# A Note from the Authors

Y ou are about to embark on an amazing journey of discovery. The study of life spans from the inner workings of cells to the complex interactions of entire ecosystems, through the information stored in DNA to the ways genetic information evolves over time. At the same time that our understanding of biology is growing in leaps and bounds, so too are great insights into how learners acquire new knowledge and skills. We are thrilled to join Scott Freeman on *Biological Science*, a book dedicated to active, research-based learning and to exploring the experimental evidence that informs what we know about biology. The next few pages highlight the features in this book and in MasteringBiology® that will help you succeed.

From left to right: Michael Black, Emily Taylor, Jon Monroe,
Lizabeth Allison, Greg Podgorski, Kim Quillin

# To the Student: How to Use This Book

New chapter-opening Roadmaps visually group and organize information to help you anticipate key ideas as well as recognize meaningful relationships and connections between them.

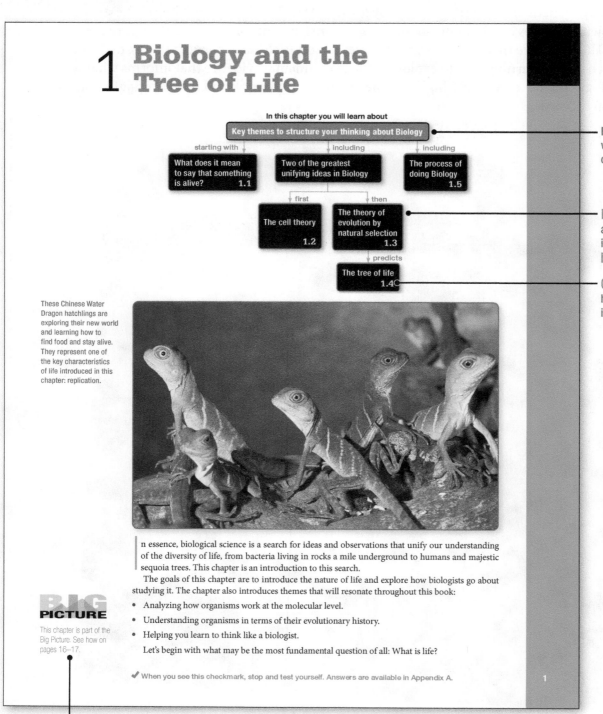

## 1 Biology and the Tree of Life

**In this chapter you will learn about**

Key themes to structure your thinking about Biology

*starting with* | *including* | *including*

What does it mean to say that something is alive? **1.1**

Two of the greatest unifying ideas in Biology

The process of doing Biology **1.5**

*first* | *then*

The cell theory **1.2**

The theory of evolution by natural selection **1.3**

*predicts*

The tree of life **1.4**

> Each Roadmap begins with a statement of why the chapter topic is important.

> Key topics from each chapter are previewed, and related ideas are connected through blue linking words.

> Chapter section numbers help you find key ideas easily in the chapter.

These Chinese Water Dragon hatchlings are exploring their new world and learning how to find food and stay alive. They represent one of the key characteristics of life introduced in this chapter: replication.

In essence, biological science is a search for ideas and observations that unify our understanding of the diversity of life, from bacteria living in rocks a mile underground to humans and majestic sequoia trees. This chapter is an introduction to this search.

The goals of this chapter are to introduce the nature of life and explore how biologists go about studying it. The chapter also introduces themes that will resonate throughout this book:

- Analyzing how organisms work at the molecular level.
- Understanding organisms in terms of their evolutionary history.
- Helping you learn to think like a biologist.

Let's begin with what may be the most fundamental question of all: What is life?

**BIG PICTURE**
This chapter is part of the Big Picture. See how on pages 16–17.

✔ When you see this checkmark, stop and test yourself. Answers are available in Appendix A.

1

> Big Picture Concept Maps are referenced on the opening page of related chapters, pointing you to summary pages that help you synthesize challenging topics.

**B**ig Picture Concept Maps integrate visuals and words to help you synthesize information about challenging topics in biology that span multiple chapters and units.

## The Big Picture

Biologists study the characteristics of life. The cell theory, the theory of evolution by natural selection, and the tree of life are some of the great ideas in biology that came about by biologists asking questions that can be answered by observing or measuring things—that is, by collecting data.

Notice that the study of life is not a series of linear steps with a beginning and an end. Instead, the process of doing biology is dynamic and ongoing. The answer to one question may lay the foundation for twenty more questions. Working together, biologists from different disciplines integrate data across many levels, from atoms to the biosphere.

Note that the gray numbers in boxes tell you where to go for more information. Also, be sure to do the blue exercises in the Check Your Understanding box.

### check your understanding

**C** **Y** **U**

**If you understand the big picture . . .**
✔ You should be able to . . .
1. Describe how biologists go about testing their ideas.
2. Provide an example of how an experimental study could span more than one level of biological organization.
3. Compare and contrast a hypothesis with a theory.
4. Propose the next step to take if data support the hypothesis you are testing.

*Answers are available in Appendix A.*

---

## Three New Big Picture topics
**have been added to the Fifth Edition:**

- NEW! Doing Biology
- NEW! The Chemistry of Life
- Energy for Life
- Genetic Information
- Evolution
- NEW! Plant and Animal Form and Function
- Ecology

## MasteringBiology®     www.masteringbiology.com

To reinforce the book's Big Picture Concept Maps, your professor may assign Interactive Big Picture Concept Map tutorials.

# Practice for success on tests and exams

**I**ntertwined color-coded "active learning threads" are embedded in the text. The gold thread helps you to identify important ideas, and the blue thread helps you to test your understanding.

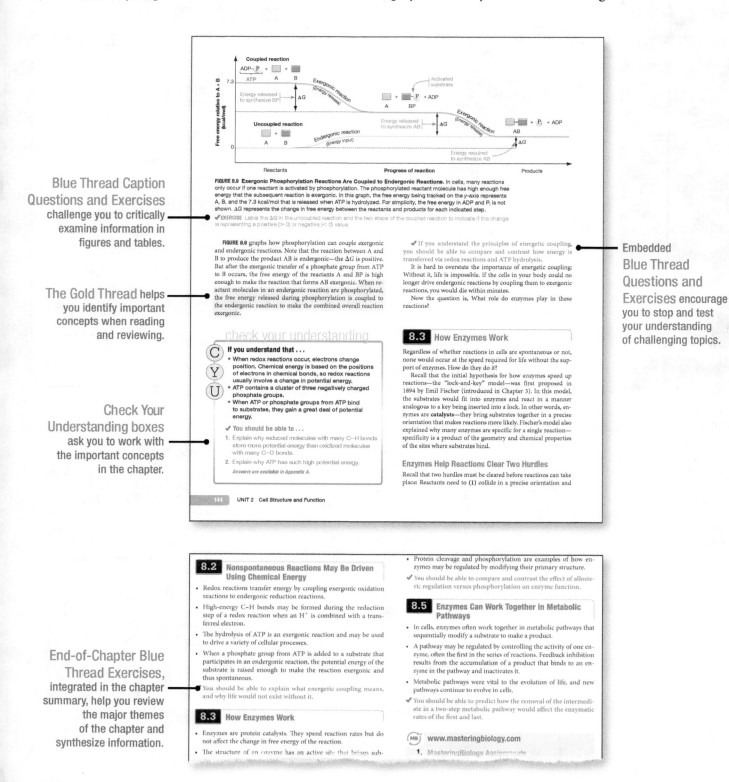

**FIGURE 8.9 Exergonic Phosphorylation Reactions Are Coupled to Endergonic Reactions.** In cells, many reactions only occur if one reactant is activated by phosphorylation. The phosphorylated reactant molecule has high enough free energy that the subsequent reaction is exergonic. In this graph, the free energy being tracked on the y-axis represents A, B, and the 7.3 kcal/mol that is released when ATP is hydrolyzed. For simplicity, the free energy in ADP and $P_i$ is not shown. $\Delta G$ represents the change in free energy between the reactants and products for each indicated step.

✔ **EXERCISE** Label the $\Delta G$ in the uncoupled reaction and the two steps of the coupled reaction to indicate if the change is representing a positive (> 0) or negative (< 0) value.

**Blue Thread Caption Questions and Exercises** challenge you to critically examine information in figures and tables.

**FIGURE 8.9** graphs how phosphorylation can couple exergonic and endergonic reactions. Note that the reaction between A and B to produce the product AB is endergonic—the $\Delta G$ is positive. But after the exergonic transfer of a phosphate group from ATP to B occurs, the free energy of the reactants A and BP is high enough to make the reaction that forms AB exergonic. When reactant molecules in an endergonic reaction are phosphorylated, the free energy released during phosphorylation is coupled to the endergonic reaction to make the combined overall reaction exergonic.

✔ If you understand the principles of energetic coupling, you should be able to compare and contrast how energy is transferred via redox reactions and ATP hydrolysis.

It is hard to overstate the importance of energetic coupling: Without it, life is impossible. If the cells in your body could no longer drive endergonic reactions by coupling them to exergonic reactions, you would die within minutes.

Now the question is, What role do enzymes play in these reactions?

**Embedded Blue Thread Questions and Exercises** encourage you to stop and test your understanding of challenging topics.

**The Gold Thread** helps you identify important concepts when reading and reviewing.

## check your understanding

**Ⓒ Ⓨ Ⓤ** **If you understand that . . .**

- When redox reactions occur, electrons change position. Chemical energy is based on the positions of electrons in chemical bonds, so redox reactions usually involve a change in potential energy.
- ATP contains a cluster of three negatively charged phosphate groups.
- When ATP or phosphate groups from ATP bind to substrates, they gain a great deal of potential energy.

✔ **You should be able to . . .**

1. Explain why reduced molecules with many C–H bonds store more potential energy than oxidized molecules with many C–O bonds.

2. Explain why ATP has such high potential energy.

*Answers are available in Appendix A.*

**Check Your Understanding boxes** ask you to work with the important concepts in the chapter.

## 8.3 How Enzymes Work

Regardless of whether reactions in cells are spontaneous or not, none would occur at the speed required for life without the support of enzymes. How do they do it?

Recall that the initial hypothesis for how enzymes speed up reactions—the "lock-and-key" model—was first proposed in 1894 by Emil Fischer (introduced in Chapter 3). In this model, the substrates would fit into enzymes and react in a manner analogous to a key being inserted into a lock. In other words, enzymes are **catalysts**—they bring substrates together in a precise orientation that makes reactions more likely. Fischer's model also explained why many enzymes are specific for a single reaction—specificity is a product of the geometry and chemical properties of the sites where substrates bind.

### Enzymes Help Reactions Clear Two Hurdles

Recall that two hurdles must be cleared before reactions can take place: Reactants need to **(1)** collide in a precise orientation and

## 8.2 Nonspontaneous Reactions May Be Driven Using Chemical Energy

- Redox reactions transfer energy by coupling exergonic oxidation reactions to endergonic reduction reactions.
- High-energy C–H bonds may be formed during the reduction step of a redox reaction when an $H^+$ is combined with a transferred electron.
- The hydrolysis of ATP is an exergonic reaction and may be used to drive a variety of cellular processes.
- When a phosphate group from ATP is added to a substrate that participates in an endergonic reaction, the potential energy of the substrate is raised enough to make the reaction exergonic and thus spontaneous.

✔ You should be able to explain what energetic coupling means, and why life would not exist without it.

**End-of-Chapter Blue Thread Exercises,** integrated in the chapter summary, help you review the major themes of the chapter and synthesize information.

## 8.3 How Enzymes Work

- Enzymes are protein catalysts. They speed reaction rates but do not affect the change in free energy of the reaction.
- The structure of an enzyme has an active site that brings sub-

- Protein cleavage and phosphorylation are examples of how enzymes may be regulated by modifying their primary structure.

✔ You should be able to compare and contrast the effect of allosteric regulation versus phosphorylation on enzyme function.

## 8.5 Enzymes Can Work Together in Metabolic Pathways

- In cells, enzymes often work together in metabolic pathways that sequentially modify a substrate to make a product.
- A pathway may be regulated by controlling the activity of one enzyme, often the first in the series of reactions. Feedback inhibition results from the accumulation of a product that binds to an enzyme in the pathway and inactivates it.
- Metabolic pathways were vital to the evolution of life, and new pathways continue to evolve in cells.

✔ You should be able to predict how the removal of the intermediate in a two-step metabolic pathway would affect the enzymatic rates of the first and last.

**Ⓜ Ⓑ** www.masteringbiology.com

**1.** MasteringBiology Assignments

# Identify gaps in your understanding, then fill them

The Fifth Edition provides many opportunities for you to test yourself and offers helpful learning strategies.

**Analyze:** Can I recognize underlying patterns and structure?

**Evaluate:** Can I make judgments on the relative value of ideas and information?

**Create:** Can I put ideas and information together to generate something new?

**Apply:** Can I use these ideas in the same way or in a new situation?

**Understand:** Can I explain this concept in my own words?

**Remember:** Can I recall the key terms and ideas?

◄ Bloom's Taxonomy describes six learning levels: Remember, Understand, Apply, Analyze, Evaluate, and Create. Questions in the book span all levels, including self-testing at the higher levels to help you develop higher-order thinking skills that will prepare you for exams.

## Steps to Building Understanding
Each chapter ends with three groups of questions that build in difficulty:

### ✓ TEST YOUR KNOWLEDGE
Begin by testing your basic knowledge of new information.

### ✓ TEST YOUR UNDERSTANDING
Once you're confident with the basics, demonstrate your deeper understanding of the material.

### ✓ TEST YOUR PROBLEM-SOLVING SKILLS
Work towards mastery of the content by answering questions that challenge you at the highest level of competency.

---

**BIOSKILL 16**   using Bloom's taxonomy

Most students have at one time or another wondered why a particular question on an exam seemed so hard, while others seemed easy. The explanation lies in the type of cognitive skills required to answer the question. Let's take a closer look.

**NEW! BioSkill Covering Bloom's Taxonomy** helps you to recognize question types using the Bloom's cognitive hierarchy, and it provides specific strategies to help you study for questions at all six levels.

**Answer Appendix Includes Bloom's Taxonomy Information** Answers to all questions in the text now include the Bloom's level being tested. You can simultaneously practice assessing your understanding of content and recognizing Bloom's levels. Combining this information with the guidance in the BioSkill on Bloom's Taxonomy will help you form a plan to improve your study skills.

### ✓ Test Your Problem-Solving Skills

**13.** *analyze* A scientific theory is not a guess—it is an idea whose validity can be tested with data. Both the cell theory and the theory of evolution have been validated by large bodies of observational and experimental data.
**14.** *apply* If all eukaryotes living today have a nucleus, then it is logical to conclude that the nucleus arose in a common ancestor of all eukaryotes, indicated by the arrow you should have added to the figure. See **FIGURE A1.2.** If it had arisen in a common ancestor of Bacteria or Archaea, then species in those groups would have had to lose the trait—an unlikely event.
**15.** *evaluate* The data set was so large and diverse that it was no longer reasonable to argue that noncellular life-forms would be discovered.
**16.** *apply* b

## MasteringBiology®
www.masteringbiology.com

**NEW! End-of-chapter questions** from the book are now available for your professor to assign as homework in MasteringBiology.

# Practice scientific thinking and scientific skills

**A** unique emphasis on the process of scientific discovery and experimental design teaches you how to think like a scientist as you learn fundamental biology concepts.

## RESEARCH

**QUESTION:** Do horses minimize the cost of locomotion?

**HYPOTHESIS:** Horses choose gaits that minimize energy use at different speeds.

**NULL HYPOTHESIS:** Horses do not choose gaits based on cost of locomotion.

**EXPERIMENTAL SETUP:**

**1.** Measure oxygen consumption of horses trained to walk, trot, and gallop at a range of speeds on a treadmill. Calculate energy used per distance travelled at different speeds.

5.6 m/s — Oxygen mask — Treadmill

**2.** Videotape the same horses locomoting freely in the paddock, and measure the gaits and speeds they choose to use naturally.

**PREDICTION:** For each gait, there is a range of speeds where energy use is minimized. Horses will favor these gaits and speeds.

**PREDICTION OF NULL HYPOTHESIS:** There will be no correlation between chosen gaits and energy consumption.

**RESULTS:**

Walking · Trotting · Galloping

Speeds and gaits chosen by free horses

Energy/distance (joules per meter) vs Speed (m/s)

©1981 Nature Publishing Group

**CONCLUSION:** Horses choose gaits that minimize energy use at different speeds and avoid speeds with high energy consumption.

**FIGURE 48.16 Horses Minimize the Cost of Locomotion by Choosing Appropriate Gaits.**
SOURCE: Hoyt, D. F., and C. R. Taylor. 1981. Gait and the energetics of locomotion in horses. *Nature* 292: 239–240.

✔ **QUANTITATIVE** Use the graph to estimate the relative energy expense of galloping rather than trotting at 3.5 meters/second (m/s).

**Research Boxes** explain how research studies are designed and give you additional practice interpreting data. Each Research Box consistently models the scientific method, presenting the research question, hypotheses, experimental setup, predictions, results, and conclusion. 15 Research Boxes are new to the Fifth Edition.

All of the Research Boxes cite the original research paper and include a question that asks you to analyze the design of the experiment or study.

# MasteringBiology®

## www.masteringbiology.com

**NEW! Solve It Tutorials** are available for homework assignments in MasteringBiology and give you an opportunity to work like a scientist through a simulated investigation that requires you to analyze and interpret data.

**Experimental Inquiry Tutorials** based on some of biology's most seminal experiments give you a chance to analyze data and the reasoning that led scientists from the data to their conclusions.

## Experimental Inquiry tutorial topics include:

- What Can You Learn About the Process of Science from Investigating a Cricket's Chirp?
- Which Wavelengths of Light Drive Photosynthesis?
- What Is the Inheritance Pattern of Sex-Linked Traits?
- Does DNA Replication Follow the Conservative, Semiconservative, or Dispersive Model?
- How Do Calcium Ions Help to Prevent Polyspermy During Egg Fertilization?
- Did Natural Selection of Ground Finches Occur When the Environment Changed?
- What Effect Does Auxin Have on Coleoptile Growth?
- What Role Do Genes Play in Appetite Regulation?
- Can a Species' Niche Be Influenced by Interspecific Competition?
- What Factors Influence the Loss of Nutrients from a Forest Ecosystem?

**B**uild important skills scientists use to perform, evaluate, and communicate scientific research.

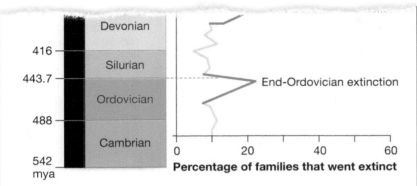

**FIGURE 28.14 The Big Five Mass Extinction Events.** This graph shows the percentage of lineages called families that went extinct over each interval in the fossil record since the Cambrian explosion. Over 50 percent of families and 90 percent of species went extinct during the end-Permian extinction.

DATA: Benton, M. J., 1995. *Science* 268: 52–58.

✔**QUANTITATIVE** Which extinction event ended the era of the dinosaurs 65 million years ago? About what percentage of families went extinct?

**NEW! Graphs and tables** now include their data sources, emphasizing the research process that leads to our understanding of biological ideas.

**NEW! Quantitative** questions are identified throughout the text, helping you practice computational problem solving and data analysis.

**Expanded BioSkills Appendix** helps you build skills that will be important to your success in biology. At relevant points in the text, you'll find references to the BioSkills appendix that will help you learn and practice foundational skills.

### BioSkills Topics include:

- The Metric System and Significant Figures
- Some Common Latin and Greek Roots Used in Biology
- Reading Graphs
- Using Statistical Tests and Interpreting Standard Error Bars
- Combining Probabilities

- Using Logarithms
- Reading a Phylogenetic Tree
- Reading Chemical Structures
- Separating and Visualizing Molecules
- Separating Cell Components by Centrifugation
- Biological Imaging: Microscopy and X-ray Crystallography

- Cell and Tissue Culture Methods
- Model Organisms
- NEW! Primary Literature and Peer Review
- Making Concept Maps
- NEW! Using Bloom's Taxonomy

## MasteringBiology®
www.masteringbiology.com

You can access self-paced BioSkills activities in the Study Area, and your instructor can assign additional activities in MasteringBiology.

# Visualize biology processes and structures

A carefully crafted visual program helps you gain a better understanding of biology through accurate, appropriately detailed figures.

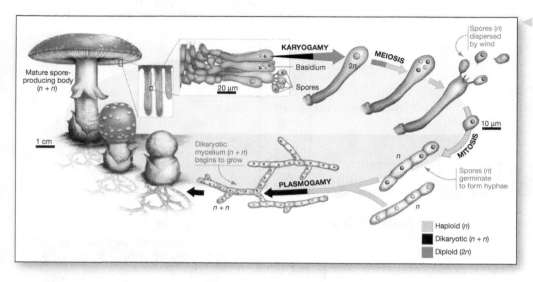

▶ NEW! Redesigned Life Cycle diagrams in Unit 6 and 7 help you compare and contrast processes among different organisms.

▲ Informative figures help you think through complex biological processes in manageable steps.

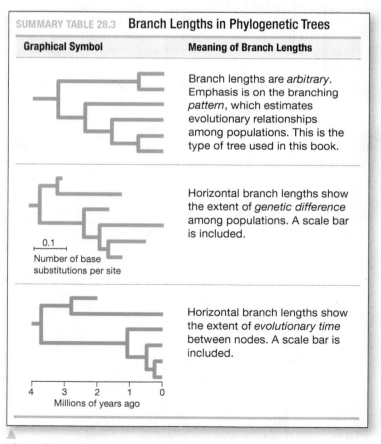

SUMMARY TABLE 28.3 **Branch Lengths in Phylogenetic Trees**

| Graphical Symbol | Meaning of Branch Lengths |
| --- | --- |
| | Branch lengths are *arbitrary*. Emphasis is on the branching *pattern*, which estimates evolutionary relationships among populations. This is the type of tree used in this book. |
| 0.1 — Number of base substitutions per site | Horizontal branch lengths show the extent of *genetic difference* among populations. A scale bar is included. |
| 4 3 2 1 0 Millions of years ago | Horizontal branch lengths show the extent of *evolutionary time* between nodes. A scale bar is included. |

▲ Visual Summary Tables pull together important information in a format that allows for easy comparison and review.

# Instructor and Student Resources

## For Instructors

### Instructor Resource DVD-ROM
978-0-321-86112-2 • 0-321-86112-4

Everything you need for lectures in one place, including video segments that demonstrate how to incorporate active-learning techniques into your own classroom. Enhanced menus make locating and assessing the digital resources for each chapter easy. The Instructor Resource CD/DVD-ROM includes PowerPoint® Lecture Outlines that integrate figures and animations for classroom presentations. All textbook figures, art, and photos are in JPEG format, and all PowerPoint slides and JPEGs have editable labels. Over 300 Instructor Animations accurately depict complex topics and dynamic processes described in the book.

### Instructor Guide (Download only)
Available in the instructor resource area of MasteringBiology.®

### TestGen® (Download only)
All of the exam questions in the Test Bank have been peer reviewed and student tested, providing questions that set the standard for quality and accuracy. To improve the Test Bank, Metadata from MasteringBiology users has been incorporated directly into the software. Test questions that are ranked according to Bloom's taxonomy and improved TestGen® software makes assembling tests that much easier.

## For Students

### Study Guide
978-0-321-85832-0 • 0-321-85832-8

The Study Guide presents a breakdown of key biological concepts, difficult topics, and quizzes to help students prepare for exams. Unique to this study guide are four introductory, stand-alone chapters that introduce students to foundational ideas and skills necessary for classroom success: Introduction to Experimentation and Research in the Biological Sciences, Presenting Biological Data, Understanding Patterns in Biology and Improving Study Techniques, and Reading and Writing to Understand Biology. "Looking Forward" and "Looking Back" sections help students make connections across the chapters instead of viewing them as discrete entities.

### Practicing Biology: A Student Workbook
978-0-321-88647-7 • 0-321-88647-X

This workbook focuses on key ideas, principles, and concepts that are fundamental to understanding biology. A variety of hands-on activities such as mapping and modeling suit different learning styles and help students discover which topics they need more help on. Students learn biology by doing biology. An instructors guide can be downloaded from the Instructor Area of MasteringBiology.

# MasteringBiology®

www.masteringbiology.com

MasteringBiology is an online homework, tutorial, and assessment system that delivers self-paced tutorials that provide individualized coaching, focus on your course objectives, and respond to each student's progress. The Mastering system helps instructors maximize class time with customizable, easy-to-assign, and automatically graded assessments that motivate students to learn outside of class and arrive prepared for lecture. MasteringBiology is also available with a complete Pearson eText edition of *Biological Science*.

Highlights of the Fifth Edition Item Library include:

* NEW! **assignment options** include Solve It activities, end-of-chapter problems, and questions that accompany new BioSkills and new Big Picture Interactive Concept Maps.

* NEW! **"best of" homework pre-built assignments** help professors assign popular, key content quickly, including a blend of tutorials, end-of-chapter problems, and test bank questions.

* *Get Ready for Biology* and **Chemistry Review assignment options** help students get up to speed with activities that review chemistry, mathematics, and basic biology.

## MasteringBiology® Virtual Labs
978-0-321-88644-6 • 0-321-88644-5

MasteringBiology: Virtual Labs is an online environment that promotes critical-thinking skills using virtual experiments and explorations that might be difficult to perform in a wet-lab environment due to time, cost, or safety concerns. MasteringBiology: Virtual Labs offers unique learning experiences in the areas of microscopy, molecular biology, genetics, ecology, and systematics.

For more information, please visit www.pearsonhighered.com/virtualbiologylabs

Scott Freeman • Lizabeth Allison • Michael Black
Greg Podgorski • Kim Quillin •Jon Monroe • Emily Taylor

# Biological Science

Second Custom Edition for University of Rhode Island

Taken from:
*Biological Science*, Fifth Edition
by Scott Freeman, Lizabeth Allison, Michael Black, Greg Podgorski,
Kim Quillin, Jon Monroe, and Emily Taylor

Cover Art: Courtesy of Photodisc/Getty Images.

Taken from:

*Biological Science*, Fifth Edition
by Scott Freeman, Lizabeth Allison, Michael Black, Greg Podgorski, Kim Quillin, Jon Monroe, and Emily Taylor
Copyright © 2014, 2011, 2008 by Pearson Education, Inc.
Boston, Massachusetts 02116

This special edition published in cooperation with Pearson Learning Solutions.

Pearson Learning Solutions, 501 Boylston Street, Suite 900, Boston, MA 02116
A Pearson Education Company
www.pearsoned.com

Printed in the United States of America

1 2 3 4 5 6 7 8 9 10 V092 17 16 15 14


000200010271900664

LA

**PEARSON**     ISBN 10: 1-269-96052-0
ISBN 13: 978-1-269-96052-6

# Brief Contents

# Detailed Contents

# About the Authors

## A Letter from Scott:

I started working on *Biological Science* in 1997 with a simple goal: To help change the way biology is taught. After just shy of 20,000 hours of work on four editions of this text, that goal still gets me out of bed in the morning. But instead of focusing my energies on textbook writing, I've decided to devote myself full-time to research on student learning and developing new courses for undergraduate and graduate students at the University of Washington.

So with this edition I am passing the torch—to an all-star cast of leading scientists and educators who have enthusiastically taught from, and contributed to, previous editions of *Biological Science*. Working with them, I have seen the new team bring their passion, talent, and creativity to the book, with expertise that spans the breadth of the life sciences. Just as important, they work beautifully together because they think alike. They are driven by a shared concern for student learning, a commitment to the craft of writing, and a background in evidence-based teaching.

These pages provide a brief introduction to Liz Allison, Michael Black, Greg Podgorski, Kim Quillin, Jon Monroe, and Emily Taylor. As a group, they've built on the book's existing strengths and infused this edition with fresh energy, perspective, and ideas. I'm full of admiration for what they have accomplished, and excited about the impact this edition will have on biology students from all over the world.—*Scott Freeman*

**Lizabeth A. Allison** is professor and chair of the Biology Department at the College of William & Mary. She received her Ph.D. in Zoology from the University of Washington, specializing in molecular and cellular biology. Before coming to William & Mary, she spent eight years as a faculty member at the University of Canterbury in New Zealand. Liz teaches introductory biology for majors and upper-division molecular biology courses. She has mentored graduate students and more than 80 undergraduate research students, many of them coauthoring papers with her on intracellular trafficking of the thyroid hormone receptor in normal and cancer cells. The recipient of numerous awards, including a State Council for Higher Education in Virginia (SCHEV) Outstanding Faculty Award in 2009, Liz received one of the three inaugural Arts & Sciences Faculty Awards for Teaching Excellence in 2011, and a Plumeri Award for Faculty Excellence in 2012. In addition to her work on this text, she is author of *Fundamental Molecular Biology*, now in its second edition.
*Lead Author; Chapter 1 and BioSkills*
laalli@wm.edu

**Scott Freeman** received a Ph.D. in Zoology from the University of Washington and was subsequently awarded an Alfred P. Sloan Postdoctoral Fellowship in Molecular Evolution at Princeton University. He has done research in evolutionary biology on topics ranging from nest parasitism to the molecular systematics of the blackbird family and is coauthor, with Jon Herron, of the standard-setting undergraduate text *Evolutionary Analysis*. Scott is the recipient of a Distinguished Teaching Award from the University of Washington and is currently a Senior Lecturer in the UW Department of Biology, where he teaches introductory biology for majors, a writing-intensive course for majors called The Tree of Life, and a graduate seminar in college science teaching. Scott's current research focuses on how active learning affects student learning and academic performance.

**Michael Black** received his Ph.D. in Microbiology & Immunology from Stanford University School of Medicine as a Howard Hughes Predoctoral Fellow. After graduation, he studied cell biology as a Burroughs Wellcome Postdoctoral Fellow at the MRC Laboratory of Molecular Biology in Cambridge, England. His current research focuses on the use of molecules to identify and track the transmission of microbes in the environment. Michael is a professor of Cell & Molecular Biology at California Polytechnic State University in San Luis Obispo, where he teaches introductory and advanced classes for majors in cell biology and microbiology. In addition to his teaching and research activities, Michael serves as the director of the Undergraduate Biotechnology Lab, where he works alongside undergraduate technicians to integrate research projects and inquiry-based activities into undergraduate classes.
*Chapters 2–12, 36, and 51*
mblack@calpoly.edu

Greg Podgorski received his Ph.D. in Molecular and Cellular Biology from Penn State University and has been a postdoctoral fellow at the Max Plank Institute for Biochemistry and Columbia University. His research interests are in biology education, developmental genetics, and computational biology. Greg's most recent work has been in mathematical modeling of how patterns of different cell types emerge during development and how tumors recruit new blood vessels in cancer. Greg has been teaching at Utah State University for more than 20 years in courses that include introductory biology for majors and for nonmajors, genetics, cell biology, developmental biology, and microbiology, and he has offered courses in nonmajors biology in Beijing and Hong Kong. He's won teaching awards at Utah State University and has been recognized by the National Academies as a Teaching Fellow and a Teaching Mentor.

*Chapters 13–24*

*greg.podgorski@usu.edu*

Jon Monroe is professor of Biology at James Madison University in Harrisonburg, Virginia. Jon completed his undergraduate work in Botany at the University of Michigan and his graduate work in Plant Physiology at Cornell University. He began his current position after a postdoc in biochemistry at Michigan State University. He currently teaches Plant Biology, and Cell and Molecular Biology. Jon's interest in plants is broad, ranging from systematics and taxonomy to physiology and biochemistry. His research, mostly with undergraduates, uses Arabidopsis thaliana to study the functions of a family of β-amylase genes in starch metabolism. Jon has been active in promoting undergraduate research through his work with the American Society of Plant Biologists (ASPB) and the Council on Undergraduate Research. He has received ASPB's Excellence in Teaching award and James Madison University Alumni Association's Distinguished Faculty Award.

*Chapters 29–32; 37–41*

*monroejd@jmu.edu*

Kim Quillin received her B.A. in Biology at Oberlin College *summa cum laude* and her Ph.D. in Integrative Biology from the University of California, Berkeley (as a National Science Foundation Graduate Fellow). Kim has worked in the trenches with Scott Freeman on every edition of *Biological Science*, starting with the ground-up development of the illustrations in the first edition in 1999 and expanding her role in each edition, always with the focus of helping students to think like biologists. Kim currently teaches introductory biology at Salisbury University, a member of the University System of Maryland, where she is actively involved in the ongoing student-centered reform of the concepts-and-methods course for biology majors. Her current research focuses on the scholarship of teaching and learning with an emphasis on measuring science process skills and the advantages and pitfalls of active multimedia learning.

*Chapters 25–28; 33–35; 48; 52–57*

*kxquillin@salisbury.edu*

Emily Taylor earned a B.A. in English at the University of California, Berkeley followed by a Ph.D. in Biological Sciences from Arizona State University, where she conducted research in the field of environmental physiology as a National Science Foundation Graduate Research Fellow. She is currently an associate professor of Biological Sciences at the California Polytechnic State University in San Luis Obispo, California. Her student-centered research program focuses on the endocrine and reproductive physiology of free-ranging reptiles, especially rattlesnakes. She teaches numerous undergraduate and graduate courses, including introductory biology, anatomy and physiology, and herpetology, and received the California Faculty Association's Distinguished Educator Award in 2010 and Cal Poly's Distinguished Teaching Award in 2012. Her revision of Unit 8 is her first foray into textbook writing.

*Chapters 42–50*

*etaylor@calpoly.edu*

# Preface to Instructors

The first edition of *Biological Science* was visionary in its unique emphasis on the process of scientific discovery and experimental design—teaching how we know what we know. The goal was for students not only to learn the language of biology and understand fundamental concepts but also to begin to apply those concepts in new situations, analyze experimental design, synthesize results, and evaluate hypotheses and data—to learn how to think like biologists. Each edition since has proudly expanded on this vision. The Fifth Edition is no exception.

A team of six dedicated teacher-scholars has joined Scott to build on and refine the original vision, and by so doing, make the book an even better teaching and learning tool. The pace of biological discovery is rapid, and with each novel breakthrough it becomes even more challenging to decide what is essential to include in an introductory biology text. Pulling together an author team with firsthand expertise from molecules to ecosystems has ensured that the content of the Fifth Edition reflects cutting-edge biology that is pitched at the right level for introductory students and is as accurate and as exciting as ever for instructors and students alike.

New findings from education research continue to inform and inspire the team's thinking about *Biological Science*—we know more today than ever before about how students learn. These findings demand that we constantly look for new ways to increase student engagement in the learning process, and to help instructors align course activities and learning goals with testing strategies.

## The New Coauthors

The new coauthor team brings a broad set of talents and interests to the project, motivated by a deep commitment to undergraduate teaching, whether at a small liberal arts college or a large university. Kim Quillin has been a partner in this textbook in every edition. For the Fifth Edition, she revised chapters across three units in addition to spearheading the continued effort to enhance the visual-teaching program. Michael Black, Greg Podgorski, Jon Monroe, and Emily Taylor, who served as unit advisors on the Fourth Edition, were already familiar with the book. And most of the authorial team have been avid users of previous editions for many years.

## Core Values

Together, the coauthor team has worked to extend the vision and maintain the core values of *Biological Science*—to provide a book for instructors who embrace the challenge of boosting students to higher levels of learning, and to provide a book for

students that helps them each step of the way in learning to think like scientists. Dedicated instructors have high expectations of their students—the Fifth Edition provides scaffolding to help students learn at the level called for by the National Academy of Sciences, the Howard Hughes Medical Institute, the American Association of Medical Academies, and the National Science Foundation.

## What's New in This Edition

The Fifth Edition contains many new or expanded features, all of them targeted at ways to help students learn to construct their own knowledge and think like biologists.

- **Road Maps** The new Road Maps at the beginning of each chapter pair with the Big Picture concept maps introduced in the Fourth Edition. Together they help students navigate chapter content and see the forest for the trees. Each Road Map starts with a purpose statement that tells students what they can expect to learn from each chapter. It then goes on to visually group and organize information to help students anticipate key ideas as well as recognize meaningful relationships and connections between the ideas.

- **The Big Picture** Introduced in the Fourth Edition, Big Picture concept maps integrate words and visuals to help students synthesize information about challenging topics that span multiple chapters and units. In response to requests from instructors and students, three new Big Pictures focused on additional tough topics have been added: Doing Biology, The Chemistry of Life, and Plant and Animal Form and Function. In addition, the Ecology Big Picture is completely revised to reflect changes to that unit.

- **New Chapters** Two new chapters are added to better serve instructors and students. Unit 2 now contains a new Chapter 8, Energy and Enzymes: An Introduction to Metabolic Pathways. This chapter consolidates these critical topics in a place where students and instructors need it most—right before the chapters on cellular respiration and photosynthesis. In the Fourth Edition, animal movement was discussed in a chapter largely focused on animal sensory systems. In the Fifth Edition, this important topic is treated in depth in a new Chapter 48, Animal Movement, that explores how muscle and skeletal systems work together to produce locomotion.

- **New BioSkills** Instructors recognize that biology students need to develop foundational science skills in addition to content knowledge. While these skills are emphasized throughout the book, *Biological Science*, beginning with the Third

Edition, has provided a robust set of materials and activities to guide students who need extra help. To promote even fuller use of this resource, the BioSkills are now updated, expanded, and reorganized. New in this edition are a discussion of significant figures within the BioSkills on the Metric System, and two new BioSkills on Primary Literature and Peer Review and Using Bloom's Taxonomy. BioSkills are located in Appendix B, and practice activities can be assigned online in MasteringBiology®.

- **Promotion of Quantitative Skills** Reports like *Biology 2010, Scientific Foundations for Future Physicians*, and *Vision and Change* all place a premium on quantitative skills. To infuse a quantitative component throughout the text, new and existing quantitative questions are flagged in each chapter to encourage students to work on developing their ability to read or create a graph, perform or interpret a calculation, or use other forms of quantitative reasoning.

- **Bloom's Taxonomy** In the Fifth Edition, all questions in the text are assigned a Bloom's Taxonomy level to help both students and instructors understand whether a question requires higher-order or lower-order cognitive skills. Questions span all six Bloom's levels. (Bloom's levels are identified in Appendix A: Answers.) The coauthors were trained by experts Mary Pat Wenderoth and Clarissa Dirks[1] to ensure we followed a process that would result in high inter-rater reliability— or agreement among raters—in assigning Bloom's levels to questions. The new BioSkill, Using Bloom's Taxonomy, explains the six Bloom's levels to students and offers a practical guide to the kinds of study activities best suited for answering questions at each level.

- **Expanded Emphasis on "Doing Biology"** A constant hallmark of this text is its emphasis on experimental evidence— on teaching how we know what we know. To reflect the progress of science, in the Fifth Edition, the coauthor team replaced many experiments with fresh examples and added new Research Boxes. And as noted earlier, they added a new Big Picture on Doing Biology, focusing on the process of science and the organizational levels of biology. Data sources are now cited for all graphs and data tables to model the importance of citing data sources to students. Updated Research Box questions continue to encourage students to analyze some aspect of experimental design. Also new to this edition is a BioSkill on Primary Literature and Peer Review.

- **Art Program** The art program is further enhanced in this edition by the addition of more illustrated summary tables. These tables make subject areas more accessible to visual learners and reinforce key concepts of the chapter. Many of the life-cycle figures in Unit 6 are significantly overhauled.

[1] Crowe, A., C. Dirks, and M. P. Wenderoth. 2008. Biology in Bloom: Implementing Bloom's Taxonomy to enhance student learning in biology. *CBE–Life Sciences Education* 7: 368–381.

## Updated Blue Thread Scaffolding

In the Third and Fourth editions of *Biological Science*, a metacognitive tool was formulated as the now popular feature known as "Blue Thread"—sets of questions designed to help students identify what they do and don't understand. The fundamental idea is that if students really understand a piece of information or a concept, they should be able to do something with it.

In the Fifth Edition, the Blue Thread is revised to reflect changes in chapter content, and to incorporate user feedback. Blue-Thread questions appear in the following locations:

- **In-text "You should be able to's"** offer exercises on topics that professors and students have identified as the most difficult concepts in each chapter.

- **Caption questions and exercises** challenge students to examine the information in a figure or table critically—not just absorb it.

- **Check Your Understanding boxes** present two to three tasks that students should be able to complete in order to demonstrate a mastery of summarized key ideas.

- **Chapter summaries** include "You should be able to" problems or exercises related to each key concept.

- **End-of-chapter** questions are organized in three levels of increasing difficulty so students can build from lower to higher-order cognitive questions.

## Integration of Media

The textbook continues to be supported by MasteringBiology®, the most powerful online homework, tutorial, and assessment system available. Tutorials follow the Socratic method, coaching students to the correct answer by offering feedback specific to a student's misconceptions as well as providing hints students can access if they get stuck. Instructors can associate content with publisher-provided learning outcomes or create their own. Content highlights include the following:

- **NEW! Solve It Tutorials** These activities allow students to act like scientists in simulated investigations. Each tutorial presents an interesting, real-world question that students will answer by analyzing and interpreting data.

- **Experimental Inquiry Tutorials** The call to teach students about the process of science has never been louder. To support such teaching, there are 10 interactive tutorials on classic scientific experiments—ranging from Meselson–Stahl on DNA replication to the Grants' work on Galápagos finches and Connell's work on competition. Students who use these tutorials should be better prepared to think critically about experimental design and evaluate the wider implications of the data—preparing them to do the work of real scientists in the future.

- **BioFlix® Animations and Tutorials** BioFlix are movie-quality, 3-D animations that focus on the most difficult core topics and are accompanied by in-depth, online tutorials that provide hints and feedback to guide student learning. Eighteen BioFlix animations and tutorials tackle topics such as meiosis, mitosis, DNA replication, photosynthesis, homeostasis, and the carbon cycle.

- **NEW! End-of-Chapter Questions** Multiple choice end-of-chapter questions are now available to assign in MasteringBiology.

- **Blue-Thread Questions** Over 500 questions based on the Blue-Thread Questions in the textbook are assignable in MasteringBiology.

- **Big Picture Tutorials** Interactive concept map activities based on the Big Picture figures in the textbook are assignable in MasteringBiology, including tutorials to support the three new Big Pictures: Doing Biology, The Chemistry of Life, and Plant and Animal Form and Function.

- **BioSkills Activities** Activities based on the BioSkills content in the textbook are assignable in MasteringBiology, including activities to support the new BioSkills on Primary Literature and Peer Review and Using Bloom's Taxonomy.

- **Reading Quiz Questions** Every chapter includes reading quiz questions you can assign to ensure students read the textbook and understand the basics. These quizzes are perfect as a pre-lecture assignment to get students into the content before class, allowing you to use class time more effectively.

## Serving a Community of Teachers

All of us on the coauthor team are deeply committed to students and to supporting the efforts of dedicated teachers. Doing biology is what we love. At various points along our diverse paths, we have been inspired by our own teachers when we were students, and now are inspired by our colleagues as we strive to become even better teacher-scholars. In the tradition of all previous editions of *Biological Science*, we have tried to infuse this textbook with the spirit and practice of evidence-based teaching. We welcome your comments, suggestions, and questions.

Thank you for your work on behalf of your students.

# Content Highlights of the Fifth Edition

As discussed in the preface, a major focus of this revision is to enhance the pedagogical utility of *Biological Science*. Another major goal is to ensure that the content reflects the current state of science and is accurate. The expanded author team has scrutinized every chapter to add new, relevant content, update descriptions when appropriate, and adjust the approach to certain topics to enhance student comprehension. In this section, some of the key content improvements to the textbook are highlighted.

**Chapter 1  Biology and the Tree of Life**  A concept map summarizing the defining characteristics of life is added. The process of doing biology coverage is expanded to include discussion of both experimental and descriptive studies, and more rigorous definitions of the terms hypothesis and theory.

**Chapter 2  Water and Carbon: The Chemical Basis of Life**  A stronger emphasis on chemical evolution is threaded throughout the chapter to bring chemistry to life for the student reader. Two prominent models for chemical evolution are introduced; the historic Miller prebiotic soup experiment was moved here. Advanced discussion of energy and chemical reactions was moved to a new chapter (see Chapter 8).

**Chapter 3  Protein Structure and Function**  The chapter is reorganized to emphasize the link between structure and function, from amino acids to folded proteins. Updated content illustrates that protein shapes are flexible and dynamic, and may remain incompletely folded until the protein interacts with other molecules or ions. Details of how enzymes work were moved to Chapter 8.

**Chapter 4  Nucleic Acids and the RNA World**  New experimental results concerning the synthesis of nucleotides and nucleic acids in a prebiotic environment are discussed. The section on the RNA world is expanded to include the artificial evolution of a novel ribozyme involved in nucleotide synthesis.

**Chapter 5  An Introduction to Carbohydrates**  The molecular basis for resistance of structural polymers, such as cellulose, to degradation is clarified. A new research box illustrates the role of carbohydrates in cellular recognition and attachment using the egg and sperm of mice as a model system.

**Chapter 6  Lipids, Membranes, and the First Cells**  New content on lipid and membrane evolution and the proposed characteristics of the first protocell is introduced. The aquaporin and potassium channel figures are updated; how key amino acids serve as selectivity filters is now highlighted.

**Chapter 7  Inside the Cell**  Several new electron micrographs were selected to more clearly illustrate cell component structure and function. A new figure is added to better depict the pulse–chase assay used to identify the secretory pathway. Coverage of nuclear transport is expanded to differentiate between passive diffusion and active nuclear import. Updated content emphasizes the role of the cytoskeleton in localizing organelles, and how polarity of microtubules and microfilaments influences their growth rate.

**Chapter 8  Energy and Enzymes: An Introduction to Pathways**  This new chapter pulls together concepts in energy, chemical reactions, and enzymes that previously were covered in three different chapters. Oxidation and reduction reactions are emphasized to prepare students for Chapters 9 and 10. The energetics behind ATP hydrolysis and its role in driving endergonic reactions is discussed, and figures are revised to better illustrate the process. Updated content on enzyme regulation and a new process figure show a model for how metabolic pathways may have evolved.

**Chapter 9  Cellular Respiration and Fermentation**  Two new summary tables for glycolysis and the citric acid cycle are added that provide the names of the enzymes and the reaction each catalyzes. New content is introduced to propose a connection between the universal nature of the proton motive force and the story of the chemical evolution of life.

**Chapter 11  Cell–Cell Interactions**  Coverage of extracellular matrix structure and function is expanded, including its role in intercellular adhesions and cell signaling. The plant apoplast and symplast are now introduced as key terms in the text and illustrated in a new figure. New content and a new figure on unicellular models for intercellular communication via pheromone sensing (yeast) and quorum sensing (slime mold) are added.

**Chapter 12  The Cell Cycle**  A new figure helps explain the pulse–chase assay for identifying phases of the cell cycle. Content is added to the text and to a figure that illustrates the similarities between chromosome segregation in eukaryotes and prokaryotes. A revised description of anaphase emphasizes how microtubule fraying at the kinetochore can drive chromosome movement. The explanation of how phosphorylation and dephosphorylation turns on MPF activity is updated to reflect current research.

**Chapter 13  Meiosis**  To improve the flow of the chapter, the section on advantages of sexual reproduction was moved to before mistakes in meiosis. The discussion of the role and timing of crossing over during meiosis I is updated. A new study that supports the hypothesis that sex evolved in response to the selective pressure of pathogens is introduced.

**Chapter 14 Mendel and the Gene** Material on gene linkage is revised to emphasize the importance of genetic mapping. A new matched set of figures on pedigree analysis brings together the various modes of transmission that were previously shown in four individual figures. A new summary table on characteristics of different patterns of inheritance is added.

**Chapter 15 DNA and the Gene: Synthesis and Repair** A new research figure is added that focuses on the relationship between telomere length and senescence in cultured somatic cells.

**Chapter 16 How Genes Work** Coverage of the evolving concept of the gene and of different types of RNA is expanded. A figure showing the karyotype of a cancer cell is revised to improve clarity.

**Chapter 17 Transcription, RNA Processing, and Translation** The sections on transcription in bacteria and eukaryotes are now separated, and content on charging tRNAs was moved to a new section. The discussion of translation is reorganized, first to emphasize the process in bacteria and then to highlight differences in eukaryotes.

**Chapter 19 Control of Gene Expression in Eukaryotes** Extensive updates to the discussion of epigenetics include a new research box and a section on DNA methylation. Coverage of transcription initiation is updated to reflect current science. A new figure illustrates the role of p53 in the cell cycle in normal and cancerous cells.

**Chapter 20 Analyzing and Engineering Genes** The material on sequencing the Neanderthal genome is updated, including evidence of limited Neanderthal genetic material in some modern human populations. New information on current generation sequencing technologies and massive parallelism is added. Recent advances in gene therapy are highlighted.

**Chapter 22 Principles of Development** New information is added on dedifferentiation in induced pluripotent stem cells, maternal genes in *Drosophila* development, how morphogens work, and tool-kit genes. The order of topics in the discussion of developmental principles is reorganized. The figure on *Hox* genes in *Drosophila* and the mouse is updated.

**Chapter 28 Phylogenies and the History of Life** The phylogenetics section is reorganized and expanded to include three illustrated summary tables and updated life-history timelines. New content is added, including the concept of the Anthropocene, the calendar analogy to the history of the Earth, the Chengjiang fossils, and a Life-in-the-Cambrian illustration. Evidence for the impact hypothesis is combined into an illustrated summary table.

**Chapter 29 Bacteria and Archaea** The chapter is updated to include a description of metagenomic experiments with an emphasis on the role of gut bacteria in digestion. A newly recognized phylum of Archaea, the Thaumarchaeota, is included, and the table comparing key characteristics of the Bacteria, Archaea, and Eukarya is streamlined.

**Chapter 30 Protists** For simplicity, protist lineages are now referred to throughout the chapter by their more familiar common names. Also, some key lineage boxes were consolidated to

**Chapter 33 An Introduction to Animals** The chapter is extensively revised to streamline and modernize the presentation, including emphasis on genetic tool kits and symmetry in the phylogeny of animals. The "Themes of Diversification" section is reorganized around five illustrated summary tables. The discussion of life cycles is revised to be more general. Insect metamorphosis has moved to Chapter 34, and a sea urchin life cycle replaces *Obelia*.

**Chapter 34 Protostome Animals** Two themes are threaded throughout the chapter: the water-to-land transition and modular body plans. The section on lophotrochozoans emphasizes spiral cleavage, indirect versus direct development, hemocoels, and radulas. The section on ecdysozoans highlights segmentation and *Hox* genes, including discussion of the origin of the wing and metamorphosis. Key lineage boxes include new phylogenies for annelids, crustaceans, and chelicerates.

**Chapter 35 Deuterostome Animals** Updates to reflect current research include revised phylogenies, evolution of flight and feathers, *Australopithecus sediba*, human migration out of Africa, and genetic evidence for interbreeding of *Homo neanderthalensis* and *Homo sapiens*.

**Chapter 42 Animal Form and Function** The chapter includes a new experiment illustrating physiological trade-offs, along with improved examples of thermoregulatory strategies in animals. Several complex figures were converted to illustrated summary tables.

**Chapter 43 Water and Electrolyte Balance in Animals** The chapter is reorganized to better integrate the relationship between excretion and water and electrolyte balance. Osmoregulatory strategies are now organized according to the challenges presented by marine, freshwater, and terrestrial habitats. Coverage of osmoregulation in bony fishes versus cartilaginous fishes, mammalian kidney function, and how nonmammalian vertebrates concentrate their urine is expanded and clarified.

**Chapter 45 Gas Exchange and Circulation** Discussion of the insect tracheal system is expanded, including new content on how respiration restricts upper limits of body size of insects. Details regarding the lymphatic system and heart anatomy in vertebrates are updated, and a new section on cardiovascular disease is added.

**Chapter 46 Electrical Signals in Animals** This chapter is greatly expanded to reflect recent research and growing interest in neuroscience. New information includes comparative anatomy of vertebrate brains, more case studies of brain injuries or dysfunctions that have led to major discoveries in neuroscience, and the concept of neuroplasticity—especially neurogenesis.

**Chapter 47 Animal Sensory Systems** Content from the Fourth Edition has been split into two chapters (47, Animal Sen-

sory Systems; 48, Animal Movement). The chapter on sensory systems is now organized by type of sensory reception: mechanoreception (with new coverage on the lateral line system of fishes), photoreception, chemoreception (with new coverage of pheromones), and a new section introducing thermoreception, electroreception, and magnetoreception.

# Acknowledgments

## Reviewers

The peer review system is the key to quality and clarity in science publishing. In addition to providing a filter, the investment that respected individuals make in vetting the material—catching errors or inconsistencies and making suggestions to improve the presentation—gives authors, editors, and readers confidence that the text meets rigorous professional standards.

Peer review plays the same role in textbook publishing. The time and care that this book's reviewers have invested is a tribute to their professional integrity, their scholarship, and their concern for the quality of teaching. Virtually every paragraph in this edition has been revised and improved based on insights from the following individuals.

Tamarah Adair, *Baylor University*
Sandra D. Adams, *Montclair State University*
Marc Albrecht, *University of Nebraska at Kearney*
Larry Alice, *Western Kentucky University*
Leo M. Alves, *Manhattan College*
David R. Angelini, *American University*
Dan Ardia, *Franklin & Marshall College*
Paul Arriola, *Elmhurst College*
Davinderjit K. Bagga, *University of Montevallo*
Susan Barrett, *Wheaton College*
Donald Baud, *University of Memphis*
Vernon W. Bauer, *Francis Marion University*
Robert Bauman, *Amarillo College*
Christopher Beck, *Emory University*
Vagner Benedito, *West Virginia University*
Scott Bingham, *Arizona State University*
Stephanie Bingham, *Barry University*
Wendy Birky, *California State University, Northridge*
Jason Blank, *California Polytechnic State University*
Kristopher A. Blee, *California State University, Chico*
Margaret Bloch-Qazi, *Gustavus Adolphus College*
Lanh Bloodworth, *Florida State College at Jacksonville*
Catherine H. Borer, *Berry College*
James Bottesch, *Brevard Community College*
Jacqueline K. Bowman, *Arkansas Tech University*
John Bowman, *University of California, Davis*
Chris Brochu, *University of Iowa*
Matthew Brown, *Dalhousie University*
Mark Browning, *Purdue University*
Carolyn J. W. Bunde, *Idaho State University*
David Byres, *Florida State College at Jacksonville*
Michael Campbell, *Penn State Erie*
Manel Camps, *University of California, Santa Cruz*
Geralyn M. Caplan, *Owensboro Community and Technical College*
Richard Cardullo, *University of California, Riverside*

David Carlini, *American University*
Dale Casamatta, *University of North Florida*
Deborah Chapman, *University of Pittsburgh*
Joe Coelho, *Quincy University*
Allen Collins, *Smithsonian Museum of Natural History*
Robert A. Colvin, *Ohio University*
Kimberly L. Conner, *Florida State College at Jacksonville*
Karen Curto, *University of Pittsburgh*
Clarissa Dirks, *Evergreen State College*
Peter Ducey, *SUNY Cortland*
Erastus Dudley, *Huntingdon College*
Jeffrey P. Duguay, *Delta State University*
Tod Duncan, *University of Colorado, Denver*
Joseph Esdin, *University of California, Los Angeles*
Brent Ewers, *University of Wyoming*
Amy Farris, *Ivy Tech Community College*
Bruce Fisher, *Roane State Community College*
Ryan Fisher, *Salem State University*
David Fitch, *New York University*
Elizabeth Fitch, *Motlow State Community College*
Michael P. Franklin, *California State University, Northridge*
Susannah French, *Utah State University*
Caitlin Gabor, *Texas State University*
Matthew Gilg, *University of North Florida*
Kendra Greenlee, *North Dakota State University*
Patricia A. Grove, *College of Mount Saint Vincent*
Nancy Guild, *University of Colorado, Boulder*
Cynthia Hemenway, *North Carolina State University*
Christopher R. Herlihy, *Middle Tennessee State University*
Kendra Hill, *South Dakota State University*
Sara Hoot, *University of Wisconsin, Milwaukee*
Kelly Howe, *University of New Mexico*
Robin Hulbert, *California Polytechnic State University*
Rick Jellen, *Brigham Young University*
Russell Johnson, *Colby College*
William Jira Katembe, *Delta State University*
Elena K. Keeling, *California Polytechnic State University*
Jill B. Keeney, *Juniata College*
Greg Kelly, *University of Western Ontario*
Scott L. Kight, *Montclair State University*
Charles Knight, *California Polytechnic State University*
Jenny Knight, *University of Colorado, Boulder*
William Kroll, *Loyola University Chicago*
Dominic Lannutti, *El Paso Community College*
Brenda Leady, *University of Toledo*
David Lindberg, *University of California, Berkeley*
Barbara Lom, *Davidson College*
Robert Maxwell, *Georgia State University*
Marshall D. McCue, *St. Mary's University*
Kurt A. McKean, *SUNY Albany*
Michael Meighan, *University of California, Berkeley*
John Merrill, *Michigan State University*

Richard Merritt, *Houston Community College*
Alan Molumby, *University of Illinois at Chicago*
Jeremy Montague, *Barry University*
Chad E. Montgomery, *Truman State University*
Kimberly D. Moore, *Lone Star College System, North Harris*
Michael Morgan, *Berry College*
James Mulrooney, *Central Connecticut State University*
John D. Nagy, *Scottsdale Community College*
Margaret Olney, *St. Martin's University*
Nathan Okia, *Auburn University at Montgomery*
Robert Osuna, *SUNY Albany*
Daniel Panaccione, *West Virginia University*
Stephanie Pandolfi, *Michigan State University*
Michael Rockwell Parker, *Monell Chemical Senses Center*
Lisa Parks, *North Carolina State University*
Nancy Pelaez, *Purdue University*
Shelley W. Penrod, *Lone Star College System, North Harris*
Andrea Pesce, *James Madison University*
Raymond Pierotti, *University of Kansas*
Melissa Ann Pilgrim, *University of South Carolina Upstate*
Paul Pillitteri, *Southern Utah University*
Debra Pires, *University of California, Los Angeles*
P. David Polly, *Indiana University, Bloomington*
Vanessa Quinn, *Purdue University North Central*
Stacey L. Raimondi, *Elmhurst College*
Stephanie Randell, *McLennan Community College*
Marceau Ratard, *Delgado Community College*
Ilona Redway, *Barry University*
Srebrenka Robic, *Agnes Scott College*
Dave Robinson, *Bellarmine University*
George Robinson, *SUNY Albany*
Adam W. Rollins, *Lincoln Memorial University*
Amanda Rosenzweig, *Delgado Community College*
Leonard C. Salvatori, *Indian River State College*
Dee Ann Sato, *Cypress College*
Meena Sawant, *Houston Community College*
Jon Scales, *Midwestern State University*
Oswald Schmitz, *Yale University*
Dan Sharp, *Simon Fraser University*
Julie Schroer, *North Dakota State University*
Timothy E. Shannon, *Francis Marion University*
Lynnette Sievert, *Emporia State University*
Susan Skambis, *Valencia College*
Ann E. Stapleton, *University of North Carolina, Wilmington*
Mary-Pat Stein, *California State University, Northridge*
Christine Strand, *California Polytechnic State University*
Denise Strickland, *Midlands Technical College*
Jackie Swanik, *Wake Technical Community College*
Billie J. Swalla, *University of Washington*
Suzana Swigonova, *University of Pittsburgh*
Briana Timmerman, *University of South Carolina*
Catherine Ueckert, *Northern Arizona University*
Sara Via, *University of Maryland, College Park*
Thomas J. Volk, *University of Wisconsin–La Crosse*
Jeffrey Walck, *Middle Tennessee State University*
Andrea Weeks, *George Mason University*
Margaret S. White, *Scottsdale Community College*
Steven D. Wilt, *Bellarmine University*
Candace Winstead, *California Polytechnic State University*
James A. Wise, *Hampton University*

## Correspondents

One of the most enjoyable interactions we have as textbook authors is correspondence or conversations with researchers and teachers who take the time and trouble to contact us to discuss an issue with the book, or who respond to our queries about a particular data set or study. We are always amazed and heartened by the generosity of these individuals. They care, deeply.

Lawrence Alice, *Western Kentucky University*
David Baum, *University of Wisconsin–Madison*
Meredith Blackwell, *Louisiana State University*
Nancy Burley, *University of California, Irvine*
Thomas Breithaupt, *University of Hull*
Philip Cantino, *Ohio University*
Allen Collins, *Smithsonian Museum of Natural History*
Robert Full, *University of California, Berkeley*
Arundhati Ghosh, *University of Pittsburgh*
Jennifer Gottwald, *University of Wisconsin–Madison*
Jon Harrison, *Arizona State University*
David Hawksworth, *Natural History Museum, London*
Jim Herrick, *James Madison University*
John Hunt, *University of Exeter*
Doug Jensen, *Converse College*
Scott Kight, *Montclair State University*
Scott Kirkton, *Union College*
Mimi Koehl, *University of California, Berkeley*
Rodger Kram, *University of Colorado*
Matthew McHenry, *University of California, Irvine*
Alison Miyamoto, *California State University, Fullerton*
Sean Menke, *Lake Forest College*
Rich Mooi, *California Academy of Sciences*
Michael Oliver, *MalawiCichlids.com*
M. Rockwell Parker, *Monell Chemical Senses Center*
Andrea Pesce, *James Madison University*
Chris Preston, *Monterey Bay Aquarium Research Institute*
Scott Sakaluk, *Illinois State University*
Kyle Seifert, *James Madison University*
Jos Snoeks, *Royal Museum for Central Africa*
Jeffrey Spring, *University of Louisiana*
Christy Strand, *California Polytechnic State University, San Luis Obispo*
Torsten Struck, *University of Osnabrueck, Germany*
Oswald Schmitz, *Yale University*
Ian Tattersal, *American Museum of Natural History*
Robert Turgeon, *Cornell University*
Tom Volk, *University of Wisconsin–La Crosse*
Naomi Wernick, *University of Massachusetts, Lowell*

## Supplements Contributors

Instructors depend on an impressive array of support materials—in print and online—to design and deliver their courses. The student experience would be much weaker without the study guide, test bank, activities, animations, quizzes, and tutorials written by the following individuals.

Brian Bagatto, *University of Akron*
Scott Bingham, *Arizona State University*
Jay L. Brewster, *Pepperdine University*

Mirjana Brockett, *Georgia Institute of Technology*
Warren Burggren, *University of North Texas*
Jeff Carmichael, *University of North Dakota*
Tim Christensen, *East Carolina University*
Erica Cline, *University of Washington—Tacoma*
Patricia Colberg, *University of Wyoming*
Elia Crisucci, *University of Pittsburgh*
Elizabeth Cowles, *Eastern Connecticut State University*
Clarissa Dirks, *Evergreen State College*
Lisa Elfring, *University of Arizona, Tucson*
Brent Ewers, *University of Wyoming*
Rebecca Ferrell, *Metropolitan State University of Denver*
Miriam Ferzli, *North Carolina State University*
Cheryl Frederick, *University of Washington*
Cindee Giffen, *University of Wisconsin–Madison*
Kathy M. Gillen, *Kenyon College*
Linda Green, *Georgia Institute of Technology*
Christopher Harendza, *Montgomery County Community College*
Cynthia Hemenway, *North Carolina State University*
Laurel Hester, *University of South Carolina*
Jean Heitz, *University of Wisconsin–Madison*
Tracey Hickox, *University of Illinois, Urbana–Champaign*
Jacob Kerby, *University of South Dakota*
David Kooyman, *Brigham Young University*
Barbara Lom, *Davidson College*
Cindy Malone, *California State University, Northridge*
Jim Manser, retired, *Harvey Mudd College*
Jeanette McGuire, *Michigan State University*
Mark Music, *Indian River State College*
Jennifer Nauen, *University of Delaware*
Chris Pagliarulo, *University of California, Davis*
Stephanie Scher Pandolfi, *Michigan State University*
Lisa Parks, *North Carolina State University*
Debra Pires, *University of California, Los Angeles*
Carol Pollock, *University of British Columbia*
Jessica Poulin, *University at Buffalo, the State University of New York*
Vanessa Quinn, *Purdue University North Central*
Eric Ribbens, *Western Illinois University*
Christina T. Russin, *Northwestern University*
Leonard Salvatori, *Indian River State College*
Joan Sharp, *Simon Fraser University*
Chrissy Spencer, *Georgia Institute of Technology*
Mary-Pat Stein, *California State University, Northridge*
Suzanne Simon-Westendorf, *Ohio University*
Fred Wasserman, *Boston University*
Cindy White, *University of Northern Colorado*
Edward Zalisko, *Blackburn College*

## Book Team

Anyone who has been involved in producing a textbook knows that many people work behind the scenes to make it all happen. The coauthor team is indebted to the many talented individuals who have made this book possible.

Development editors Mary Catherine Hager, Moira Lerner-Nelson, and Bill O'Neal provided incisive comments on the revised manuscript. Fernanda Oyarzun and Adam Steinberg used their artistic sense, science skills, and love of teaching to hone the figures for many chapters.

The final version of the text was copyedited by Chris Thillen and expertly proofread by Pete Shanks. The final figure designs were rendered by Imagineering Media Services and carefully proofread by Frank Purcell. Maureen Spuhler, Eric Schrader, and Kristen Piljay researched images for the Fifth Edition.

The book's clean, innovative design was developed by Mark Ong and Emily Friel. Text and art were skillfully set in the design by S4Carlisle Publishing Services. The book's production was supervised by Lori Newman and Mike Early.

The extensive supplements program was managed by Brady Golden and Katie Cook. All of the individuals mentioned—and more—were supported with cheerful, dedicated efficiency by Editorial Assistant Leslie Allen for the first half of the project; Eddie Lee has since stepped in to skillfully fill this role.

Creating MasteringBiology® tutorials and activities also requires a team. Media content development was overseen by Tania Mlawer and Sarah Jensen, who benefited from the program expertise of Caroline Power and Caroline Ross. Joseph Mochnick and Daniel Ross worked together as media producers. Lauren Fogel (VP, Director, Media Development), Stacy Treco (VP, Director, Media Product Strategy), and Laura ensured that the complete media program that accompanies the Fifth Edition, including MasteringBiology, will meet the needs of the students and professors who use our offerings.

Pearson's talented sales reps, who listen to professors, advise the editorial staff, and get the book in students' hands, are supported by tireless Executive Marketing Manager Lauren Harp and Director of Marketing Christy Lesko. The marketing materials that support the outreach effort were produced by Lillian Carr and her colleagues in Pearson's Marketing Comunications group. David Theisen, national director for Key Markets, tirelessly visits countless professors each year, enthusiastically discussing their courses and providing us with meaningful editorial guidance.

The vision and resources required to run this entire enterprise are the responsibility of Vice President and Editor-in-Chief Beth Wilbur, who provided inspirational and focused leadership, and President of Pearson Science Paul Corey, who displays unwavering commitment to high-quality science publishing.

Becky Ruden recruited the coauthor team, drawing us to the project with her energy and belief in this book. The editorial team was skillfully directed by Executive Director of Development Deborah Gale. Finally, we are deeply grateful for three key drivers of the Fifth Edition. Project Editor Anna Amato's superb organizational skills and calm demeanor assured that all the wheels and cogs of the process ran smoothly to keep the mammoth project steadily rolling forward. Supervising Development Editor Sonia DiVittorio's deep expertise, creative vision, keen attention to detail, level, and clarity, and inspiring insistence on excellence kept the bar high for everyone on every aspect of the project. Lastly, Senior Acquisitions Editor Michael Gillespie's boundless energy and enthusiasm, positive attitude, and sharp intellect have fueled and united the team and also guided the book through the hurdles to existence. The coauthor team thanks these exceptional people for making the art and science of book writing a productive and exhilarating process.

# 1 Biology and the Tree of Life

**In this chapter you will learn about**

Key themes to structure your thinking about Biology

starting with
**What does it mean to say that something is alive?** 1.1

including
**Two of the greatest unifying ideas in Biology**

including
**The process of doing Biology** 1.5

first
**The cell theory** 1.2

then
**The theory of evolution by natural selection** 1.3

predicts
**The tree of life** 1.4

These Chinese water dragon hatchlings are exploring their new world and learning how to find food and stay alive. They represent one of the key characteristics of life introduced in this chapter—replication.

n essence, biological science is a search for ideas and observations that unify our understanding of the diversity of life, from bacteria living in rocks a mile underground to humans and majestic sequoia trees. This chapter is an introduction to this search.

The goals of this chapter are to introduce the nature of life and explore how biologists go about studying it. The chapter also introduces themes that will resonate throughout this book:

- Analyzing how organisms work at the molecular level.
- Understanding organisms in terms of their evolutionary history.
- Helping you learn to think like a biologist.

Let's begin with what may be the most fundamental question of all: What is life?

This chapter is part of the Big Picture. See how on pages 16–17.

✔ When you see this checkmark, stop and test yourself. Answers are available in Appendix A.

## 1.1 What Does It Mean to Say That Something Is Alive?

An **organism** is a life-form—a living entity made up of one or more cells. Although there is no simple definition of life that is endorsed by all biologists, most agree that organisms share a suite of five fundamental characteristics.

- *Energy*  To stay alive and reproduce, organisms have to acquire and use energy. To give just two examples: plants absorb sunlight; animals ingest food.

- *Cells*  Organisms are made up of membrane-bound units called cells. A cell's membrane regulates the passage of materials between exterior and interior spaces.

- *Information*  Organisms process hereditary, or genetic, information encoded in units called genes. Organisms also respond to information from the environment and adjust to maintain stable internal conditions. Right now, cells throughout your body are using information to make the molecules that keep you alive; your eyes and brain are decoding information on this page that will help you learn some biology, and if your room is too hot you might be sweating to cool off.

- *Replication*  One of the great biologists of the twentieth century, François Jacob, said that the "dream of a bacterium is to become two bacteria." Almost everything an organism does contributes to one goal: replicating itself.

- *Evolution*  Organisms are the product of evolution, and their populations continue to evolve.

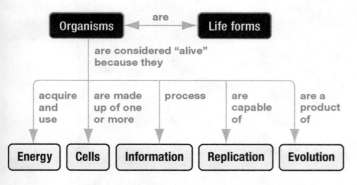

You can think of this text as one long exploration of these five traits. Here's to life!

## 1.2 The Cell Theory

Two of the greatest unifying ideas in all of science laid the groundwork for modern biology: the cell theory and the theory of evolution by natural selection. Formally, scientists define a **theory** as an explanation for a very general class of phenomena or observations that are supported by a wide body of evidence. The cell theory and theory of evolution address fundamental questions: What are organisms made of? Where do they come from?

When these concepts emerged in the mid-1800s, they revolutionized the way biologists think about the world. They established

two of the five attributes of life: Organisms are cellular, and their populations change over time.

Neither insight came easily, however. The cell theory, for example, emerged after some 200 years of work. In 1665 the Englishman Robert Hooke devised a crude microscope to examine the structure of cork (a bark tissue) from an oak tree. The instrument magnified objects to just 30× (30 times) their normal size, but it allowed Hooke to see something extraordinary. In the cork he observed small, pore-like compartments that were invisible to the naked eye. Hooke coined the term "cells" for these structures because of their resemblance to the cells inhabited by monks in a monastery.

Soon after Hooke published his results, a Dutch scientist named Anton van Leeuwenhoek succeeded in developing much more powerful microscopes, some capable of magnifications up to 300×. With these instruments, van Leeuwenhoek inspected samples of pond water and made the first observations of a dazzling collection of single-celled organisms that he called "animalcules." He also observed and described human blood cells and sperm cells, shown in **FIGURE 1.1**.

In the 1670s an Italian researcher who was studying the leaves and stems of plants with a microscope concluded that plant tissues were composed of many individual cells. By the early 1800s, enough data had accumulated for a German biologist to claim that *all* organisms consist of cells. Did this claim hold up?

### All Organisms Are Made of Cells

Advances in microscopy have made it possible to examine the amazing diversity and complexity of cells at higher and higher magnifications. Biologists have developed microscopes that are tens of thousands of times more powerful than van Leeuwenhoek's and have described over a million new species. The basic conclusion made in the 1800s remains intact, however: All organisms are made of cells.

The smallest organisms known today are bacteria that are barely 200 nanometers wide, or 200 *billionths* of a meter. (See **BioSkills 1** in Appendix B to review the metric system and its prefixes.[1]) It would take 5000 of these organisms lined up side by side to span a millimeter. This is the distance between the smallest hash marks on a metric ruler. In contrast, sequoia trees can be over 100 meters tall. This is the equivalent of a 20-story building. Bacteria and sequoias are composed of the same fundamental building block, however—the cell. Bacteria consist of a single cell; sequoias are made up of many cells.

Today a **cell** is defined as a highly organized compartment that is bounded by a thin, flexible structure called a plasma membrane and that contains concentrated chemicals in an aqueous (watery) solution. The chemical reactions that sustain life take place inside cells. Most cells are also capable of reproducing by dividing—in effect, by making a copy of themselves.

The realization that all organisms are made of cells was fundamentally important, but it formed only the first part of the cell

---

[1]BioSkills are located in the second appendix at the back of the book. They focus on general skills that you'll use throughout this course. More than a few students have found them to be a life-saver. Please use them!

**(a)** van Leeuwenhoek built his own microscopes—which, while small, were powerful. They allowed him to see, for example . . .

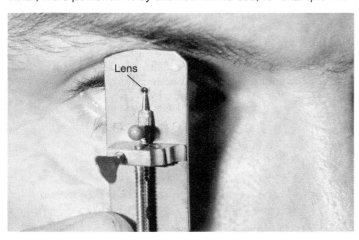

**(b)** . . . human blood cells (this modern photo was shot through one of van Leeuwenhoek's original microscopes) . . .

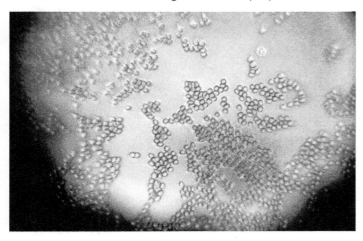

**(c)** . . . and animal sperm (drawing by van Leeuwenhoek of canine sperm cells on left, human on right).

**FIGURE 1.1 Van Leeuwenhoek's Microscope Made Cells Visible.**

theory. In addition to understanding what organisms are made of, scientists wanted to understand how cells come to be.

## Where Do Cells Come From?

Most scientific theories have two components: The first describes a pattern in the natural world; the second identifies a mechanism or process that is responsible for creating that pattern. Hooke and his fellow scientists articulated the pattern component of the cell theory. In 1858, a German scientist named Rudolph Virchow added the process component by stating that all cells arise from preexisting cells.

The complete **cell theory** can be stated as follows: All organisms are made of cells, and all cells come from preexisting cells.

**Two Hypotheses**    The cell theory was a direct challenge to the prevailing explanation of where cells come from, called spontaneous generation. In the mid-1800s, most biologists believed that organisms could arise spontaneously under certain conditions. For example, the bacteria and fungi that spoil foods such as milk and wine were thought to appear in these nutrient-rich media of their own accord—springing to life from nonliving materials. In contrast, the cell theory maintained that cells do not spring to life spontaneously but are produced only when preexisting cells grow and divide. The all-cells-from-cells explanation was a **hypothesis:** a testable statement to explain a phenomenon or a set of observations.

Biologists usually use the word theory to refer to proposed explanations for broad patterns in nature and prefer hypothesis to refer to explanations for more tightly focused questions. A theory serves as a framework for the development of new hypotheses.

**An Experiment to Settle the Question**    Soon after Virchow's all-cells-from-cells hypothesis appeared in print, a French scientist named Louis Pasteur set out to test its predictions experimentally. An experimental **prediction** describes a measurable or observable result that must be correct if a hypothesis is valid.

Pasteur wanted to determine whether microorganisms could arise spontaneously in a nutrient broth or whether they appear only when a broth is exposed to a source of preexisting cells. To address the question, he created two treatment groups: a broth that was not exposed to a source of preexisting cells and a broth that was.

The spontaneous generation hypothesis predicted that cells would appear in both treatment groups. The all-cells-from-cells hypothesis predicted that cells would appear only in the treatment exposed to a source of preexisting cells.

**FIGURE 1.2** (on page 4) shows Pasteur's experimental setup. Note that the two treatments are identical in every respect but one. Both used glass flasks filled with the same amount of the same nutrient broth. Both were boiled for the same amount of time to kill any existing organisms such as bacteria or fungi. But because the flask pictured in Figure 1.2a had a straight neck, it was exposed to preexisting cells after sterilization by the heat treatment. These preexisting cells are the bacteria and fungi that cling to dust particles in the air. They could drop into the nutrient broth because the neck of the flask was straight.

In contrast, the flask drawn in Figure 1.2b had a long swan neck. Pasteur knew that water would condense in the crook of the swan neck after the boiling treatment and that this pool of water

**QUESTION: Do cells arise spontaneously or from other cells?**

**SPONTANEOUS GENERATION HYPOTHESIS:** Cells arise spontaneously from nonliving materials.

**ALL-CELLS-FROM-CELLS HYPOTHESIS:** Cells are produced only when preexisting cells grow and divide.

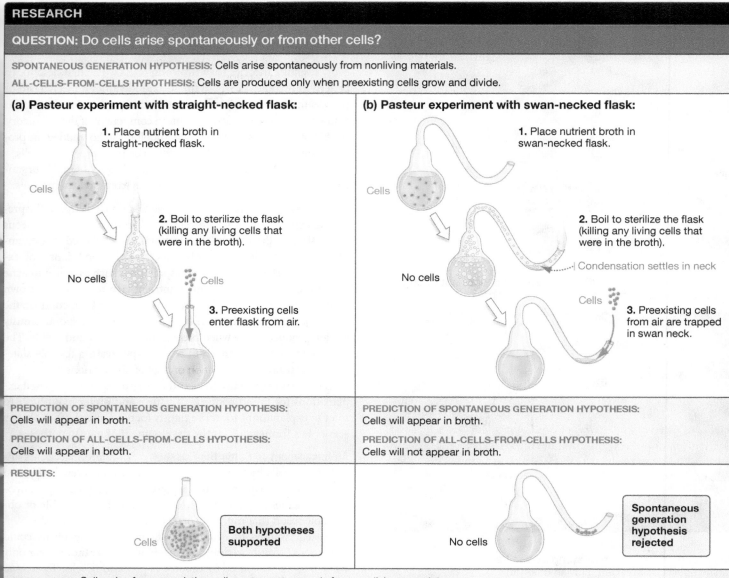

**(a) Pasteur experiment with straight-necked flask:**

1. Place nutrient broth in straight-necked flask.

Cells

2. Boil to sterilize the flask (killing any living cells that were in the broth).

No cells

Cells

3. Preexisting cells enter flask from air.

**(b) Pasteur experiment with swan-necked flask:**

1. Place nutrient broth in swan-necked flask.

Cells

2. Boil to sterilize the flask (killing any living cells that were in the broth).

Condensation settles in neck

No cells

Cells

3. Preexisting cells from air are trapped in swan neck.

**PREDICTION OF SPONTANEOUS GENERATION HYPOTHESIS:** Cells will appear in broth.

**PREDICTION OF ALL-CELLS-FROM-CELLS HYPOTHESIS:** Cells will appear in broth.

**PREDICTION OF SPONTANEOUS GENERATION HYPOTHESIS:** Cells will appear in broth.

**PREDICTION OF ALL-CELLS-FROM-CELLS HYPOTHESIS:** Cells will not appear in broth.

**RESULTS:**

Cells

Both hypotheses supported

No cells

Spontaneous generation hypothesis rejected

**CONCLUSION:** Cells arise from preexisting cells, not spontaneously from nonliving material.

**FIGURE 1.2 The Spontaneous Generation and All-Cells-from-Cells Hypotheses Were Tested Experimentally.**

✔**QUESTION** What problem would arise in interpreting the results of this experiment if Pasteur had (1) put different types of broth in the two treatments, (2) heated them for different lengths of time, or (3) used a ceramic flask for one treatment and a glass flask for the other?

would trap any bacteria or fungi that entered on dust particles. Thus, the contents of the swan-necked flask were isolated from any source of preexisting cells even though still open to the air.

Pasteur's experimental setup was effective because there was only one difference between the two treatments and because that difference was the factor being tested—in this case, a broth's exposure to preexisting cells.

**One Hypothesis Supported** And Pasteur's results? As Figure 1.2 shows, the treatment exposed to preexisting cells quickly filled with bacteria and fungi. This observation was important because it showed that the heat sterilization step had not altered the nutrient broth's capacity to support growth.

The broth in the swan-necked flask remained sterile, however. Even when the flask was left standing for months, no organisms appeared in it. This result was inconsistent with the hypothesis of spontaneous generation.

Because Pasteur's data were so conclusive—meaning that there was no other reasonable explanation for them—the results persuaded most biologists that the all-cells-from-cells hypothesis was correct. However, you will see that biologists now have evidence that life did arise from nonlife early in Earth's history, through a process called chemical evolution (Chapters 2–6).

The success of the cell theory's process component had an important implication: If all cells come from preexisting cells, it follows that all individuals in an isolated population of single-celled organisms are related by common ancestry. Similarly, in you and most other multicellular individuals, all the cells present are descended from preexisting cells, tracing back to a fertilized egg. A fertilized egg is a cell created by the fusion of sperm and egg—cells that formed in individuals of the previous generation. In this way, all the cells in a multicellular organism are connected by common ancestry.

The second great founding idea in biology is similar, in spirit, to the cell theory. It also happened to be published the same year as the all-cells-from-cells hypothesis. This was the realization, made independently by the English scientists Charles Darwin and Alfred Russel Wallace, that all species—all distinct, identifiable types of organisms—are connected by common ancestry.

## 1.3 The Theory of Evolution by Natural Selection

In 1858 short papers written separately by Darwin and Wallace were read to a small group of scientists attending a meeting of the Linnean Society of London. A year later, Darwin published a book that expanded on the idea summarized in those brief papers. The book was called *The Origin of Species*. The first edition sold out in a day.

### What Is Evolution?

Like the cell theory, the theory of evolution by natural selection has a pattern and a process component. Darwin and Wallace's theory made two important claims concerning patterns that exist in the natural world.

1. Species are related by common ancestry. This contrasted with the prevailing view in science at the time, which was that species represent independent entities created separately by a divine being.

2. In contrast to the accepted view that species remain unchanged through time, Darwin and Wallace proposed that the characteristics of species can be modified from generation to generation. Darwin called this process descent with modification.

**Evolution** is a change in the characteristics of a population over time. It means that species are not independent and unchanging entities, but are related to one another and can change through time.

### What Is Natural Selection?

This pattern component of the theory of evolution was actually not original to Darwin and Wallace. Several scientists had already come to the same conclusions about the relationships between species. The great insight by Darwin and Wallace was in proposing a process, called **natural selection,** that explains *how* evolution occurs.

**Two Conditions of Natural Selection**    Natural selection occurs whenever two conditions are met.

1. Individuals within a population vary in characteristics that are **heritable**—meaning, traits that can be passed on to offspring.

A **population** is defined as a group of individuals of the same species living in the same area at the same time.

2. In a particular environment, certain versions of these heritable traits help individuals survive better or reproduce more than do other versions.

If certain heritable traits lead to increased success in producing offspring, then those traits become more common in the population over time. In this way, the population's characteristics change as a result of natural selection acting on individuals. This is a key insight: Natural selection acts on individuals, but evolutionary change occurs in populations.

**Selection on Maize as an Example**    To clarify how selection works, consider an example of **artificial selection**—changes in populations that occur when *humans* select certain individuals to produce the most offspring. Beginning in 1896, researchers began a long-term selection experiment on maize (corn).

1. In the original population, the percentage of protein in maize kernels was variable among individuals. Kernel protein content is a heritable trait—parents tend to pass the trait on to their offspring.

2. Each year for many years, researchers chose individuals with the highest kernel protein content to be the parents of the next generation. In this environment, individuals with high kernel protein content produced more offspring than individuals with low kernel protein content.

**FIGURE 1.3** shows the results. Note that this graph plots generation number on the *x*-axis, starting from the first generation (0 on the graph) and continuing for 100 generations. The average percentage of protein in a kernel among individuals in this population is plotted on the *y*-axis.

**FIGURE 1.3 Response to Selection for High Kernel Protein Content in Maize.**

DATA: Moose, S. P., J. W. Dudley, and T. R. Rocheford. 2004. *Trends in Plant Sciences* 9: 358–364; and the Illinois long-term selection experiment for oil and protein in corn (University of Illinois at Urbana–Champaign).

To read this graph, put your finger on the *x*-axis at generation 0. Then read up the *y*-axis, and note that kernels averaged about 11 percent protein at the start of the experiment. Now read the graph to the right. Each dot is a data point, representing the average kernel protein concentration in a particular generation. (A generation in maize is one year.) The lines on this graph simply connect the dots, to make the pattern in the data easier to see. During a few years the average protein content goes down, because of poor growing conditions or chance changes in how the many genes responsible for this trait interact. However, at the end of the graph, after 100 generations of selection, average kernel protein content is about 29 percent. (For more help with reading graphs, see **BioSkills 3** in Appendix B.)

This sort of change in the characteristics of a population, over time, is evolution. Humans have been practicing artificial selection for thousands of years, and biologists have now documented evolution by *natural* selection—where humans don't do the selecting—occurring in thousands of different populations, including humans. Evolution occurs when heritable variation leads to differential success in reproduction.

✔ **QUANTITATIVE** If you understand the concepts of selection and evolution, you should be able to describe how protein content in maize kernels changed over time, using the same *x*-axis and *y*-axis as in Figure 1.3, when researchers selected individuals with the *lowest* kernel protein content to be the parents of the next generation. (This experiment was actually done, starting with the same population at the same time as selection for high protein content.)

**Fitness and Adaptation** Darwin also introduced some new terminology to identify what is happening during natural selection.

- In everyday English, fitness means health and well-being. But in biology, **fitness** means the ability of an individual to produce viable offspring. Individuals with high fitness produce many surviving offspring.

- In everyday English, adaptation means that an individual is adjusting and changing to function in new circumstances. But in biology, an **adaptation** is a trait that increases the fitness of an individual in a particular environment.

Once again, consider kernel protein content in maize: In the environment of the experiment graphed in Figure 1.3, individuals with high kernel protein content produced more offspring and had higher fitness than individuals with lower kernel protein content. In this population and this environment, high kernel protein content was an adaptation that allowed certain individuals to thrive.

Note that during this process, the amount of protein in the kernels of any individual maize plant did not change within its lifetime—the change occurred in the characteristics of the population over time.

Together, the cell theory and the theory of evolution provided the young science of biology with two central, unifying ideas:

1. The cell is the fundamental structural unit in all organisms.

2. All species are related by common ancestry and have changed over time in response to natural selection.

**If you understand that . . .**

- Natural selection occurs when heritable variation in certain traits leads to improved success in reproduction. Because individuals with these traits produce many offspring with the same traits, the traits increase in frequency and evolution occurs.
- Evolution is a change in the characteristics of a population over time.

✔ **You should be able to . . .**

Using the graph you just analyzed in Figure 1.3, describe the average kernel protein content over time in a maize population where *no* selection occurred.

*Answers are available in Appendix A.*

## 1.4 The Tree of Life

Section 1.3 focuses on how individual populations change through time in response to natural selection. But over the past several decades, biologists have also documented dozens of cases in which natural selection has caused populations of one species to diverge and form new species. This divergence process is called **speciation.**

Research on speciation has two important implications: All species come from preexisting species, and all species, past and present, trace their ancestry back to a single common ancestor.

The theory of evolution by natural selection predicts that biologists should be able to construct a **tree of life**—a family tree of organisms. If life on Earth arose just once, then such a diagram would describe the genealogical relationships between species with a single, ancestral species at its base.

Has this task been accomplished? If the tree of life exists, what does it look like?

### Using Molecules to Understand the Tree of Life

One of the great breakthroughs in research on the tree of life occurred when American biologist Carl Woese (pronounced *woze*) and colleagues began analyzing the chemical components of organisms as a way to understand their evolutionary relationships. Their goal was to understand the **phylogeny** of all organisms—their actual genealogical relationships. Translated literally, phylogeny means "tribe-source."

To understand which organisms are closely versus distantly related, Woese and co-workers needed to study a molecule that is found in all organisms. The molecule they selected is called small subunit ribosomal RNA (rRNA). It is an essential part of the machinery that all cells use to grow and reproduce.

Although rRNA is a large and complex molecule, its underlying structure is simple. The rRNA molecule is made up of sequences of four smaller chemical components called ribonucleotides. These ribonucleotides are symbolized by the letters A, U, C, and G. In rRNA, ribonucleotides are connected to one another linearly, like the boxcars of a freight train.

**Analyzing rRNA**  Why might rRNA be useful for understanding the relationships between organisms? The answer is that the ribonucleotide sequence in rRNA is a trait that can change during the course of evolution. Although rRNA performs the same function in all organisms, the sequence of ribonucleotide building blocks in this molecule is not identical among species.

In land plants, for example, the molecule might start with the sequence A-U-A-U-C-G-A-G (**FIGURE 1.4**). In green algae, which are closely related to land plants, the same section of the molecule might contain A-U-A-U-G-G-A-G. But in brown algae, which are not closely related to green algae or to land plants, the same part of the molecule might consist of A-A-A-U-G-G-A-C.

The research that Woese and co-workers pursued was based on a simple premise: If the theory of evolution is correct, then rRNA sequences should be very similar in closely related organisms but less similar in organisms that are less closely related. Species that are part of the same evolutionary lineage, like the plants, should share certain changes in rRNA that no other species have.

To test this premise, the researchers determined the sequence of ribonucleotides in the rRNA of a wide array of species. Then they considered what the similarities and differences in the sequences implied about relationships between the species. The goal was to produce a diagram that described the phylogeny of the organisms in the study.

A diagram that depicts evolutionary history in this way is called a phylogenetic tree. Just as a family tree shows relationships between individuals, a phylogenetic tree shows relationships between species. On a phylogenetic tree, branches that share a recent common ancestor represent species that are closely related; branches that don't share recent common ancestors represent species that are more distantly related.

**The Tree of Life Estimated from Genetic Data**  To construct a phylogenetic tree, researchers use a computer to find the arrangement of branches that is most consistent with the similarities and differences observed in the data.

Although the initial work was based only on the sequences of ribonucleotides observed in rRNA, biologists now use data sets that include sequences from a wide array of genetic material. **FIGURE 1.5** shows a recent tree produced by comparing these sequences. Because this tree includes such a diverse array of

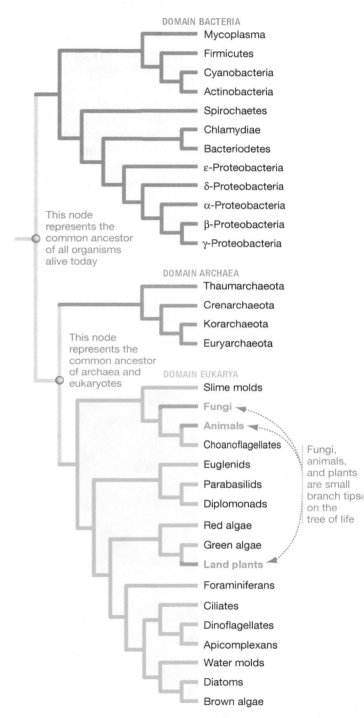

**FIGURE 1.5 The Tree of Life.** A phylogenetic tree estimated from a large amount of genetic sequence data. The three domains of life revealed by the analysis are labeled. Common names are given for lineages in the domains Bacteria and Eukarya. Phyla names are given for members of the domain Archaea, because most of these organisms have no common names.

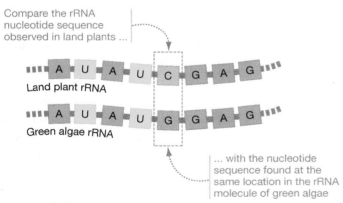

**FIGURE 1.4 RNA Molecules Are Made Up of Smaller Molecules.** A complete small subunit rRNA molecule contains about 2000 ribonucleotides; just 8 are shown in this comparison.

✔ **QUESTION** Suppose that in the same section of rRNA, molds and other fungi have the sequence A-U-A-U-G-G-A-C. Are fungi more closely related to green algae or to land plants? Explain your logic.

pecies, it is often called the universal tree, or the tree of life. (For help in learning how to read a phylogenetic tree, see **BioSkills 7** in Appendix B.) Notice that the tree's main node is the common ancestor of all living organisms. Researchers who study the origin of life propose that the tree's root extends even further back to the "*last universal common ancestor*" of cells, or **LUCA.**

The tree of life implied by rRNA and other genetic data established that there are three fundamental groups or lineages of organisms: (1) the Bacteria, (2) the Archaea, and (3) the Eukarya. In all **eukaryotes,** cells have a prominent component called the nucleus (**FIGURE 1.6a**). Translated literally, the word eukaryotes means "true kernel." Because the vast majority of bacterial and archaeal cells lack a nucleus, they are referred to as **prokaryotes** (literally, "before kernel"; see **FIGURE 1.6b**). The vast majority of bacteria and archaea are unicellular ("one-celled"); many eukaryotes are multicellular ("many-celled").

When results based on genetic data were first published, biologists were astonished. For example:

Prior to Woese's work and follow-up studies, biologists thought that the most fundamental division among organisms was between prokaryotes and eukaryotes. The Archaea were virtually unknown—much less recognized as a major and highly distinctive branch on the tree of life.

Fungi were thought to be closely related to plants. Instead, they are actually much more closely related to animals.

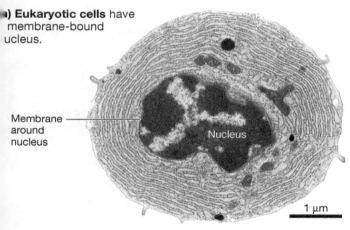

**a) Eukaryotic cells** have membrane-bound nucleus.

Membrane around nucleus

Nucleus

1 μm

**b) Prokaryotic cells** do *not* have a membrane-bound nucleus.

No nucleus

0.1 μm

**FIGURE 1.6 Eukaryotes and Prokaryotes.**

**QUANTITATIVE** How many times larger is the eukaryotic cell in this figure than the prokaryotic cell? (Hint: Study the scale bars.)

Traditional approaches for classifying organisms—including the system of five kingdoms divided into various classes, orders, and families that you may have learned in high school—are inaccurate in many cases, because they do not reflect the actual evolutionary history of the organisms involved.

**The Tree of Life Is a Work in Progress** Just as researching your family tree can help you understand who you are and where you came from, so the tree of life helps biologists understand the relationships between organisms and the history of species. The discovery of the Archaea and the accurate placement of lineages such as the fungi qualify as exciting breakthroughs in our understanding of evolutionary history and life's diversity.

Work on the tree of life continues at a furious pace, however, and the location of certain branches on the tree is hotly debated. As databases expand and as techniques for analyzing data improve, the shape of the tree of life presented in Figure 1.5 will undoubtedly change. Our understanding of the tree of life, like our understanding of every other topic in biological science, is dynamic.

## How Should We Name Branches on the Tree of Life?

In science, the effort to name and classify organisms is called **taxonomy.** Any named group is called a **taxon** (plural: **taxa**). Currently, biologists are working to create a taxonomy, or naming system, that accurately reflects the phylogeny of organisms.

Based on the tree of life implied by genetic data, Woese proposed a new taxonomic category called the **domain.** The three domains of life are the Bacteria, Archaea, and Eukarya.

Biologists often use the term **phylum** (plural: **phyla**) to refer to major lineages within each domain. Although the designation is somewhat arbitrary, each phylum is considered a major branch on the tree of life. Within the lineage called animals, biologists currently name 30–35 phyla—each of which is distinguished by distinctive aspects of its body structure as well as by distinctive gene sequences. For example, the mollusks (clams, squid, octopuses) constitute a phylum, as do chordates (the vertebrates and their close relatives).

Because the tree of life is so new, though, naming systems are still being worked out. One thing that hasn't changed for centuries, however, is the naming system for individual species.

**Scientific (Latin) Names** In 1735, a Swedish botanist named Carolus Linnaeus established a system for naming species that is still in use today. Linnaeus created a two-part name unique to each type of organism.

- *Genus* The first part indicates the organism's **genus** (plural: **genera**). A genus is made up of a closely related group of species. For example, Linnaeus put humans in the genus *Homo*. Although humans are the only living species in this genus, at least six extinct organisms, all of which walked upright and made extensive use of tools, were later also assigned to *Homo*.

- *Species* The second term in the two-part name identifies the organism's species. Linnaeus gave humans the species name *sapiens*.

An organism's genus and species designation is called its **scientific name** or Latin name. Scientific names are always italicized. Genus names are always capitalized, but species names are not—as in *Homo sapiens*.

Scientific names are based on Latin or Greek word roots or on words "Latinized" from other languages. Linnaeus gave a scientific name to every species then known, and also Latinized his own name—from Karl von Linné to Carolus Linnaeus.

Linnaeus maintained that different types of organisms should not be given the same genus and species names. Other species may be assigned to the genus *Homo*, and members of other genera may be named *sapiens*, but only humans are named *Homo sapiens*. Each scientific name is unique.

**Scientific Names Are Often Descriptive**  Scientific names and terms are often based on Latin or Greek word roots that are descriptive. For example, *Homo sapiens* is derived from the Latin *homo* for "man" and *sapiens* for "wise" or "knowing." The yeast that bakers use to produce bread and that brewers use to brew beer is called *Saccharomyces cerevisiae*. The Greek root *saccharo* means "sugar," and *myces* refers to a fungus. *Saccharomyces* is aptly named "sugar fungus" because yeast is a fungus and because the domesticated strains of yeast used in commercial baking and brewing are often fed sugar. The species name of this organism, *cerevisiae*, is Latin for "beer." Loosely translated, then, the scientific name of brewer's yeast means "sugar-fungus for beer."

Scientific names and terms often seem daunting at first glance. So, most biologists find it extremely helpful to memorize some of the common Latin and Greek roots. To aid you in this process, new terms in this text are often accompanied by a translation of their Latin or Greek word roots in parentheses. (A glossary of common root words with translations and examples is also provided in **BioSkills 2** in Appendix B.)

## check your understanding

**C Y U**

**If you understand that . . .**
- A phylogenetic tree shows the evolutionary relationships between species.
- To infer where species belong on a phylogenetic tree, biologists examine genetic and other characteristics of the species involved. Closely related species should have similar characteristics, while less closely related species should be less similar.

✔ **You should be able to . . .**

Examine the following rRNA ribonucleotide sequences and draw a phylogenetic tree showing the relationships between species A, B, and C that these data imply:

**Species A:**  A A C T A G C G C G A T
**Species B:**  A A C T A G C G C C A T
**Species C:**  T T C T A G C G G T A T

*Answers are available in Appendix A.*

## 1.5 Doing Biology

This chapter has introduced some of the great ideas in biology. The development of the cell theory and the theory of evolution by natural selection provided cornerstones when the science was young; the tree of life is a relatively recent insight that has revolutionized our understanding of life's diversity.

These theories are considered great because they explain fundamental aspects of nature, and because they have consistently been shown to be correct. They are considered correct because they have withstood extensive testing.

How do biologists go about testing their ideas? Before answering this question, let's step back a bit and consider the types of questions that researchers can and cannot ask.

### The Nature of Science

Biologists ask questions about organisms, just as physicists and chemists ask questions about the physical world or geologists ask questions about Earth's history and the ongoing processes that shape landforms.

No matter what their field, all scientists ask questions that can be answered by observing or measuring things—by collecting data. Conversely, scientists cannot address questions that can't be answered by observing or measuring things.

This distinction is important. It is at the root of continuing controversies about teaching evolution in publicly funded schools. In the United States and in Turkey, in particular, some Christian and Islamic leaders have been particularly successful in pushing their claim that evolution and religious faith are in conflict. Even though the theory of evolution is considered one of the most successful and best-substantiated ideas in the history of science, they object to teaching it.

The vast majority of biologists and many religious leaders reject this claim; they see no conflict between evolution and religious faith. Their view is that science and religion are compatible because they address different types of questions.

- Science is about formulating hypotheses and finding evidence that supports or conflicts with those hypotheses.

- Religious faith addresses questions that cannot be answered by data. The questions addressed by the world's great religions focus on why we exist and how we should live.

Both types of questions are seen as legitimate and important.

So how do biologists go about answering questions? After formulating hypotheses, biologists perform experimental studies, or studies that yield descriptive data, such as observing a behavior, characterizing a structure within a cell by microscopy, or sequencing rRNA. Let's consider two recent examples of this process.

### Why Do Giraffes Have Long Necks? An Introduction to Hypothesis Testing

If you were asked why giraffes have long necks, you might say, based on your observations that long necks enable giraffes to reach food that is unavailable to other mammals. This hypothesis is expressed in African folktales and has traditionally been accepted by many biologists. The food competition hypothesis is so plausible, in fact, that for decades no one thought to test it.

In the mid-1990s, however, Robert Simmons and Lue Scheepers assembled data suggesting that the food competition hypothesis is only part of the story. Their analysis supports an alternative hypothesis—that long necks allow giraffes to use their heads as effective weapons for battering their opponents, and that longer-necked giraffes would have a competitive advantage in fights.

Before exploring these alternative explanations, it's important to recognize that hypothesis testing is a two-step process:

**Step 1** State the hypothesis as precisely as possible and list the predictions it makes.

**Step 2** Design an observational or experimental study that is capable of testing those predictions.

If the predictions are accurate, the hypothesis is supported. If the predictions are not met, then researchers do further tests, modify the original hypothesis, or search for alternative explanations. But the process does not end here. Biologists also talk to other researchers. Over coffee, at scientific meetings, or through publications, biologists communicate their results to the scientific community and beyond. (You can see the Big Picture of the process of doing biology on pages 16–17.)

Now that you understand more about hypothesis testing, let's return to the giraffes. How did biologists test the food competition hypothesis? What data support their alternative explanation?

**The Food Competition Hypothesis: Predictions and Tests** The food competition hypothesis claims that giraffes compete for food with other species of mammals. When food is scarce, as it is during the dry season, giraffes with longer necks can reach food that is unavailable to other species and to giraffes with shorter necks. As a result, the longest-necked individuals in a giraffe population survive better and produce more young than do shorter-necked individuals, and average neck length of the population increases with each generation.

To use the terms introduced earlier, long necks are adaptations that increase the fitness of individual giraffes during competition for food. This type of natural selection has gone on so long that the population has become extremely long necked.

The food competition hypothesis makes several explicit predictions. For example, the food competition hypothesis predicts that:

- neck length is variable among giraffes;
- neck length in giraffes is heritable; and
- giraffes feed high in trees, especially during the dry season, when food is scarce and the threat of starvation is high.

The first prediction is correct. Studies in zoos and natural populations confirm that neck length is variable among individuals.

The researchers were unable to test the second prediction, however, because they studied giraffes in a natural population and were unable to do breeding experiments. As a result, they simply had to accept this prediction as an assumption. In

(a) Most feeding is done at about shoulder height.

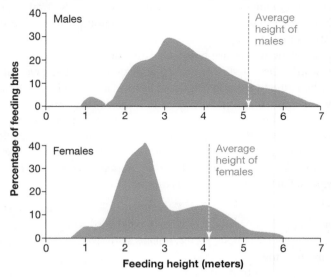

(b) Typical feeding posture in giraffes

**FIGURE 1.7 Giraffes Do Not Usually Extend Their Necks Upward to Feed.**

DATA: Young, T. P., L. A. Isbell. 1991. *Ethology* 87: 79–89.

general, though, biologists prefer to test every assumption behind a hypothesis.

What about the prediction regarding feeding high in trees? According to Simmons and Scheepers, this is where the food competition hypothesis breaks down.

Consider, for example, data collected by a different research team on the amount of time that giraffes spend feeding in vegetation of different heights. **FIGURE 1.7a** plots the height of vegetation versus the percentage of bites taken by a giraffe, for males and for females from the same population in Kenya. The dashed line on each graph indicates the average height of a male or female in this population.

Note that the average height of a giraffe in this population is much greater than the height where most feeding takes place. In this population, both male and female giraffes spend most of their feeding time eating vegetation that averages just 60 percent of their full height. Studies on other populations of giraffes, during both the wet and dry seasons, are consistent with these data. Giraffes usually feed with their necks bent (**FIGURE 1.7b**).

These data cast doubt on the food competition hypothesis, because one of its predictions does not appear to hold. Biologists have not abandoned this hypothesis completely, though, because feeding high in trees may be particularly valuable during extreme droughts, when a giraffe's ability to reach leaves far above the ground could mean the difference between life and death. Still, Simmons and Scheepers have offered an alternative explanation for why giraffes have long necks. The new hypothesis is based on the mating system of giraffes.

**The Sexual Competition Hypothesis: Predictions and Tests**   Giraffes have an unusual mating system. Breeding occurs year round rather than seasonally. To determine when females are coming into estrus or "heat" and are thus receptive to mating, the males nuzzle the rumps of females. In response, the females urinate into the males' mouths. The males then tip their heads back and pull their lips to and fro, as if tasting the liquid. Biologists who have witnessed this behavior have proposed that the males taste the females' urine to detect whether estrus has begun.

Once a female giraffe enters estrus, males fight among themselves for the opportunity to mate. Combat is spectacular. The bulls stand next to one another, swing their necks, and strike thunderous blows with their heads. Researchers have seen males knocked unconscious for 20 minutes after being hit and have cataloged numerous instances in which the loser died. Giraffes are not the only animals known to fight in this way—male giraffe weevils also use enormously long necks to fight for mating rights.

These observations inspired a new explanation for why giraffes have long necks. The sexual competition hypothesis is based on the idea that longer-necked giraffes are able to strike harder blows during combat than can shorter-necked giraffes. In engineering terms, longer necks provide a longer "moment arm." A long moment arm increases the force of an impact. (Think about the type of sledgehammer you'd use to bash down a concrete wall—one with a short handle or one with a long handle?)

The idea here is that longer-necked males should win more fights and, as a result, father more offspring than shorter-necked males do. If neck length in giraffes is inherited, then the average neck length in the population should increase over time. Under the sexual competition hypothesis, long necks are adaptations that increase the fitness of males during competition for females.

Although several studies have shown that long-necked males are more successful in fighting and that the winners of fights gain access to estrous females, the question of why giraffes have long necks is not closed. With the data collected to date, most biologists would probably concede that the food competition hypothesis needs further testing and refinement and that the sexual competition hypothesis appears promising. It could also be true that both hypotheses are correct. For our purposes, the important take-home message is that all hypotheses must be tested rigorously.

In many cases in biological science, testing hypotheses rigorously involves experimentation. Experimenting on giraffes is difficult. But in the case study considered next, biologists were able to test an interesting hypothesis experimentally.

## How Do Ants Navigate? An Introduction to Experimental Design

Experiments are a powerful scientific tool because they allow researchers to test the effect of a single, well-defined factor on a particular phenomenon. Because experiments testing the effect of neck length on food and sexual competition in giraffes haven't been done yet, let's consider a different question: When ants leave their nest to search for food, how do they find their way back?

The Saharan desert ant lives in colonies and makes a living by scavenging the dead carcasses of insects. Individuals leave the burrow and wander about searching for food at midday, when temperatures at the surface can reach 60°C (140°F) and predators are hiding from the heat.

Foraging trips can take the ants hundreds of meters—an impressive distance when you consider that these animals are only about a centimeter long. But when an ant returns, it doesn't follow the same long, wandering route it took on its way away from the nest. Instead, individuals return in a straight line (**FIGURE 1.8**).

Once individuals are close to the nest, they engage in a characteristic set of back-and-forth U-turns until they find their nest hole. How do they do know how far they are from the nest?

**The Pedometer Hypothesis**   Early work on navigation in desert ants showed that they use the Sun's position as a compass—meaning that they always know the approximate direction of the nest relative to the Sun. But how do they know how far to go?

After experiments had shown that the ants do not use landmarks to navigate, Matthias Wittlinger and co-workers set out to test a novel idea. The biologists proposed that Saharan desert ants know how far they are from the nest by integrating information from leg movements.

According to this pedometer hypothesis, the ants always know how far they are from the nest because they track the number

Observation:

Saharan desert ants meander long distances to find food (insect carcasses) but then return to the nest in a straight line.

Food

Nest    Question:  How do they find their way back?

**FIGURE 1.8  Navigation in Foraging Desert Ants.**

of steps they have taken and their stride length. The idea is that they can make a beeline back toward the burrow because they integrate information on the angles they have traveled *and* the distance they have gone—based on step number and stride length.

If the pedometer hypothesis is wrong, however, then stride length and step number should have no effect on the ability of an ant to get back to its nest. This latter possibility is called a **null hypothesis.** A null hypothesis specifies what should be observed when the hypothesis being tested isn't correct.

**Testing the Hypothesis**   To test their idea, Wittlinger's group allowed ants to walk from a nest to a feeder through a channel—a distance of 10 m. Then they caught ants at the feeder and created three test groups, each with 25 individuals (**FIGURES 1.9** and **1.10**):

- *Stumps*   By cutting the lower legs of some individuals off, they created ants with shorter-than-normal legs.
- *Normal*   Some individuals were left alone, meaning that they had normal leg length.

---

## RESEARCH

**QUESTION:** How do desert ants find their way back to their nest?

**PEDOMETER HYPOTHESIS:** Desert ants keep track of stride number and length to calculate how far they are from the nest.

**NULL HYPOTHESIS:** Stride number and length have nothing to do with navigation (the ants use some other mechanism to navigate).

**EXPERIMENTAL SETUP (TEST 1):**

1. Ants walk from nest to feeder. 75 ants are collected.

Nest ———→ Feeder
0    5    10 m

2. Manipulation of legs. Three treatments, 25 ants each.

Cut legs to create "stumps"      Leave legs normal length      Add pig bristles as "stilts"

3. Ants return "home" from feeder and search for nest hole.

Feeder ————?————
0    5    10    15    20 m

**EXPERIMENTAL SETUP (TEST 2):**

1. Recapture manipulated ants from Test 1.

"stumps"      normal      "stilts"

2. The three treatments of ants walk from nest to feeder again.

Nest ———→ Feeder
0    5    10 m

3. Ants walk back "home" from feeder again.

Feeder ————?————
0    5    10    15    20 m

**PREDICTION:**
Ants with stilts will go too far; ants with stumps will stop short.

**PREDICTION OF NULL HYPOTHESIS:**
No differences among the three groups.

**PREDICTION:**
All three groups will start looking for nest after walking 10 m.

**PREDICTION OF NULL HYPOTHESIS:**
No difference from the observed results in Test 1.

**RESULTS:**

Stilts / Normal / Stumps
Homebound run (m)
0    5    10    15    20

Stilts / Normal / Stumps
Homebound run (m)
0    5    10    15    20

**CONCLUSION:** Desert ants use information on stride length and number to calculate how far they are from the nest.

**FIGURE 1.9  An Experimental Test: Do Desert Ants Use a "Pedometer"?**

SOURCE: Wittlinger, M., R. Wehner, and H. Wolf. 2006. The ant odometer: Stepping on stilts and stumps. *Science* 312: 1965–1967.

✓**QUESTION**  What is the advantage of using 25 ants in each group instead of just one?

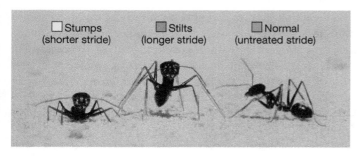

**FIGURE 1.10 Manipulation of Desert Ant Stride Length.**

- *Stilts*  By gluing pig bristles onto each leg, the biologists created ants with longer-than-normal legs.

Next they put the ants in a different channel and recorded how far they traveled in a direct line before starting their nest-searching behavior. To see the data they collected, look at the graph on the left side of the "Results" section in Figure 1.9.

- *Stumps*  The ants with stumps stopped short, by about 5 m, before starting to search for the nest opening.
- *Normal*  The normal ants walked the correct distance—about 10 m.
- *Stilts*  The ants with stilts walked about 5 m too far before starting to search for the nest opening.

To check the validity of this result, the researchers put the test ants back in the nest and recaptured them one to several days later, when they had walked to the feeder on their stumps, normal legs, or stilts. Now when the ants were put into the other channel to "walk back," they all traveled the correct distance—10 m—before starting to search for the nest (see the graph on the right side of the "Results" section in Figure 1.9).

The graphs in the "Results" display "box-and-whisker" plots that allow you to easily see where most of the data fall. Each box indicates the range of distances where 50 percent of the ants stopped to search for the nest. The whiskers indicate the lower extreme (stopping short of the nest location) and the upper extreme (going too far) of where the ants stopped to search. The vertical line inside each box indicates the median—meaning that half the ants stopped above this distance and half below. (For more details on how biologists report medians and indicate the variability and uncertainty in data, see **BioSkills 4** in Appendix B.)

**Interpreting the Results**  The pedometer hypothesis predicts that an ant's ability to walk home depends on the number and length of steps taken on its outbound trip. Recall that a prediction specifies what we should observe if a hypothesis is correct. Good scientific hypotheses make testable predictions—predictions that can be supported or rejected by collecting and analyzing data. In this case, the researchers tested the prediction by altering stride length and recording the distance traveled on the return trip. Under the null hypothesis in this experiment, all the ants—altered and unaltered—should have walked 10 m in the first test before they started looking for their nest.

**Important Characteristics of Good Experimental Design**  In relation to designing effective experiments, this study illustrates several important points:

- It is critical to include **control** groups. A control checks for factors, other than the one being tested, that might influence the experiment's outcome. In this case, there were two controls. Including a normal, unmanipulated individual controlled for the possibility that switching the individuals to a new channel altered their behavior. In addition, the researchers had to control for the possibility that the manipulation itself—and not the change in leg length—affected the behavior of the stilts and stumps ants. This is why they did the second test, where the outbound and return runs were done with the same legs.

- The experimental conditions must be as constant or equivalent as possible. The investigators used ants of the same species, from the same nest, at the same time of day, under the same humidity and temperature conditions, at the same feeders, in the same channels. Controlling all the variables except one—leg length in this case—is crucial because it eliminates alternative explanations for the results.

- Repeating the test is essential. It is almost universally true that larger sample sizes in experiments are better. By testing many individuals, the amount of distortion or "noise" in the data caused by unusual individuals or circumstances is reduced.

✔ If you understand these points, you should be able to explain: (1) What you would conclude if in the first test, the normal individual had not walked 10 m on the return trip before

**If you understand that . . .**

- Hypotheses are proposed explanations that make testable predictions.
- Predictions describe observable outcomes of particular conditions.
- Well-designed experiments alter just one condition—a condition relevant to the hypothesis being tested.

✔ **You should be able to . . .**

Design an experiment to test the hypothesis that desert ants feed during the hottest part of the day because it allows them to avoid being eaten by lizards. Then answer the following questions about your experimental design:

1. How does the presence of a control group in your experiment allow you to test the hypothesis?

2. How are experimental conditions controlled or standardized in a way that precludes alternative explanations of the data?

*Answers are available in Appendix A.*

looking for the nest; and (2) What you would conclude if the stilts and stumps ants had not navigated normally during the second test.

From the outcomes of these experiments, the researchers concluded that desert ants use stride length and number to measure how far they are from the nest. They interpreted their results as strong support for the pedometer hypothesis.

The giraffe and ant studies demonstrate a vital point: Biologists practice evidence-based decision making. They ask questions about how organisms work, pose hypotheses to answer those questions, and use experimental or observational evidence to decide which hypotheses are correct.

The data on giraffes and ants are a taste of things to come. In this text you will encounter hypotheses and research on questions ranging from how water gets to the top of 100-meter-tall sequoia trees to how the bacterium that causes tuberculosis has become resistant to antibiotics. As you work through this book, you'll get lots of practice thinking about hypotheses and predictions, analyzing the nature of control treatments, and interpreting graphs.

A commitment to tough-minded hypothesis testing and sound experimental design is a hallmark of biological science. Understanding their value is an important first step in becoming a biologist.

---

## CHAPTER 1    REVIEW

For media, go to MasteringBiology

## If you understand . . .

### 1.1    What Does It Mean to Say That Something Is Alive?

- There is no single, well-accepted definition of life. Instead, biologists point to five characteristics that organisms share.

✓ You should be able to explain why the cells in a dead organism are different from the cells in a live organism.

### 1.2    The Cell Theory

- The cell theory identified the fundamental structural unit common to all life.

✓ You should be able to describe the evidence that supported the pattern and the process components of the cell theory.

### The Theory of Evolution by Natural Selection

- The theory of evolution states that all organisms are related by common ancestry.

- Natural selection is a well-tested explanation for why species change through time and why they are so well adapted to their habitats.

✓ You should be able to explain why the average protein content of seeds in a natural population of a grass species would increase over time, if seeds with higher protein content survive better and grow into individuals that produce many seeds with high protein content when they mature.

### 1.4    The Tree of Life

- The theory of evolution predicts that all organisms are part of a genealogy of species, and that all species trace their ancestry back to a single common ancestor.

- To construct this phylogeny, biologists have analyzed the sequences in rRNA and in an array of genetic material found in all cells.

- A tree of life, based on similarities and differences in these molecules, has three fundamental lineages, or domains: the Bacteria, the Archaea, and the Eukarya.

✓ You should be able to explain how biologists can determine which of the three domains a newly discovered species belongs to by analyzing its rRNA.

### 1.5    Doing Biology

- Biology is a hypothesis-driven, experimental science.

✓ You should be able to explain (1) the relationship between a hypothesis and a prediction and (2) why experiments are convincing ways to test predictions.

### (MB)  MasteringBiology

1. **MasteringBiology Assignments**

   **Tutorials and Activities** An Introduction to Graphing; Experimental Inquiry: What Can You Learn about the Process of Science from Investigating a Cricket's Chirp?; Introduction to Experimental Design; Levels of Life Card Game; Metric System Review; The Scientific Method

   **Questions** Reading Quizzes, Blue-Thread Questions, Test Bank

2. **eText** Read your book online, search, take notes, highlight text, and more.

3. **The Study Area** Practice Test, Cumulative Test, BioFlix® 3-D Animations, Videos, Activities, Audio Glossary, Word Study Tools, Art

## You should be able to . . .

1. Anton van Leeuwenhoek made an important contribution to the development of the cell theory. How?
   a. He articulated the pattern component of the theory—that all organisms are made of cells.
   b. He articulated the process component of the theory—that all cells come from preexisting cells.
   c. He invented the first microscope and saw the first cell.
   d. He invented more powerful microscopes and was the first to describe the diversity of cells.

2. What does it mean to say that experimental conditions are controlled?
   a. The test groups consist of the same individuals.
   b. The null hypothesis is correct.
   c. There is no difference in outcome between the control and experimental treatment.
   d. All physical conditions except for one are identical for all groups tested.

3. The term *evolution* means that _____ change through time.

4. What does it mean to say that a characteristic of an organism is heritable?
   a. The characteristic evolves.
   b. The characteristic can be passed on to offspring.
   c. The characteristic is advantageous to the organism.
   d. The characteristic does not vary in the population.

5. In biology, to what does the term *fitness* refer?

6. Could *both* the food competition hypothesis and the sexual competition hypothesis explain why giraffes have long necks? Why or why not?
   a. No. In science, only one hypothesis can be correct.
   b. No. Observations have shown that the food competition hypothesis cannot be correct.
   c. Yes. Long necks could be advantageous for more than one reason.
   d. Yes. All giraffes have been shown to feed at the highest possible height and fight for mates.

7. What would researchers have to demonstrate to convince you that they had discovered life on another planet?

8. What did Linnaeus's system of naming organisms ensure?
   a. Two different organisms never end up with the same genus and species name.
   b. Two different organisms have the same genus and species name if they are closely related.
   c. The genus name is different for closely related species.
   d. The species name is the same for each organism in a genus.

9. What does it mean to say that a species is adapted to a particular habitat?

10. Explain how selection occurs during natural selection. What is selected, and why?

11. The following two statements explain the logic behind the use of molecular sequence data to estimate evolutionary relationships:

    "If the theory of evolution is true, then rRNA sequences should be very similar in closely related organisms but less similar in organisms that are less closely related."

    "On a phylogenetic tree, branches that share a recent common ancestor represent species that are closely related; branches that don't share recent common ancestors represent species that are more distantly related."

    Is the logic of these statements sound? Why or why not?

12. Explain why researchers formulate a null hypothesis in addition to a hypothesis when designing an experimental study.

13. A scientific theory is a set of propositions that defines and explains some aspect of the world. This definition contrasts sharply with the everyday usage of the word theory, which often carries meanings such as "speculation" or "guess." Explain the difference between the two definitions, using the cell theory and the theory of evolution by natural selection as examples.

14. Turn back to the tree of life shown in Figure 1.5. Note that Bacteria and Archaea are prokaryotes, while Eukarya are eukaryotes. On the simplified tree below, draw an arrow that points to the branch where the structure called the nucleus originated. Explain your reasoning.

    BACTERIA

    ARCHAEA

    EUKARYA

15. The proponents of the cell theory could not "prove" that it was correct in the sense of providing incontrovertible evidence that all organisms are made up of cells. They could state only that all organisms examined to date were made of cells. Why was it reasonable for them to conclude that the theory was valid?

16. Some humans have heritable traits that make them resistant to infection by HIV. In areas of the world where HIV infection rates are high, are human populations evolving? Explain your logic.
    a. No. HIV infection rates would not affect human evolution.
    b. Yes. The heritable traits that confer resistance to HIV should increase over time.
    c. No. The heritable traits that confer resistance to HIV should decrease over time.
    d. Yes. The heritable traits that confer resistance to HIV should decrease over time.

Biologists study the characteristics of life. The cell theory, the theory of evolution by natural selection, and the tree of life are some of the great ideas in biology that came about by biologists asking questions that can be answered by observing or measuring things—that is, by collecting data.

Notice that the study of life is not a series of linear steps with a beginning and an end. Instead, the process of doing biology is dynamic and ongoing. The answer to one question may lay the foundation for twenty more questions. Working together, biologists from different disciplines integrate data across many levels, from atoms to the biosphere.

Note that the gray numbers in boxes tell you where to go for more information. Also, be sure to do the blue exercises in the Check Your Understanding box.

**Characteristics of living things**
- Energy
- Cells
- Information
- Replication
- Evolution

1.1

focuses on

Text section where you can find more information

Scientists regularly integrate across many of these levels

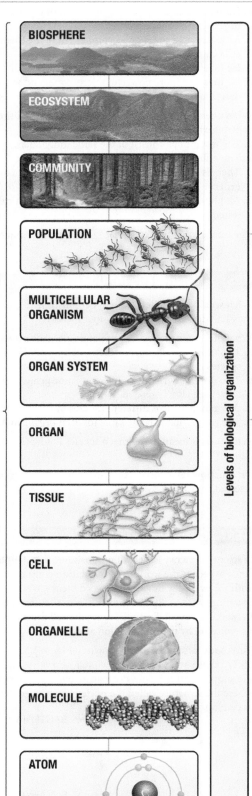

Levels of biological organization

BIOSPHERE

ECOSYSTEM

COMMUNITY

POPULATION

MULTICELLULAR ORGANISM

ORGAN SYSTEM

ORGAN

TISSUE

CELL

ORGANELLE

MOLECULE

ATOM

## check your understanding

**If you understand the big picture . . .**

✓ You should be able to . . .

1. Describe how biologists go about testing their ideas.
2. Provide an example of how an experimental study could span more than one level of biological organization.
3. Compare and contrast a hypothesis with a theory.
4. Propose the next step to take if data support the hypothesis you are testing.

*Answers are available in Appendix A.*

# DOING BIOLOGY

**Evidence-based study of life** 1.1

*involves the*

*reveals*

**The Tree of Life**
Describes the evolutionary relationships among species

**1.4, Ch 28, Unit 6**

*begins with*

**Observations** (planned or chance)

**Exploring the literature**
BioSkills 14

**Sharing ideas with other scientists**

**Inspiration**

*provides*

*lead to*

*leads to*

*enables*

**Defining a problem and forming a question**

*leads to*

**Society**

*may involve one or many*

*leads to*

**Stating a hypothesis and a null hypothesis, and making predictions**

*reject hypothesis; propose alternative hypothesis*

**Scientific community**
• Discussions with colleagues
• Scientific meetings
• Peer-reviewed publications

BioSkills 14

*leads to*

*to*

*may involve one or many*

**Designing a study (either observational or experimental) to test predictions**

*revisit assumptions of study*

**Characteristics of good experimental design**
• Controls
• Consistent experimental conditions
• Large sample sizes 1.5

*usually involves*

*leads to*

**Gathering data**

*then*

**Communicate findings**

*then*

**Theory**
• Explains fundamental aspects of nature
• Consistently shown to be correct after extensive testing
• Serves as a framework for developing new hypotheses 1.2

*leads to*

**Analyzing and interpreting data**
BioSkills 1, 3, 4, 7, 9

*relate to larger*

*evaluated by asking*

*such as*

**Do the data support the hypothesis?**

*if NO*

*if YES*

**Cell theory** 1.2

*and*

**Theory of natural selection** 1.3, Ch 25

# 2 Water and Carbon: The Chemical Basis of Life

**In this chapter you will learn that**

**Chemistry is intimately linked to the evolution of life**

*by reviewing*

| | | |
|---|---|---|
| **How are atoms bonded together in molecules?** | *and asking* **The structure of atoms, ions, and molecules 2.1** | *and asking* **How do chemical reactions occur? 2.3** |

*then examining* ⟶

**The unique properties of water 2.2**  **Current models for chemical evolution 2.4**  **Carbon: The most versatile atom on Earth 2.5**

These deep-sea hydrothermal vents produce hydrogen-rich, highly basic fluids at temperatures that range from 40° to 90°C. It has been proposed that life emerged from similar seafloor chimneys early in Earth's history via chemical evolution.

A classic experiment on spontaneous generation by Louis Pasteur tested the idea that life arises from nonliving materials (see Chapter 1). This work helped build a consensus that spontaneous generation does not occur. But for life to exist, spontaneous generation must have occurred at least once, early in Earth's history.

How did life begin? This simple query has been called "the mother of all questions." This chapter examines a theory, called **chemical evolution,** that is the leading scientific explanation for the origin of life. Like all scientific theories, the theory of chemical evolution has a *pattern component* that makes a claim about the natural world and a *process component* that explains that pattern.

- *The pattern component*  In addition to small molecules, complex carbon-containing substances exist and are required for life.

- *The process component*  Early in Earth's history, simple chemical compounds combined to form more complex carbon-containing substances before the evolution of life.

This chapter is part of the Big Picture. See how on pages 104–105.

✔ When you see this checkmark, stop and test yourself. Answers are available in Appendix A.

The theory maintains that inputs of energy led to the formation of increasingly complex carbon-containing substances, culminating in a compound that could replicate itself. At this point, there was a switch from chemical evolution to biological evolution.

As the original molecule multiplied, the process of evolution by natural selection took over. Eventually a descendant of the original molecule became metabolically active and acquired a membrane. When this occurred, the five attributes of life (discussed in Chapter 1) were fulfilled. Life had begun.

At first glance, the theory of chemical evolution may seem implausible. But is it? What evidence do biologists have that chemical evolution occurred? What approaches do they take to gathering this evidence?

Let's start with the fundamentals—the atoms and molecules that would have combined to get chemical evolution started.

## 2.1 Atoms, Ions, and Molecules: The Building Blocks of Chemical Evolution

Just four types of atoms—hydrogen, carbon, nitrogen, and oxygen—make up 96 percent of all matter found in organisms today. Many of the molecules found in your cells contain thousands, or even millions, of these atoms bonded together. But early in Earth's history, these elements existed only in simple substances such as water and carbon dioxide, which contain just three atoms apiece.

Two questions are fundamental to understanding how elements could have evolved into the more complex substances found in living cells:

1. What is the physical structure of the hydrogen, carbon, nitrogen, and oxygen atoms found in living cells?

2. What is the structure of the simple molecules—water, carbon dioxide, and others—that served as the building blocks of chemical evolution?

The focus on structure follows from one of the most central themes in biology: *Structure affects function*. To understand how a molecule affects your body or the role it played in chemical evolution, you have to understand how it is put together.

### Basic Atomic Structure

**FIGURE 2.1a** shows a simple way of depicting the structure of an atom, using hydrogen and carbon as examples. Extremely small particles called electrons orbit an atomic nucleus made up of larger particles called protons and neutrons. **FIGURE 2.1b** provides a sense of scale at the atomic level.

Protons have a positive electric charge (+1), neutrons are electrically neutral, and electrons have a negative electric charge (−1). When the number of protons and the number of electrons in an atom are the same, the charges balance and the atom is electrically neutral.

**(a)** Diagrams of atoms

Hydrogen

Carbon

**(b)** Most of an atom's volume is empty space.

If an atom occupied the same volume as this stadium, the nucleus would be about the size of a pea

**FIGURE 2.1 Parts of an Atom.** The atomic nucleus, made up of protons and neutrons, is surrounded by orbiting electrons. In reality, electrons do not orbit the nucleus in circles; their actual orbits are complex.

**FIGURE 2.2** shows a segment of the periodic table of the elements. Notice that each atom of a given **element** contains a characteristic number of protons, called its **atomic number**. The atomic number is written as a subscript to the left of an element's symbol in Figure 2.2. The sum of the protons and neutrons in an atom is called its **mass number** and is written as a superscript to the left of its symbol.

Mass number
(number of protons + neutrons)

Atomic number
(number of protons)

$^1_1$H $\quad$ $^4_2$He

$^7_3$Li $\quad$ $^9_4$Be $\quad$ $^{11}_5$B $\quad$ $^{12}_6$C $\quad$ $^{14}_7$N $\quad$ $^{16}_8$O $\quad$ $^{19}_9$F $\quad$ $^{20}_{10}$Ne

$^{23}_{11}$Na $\quad$ $^{24}_{12}$Mg $\quad$ $^{27}_{13}$Al $\quad$ $^{28}_{14}$Si $\quad$ $^{31}_{15}$P $\quad$ $^{32}_{16}$S $\quad$ $^{35}_{17}$Cl $\quad$ $^{40}_{18}$Ar

**FIGURE 2.2 A Portion of the Periodic Table.** Each element has a unique atomic number and is represented by a unique one- or two-letter symbol. The mass numbers given here are the most common for each element. (Appendix C provides a complete periodic table of elements.)

The number of protons in an element does not vary—if the atomic number of an atom changes, then it is no longer the same element. The number of neutrons present in an element can vary, however. Forms of an element with different numbers of neutrons are known as **isotopes** (literally, "equal-places" in regard to position in the periodic table).

Different isotopes have different masses, yet are the same element. For example, all atoms of the element carbon have 6 protons. But naturally occurring isotopes of carbon can have 6, 7, or even 8 neutrons, giving them a mass number of 12, 13, or 14, respectively. The **atomic weight** of an element is an average of all the mass numbers of the naturally occurring isotopes based on their abundance. This is why the atomic weights for elements are often slightly different from the mass numbers—the atomic weight of carbon, for example, is 12.01.

Most isotopes are stable, but not all. For example, $^{14}C$, with 6 protons and 8 neutrons, represents an unstable **radioactive isotope.** Its nucleus will eventually decay and release energy (radiation). When $^{14}C$ decays, one of its neutrons changes into a proton, converting $^{14}C$ to the stable $^{14}N$ isotope of nitrogen, with 7 protons and 7 neutrons. Timing of decay is specific to each radioisotope, a fact that has been very useful in estimating the rates of key events in the fossil record (see Chapter 25).

Although the masses of protons, neutrons, and electrons can be measured in grams, the numbers involved are so small that biologists prefer to use a special unit called the **dalton.** The masses of protons and neutrons are virtually identical and are routinely rounded to 1 dalton. A carbon atom that contains 6 protons and 6 neutrons has a mass of 12 daltons, while a carbon atom with 6 protons and 7 neutrons would have a mass of 13 daltons. These isotopes would be written as $^{12}C$ and $^{13}C$,

respectively. The mass of an electron is so small that it is normally ignored.

To understand how the atoms involved in chemical evolution behave, focus on how electrons are arranged around the nucleus:

- Electrons move around atomic nuclei in specific regions called **orbitals.**
- Each orbital can hold up to two electrons.
- Orbitals are grouped into levels called **electron shells.**
- Electron shells are numbered 1, 2, 3, and so on, to indicate their relative distance from the nucleus. Smaller numbers are closer to the nucleus.
- Each electron shell contains a specific number of orbitals. An electron shell comprising a single orbital can hold up to two electrons; a shell with four orbitals can contain up to eight electrons.
- The electrons of an atom fill the innermost shells first, before filling outer shells.

To understand how the structures of atoms differ, take a moment to study **FIGURE 2.3**. This chart highlights the elements that are most abundant in living cells. The gray ball in the center of each box represents an atomic nucleus, and the orange circle or circles represent the electron shells around that nucleus. The small orange balls on the circles indicate the number of electrons that are distributed in the shells of each element. Electrons shown as pairs share the same orbital within a shell.

Now focus on the outermost shell of each atom. This is the element's **valence shell.** The electrons found in this shell are referred to as **valence electrons.** Two observations are important:

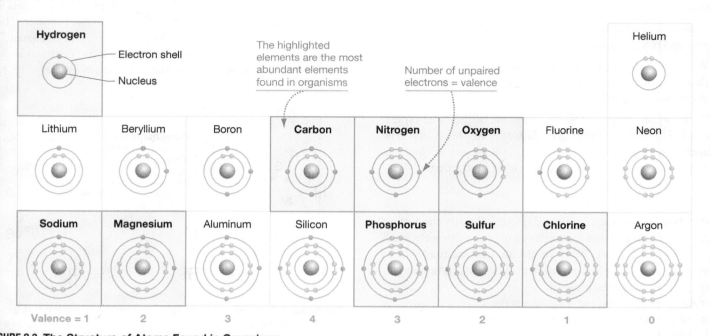

**FIGURE 2.3 The Structure of Atoms Found in Organisms.**

**QUESTION** If the mass number of phosphorus is 31, how many neutrons exist in the most common isotope phosphorus?

1. In each of the highlighted elements, the outermost electron shell is not full—not all orbitals in the valence shell have two electrons. The highlighted elements have at least one unpaired valence electron—meaning at least one unfilled valence shell orbital.

2. The number of unpaired valence electrons varies among elements. Carbon, for example, has four valence electrons, all unpaired. Oxygen has six valence electrons; four are paired, two are not. The number of unpaired electrons found in an atom is called its **valence.** Carbon's valence is four, oxygen's is two.

These observations are significant because an atom is most stable when its valence shell is filled. One way that shells can be filled is through the formation of strong **chemical bonds**—attractions that bind atoms together. A strong attraction where two atoms share one or more pairs of electrons is called a **covalent bond.**

## How Does Covalent Bonding Hold Molecules Together?

To understand how atoms can become more stable by making covalent bonds, consider hydrogen. The hydrogen atom has just one electron, which resides in a shell that can hold two electrons.

Because it has an unpaired valence electron, the hydrogen atom is not very stable. But when two atoms of hydrogen come into contact, the two electrons become shared by the two nuclei (**FIGURE 2.4**). Both atoms now have a completely filled outer shell. Together, the hydrogen atoms are more stable than the two individual hydrogen atoms.

Shared electrons "glue" two hydrogen atoms together. Substances held together by covalent bonds are called **molecules.** In the case of two hydrogen atoms, the bonded atoms form a single molecule of hydrogen, written as H–H or H₂.

It can also be helpful to think about covalent bonding as electrical attraction and repulsion. Opposite charges attract; like charges repel. As two hydrogen atoms move closer together, their positively charged nuclei repel each other and their negatively charged electrons repel each other. But each proton attracts both electrons, and each electron attracts both protons. Covalent bonds form when the attractive forces overcome the repulsive forces. This is the case when hydrogen atoms interact to form the hydrogen molecule ($H_2$).

**Nonpolar and Polar Bonds** In **FIGURE 2.5a**, the covalent bond between hydrogen atoms is represented by a dash and the electrons are drawn as dots halfway between the two nuclei. This depiction shows that the electrons are shared equally between the two hydrogen atoms, resulting in a covalent bond that is symmetrical.

It's important to note, though, that the electrons participating in a covalent bond are not always shared equally between the atoms involved. This happens because some atoms hold the electrons in covalent bonds much more tightly than do other atoms. Chemists call this property **electronegativity.**

What is responsible for an atom's electronegativity? It's a combination of two things—the number of protons in the nucleus and the distance between the nucleus and the valence shell. If

Hydrogen atoms each have one unpaired electron

$H_2$ molecule has two shared electrons

**FIGURE 2.4 Covalent Bonds Result from Electron Sharing.** When two hydrogen atoms come into contact, their electrons are attracted to the positive charge in each nucleus. As a result, their orbitals overlap, the electrons are shared by each nucleus, and a covalent bond forms.

you return to Figure 2.3 and move your finger along a row from left to right, you will be moving toward elements that increase in protons and in electronegativity (ignoring the elements in the far right column, which have full outer shells). Each row, however, represents shells of electrons, so if your finger moved down the table, the elements would decrease in electronegativity.

Oxygen, which has eight protons and only two electron shells, is among the most electronegative of all elements. It attracts covalently bonded electrons more strongly than does any other atom commonly found in organisms. Nitrogen's electronegativity is somewhat lower than oxygen's. Carbon and hydrogen, in turn, have relatively low and approximately equal electronegativities. Thus, the electronegativities of the four most abundant elements in organisms are related as follows: $O > N > C \cong H$.

Because carbon and hydrogen have approximately equal electronegativity, the electrons in a C–H bond are shared equally or symmetrically. The result is a **nonpolar covalent bond.** In contrast, asymmetric sharing of electrons results in a **polar covalent bond.** The electrons in a polar covalent bond spend most of their time close to the nucleus of the more electronegative atom. Why is this important?

**Polar Bonds Produce Partial Charges on Atoms** To understand the consequences of differences in electronegativity and the formation of polar covalent bonds, consider the water molecule.

Water consists of an oxygen bonded to two hydrogen atoms, and is written $H_2O$. As **FIGURE 2.5b** illustrates, the electron

**(a)** Nonpolar covalent bond in hydrogen molecule

$$H \overset{\bullet}{\underset{\bullet}{-}} H$$

Electrons are halfway between the two atoms, shared equally

**(b)** Polar covalent bonds in water molecule

Electrons are not shared equally (O is more electronegative than H), so partial charges exist on the O and H atoms

**FIGURE 2.5 Electron Sharing and Bond Polarity.** Delta (δ) symbols in polar covalent bonds refer to partial positive and negative charges that arise owing to unequal electron sharing.

volved in the covalent bonds in water are not shared equally but are held much more tightly by the oxygen nucleus than by the hydrogen nuclei. Hence, water has two polar covalent bonds—one between the oxygen atom and each of the hydrogen atoms.

Here's the key observation: Because electrons are shared unequally in each O—H bond, they spend more time near the oxygen atom, giving it a partial negative charge, and less time near the hydrogen atoms, giving them a partial positive charge. These partial charges are symbolized by the lowercase Greek letter delta, δ.

As Section 2.2 shows, the partial charges on water molecules—due simply to the difference in electronegativity between oxygen and hydrogen—are one of the primary reasons that life exists.

## Ionic Bonding, Ions, and the Electron-Sharing Continuum

Ionic bonds are similar in principle to covalent bonds, but instead of being shared between two atoms, the electrons in ionic bonds are completely transferred from one atom to the other. The electron transfer occurs because it gives the resulting atoms a full outermost shell.

Sodium atoms (Na), for example, tend to lose an electron, leaving them with a full second shell. This is a much more stable arrangement, energetically, than having a lone electron in their third shell (FIGURE 2.6a). The atom that results has a net electric charge of +1, because it has one more proton than it has electrons.

An atom or molecule that carries a full charge, rather than the partial charges that arise from polar covalent bonds, is called an ion. The sodium ion is written Na$^+$ and, like other positively charged ions, is called a cation (pronounced KAT-eye-un).

Chlorine atoms (Cl), in contrast, tend to gain an electron, filling their outermost shell (FIGURE 2.6b). The ion has a net charge of −1, because it has one more electron than protons. This

negatively charged ion, or anion (pronounced AN-eye-un), is written Cl$^-$ and is called chloride.

When sodium and chlorine combine to form sodium chloride (NaCl, common table salt), they pack into a crystal structure consisting of sodium cations and chloride anions (FIGURE 2.6c). The electrical attraction between the ions is so strong that salt crystals are difficult to break apart.

This discussion of covalent and ionic bonding supports an important general observation: The degree to which electrons are shared in chemical bonds forms a continuum from equal sharing in nonpolar covalent bonds to unequal sharing in polar covalent bonds to the transfer of electrons in ionic bonds.

As the left-hand side of FIGURE 2.7 shows, covalent bonds between atoms with exactly the same electronegativity—for example, between the atoms of hydrogen in H$_2$—represent one end of the continuum. The electrons in these nonpolar bonds are shared equally.

In the middle of the continuum are bonds where one atom is much more electronegative than the other. In these asymmetric bonds, substantial partial charges exist on each of the atoms. These types of polar covalent bonds occur when a highly electronegative atom such as oxygen or nitrogen is bonded to an atom with a lower affinity for electrons, such as carbon or hydrogen. Ammonia (NH$_3$) and water (H$_2$O) are examples of molecules with polar covalent bonds.

At the right-hand side of the continuum are molecules made up of atoms with extreme differences in their electronegativities. In this case, electrons are transferred rather than shared, the atoms have full charges, and the bonding is ionic. Sodium chloride (NaCl) is a familiar example of a molecule formed by ionic bonds.

Most chemical bonds that occur in biological molecules are on the left-hand side and the middle of the continuum; in the molecules found in organisms, ionic bonding is less common.

(a) A sodium ion being formed

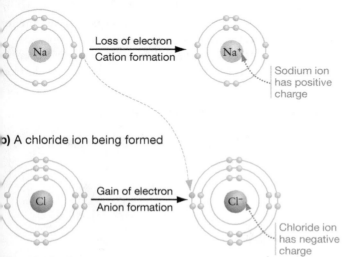

(b) A chloride ion being formed

(c) Table salt (NaCl) is a crystal composed of two ions.

FIGURE 2.6 Ion Formation and Ionic Bonding. The sodium ion (Na$^+$) and the chloride ion (Cl$^-$) are stable because they have full valence shells. In table salt (NaCl), sodium and chloride ions pack into a crystal structure held together by electrical attraction between their positive and negative charges.

Equal sharing of electrons ◄————————————————————► Transfer of electrons

| **Nonpolar covalent bonds**<br>(atoms have no charge) | | **Polar covalent bonds**<br>(atoms have partial charge) | | **Ionic bonds**<br>(atoms have full charge) |

Hydrogen | Methane | Ammonia | Water | Sodium chloride

**FIGURE 2.7 The Electron-Sharing Continuum.** The degree of electron sharing in chemical bonds can be thought of as a continuum, from equal sharing in nonpolar covalent bonds to no sharing in ionic bonds.

✔**QUESTION** Why do most polar covalent bonds involve nitrogen or oxygen?

## Some Simple Molecules Formed from C, H, N, and O

Look back at Figure 2.3 and count the number of unpaired electrons in the valence shells of carbon, nitrogen, oxygen, and hydrogen atoms. Each unpaired electron in a valence shell can make up half of a covalent bond. It should make sense to you that a carbon atom can form a total of four covalent bonds; nitrogen can form three; oxygen can form two; and hydrogen, one.

When each of the four unpaired electrons of a carbon atom covalently bonds with a hydrogen atom, the molecule that results is written $CH_4$ and is called methane (**FIGURE 2.8a**). Methane is the most common molecule found in natural gas. When a nitrogen atom's three unpaired electrons bond with three hydrogen atoms, the result is $NH_3$, or ammonia. Similarly, an atom of oxygen can form covalent bonds with two atoms of hydrogen, resulting in a water molecule ($H_2O$). As Figure 2.4 showed, a hydrogen atom can bond with another hydrogen atom to form hydrogen gas ($H_2$).

In addition to forming more than one single bond, atoms with more than one unpaired electron in the valence shell can form double bonds or triple bonds. **FIGURE 2.8b** shows how carbon forms double bonds with oxygen atoms to produce carbon dioxide ($CO_2$). Triple bonds result when three pairs of electrons are shared. **FIGURE 2.8c** shows the structure of molecular nitrogen ($N_2$), which forms when two nitrogen atoms establish a triple bond.

✔ If you understand how electronegativity affects covalent bonds, you should be able to draw arrows between the atoms in each molecule shown in Figure 2.8 to indicate the relative position of the shared electrons. If they are equally shared, then draw a double-headed arrow.

## The Geometry of Simple Molecules

In many cases, the overall shape of a molecule dictates how it behaves. In chemistry and in biology, function is based on structure.

The shapes of the simple molecules you've just learned about are governed by the geometry of their bonds. Nitrogen ($N_2$) and

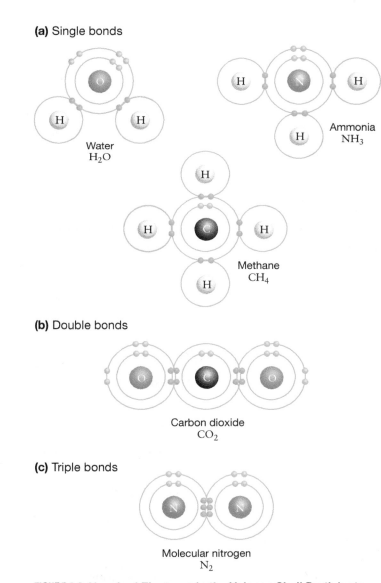

**(a)** Single bonds

Water
$H_2O$

Ammonia
$NH_3$

Methane
$CH_4$

**(b)** Double bonds

Carbon dioxide
$CO_2$

**(c)** Triple bonds

Molecular nitrogen
$N_2$

**FIGURE 2.8 Unpaired Electrons in the Valence Shell Participate in Covalent Bonds.** Covalent bonding is based on sharing of electrons in the outermost shell. Covalent bonds can be **(a)** single, **(b)** double, or **(c)** triple.

**(a)** Methane (CH₄)    **(b)** Water (H₂O)

**FIGURE 2.9 The Geometry of Methane and Water.**

carbon dioxide ($CO_2$), for example, have linear structures (see Figure 2.8). Molecules with more complex geometries include

- Methane ($CH_4$)—which is tetrahedral, a structure with four triangular faces like a pyramid (**FIGURE 2.9a**). The tetrahedron forms because the electrons in the four C—H bonds repulse each other equally. The electron pairs are as far apart as they can get.

- Water ($H_2O$)—which is bent and two-dimensional, or planar (**FIGURE 2.9b**). Why? The electrons in the four orbitals of oxygen's valence shell repulse each other, just as they do in methane. But in water, two of the orbitals are filled with electron pairs from the oxygen atom, and two are filled with electron pairs from covalent bonds between oxygen and hydrogen. The shared electrons form a molecule that is V-shaped and flat.

Section 2.2 explores how water's shape, in combination with the partial charges on the oxygen and hydrogen atoms, makes it the most important molecule on Earth.

## Representing Molecules

Molecules can be represented in a variety of increasingly complex ways—only some of which reflect their actual shape. Each method has advantages and disadvantages.

- **Molecular formulas** are compact, but don't contain a great deal of information—they indicate only the numbers and types of atoms in a molecule (**FIGURE 2.10a**).

- **Structural formulas** indicate which atoms in a molecule are bonded together. Single, double, and triple bonds are represented by single, double, and triple dashes, respectively. Structural formulas also indicate geometry in two dimensions (**FIGURE 2.10b**). This method is useful for planar molecules such as water and $O_2$.

- **Ball-and-stick models** take up more space than structural formulas, but provide information on the three-dimensional shape of molecules and indicate the relative sizes of the atoms involved (**FIGURE 2.10c**).

- **Space-filling models** are more difficult to read than ball-and-stick models but more accurately depict the spatial relationships between atoms. (**FIGURE 2.10d**).

In both ball-and-stick and space-filling models, biologists use certain colors to represent certain atoms. A black ball, for

|  | Methane | Ammonia | Water | Oxygen |
|---|---|---|---|---|
| **(a)** Molecular formulas: | $CH_4$ | $NH_3$ | $H_2O$ | $O_2$ |
| **(b)** Structural formulas: | H—C—H with H above and below | H—N—H with H below | O with H and H | O=O |
| **(c)** Ball-and-stick models: |  | | | |
| **(d)** Space-filling models: |  | | | |

**FIGURE 2.10 Molecules Can Be Represented Several Ways.** Each method of representing a molecule has particular advantages.

example, always symbolizes carbon. (For more information on interpreting chemical structures, see **BioSkills 8** in Appendix B.)

Some of the small molecules you've just learned about are found in volcanic gases, the atmospheres of nearby planets, and in deep-sea hydrothermal vents, like those shown in the photograph at the start of this chapter. Based on these observations, researchers claim that they were important components of Earth's ancient atmosphere and oceans. If so, then they provided the building blocks for chemical evolution. The question is: How did these simple building blocks combine to form more complex products, early in Earth's history?

Researchers postulate that most of the critical reactions in chemical evolution occurred in an aqueous, or water-based, environment. To understand what happened and why, let's delve into the properties of water and then turn to analyzing the reactions that triggered chemical evolution.

check your understanding

**C Y U**

**If you understand that . . .**

- Covalent bonds are based on electron sharing. Electron sharing allows atoms to fill all the orbitals in their valence shell, making them more stable.
- Covalent bonds can be polar or nonpolar, depending on whether the electronegativities of the two atoms involved are the same or different.

✓ **You should be able to . . .**

Draw the structural formula of formaldehyde ($CH_2O$) and add dots to indicate the relative locations of the electrons being shared in each covalent bond, based on the relative electronegativities of C, H, and O.

*Answers are available in Appendix A.*

## 2.2 Properties of Water and the Early Oceans

Life is based on water. It arose in an aqueous environment and remains dependent on water today. In fact, 75 percent of the volume in a typical cell is water; water is the most abundant molecule in organisms (**FIGURE 2.11**). You can survive for weeks without eating, but you aren't likely to live more than 3 or 4 days without drinking.

Water is vital for a simple reason: It is an excellent **solvent**—that is, an agent for dissolving substances and getting them into **solution.** The reactions that were responsible for chemical evolution some 3.5 billion years ago, like those occurring inside your body right now, depend on direct, physical interaction between molecules. Substances are most likely to come into contact with one another and react as **solutes**—meaning, when they are dissolved in a solvent like water. The formation of Earth's first ocean, about 3.8 billion years ago, was a turning point in chemical evolution because it gave the process a place to happen.

### Why Is Water Such an Efficient Solvent?

To understand why water is such an effective solvent, recall that

1. Both of the O–H bonds in a water molecule are polar, owing to the difference in the electronegativities of hydrogen and oxygen. As a result, the oxygen atom has a partial negative charge and each hydrogen atom has a partial positive charge.

2. The molecule is bent. Consequently, the partial negative charge on the oxygen atom sticks out, away from the partial positive charges on the hydrogen atoms, giving a water molecule an overall polarity (**FIGURE 2.12a**).

**FIGURE 2.12b** illustrates how water's structure affects its interactions with other water molecules. When two water molecules approach each other, the partial positive charge on hydrogen attracts the partial negative charge on oxygen. This weak electrical attraction forms a **hydrogen bond** between the molecules.

✔ If you understand how water's structure makes hydrogen bonding possible, you should be able to (1) draw a fictional version of Figure 2.12b that shows water as a linear (not bent)

**(a)** Water is polar.

Electrons are pulled toward oxygen

**(b)** Hydrogen bonds form between water molecules.

**FIGURE 2.12 Water Is Polar and Participates in Hydrogen Bonds. (a)** Because of oxygen's high electronegativity, the electrons that are shared between hydrogen and oxygen spend more time close to the oxygen nucleus, giving the oxygen atom a partial negative charge and the hydrogen atom a partial positive charge. **(b)** The electrical attraction that occurs between the partial positive and negative charges on water molecules forms a hydrogen bond.

molecule with partial charges on the oxygen and hydrogen atoms; and (2) explain why electrostatic attractions between such water molecules would be much weaker as a result.

In an aqueous solution, hydrogen bonds also form between water molecules and other polar molecules. Similar interactions occur between water and ions. Ions and polar molecules stay in solution because of their interactions with water's partial charges (**FIGURE 2.13**). Substances that interact with water in this way are said to be **hydrophilic** ("water-loving"). Hydrogen bonding makes it possible for almost any charged or polar molecule to dissolve in water.

In contrast, compounds that are uncharged and nonpolar do not interact with water through hydrogen bonding and do not dissolve in water. Substances that do not interact with water are said to be **hydrophobic** ("water-fearing"). Because their interactions with water are minimal or nonexistent, they are forced to interact with each other (**FIGURE 2.14**, see page 26). The water molecules surrounding nonpolar molecules form hydrogen bonds with one another and increase the stability of these **hydrophobic interactions.**

Although individual hydrogen bonds are not as strong as covalent or ionic bonds, many of them occur in a solution. Hydrogen bonding is extremely important in biology owing to the

**FIGURE 2.11 Fruits Shrink When They Are Dried Because They Consist Primarily of Water.**

Salt in absence of water

Salt dissolved in water

**FIGURE 2.13 Polar Molecules and Ions Dissolve Readily in Water.** Water's polarity makes it a superb solvent for polar molecules and ions.

**FIGURE 2.14 Nonpolar Molecules Do Not Dissolve in Water.**
In aqueous solution, nonpolar molecules and compounds are forced to interact with each other. This occurs because water is much more stable when it interacts with itself rather than with the nonpolar molecules.

✓**QUESTION** What is the physical basis of the expression, "Oil and water don't mix"?

sheer number of hydrogen bonds that form between water and hydrophilic molecules.

## What Properties Are Correlated with Water's Structure?

Water's small size, highly polar covalent bonds, and bent shape resulting in overall polarity are unique among molecules. Because the structure of molecules routinely correlates with their function, it's not surprising that water has some remarkable properties, in addition to its extraordinary capacity to act as a solvent.

**Cohesion, Adhesion, and Surface Tension**   Attraction between like molecules is called **cohesion.** Water is cohesive—meaning that it stays together—because of the hydrogen bonds that form between individual molecules.

Attraction between unlike molecules, in contrast, is called **adhesion.** Adhesion is usually analyzed in regard to interactions between a liquid and a solid surface. Water adheres to surfaces that have any polar or charged components.

Cohesion and adhesion are important in explaining how water can move from the roots of plants to their leaves against the force of gravity (see Chapter 38). But you can also see them in action in the concave surface, or meniscus, that forms in a glass tube (**FIGURE 2.15a**). A meniscus forms as a result of two forces:

1. Water molecules at the perimeter of the surface adhere to the glass, resulting in an upward pull.

2. Water molecules at the surface hydrogen-bond with water molecules next to them and below them, resulting in a net lateral and downward pull that resists the upward pull of adhesion.

Cohesion is also instrumental in the phenomenon known as **surface tension.** When water molecules are at the surface, there

**(a)** A meniscus forms where water meets a solid surface, as a result of two forces.

Adhesion: Water molecules that adhere to the glass pull upward at the perimeter.

Cohesion: Water molecules at the surface form hydrogen bonds with nearby water molecules and resist the upward pull of adhesion.

**(b)** Water has high surface tension.

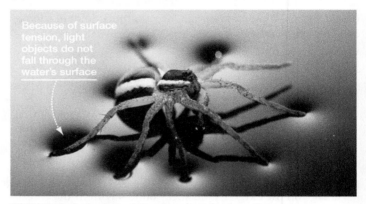

Because of surface tension, light objects do not fall through the water's surface

**FIGURE 2.15 Cohesion, Adhesion, and Surface Tension.**
**(a)** Meniscus formation is based on hydrogen bonding. **(b)** Water resists forces—like the weight of a spider—that increase its surface area. The resistance is great enough that light objects do not break the surface.

are no water molecules above them for hydrogen bonding. As a result, they exhibit stronger attractive forces between their nearest neighboring molecules. This enhanced attraction between the surface water molecules results in tension that minimizes the total surface area.

This fact has an important consequence: Water resists any force that increases its surface area. More specifically, any force that depresses a water surface meets with resistance. This resistance makes a water surface act like an elastic membrane (**FIGURE 2.15b**).

In water, the "elastic membrane" is stronger than it is in other liquids. Water's surface tension is extraordinarily high because of the stronger hydrogen bonding that occurs between molecules at the surface. This explains why it is better to cut the water's surface with your fingertips when you dive into a pool, instead of doing a belly flop.

**Water Is Denser as a Liquid than as a Solid**   When factory workers pour molten metal or plastic into a mold and allow it to cool to the solid state, the material shrinks. When molten lava pours out of a volcano and cools to solid rock, it shrinks. But when you fill an ice tray with water and put it in the freezer to make ice, the water expands.

Unlike most substances, water is denser as a liquid than it is as a solid. In other words, there are more molecules of water in a given volume of liquid water than there are in the same volume of solid water, or ice. **FIGURE 2.16** illustrates why this is so.

Note that in ice, each water molecule participates in four hydrogen bonds. These hydrogen bonds cause the water molecules to form a regular and repeating structure, or crystal (Figure 2.16a). The crystal structure of ice is fairly open, meaning that there is a relatively large amount of space between molecules.

Now compare the extent of hydrogen bonding and the density of ice with that of liquid water, illustrated in Figure 2.16b. Note that the extent of hydrogen bonding in liquid water is much less than that found in ice, and that the hydrogen bonds in liquid water are constantly being formed and broken. As a result, molecules in the liquid phase are packed much more closely together than in the solid phase.

Normally, heating a substance causes it to expand because molecules begin moving faster and colliding more often and with greater force. But heating ice causes hydrogen bonds to break and the open crystal structure to collapse. In this way, hydrogen bonding explains why water is denser as a liquid than as a solid.

This property of water has an important result: Ice floats (Figure 2.16c). If it didn't, ice would sink to the bottom of lakes, ponds, and oceans soon after it formed. The ice would stay frozen in the cold depths. Instead, ice serves as a blanket, insulating the liquid below from the cold air above. If water weren't so unusual, it is almost certain that Earth's oceans would have frozen solid before life had a chance to start.

**Water Has a High Capacity for Absorbing Energy** Hydrogen bonding is also responsible for another of water's remarkable physical properties: Water has a high capacity for absorbing energy.

**Specific heat,** for example, is the amount of energy required to raise the temperature of 1 gram of a substance by 1°C. Water has a high specific heat because when a source of energy hits it, hydrogen bonds must be broken before heat can be transferred and the water molecules begin moving faster. As **TABLE 2.1** indicates, as molecules increase in overall polarity, and thus in their ability to form hydrogen bonds, it takes an extraordinarily large amount of energy to change their temperature.

TABLE 2.1 **Specific Heats of Some Liquids**

The specific heats reported in this table were measured at 25°C and are given in units of joules per gram of substance per degree Celsius. (The joule is a unit of energy.)

| With extensive hydrogen bonding | Specific Heat |
|---|---|
| Water ($H_2O$) | 4.18 |
| **With some hydrogen bonding** | |
| Ethanol ($C_2H_6O$) | 2.44 |
| Glycerol ($C_3H_8O_3$) | 2.38 |
| **With little or no hydrogen bonding** | |
| Benzene ($C_6H_6$) | 1.74 |
| Xylene ($C_8H_{10}$) | 1.72 |

DATA: D. R. Lide (editor). 2008. Standard Thermodynamic Properties of Chemical Substances, in *CRC Handbook of Physics and Chemistry.* 89th ed. Boca Raton, FL: CRC Press.

**(a)** In ice, water molecules form a crystal lattice.

**(b)** In liquid water, no crystal lattice forms.

**(c)** Liquid water is denser than ice. As a result, ice floats.

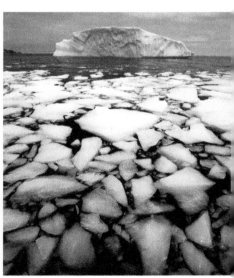

**FIGURE 2.16 Hydrogen Bonding Forms the Crystal Structure of Ice.** In ice, each molecule can form four hydrogen bonds at one time. Each oxygen atom can form two; each hydrogen atom can form one.

| Property | Cause | Biological Consequences |
|---|---|---|
| Solvent for charged or polar compounds | _____ _____ _____ _____ | Most chemical reactions important for life take place in aqueous solution. |
| Denser as a liquid than a solid | As water freezes, each molecule forms a total of four hydrogen bonds, leading to the formation of the low-density crystal structure called ice. | _____ _____ _____ |
| High specific heat | Water molecules must absorb lots of heat energy to break hydrogen bonds and experience increased movement (and thus temperature). | Oceans absorb and release heat slowly, moderating coastal climates. |
| High heat of vaporization | _____ _____ _____ | Evaporation of water from an organism cools the body. |

✔**EXERCISE** You should be able to fill in the missing cells in this table.

Similarly, it takes a large amount of energy to break the hydrogen bonds in liquid water and change the molecules from the liquid phase to the gas phase. Water's **heat of vaporization**—the energy required to change 1 gram of it from a liquid to gas—is higher than that of most molecules that are liquid at room temperature. As a result, water has to absorb a great deal of energy to evaporate. Water's high heat of vaporization is the reason that sweating or dousing yourself with water is an effective way to cool off on a hot day. Water molecules absorb a great deal of energy from your body before they evaporate, so you lose heat.

Water's ability to absorb energy is critical to the theory of chemical evolution. Molecules that were formed in the ocean were well protected from sources of energy that could break them apart, such as intense sunlight. As a result, they would have persisted and slowly increased in concentration over time, making them more likely to react and continue the process.

**TABLE 2.2** summarizes some of the key properties of water.

## The Role of Water in Acid–Base Reactions

You've seen that water's high specific heat and heat of vaporization tend to keep its temperature and liquid form stable. One other aspect of water's chemistry is important for understanding chemical evolution and how organisms work: Water is not a completely stable molecule. In reality, water molecules continually undergo a chemical reaction with themselves. When a **chemical reaction** occurs, one substance is combined with others or broken down into another substance. Atoms may also be rearranged; in most cases, chemical bonds are broken and new bonds form. The chemical reaction that takes place between water molecules is called a "dissociation" reaction. It can be written as follows:

$$H_2O \rightleftharpoons H^+ + OH^-$$

The double arrow indicates that the reaction proceeds in both directions.

The substances on the right-hand side of the expression are the **hydrogen ion** ($H^+$) and the **hydroxide ion** ($OH^-$). A hydrogen ion is simply a proton. In reality, however, protons do not exist by themselves. In water, for example, protons associate with water molecules to form hydronium ions ($H_3O^+$). Thus, the dissociation of water is more accurately written as:

$$H_2O + H_2O \rightleftharpoons H_3O^+ + OH^-$$

One of the water molecules on the left-hand side of the expression has given up a proton, while the other water molecule has accepted a proton.

Substances that give up protons during chemical reactions and raise the hydronium ion concentration of water are called **acids;** molecules or ions that acquire protons during chemical reactions and lower the hydronium ion concentration of water are called **bases.** Most acids act only as acids, and most bases act only as bases; but water can act as both an acid and a base.

A chemical reaction that involves a transfer of protons is called an acid–base reaction. Every acid–base reaction requires a proton donor and a proton acceptor—an acid and a base, respectively.

Water is an extremely weak acid—very few water molecules dissociate to form hydronium ions and hydroxide ions. In contrast, strong acids like the hydrochloric acid (HCl) in your stomach readily give up a proton when they react with water.

$$HCl + H_2O \rightleftharpoons H_3O^+ + Cl^-$$

Strong bases readily acquire protons when they react with water. For example, sodium hydroxide (NaOH, commonly called lye) dissociates completely in water to form $Na^+$ and $OH^-$. The hydroxide ion produced by that reaction then accepts a proton from a hydronium ion in the water, forming two water molecules.

$$NaOH(aq) \longrightarrow Na^+ + OH^-$$
$$OH^- + H_3O^+ \rightleftharpoons 2\, H_2O$$

(The "*aq*" in the first expression indicates that NaOH is in aqueous solution.)

To summarize, adding an acid to a solution increases the concentration of protons; adding a base to a solution lowers the concentration of protons. Water is both a weak acid and a weak base.

**Determining the Concentration of Protons**  In a solution, the tendency for acid–base reactions to occur is largely a function of the number of protons present. The problem is, there's no simple way to count the actual number of protons present in a sample. Researchers solve this problem using the mole concept.

A **mole** refers to the number $6.022 \times 10^{23}$—just as the unit called the dozen refers to the number 12 or the unit million refers to the number $1 \times 10^{6}$. The mole is a useful unit because the mass of one mole of any substance is the same as its molecular weight expressed in grams. **Molecular weight** is the sum of the atomic weights of all the atoms in a molecule.

For example, to get the molecular weight of $H_2O$, you sum the atomic weights of two atoms of hydrogen and one atom of oxygen. Since the atomic weights of hydrogen and oxygen are very close to their mass numbers (see Figure 2.2), the molecular weight of water would be $1 + 1 + 16$, or a total of 18. Thus, if you weighed a sample of 18 grams of water, it would contain around $6 \times 10^{23}$ water molecules, or about 1 mole of water molecules.

When substances are dissolved in water, their concentration is expressed in terms of molarity (symbolized by "M"). **Molarity** is the number of moles of the substance present per liter of solution. A 1-molar solution of protons in water, for example, means that 1 mole of protons is contained in 1 liter of solution.

Chemists can measure the concentration of protons in a solution directly using molarity and an instrument called a pH meter. In a sample of pure water at 25°C, the concentration of $H^+$ is $1.0 \times 10^{-7}$M, or 1 ten-millionth molar.

**The pH of a Solution Reveals Whether It Is Acidic or Basic**  Because the concentration of protons in water is such a small number, exponential notation is cumbersome. So chemists and biologists prefer to express the concentration of protons in a solution, and thus whether it is acidic or basic, with a logarithmic notation called **pH**.[1]

By definition, the pH of a solution is the negative of the base-10 logarithm, or log, of the hydrogen ion concentration:

$$pH = -\log [H^+]$$

(To review logarithms, see **BioSkills 6** in Appendix B. The square brackets are a standard notation for indicating "concentration" of a substance in solution.)

Taking antilogs gives

$$[H^+] = \text{antilog}(-pH) = 10^{-pH}$$

Solutions that contain acids have a proton concentration larger than $1 \times 10^{-7}$M and thus a pH < 7. This is because acidic

molecules tend to release protons into solution. In contrast, solutions that contain bases have a proton concentration less than $1 \times 10^{-7}$M and thus a pH > 7. This is because basic molecules tend to accept protons from solution.

pH is a convenient way to indicate the concentration of protons in a solution, but take note of what the number represents. For example, if the concentration of $H^+$ in a sample of water is $1.0 \times 10^{-7}$M, then its pH is 7. If the pH changes to 5, then the sample contains 100 times more protons and has become 100 times more acidic. ✔ QUANTITATIVE If you understand how pH is related to [$H^+$], you should be able to calculate the concentration of protons in a solution that has a pH of 8.5.

**FIGURE 2.17** shows the pH scale and reports the pH of some selected solutions. Pure water is used as a standard, or point of reference, for pH 7 on the pH scale. The solution inside living cells is about pH 7, which is considered neutral—neither acidic nor basic. The normal function of a cell is dependent on maintaining this neutral internal environment. What is responsible for regulating pH?

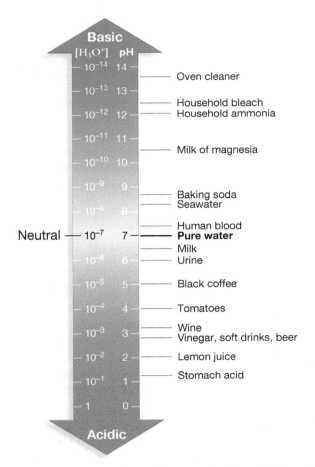

**FIGURE 2.17 The pH Scale.** Because the pH scale is logarithmic, a change in one unit of pH represents a change in the concentration of hydrogen ions equal to a factor of 10. Coffee has a hundred times more $H^+$ than pure water has.

✔QUESTION What happens to the concentration of protons in black coffee after you add milk?

---

[1]The term pH is derived from the French *puissance d'hydrogéne*, or "power of hydrogen."

**Buffers Protect Against Damaging Changes in pH** Life is sensitive to changes in pH. Changes in proton concentration affect the structure and function of polar or charged substances as well as the tendency of acid–base reactions to occur.

Compounds that minimize changes in pH are called **buffers** because they reduce the impact of adding acids or bases on the overall pH of a solution. Buffers are important in maintaining relatively constant conditions, or **homeostasis,** in cells and tissues. In cells, a wide array of naturally occurring molecules act as buffers.

Most buffers are weak acids, meaning that they are somewhat likely to give up a proton in solution, but once the proton concentration rises, the acid is regenerated. To see how buffers work, consider the disassociation of carbonic acid in water to form bicarbonate ions and protons:

$$CH_2O_3 \rightleftharpoons CHO_3^- + H^+$$
$$\text{carbonic acid} \qquad \text{bicarbonate}$$

When carbonic acid and bicarbonate are present in about equal concentrations in a solution, they function as a buffering system. If the concentration of protons increases slightly, the protons react with bicarbonate ions to form carbonic acid and pH does not change. If the concentration of protons decreases slightly, carbonic acid gives up protons and pH does not change.
✔ If you understand this concept, you should be able to predict what would happen to the concentration of bicarbonate ions if a base like sodium hydroxide (NaOH) were added to the solution of carbonic acid.

As chemical evolution began, then, water provided the physical environment for key reactions to take place. In some cases water also acted as an important reactant. Although acid–base reactions were not critical to the initial stages of chemical evolution, they became extremely important once the process was under way. Now let's consider what happened in solution, some 3.5 billion years ago.

## 2.3 Chemical Reactions, Energy, and Chemical Evolution

Proponents of the theory of chemical evolution contend that simple molecules present in the atmosphere and oceans of early Earth participated in chemical reactions that eventually produced larger, more complex organic (carbon-containing) molecules—such as the proteins, nucleic acids, sugars, and lipids introduced in the next four chapters. Currently, researchers are investigating two environments where these reactions may have occurred:

1. *The atmosphere,* which was probably dominated by gases ejected from volcanoes. Water vapor, carbon dioxide ($CO_2$), and nitrogen ($N_2$) are the dominant gases ejected by volcanoes today; a small amount of molecular hydrogen ($H_2$) and carbon monoxide (CO) may also be present.

2. *Deep-sea hydrothermal vents,* where extremely hot rocks contact deep cracks in the seafloor. In addition to gases such as $CO_2$ and $H_2$, certain deep-sea vents are rich in minerals containing reactive metals such as nickel and iron.

When gases like $CO_2$, $N_2$, $H_2$, and CO are put together and allowed to interact on their own, however, very little happens. They do not suddenly link together to create large, complex substances like those found in living cells. Instead, their bonds remain intact. To understand why the bonds of these molecules remain unchanged, you must first learn about how chemical reactions proceed.

## How Do Chemical Reactions Happen?

Chemical reactions are written in a format similar to mathematical equations: The initial, or **reactant,** molecules are shown on the left and the resulting reaction **product(s)** shown on the right. For example, the most common reaction in the mix of gases and water vapor that emerges from volcanoes results in the production of carbonic acid, which can be precipitated with water as acid rain:

$$CO_2(g) + H_2O(l) \rightleftharpoons CH_2O_3(aq)$$
$$\text{carbonic acid}$$

The physical state of each reactant and product is indicated as gas (*g*), liquid (*l*), solid (*s*), or in aqueous solution (*aq*).

Note that the expression is balanced; that is, 1 carbon, 3 oxygen, and 2 hydrogen atoms are present on each side of the expression. This illustrates the conservation of mass in closed systems—mass cannot be created or destroyed, but it may be rearranged through chemical reactions.

Note also that the expression contains a double arrow, meaning that the reaction is reversible. When the forward and reverse reactions proceed at the same rate, the quantities of reactants and products remain constant, although not necessarily equal. A dynamic but stable state such as this is termed a **chemical equilibrium.**

Changing the concentration of reactants or products can disturb a chemical equilibrium. For example, adding more $CO_2$ to the mixture would drive the reaction to the right, creating more $CH_2O_3$ until the equilibrium proportions of reactants and products are reestablished. Removing $CO_2$ or adding more $CH_2O_3$ would drive the reaction to the left.

A chemical equilibrium can also be altered by changes in temperature. For example, the water molecules in the following set of interacting elements, or **system,** would be present as a combination of liquid water and water vapor:

$$H_2O(l) \rightleftharpoons H_2O(g)$$

If liquid water molecules absorb enough energy, like the heat released from a volcano, they transform to the gaseous state. (You may recall that water has a high heat of vaporization and requires a large amount of energy to change its state from liquid to gas.) As a result, this change is termed **endothermic** ("within heating") because heat is absorbed during the process. In contrast, the transformation of water vapor to liquid water releases heat and is **exothermic** ("outside heating"). Raising the temperature of this system drives the equilibrium to the right; cooling the system drives it to the left.

In relation to chemical evolution, though, these reactions and changes of physical state are not particularly interesting. Carbonic acid is not an important intermediate in the formation of more complex molecules. However, interesting things do begin to happen when energy is added to mixtures of volcanic gases.

## What Is Energy?

**Energy** can be defined as the capacity to do work or to supply heat. This capacity exists in one of two ways—as a stored potential or as an active motion.

Stored energy is called **potential energy.** An object gains or loses its ability to store energy because of its position. An electron that resides in an outer electron shell will, if the opportunity arises, fall into a lower electron shell closer to the positive charges on the protons in the nucleus. Because of its position farther from the positive charges in the nucleus, an electron in an outer electron shell has more potential energy than does an electron in an inner shell (**FIGURE 2.18**). When stored in chemical bonds, this form of potential energy is called **chemical energy.**

**Kinetic energy** is energy of motion. Molecules have kinetic energy because they are constantly in motion.

- The kinetic energy of molecular motion is called **thermal energy.**
- The **temperature** of an object is a measure of how much thermal energy its molecules possess. If an object has a low temperature, its molecules are moving slowly. (We perceive this as "cold.") If an object has a high temperature, its molecules are moving rapidly. (We perceive this as "hot.")
- When two objects with different temperatures come into contact, thermal energy is transferred between them. This transferred energy is called **heat.**

There are many forms of potential energy and kinetic energy, and energy can change from one form into another. However, according to the **first law of thermodynamics,** energy is conserved—it cannot be created or destroyed, but only transferred and transformed. (A more thorough explanation of energy transformation is provided in Chapter 8 in the context of cellular metabolism.)

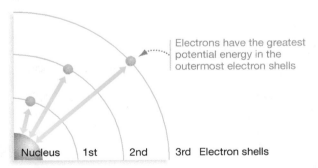

**FIGURE 2.18 Potential Energy as a Function of Electron Shells.** Electrons in outer shells have more potential energy than do electrons in inner shells, because the negative charges of the electrons in outer shells are farther from the positive charges of the protons in the nucleus. Each shell represents a distinct level of potential energy.

Energy transformation is the heart of chemical evolution. According to the best data available, molecules that were part of the early Earth were exposed to massive inputs of energy. Kinetic energy, in the form of heat, was present in the gradually cooling molten mass that initially formed the planet. The atmosphere and surface of the early Earth were also bombarded with electricity from lightening and radiation from the Sun. Energy stored as potential energy in the chemical bonds of small molecules was also abundant.

Now that you understand that energy transformations are involved in chemical reactions, a big question remains: What determines if a reaction will take place?

## What Makes a Chemical Reaction Spontaneous?

When chemists say that a reaction is spontaneous, they have a precise meaning in mind: Chemical reactions are spontaneous if they are able to proceed on their own, without any continuous external influence, such as added energy. Two factors determine if a reaction will proceed spontaneously:

1. Reactions tend to be spontaneous when the product molecules are less ordered than the reactant molecules. For example, nitroglycerin is a single, highly ordered molecule. But when nitroglycerin explodes, it breaks up into gases like carbon dioxide, nitrogen, oxygen, and water vapor. These molecules are much less ordered than the reactant nitroglycerin molecules. The heat that is given off from this explosion also contributes to increasing disorder in the environment. The amount of disorder in a system is called **entropy.** When the products of a chemical reaction are less ordered than the reactant molecules are, entropy increases and the reaction tends to be spontaneous. The **second law of thermodynamics,** in fact, states that entropy always increases in an isolated system.

2. Reactions tend to be spontaneous if the products have lower potential energy than the reactants. If the electrons in the reaction products are held more tightly than those in the reactants, then they have lower potential energy. Recall that highly electronegative atoms such as oxygen or nitrogen hold electrons in covalent bonds much more tightly than do atoms with a lower electronegativity, such as hydrogen or carbon. For example, when hydrogen and oxygen gases react, water is produced spontaneously:

$$2\ H_2(g) + O_2(g) \longrightarrow 2\ H_2O(g)$$

The electrons involved in the O—H bonds of water are held much more tightly by the more electronegative oxygen atom than when they were shared equally in the H—H and O=O bonds of hydrogen and oxygen (see **FIGURE 2.19a** on page 32). As a result, the products have much lower potential energy than the reactants. The difference in chemical energy between reactants and products is given off as heat, so the reaction is exothermic. And although the reaction between hydrogen and oxygen results in less entropy—three molecules of gas produce two molecules of water vapor—the reaction is still spontaneous due to the large drop in potential energy.

**(a)** When hydrogen and oxygen gas react, the product has much lower potential energy than the reactants.

**(b)** The difference in potential energy is released as heat and light, which vaporizes the water produced.

Electrons are held "loosely" in bonds between atoms with equal electronegativities

Electrons are held tightly by highly electronegative atoms

H——H  +  O═══O  $\xrightarrow{\text{Potential energy drops}}$  H——O——H  +  Released energy

Hydrogens ($H_2$)    1 Oxygen ($O_2$)    2 Waters ($H_2O$)

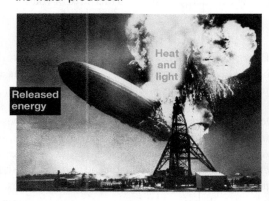

Heat and light

**FIGURE 2.19 Potential Energy May Change during Chemical Reactions.** In the Hindenburg disaster of 1937, the hydrogen gas from this lighter-than-air craft reacted with oxygen in the atmosphere, with devastating results.

✔ **EXERCISE** Label which electrons have relatively low potential energy and which electrons have relatively high potential energy.

released as heat. Since heat increases disorder in the environment, the second law of thermodynamics remains intact. The Hindenburg disaster of 1937 illustrates the large and terrifying amount of heat energy that is given off from this relatively simple reaction (**FIGURE 2.19b**).

To summarize: In general, physical and chemical processes proceed in the direction that results in increased entropy and lower potential energy (**FIGURE 2.20**). These two factors—potential energy and entropy—are used to figure out whether a reaction is spontaneous (see Chapter 8 for more detail). Were the reactions that led to chemical evolution spontaneous? Section 2.4 explores how researchers address this question.

**Reactants:**
high potential energy
more order
(lower entropy)

$C_6H_{12}O_6$
Glucose (a sugar)    +    $6\ O_2$

This reaction occurs in your cells and when wood burns

**Products:**
low potential energy
less order
(higher entropy)

+ Released heat

$6\ CO_2\ +\ 6\ H_2O$

**FIGURE 2.20 Spontaneous Processes Result in Lower Potential Energy, Increased Disorder, or Both.**

# check your understanding

**C Y U**

**If you understand that . . .**

- Chemical reactions result in the transformation of energy, either through the release of energy stored in chemical bonds or the uptake of energy from external sources.
- Chemical reactions tend to be spontaneous if they lead to lower potential energy and higher entropy (more disorder).

✔ **You should be able to . . .**

1. Determine if the reaction between methane ($CH_4$) and oxygen ($O_2$) shown here is spontaneous or not, addressing both potential energy and entropy:

$$CH_4 + 2\ O_2 \longrightarrow CO_2 + 2\ H_2O$$

2. Explain how the positions of the valence electrons in carbon and hydrogen change as methane is converted into carbon dioxide and water.

*Answers are available in Appendix A.*

**2.4 Investigating Chemical Evolution: Approaches and Model Systems**

To probe the kinds of reactions that may have set chemical evolution in motion, researchers have used two different approaches—one looking from the "top down" and the other from the "bottom up."

1. In the top-down approach, researchers examine modern cells to identify chemistry that is shared throughout the tree of life. Such ancient reactions are prime candidates for being involved in the chemical evolution that led up to **LUCA,** or last universal common ancestor (introduced in Chapter 1).

2. In the bottom-up approach, the primary focus is on the small molecules and environmental conditions that were present in

early Earth. Here, researchers attempt to identify reactions that could build the molecules found in life using only what was available at the time, without regard to reactions used by modern cells.

These approaches have been used to investigate two different model systems that attempt to explain the process component of the theory of chemical evolution:

1. The **prebiotic soup model** proposes that certain molecules were synthesized from gases in the atmosphere or arrived via meteorites. Afterward they would have condensed with rain and accumulated in oceans. This process would result in an "organic soup" that allowed for continued construction of larger, even more complex molecules.

2. The **surface metabolism model** suggests that dissolved gases came in contact with minerals lining the walls of deep-sea vents and formed more complex, organic molecules.

Since it is impossible to directly examine how and where chemical evolution occurred, the next best thing is to re-create the conditions in the lab and test predictions made by these models. In the following sections, you will learn about how biologists used the top-down and bottom-up approaches to identify reactions that support each of these models for chemical evolution.

## Early Origin-of-Life Experiments

Chemical evolution was first taken seriously in 1953 when a graduate student named Stanley Miller performed a breakthrough experiment in the study of the prebiotic soup model.

Miller wanted to answer a simple question: Can complex organic compounds be synthesized from the simple molecules present in Earth's early atmosphere? In other words, is it possible to re-create the first steps in chemical evolution by simulating early-Earth conditions in the laboratory?

Miller's experimental setup (**FIGURE 2.21**) was designed to produce a microcosm of early Earth. The large glass flask represented the atmosphere and contained the gases methane ($CH_4$), ammonia ($NH_3$), and hydrogen ($H_2$), all of which have high potential energy. This large flask was connected to a smaller flask by glass tubing. The small flask held a tiny ocean—200 milliliters (mL) of liquid water.

To connect the mini-atmosphere with the mini-ocean, Miller boiled the water constantly. This added water vapor to the mix of gases in the large flask. As the vapor cooled and condensed, it flowed back into the smaller flask, where it boiled again. In this way, water vapor circulated continuously through the system. This was important: If the molecules in the simulated atmosphere reacted with one another, the "rain" would carry them into the mini-ocean, forming a simulated version of the prebiotic soup.

Had Miller stopped at merely boiling the molecules, little or nothing would have happened. Even at the boiling point of water (100°C), the starting molecules used in the experiment are stable and do not undergo spontaneous chemical reactions.

Something did start to happen in the apparatus, however, when Miller sent electrical discharges across the electrodes he'd inserted into the atmosphere. These miniature lightning bolts

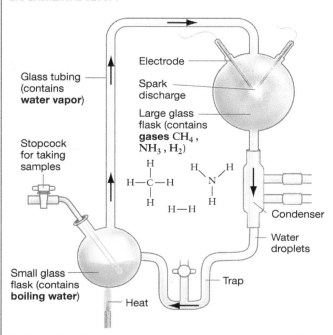

**RESEARCH**

**QUESTION:** Can simple molecules and kinetic energy lead to chemical evolution?

**HYPOTHESIS:** If kinetic energy is added to a mix of simple molecules, reactions will occur that produce more complex molecules, perhaps including some with C–C bonds.

**NULL HYPOTHESIS:** Chemical evolution will not occur, even with an input of energy.

**EXPERIMENTAL SETUP:**

**PREDICTION:** Complex organic compounds will be found in the liquid water.

**PREDICTION OF NULL HYPOTHESIS:** Only the starting molecules will be found in the liquid water.

**RESULTS**

Samples taken from the liquid water contain formaldehyde, hydrogen cyanide, and several complex compounds with carbon–carbon bonds, including amino acids

**CONCLUSION:** Chemical evolution occurs readily if simple molecules with high free energy are exposed to a source of kinetic energy.

**FIGURE 2.21 Miller's Spark-Discharge Experiment.** The arrows in the "Experimental setup" diagram indicate the flow of water vapor o liquid. The condenser is a jacket with cold water flowing through it.

SOURCE: Miller, S. L. 1953. A production of amino acids under possible primitive Earth conditions. *Science* 117: 528–529.

✔**QUESTION** Which parts of the apparatus mimic the ocean, atmosphere, rain, and lightning?

added a crucial element to the reaction mix—pulses of intense electrical energy. After a day of continuous boiling and sparking, the solution in the boiling flask began to turn pink. After a week, it was deep red and cloudy.

When Miller analyzed samples from the mini-ocean, he found large quantities of hydrogen cyanide and formaldehyde. Even more exciting, the sparks and heating had led to the synthesis of additional, more complex organic compounds, including amino acids, which are the building blocks of proteins (see Chapter 3).

## Recent Origin-of-Life Experiments

The production of more complex molecules from simple molecules in Miller's experiment supported his claim that the formation of a prebiotic soup was possible. The results came under fire, however, when other researchers pointed out that the early atmosphere was dominated by volcanic gases like CO, $CO_2$, and $H_2$, not the $CH_4$ and $NH_3$ used in Miller's experiment.

This controversy stimulated a series of follow-up experiments, which showed that the assembly of small molecules into more complex molecules can also occur under more realistic early Earth conditions.

**Synthesis of Precursors Using Light Energy** One such reaction that may have played a role in chemical evolution is the synthesis of formaldehyde ($CH_2O$) from carbon dioxide and hydrogen:

$$CO_2(g) + 2\,H_2(g) \longrightarrow \underset{\text{formaldehyde}}{CH_2O(g)} + H_2O(g)$$

This reaction has not been observed in cells—like Miller's experiment, it represents the bottom-up approach. But researchers have shown that when molecules of formaldehyde are heated, they react with one another to produce larger organic compounds, including energy-rich molecules like sugars (see Chapter 5). Note, however, that this reaction does not occur spontaneously—a large input of energy is required.

To explore the possibility of early formaldehyde synthesis, a research group constructed a computer model of the early atmosphere of Earth. The model consisted of a list of all possible chemical reactions that can occur among the molecules now thought to have dominated the early atmosphere: $CO_2$, $H_2O$, $N_2$, CO, and $H_2$. In this model, they included reactions that occur when these molecules are struck by sunlight. This was crucial because sunlight represents a source of energy.

The sunlight that strikes Earth is made up of packets of light energy called **photons.** Today, Earth is protected by a blanket of ozone ($O_3$) in the upper atmosphere that absorbs most of the higher-energy photons in sunlight. But since Earth's early atmosphere was filled with volcanic gases released as the molten planet cooled, and ozone is not among these gases, it is extremely unlikely that appreciable quantities of ozone existed. Based on this logic, researchers infer that when chemical evolution was occurring, large quantities of high-energy photons bombarded the planet.

To understand why this energy source was so important, recall that the atoms in hydrogen and carbon dioxide molecules have full valence shells through covalent bonding. This arrangement makes these molecules largely unreactive. However, energy

from photons can break up molecules by knocking apart shared electrons. The fragments that result, called **free radicals,** have unpaired electrons in their outermost shells and are extremely reactive (**FIGURE 2.22**). To mimic the conditions on early Earth more accurately, the computer model included several reactions that produce highly reactive free radicals.

The result? The researchers calculated that, under conditions accepted as reasonable approximations of early Earth by most scientists, appreciable quantities of formaldehyde would have been produced. The energy in sunlight was converted to chemical energy in the form of new bonds in formaldehyde.

The complete reaction that results in the formation of formaldehyde is written as

$$CO_2(g) + 2\,H_2(g) + \text{sunlight} \longrightarrow CH_2O(g) + H_2O(g)$$

Notice that the reaction is balanced in terms of the atoms *and* the energy involved. The sunlight on the reactant side balances the higher energy required for the formation of formaldehyde and water. This result makes sense if you take a moment to think about it. Energy is the capacity to do work, and building larger, more complex molecules requires work to be done.

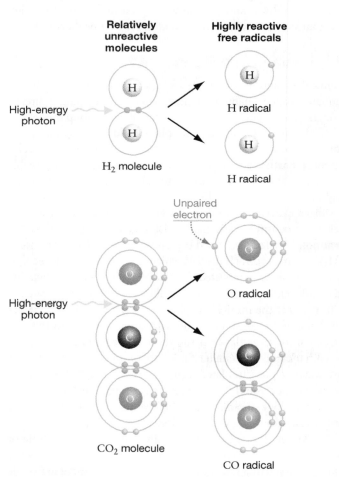

**FIGURE 2.22 Free Radicals Are Extremely Reactive.** When high-energy photons or pulses of intense electrical energy, such as lightning, strike molecules of hydrogen or carbon dioxide, free radicals can be created. Formation of free radicals is thought to be responsible for some key reactions in chemical evolution.

Using a similar model, other researchers have shown that hydrogen cyanide (HCN)—another important precursor of molecules required for life—could also have been produced in the early atmosphere. According to this research, large quantities of potential precursors for chemical evolution would have formed in the atmosphere and rained out into the early oceans. As a result, organic compounds with relatively high potential energy could have accumulated, and the groundwork would have been in place for the prebiotic soup model of chemical evolution to take off (FIGURE 2.23a).

**Concentration and Catalysis in Hydrothermal Vents** A major stumbling block in the prebiotic soup model is that precursor molecules would have become diluted when they entered the early oceans. Without some means of localized concentration, the formaldehyde and hydrogen cyanide mentioned in the previous section would have been unlikely to meet and react to form larger, more complex molecules. The surface metabolism model offers one possible solution to this dilution effect.

In the surface metabolism model, reactants are recruited to a defined space—a layer of reactive minerals deposited on the

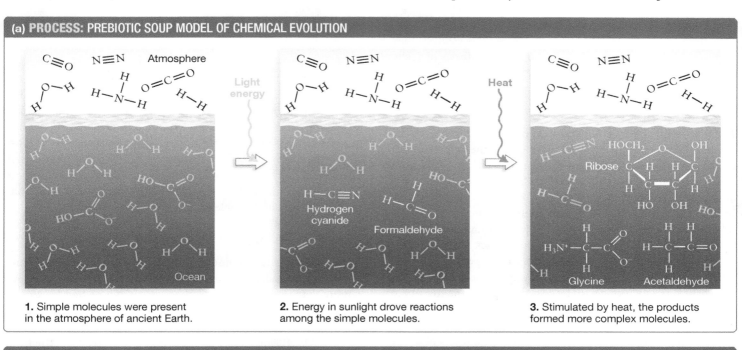

**(a) PROCESS: PREBIOTIC SOUP MODEL OF CHEMICAL EVOLUTION**

1. Simple molecules were present in the atmosphere of ancient Earth.

2. Energy in sunlight drove reactions among the simple molecules.

3. Stimulated by heat, the products formed more complex molecules.

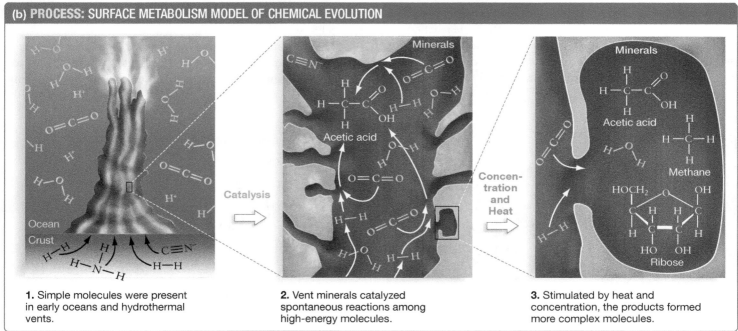

**(b) PROCESS: SURFACE METABOLISM MODEL OF CHEMICAL EVOLUTION**

1. Simple molecules were present in early oceans and hydrothermal vents.

2. Vent minerals catalyzed spontaneous reactions among high-energy molecules.

3. Stimulated by heat and concentration, the products formed more complex molecules.

**FIGURE 2.23 The Start of Chemical Evolution—Two Models.** The prebiotic soup and surface metabolism models illustrate how simple molecules containing C, H, O, and N reacted to form organic compounds that served as building blocks for more complex molecules.

walls of deep-sea vent chimneys. Dissolved gases would be attracted by the minerals and concentrated on vent-wall surfaces (**FIGURE 2.23b**).

Here's a key point of this model: Not only would vent-wall minerals bring reactants together, they would also be critical to the rate at which reaction products formed. Even if a potential reaction were spontaneous, it would probably not occur at a level useful for chemical evolution without the support of a **catalyst.** A catalyst provides the appropriate chemical environment for reactants to interact with one another effectively. (You will learn in Chapter 8 that a catalyst only influences the rate of a reaction—it does not provide energy or alter spontaneity.)

A reaction that provides an example of the role catalysts may have played during chemical evolution is the synthesis of acetic acid ($CH_3COOH$) from carbon dioxide and hydrogen:

$$2\ CO_2(aq) + 4\ H_2(aq) \longrightarrow CH_3COOH(aq) + 2\ H_2O(l)$$
$$\text{acetic acid}$$

The reaction is driven by chemical energy stored in one of the reactants—$H_2$—and is spontaneous despite the apparent decrease in entropy. It is employed by certain groups of Bacteria and Archaea today as a step toward building even more complex organic molecules.

This reaction has grabbed wide attention among the chemical evolution research community, for two reasons in particular: **(1)** Acetic acid can be formed under conditions that simulate a hydrothermal vent environment (bottom-up approach). **(2)** It is a key intermediate in an ancient pathway that produces acetyl CoA, which is a molecule used by cells throughout the tree of life (top-down approach). (The role of acetyl CoA in modern cells is discussed in Chapter 9.)

Did vent minerals serve as catalysts in the synthesis of acetic acid in early Earth? Evidence from modern cells suggests the answer may be yes. The catalysts that perform the same reaction in modern cells contain minerals similar to those found in hydrothermal vents. These minerals may represent a form of molecular luggage taken from the deep-sea hydrothermal vents as LUCA evolved its independence.

Research is currently under way to establish laboratory systems to more closely mimic surface metabolism conditions in hydrothermal vents. Preliminary results show that in addition to the production of acetic acid, a variety of larger carbon-based molecules can be formed under early Earth conditions. Among these are precursors for the synthesis of nucleotides, the building blocks for the molecules of inheritance used by every living organism on Earth (see Chapter 4).

## 2.5 The Importance of Organic Molecules

Life has been called a carbon-based phenomenon, and with good reason. Except for water, almost all of the molecules found in organisms contain this atom. Molecules that contain carbon bonded to other elements, such as hydrogen, are called **organic** molecules. (Other types of molecules are referred to as *inorganic* compounds.)

Carbon has great importance in biology because it is the most versatile atom on Earth. Because of its four valence electrons, it will form four covalent bonds. This results in an almost limitless array of molecular shapes, made possible by different combinations of single and double bonds.

### Linking Carbon Atoms Together

You have already examined the tetrahedral structure of methane and the linear shape of carbon dioxide. When molecules contain more than one carbon atom, these atoms can be bonded to one another in long chains, as in the component of gasoline called octane ($C_8H_{18}$; **FIGURE 2.24a**), or in a ring, as in the sugar glucose ($C_6H_{12}O_6$; **FIGURE 2.24b**). Carbon atoms provide the structural framework for virtually all the important compounds associated with life, with the exception of water.

The formation of carbon–carbon bonds was an important event in chemical evolution: It represented a crucial step toward the production of the types of molecules found in living organisms.

**(a)** Carbons linked in a chain

**(b)** Carbons linked in a ring

$C_8H_{18}$ Octane

$C_6H_{12}O_6$ Glucose

**FIGURE 2.24 The Shapes of Carbon-Containing Molecules.**
**(a)** Octane is a hydrocarbon chain, and one of the primary ingredients in gasoline. **(b)** Glucose is a sugar that can form a ring-like structure.

## Functional Groups

In general, the carbon atoms in an organic molecule furnish a skeleton that gives the molecule its overall shape. But the chemical behavior of the compound—meaning the types of reactions that it participates in—is dictated by groups of H, N, O, P, or S atoms that are bonded to one of the carbon atoms in a specific way.

The critically important H-, N-, O-, P-, and S-containing groups found in organic compounds are called **functional groups.** The composition and properties of six prominent functional groups that are commonly found in organic molecules and recognized by organic chemists are summarized in **TABLE 2.3**. To understand the role that organic compounds play in organisms, it is important to analyze how these functional groups behave.

**SUMMARY TABLE 2.3** **Six Functional Groups Commonly Attached to Carbon Atoms**

| Functional Group | Formula* | Family of Molecules | Properties of Functional Group | Example |
|---|---|---|---|---|
| Amino | | Amines | Acts as a base—tends to attract a proton to form: | Glycine (an amino acid) |
| Carboxyl | | Carboxylic acids | Acts as an acid—tends to lose a proton in solution to form: | Acetic acid |
| Carbonyl | | Aldehydes | Aldehydes, especially, react with certain compounds to produce larger molecules to form: | Acetaldehyde |
| | | Ketones | | Acetone |
| Hydroxyl | R—OH | Alcohols | Highly polar, so makes compounds more soluble through hydrogen bonding with water; may also act as a weak acid and drop a proton | Ethanol |
| Phosphate | | Organic phosphates | Molecules with more than one phosphate linked together store large amounts of chemical energy | 3–Phosphoglyceric acid |
| Sulfhydryl | R—SH | Thiols | When present in proteins, can form disulfide (S–S) bonds that contribute to protein structure | Cysteine |

*In these structural formulas, "R" stands for the rest of the molecule.

✔ **EXERCISE** Based on the electronegativities of the atoms involved, predict whether each functional group is polar or nonpolar.

*Amino and carboxyl functional groups* tend to attract or drop a proton, respectively, when in solution. Amino groups function as bases; carboxyl groups act as acids. During chemical evolution and in organisms today, the most important types of amino- and carboxyl-containing molecules are the amino acids (which Chapter 3 analyzes in detail). Amino acids contain both an amino group and a carboxyl group. (It's common for organic compounds to contain more than one functional group.) Amino acids can be linked together by covalent bonds that form between amino and carboxyl groups. In addition, both of these functional groups participate in hydrogen bonding.

*Carbonyl groups* are found on aldehyde and ketone molecules such as formaldehyde, acetaldehyde, and acetone. This functional group is the site of reactions that link these molecules into larger, more complex organic compounds.

*Hydroxyl groups* are important because they act as weak acids. In many cases, the protons involved in acid–base reactions that occur in cells come from hydroxyl groups on organic compounds. Because hydroxyl groups are polar, molecules containing hydroxyl groups will form hydrogen bonds and tend to be soluble in water.

*Phosphate groups* carry two negative charges. When phosphate groups are transferred from one organic compound to another, the change in charge often dramatically affects the structure of the recipient molecule. In addition, phosphates that are bonded together store chemical energy that can be used in chemical reactions (some of these are discussed in Chapter 3).

*Sulfhydryl groups* consist of a sulfur atom bonded to a hydrogen atom. They are important because sulfhydryl groups can link to one another via disulfide (S—S) bonds.

To summarize, functional groups make things happen. The number and types of functional groups attached to a framework of carbon atoms imply a great deal about how that molecule is going to behave.

When you encounter an organic compound that is new to you, it's important to do the following three things:

1. Examine the overall size and shape provided by the carbon framework.

2. Identify the types of covalent bonds present based on the electronegativities of the atoms. Use this information to estimate the polarity of the molecule and the amount of potential energy stored in its chemical bonds.

3. Locate any functional groups and note the properties these groups give to the molecule.

Understanding these three features will help you to predict the molecule's role in the chemistry of life.

Once carbon-containing molecules with functional groups had appeared early in Earth's history, what happened next? For chemical evolution to continue, small carbon-based molecules had to form still larger, more complex molecules like those found in living cells. How were the molecules of life—proteins, nucleic acids, carbohydrates, and lipids—formed, and how do they function in organisms today? The rest of this unit explores the next steps in chemical evolution, culminating in the formation of the first living cell.

---

## CHAPTER 2 REVIEW

*For media, go to MasteringBiology*

### If you understand . . .

### 2.1 Atoms, Ions, and Molecules: The Building Blocks of Chemical Evolution

- When atoms participate in chemical bonds to form molecules, the shared electrons give the atoms full valence shells and thus contribute to the atoms' stability.

- The electrons in a chemical bond may be shared equally or unequally, depending on the relative electronegativities of the two atoms involved.

- Nonpolar covalent bonds result from equal sharing; polar covalent bonds are due to unequal sharing. Ionic bonds form when an electron is completely transferred from one atom to another.

✓ You should be able to compare and contrast the types of bonds found in methane ($CH_4$), ammonia ($NH_3$), and sodium chloride (NaCl).

### 2.2 Properties of Water and the Early Oceans

- The chemical reactions required for life take place in water.

- Water is polar—meaning that it has partial positive and negative charges—because it is bent and has two polar covalent bonds.

- Polar molecules and charged substances, including ions, interact with water and stay in solution via hydrogen bonding and electrostatic attraction.

- Water's ability to participate in hydrogen bonding also gives it an extraordinarily high capacity to absorb heat and cohere to other water molecules.

- Water spontaneously dissociates into hydrogen ions (or protons, $H^+$) and hydroxide ions ($OH^-$). The concentration of protons in a solution determines the pH, which can be altered by acids and bases or stabilized by buffers.

✓ You should be able to predict what part of water molecules would interact with amino, carboxyl, and hydroxyl functional groups in solution and the types of bonds that would be involved.

## 2.3 Chemical Reactions, Energy, and Chemical Evolution

- The first step in chemical evolution was the formation of small organic compounds from molecules such as molecular hydrogen ($H_2$) and carbon dioxide ($CO_2$).

- Chemical reactions typically involve bonds being broken, atoms being rearranged, and new bonds being formed. This process involves energy, either from the reactants or external sources (e.g., heat).

- Energy comes in different forms. Although energy cannot be created or destroyed, one form of energy can be transformed into another.

✓ You should be able to explain how the energy in electricity can drive a reaction that is nonspontaneous.

## 2.4 Investigating Chemical Evolution: Approaches and Model Systems

- Experiments suggest that early in Earth's history, external sources of energy, such as sunlight or lightning, could have driven chemical reactions between simple molecules to form molecules with higher potential energy. In this way, energy in the form of radiation or electricity was transformed into chemical energy.

- The prebiotic soup and surface metabolism models for chemical evolution have been supported by the synthesis of organic molecules in laboratory simulations of the early Earth environment.

✓ You should be able to explain how the surface metabolism model is supported by both the top-down and bottom-up approaches used to investigate reactions involved in chemical evolution.

## 2.5 The Importance of Organic Molecules

- Carbon is the foundation of organic molecules based on its valence, which allows for the construction of molecules with complex shapes.

- Organic molecules are critical to life because they possess versatility of chemical behavior due to the presence of functional groups.

✓ You should be able to predict how adding hydroxyl groups to the octane molecule in Figure 2.24 would affect the properties of the molecule.

### (MB) MasteringBiology

**1. MasteringBiology Assignments**

**Tutorials and Activities** Acids, Bases, and pH; Anatomy of Atoms; Atomic Number and Mass Number; BioSkill: Using Logarithms; Carbon Bonding and Functional Groups; Cohesion of Water; Covalent Bonds; Dissociation of Water Molecules; Diversity of Carbon-Based Molecules; Electron Arrangement; Energy Transformations; Functional Groups; Hydrogen Bonding and Water; Hydrogen Bonds; Ionic Bonds; Nonpolar and Polar Molecules; pH Scale; Polarity of Water; Properties of Water; Structure of the Atomic Nucleus

**Questions** Reading Quizzes, Blue-Thread Questions, Test Bank

**2. eText** Read your book online, search, take notes, highlight text, and more.

**3. The Study Area** Practice Test, Cumulative Test, BioFlix® 3-D Animations, Videos, Activities, Audio Glossary, Word Study Tools, Art

## You should be able to . . .

### ✓ TEST YOUR KNOWLEDGE

Answers are available in Appendix A

1. Which of the following occurs when a covalent bond forms?
   a. The potential energy of electrons drops.
   b. Electrons in valence shells are shared between nuclei.
   c. Ions of opposite charge interact.
   d. Polar molecules interact.

2. If a reaction is exothermic, then which of the following statements is true?
   a. The products have lower potential energy than the reactants.
   b. Energy must be added for the reaction to proceed.
   c. The products have lower entropy (are more ordered) than the reactants.
   d. It occurs extremely quickly.

3. Which of the following is most likely to have been the energy source responsible for the formation of acetic acid in deep-sea hydrothermal vents?

   a. heat released from the vents
   b. solar radiation that passed through the ocean water
   c. chemical energy present in the reactants
   d. the increase in entropy in the products

4. What is thermal energy?
   a. a form of potential energy
   b. the temperature increase that occurs when any form of energy is added to a system
   c. mechanical energy
   d. the kinetic energy of molecular motion, measured as heat

5. What factors determine whether a chemical reaction is spontaneous or not?

6. What are the two models that have been proposed to explain the process component of chemical evolution?

7. Which of the following molecules would you predict to have the largest number of polar covalent bonds based on their molecular formulas?
   a. $C_2H_6O$ (ethanol)
   b. $C_2H_6$ (ethane)
   c. $C_2H_4O_2$ (acetic acid)
   d. $C_3H_8O$ (propanol)

8. Locate fluorine (F) on the partial periodic table provided in Figure 2.2. Predict its relative electronegativity compared to hydrogen, sodium, and oxygen. State the number and type of bond(s) you expect it would form if it reacted with sodium.

9. Oxygen is extremely electronegative, meaning that its nucleus pulls electrons shared in covalent bonds very strongly. Explain the changes in electron position that are illustrated in Figure 2.19 based on oxygen's electronegativity.

10. Draw the electron-sharing continuum and place molecular oxygen ($O_2$), magnesium chloride ($MgCl_2$), and carbon dioxide ($CO_2$) on it.

11. Consider the reaction between carbon dioxide and water, which forms carbonic acid:

$$CO_2(g) + H_2O(l) \rightleftharpoons CH_2O_3(aq)$$

In aqueous solution, carbonic acid immediately dissociates to form a proton and bicarbonate ion, as follows:

$$CH_2O_3(aq) \rightleftharpoons H^+(aq) + CHO_3^-(aq)$$

If an underwater volcano bubbled additional $CO_2$ into the ocean, would this sequence of reactions be driven to the left or the right? How would this affect the pH of the ocean?

12. What is the relationship between the carbon framework in an organic molecule (the "R" in Table 2.3) and its functional groups?

13. When $H_2$ and $CO_2$ react, acetic acid can be formed spontaneously while the production of formaldehyde requires an input of energy. Which of the following conclusions may be drawn from this observation?
    a. More heat is released when formaldehyde is produced compared to the production of acetic acid.
    b. Compared to the reactants from which it is formed, formaldehyde has more potential energy than does acetic acid.
    c. Entropy decreases when acetic acid is produced and increases when formaldehyde is produced.
    d. The mineral catalyst involved in acetic acid production provides energy to make the reaction spontaneous.

14. When chemistry texts introduce the concept of electron shells, they emphasize that shells represent distinct potential energy levels. In introducing electron shells, this chapter also emphasizes that they represent distinct distances from the positive charges in the nucleus. Are these two points of view in conflict? Why or why not?

15. Draw a concept map relating water's structure to its properties. (For an introduction to concept mapping, see **BioSkills 15** in Appendix B.) Your concept map should include the following terms or phrases: polar covalent bonds, polarity (on the water molecule), hydrogen bonding, high heat of vaporization, high specific heat, less dense as a solid, effective solvent, unequal sharing of electrons, high energy input required to break bonds, high electronegativity of oxygen.

16. From what you have learned about water, why do coastal regions tend to have climates with lower annual variation in temperature than do inland areas at the same latitude?

# 3 Protein Structure and Function

**In this chapter you will learn that**

Proteins are the most abundant and versatile macromolecules in life

composed of

20 amino acids with unique side chains
**3.1**

polymerize to form

Protein structure:
Primary – Secondary – Tertiary – Quaternary
**3.2**

determines

Protein function
**3.3**

informs

determines

Importance of proteins for life
**3.4**

A space-filling model of hemoglobin—a protein that is carrying oxygen in your blood right now.

This chapter is part of the Big Picture. See how on pages 104–105.

hemical reactions in the atmosphere and ocean of ancient Earth are thought to have led to the formation of the first complex carbon-containing compounds. This idea, called chemical evolution, was first proposed by Alexander I. Oparin in 1924. The hypothesis was published again—independently and five years later—by J. B. S. Haldane.

Today, the Oparin–Haldane proposal is considered a formal scientific theory (see Chapter 1). Scientific theories are continuously refined as new information comes to light, and many of Oparin

✔ When you see this checkmark, stop and test yourself. Answers are available in Appendix A.

and Haldane's original ideas have been revised. In its current form, the theory can be broken into four steps.

**Step 1** Chemical evolution began with the production of small organic compounds from reactants such as $H_2$, $N_2$, $NH_3$, and $CO_2$. (Chapter 2 focuses on this step.)

**Step 2** These small, simple organic compounds reacted to form mid-sized molecules, such as amino acids, nucleotides, and sugars. (Amino acids are introduced in this chapter. Nucleotides and sugars are discussed in Chapters 4 and 5, respectively.)

**Step 3** Mid-sized, building-block molecules linked to form the types of large molecules found in cells today, including proteins, nucleic acids, and complex carbohydrates. Each of these large molecules is composed of distinctive chemical subunits that join together: Proteins are composed of amino acids, nucleic acids are composed of nucleotides, and complex carbohydrates are composed of sugars.

**Step 4** Life became possible when one of these large, complex molecules acquired the ability to replicate itself. By increasing in copy number, this molecule would then emerge from the pool of chemicals. At that point, life had begun—chemical evolution gave way to biological evolution.

What type of molecule was responsible for the origin of life? Answering this question is a recurring theme in this and the next three chapters.

To address this question, researchers first designed experiments to identify the types of molecules that could be produced in the waters of prebiotic Earth (Chapter 2). One series of results sparked particular excitement for origin-of-life researchers—the repeated discovery of amino acids among the products of early Earth simulations.

Amino acids have also been found in meteorites and produced in experiments that approximate the environment of interstellar space. Taken together, these observations have led researchers to conclude that amino acids were present and probably abundant during chemical evolution. Since amino acids are the building blocks of proteins, many researchers have therefore asked, Could a protein have been the initial spark of life?

For this question to be valid, proteins would need to possess three of the fundamental attributes of life, namely: information, replication, and evolution. To determine if they do, let's look at the molecules themselves. What are amino acids, and how are they linked to form proteins?

## 3.1 Amino Acids and Their Polymerization

Modern cells, such as those that make up your body, produce tens of thousands of distinct proteins. Most of these molecules are composed of just 20 different building blocks, called **amino acids.** All 20 of these building blocks have a common structure.

**(a) Non-ionized** form of amino acid

**(b) Ionized** form of amino acid

**FIGURE 3.1 All Amino Acids Have the Same General Structure.** The central α-carbon is shown in red.

## The Structure of Amino Acids

To understand how amino acids are put together, recall that carbon atoms have a valence of four—they form four covalent bonds (Chapter 2). All 20 amino acids thus have a common core structure—with a central carbon atom (referred to as the α-carbon) bonded to the four different atoms or groups of atoms diagrammed in **FIGURE 3.1a**:

1. H—a hydrogen atom
2. $NH_2$—an amino functional group
3. COOH—a carboxyl functional group
4. a distinctive "R-group" (often referred to as a "side chain")

The combination of amino and carboxyl groups not only inspired the name amino acid, but is key to how these molecules behave. In water at pH 7, the concentration of protons causes the amino group to act as a base. It attracts a proton to form $NH_3^+$ (**FIGURE 3.1b**). The carboxyl group, in contrast, is acidic because its two oxygen atoms are highly electronegative. They pull electrons away from the hydrogen atom, which means that it is relatively easy for this group to lose a proton to form $COO^-$.

The charges on these functional groups are important for two reasons: (1) They help amino acids stay in solution, where they can interact with one another and with other solutes, and (2) they affect the amino acid's chemical reactivity.

## The Nature of Side Chains

What about the R-group? The R-groups, or side chains, on amino acids vary from a single hydrogen atom to large structures containing carbon atoms linked into rings. While all amino acids share the same core structure, each of the 20 R-groups is unique. The properties of amino acids vary because their R-groups vary.

**FIGURE 3.2** highlights the R-groups on the 20 most common amino acids found in cells.[1] As you examine these side chains,

---
[1]There are actually 22 amino acids found in proteins that occur in organisms, but two are very rare.

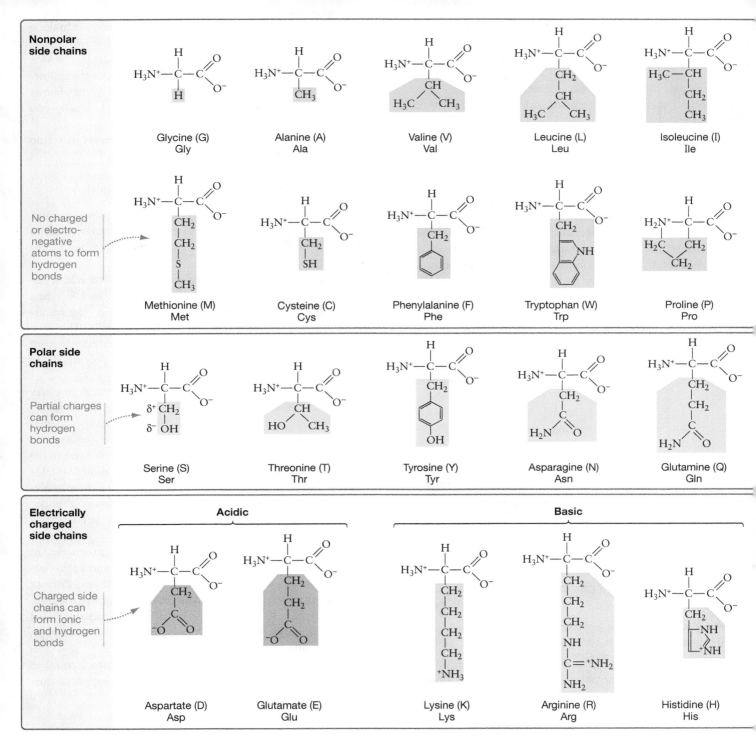

**FIGURE 3.2 The 20 Major Amino Acids Found in Organisms.** At the pH (about 7.0) found in cells, the 20 major amino acids found in organisms have the structural formulas shown here. The side chains are highlighted, and standard single-letter and three-letter abbreviations for each amino acid are given. For clarity, the carbon atoms in the ring structures of phenylalanine, tyrosine, tryptophan, and histidine are not shown; each bend in a ring is the site of a carbon atom. The hydrogen atoms in these structures are also not shown. A double line inside a ring indicates a double bond.

✔**EXERCISE** Explain why the green R-groups are nonpolar and why the pink R-groups are polar, based on the relative electronegativities of O, N, C, and H (see Chapter 2). Note that sulfur (S) has an electronegativity almost equal to that of carbon and slightly higher than that of hydrogen, making cysteine's side chain mildly hydrophobic.

ask yourself two questions (while referring to Table 2.3): Is this R-group likely to participate in chemical reactions? Will it help this amino acid stay in solution?

**Functional Groups Affect Reactivity** Several of the side chains found in amino acids contain carboxyl, sulfhydryl, hydroxyl, or amino functional groups. Under the right conditions, these functional groups can participate in chemical reactions. For example, amino acids with a sulfhydryl group (SH) in their side chains can form disulfide (S—S) bonds that help link different parts of large proteins. Such bonds naturally form between the proteins in your hair; curly hair contains many cross-links and straight hair far fewer.

In contrast, some amino acids contain side chains that are devoid of functional groups—consisting solely of carbon and hydrogen atoms. These R-groups rarely participate in chemical reactions. As a result, the influence of these amino acids on protein function depends primarily on their size and shape rather than reactivity.

**The Polarity of Side Chains Affects Solubility** The nature of its R-group affects the polarity, and thus the solubility, of an amino acid in water.

Nonpolar side chains lack charged or highly electronegative atoms capable of forming hydrogen bonds with water. These R-groups are **hydrophobic,** meaning that they do not interact with water. Instead of dissolving, hydrophobic side chains tend to coalesce in aqueous solution.

Polar or charged side chains interact readily with water and are **hydrophilic.** Hydrophilic side chains dissolve in water easily.

Amino acid side chains distinguish the different amino acids and can be grouped into four general types: acidic, basic, uncharged polar, and nonpolar. If given a structural formula for an amino acid, as in Figure 3.2, you can determine which type of amino acid it is by asking three questions:

- Does the side chain have a negative charge? If so, it has lost a proton, so it must be acidic.

- Does the side chain have a positive charge? If so, it has taken on a proton, so it must be basic.

- If the side chain is uncharged, does it have an oxygen atom? If so, the highly electronegative oxygen will result in a polar covalent bond and thus is uncharged polar.

If the answers to all three questions are no, then you are looking at a nonpolar amino acid. ✔ If you understand how the interaction between amino acids and water is affected by the side chains, you should be able to use Figure 3.2 to order the following amino acids from most hydrophilic to most hydrophobic: valine, aspartate, asparagine, and tyrosine. Explain why you have chosen this order.

Now that you have seen the diversity of structures in amino acids, let's put them together to make a protein.

## How Do Amino Acids Link to Form Proteins?

Amino acids are linked to one another to form proteins. Similarly, the molecular building blocks called nucleotides attach to one another to form nucleic acids, and simple sugars connect to form complex carbohydrates.

In general, a molecular subunit such as an amino acid, a nucleotide, or a sugar is called a **monomer** ("one-part"). When a large number of monomers are bonded together, the resulting structure is called a **polymer** ("many-parts"). The process of linking monomers together is called **polymerization** (**FIGURE 3.3**). Thus, amino acid monomers can polymerize to form proteins.

Biologists also use the word **macromolecule** to denote a very large molecule that is made up of smaller molecules joined together. Proteins are macromolecules—polymers—that consist of linked amino acid monomers.

The theory of chemical evolution states that monomers in the prebiotic soup polymerized to form larger and more complex molecules, such as the proteins and other types of macromolecules found in organisms. This is a difficult step, because monomers such as amino acids do not spontaneously self-assemble into macromolecules such as proteins.

According to the second law of thermodynamics (reviewed in Chapter 2), this fact is not surprising. Complex and highly organized molecules are not expected to form spontaneously from simpler constituents, because polymerization organizes the molecules involved into a more complex, ordered structure. Stated another way, polymerization decreases the disorder, or entropy, of the molecules involved.

For monomers to link together and form macromolecules, an input of energy is required. How could this have happened during chemical evolution?

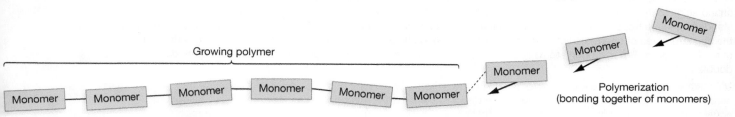

**FIGURE 3.3 Monomers Are the Building Blocks of Polymers.**

**(a) Condensation reaction:**
monomer in, water out

(Water)

**(b) Hydrolysis:**
water in, monomer out

H — OH (Water)

**FIGURE 3.4 Polymers Can Be Extended or Broken Apart.**

**Could Polymerization Occur in the Energy-Rich Environment of Early Earth?** Monomers polymerize through **condensation reactions,** also known as **dehydration reactions.** These reactions are aptly named because the newly formed bond results in the loss of a water molecule (**FIGURE 3.4a**). The reverse reaction, called **hydrolysis,** breaks polymers apart by adding a water molecule (**FIGURE 3.4b**). The water molecule reacts with the bond linking the monomers, separating one monomer from the polymer chain.

In a solution such as the prebiotic soup, condensation and hydrolysis represent the forward and reverse reactions of a chemical equilibrium:

$$\text{Monomer 1} + \text{Monomer 2} \underset{\text{hydrolysis}}{\overset{\text{condensation}}{\rightleftharpoons}} \text{Monomer 1} - \text{Monomer 2}$$

Hydrolysis dominates because it increases entropy and is favorable energetically.

This means that, in the prebiotic soup, polymerization would occur only if there were a very high concentration of amino acids to push the reaction toward condensation. Since the equilibrium favors free monomers over polymers even under concentrated conditions, a polymer is unlikely to have grown much beyond a short chain.

According to recent experiments, though, there are several ways that amino acids could have polymerized early in chemical evolution.

- Researchers evaluating the surface metabolism model of chemical evolution have been able to generate stable polymers by mixing free amino acids with a source of chemical energy and tiny mineral particles. Apparently, growing macromolecules are protected from hydrolysis if they cling, or adsorb, to a mineral surface. One such experiment produced polymers that were 55 amino acids long.

- In conditions that simulate the hot, metal-rich environments of undersea volcanoes, researchers have observed not only amino acid formation but also their polymerization.

- Amino acids have also joined into polymers in experiments in cooler water if a carbon- and sulfur-containing gas—one that is commonly ejected from undersea volcanoes—is present.

The current consensus is that several mechanisms could have led to polymerization reactions between amino acids, early in chemical evolution. What kind of bond is responsible for linking these monomers?

**The Peptide Bond** As **FIGURE 3.5** shows, amino acids polymerize when a bond forms between the carboxyl group of one amino acid and the amino group of another. The C—N covalent bond that results from this condensation reaction is called a **peptide bond.** When a water molecule is removed in the condensation reaction, the carboxyl group is converted to a carbonyl functional group (C=O) in the resulting polymer, and the amino group is reduced to an N—H.

Peptide bonds are unusually stable compared to linkages in other types of macromolecules. This is because a pair of valence electrons on the nitrogen is partially shared in the C—N bond (see Figure 3.5). The degree of electron sharing is great enough that peptide bonds actually have some of the characteristics of a double bond. For example, the peptide bond is planar, limiting the movement of the atoms participating in the peptide bond.

When amino acids are linked by peptide bonds into a chain, the amino acids are referred to as residues to distinguish them from free monomers.

**FIGURE 3.5 Peptide Bonds Form When the Carboxyl Group of One Amino Acid Reacts with the Amino Group of a Second Amino Acid.**

**(a)** Peptide chain

**(b)** Numbering system

**FIGURE 3.6  Amino Acids Polymerize to Form Chains.**

**FIGURE 3.6a** shows how the chain of peptide bonds in a short polymer gives the molecule a structural framework, or a "backbone." There are three key points to note about the peptide-bonded backbone:

1. **R-group orientation**   The side chains present in each residue extend out from the backbone, making it possible for them to interact with each other and with water.

2. **Directionality**   There is an amino group ($NH_3^+$) on one end of the backbone and a carboxyl group ($COO^-$) on the other. The end of the sequence that has the free amino group is called the N-terminus, or amino-terminus, and the end with the free carboxyl group is called the C-terminus, or carboxy-terminus. By convention, biologists always write amino acid sequences

from the N-terminus to the C-terminus (**FIGURE 3.6b**), because the N-terminus is the start of the chain when proteins are synthesized in cells.

3. **Flexibility**   Although the peptide bond itself cannot rotate because of its double-bond nature, the single bonds on either side of the peptide bond can rotate. As a result, the structure as a whole is flexible (**FIGURE 3.7**).

When fewer than 50 amino acids are linked together in this way, the resulting polymer is called an **oligopeptide** ("few peptides") or simply a **peptide**. Polymers that contain 50 or more amino acids are called **polypeptides** ("many peptides").

The term **protein** is often used to describe any chain of amino acid residues, but formally protein refers to the complete, often

**FIGURE 3.7  Peptide Chains Are Flexible.**

functional form of the molecule. In Section 3.2, you'll see that some proteins consist of a single polypeptide while others are functional only when multiple polypeptides are bonded to one another.

Proteins are the stuff of life. Let's take a look at how they are put together and then see what they do.

## check your understanding

### If you understand that . . .

- Amino acids are small molecules with a central carbon atom bonded to a carboxyl group, an amino group, a hydrogen atom, and a side chain called an R-group.
- Each amino acid has distinctive chemical properties because each has a unique R-group.
- Proteins are polymers made up of amino acids.
- When the carboxyl group of one amino acid reacts with the amino group of another amino acid, a strong covalent bond called a peptide bond forms. Small chains are called oligopeptides; large chains are called polypeptides, or proteins.

### ✔ You should be able to . . .

Draw the structural formulas of two glycine residues (glycine's R-group is an H) linked by a peptide bond, and label the amino- and carboxy-terminus.

*Answers are available in Appendix A.*

## 3.2 What Do Proteins Look Like?

The unparalleled diversity of proteins—in size, shape, and other aspects of structure—is important because function follows from structure. Proteins can serve diverse functions in cells because they are diverse in size and shape as well as in the chemical properties of their amino acid residues.

**FIGURE 3.8** illustrates some of the variety in the sizes and shapes observed in proteins. In the case of the TATA box–binding protein in **FIGURE 3.8a** and the porin protein in **FIGURE 3.8b**, the shape of the molecule has a clear correlation with its function. The TATA box–binding protein has a groove where DNA molecules fit; porin has a hole that forms a pore. The groove in the TATA box–binding protein interacts with specific regions of a DNA molecule, while porin fits in cell membranes and allows certain hydrophilic molecules to pass through. Proteins that provide structural support for cells or tissues, such as the collagen triple helix in **FIGURE 3.8d**, often form long, cable-like fibers.

But many of the proteins found in cells do not have shapes that are noticeably correlated with their functions. For example, the trypsin protein in **FIGURE 3.8c** has an overall globular shape that tells little about its function, which is to bind and cleave peptide bonds of other proteins.

How can biologists make sense of this diversity of protein size and shape? Initially, the amount of variation seems overwhelming. Fortunately, it is not. No matter how large or complex a protein may be, its underlying structure can be broken down into just four basic levels of organization.

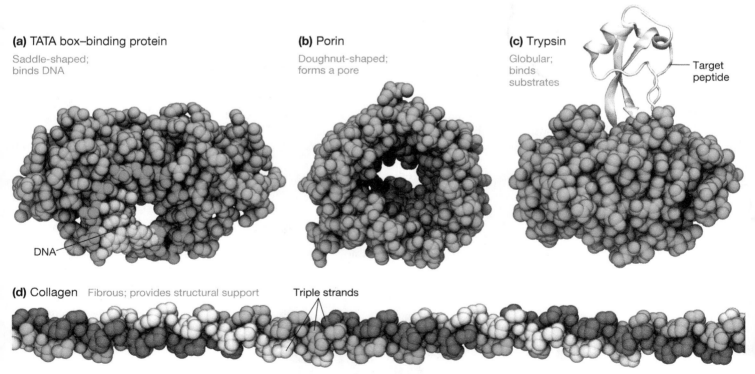

**(a)** TATA box–binding protein
Saddle-shaped;
binds DNA

DNA

**(b)** Porin
Doughnut-shaped;
forms a pore

**(c)** Trypsin
Globular;
binds
substrates

Target peptide

**(d)** Collagen   Fibrous; provides structural support

Triple strands

**FIGURE 3.8 In Overall Shape, Proteins Are the Most Diverse Class of Molecules Known.**

# Primary Structure

Each protein has a unique sequence of amino acids. That simple conclusion was the culmination of 12 years of study by Frederick Sanger and co-workers during the 1940s and 1950s. Sanger's group worked out the first techniques for determining the amino acid sequence of insulin, a hormone that helps regulate sugar concentrations in the blood of humans and other mammals. When other proteins were analyzed, it rapidly became clear that each protein has a definite and distinct amino acid sequence.

Biochemists call the unique sequence of amino acids in a protein the **primary structure** of that protein. The sequence of amino acid residues in Figure 3.6, for example, defines the peptide's primary structure.

With 20 types of amino acids available and length ranging from two amino acid residues to tens of thousands, the number of primary structures that are possible is practically limitless. There may, in fact, be $20^n$ different combinations of amino acid residues for a polymer with a given length of $n$. For example, a peptide that is just 10 amino acids long has $20^{10}$ possible sequences. This is over 10,000 billion.

Why is the order and type of residues in the primary structure of a protein important? Recall that the R-groups present on each amino acid affect its chemical reactivity and solubility. It's therefore reasonable to predict that the R-groups present in a polypeptide will affect that molecule's properties and function.

This prediction is correct. In some cases, even a single change in the sequence of amino acids can cause radical changes in the way the protein as a whole behaves.

As an example, consider hemoglobin, an oxygen-binding protein in human red blood cells. In some individuals, hemoglobin has a valine instead of a glutamate at the 6th position of a strand containing 146 amino acid residues (**FIGURE 3.9a**). Valine's side chain is radically different from the R-group in glutamate. The change in R-group produces hemoglobin molecules that stick to one another and form fibers when oxygen concentrations in the blood are low. Red blood cells that carry these fibers adopt a sickle-like shape (**FIGURE 3.9b**). Sickled red blood cells get stuck in the small blood vessels called capillaries and starve downstream cells of oxygen. A debilitating illness called sickle-cell disease results.

A protein's primary structure is fundamental to its function. Primary structure is also fundamental to the higher levels of protein structure: secondary, tertiary, and quaternary.

## Secondary Structure

Even though variation in the amino acid sequence of a protein is virtually limitless, it is only the tip of the iceberg in terms of generating structural diversity.

The next level of organization in proteins—**secondary structure**—is created in part by hydrogen bonding between components of the peptide-bonded backbone. Secondary structures are distinctively shaped sections of proteins that are stabilized largely by hydrogen bonding that occurs between the oxygen on the C=O group of one amino acid residue and the hydrogen on the N—H groups of another (**FIGURE 3.10a**). The oxygen atom in the C=O group has a partial negative charge due to its high electronegativity, while the hydrogen atom in the N—H group has a partial positive charge because it is bonded to nitrogen, which has high electronegativity.

Note a key point: Hydrogen bonding between sections of the same backbone is possible only when a polypeptide bends in a way that puts C=O and N—H groups close together. In most proteins, these polar groups are aligned and form hydrogen bonds with one another when the backbone bends to form one of two possible structures (**FIGURE 3.10b**):

1. an **α-helix** (alpha-helix), in which the polypeptide's backbone is coiled; or

2. a **β-pleated sheet** (beta-pleated sheet), in which segments of a peptide chain bend 180° and then fold in the same plane.

In both structures, the distance between residues that hydrogen-bond to one another is small. In an α-helix, for example, H-bonds form between residues that are just four linear positions apart in the polypeptide's primary sequence (Figure 3.10a).

When biologists use illustrations called ribbon diagrams to represent the shape of a protein, α-helices are shown as coils; β-pleated sheets are shown by groups of arrows in a plane (**FIGURE 3.10c**).

In most cases, secondary structure consists of α-helices and β-pleated sheets. Which one forms, if either, depends on the molecule's primary structure—specifically, the geometry and

**(a)** Normal amino acid sequence

Normal red blood cells

**(b)** Single change in amino acid sequence

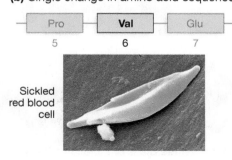

Sickled red blood cell

**FIGURE 3.9 Changes in Primary Structure Affect Protein Function.** Compare the primary structure of normal hemoglobin **(a)** with that of hemoglobin molecules in people with sickle-cell disease **(b)**. The single amino acid change causes red blood cells to change from their normal disc shape in (a) to a sickled shape in (b) when oxygen concentrations are low.

properties of the amino acids in the sequence. Certain amino acids are more likely to be involved in α-helices than in β-pleated sheets, and vice versa, due to the specific geometry of their side chains. Proline, for example, may be present in β-pleated sheets,

**(a)** Hydrogen bonds can form between nearby amino and carbonyl groups on the same polypeptide chain.

**(b)** Secondary structures of proteins result.

α-helix                β-pleated sheet

**(c)** Ribbon diagrams of secondary structure

Arrowheads point toward the carboxyl end of the primary structure

α-helix                β-pleated sheet

**FIGURE 3.10 Secondary Structures of Proteins.** A polypeptide chain can coil or fold in on itself when hydrogen bonds form between N–H and C=O groups on its peptide-bonded backbone.

but it will terminate α-helices due to its unusual side chain. The bond formed between proline's R-group and the nitrogen of the core amino group introduces kinks in the backbone that do not conform to the shape of the helix.

Although each of the hydrogen bonds in an α-helix or a β-pleated sheet is weak relative to a covalent bond, the large number of hydrogen bonds in these structures makes them highly stable. As a result, they increase the stability of the molecule as a whole and help define its shape. In terms of overall shape and stability, though, the tertiary structure of a protein is even more important.

## Tertiary Structure

Most of the overall shape, or **tertiary structure,** of a polypeptide results from interactions between R-groups or between R-groups and the backbone. In contrast to the secondary structures, where hydrogen bonds link backbone components together, these side chains can be involved in a wide variety of bonds and interactions. In addition, the amino acid residues that interact with one another are often far apart in the linear sequence. Because each contact between R-groups causes the peptide-bonded backbone to bend and fold, each contributes to the distinctive three-dimensional shape of a polypeptide.

Five types of interactions involving side chains are particularly important:

1. ***Hydrogen bonding*** Hydrogen bonds form between polar R-groups and opposite partial charges either in the peptide backbone or other R-groups.

2. ***Hydrophobic interactions*** In an aqueous solution, water molecules interact with the hydrophilic polar side chains of a polypeptide and force the hydrophobic nonpolar side chains to coalesce into globular masses. When these nonpolar R-groups come together, the surrounding water molecules form more hydrogen bonds with each other, increasing the stability of their own interactions.

3. ***van der Waals interactions*** Once hydrophobic side chains are close to one another, their association is further stabilized by electrical attractions known as **van der Waals interactions.** These weak attractions occur because the constant motion of electrons gives molecules a tiny asymmetry in charge that changes with time. If nonpolar molecules get extremely close to each other, the minute partial charge on one molecule induces an opposite partial charge in the nearby molecule and causes an attraction. Although the interaction is very weak relative to covalent bonds or even hydrogen bonds, a large number of van der Waals attractions can significantly increase the stability of the structure.

4. ***Covalent bonding*** Covalent bonds can form between the side chains of two cysteines through a reaction between the sulfhydryl groups. These **disulfide ("two-sulfur") bonds** are frequently referred to as bridges, because they create strong links between distinct regions of the same polypeptide or two separate polypeptides.

**(a)** Interactions that determine the tertiary structure of proteins

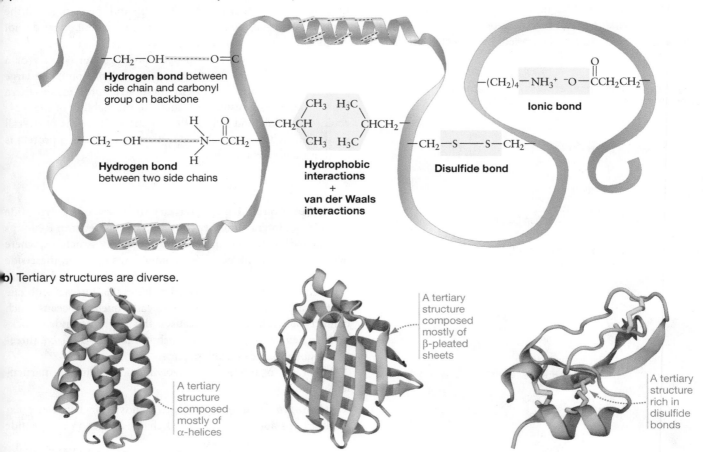

**(b)** Tertiary structures are diverse.

A tertiary structure composed mostly of α-helices

A tertiary structure composed mostly of β-pleated sheets

A tertiary structure rich in disulfide bonds

**FIGURE 3.11 Tertiary Structure of Proteins Results from Interactions Involving R-Groups. (a)** The overall shape of a single polypeptide is called its tertiary structure. This level of structure is created by bonds and other interactions that cause it to fold. **(b)** The tertiary structure of these proteins includes interactions between α-helices and β-pleated sheets.

5. **Ionic bonding**   Ionic bonds form between groups that have full and opposing charges, such as the ionized acidic and basic side chains highlighted on the right in **FIGURE 3.11a**.

In addition, the overall shape of many proteins depends in part on the presence of secondary structures like α-helices and β-pleated sheets. Thus, tertiary structure depends on both primary and secondary structures.

With so many interactions possible between side chains and peptide-bonded backbones, it's not surprising that polypeptides vary in shape from rod-like filaments to ball-like masses. (See FIGURE 3.11b, and look again at Figure 3.8.)

## Quaternary Structure

The first three levels of protein structure involve individual polypeptides. But some proteins contain multiple polypeptides that interact to form a single structure. The combination of polypeptides, referred to as subunits, gives a protein **quaternary structure.** The individual polypeptides are held together by the same types of bonds and interactions found in the tertiary level of structure.

In the simplest case, a protein with quaternary structure can consist of just two subunits that are identical. The Cro protein found in a virus called bacteriophage λ (pronounced *LAMB-da*) is an example (**FIGURE 3.12a**). Proteins with two polypeptide subunits are called dimers ("two-parts").

More than two polypeptides can be linked into a single protein, however, and the polypeptides involved may be distinct in primary, secondary, and tertiary structure. For example hemoglobin, an oxygen-binding protein, is a tetramer ("four-parts"). It consists of two copies of two different polypeptides (**FIGURE 3.12b**).

In addition, cells contain **macromolecular machines:** groups of multiple proteins that assemble to carry out a particular function. Some proteins are also found in complexes that include other types of macromolecules. The ribosome (introduced in Chapter 7) provides an example; it consists of several nucleic acid molecules and over 50 different proteins.

**TABLE 3.1** summarizes the four levels of protein structure, using hemoglobin as an example. The key thing to note is that protein structure is hierarchical. Quaternary structure is based on tertiary structure, which is based in part on secondary

**(a)** Cro protein, a dimer

**(b)** Hemoglobin, a tetramer

**FIGURE 3.12 Quaternary Structures of Proteins Are Created by Multiple Polypeptides.** These diagrams represent primary sequences as ribbons. **(a)** The Cro protein is a dimer—it consists of two polypeptide subunits, colored light and dark green. The subunits are identical in this case. **(b)** Hemoglobin is a tetramer—it consists of four polypeptide subunits. The α subunits (light and dark green) are identical; so are the β subunits (light and dark blue).

structure. All three of the higher-level structures are based on primary structure.

The summary table and preceding discussion convey three important messages:

1. The combination of primary, secondary, tertiary, and quaternary levels of structure is responsible for the fantastic diversity of sizes and shapes observed in proteins.

2. Protein folding is directed by the sequence of amino acids present in the primary structure.

3. Most elements of protein structure are based on folding of polypeptide chains.

Does protein folding occur spontaneously? What happens to the function of a protein if normal folding is disrupted? Let's use these questions as a guide to dig deeper into how proteins fold.

**SUMMARY TABLE 3.1** Protein Structure

| Level | Description | Stabilized by | Example: Hemoglobin |
|---|---|---|---|
| **Primary** | The sequence of amino acids in a polypeptide | Peptide bonds | Gly — Ser — Asp — Cys |
| **Secondary** | Formation of α-helices and β-pleated sheets in a polypeptide | Hydrogen bonding between groups along the peptide-bonded backbone; thus, depends on primary structure | One α-helix |
| **Tertiary** | Overall three-dimensional shape of a polypeptide (includes contribution from secondary structures) | Bonds and other interactions between R-groups, or between R-groups and the peptide-bonded backbone; thus, depends on primary structure | One of hemoglobin's subunits |
| **Quaternary** | Shape produced by combinations of polypeptides (thus, combinations of tertiary structures) | Bonds and other interactions between R-groups, and between peptide backbones of different polypeptides; thus, depends on primary structure | Hemoglobin consists of four polypeptide subunits |

## 3.3 Folding and Function

If you were able to synthesize one of the polypeptides in hemoglobin from individual amino acids, and you then placed the resulting chain in an aqueous solution, it would spontaneously fold into the shape of the tertiary structure shown in Table 3.1.

In terms of entropy, this result probably seems counterintuitive. Because an unfolded protein has many more ways to move about, it has much higher entropy than the folded version. Folding *does* tend to be spontaneous, however, because the chemical bonds, hydrophobic interactions, and van der Waals forces that occur release enough energy to overcome the decrease in entropy. In terms of energy, the folded molecule is more stable than the unfolded molecule.

Folding is crucial to the function of a completed protein. This relationship between protein structure and function was hammered home in a set of classic experiments by Christian Anfinsen and colleagues during the 1950s.

### Normal Folding Is Crucial to Function

Anfinsen studied a protein called ribonuclease that is found in many organisms. Ribonuclease is an enzyme that cleaves ribonucleic acid polymers. Anfinsen found that ribonuclease could be unfolded, or **denatured,** by treating it with compounds that break hydrogen bonds and disulfide bonds. The denatured ribonuclease was unable to function normally—it could no longer break apart nucleic acids (**FIGURE 3.13**).

When the denaturing agents were removed, however, the molecule refolded and began to function normally again. These experiments confirmed that ribonuclease folds spontaneously and that folding is essential for normal function.

More recent work has shown that in cells, folding is often facilitated by specific proteins called **molecular chaperones.** Many molecular chaperones belong to a family of molecules called the heat-shock proteins. Heat-shock proteins are produced in large quantities after cells experience high temperatures or other

Ribonuclease protein, **folded**

Ribonuclease protein, denatured **(unfolded)**

Denaturant added

Denaturant removed

Disulfide bonds form

Hydrogen bonds form

Disulfide bonds and hydrogen bonds are broken

**FIGURE 3.13 Protein Structure Determines Function. (left)** Ribonuclease is functional when properly folded via hydrogen and disulfide bonds. **(right)** When the disulfide and various noncovalent bonds are broken, ribonuclease is no longer able to function. The double arrow indicates that this process is reversible.

treatments that make other proteins lose their tertiary structure. Heat-shock proteins recognize denatured proteins by binding to hydrophobic patches that would not normally be exposed in properly folded proteins. This interaction blocks inappropriate interactions with other molecules and allows the proteins to refold.

So what is the "normal shape" of a protein? Is only one shape possible for each protein, or could there be several different folded shapes with only one serving as the functional form?

## Protein Shape Is Flexible

Although each protein has a characteristic folded shape that is necessary for its function, most proteins are flexible and dynamic, not rigid and static. As it turns out, many polypeptides are unable to fold into their active shape on their own. Over half of the proteins that have been analyzed to date have been found to contain disordered regions lacking any apparent structure. These proteins exist in an assortment of shapes. Only when they interact with particular ions or molecules, or are chemically modified, will they adopt the shape, or conformation, that allows them to perform their function in the cell.

**Protein Folding Is Often Regulated** Since the function of a protein is dependent on its shape, controlling when or where it is folded will regulate the protein's activity.

For example, proteins involved in cell signaling are often regulated by controlling their shape. The inactive form of calmodulin—a protein that helps maintain normal blood pressure—has a disordered shape. When the concentration of calcium ions increases in the cell, calmodulin binds these ions, folds into an ordered, active conformation, and sends a signal to increase the diameter of blood vessels. **FIGURE 3.14** illustrates the major shape change that is induced in calmodulin when it binds to calcium.

**Misfolding Can Be "Infectious"** In 1982, Stanley Prusiner published what may be the most surprising result to emerge from research on protein folding: Certain proteins can be folded into infectious, disease-causing agents. These proteins are called **prions** (pronounced *PREE-ons*), or proteinaceous infectious particles.

Infectious prions are alternate forms of normal proteins that are present in healthy individuals. The infectious and normal forms do not necessarily differ in amino acid sequence, but their *shapes* are radically different. The infectious form propagates by inducing conformational changes in normal proteins that cause them to adopt the alternate, infectious shape.

**FIGURE 3.15** illustrates the differences in shape observed between the normal and infectious forms of the prion responsible for "mad cow disease" in cattle. The molecule in Figure 3.15a is called the prion protein (PrP) and is a normal component of mammalian cells. The improperly folded version of this protein, like the one in Figure 3.15b, represents the infectious form of the prion.

Prions cause a family of diseases known as the spongiform encephalopathies—literally, "sponge-brain-illnesses." Sheep, cows, goats, and humans afflicted with these diseases undergo massive degeneration of the brain. Although some spongiform encephalopathies

**(a) Disordered, inactive** calmodulin

Protein is not properly folded, and form is variable (one of many forms is shown)

**(b) Ordered, active** calmodulin

+ Ca²⁺

Calcium ion

After binding calcium, calmodulin folds to a single, functional form

**FIGURE 3.14 Calmodulin Requires Calcium to Fold Properly.** Many proteins, like calmodulin, do not complete their folding until after interacting with ions or other molecules. Once calmodulin binds to calcium, it assumes its functional shape.

can be inherited, in many cases the disease is transmitted when individuals eat tissues containing the infectious form of PrP. All the prion illnesses are fatal.

Prions are a particularly dramatic example of how a protein's function depends on its shape as well as how the final shape of a protein depends on folding.

**(a) Normal** prion protein

**(b) Infectious** prion protein

α-helixes in normal prion

β-pleated sheet in infectious prion

**FIGURE 3.15 Prion Infectivity Is Linked to Structure.** Ribbon model of **(a)** a normal, noninfectious prion protein; and **(b)** the infectious form that causes mad cow disease in cattle. Secondary structure is represented by coils (α-helices) and arrows (β-pleated sheets).

## 3.4 Proteins Are the Most Versatile Macromolecules in Cells

As a group, proteins perform more types of cell functions than any other type of molecule does. It makes sense to hypothesize that life began with proteins, simply because proteins are so vital to the life of today's cells.

Consider the red blood cells that are moving through your arteries right now. Each of these cells contains about 300 million copies of hemoglobin. Hemoglobin carries oxygen from your lungs to cells throughout the body. But every red blood cell also has thousands of copies of a protein called carbonic anhydrase, which is important for moving carbon dioxide from cells back to the lungs, where it can be breathed out. Other proteins form the cell's internal "skeleton" or reside on the cell's membrane to interact with neighboring cells.

Proteins are crucial to most tasks required for cells to exist:

- *Catalysis* Many proteins are specialized to **catalyze,** or speed up, chemical reactions. A protein that functions as a catalyst is called an **enzyme.** The carbonic anhydrase molecules in red blood cells are catalysts. So is the protein called salivary amylase, found in your mouth. Salivary amylase helps begin the digestion of starch and other complex carbohydrates into simple sugars. Most chemical reactions that make life possible depend on enzymes.

- *Defense* Proteins called antibodies and complement proteins attack and destroy viruses and bacteria that cause disease.

- *Movement* Motor proteins and contractile proteins are responsible for moving the cell itself, or for moving large molecules and other types of cargo inside the cell. As you turn this page, for example, specialized proteins called actin and myosin will slide past one another to flex or extend muscle cells in your fingers and arm.

- *Signaling* Proteins are involved in carrying and receiving signals from cell to cell inside the body. If sugar levels in your blood are low, a small protein called glucagon will bind to receptor proteins on your liver cells, triggering enzymes inside to release sugar into your bloodstream.

- *Structure* Structural proteins make up body components such as fingernails and hair, and define the shape of individual cells. Structural proteins keep red blood cells flexible and in their normal disc-like shape.

- *Transport* Proteins allow particular molecules to enter and exit cells or carry them throughout the body. Hemoglobin is a particularly well-studied transport protein, but virtually every cell is studded with membrane proteins that control the passage of specific molecules and ions.

Of all the functions that proteins perform in cells, catalysis may be the most important. The reason is speed. Life, at its most basic level, consists of chemical reactions. But most don't occur fast enough to support life unless a catalyst is present. Enzymes are the most effective catalysts on Earth. Why is this so?

## Why Are Enzymes Good Catalysts?

Part of the reason enzymes are such effective catalysts is that they bring reactant molecules—called **substrates**—together in a precise orientation so the atoms involved in the reaction can interact.

The initial hypothesis for how enzymes work was proposed by Emil Fischer in 1894. According to Fischer's "lock-and-key" model, enzymes are analogous to a lock and the keys are substrates that fit into the lock and then react.

Several important ideas in this model have stood the test of time. For example, Fischer was correct in proposing that enzymes bring substrates together in a precise orientation that makes reactions more likely. His model also accurately explained why most enzymes catalyze one specific reaction effectively. Enzyme specificity is a product of the geometry and types of functional groups in the sites where substrates bind.

As researchers began to test Fischer's model, the location where substrates bind and react became known as the enzyme's **active site.** The active site is where catalysis actually occurs.

When techniques for solving the three-dimensional structure of enzymes became available, the active sites were identified as clefts or cavities within the globular shapes. The digestive enzyme trypsin, which is at work in your body now, is a good example. As **FIGURE 3.16** shows, the active site in trypsin is a small notch that contains three key amino acid residues with functional groups that catalyze the cleavage of peptide bonds in other proteins. No other class of macromolecule can match proteins for their catalytic potential. The variety of reactive functional groups present in amino acids is much better suited for this activity than those found in nucleotides or sugars.

The role of enzymes in catalyzing reactions is discussed in more detail in the next unit (see Chapter 8). There you will see that Fischer's model had to be modified as research on enzyme action progressed.

Key residues inside trypsin's active site cut protein like molecular scissors

Peptide substrate in active site

**FIGURE 3.16 Substrates Bind to a Specific Location in an Enzyme Called the Active Site.** The active site in trypsin, as in many enzymes, is a cleft that contains key amino acid residues that bind substrates and catalyze a reaction.

## Was the First Living Entity a Protein Catalyst?

Several observations in the preceding sections could argue that a protein was the first molecule capable of replication. Experimental studies have shown that amino acids were likely abundant during chemical evolution, and that they could have polymerized to form small proteins. In addition, proteins are the most efficient catalysts known.

To date, however, attempts to simulate the origin of life with proteins have not been successful. The only experimental glimpse of a protein's potential to replicate involved an enzyme that could link two oligopeptides together to form a functional duplicate of itself. However, this result required a high concentration of preformed, specific oligopeptides that would not have been present during chemical evolution.

Although it is too early to arrive at definitive conclusions, most origin-of-life researchers are increasingly skeptical that life began with a protein. Their reasoning is that to make a copy of something, a mold or template is required. Proteins cannot furnish this information. Nucleic acids, in contrast, *can*. How they do so is the subject of the next chapter.

  check your understanding

**If you understand that . . .**

- Proteins are the most versatile large molecules in cells, and each function is directly connected to structure.
- Enzymes speed up chemical reactions by binding substrates at their active site, where catalysis takes place.

✔ **You should be able to . . .**

Predict where amino acid changes would most likely occur in an enzyme that would result in it catalyzing a reaction with a new substrate, and explain how these changes could result in the new activity.

*Answers are available in Appendix A.*

---

## CHAPTER 3 REVIEW

*For media, go to MasteringBiology*

### If you understand . . .

#### 3.1 Amino Acids and Their Polymerization

- Amino acids have a central carbon bonded to an amino group, a hydrogen atom, a carboxyl group, and an R-group.
- The structure of the R-group affects the chemical reactivity and solubility of the amino acid.
- In proteins, amino acids are joined by a peptide bond between the carboxyl group of one amino acid and the amino group of another amino acid.

✔ You should be able to explain how you could use the structural formula of an amino acid to determine if it is acidic, basic, uncharged polar, or nonpolar.

#### 3.2 What Do Proteins Look Like?

- A protein's primary structure, or sequence of amino acids, is responsible for most of its chemical properties.
- Interactions that take place between C=O and N—H groups in the same peptide-bonded backbone create secondary structures, which are stabilized primarily by hydrogen bonding.
- Tertiary structure results from interactions between R-groups—or R-groups and the peptide-bonded backbone—that stabilize a folded protein into a characteristic overall shape.
- In many cases, a complete protein consists of several different polypeptides, bonded together. The combination of polypeptides represents the protein's quaternary structure.

✔ You should be able to predict where nonpolar amino acid residues would be found in a globular protein, such as the trypsin molecule shown in Figure 3.8c.

#### 3.3 Folding and Function

- Protein folding is a spontaneous process.
- A protein's normal folded shape is essential to its function.
- Many proteins must first bind to other molecules or ions before they can adopt their active conformation.
- Improperly folded proteins can be detrimental to life, and certain proteins even cause deadly infectious diseases.

✔ You should be able to identify one way in which the process of folding in calmodulin and infectious prions is similar.

#### 3.4 Proteins Are the Most Versatile Macromolecules in Cells

- In organisms, proteins function in catalysis, defense, movement, signaling, structural support, and transport of materials.
- Proteins can have diverse functions in cells because they have such diverse structures and chemical properties.
- Catalysis takes place at the enzyme's active site, which has unique chemical properties and a distinctive size and shape.

✔ You should be able to provide the characteristics of proteins that make them especially useful for the following cellular activities: catalysis, defense, and signaling.

# MasteringBiology

## 1. MasteringBiology Assignments

**Tutorials and Activities** Activation Energy and Enzymes; Amino Acid Functional Groups; Condensation and Hydrolysis Reactions; Enzyme and Substrate Concentrations; Enzyme Inhibition; Factors That Affect Reaction Rate; How Enzymes Function; How Enzymes Work; Levels of Structure in Proteins; Making and Breaking Polymers; Protein Functions, Protein Structure; Regulating Enzyme Action

**Questions** Reading Quizzes, Blue-Thread Questions, Test Bank

## 2. eText Read your book online, search, take notes, highlight text, and more.

## 3. The Study Area Practice Test, Cumulative Test, BioFlix® 3-D Animations, Videos, Activities, Audio Glossary, Word Study Tools, Art

# You should be able to . . .

## ✓ TEST YOUR KNOWLEDGE
Answers are available in Appendix A

1. What two functional groups are present on every amino acid?
   a. a carbonyl (C=O) group and a carboxyl group
   b. an N–H group and a carbonyl group
   c. an amino group and a hydroxyl group
   d. an amino group and a carboxyl group

2. Twenty different amino acids are found in the proteins of cells. What distinguishes these molecules?

3. By convention, biologists write the sequence of amino acids in a polypeptide in which direction?
   a. carboxy- to amino-terminus
   b. amino- to carboxy-terminus
   c. polar residues to nonpolar residues
   d. charged residues to uncharged residues

4. In a polypeptide, what bonds are responsible for the secondary structure called an α-helix?
   a. peptide bonds
   b. hydrogen bonds that form between the core C=O and N–H groups on different residues
   c. hydrogen bonds and other interactions between side chains
   d. disulfide bonds that form between cysteine residues

5. Where is the information stored that directs different polypeptides to fold into different shapes?

6. What is an active site?
   a. the position in an enzyme where substrates bind
   b. the place where a molecule or ion binds to a protein to induce a shape change
   c. the portion of a motor protein that is involved in moving cargo in a cell
   d. the site on an antibody where it binds to bacterial cells or viruses

## ✓ TEST YOUR UNDERSTANDING
Answers are available in Appendix A

7. Explain how water participates in the development of the interactions that glue nonpolar amino acids together in the interior of globular proteins.

8. If amino acids were mixed together in a solution, resembling the prebiotic soup, would they spontaneously polymerize into polypeptides? Why or why not?

9. Provide an example of how a specific shape of a protein is correlated with its function.

10. A major theme in this chapter is that the structure of molecules correlates with their function. Use this theme to explain why proteins can perform so many different functions in organisms and why enzymes are such effective catalysts.

11. Why are proteins not considered to be a good candidate for the first living molecule?
    a. Their catalytic capability is insufficient.
    b. Their amino acid monomers were likely not present during chemical evolution.
    c. They cannot serve as a template for replication.
    d. They could not have polymerized on their own from amino acids during chemical evolution.

12. If proteins folded only into rigid, inflexible structures, how might this affect the cell's ability to regulate protein function?

## ✓ TEST YOUR PROBLEM-SOLVING SKILLS
Answers are available in Appendix A

13. Based on what you know of the peptide bonds that link together amino acid residues, why would proline's side chain reduce the flexibility of the backbone?

14. Make a concept map (see **BioSkills 15** in Appendix B) that relates the four levels of protein structure and shows how they can contribute to the formation of an active site. Your map should include the following boxed terms: Primary structure, Secondary structure, Tertiary structure, Quaternary structure, Active site, Amino acid sequence, R-groups, Helices and sheets, 3-D shape.

15. Proteins that interact with DNA often interact with the phosphates that are part of this molecule. Which of the following types of amino acids would you predict to be present in the DNA binding sites of these proteins?
    a. acidic amino acids
    b. basic amino acids
    c. uncharged polar amino acids
    d. nonpolar amino acids

16. Some prion-associated diseases are inherited, such as fatal familial insomnia. What is likely to be different between the infectious forms of these inherited prions compared to those that arise via transmission from one animal to another?

**6**    UNIT 1    The Molecular Origin and Evolution of Life

# 4 Nucleic Acids and the RNA World

## In this chapter you will learn that

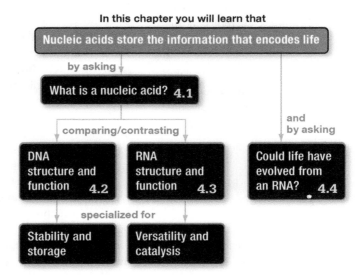

**Nucleic acids store the information that encodes life**

by asking ↓

**What is a nucleic acid?** 4.1

comparing/contrasting

**DNA structure and function** 4.2 | **RNA structure and function** 4.3

and by asking

**Could life have evolved from an RNA?** 4.4

specialized for

**Stability and storage** | **Versatility and catalysis**

This is part of the sheet-metal-and-wire model that James Watson and Francis Crick used to figure out the secondary structure of DNA. The large "T" stands for the nitrogen-containing base thymine.

This chapter is part of the Big Picture. See how on pages 104–105.

ife began when chemical evolution led to the production of a molecule that could promote its own replication. The nature of this first "living molecule," however, has been the subject of many investigations and heated debates. Even though proteins are the workhorse molecules of today's cells, relatively few researchers favor the hypothesis that life began as a protein molecule. Instead, the vast majority of biologists contend that life began as a polymer called a nucleic acid—specifically, a molecule of ribonucleic acid (RNA). This proposal is called the **RNA world hypothesis.**

The RNA world hypothesis contends that chemical evolution led to the existence of an RNA molecule that could replicate itself. Once this molecule existed, chance errors in the copying process

✔ When you see this checkmark, stop and test yourself. Answers are available in Appendix A.

created variations that would undergo natural selection—the evolutionary process by which individuals with certain attributes are selectively reproduced (see Chapter 1). At this point, chemical evolution was over and biological evolution was off and running.

To test this hypothesis, several groups around the world have been working to synthesize a self-replicating RNA molecule in the laboratory. If they ever succeed, they will have created a life-form in a test tube.

This chapter focuses on the structure and function of nucleic acids. Let's begin with an analysis of nucleic acid monomers and how they are linked together into polymers. Afterwards, you will learn about the experiments used to determine if a nucleic acid could have triggered the evolution of life on Earth.

## 4.1 What Is a Nucleic Acid?

Nucleic acids are polymers, just as proteins are polymers. But instead of being made up of monomers called amino acids, **nucleic acids** are made up of monomers called **nucleotides.**

**FIGURE 4.1a** diagrams the three components of a nucleotide: (1) a phosphate group, (2) a five-carbon sugar, and (3) a nitrogenous (nitrogen-containing) base. The phosphate is bonded to the sugar molecule, which in turn is bonded to the nitrogenous base.

The sugar component of a nucleotide is an organic compound bearing reactive hydroxyl (−OH) functional groups. Notice that the prime symbols (′) in Figure 4.1 indicate that the carbon being referred to is part of the sugar—not of the attached nitrogenous base. The phosphate group in a nucleotide is attached to the 5′ carbon.

Although a wide variety of nucleotides are found in living cells, origin-of-life researchers concentrate on two types: **ribonucleotides,** the monomers of **ribonucleic acid (RNA)**, and **deoxyribonucleotides,** the monomers of **deoxyribonucleic acid (DNA)**. In ribonucleotides, the sugar is ribose; in deoxyribonucleotides, it is deoxyribose (*deoxy* means "lacking oxygen"). As **FIGURE 4.1b** shows, these two sugars differ by a single oxygen atom. Ribose has an −OH group bonded to the 2′ carbon. Deoxyribose has an H instead at the same location. In both of these sugars, an −OH group is bonded to the 3′ carbon.

In addition to the type of sugar, nucleotides also differ in the type of nitrogenous base. These bases, diagrammed in **FIGURE 4.1c**, belong to structural groups called **purines** and **pyrimidines.** The purines are adenine (A) and guanine (G); the pyrimidines are cytosine (C), uracil (U), and thymine (T). Note that the two rings in adenine and guanine are linked together by nine atoms, compared to the six atoms that make a single ring in each pyrimidine. This makes remembering which bases are purines easy, since both adenine and guanine include "nine" in their names.

As Figure 4.1c shows, ribonucleotides and deoxyribonucleotides also differ in one of their pyrimidine bases. Ribonucleotides

**FIGURE 4.1 The General Structure of a Nucleotide.** Note that in the bases, the nitrogen that bonds to the sugar is colored blue.

use uracil (U) while deoxyribonucleotides use the closely related base thymine (T).

✔ You should be able to diagram a ribonucleotide and a deoxyribonucleotide. Use a ball for the phosphate group, a pentagon to represent the sugar subunit, and a hexagon to represent the nitrogenous base. Label the 2′, 3′, and 5′ carbons on the sugar molecule, and add the atoms or groups that are bonded to each.

To summarize: After the different sugars and bases are taken into account, eight different nucleotides are used to build nucleic acids—four ribonucleotides (A, G, C, and U) and four deoxyribonucleotides (A, G, C, and T). If nucleic acids played any role in the chemical evolution of life, then at least some of these nucleotides must have been present in the prebiotic oceans. Is there any evidence to suggest that this was possible?

## Could Chemical Evolution Result in the Production of Nucleotides?

Based on data from Stanley Miller and researchers who followed (Chapter 2), most biologists contend that amino acids could have been synthesized early in Earth's history. The reactions behind the prebiotic synthesis of nucleotides, however, have been more difficult to identify.

Miller-like laboratory simulations have shown that nitrogenous bases and many different types of sugars can be synthesized readily under conditions that mimic the prebiotic soup. In these experiments, almost all the sugars that have five or six carbons—called pentoses and hexoses, respectively—are produced in approximately equal amounts. If nucleic acids were to form in the prebiotic soup, however, ribose would have had to predominate.

How ribose came to be the dominant sugar during chemical evolution (i.e., what selective process was at work) is still a mystery. Origin-of-life researchers refer to this issue as the "ribose problem." Recent work focusing on the conditions that exist in deep-sea hydrothermal vent systems (see Chapter 2) may point to a possible solution.

Here's the line of reasoning researchers are currently pursuing: Ribose molecules may have been selectively enriched from the mix of sugars in certain early Earth deep-sea vent systems. In one experiment, researchers simulated the conditions that exist in these vents. Then they tested whether minerals that are predicted to have existed in the vent chimneys are able to bind sugars. What they found was striking—the minerals preferentially bound to ribose over other pentoses and hexoses. Did this occur in the ancient vents? If so, the implications are exciting: A high concentration of ribose would be present in the same deep-sea vent environment where chemical evolution is thought to have taken place.

Despite the observed synthesis of nitrogenous bases and the recent discovery of ribose enrichment, the production of nucleotides remains a serious challenge for the theory of chemical evolution. At this time, experiments that attempt to simulate early

**FIGURE 4.2 Nucleotides Polymerize via Phosphodiester Linkages.** Ribonucleotides can polymerize via condensation reactions. The resulting phosphodiester linkage connects the 3′ carbon of one ribonucleotide and the 5′ carbon of another ribonucleotide.

Earth environments have yet to synthesize complete nucleotides. But research on this issue continues.

In the meantime, let's consider the next question: Once nucleotides formed, how would they polymerize to form RNA and DNA? This question has an answer.

## How Do Nucleotides Polymerize to Form Nucleic Acids?

Nucleic acids form when nucleotides polymerize. As **FIGURE 4.2** shows, the polymerization reaction involves the formation of a bond between a hydroxyl on the sugar component of one nucleotide and the phosphate group of another nucleotide. The result of this condensation reaction is called a **phosphodiester linkage,** or a phosphodiester bond.

A phosphodiester linkage joins the 5′ carbon on the sugar of one nucleotide to the 3′ carbon on the sugar of another. When the nucleotides involved contain the sugar ribose, the polymer that is produced is RNA. If the nucleotides contain the sugar deoxyribose instead, then the resulting polymer is DNA.

**DNA and RNA Strands Are Directional** **FIGURE 4.3** (see page 60) shows how the chain of phosphodiester linkages in a nucleic acid acts as a backbone, analogous to the peptide-bonded backbone found in proteins.

Like the peptide-bonded backbone of a polypeptide, the sugar-phosphate backbone of a nucleic acid is directional. In a strand of RNA or DNA, one end has an unlinked 5′ phosphate while the other end has an unlinked 3′ hydroxyl—meaning the groups are not linked to another nucleotide. By convention, the

## The sugar-phosphate backbone of RNA

5' end of nucleic acid

**5'**

O⁻
|
⁻O—P=O
|
O
|
CH₂   O   (uracil base: NH, O)
5'

3'
O   OH
|
⁻O—P=O
|
O
|
CH₂   O   (adenine base: NH₂, N, N, N)
5'

3'
O   OH
|
⁻O—P=O
|
O
|
CH₂   O   (guanine base: O, NH, NH₂)
5'

3' and 5' carbons joined by phosphodiester linkage

3'
O   OH
|
⁻O—P=O
|
O
|
CH₂   O   (cytosine base: NH₂, N, O)
5'

3' end of nucleic acid: new nucleotides are added to the unlinked 3' hydroxyl

3'
OH   OH

**3'**

**FIGURE 4.3 RNA Has a Sugar-Phosphate Backbone.**

✔**EXERCISE** Identify the four bases in this RNA strand, using Figure 4.1c as a key. Then write down the base sequence, starting at the 5' end.

sequence of bases found in an RNA or DNA strand is always written in the 5'→3' direction. (This system is logical because in cells, RNA and DNA are always synthesized in this direction. Bases are added only at the 3' end of the growing molecule.)

The order of the different nitrogenous bases in a nucleic acid forms the primary structure of the molecule. When biologists write the primary structure of a stretch of DNA or RNA, they simply list the sequence of nucleotides in the 5'→3' direction, using their single-letter abbreviations. For example, a six-base-long DNA sequence might be ATTAGC. It would take roughly

6 billion of these letters to write the primary structure of the DNA in most of your cells.

**Polymerization Requires an Energy Source** In cells, the polymerization reactions that join nucleotides into nucleic acids are catalyzed by enzymes. Like other polymerization reactions, the process is not spontaneous. An input of energy is needed to tip the energy balance in favor of the process.

Polymerization can take place in cells because the potential energy of the nucleotide monomers is first raised by reactions that add two phosphate groups to the ribonucleotides or deoxyribonucleotides, creating nucleoside triphosphates.[1] In the case of nucleic acid polymerization, researchers refer to these nucleotides as "activated." **FIGURE 4.4a** shows an example of an activated nucleotide; this molecule is called **adenosine triphosphate,** or **ATP.**

Why do added phosphate groups raise the energy content of a molecule? Recall that phosphates are negatively charged and that like charges repel (Chapter 2). Linking two or more phosphates with covalent bonds generates strong repulsive forces. These bonds therefore carry a large amount of potential energy, which can be harvested to power other chemical reactions (**FIGURE 4.4b**). You will see in later chapters that the potential energy stored in ATP is used to drive other cellular activities, independent of nucleotide polymerization.

This is a key point, and one that you will encounter again and again in this text: The addition of one or more phosphate groups raises the potential energy of substrate molecules enough to make an otherwise nonspontaneous reaction possible. (Chapter 8 explains how this happens in more detail.)

**Could Nucleic Acids Have Formed in the Absence of Cellular Enzymes?** Accumulating data suggest that the answer is yes.

Activation of nucleotides has been observed when prebiotic conditions are simulated experimentally. In a suite of follow-up experiments, researchers have produced RNA molecules by incubating activated nucleotides with tiny mineral particles—in one case, molecules up to 50 nucleotides long were observed. These results support the hypothesis that polymerization of activated nucleotides in the prebiotic world may have been catalyzed by minerals. This model would be in line with the surface metabolism model for chemical evolution (introduced in Chapter 2).

More recent work has shown that under certain conditions, up to 100 nucleotides can be linked together, even without first being activated. To accomplish this, heat was introduced as a source of energy and small nonpolar molecules, called lipids, were added to help the monomers interact. This experiment is particularly interesting with respect to the setting for chemical evolution, because both of these factors—heat and lipids—are thought to have been present in prebiotic hydrothermal vents. (The chemical origins and properties of lipids are covered in Chapter 6.)

---

[1] A molecule consisting of a sugar and one of the bases in Figure 4.1c is called a nucleoside (a nucleotide is a sugar, a base, and one or more phosphate groups). Thus, a sugar attached to a base and three phosphate groups is called a nucleoside triphosphate.

**(a)** ATP is an example of an activated nucleotide.

The addition of phosphate groups raises the potential energy of the monomer

Adenine

Ribose

**FIGURE 4.4 Activated Monomers Drive Polymerization Reactions.** Polymerization reactions are generally nonspontaneous, but those reactions involving nucleoside triphosphates, such as ATP, are spontaneous. The potential energy stored in activated nucleotides is released when the pyrophosphate ($PP_i$) is removed before the polymerizing condensation reaction shown in Figure 4.2.

**(b)** Energy is released when phosphates are removed by hydrolysis.

ATP          +    H₂O    ⟶    AMP    +    Inorganic pyrophosphate    +    10.9 kcal/mol ATP

Water                                                                   Energy used to link
                                                                        nucleotide to RNA

Based on these results, there is a strong consensus that if ribonucleotides and deoxyribonucleotides were able to form during chemical evolution, they would be able to polymerize into DNA and RNA. Now, what do these nucleic acids look like, and what can they do?

## 4.2 DNA Structure and Function

The primary structure of nucleic acids is somewhat similar to the primary structure of proteins. Proteins have a peptide-bonded backbone with a series of R-groups that extend from it. DNA and RNA molecules have a sugar-phosphate backbone, created by phosphodiester linkages, and a sequence of any of four nitrogenous bases that extend from it.

Like proteins, DNA and RNA also have secondary structure. While the α-helices and β-pleated sheets of proteins are formed by hydrogen bonding between groups in the backbone, the secondary structure of nucleic acids is formed by hydrogen bonding between the nitrogenous bases.

Let's analyze the secondary structure and function of DNA first, and then dig into the secondary structure and function of RNA.

## What Is the Nature of DNA's Secondary Structure?

The solution to DNA's secondary structure, announced in 1953, ranks among the great scientific breakthroughs of the twentieth century. James Watson and Francis Crick presented a model for the secondary structure of DNA in a one-page paper published in the scientific journal *Nature*.

**Early Data Provided Clues**   Watson and Crick's finding was a hypothesis based on a series of results from other laboratories. They were trying to propose a secondary structure that could explain several important observations about the DNA found in cells:

- Chemists had worked out the structure of nucleotides and knew that DNA polymerized through the formation of phosphodiester linkages. Thus, Watson and Crick knew that the molecule had a sugar-phosphate backbone.

- By analyzing the nitrogenous bases in DNA samples from different organisms, Erwin Chargaff had established two empirical rules: (**1**) The number of purines in a given DNA molecule is equal to the number of pyrimidines, and (**2**) the number of T's and A's in DNA are equal, and the number of C's and G's in DNA are equal.

- By bombarding DNA with X-rays and analyzing how it scattered the radiation, Rosalind Franklin and Maurice Wilkins had calculated the distances between groups of atoms in the molecule (see **BioSkills 11** in Appendix B for an introduction to this technique, called **X-ray crystallography**). The scattering patterns showed that three distances were repeated many times: 0.34 nanometer (nm), 2.0 nm, and 3.4 nm. Because the measurements repeated, the researchers inferred that DNA molecules had a regular and repeating structure. The pattern of X-ray scattering suggested that the molecule was helical, or spiral, in nature.

Based on this work, understanding DNA's structure boiled down to understanding the nature of the helix involved. What type of helix would have a sugar-phosphate backbone and explain both Chargaff's rules and the Franklin–Wilkins measurements?

**DNA Strands Are Antiparallel** Watson and Crick began by analyzing the size and geometry of deoxyribose, phosphate groups, and nitrogenous bases. The bond angles and measurements suggested that the distance of 2.0 nm probably represented the width of the helix and that 0.34 nm was likely to be the distance between bases stacked in a spiral.

How could they make sense of Chargaff's rules and the 3.4-nm distance, which appeared to be exactly 10 times the distance between a single pair of bases?

To solve this problem, Watson and Crick constructed a series of physical models like the one pictured in **FIGURE 4.5**. The models allowed them to tinker with different types of helical configurations. After many false starts, something clicked:

- They arranged two strands of DNA side by side and running in opposite directions—meaning that one strand ran in the 5′ → 3′ direction while the other strand was oriented 3′ → 5′. Strands with this orientation are said to be **antiparallel.**

- If the antiparallel strands are twisted together to form a **double helix,** the coiled sugar-phosphate backbones end up on the outside of the spiral and the nitrogenous bases on the inside.

**FIGURE 4.5 Building a Physical Model of DNA Structure.** Watson (left) and Crick (right) represented the arrangement of the four deoxyribonucleotides in a double helix, using metal plates and wires with precise lengths and geometries.

- For the bases from each backbone to fit in the interior of the 2.0-nm-wide structure, they have to form purine-pyrimidine pairs (see **FIGURE 4.6a**). This is a key point: The pairing allows hydrogen bonds to form between certain purines and pyrimidines. Adenine forms hydrogen bonds with thymine, and guanine forms hydrogen bonds with cytosine (**FIGURE 4.6b**).

- The A-T and G-C bases were said to be complementary. Two hydrogen bonds form when A and T pair, and three hydrogen bonds form when G and C pair. As a result, the G-C interaction is slightly stronger than the A-T bond. In contrast, A-C and G-T pairs allowed no or only one hydrogen bond.

**(a)** Only purine-pyrimidine pairs fit inside the double helix.

Purine-purine pair
NOT ENOUGH SPACE

Pyrimidine-pyrimidine pair
TOO MUCH SPACE

Purine-pyrimidine pair
JUST RIGHT

Space inside sugar-phosphate backbones

**(b)** Hydrogen bonds form between G-C pairs and A-T pairs.

**FIGURE 4.6 Complementary Base Pairing Is Based on Hydrogen Bonding.**

Watson and Crick had discovered **complementary base pairing.** In fact, the term **Watson–Crick pairing** is now used interchangeably with the phrase complementary base pairing. The physical restraints posed by these interactions resulted in a full helical twist every 10 bases, or 3.4 nm.

**The Double Helix** **FIGURE 4.7a** shows how antiparallel strands of DNA form when complementary bases line up and form hydrogen bonds. As you study the figure, notice that DNA is put together like a ladder whose ends have been twisted in opposite directions. The sugar-phosphate backbones form the supports of the ladder; the base pairs represent the rungs of the ladder. The twisting allows the nitrogenous bases to line up in a way that makes hydrogen bonding between them possible.

The nitrogenous bases in the middle of the molecule are hydrophobic. This is a key point, because twisting into a double helix minimizes contact between the bases and surrounding water molecules. In addition to hydrogen bonding, van der Waals interactions between the tightly stacked bases in the interior further contribute to the stability of the helix. You see the same forces—hydrogen bonding, hydrophobicity, and van der Waals interactions—play similar roles in protein folding (Chapter 3). But DNA as a whole is hydrophilic and water soluble because the backbones, which face the exterior of the molecule, contain negatively charged phosphate groups that interact with water.

**FIGURE 4.7b** highlights additional features of DNA's secondary structure. It's important to note that the outside of the helical DNA molecule forms two types of grooves. The larger of the two is known as the major groove, and the smaller one is known as the minor groove. From this figure, you can identify how DNA's secondary structure explains the measurements observed by Franklin and Wilkins.

Since the model of the double helix was published, experimental tests have shown that the hypothesis is correct in almost every detail. To summarize:

- DNA's secondary structure consists of two antiparallel strands twisted into a double helix.

- The molecule is stabilized by hydrophobic interactions in its interior and by hydrogen bonding between the complementary base pairs A-T and G-C.

✔ You should be able to explain why complementary base pairing would not be possible if two DNA strands were aligned in a parallel fashion—instead of the antiparallel alignment shown in Figure 4.6b.

Now the question is, how does this secondary structure affect the molecule's function?

**(a)** Cartoons of DNA structure

Base pairing          Double helix

**(b)** Space-filling model of DNA double helix

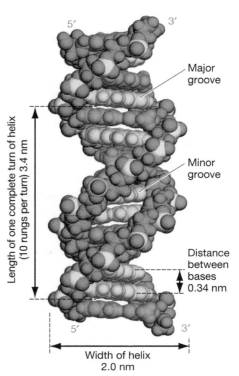

Length of one complete turn of helix (10 rungs per turn) 3.4 nm

Major groove

Minor groove

Distance between bases 0.34 nm

Width of helix 2.0 nm

**FIGURE 4.7 The Secondary Structure of DNA Is a Double Helix. (a)** The cartoons illustrate complementary base pairing and how strands are twisted into a double helix. **(b)** The space-filling model shows tight packing of the bases inside the double helix. The double-helix structure explains the measurements inferred from X-ray analysis of DNA molecules.

## DNA Functions as an Information-Containing Molecule

Watson and Crick's model created a sensation for a simple reason: It revealed how DNA could store and transmit biological information. In literature, information consists of letters on a page. In music, information is composed of the notes on a staff. But inside cells, information consists of a sequence of nucleotides in a nucleic acid. The four nitrogenous bases function like letters of the alphabet. A sequence of bases is like the sequence of letters in a word—it has meaning.

In all organisms that have been examined to date, from tiny bacteria to gigantic redwood trees, DNA carries the information required for the organism's growth and reproduction. Exploring how hereditary information is encoded and translated into action is the heart of several later chapters (Chapters 16 through 19).

Here, however, our focus is on how life began. The theory of chemical evolution holds that life began once a molecule emerged that could make a copy of itself. Does the information contained within DNA allow it to be replicated?

Watson and Crick ended their paper on the double helix with one of the classic understatements in the scientific literature: "It has not escaped our notice that the specific pairing we have postulated immediately suggests a possible copying mechanism." Here's the key insight: DNA's primary structure serves as a mold or template for the synthesis of a complementary strand. DNA contains the information required for a copy of itself to be made. **FIGURE 4.8** shows how a copy of DNA can be made by complementary base pairing.

**Step 1** Heating or enzyme-catalyzed reactions can cause the double helix to separate.

**Step 2** Free deoxyribonucleotides form hydrogen bonds with complementary bases on the original strand of DNA—also called a **template strand.** As they do, their sugar-phosphate groups form phosphodiester linkages to create a new strand—also called a **complementary strand.** Note that the $5' \rightarrow 3'$ directionality of the complementary strand is opposite that of the template strand.

**Step 3** Complementary base pairing allows each strand of a DNA double helix to be copied exactly, producing two identical daughter molecules.

DNA copying is the basis for a second of the five characteristics of life (introduced in Chapter 1): replication. But can DNA catalyze the reactions needed to *self*-replicate? In today's cells and in laboratory experiments, the answer is no. Instead, the molecule is copied through a complicated series of energy-demanding reactions, catalyzed by a large suite of enzymes. Why can't DNA catalyze these reactions itself?

## Is DNA a Catalytic Molecule?

The DNA double helix is highly structured. It is regular, symmetric, and held together by hydrogen bonding, hydrophobic

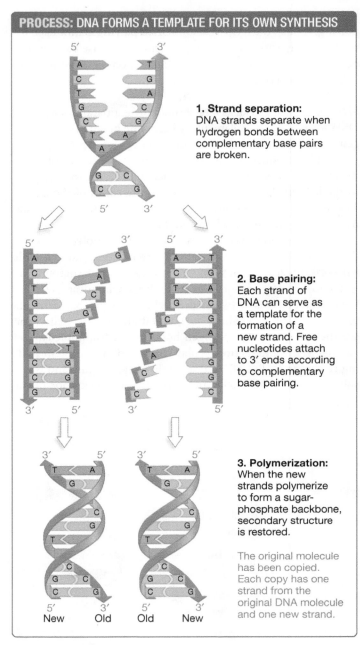

**PROCESS: DNA FORMS A TEMPLATE FOR ITS OWN SYNTHESIS**

**1. Strand separation:** DNA strands separate when hydrogen bonds between complementary base pairs are broken.

**2. Base pairing:** Each strand of DNA can serve as a template for the formation of a new strand. Free nucleotides attach to 3' ends according to complementary base pairing.

**3. Polymerization:** When the new strands polymerize to form a sugar-phosphate backbone, secondary structure is restored.

The original molecule has been copied. Each copy has one strand from the original DNA molecule and one new strand.

New   Old      Old   New

**FIGURE 4.8 Making a Copy of DNA.** If new bases are added to each of the two strands of DNA via complementary base pairing, a copy of the DNA molecule can be produced.

✓**QUESTION** When double-stranded DNA is heated to 95°C, the bonds between complementary base pairs break and single-stranded DNA results. Considering this observation, is the reaction shown in step 1 spontaneous?

interactions, and phosphodiester linkages. In addition, the molecule has few functional groups exposed that can participate in chemical reactions. For example, the lack of a 2′ hydroxyl group on each deoxyribonucleotide makes the polymer much less reactive than RNA, and thus much more resistant to degradation.

Intact stretches of DNA have been recovered from fossils that are tens of thousands of years old. The molecules have the same sequence of bases as the organisms had when they were alive, despite death and exposure to a wide array of pH, temperature, and chemical conditions. DNA's stability is the key to its effectiveness as a reliable information-bearing molecule. DNA's structure is consistent with its function in cells.

The orderliness and stability that make DNA such a dependable information repository also make it extraordinarily inept at catalysis, however. Recall that enzyme function is based on a specific binding event between a substrate and a protein catalyst (Chapter 3). Thanks to variation in reactivity among R-groups in amino acids, and the enormous diversity of shapes found in proteins, a wide array of catalytic activities can be generated. In comparison, DNA's primary and secondary structures are simple. It is not surprising, then, that DNA has never been observed to catalyze any reaction in any organism. Although researchers have been able to construct single-stranded DNA molecules that can catalyze some reactions in the laboratory, the number and diversity of reactions involved is a minute fraction of the activity catalyzed by enzymes.

In short, DNA furnishes an extraordinarily stable template for copying itself and for storing information encoded in a sequence of bases. But owing to its inability to act as an effective catalyst, there is virtually no support for the hypothesis that the first life-form consisted of DNA. Instead, most biologists who are working on the origin of life support the hypothesis that life began with RNA. How does the structure of RNA differ from DNA?

## check your understanding

**If you understand that . . .**

- DNA's primary structure consists of a sequence of deoxyribonucleotides.
- DNA's secondary structure consists of two DNA molecules that run in opposite orientations to each other. The two strands are twisted into a double helix, and they are held together by hydrogen bonds between A-T and G-C pairs and hydrophobic interactions that drive bases into the interior of the helix.
- The sequence of deoxyribonucleotides in DNA contains information. Owing to complementary base pairing, each DNA strand also contains the information required to form its complementary strand.

✔ **You should be able to . . .**

Make a sketch of a double-stranded DNA molecule in the form of a ladder with the sequence of A-G-C-T. Label the 5′ and 3′ ends, the sugar-phosphate backbones, the hydrogen bonds between complementary bases, and the location of hydrophobic interactions.

*Answers are available in Appendix A.*

## 4.3 RNA Structure and Function

The first living molecule would have needed to perform two key functions: carry information and catalyze reactions that promoted its own replication. At first glance, these two functions appear to conflict. Information storage requires regularity and stability; catalysis requires variation in chemical composition and flexibility in shape. How is it possible for a molecule to do both? The answer lies in structure.

### Structurally, RNA Differs from DNA

Recall that proteins can have up to four levels of structure. Single-chain proteins possess a primary sequence of amino acids, secondary folds that are stabilized by hydrogen bonding between atoms in the peptide-bonded backbone, and tertiary folds that are stabilized by interactions involving R-groups. Quaternary structure is found in proteins consisting of multiple polypeptides.

DNA has only primary and secondary structure. But RNA, like single-chained proteins, can have up to three levels of structure.

**Primary Structure** Like DNA, RNA has a primary structure consisting of a sugar-phosphate backbone formed by phosphodiester linkages and, extending from that backbone, a sequence of four types of nitrogenous bases. But it's important to recall two significant differences between these nucleic acids:

1. The sugar in the sugar-phosphate backbone of RNA is ribose, not deoxyribose as in DNA.

2. The pyrimidine base thymine does not exist in RNA. Instead, RNA contains the closely related pyrimidine base uracil.

The first point is critical. Look back at Figure 4.1b and compare the functional groups attached to ribose and deoxyribose. Notice the hydroxyl (−OH) group on the 2′ carbon of ribose. This additional hydroxyl is much more reactive than the hydrogen atom on the 2′ carbon of deoxyribose. When RNA molecules fold in certain ways, the hydroxyl group can attack the phosphate linkage between nucleotides, which would generate a break in the sugar-phosphate backbone. While this −OH group makes RNA much less stable than DNA, it can also support catalytic activity by the molecule.

**Secondary Structure** Like DNA molecules, most RNA molecules have secondary structure that results from complementary base pairing between purine and pyrimidine bases. In RNA, adenine forms hydrogen bonds only with uracil, and guanine again forms hydrogen bonds with cytosine. (Other, non-Watson–Crick base pairs occur, although less frequently.) Three hydrogen bonds form between guanine and cytosine, but only two form between adenine and uracil.

This hydrogen bonding should seem familiar, since DNA bonds together in a similar manner—so how do the secondary structures of RNA and DNA differ? In the vast majority of cases, the purine and pyrimidine bases in RNA undergo hydrogen

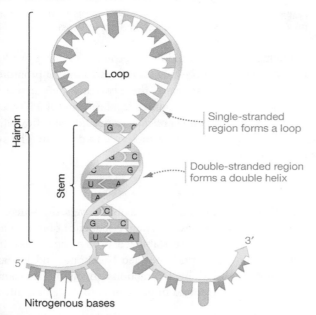

**FIGURE 4.9 Complementary Base Pairing and Secondary Structure in RNA: Stem-and-Loop Structures.** This RNA molecule has secondary structure. The double-stranded "stem" and single-stranded "loop" form a hairpin. The bonded bases in the stem are antiparallel, meaning that they are oriented in opposite directions.

If the section where the fold occurs includes unpaired bases, then the stem-and-loop configuration shown in Figure 4.9 results. This type of secondary structure is called a **hairpin.** Several other types of RNA secondary structures are possible, each involving a different length and arrangement of base-paired segments.

Like the α-helices and β-pleated sheets observed in many proteins, RNA secondary structures can form spontaneously. They are directed by hydrophobic interactions and stabilized by hydrogen bonding between the bases. Even though hairpins and other types of secondary structure reduce the entropy of RNA molecules, the energy released in these interactions makes the overall process favorable.

**Tertiary Structure** RNA molecules can also have tertiary structure, which arises when secondary structures fold into more complex shapes. As a result, RNA molecules with different base sequences can have very different overall shapes and chemical properties. RNA molecules are much more diverse in size, shape, and reactivity than DNA molecules are. Structurally and chemically, RNA is intermediate between the complexity of proteins and the simplicity of DNA.

**TABLE 4.1** summarizes the similarities and differences in the structures of RNA and DNA.

bonding with complementary bases on the *same strand*, rather than forming hydrogen bonds with complementary bases on a different strand, as in DNA.

**FIGURE 4.9** shows how within-strand base pairing works. The key is that when bases on one part of an RNA strand fold over and align with ribonucleotides on another part of the same strand, the two sugar-phosphate strands are antiparallel. In this orientation, hydrogen bonding between complementary bases results in a stable double helix.

## RNA's Structure Makes It an Extraordinarily Versatile Molecule

In terms of structure, you've seen that RNA is intermediate between DNA and proteins. RNA is intermediate in terms of function as well. RNA molecules cannot archive information nearly as efficiently as DNA molecules do, but they do perform key functions in information processing. Likewise, they cannot catalyze as many reactions as proteins do. But as it turns out, the reactions they do catalyze are particularly important.

In cells, RNA molecules function like a jackknife or a pocket tool with an array of attachments: They perform a wide variety of

SUMMARY TABLE 4.1 **DNA and RNA Structure**

| Level of Structure | DNA | | RNA | |
|---|---|---|---|---|
| **Primary** | Sequence of deoxyribonucleotides; bases are A, T, G, C | 5′ A A T G T G C C G 3′ | Sequence of ribonucleotides; bases are A, U, G, C | 5′ U U A C A C G G C 3′ |
| **Secondary** | Two antiparallel strands twist into a double helix, stabilized by hydrogen bonding between complementary bases (A-T, G-C) and hydrophobic interactions | | Most common are hairpins, formed when a single strand folds back on itself to form a double-helix "stem" and a single-stranded "loop" | |
| **Tertiary** | None* | | Folds that form distinctive three-dimensional shapes | Example: tRNA |

*In cells, DNA coils around proteins that bind to the double helix. In many cases the DNA-protein complex folds into highly organized, compact structures. But DNA does not form tertiary structure on its own.

tasks reasonably well. Some of the most surprising results in the last decade of biological science, in fact, involve new insights into the diversity of roles that RNAs play in cells. These molecules process information stored in DNA, synthesize proteins, and defend against attack by viruses, among other things.

Next let's focus on the roles that RNA could have played in the origin of life—as an information-containing entity and as a catalyst.

## RNA Is an Information-Containing Molecule

Because RNA contains a sequence of bases analogous to the letters in a word, it can function as an information-containing molecule. And because hydrogen bonding occurs specifically between A-U pairs and G-C pairs in RNA, it is possible for RNA to furnish the information required to make a copy of itself.

FIGURE 4.10 illustrates how the information stored in an RNA molecule can be used to direct its own replication.

First, a complementary copy of the RNA is made when free ribonucleotides form hydrogen bonds with complementary bases on the original strand of RNA—the template strand. As they do, their sugar-phosphate groups form phosphodiester linkages to produce a double-stranded RNA molecule (steps 1 and 2).

To make a copy of the original single-stranded RNA, the hydrogen bonds between the double-stranded product must first be broken by heating or by a catalyzed reaction (step 3). The newly made complementary RNA molecule now exists independently of the original template strand. If steps 1–3 were repeated with the new strand serving as a template (steps 4–6), the resulting molecule would be a copy of the original. In this way, the primary sequence of an RNA serves as a mold.

## RNA Can Function as a Catalytic Molecule

In terms of diversity in chemical reactivity and overall shape, RNA molecules are no match for proteins. The primary structure of RNA molecules is much more restricted because RNA has only four types of nucleotides versus the 20 types of amino acids found in proteins. Secondary through tertiary structure is more limited as a result, meaning that RNA cannot form the wide array of catalysts observed among proteins.

But because RNA has a degree of structural and chemical complexity, it is capable of catalyzing a number of chemical reactions. Sidney Altman and Thomas Cech shared the 1989 Nobel Prize in chemistry for showing that catalytic RNAs, or ribozymes, exist in organisms.

FIGURE 4.11 (on page 68) shows the structure of a ribozyme Cech isolated from a single-celled organism called *Tetrahymena*. This ribozyme catalyzes both the hydrolysis and the condensation of phosphodiester linkages in RNA. Researchers have since discovered a variety of ribozymes that catalyze an array of reactions in cells. For example, ribozymes catalyze the formation of peptide bonds when amino acids polymerize to form polypeptides. Ribozymes are at work in your cells right now.

The three-dimensional nature of ribozymes is vital to their catalytic activity. To catalyze a chemical reaction, substrates must

PROCESS: RNA FORMS A TEMPLATE FOR ITS OWN SYNTHESIS

1. Complementary bases pair.

2. Copied strand polymerizes.

3. Copy and template separate.

4. Copy serves as new template.

5. New copy polymerizes.

6. New copy is identical to original template.

FIGURE 4.10 RNA Molecules Contain Information That Allows Them to Be Replicated. For a single-stranded RNA to be copied, it must pass through double-stranded RNA intermediates.

folding brings
widely spaced
nucleotides
together at the
active site of
this catalytic
RNA

**FIGURE 4.11 Tertiary Structure of the *Tetrahymena* Ribozyme.** The folded structure brings together bases from distant locations in the primary structure to form the active site.

brought together in an environment that will promote the reaction. As with protein enzymes, the region of the ribozyme that is responsible for this activity is called the active site. When the *Tetrahymena* ribozyme was compared to protein enzymes that catalyze similar reactions, their active sites were found to be similar in structure. This observation about two very different molecules demonstrates the critical relationship between structure and function

The discovery of ribozymes was a watershed event in origin-of-life research. Before Altman and Cech published their results, most biologists thought that the only molecules capable of catalyzing reactions in cells were proteins. The fact that a ribozyme in *Tetrahymena* catalyzed a condensation reaction raised the possibility that an RNA molecule could make a copy of itself. Such a molecule could qualify as the first living entity. Is there any experimental evidence to support this hypothesis?

## 4.4 In Search of the First Life-Form

The theory of chemical evolution maintains that life began as a naked self-replicator—a molecule that existed by itself in solution, without being enclosed in a membrane. To make a copy of itself, that first living molecule had to (1) provide a template that could be copied, and (2) catalyze polymerization reactions that would link monomers into a copy of that template. Because RNA is capable of both processes, most origin-of-life researchers propose that the first life-form was made of RNA.

No self-replicating RNA molecules have been discovered in nature, however, so researchers test the hypothesis by trying to simulate the RNA world in the laboratory. The eventual goal is to create an RNA molecule that can catalyze its own replication.

### How Biologists Study the RNA World

To understand how researchers go about testing the RNA world hypothesis, consider two recent experiments by researchers in David Bartel's laboratory. In one study, the team attempted to generate an RNA molecule that could catalyze the kind of template-directed polymerization needed for RNA replication—an RNA "replicase." Starting with a ribozyme capable of joining two ribonucleotides together, they generated billions of copies into which random mutations were introduced.

Next they incubated the mutants with free ribonucleotides and began selecting for replicase activity. Molecules that exhibited such activity were isolated and copied. After two weeks and 18 rounds of selection, the team succeeded in isolating a ribozyme that could add 14 nucleotides to an existing RNA strand.

Note that the team's experimental protocol was designed to mimic the process of natural selection introduced in Chapter 1. The population of RNAs from each round had variable characteristics that could be replicated and passed on to the next generation of ribozymes. In addition, the researchers were able to select the most efficient RNAs to be the "parents" of the next generation—and in the process introduce new mutations that potentially could make some of the "offspring" even better ribozymes.

This research created considerable excitement among biologists interested in the origin of life, because adding ribonucleotides to a growing strand is a key attribute of an RNA replicase. However, since the maximum product length generated was less than 10 percent of the ribozyme's own length, an RNA replicase capable of making a full-length copy of itself was far from being discovered. In fact, the difficulty in creating an effective RNA replicase has led many researchers to question the idea of a replicase being the first ribozyme to emerge in the RNA world.

In another study, Bartel's group asked a different question: Would it be possible to select for a ribozyme that could make ribonucleotides? This type of ribozyme is not known to exist in nature but would be a key component in the RNA world.

Recall that the direction of a chemical reaction and how much product it makes is influenced by the amount of reactants present (Chapter 2). Since the chemical evolution of nucleotides is thought to have been inefficient, nucleotides would have been a scarce resource on early Earth. Ribozymes that could catalyze the production of nucleotides would be more likely to be copied due to local accumulation of monomers.

Starting with a large pool of randomly generated RNA sequences, the researchers selected for RNAs that could catalyze the addition of a uracil base to a ribose sugar. By round 11, the group had recovered ribozymes that were 50,000 times better at catalyzing the reaction than those found in the fourth round and over 1 million times more efficient than the uncatalyzed reaction. In effect, molecular evolution had occurred in the reaction tubes.

Thanks to similar efforts at other laboratories around the world, biologists have produced an increasingly impressive set of catalytic activities from RNA molecules. The results from each of these studies help clarify our view of what occurred in the RNA world. If a living ribozyme ever existed, then each round of simulated molecular evolution brings us closer to resurrecting it.

## The RNA World May Have Sparked the Evolution of Life

Although ribozymes like these lab-generated molecules may have been present in the RNA world, they have not been observed in nature. Of those that have been discovered in modern cells, most play key roles in the synthesis of proteins. This relationship suggests the order of events in chemical evolution—the RNA world preceded proteins.

The evolution of protein enzymes would have marked the end of the RNA world—providing the means for catalyzing reactions necessary for life to emerge in a cellular form. After this milestone, three of the five fundamental characteristics of life (see Chapter 1) were solidly in place:

1. **Information** Proteins and ribozymes were processing information stored in nucleic acids for the synthesis of more proteins.

2. **Replication** Enzymes, and possibly ribozymes, were replicating the nucleic acids that stored the hereditary information.

3. **Evolution** Random changes in the synthesis of proteins, and selective advantages resulting from some of these changes, allowed for the evolution of new proteins and protein families.

If these events occurred in a hydrothermal vent, the molecular assemblages of nucleic acids and proteins would have been constantly fed with thermal and chemical energy. To gain independence from their undersea hatchery, enzymes would have evolved to store this energy as something more portable—carbohydrates. The structure and function of carbohydrates will be the focus of the next chapter.

---

## If you understand . . .

### 4.1 What Is a Nucleic Acid?

- Nucleic acids are polymers of nucleotide monomers, which consist of a sugar, a phosphate group, and a nitrogenous base. Ribonucleotide monomers polymerize to form RNA. Deoxyribonucleotide monomers polymerize to form DNA.

- Ribonucleotides have a hydroxyl (—OH) group on their 2′ carbon; deoxyribonucleotides do not.

- Nucleic acids polymerize when condensation reactions join nucleotides together via phosphodiester linkages.

- Nucleic acids are directional: they have a 5′ end and a 3′ end. During polymerization, new nucleotides are added only to the 3′ end.

✓ You should be able to state what cells do to activate nucleotides for incorporation into a polymer and explain why activation is required.

### 4.2 DNA Structure and Function

- DNA's primary structure consists of a sequence of linked nitrogenous bases. Its secondary structure consists of two DNA strands running in opposite directions that are twisted into a double helix.

- DNA is an extremely stable molecule that serves as a superb archive for information in the form of base sequences. It lacks a reactive 2′ hydroxyl group, and its secondary structure is stabilized by hydrophobic interactions and hydrogen bonds that form between complementary bases stacked on the inside of the helix.

- DNA is readily copied via complementary base pairing. Complementary base pairing occurs between A-T and G-C pairs in DNA.

- DNA's structural stability and regularity are advantageous for information storage, but they make DNA an ineffective catalyst.

✓ You should be able to explain why DNA molecules with a high percentage of guanine and cytosine are particularly stable.

### 4.3 RNA Structure and Function

- Like DNA, RNA's primary structure consists of a sequence of linked nitrogenous bases. RNA's secondary structure includes short regions of double helices and looped structures called hairpins.

- RNA molecules are usually single stranded. They have secondary structure because of complementary base pairing between A-U and G-C pairs on the same strand.

- Unlike DNA, the secondary structures of RNA can fold into more complex shapes, stabilized by hydrogen bonding, which gives the molecule tertiary structure.

- RNA is versatile. The primary function of proteins is to catalyze chemical reactions, and the primary function of DNA is to carry information. But RNA is an "all-purpose" macromolecule that can do both.

✓ You should be able to explain why many RNA molecules exhibit tertiary structure, while most DNA molecules do not.

To test the RNA world hypothesis, researchers are attempting to synthesize new ribozymes in the laboratory. Using artificial selection strategies, they have succeeded in identifying RNAs that catalyze several different reactions.

Ribozymes that catalyze reactions necessary for the production of nucleotides may have preceded the evolution of RNA replicases.

✓ You should be able to provide two examples of activities in the RNA world you expect would benefit from catalysis and justify your choices.

## MB MasteringBiology

**1. MasteringBiology Assignments**

**Tutorials and Activities** Double Helix; Heritable Information: DNA; Nucleic Acid Building Blocks; Nucleic Acid Structure; Structure of RNA and DNA

**Questions** Reading Quizzes, Blue-Thread Questions, Test Bank

**2. eText** Read your book online, search, take notes, highlight text, and more.

**3. The Study Area** Practice Test, Cumulative Test, BioFlix® 3-D Animations, Videos, Activities, Audio Glossary, Word Study Tools, Art

# You should be able to . . .

## ✓ TEST YOUR KNOWLEDGE
*Answers are available in Appendix A*

1. What are the four nitrogenous bases found in RNA?
   a. uracil, guanine, cytosine, thymine (U, G, C, T)
   b. adenine, guanine, cytosine, thymine (A, G, C, T)
   c. adenine, uracil, guanine, cytosine (A, U, G, C)
   d. alanine, threonine, glycine, cysteine (A, T, G, C)

2. What determines the primary structure of a DNA molecule?
   a. the sugar-phosphate backbone
   b. complementary base pairing and the formation of hairpins
   c. the sequence of deoxyribonucleotides
   d. the sequence of ribonucleotides

3. DNA attains a secondary structure when hydrogen bonds form between the nitrogenous bases called purines and pyrimidines. What are the complementary base pairs that form in DNA?
   a. A-T and G-C
   b. A-U and G-C
   c. A-G and T-C
   d. A-T and G-U

4. Which of the following rules apply to the synthesis of nucleic acids?
   a. Nucleotides are added to the 5′ end of nucleic acids.
   b. The synthesis of nucleic acids cannot occur without the presence of an enzyme to catalyze the reaction.
   c. Strands are synthesized in a parallel direction such that one end of the double-stranded product has the 3′ ends and other has the 5′ ends.
   d. Complementary pairing between bases is required for copying nucleic acids.

5. Nucleic acids are directional, meaning that there are two different ends. What functional groups define the two different ends of a DNA strand?

6. What is responsible for the increased stability of DNA compared to RNA?

## ✓ TEST YOUR UNDERSTANDING
*Answers are available in Appendix A*

7. Explain how Chargaff's rules relate to the complementary base pairing seen in the secondary structure of DNA. Would you expect these rules to apply to RNA as well? Explain why or why not.

8. QUANTITATIVE If nucleotides from the DNA of a human were quantified and 30 percent of them consisted of adenine, what percentage of guanine nucleotides would be present?
   a. 20 percent
   b. 30 percent
   c. 40 percent
   d. 70 percent

9. What would be the sequence of the strand of DNA that is made from the following template: 5′-GATATCGAT-3′ (Your answer must be written 5′→3′.) How would this sequence be different if RNA were made from this DNA template?

10. A major theme in this chapter is that the structure of molecules correlates with their function. Explain how DNA's secondary structure limits its catalytic abilities compared with that of RNA. Why is it expected that RNA molecules can catalyze a modest but significant array of reactions?

11. To replicate a ribozyme, a complete complementary copy must be made. Would you expect the double-stranded intermediate to maintain its catalytic activity? Justify your answer with an explanation.

12. Suppose that Bartel's research group succeeded in producing a molecule that could make a copy of itself. Which of the five fundamental characteristics of life (provided in Chapter 1) would support the claim that this molecule is alive?

**13.** Make a concept map (see **BioSkills 15** in Appendix B) that relates DNA's primary structure to its secondary structure. Your diagram should include deoxyribonucleotides, hydrophobic interactions, purines, pyrimidines, phosphodiester linkages, DNA primary structure, DNA secondary structure, complementary base pairing, and antiparallel strands.

**14.** Viruses are particles that infect cells. In some viruses, the genetic material consists of two strands of RNA, bonded together via complementary base pairing. Would these antiparallel strands form a double helix? Explain why or why not.

**15.** Before Watson and Crick published their model of the DNA double helix, Linus Pauling offered a model based on a triple helix. If the three sugar-phosphate backbones were on the outside of such a molecule, would hydrogen bonding or hydrophobic interactions be more important in keeping such a secondary structure together?

**16.** How would you expect the structure of ribozymes in organisms that grow in very hot environments, such as hot springs or deep-sea vents, to differ from those in organisms that grow in cooler environments?
   **a.** These ribozymes would have more hairpin secondary structures.
   **b.** The hairpins would have more G's and C's in the primary structure.
   **c.** The hairpins would have more A's and U's in the primary structure.
   **d.** These ribozymes would exhibit no tertiary structure.

# 5 An Introduction to Carbohydrates

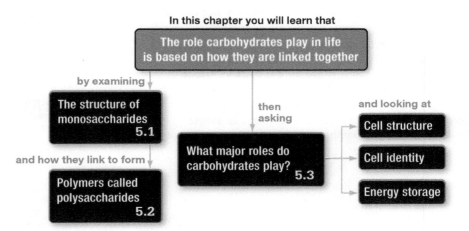

**In this chapter you will learn that**

The role carbohydrates play in life is based on how they are linked together

by examining

The structure of monosaccharides
**5.1**

and how they link to form

Polymers called polysaccharides
**5.2**

then asking

What major roles do carbohydrates play? **5.3**

and looking at

Cell structure

Cell identity

Energy storage

A cross section through a buttercup root. Cellulose-rich cell walls are stained green; starch-filled structures are stained purple. Cellulose is a structural carbohydrate; starch is an energy-storage carbohydrate.

This unit highlights the four types of macromolecules that were key to the evolution of the cell: proteins, nucleic acids, carbohydrates, and lipids. Understanding the structure and function of macromolecules is a basic requirement for exploring how life began and how organisms work. Recall that proteins and nucleic acids could satisfy only three of the five fundamental characteristics of life: information, replication, and evolution (Chapter 4). Carbohydrates, the subject of this chapter, play an important role in a fourth characteristic—energy.

The term **carbohydrate,** or **sugar,** encompasses the monomers called **monosaccharides** (literally, "one-sugar"), small polymers called **oligosaccharides** ("few-sugars"), and the large polymers called **polysaccharides** ("many-sugars"). The name carbohydrate is logical because the molecular formula of many of these molecules is $(CH_2O)_n$, where the $n$ refers to the number of "carbohydrate" groups. The value of $n$ can vary from 3, for the smallest sugar, to well over a thousand for some of the large polymers.

This chapter is part of the Big Picture. See how on pages 104–105.

✔ When you see this checkmark, stop and test yourself. Answers are available in Appendix A.

**An aldose**
Carbonyl group at
end of carbon chain

**A ketose**
Carbonyl group in
middle of carbon chain

The name can also be misleading, though, because carbohydrates do not consist of carbon atoms bonded to water molecules. Instead, they are molecules with a carbonyl (C=O) and several hydroxyl (−OH) functional groups, along with several to many carbon–hydrogen (C−H) bonds. Consider formaldehyde, which was introduced as one of the molecules present in early Earth (Chapter 2). Even though formaldehyde has the same molecular formula as the one given above ($CH_2O$), it is not a carbohydrate since it does not contain a hydroxyl group.

Let's begin with monosaccharides, put them together into polysaccharides, and then explore how carbohydrates figured in the origin of life and what they do in cells today. As you study this material, be sure to ask yourself the central question of biological chemistry: How does this molecule's structure relate to its properties and function?

# 5.1 Sugars as Monomers

Sugars are fundamental to life. They provide chemical energy in cells and furnish some of the molecular building blocks required for the synthesis of larger, more complex compounds. Monosaccharides were important during chemical evolution, early in Earth's history. For example, as you've seen, the sugar called ribose is required for the formation of the nucleotides that make up nucleic acids (Chapter 4).

## What Distinguishes One Monosaccharide from Another?

Monosaccharides, or simple sugars, are the monomers of carbohydrates. **FIGURE 5.1** illustrates two of the smallest monosaccharides. Although their molecular formulas are identical ($C_3H_6O_3$), their molecular structures are different. The carbonyl group that serves as one of monosaccharides' distinguishing features can be found either at the end of the molecule, forming an aldehyde sugar (an aldose), or within the carbon chain, forming a ketone sugar (a ketose). The presence of a carbonyl group along with multiple hydroxyl groups provides sugars with an array of reactive and hydrophilic functional groups. Based on this observation, it's not surprising that sugars are able to participate in a large number of chemical reactions.

The number of carbon atoms present also varies in monosaccharides. By convention, the carbons in a monosaccharide are numbered consecutively, starting with the end nearest the carbonyl group. Figure 5.1 features three-carbon sugars, or **trioses.** Ribose, which acts as a building block for nucleotides, has five carbons and is called a **pentose;** the glucose that is coursing through your bloodstream right now is a six-carbon sugar, or a **hexose.**

Besides varying in the location of the carbonyl group and the total number of carbon atoms present, monosaccharides can vary in the spatial arrangement of their atoms. There is, for example, a wide array of pentoses and hexoses. Each is distinguished by the configuration of its hydroxyl functional groups. **FIGURE 5.2**

**Glucose**

**Galactose**

**FIGURE 5.2 Sugars May Vary in the Configuration of Their Hydroxyl Groups.** The two six-carbon sugars shown here vary only in the spatial orientation of their hydroxyl groups on carbon number 4.

✔**EXERCISE** Mannose is a six-carbon sugar that is identical to glucose, except that the hydroxyl (−OH) group on carbon number 2 is switched in orientation. Circle carbon number 2 in glucose and galactose; then draw the structural formula of mannose.

illustrates glucose and galactose, which are six-carbon sugars. Notice that the two molecules have the same molecular formula ($C_6H_{12}O_6$) but not the same structure. Both are aldose sugars with six carbons, but they differ in the spatial arrangement of the hydroxyl group at the fourth carbon (highlighted in Figure 5.2).

This is a key point: Because the structures of glucose and galactose differ, their functions differ. In cells, glucose is used as a source of carbons for the construction of other molecules and chemical energy that sustains life. But for galactose to be used in these roles, it first has to be converted to glucose via an enzyme-catalyzed reaction. This example underscores a general theme: Even seemingly simple changes in structure—like the location of a single hydroxyl group—can have enormous consequences for function. This is because molecules interact in precise ways, based on their shape.

It's rare for sugars consisting of five or more carbons to exist in the form of the linear chains illustrated in Figure 5.2, however. In aqueous solution they tend to form ring structures. The bond responsible for ring formation occurs only between the carbon containing the carbonyl group and one of the carbons with a hydroxyl group. Glucose serves as the example in **FIGURE 5.3**. When the cyclic structure forms in glucose, the C-1 carbon (the carbon numbered 1 in the linear chain) forms a bond with the oxygen atom of the C-5 hydroxyl and transfers its hydrogen to the C-1 carbonyl, turning it into a hydroxyl group.

Transfer of hydrogen between the C-5 and C-1 functional groups preserves the number of atoms and hydroxyls found in the ring and linear forms. The newly formed C-1 hydroxyl group can be oriented in two distinct ways: above or below the plane of the ring. The different configurations produce the molecules α-glucose and β-glucose.

To summarize, many distinct monosaccharides exist because so many aspects of their structure are variable: aldose or ketose placement of the carbonyl group, variation in carbon number, different arrangements of hydroxyl groups in space, and alternative ring forms. Each monosaccharide has a unique structure and function.

## Monosaccharides and Chemical Evolution

Laboratory simulations, like those you read about in Chapter 2, have shown that most monosaccharides are readily synthesized under conditions that mimic the conditions of early Earth. For example, when formaldehyde ($CH_2O$) molecules are heated in solution, they react with one another to form almost all the pentoses and hexoses.

In addition, researchers have discovered the three-carbon ketose illustrated in Figure 5.1, along with a wide array of compounds closely related to sugars, on a meteorite that struck Murchison, Australia, in 1969. Based on these observations, investigators suspect that sugars are synthesized on dust particles and other debris in interstellar space and could have rained down onto Earth as the planet was forming, as well as being synthesized in the hot water near ancient undersea volcanoes.

More recent evidence suggests that synthesis of sugars could have been catalyzed by minerals found in the walls of deep-sea hydrothermal vents. Most researchers interested in chemical evolution maintain that one or more of the above mechanisms led to the accumulation of monosaccharides in the early oceans.

Modern cells display a wide range of carbohydrates beyond monosaccharides. How do these monomers join together to form polymers? Is the process similar to how amino acids link together to form proteins and nucleotides join to form nucleic acids? Let's explore how the array of functional groups in monosaccharides influences the polymerization of carbohydrates.

**(a)** Linear form of glucose    **(b)** Ring forms of glucose

Oxygen from the 5-carbon bonds to the 1-carbon, resulting in a ring structure

α-Glucose

β-Glucose

**FIGURE 5.3 Sugars Exist in Linear and Ring Forms. (a)** The linear form of glucose is rare. **(b)** In solution, almost all glucose molecules spontaneously react to form one of two ring structures, called the α and β forms of glucose. The two forms exist in equilibrium, but the β form is more common because it is slightly more stable than the α form.

**If you understand that . . .**

- Simple sugars differ from each other in three respects:
  1. the location of their carbonyl group,
  2. the number of carbon atoms present, and
  3. the spatial arrangement of their atoms—particularly the relative positions of hydroxyl (−OH) groups.

✔ **You should be able to . . .**

Draw the structural formula of a three-carbon monosaccharide ($C_3H_6O_3$) in linear form and then draw three other sugars that illustrate the three differences listed above.

*Answers are available in Appendix A.*

## 5.2 The Structure of Polysaccharides

Simple sugars can be covalently linked into chains of varying lengths, also known as complex carbohydrates. These chains range in size from small oligomers, or oligosaccharides, to the large polymers called polysaccharides. When only two sugars are linked together, they are known as **disaccharides.**

Similar to proteins and nucleic acids, the structure and function of larger carbohydrates depends on the types of monomers involved and how they are linked together. For example, maltose, also known as malt sugar, and lactose, an important sugar in milk, are two disaccharides that differ by just one monosaccharide. Maltose consists of two identical glucose molecules (**FIGURE 5.4a**), while lactose is made up of glucose and galactose (**FIGURE 5.4b**).

Monosaccharides polymerize when a condensation reaction occurs between two hydroxyl groups, resulting in a covalent interaction called a **glycosidic linkage.** The inverse reaction, hydrolysis, cleaves these linkages. (To review condensation and hydrolysis reactions, see Chapter 3.)

**(a)** Formation of α-glycosidic linkage

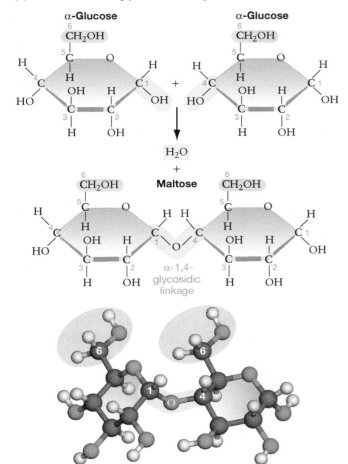

**(b)** Formation of β-glycosidic linkage

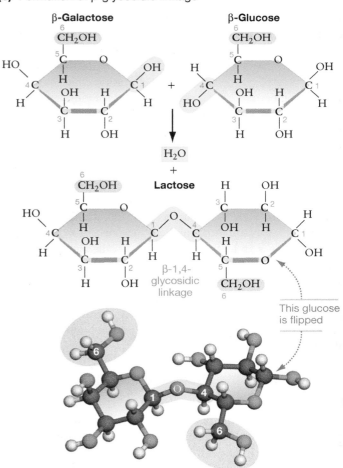

**FIGURE 5.4 Monosaccharides Polymerize through Formation of Glycosidic Linkages.** A glycosidic linkage occurs when hydroxyl groups on two monosaccharides undergo a condensation reaction. Maltose and lactose are disaccharides.

In that they hold monomers together, glycosidic linkages are analogous to the peptide bonds and phosphodiester linkages in proteins and nucleic acids. There is an important difference, however. Peptide bonds and phosphodiester linkages form between the same locations in their monomers, giving proteins and nucleic acids a standard backbone structure, but this is not the case for polysaccharides. Because glycosidic linkages form between hydroxyl groups, and because every monosaccharide contains at least two hydroxyls, the location and geometry of glycosidic linkages can vary widely among polysaccharides.

Maltose and lactose illustrate two of the most common glycosidic linkages, called the $\alpha$-1,4-glycosidic linkage and the $\beta$-1,4-glycosidic linkage. The numbers refer to the carbons on either side of the linkage, indicating that both linkages are between the C-1 and C-4 carbons. Their geometry, however, is different: $\alpha$ and $\beta$ refer to the contrasting orientations of the C-1 hydroxyls—on opposite sides of the plane of the glucose rings (i.e., "above" versus "below" the plane).

As Section 5.3 explains, the orientation of this hydroxyl in glycosidic linkages is particularly important in the structure, function, and durability of the molecules. In essence, the difference between polysaccharides used for storage and structural polysaccharides is a simple twist of a link.

To drive this point home, let's consider the structures of the most common polysaccharides found in organisms today: starch, glycogen, cellulose, and chitin, along with a modified polysaccharide called peptidoglycan. Each of these macromolecules is joined by particular $\alpha$-1,4- or $\beta$-1,4-glycosidic linkages and can consist of a few hundred to many thousands of monomers.

## Starch: A Storage Polysaccharide in Plants

In plant cells, some monosaccharides are stored for later use in the form of starch. **Starch** consists entirely of $\alpha$-glucose monomers joined by glycosidic linkages. As the top panel in **TABLE 5.1** shows, the angle of the linkages between C-1 and C-4 carbons causes a chain of glucose subunits to coil into a helix.

Starch is actually a mixture of two such polysaccharides, however. One is an unbranched molecule called amylose, which contains only $\alpha$-1,4-glycosidic linkages. The other is a branched molecule called amylopectin. The branching in amylopectin occurs when glycosidic linkages form between the C-1 carbon of a glucose monomer on one strand and the C-6 carbon of a glucose monomer on another strand. In amylopectin, branches occur at about one out of every 30 monomers.

## Glycogen: A Highly Branched Storage Polysaccharide in Animals

**Glycogen** performs the same storage role in animals that starch performs in plants. In humans, for example, glycogen is stored in the liver and in muscles. When you start exercising, enzymes begin breaking glycogen into glucose monomers, which are then processed in muscle cells to supply energy. Glycogen is a polymer of $\alpha$-glucose and is nearly identical to the branched form of starch. However, instead of an $\alpha$-1,6-glycosidic linkage occurring in about 1 out of every 30 monomers, a branch occurs in about 1 out of every 10 glucose subunits (see Table 5.1).

## Cellulose: A Structural Polysaccharide in Plants

All cells are enclosed by a membrane (Chapter 1). In most organisms living today, the cell is also surrounded by a layer of material called a wall. A **cell wall** is a protective sheet that occurs outside the membrane. In plants, bacteria, fungi, and many other groups, the cell wall is composed primarily of one or more polysaccharides.

In plants, cellulose is the major component of the cell wall. **Cellulose** is a polymer of $\beta$-glucose monomers, joined by $\beta$-1,4-glycosidic linkages. As Table 5.1 shows, the geometry of the linkage is such that each glucose monomer in the chain is flipped in relation to the adjacent monomer. The flipped orientation is important because **(1)** it generates a linear molecule, rather than the helix seen in starch; and **(2)** it permits multiple hydrogen bonds to form between adjacent, parallel strands of cellulose. As a result, cellulose forms long, parallel strands that are joined by hydrogen bonds. The linked cellulose fibers are strong and give the cell structural support.

## Chitin: A Structural Polysaccharide in Fungi and Animals

**Chitin** is a polysaccharide that stiffens the cell walls of fungi. It is also found in a few types of protists and in many animals. It is, for example, the most important component of the external skeletons of insects and crustaceans.

Chitin is similar to cellulose, but instead of consisting of glucose monomers, the monosaccharide involved is one called *N*-acetylglucosamine (abbreviated as NAG). These NAG monomers are joined by $\beta$-1,4-glycosidic linkages (see Table 5.1). As in cellulose, the geometry of these bonds results in every other residue being flipped in orientation.

Like the glucose monomers in cellulose, the NAG subunits in chitin form hydrogen bonds between adjacent strands. The result is a tough sheet that provides stiffness and protection.

## Peptidoglycan: A Structural Polysaccharide in Bacteria

Most bacteria, like all plants, have cell walls. But unlike plants, in bacteria the ability to produce cellulose is extremely rare. Instead, a polysaccharide called **peptidoglycan** gives bacterial cell walls strength and firmness.

Peptidoglycan is the most complex of the polysaccharides discussed thus far. It has a long backbone formed by two types of monosaccharides that alternate with each other and are linked by $\beta$-1,4-glycosidic linkages (see Table 5.1). In addition, a short chain of amino acids is attached to one of the two sugar types. When molecules of peptidoglycan align, peptide bonds link the amino acid chains on adjacent strands. These links serve the same purpose as the hydrogen bonds between the parallel strands of cellulose and chitin in the cell walls of other organisms.

**Polysaccharides Differ in Structure**

| Polysaccharide | Chemical Structure | Three-dimensional Structure |
|---|---|---|

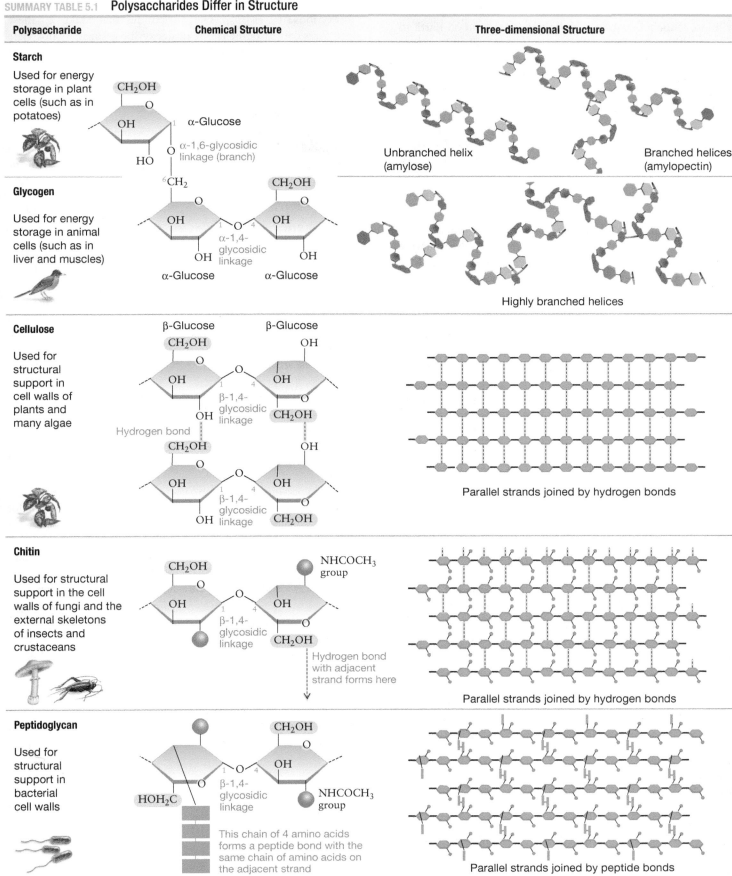

**Starch**

Used for energy storage in plant cells (such as in potatoes)

$CH_2OH$
α-Glucose
α-1,6-glycosidic linkage (branch)

Unbranched helix (amylose)

Branched helices (amylopectin)

**Glycogen**

Used for energy storage in animal cells (such as in liver and muscles)

$^6CH_2$
$CH_2OH$
$CH_2OH$
α-1,4-glycosidic linkage
α-Glucose
α-Glucose

Highly branched helices

**Cellulose**

Used for structural support in cell walls of plants and many algae

β-Glucose
β-Glucose
$CH_2OH$
OH
β-1,4-glycosidic linkage
$CH_2OH$
Hydrogen bond
$CH_2OH$
OH
β-1,4-glycosidic linkage
$CH_2OH$

Parallel strands joined by hydrogen bonds

**Chitin**

Used for structural support in the cell walls of fungi and the external skeletons of insects and crustaceans

$CH_2OH$
$NHCOCH_3$ group
OH
β-1,4-glycosidic linkage
$CH_2OH$
Hydrogen bond with adjacent strand forms here

Parallel strands joined by hydrogen bonds

**Peptidoglycan**

Used for structural support in bacterial cell walls

$CH_2OH$
OH
β-1,4-glycosidic linkage
$HOH_2C$
$NHCOCH_3$ group
This chain of 4 amino acids forms a peptide bond with the same chain of amino acids on the adjacent strand

Parallel strands joined by peptide bonds

## Polysaccharides and Chemical Evolution

Cellulose is the most abundant organic compound on Earth to-day, and chitin is probably the second most abundant by weight. Virtually all organisms depend on glycogen or starch as an energy source. But despite their current importance to life, polysaccharides probably played little to no role in the origin of life. This conclusion is supported by several observations:

- *No plausible mechanism exists for the polymerization of monosaccharides under conditions that prevailed early in Earth's history.* In cells and in laboratory experiments, the glycosidic linkages illustrated in Figure 5.4 and Table 5.1 form only with the aid of protein enzymes. No enzyme-like RNAs are known to catalyze these reactions.

- *To date, no polysaccharide has been discovered that can catalyze polymerization reactions.* Even though polysaccharides contain reactive hydroxyl and carbonyl groups, they lack the structural and chemical complexity that makes proteins, and to a lesser extent RNA, effective catalysts.

- *The monomers in polysaccharides are not capable of complementary base pairing.* Like proteins, but unlike nucleic acids, polysaccharides cannot act as templates for their own replication.

Even though polysaccharides probably did not play a significant role in the earliest forms of life, they became enormously important once cellular life evolved. In the next section, let's take a detailed look at how they function in today's cells.

## check your understanding

**If you understand that . . .**

- Polysaccharides form when enzymes catalyze the formation of glycosidic linkages between monosaccharides that are in the α or β form.
- Most polysaccharides are long chains of monosaccharides, but some branch extensively. Among linear forms, it is common for adjacent strands to be connected by hydrogen bonding or other types of linkages.

✓ **You should be able to . . .**

Provide four structural differences that could result in different oligosaccharides consisting of two glucose monomers and two galactose monomers.

*Answers are available in Appendix A.*

## 5.3 What Do Carbohydrates Do?

One of the basic functions that carbohydrates perform in organisms is to serve as a substrate for synthesizing more-complex molecules. For example, recall that RNA contains the five-carbon sugar ribose ($C_5H_{10}O_5$) and DNA contains the modified sugar deoxyribose ($C_5H_{10}O_4$). The nucleotides that make up these polymers consist of the ribose or deoxyribose sugar, a phosphate group, and a nitrogenous base (Chapter 4). The sugar itself acts as a subunit of each of these monomers.

In addition, sugars frequently furnish the raw "carbon skeletons" that are used as building blocks in the synthesis of important molecules. Your cells are producing amino acids right now, for example, using sugars as a starting point.

Carbohydrates have diverse functions in cells: In addition to serving as precursors to larger molecules, they (1) provide fibrous structural materials, (2) indicate cell identity, and (3) store chemical energy. Let's look at each function in turn.

## Carbohydrates Can Provide Structural Support

Cellulose and chitin, along with the modified polysaccharide peptidoglycan, are key structural compounds. They form fibers that give cells and organisms strength and elasticity.

To appreciate why cellulose, chitin, and peptidoglycan are effective structural molecules, recall that they form long strands and that bonds can form between adjacent strands. In the cell walls of plants, for example, a collection of about 80 cellulose molecules are cross-linked by hydrogen bonding to create a tough fiber. These cellulose fibers, in turn, crisscross to form a tough sheet that is able to withstand pulling and pushing forces—what an engineer would call tension and compression.

Besides being stiff and strong, the structural carbohydrates are durable. Almost all organisms have the enzymes required to break the various α-glycosidic linkages that hold starch and glycogen molecules together, but only a few organisms have enzymes capable of hydrolyzing cellulose, chitin, and peptidoglycan. Due to the strong interactions between strands consisting of β-1,4-glycosidic linkages, water is excluded and the fibers tend to be insoluble. The absence of water within these fibers makes their hydrolysis more difficult. As a result, the structural polysaccharides are resistant to degradation and decay.

Ironically, the durability of cellulose supports digestion. The cellulose that you ingest when you eat plant cells—what biologists call dietary fiber—forms a porous mass that absorbs and retains water. This sponge-like mass adds moisture and bulk that helps fecal material move through the intestinal tract more quickly, preventing constipation and other problems.

## The Role of Carbohydrates in Cell Identity

Structural polymers tend to be repetitive, with only one or two types of monosaccharides. The same is not true for all complex carbohydrates. Some types exhibit enormous structural diversity, because their component monomers—and the linkages between them—vary a lot. As a result, they are capable of displaying information to other cells through their structure. More specifically, polysaccharides act as an identification badge on the outer surface of the plasma membrane that surrounds a cell. (Chapter 6 describes plasma membranes in detail.)

Outside of cell
Oligosaccharide
Plasma membrane
Protein
Inside of cell
Glycoprotein

**FIGURE 5.5 Carbohydrates Are an Identification Badge for Cells.**
Glycoproteins contain sugar groups that project outside the cell from the surface of the plasma membrane enclosing the cell. These sugar groups have distinctive structures that identify the type or species of the cell.

**FIGURE 5.5** shows how this information about cell identity is displayed. Molecules called glycoproteins project outward from the cell surface into the surrounding environment. A **glycoprotein** is a protein that has one or more carbohydrates covalently bonded to it—usually relatively short oligosaccharides.

Glycoproteins are key molecules in what biologists call cell–cell recognition and cell–cell signaling. Each cell in your body has glycoproteins on its surface that identify it as part of your body. Immune system cells use these glycoproteins to distinguish your body's cells from foreign cells, such as bacteria. In addition, each distinct type of cell in a multicellular organism—for example, the nerve cells and muscle cells in your body—displays a different set of glycoproteins on its surface.

The identification information displayed by glycoproteins helps cells recognize and communicate with each other.

The key point here is to recognize that the variety in the types of monosaccharides and how they can be linked together makes it possible for an enormous number of unique oligosaccharides to exist. As a result, each cell type and each species can display a unique identity.

During the 1980s, Paul Wassarman and colleagues investigated the role of glycoproteins in one of the most important cell–cell recognition events in the life of a plant or animal—the attachment of sperm to eggs during fertilization. This step guarantees specificity—sperm recognize and bind only to eggs of their own species.

In one experiment, the researchers mixed sperm with purified egg-surface glycoproteins and discovered that most of the sperm lost their ability to attach to eggs (**FIGURE 5.6**). Such loss of function is an example of what researchers call competitive inhibition. The glycoproteins had bound to—and thus blocked—the same structure on the sperm that it uses to bind to eggs. This result showed that sperm attach to eggs via egg glycoproteins.

**RESEARCH**

**QUESTION:** What part of surface glycoproteins do sperm recognize when they attach to eggs?

**HYPOTHESIS:** Sperm attach to the carbohydrate component.

**NULL HYPOTHESIS:** Sperm attach to the protein component.

EXPERIMENTAL SETUP:

Glycoprotein

Carbohydrate            Protein

Sperm

Egg

1. **Isolate glycoproteins** from the surface of a mouse egg.

2. **Separate protein and carbohydrate components.**

3. **Treat sperm** with components; allow time for component binding.

4. **Test attachment inhibition:** Add mouse eggs to treated sperm; allow time for sperm binding.

PREDICTION: The carbohydrate component of the glycoprotein will bind to sperm and block their attachment to eggs.

PREDICTION OF NULL HYPOTHESIS: The protein component of the glycoprotein will block sperm attachment to eggs.

RESULTS:

Results from this experiment

Results from previous experiments

Attachment inhibition (%)

Pure protein blocks few sperm from attaching

Pure carbohydrate blocks sperm attachment as much as intact glycoprotein

Carbohydrate    Protein

Intact glycoprotein    Untreated (control)

CONCLUSION: Sperm recognize and bind to the carbohydrates of egg-surface glycoproteins when they attach to egg cells.

**FIGURE 5.6 Carbohydrates Are Required for Cellular Recognition and Attachment.**

SOURCES: Florman, H. M., K. B. Bechtol, and P. M. Wassarman. 1984. Enzymatic dissection of the functions of the mouse egg's receptor for sperm. *Developmental Biology* 106: 243–255. Also Florman, H. M., and P. M. Wassarman. 1985. O-linked oligosaccharides of mouse egg ZP3 account for its sperm receptor activity. *Cell* 41: 313–324.

✔ **QUANTITATIVE** How would the bars change in the graph if sperm attachment required only the protein portion of egg glycoproteins?

But which part of the egg glycoproteins is essential for recognition and attachment—the protein or the carbohydrate? In follow-up experiments, Wassarman's group used the same type of competitive-binding assay to answer this question. When sperm were mixed with purified carbohydrates alone, most were unable to attach to eggs. In contrast, most sperm treated with purified protein alone were not inhibited and still attached to eggs. Both results show that the carbohydrate component plays a fundamental role in the process of egg-cell recognition.

## Carbohydrates and Energy Storage

Candy-bar wrappers promise a quick energy boost, and ads for sports drinks claim that their products provide the "carbs" needed for peak activity. If you were to ask friends or family members what carbohydrates do in your body, they would probably say something like "They give you energy." And after pointing out that carbohydrates are also used in cell identity, as structural material, and as a source of carbon skeletons for the synthesis of other complex molecules, you'd have to agree.

Carbohydrates store and provide chemical energy in cells. What aspect of carbohydrate structure makes this function possible?

**Carbohydrates Store Sunlight as Chemical Energy**   Recall that the essence of chemical evolution was energy transformations (Chapter 2). For example, it was proposed that the kinetic energy of sunlight may have been converted into chemical energy and stored in bonds of molecules such as formaldehyde ($CH_2O$).

This same type of transformation from light energy to chemical energy occurs in cells today, but instead of making formaldehyde, cells produce sugars. For example, plants harvest the kinetic energy in sunlight and store it in the bonds of carbohydrates by the process known as **photosynthesis.** (Photosynthesis is the focus of Chapter 10.)

Photosynthesis entails a complex set of reactions that can be summarized most simply as follows:

$$CO_2 + H_2O + \text{sunlight} \longrightarrow (CH_2O)_n + O_2$$

where $(CH_2O)_n$ represents a carbohydrate. The key to understanding the energy conversion that is taking place in this reaction is to compare the positions of the electrons in the reactants to those in the products.

- The electrons in the C=O bonds of carbon dioxide and the C–O bonds of carbohydrates are held tightly because of oxygen's high electronegativity. Thus, they have relatively low potential energy.

- The electrons involved in the C–H bonds of carbohydrates are shared equally because the electronegativity of carbon and hydrogen is about the same. Thus, these electrons have relatively high potential energy.

- Electrons are also shared equally in the carbon–carbon C–C bonds of carbohydrates—meaning that they, too, have relatively high potential energy.

(a) Carbon dioxide

(b) A carbohydrate

(c) A fatty acid (a component of fat molecules)

**FIGURE 5.7 In Organisms, Potential Energy Is Stored in C–H and C–C Bonds. (a)** In carbon dioxide, the electrons involved in covalent bonds are held tightly by oxygen atoms. **(b)** In carbohydrates such as the sugar shown here, many of the covalently bonded electrons are held equally between C and H atoms. **(c)** The fatty acids found in fat molecules have more C–H bonds and fewer C–O bonds than carbohydrates do. ("R" stands for the rest of the molecule.)

✔**EXERCISE** Circle the bonds in this diagram that have high potential energy.

C–C and C–H bonds have much higher potential energy than C–O bonds have. As a result, carbohydrates have much more chemical energy than carbon dioxide has.

**FIGURE 5.7** summarizes and extends these points. Start by comparing the structure of carbon dioxide in Figure 5.7a with the carbohydrate in Figure 5.7b. The main difference is the presence of C–C and C–H bonds in the carbohydrate. Now compare the carbohydrate in Figure 5.7b with the fatty acid—a subunit of a fat molecule—in Figure 5.7c. Compared with carbohydrates, fats contain many more C–C and C–H bonds and many fewer C–O bonds.

This point is important. C–C and C–H bonds have high potential energy because the electrons are shared equally by atoms with low electronegativities. C–O bonds, in contrast, have low potential energy because the highly electronegative oxygen atom holds the electrons so tightly. Both carbohydrates and fats are used as fuel in cells, but fats store twice as much energy per gram compared with carbohydrates. (Fats are discussed in more detail in Chapter 6.)

**Enzymes Hydrolyze Polysaccharides to Release Glucose**   Starch and glycogen are efficient energy-storage molecules because they polymerize via α-glycosidic linkages instead of the β-glycosidic linkages observed in the structural polysaccharides. The α-linkages in storage polysaccharides are readily hydrolyzed to release glucose, while the structural polysaccharides resist enzymatic degradation.

The most important enzyme involved in catalyzing the hydrolysis of α-glycosidic linkages in glycogen molecules is a protein called **phosphorylase.** Many of your cells contain phosphorylase, so they can break down glycogen to provide glucose on demand.

The enzymes involved in breaking the α-glycosidic linkages in starch are called **amylases.** Your salivary glands and pancreas produce amylases that are secreted into your mouth and small intestine, respectively. These amylases are responsible for digesting the starch that you eat.

The glucose subunits that are hydrolyzed from glycogen and starch are processed in reactions that result in the production of chemical energy that can be used in the cell. Glycogen and starch are like a candy bar that has segments, so you can break off chunks whenever you need a boost.

**Energy Stored in Glucose is Used to Make ATP** When a cell needs energy, reactions lead to the breakdown of the glucose and capture of the released energy through synthesis of the nucleotide adenosine triphosphate (ATP) (introduced in Chapter 4).

More specifically, the energy that is released when sugars are processed is used to synthesize ATP from a precursor called adenosine diphosphate (ADP) plus a free inorganic phosphate ($P_i$) molecule. The overall reaction can be written as follows:

$$(CH_2O)_n + O_2 + ADP + P_i \longrightarrow CO_2 + H_2O + ATP$$

To put this in words, the chemical energy stored in the C−H and C−C bonds of carbohydrate is transferred to a new bond linking a third phosphate group to ADP to form ATP.

How much energy does it take to form ATP? Consider this example: A cell can use the 10 calories of energy stored in a LifeSavers candy to produce approximately $2 \times 10^{23}$ molecules of ATP. Although this sounds like a lot of ATP, an average human's energy needs would burn through all of this ATP energy in a little over a minute! The energy in ATP drives reactions like polymerization and cellular processes like moving your muscles.

Carbohydrates are like the water that piles up behind a dam. ATP is like the electricity generated at a dam, which lights up your home. Carbohydrates store chemical energy; ATP makes chemical energy useful to the cell.

Later chapters analyze in detail how cells capture and store energy in sugars and how these sugars are then broken down to provide cells with usable chemical energy in the form of ATP (Chapters 8, 9, and 10). For both of these processes to occur, however, a selectively permeable membrane barrier is required. The following chapter introduces the lipids needed to build these membranes and the role they played in the evolution of the first cell.

## check your understanding

**If you understand that . . .**

- Carbohydrates provide building blocks for the synthesis of more complex compounds.
- Polysaccharides such as cellulose, chitin, and peptidoglycan form cell walls, which give cells structural strength.
- Glycoproteins project from the surface of cells. They provide a molecular badge that identifies the cell's type or species.
- Starch and glycogen store sugars for later use in reactions that produce ATP. Sugars contain large amounts of chemical energy because they contain carbon atoms that are bonded to hydrogen atoms or other carbon atoms. The C−H and C−C bonds have high potential energy because the electrons are shared equally by atoms with low electronegativity.

✔ **You should be able to . . .**

1. Identify two aspects of the structures of cellulose, chitin, and peptidoglycan that correlate with their function as structural molecules.

2. Describe how the carbohydrates you ate during breakfast today are functioning in your body right now.

*Answers are available in Appendix A.*

---

**CHAPTER 5 REVIEW**          *For media, go to MasteringBiology*

## If you understand . . .

### 5.1  Sugars as Monomers

- Monosaccharides are organic compounds that have a carbonyl group and several hydroxyl groups. The molecular formula for a sugar is typically $(CH_2O)_n$, but the number of "carbon-hydrate" groups may vary between sugars, as indicated by the $n$.

- Although some monosaccharides may have the same molecular formula, the arrangement of functional groups can lead to differences in the molecular structure of the sugars.

- Individual monosaccharides may form ring structures that differ from one another in the orientation of a hydroxyl group.

✔ You should be able to explain how a relatively small difference in the location of a carbonyl or hydroxyl group can lead to dramatic changes in the properties and function of a monosaccharide.

## 5.2 The Structure of Polysaccharides

Monosaccharides can be covalently bonded to one another via glycosidic linkages, which join hydroxyl groups on adjacent molecules.

In contrast to proteins and nucleic acids, polysaccharides do not always form a single uniform backbone structure. The numerous hydroxyls found in each monosaccharide allow glycosidic linkages to form at different sites and new strands to branch from existing chains.

The types of monomers involved and the geometries of the glycosidic linkages between monomers distinguish different polysaccharides from one another.

The most common polysaccharides in organisms today are starch, glycogen, cellulose, and chitin; peptidoglycan is an abundant polysaccharide that has short chains of amino acids attached.

✓ You should be able to compare and contrast glycosidic linkages in polysaccharides with the linkages between monomers in proteins and nucleic acids.

## 5.3 What Do Carbohydrates Do?

In carbohydrates, as in proteins and nucleic acids, structure correlates with function.

Cellulose, chitin, and peptidoglycan are polysaccharides that function in support. They are made up of monosaccharide monomers joined by β-1,4-glycosidic linkages. When individual molecules of these polysaccharides align side by side, bonds form between them—resulting in strong, flexible fibers or sheets that resist hydrolysis.

- The oligosaccharides on cell-surface glycoproteins can function as specific signposts or identity tags because their constituent monosaccharides are so diverse in geometry and composition.

- Both starch and glycogen function as energy-storage molecules. They are made up of glucose molecules that are joined by α-glycosidic linkages. These linkages are readily hydrolyzed to release glucose for the production of ATP.

✓ You should be able to describe four key differences in the structure of polysaccharides that function in energy storage versus structural support.

(MB) **MasteringBiology**

**1. MasteringBiology Assignments**

**Tutorials and Activities** Carbohydrates; Carbohydrate Structure and Function; Types of Carbohydrates

**Questions** Reading Quizzes, Blue-Thread Questions, Test Bank

**2. eText** Read your book online, search, take notes, highlight text, and more.

**3. The Study Area** Practice Test, Cumulative Test, BioFlix® 3-D Animations, Videos, Activities, Audio Glossary, Word Study Tools, Art

## You should be able to . . .

## ✓ TEST YOUR KNOWLEDGE

Answers are available in Appendix A

1. What is the difference between a monosaccharide, an oligosaccharide, and a polysaccharide?
   a. the number of carbon atoms in the molecule
   b. the type of glycosidic linkage between monomers
   c. the spatial arrangement of the various hydroxyl residues in the molecule
   d. the number of monomers in the molecule

2. What are three ways monosaccharides differ from one another?

3. What type of bond is formed between two sugars in a disaccharide?
   a. glycosidic linkage
   b. phosphodiester bond
   c. peptide bond
   d. hydrogen bond

4. What holds cellulose molecules together in bundles large enough to form fibers?
   a. the cell wall
   b. peptide bonds
   c. hydrogen bonds
   d. hydrophobic interactions between different residues in the cellulose helix

5. What are the primary functions of carbohydrates in cells?
   a. energy storage, cell identity, structure, and building blocks for synthesis
   b. catalysis, structure, and energy storage
   c. information storage and catalysis
   d. source of carbon, information storage, and energy storage

6. What is responsible for the difference in potential energy between carbohydrates and carbon dioxide?

7. Which of the differences listed here could be found in the same monosaccharide?

a. different orientation of a hydroxyl in the linear form
b. different number of carbons
c. different orientation of a hydroxyl in the ring form
d. different position of the carbonyl group in the linear form

8. What would most likely occur if the galactose in lactose were replaced with glucose?
   a. It would not be digested by human infants or adults.
   b. It would be digested by most adult humans.
   c. It would be digested by human infants, but not adults.
   d. It would be digested by human adults, but not infants.

9. Explain how the structure of carbohydrates supports their function in displaying the identity of a cell.

10. What is the difference between linking glucose molecules with $\alpha$-1,4-glycosidic linkages versus $\beta$-1,4-glycosidic linkages? What are the consequences?

11. Give three reasons why researchers have concluded that polysaccharides were unlikely to play a large role in the origin of life.

12. Compare and contrast the structures and functions of starch and glycogen. How are these molecules similar? How are they different?

13. A weight-loss program for humans that emphasized minimal consumption of carbohydrates was popular in some countries

in the early 2000s. What was the logic behind this diet? (Note: This diet plan caused controversy and is not endorsed by some physicians and researchers).

14. Galactosemia is a potentially fatal disease that occurs in humans who lack the enzyme that converts galactose to glucose. To treat this disease, physicians exclude the monosaccharide galactose from the diet. Which of the following would you also predict to be excluded from the diet?
    a. maltose    b. starch    c. mannose    d. lactose

15. If you hold a salty cracker in your mouth long enough, it will begin to taste sweet. What is responsible for this change in taste?

16. Lysozyme, an enzyme found in human saliva, tears, and other secretions, catalyzes the hydrolysis of the $\beta$-1,4-glycosidic linkages in peptidoglycan. Predict the effect of this enzyme on bacteria, and explain the role its activity plays in human health.

# 6 Lipids, Membranes, and the First Cells

In this chapter you will learn how

Life's defining barrier—the plasma membrane—is built of lipids and proteins

by looking at

Lipid structure and function **6.1**

and how

Lipids spontaneously form bilayers **6.2**

How do substances move across bilayers?

then asking

via

Diffusion and osmosis **6.3**

Membrane proteins **6.4**

A space-filling model of a phospholipid bilayer. In single-celled organisms, this cluster of molecules forms part of the boundary between life (inside the cell) and nonlife (outside the cell)—the cell membrane.

Currently, most biologists support the hypothesis that biological evolution began with a catalytic RNA molecule that could replicate itself. As the offspring of this molecule multiplied, natural selection would have favored the most efficient versions. A second great milestone in the history of life occurred when descendants of these replicators became enclosed within a membrane.

Why is the presence of a membrane so important? The **plasma membrane,** or **cell membrane,** separates life from nonlife. It is a layer of molecules that surrounds the cell interior and separates it from the environment.

- The plasma membrane serves as a selective barrier: It keeps damaging compounds out of the cell and allows entry of compounds needed by the cell.

- Because the plasma membrane sequesters the appropriate chemicals in an enclosed area, reactants collide more frequently—the chemical reactions necessary for life occur much more efficiently.

This chapter is part of the Big Picture. See how on pages 104–105.

✓ When you see this checkmark, stop and test yourself. Answers are available in Appendix A.

While researchers of chemical evolution are currently debating when membranes arose—whether early or late during the emergence of life—there is little argument about the importance of this event. After life secured a membrane, it continued to evolve into an efficient and dynamic reaction vessel—the cell.

How do membranes form? Which ions and molecules can pass through a membrane and which cannot, and why? These are some of the most fundamental questions in all of biological science. Let's delve into them, beginning with the membrane's foundation—lipids.

## 6.1 Lipid Structure and Function

**Lipid** is a catchall term for carbon-containing compounds that are found in organisms and are largely nonpolar and hydrophobic—meaning that they do not dissolve readily in water. (Recall from Chapter 2 that water is a polar solvent.) Lipids do dissolve, however, in liquids consisting of nonpolar organic compounds.

To understand why lipids are insoluble in water, examine the five-carbon compound called isoprene, illustrated in **FIGURE 6.1a**. Note that isoprene consists of carbon atoms bonded to hydrogen atoms. The figure also shows the structural formula of a chain of linked isoprenes, called an isoprenoid.

Molecules that contain only carbon and hydrogen are known as **hydrocarbons.** Hydrocarbons are nonpolar because electrons are shared equally in C—H bonds—owing to the approximately equal electronegativity of carbon and hydrogen. Since these bonds form no partial charges, hydrocarbons are hydrophobic. Thus lipids do not dissolve in water, because they have a significant hydrocarbon component.

## Bond Saturation Is an Important Aspect of Hydrocarbon Structure

**FIGURE 6.1b** gives the structural formula of a **fatty acid,** a simple lipid consisting of a hydrocarbon chain bonded to a carboxyl (—COOH) functional group. Fatty acids and isoprenes are key building blocks of important lipids found in organisms. Just as subtle differences in the orientation of hydroxyls in sugars can lead to dramatic effects in their structure and function, the type of C—C bond used in hydrocarbon chains is a key factor in lipid structure.

When two carbon atoms form a double bond, the attached atoms are found in a plane instead of a three-dimensional tetrahedron. The carbon atoms involved are also locked into place. They cannot rotate freely, as they do in carbon–carbon single bonds. As a result, certain double bonds between carbon atoms produce a "kink" in an otherwise straight hydrocarbon chain (Figure 6.1b, left).

Hydrocarbon chains that consist of only single bonds between the carbons are called **saturated.** If one or more double bonds exist in the hydrocarbon chains, then they are **unsaturated.** The choice of terms is logical. If a hydrocarbon chain does not contain a double bond, it is saturated with the maximum number of hydrogen atoms that can attach to the carbon skeleton. If it is unsaturated, then a C—H bond is removed to form a C=C double bond, resulting in fewer than the maximum number of attached hydrogen atoms.

Foods that contain lipids with many double bonds are said to be polyunsaturated and are advertised as healthier than foods with saturated fats. Recent research suggests that polyunsaturated fats help protect the heart from disease. Exactly how this occurs is under investigation.

**(a)** Isoprenes can be linked into chains called isoprenoids.

**(b)** Fatty acids can be saturated or unsaturated.

Isoprene

Carboxyl group

Hydrocarbon chains

cis double bonds cause kinks in hydrocarbon chains

**Isoprenoid**  **Saturated fatty acid**  **Unsaturated fatty acid**

**FIGURE 6.1 Hydrocarbon Structure. (a)** Isoprene subunits, like the one shown to the left, can be linked to each other, end to end, to form long hydrocarbon chains called isoprenoids. **(b)** Fatty acids typically contain a total of 14–20 carbon atoms, most found in their long hydrocarbon "tails." Unsaturated hydrocarbons contain carbon–carbon double bonds; saturated hydrocarbons do not.

**(a) Saturated lipids**

Butter

**(b) Saturated lipids with long hydrocarbon tails**

Beeswax

**(c) Unsaturated lipids**

Safflower oil

**FIGURE 6.2 The Fluidity of Lipids Depends on the Length and Saturation of Their Hydrocarbon Chains. (a)** Butter consists primarily of saturated lipids. **(b)** Waxes are lipids with extremely long saturated hydrocarbon chains. **(c)** Oils are dominated by "polyunsaturates"—lipids with hydrocarbon chains that contain multiple C=C double bonds.

Bond saturation also profoundly affects the physical state of lipids. Highly saturated fats, such as butter, are solid at room temperature (**FIGURE 6.2a**). Saturated lipids that have extremely long hydrocarbon tails, like **waxes** do, form particularly stiff solids at room temperature (**FIGURE 6.2b**). Highly unsaturated fats are liquid at room temperature (**FIGURE 6.2c**).

## A Look at Three Types of Lipids Found in Cells

Unlike amino acids, nucleotides, and monosaccharides, lipids are characterized by a physical property—their insolubility in water—instead of a shared chemical structure. This insolubility is based on the high proportion of nonpolar C–C and C–H bonds

relative to polar functional groups. As a result, the structure of lipids varies widely. For example, consider the most important types of lipids found in cells: fats, steroids, and phospholipids.

**Fats** **Fats** are nonpolar molecules composed of three fatty acids that are linked to a three-carbon molecule called **glycerol.** Because of this structure, fats are also called triacylglycerols or triglycerides. When the fatty acids are polyunsaturated, they form liquid triacylglycerols called **oils.** In organisms, the primary role of fats is energy storage.

As **FIGURE 6.3a** shows, fats form when a dehydration reaction occurs between a hydroxyl group of glycerol and the carboxyl

**(a) Fats form via dehydration reactions.**

Glycerol

Dehydration reaction

Fatty acid

**(b) Fats consist of glycerol linked by ester linkages to three fatty acids.**

Ester linkages

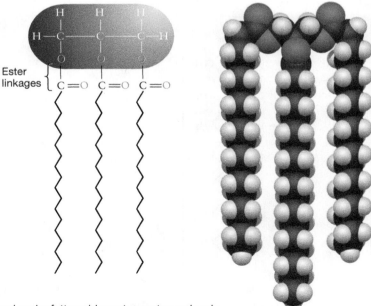

**FIGURE 6.3 Fats Are One Type of Lipid Found in Cells. (a)** When glycerol and a fatty acid react, a water molecule leaves. The covalent bond that results from this reaction is termed an ester linkage. **(b)** The structural formula and a space-filling model of tristearin, the most common type of fat in beef.

group of a fatty acid. The glycerol and fatty acid molecules become joined by an **ester linkage.** Fats are not polymers, however, and fatty acids are not monomers. As **FIGURE 6.3b** shows, fatty acids are not linked together to form a macromolecule in the way that amino acids, nucleotides, and monosaccharides are.

**Steroids**   **Steroids** are a family of lipids distinguished by the bulky, four-ring structure shown in orange in **FIGURE 6.4a.** The various steroids differ from one another by the functional groups or side groups attached to different carbons in those hydrophobic rings. The steroid shown in the figure is cholesterol, which has a hydrophilic hydroxyl group attached to the top ring and an isoprenoid "tail" attached at the bottom. Cholesterol is an important component of plasma membranes in many organisms.

**Phospholipids**   **Phospholipids** consist of a glycerol that is linked to a phosphate group and two hydrocarbon chains of either isoprenoids or fatty acids. The phosphate group is also bonded to a small organic molecule that is charged or polar (**FIGURE 6.4b**).

Phospholipids composed of fatty acids are found in the domains Bacteria and Eukarya; phospholipids with isoprenoid chains are found in the domain Archaea. (The domains of life were introduced in Chapter 1.) In all three domains, phospholipids are crucial components of the plasma membrane.

The lipids found in organisms have a wide array of structures and functions. In addition to storing chemical energy, lipids act as pigments that capture or respond to sunlight, serve as signals between cells, form waterproof coatings on leaves and skin, and act as vitamins used in many cellular processes. The most prominent function of lipids, however, is their role in cell membranes.

## The Structures of Membrane Lipids

Not all lipids can form membranes. Membrane-forming lipids have a polar, hydrophilic region—in addition to the nonpolar, hydrophobic region found in all lipids.

To better understand this structure, take another look at the phospholipid illustrated in Figure 6.4b. Notice that the molecule has a "head" region containing highly polar covalent bonds as well as a negatively charged phosphate attached to a polar or charged group. The charges and polar bonds in the head region interact with water molecules when a phospholipid is placed in solution. In contrast, the long hydrocarbon tails of a phospholipid are nonpolar and hydrophobic. Water molecules cannot form hydrogen bonds with the hydrocarbon tail, so they do not interact extensively with this part of the molecule.

Compounds that contain both hydrophilic and hydrophobic elements are **amphipathic** (literally, "dual-sympathy"). Phospholipids are amphipathic. As Figure 6.4a shows, cholesterol is also amphipathic. Because it has a hydroxyl functional group attached to its rings, it has both hydrophilic and hydrophobic regions. ✔ If you understand these concepts, you should be able to look back at Figure 6.1b and explain why fatty acids are also amphipathic.

**(a)** A steroid          Schematic          Space-filling

Polar (hydrophilic)

Nonpolar (hydrophobic)

**(b)** A phospholipid

Polar head (hydrophilic)

Polar or charged group

Phosphate

Glycerol

Nonpolar tail (hydrophobic)

Fatty acid   Fatty acid

**FIGURE 6.4 Some Lipids Contain Hydrophilic and Hydrophobic Regions. (a)** All steroids have the distinctive four-ring structure shown in orange. Cholesterol has a polar hydroxyl group and an isoprenoid chain attached to these rings. **(b)** Most phospholipids consist of two fatty acid or isoprenoid chains that are linked to glycerol, which is linked to a phosphate group, which is linked to a small organic molecule that is polar or charged.

✔**QUESTION** If cholesterol and phospholipids were in solution, which part of the molecules would interact with water molecules?

The amphipathic nature of phospholipids is far and away their most important feature biologically. It is responsible for life's defining barrier—the plasma membrane. If the membrane defines life, then amphipathic lipids must have existed when life first originated during chemical evolution. Was that possible?

# Were Lipids Present during Chemical Evolution?

Like amino acids, nucleic acids, and carbohydrates (Chapters 3–5), there is evidence that lipids were present during chemical evolution. Laboratory experiments have shown that simple lipids, such as fatty acids, can be synthesized from $H_2$ and $CO_2$ via reactions with mineral catalysts under conditions thought to be present in prebiotic hydrothermal vent systems (Chapter 2).

It is also possible that lipids literally fell from the sky early in Earth's history. Modern meteorites have been found to contain not only amino acids and carbohydrates but also lipids that exhibit amphipathic qualities. For example, lipids extracted from the meteorite that struck Murchison, Australia, in 1969 spontaneously formed lipid "bubbles" that resembled small cells. Why do amphipathic lipids do this?

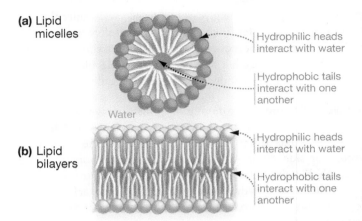

**FIGURE 6.5 Lipids Form Micelles and Bilayers in Solution.** In **(a)** a micelle or **(b)** a lipid bilayer, the hydrophilic heads of lipids face out, toward water; the hydrophobic tails face in, away from water. Lipid bilayers are the foundation of plasma membranes.

## 6.2 Phospholipid Bilayers

Amphipathic lipids do not dissolve when they are placed in water. Their hydrophilic heads interact with water, but their hydrophobic tails do not. Instead of dissolving in water, then, amphipathic lipids assume one of two types of structures: micelles or lipid bilayers.

Micelles (**FIGURE 6.5a**) are tiny droplets created when the hydrophilic heads of a set of lipids face the water and form hydrogen bonds, while the hydrophobic tails interact with each other in the interior, away from the water.

A **lipid bilayer** is created when two sheets of lipid molecules align. As **FIGURE 6.5b** shows, the hydrophilic heads in each layer face the surrounding solution while the hydrophobic tails face one another inside the bilayer. In this way, the hydrophilic heads interact with water while the hydrophobic tails interact with one another.

Micelles tend to form from fatty acids or other simple amphipathic hydrocarbon chains. Bilayers tend to form from phospholipids that contain two hydrocarbon tails. For this reason, bilayers are often called phospholipid bilayers.

It's critical to recognize that micelles and phospholipid bilayers form spontaneously—no input of energy is required. This concept can be difficult to grasp because entropy clearly decreases when these structures form. The key is to recognize that micelles and lipid bilayers are much more stable energetically than are independent phospholipids in solution.

Independent lipids are unstable in water because their hydrophobic tails disrupt hydrogen bonds that could otherwise form between water molecules. As a result, the tails of amphipathic molecules are forced together and participate in hydrophobic interactions (introduced in Chapter 2). This point should also remind you of the aqueous behavior of hydrophobic side chains in proteins and bases in nucleic acids.

## Artificial Membranes as an Experimental System

When phospholipids are added to an aqueous solution and agitated, lipid bilayers spontaneously form small spherical structures. The hydrophilic heads on both sides of the bilayer remain in contact with the aqueous solution—water is present both inside and outside the vesicle. Artificial membrane-bound vesicles like these are called liposomes (**FIGURE 6.6**).

To explore how membranes work, researchers began creating and experimenting with liposomes and planar bilayers—lipid bilayers constructed across a hole in a glass or plastic wall separating two aqueous solutions (**FIGURE 6.7a**). Some of the first questions they posed concerned the permeability of lipid bilayers. The **permeability** of a structure is its tendency to allow a given substance to pass through it.

Using liposomes and planar bilayers, researchers can study what happens when a known ion or molecule is added to one side of a lipid bilayer (**FIGURE 6.7b**). Does the substance cross the

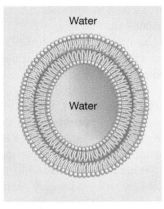

25 nm

**FIGURE 6.6 Liposomes Are Artificial Membrane-Bound Vesicles.** Electron micrograph of liposomes in cross section (left) and a cross-sectional diagram of the lipid bilayer in a liposome (right).

**(a) Planar bilayers:** Artificial membranes

**(b)** Artificial-membrane experiments

How rapidly can different solutes cross the membrane (if at all) when …

**1.** Different types of phospholipids are used to make the membrane?

**2.** Proteins or other molecules are added to the membrane?

**FIGURE 6.7 Use of Planar Bilayers in Experiments. (a)** The construction of a planar bilayer across a hole in a wall separating two water-filled compartments. **(b)** A wide variety of experiments are possible with planar bilayers; a few are suggested here.

membrane and show up on the other side? If so, how rapidly does the movement take place? What happens when a different type of phospholipid is used to make the artificial membrane? Does the membrane's permeability change when proteins or other types of molecules become part of it?

Biologists describe such an experimental system as elegant and powerful because it gives them precise control over which factor changes from one experimental treatment to the next.

Control, in turn, is why experiments are such an effective way to explore scientific questions. Recall that good experimental design allows researchers to alter one factor at a time and determine what effect, if any, each has on the process being studied (Chapter 1).

## Selective Permeability of Lipid Bilayers

When researchers put molecules or ions on one side of a liposome or planar bilayer and measure the rate at which the molecules arrive on the other side, a clear pattern emerges: Lipid bilayers are highly selective.

**Selective permeability** means that some substances cross a membrane more easily than other substances do. Small nonpolar molecules move across bilayers quickly. In contrast, large molecules and charged substances cross the membrane slowly, if at all. This difference in membrane permeability is a critical issue because controlling what passes between the exterior and interior environments is a key characteristic of cells.

According to the data in **FIGURE 6.8**, small nonpolar molecules such as oxygen ($O_2$) move across selectively permeable membranes more than a billion times faster than do chloride ions ($Cl^-$). In essence, ions cannot cross membranes at all—unless they have "help" in the form of membrane proteins introduced later in the chapter. Very small and uncharged molecules such as water ($H_2O$) can cross membranes relatively rapidly, even if they are polar. Small polar molecules such as glycerol have intermediate permeability.

The leading hypothesis to explain this pattern is that charged compounds and large polar molecules are more stable dissolved in water than they are in the nonpolar interior of membranes. ✔ If you understand this hypothesis, you should be able to predict where amino acids and nucleotides would be placed in Figure 6.8 and explain your reasoning.

**FIGURE 6.8 Lipid Bilayers Show Selective Permeability.** Only certain substances cross lipid bilayers readily. Size and polarity or charge affect the rate of diffusion across a membrane.

# How Does Lipid Structure Affect Membrane Permeability?

The amphipathic nature of phospholipids allows them to spontaneously form membranes. But not all phospholipid bilayers are the same. The nature of the hydrocarbon tails, in addition to the presence of cholesterol molecules, profoundly influences how a membrane behaves.

**Bond Saturation and Hydrocarbon Chain Length Affect Membrane Fluidity and Permeability**  The degree of saturation in a phospholipid—along with the length of its hydrocarbon tails—affects key aspects of a lipid's behavior in a membrane.

- When unsaturated hydrocarbon tails are packed into a lipid bilayer, kinks created by double bonds produce spaces among the tails. These spaces reduce the strength of the van der Waals interactions (see Chapter 3) that hold the hydrophobic tails together, weakening the barrier to solutes.

- Packed saturated hydrocarbon tails have fewer spaces and stronger van der Waals interactions. As the length of saturated hydrocarbon tails increases, the forces that hold them together also grow stronger, making the membrane even denser.

These observations have profound impacts on membrane fluidity and permeability—two closely related properties. As **FIGURE 6.9** shows, lipid bilayers are more permeable as well as more fluid when they contain short, kinked, unsaturated hydrocarbon tails. An unsaturated membrane allows more materials to pass because its interior is held together less tightly. Bilayers containing long, straight, saturated hydrocarbon tails are much less permeable and fluid. Experiments on liposomes have shown exactly these patterns.

**Cholesterol Reduces Membrane Permeability**  Cholesterol molecules are present, to varying extents, in the membranes of every cell in your body. What effect does adding cholesterol have on a membrane? Researchers have found that adding cholesterol molecules to liposomes dramatically reduces the permeability of

lipid bilayers. The data behind this conclusion are presented in **FIGURE 6.10**.

To read the graph in the "Results" section of Figure 6.10, put your finger on the *x*-axis at the point marked 20°C, and note that permeability to glycerol is much higher at this temperature in membranes that contain no cholesterol versus 20 percent or 50 percent cholesterol. Using this procedure at other temperature points should convince you that membranes lacking cholesterol are more permeable than the other two membranes at every temperature tested in the experiment.

What explains this result? Because the steroid rings in cholesterol are bulky, adding cholesterol fills gaps that would otherwise be present in the hydrophobic section of the membrane.

## How Does Temperature Affect the Fluidity and Permeability of Membranes?

At about 25°C—or "room temperature"—the phospholipids in a plasma membrane have a consistency resembling olive oil. This fluid physical state allows individual lipid molecules to move laterally within each layer (**FIGURE 6.11**), a little like a person moving about in a dense crowd. By tagging individual phospholipids and following their movement, researchers have clocked average speeds of 2 micrometers (μm)/second at room temperature. At these speeds, a phospholipid could travel the length of a small bacterial cell in a second.

Recall that permeability is closely related to fluidity. As temperature drops, molecules in a bilayer move more slowly. As a result, the hydrophobic tails in the interior of membranes pack together more tightly. At very low temperatures, lipid bilayers even begin to solidify. As the graph in Figure 6.10 indicates, low temperatures can make membranes impervious to molecules that would normally cross them readily. Put your finger on the *x*-axis of that graph, just about the freezing point

![figure 6.9]

**Lipid bilayer with short and unsaturated hydrocarbon tails**

**Higher permeability and fluidity**

**Lipid bilayer with long and saturated hydrocarbon tails**

**Lower permeability and fluidity**

**FIGURE 6.9 Fatty Acid Structure Changes the Permeability of Membranes.** Lipid bilayers consisting of phospholipids containing unsaturated fatty acids should have more gaps and be more permeable than those with saturated fatty acids.

**RESEARCH**

## QUESTION: Does adding cholesterol to a membrane affect its permeability?

**HYPOTHESIS:** Cholesterol reduces permeability because it fills spaces in phospholipid bilayers.

**NULL HYPOTHESIS:** Cholesterol has no effect on permeability.

**EXPERIMENTAL SETUP:**

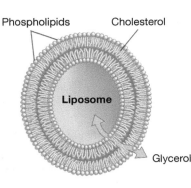

Phospholipids    Cholesterol

**Liposome**

Glycerol

**1. Construct liposomes:** Create with no cholesterol, 20% cholesterol, and 50% cholesterol.

**2. Measure glycerol movement:** Record how quickly glycerol moves across each type of membrane at different temperatures.

**PREDICTION:** Liposomes with higher cholesterol levels will have reduced permeability.

**PREDICTION OF NULL HYPOTHESIS:** All liposomes will have the same permeability.

**RESULTS:**

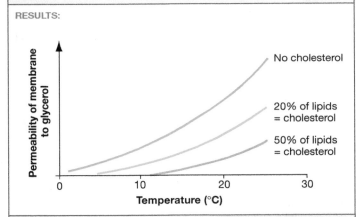

No cholesterol

20% of lipids = cholesterol

50% of lipids = cholesterol

Permeability of membrane to glycerol

Temperature (°C)

**CONCLUSION:** Adding cholesterol to membranes decreases their permeability to glycerol. The permeability of all membranes analyzed in this experiment increases with increasing temperature.

**FIGURE 6.10 The Permeability of a Membrane Depends on Its Composition.**

SOURCE: de Gier, J., et al. (1968). Lipid composition and permeability of liposomes. *Biochimica et Biophysica Acta* 150: 666–675.

✔**QUANTITATIVE** Suppose the investigators had instead created liposomes using phospholipids with fully saturated tails and compared them to two other sets of liposomes where either 20 percent or 50 percent of the phospholipids contained polyunsaturated tails. Label the three lines on the graph above with your prediction for the three different liposomes in this new experiment.

Phospholipids are in constant lateral motion, but rarely flip to the other side of the bilayer

**FIGURE 6.11 Phospholipids Move within Membranes.** Membranes are dynamic—in part because phospholipid molecules randomly move laterally within each layer in the structure.

of water (0°C), and note that even membranes that lack cholesterol are almost completely impermeable to glycerol. Indeed trace any of the three lines in Figure 6.10, and as you move to the right (increasing temperature), you also move up (increasing permeability).

These observations on glycerol and lipid movement demonstrate that membranes are dynamic. Phospholipid molecules whiz around each layer, while water and small nonpolar molecules shoot in and out of the membrane. How quickly molecules move within and across membranes is a function of temperature, the structure of hydrocarbon tails, and the number of cholesterol molecules in the bilayer.

## 6.3 How Molecules Move across Lipid Bilayers: Diffusion and Osmosis

Small uncharged molecules and hydrophobic compounds can cross membranes readily and spontaneously—without an input of energy. The question now is: How is this possible? What process is responsible for movement of molecules across lipid bilayers?

### Diffusion

A thought experiment can help explain how substances can cross membranes spontaneously. Suppose you rack up a set of billiard balls in the middle of a pool table and then begin to vibrate the table.

1. Because of the vibration, the billiard balls will move about randomly. They will also bump into one another.

2. After these collisions, some balls will move outward—away from their original position.

3. As movement and collisions continue, the overall or net movement of balls will be outward. This occurs because the random motion of the balls disrupts their original, nonrandom position. As the balls move at random, they are more likely to move away from one another than to stay together.

4. Eventually, the balls will be distributed randomly across the table. The entropy of the billiard balls has increased. Recall that entropy is a measure of the randomness or disorder in

a system (Chapter 2). The second law of thermodynamics states that in an isolated system, entropy always increases.

This hypothetical example illustrates how vibrating billiard balls move at random. More to the point, it also explains how substances located on one side of a lipid bilayer can move to the other side spontaneously. All dissolved molecules and ions, or **solutes,** have thermal energy and are in constant, random motion. Movement of molecules and ions that results from their kinetic energy is known as **diffusion.**

A difference in solute concentrations creates what is called a **concentration gradient.** Solutes move randomly in all directions, but when a concentration gradient exists, there is a net movement from regions of high concentration to regions of low concentration. Diffusion down a concentration gradient, or away from the higher concentration, is a spontaneous process because it results in an increase in entropy.

Once the molecules or ions are randomly distributed throughout a solution, a chemical equilibrium is established. For example, consider two aqueous solutions separated by a lipid bilayer. **FIGURE 6.12** shows how molecules that can pass through the bilayer diffuse to the other side. At equilibrium, these molecules continue to move back and forth across the membrane, but at equal rates—simply because they are equally likely to move in any direction. This means that there is no longer a net movement of molecules across the membrane. ✔ If you understand diffusion, you should be able to predict how a difference in temperature across a membrane would affect the concentration of a solute at equilibrium.

## Osmosis

What about water? As the data in Figure 6.8 show, water moves across lipid bilayers relatively quickly. The movement of water is a special case of diffusion that is given its own name: **osmosis.** Osmosis occurs only when solutions are separated by a membrane that permits water to cross, but holds back some or all of the solutes—that is, a selectively permeable membrane.

It's important to note that some of the water molecules in a solution are unavailable to diffuse across the membrane. Recall that solutes form ionic or hydrogen bonds with water molecules (Chapter 2). Water molecules that are bound to a solute that can't cross the membrane are themselves prevented from crossing.

Only unbound water molecules are able to diffuse across the membrane during osmosis. When these unbound water molecules move across a membrane, they flow from the solution with the lower solute concentration into the solution with the higher solute concentration.

To drive this point home, let's suppose the concentration of a particular solute is higher on one side of a selectively permeable membrane than it is on the other side (**FIGURE 6.13**, step 1). Further, suppose that this solute cannot diffuse through the membrane to establish equilibrium. What happens? Water will move from the side with a lower concentration of solute to the side with a higher concentration of solute (Figure 6.13, step 2). Osmosis dilutes the higher concentration and equalizes the concentrations

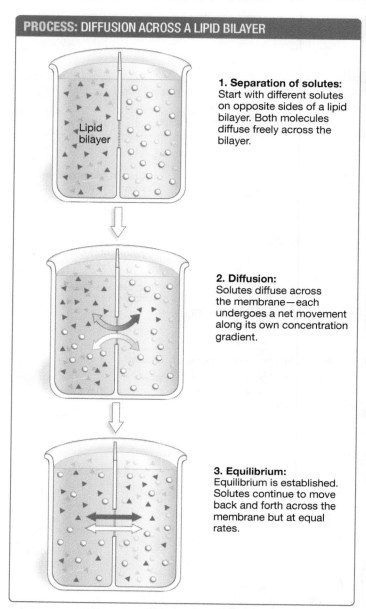

**1. Separation of solutes:** Start with different solutes on opposite sides of a lipid bilayer. Both molecules diffuse freely across the bilayer.

Lipid bilayer

**2. Diffusion:** Solutes diffuse across the membrane—each undergoes a net movement along its own concentration gradient.

**3. Equilibrium:** Equilibrium is established. Solutes continue to move back and forth across the membrane but at equal rates.

**FIGURE 6.12 Diffusion across a Selectively Permeable Membrane Establishes an Equilibrium.**

on both sides. The movement of water is spontaneous. It is driven by the increase in entropy achieved when solute concentrations are equal on both sides of the membrane.

Movement of water by osmosis is important because it can swell or shrink a membrane-bound vesicle. Consider the liposomes illustrated in **FIGURE 6.14**. (Remember that osmosis occurs only when a solute cannot pass through a separating membrane.)

- *Left* If the solution inside the membrane has a lower concentration of solutes than the exterior has, water moves out of the vesicle into the solution outside. The solution inside is said to be **hypotonic** ("lower-tone") relative to the outside of the vesicle. As water leaves, the vesicle shrinks and the membrane shrivels, resulting in lower vesicle firmness.

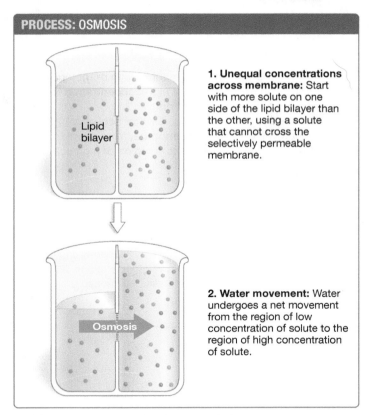

**1. Unequal concentrations across membrane:** Start with more solute on one side of the lipid bilayer than the other, using a solute that cannot cross the selectively permeable membrane.

Lipid bilayer

Osmosis

**2. Water movement:** Water undergoes a net movement from the region of low concentration of solute to the region of high concentration of solute.

**FIGURE 6.13 Osmosis Is the Diffusion of Water.**

✔**QUESTION** Suppose you doubled the number of solute molecules on the left side of the membrane (at the start). At equilibrium, would the water level on the left side be higher or lower than what is shown in the second drawing?

- *Middle* If the solution inside the membrane has a higher concentration of solutes than the exterior has, water moves into the vesicle via osmosis. The inside solution is said to be **hypertonic** ("excess-tone") relative to the outside of the vesicle. The incoming water causes the vesicle to swell and increase in firmness, or even burst.

- *Right* If solute concentrations are equal on both sides of the membrane, the liposome maintains its size. When the inside solution does not affect the membrane's shape, that solution is called **isotonic** ("equal-tone").

Note that the terms hypertonic, hypotonic, and isotonic are relative—they can be used only to express the relationship between a given solution and another solution separated by a membrane. Biologists also commonly use these terms to describe the solution that is exterior to the cells or vesicles.

## Membranes and Chemical Evolution

What do diffusion and osmosis have to do with the first membranes floating in the prebiotic soup? Both processes tend to *reduce* differences in chemical composition between the inside and outside of membrane-bound compartments.

If liposome-like structures first arose in the oceans of early Earth, their interiors probably didn't offer a radically different environment from the surrounding solution. In all likelihood, the primary importance of the first lipid bilayers was simply to provide a container for replicating RNA, the macromolecule most likely to have been the first "living" molecule (see Chapter 4). But ribonucleotide monomers would need to be available for these

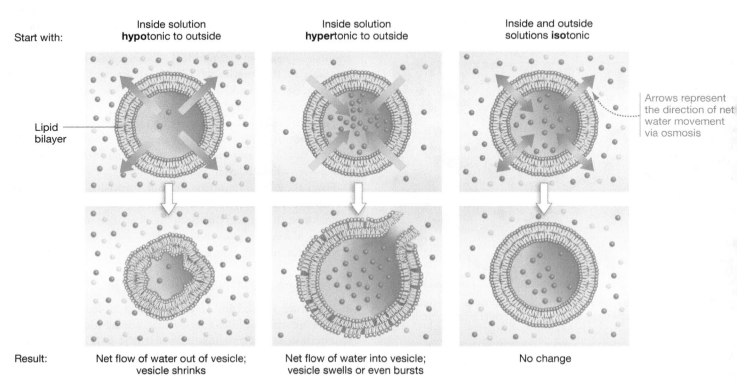

Start with:

Inside solution **hypo**tonic to outside

Inside solution **hyper**tonic to outside

Inside and outside solutions **iso**tonic

Lipid bilayer

Arrows represent the direction of net water movement via osmosis

Result:  Net flow of water out of vesicle; vesicle shrinks

Net flow of water into vesicle; vesicle swells or even bursts

No change

**FIGURE 6.14 Osmosis Can Shrink or Burst Membrane-Bound Vesicles.**

RNAs to replicate. Can negatively charged ribonucleotides get across lipid bilayers and inside lipid-bounded vesicles?

The answer is yes. Jack Szostak and colleagues first set out to study the permeability of membranes consisting of fatty acids and other simple amphipathic lipids thought to be present in the early oceans. Like phospholipids, fatty acids will spontaneously assemble into lipid bilayers and water-filled vesicles. Their experiments showed that ions, and even ribonucleotides, can diffuse across the fatty acid vesicle membranes—meaning that monomers could have been available for RNA synthesis.

Lending support to this hypothesis, the same minerals found to catalyze the polymerization of RNA from activated nucleotides (see Chapter 4) will also promote the formation of fatty acid vesicles—and in the process, often incorporate themselves and RNA inside. Simple vesicle-like structures that harbor nucleic acids are referred to as **protocells** (**FIGURE 6.15**). Most origin-of-life researchers view protocells as possible intermediates in the evolution of the cell.

Laboratory simulations also showed that free lipids and micelles can become incorporated into fatty acid bilayers, causing protocells to grow. Shearing forces, as from bubbling, shaking, or wave action, cause protocells to divide. Based on these observations, it is reasonable to hypothesize that once replicating RNAs became surrounded by a lipid bilayer, this simple lifeform and its descendants would occupy cell-like structures that grew and divided.

Now let's investigate the next great innovation in the evolution of the cell: the ability to create and maintain a specialized internal environment that is conducive to life. What is necessary to construct an effective plasma membrane—one that imports ions and molecules needed for life while excluding ions and molecules that might damage it?

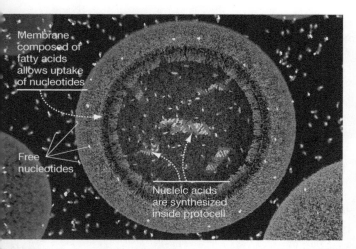

Membrane composed of fatty acids allows uptake of nucleotides

Free nucleotides

Nucleic acids are synthesized inside protocell

**FIGURE 6.15 Protocells May Have Possessed Simple, Permeable Membranes.** This image shows a computer model of a protocell. Like this model, the membranes of early cells may have been built of fatty acids. Passive transport of nucleotides across these membranes, as well as replication of nucleic acids inside, has been observed in the laboratory.

## 6.4 Membrane Proteins

What sort of molecule could become incorporated into a lipid bilayer and affect the bilayer's permeability? The title of this section gives the answer away. Proteins that are amphipathic can be inserted into lipid bilayers.

Proteins can be amphipathic because their monomers, amino acids, have side chains that range from highly nonpolar to highly polar or charged (see Figure 3.2). It's conceivable, then, that a protein could have a series of nonpolar amino acid residues in the middle of its primary structure flanked by polar or charged amino acid residues (**FIGURE 6.16a**). The nonpolar residues would be stable in the interior of a lipid bilayer, while the polar or charged residues would be stable alongside the polar lipid heads and surrounding water (**FIGURE 6.16b**).

Further, because the secondary and tertiary structures of proteins are almost limitless in their variety, it is possible for proteins to form openings and thus function as some sort of channel or pore across a lipid bilayer.

From these considerations, it's not surprising that when researchers began analyzing the chemical composition of plasma membranes, they found that proteins were often just as common, in terms of mass, as phospholipids. How were these two types of molecules arranged?

### Development of the Fluid-Mosaic Model

In 1935 Hugh Davson and James Danielli proposed that cell membranes were structured like a sandwich in which hydrophilic proteins coat both sides of a pure lipid bilayer (**FIGURE 6.17a**). Early electron micrographs of plasma membranes seemed to be consistent with the sandwich model, and for decades it was widely accepted.

**(a)** Proteins can be amphipathic.

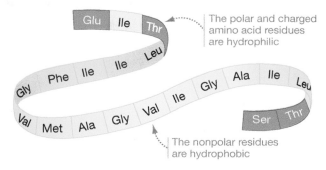

The polar and charged amino acid residues are hydrophilic

The nonpolar residues are hydrophobic

**(b)** Amphipathic proteins can integrate into lipid bilayers.

Outside cell

Inside cell

**FIGURE 6.16 Amphipathic Proteins Are Anchored in Lipid Bilayers.**

**(a)** Sandwich model

Cell exterior

Membrane proteins on cell exterior

Phospholipid bilayer

Membrane proteins on cell interior

Cell interior

**(b)** Fluid-mosaic model

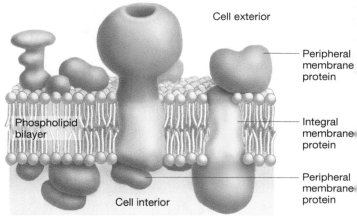

Cell exterior

Peripheral membrane protein

Phospholipid bilayer

Integral membrane protein

Peripheral membrane protein

Cell interior

**FIGURE 6.17 Past and Current Models of Membrane Structure Differ in Where Membrane Proteins Reside. (a)** The protein-lipid-lipid-protein sandwich model was the first hypothesis for the arrangement of lipids and proteins in cell membranes. **(b)** The fluid-mosaic model was a radical departure from the sandwich hypothesis.

The realization that membrane proteins could be amphipathic, however, led S. Jon Singer and Garth Nicolson to suggest an alternative hypothesis. In 1972, they proposed that at least some proteins span the membrane instead of being found only outside the lipid bilayer. Their hypothesis was called the **fluid-mosaic model** (**FIGURE 6.17b**). Singer and Nicolson suggested that membranes are a mosaic of phospholipids and different types of proteins. The overall structure was proposed to be dynamic and fluid.

The controversy over the nature of the cell membrane was resolved in the early 1970s with the development of an innovative technique for visualizing the surface of plasma membranes. The method is called freeze-fracture electron microscopy because the steps involve freezing and fracturing the membrane before examining it with a **scanning electron microscope (SEM),** which produces images of an object's surface (see **BioSkills 11** in Appendix B).

As **FIGURE 6.18** (see page 96) shows, the freeze-fracture technique allows researchers to split cell membranes and view the middle of the structure. The scanning electron micrographs that result show pits and mounds studding the inner surfaces of the lipid bilayer. Researchers interpreted these structures as the locations of membrane proteins. As step 4 in the figure shows, the mounds represent proteins that remained attached to one side of the split lipid bilayer and the pits are the holes they left behind.

These observations conflicted with the sandwich model but were consistent with the fluid-mosaic model. Based on these and subsequent observations, the fluid-mosaic model is now widely accepted.

Notice in Figure 6.17b that some proteins span the membrane and have segments facing both the interior and the exterior surfaces. Proteins like these are called **integral membrane proteins,** or **transmembrane proteins.** Proteins that bind to the membrane without passing through it are called **peripheral membrane proteins.**

Certain peripheral proteins are found only on the interior surface of a cellular membrane, while others are found only on the exterior surface. As a result, the interior and exterior surfaces of the plasma membrane are distinct—the peripheral proteins and the ends of transmembrane proteins differ. Peripheral membrane proteins are often attached to transmembrane proteins.

How do these proteins affect the permeability of membranes? The answer to this question starts with an investigation of the structure of proteins involved in the transport of molecules and ions across the plasma membrane.

1. **Fracture cell:** Strike frozen cell with a knife. Fracture splits the lipid bilayer.

2. **Separate the parts** and prepare for scanning electron microscopy.

3. **Microscopy:** Observe pits and mounds in the membrane interior.

4. **Interpretation:** Image supports fluid-mosaic model of membrane structure.

**FIGURE 6.18 Freeze-Fracture Preparations Allow Biologists to View Membrane Proteins.**

✔**QUESTION** What would be an appropriate control to show that the pits and mounds were not simply irregularities in the lipid bilayer caused by the freeze-fracture process?

## Systems for Studying Membrane Proteins

The discovery of transmembrane proteins was consistent with the hypothesis that proteins affect membrane permeability. To test this hypothesis, researchers needed some way to isolate and purify membrane proteins.

**FIGURE 6.19** outlines one method that researchers developed to separate proteins from membranes. The key to the technique is the use of detergents. A **detergent** is a small amphipathic molecule. When detergents are added to the solution surrounding a lipid bilayer, the hydrophobic tails of the detergent molecule interact with the hydrophobic tails of the lipids and with the

1. **Addition of detergents:** Detergents are small, amphipathic molecules that tend to form micelles in water.

2. **Binding by detergents:** Detergents break up plasma membranes; they coat hydrophobic portions of membrane proteins and phospholipids.

3. **Isolation of proteins:** Treating a plasma membrane with a detergent is an effective way to isolate membrane proteins so they can be purified and studied in detail.

**FIGURE 6.19 Detergents Can Be Used to Isolate Proteins from Membranes.**

hydrophobic portions of transmembrane proteins. These interactions displace the membrane phospholipids and end up forming water-soluble detergent–protein complexes that can be isolated.

Since intensive experimentation on membrane proteins began, researchers have identified three broad classes of proteins that affect membrane permeability: channels, carriers, and pumps. Let's consider each class in turn.

## Facilitated Diffusion via Channel Proteins

As the data in Figure 6.8 show, ions almost never cross pure phospholipid bilayers on their own. But in cells, ions routinely cross membranes through specialized membrane proteins called **ion channels.**

Ion channels form pores, or openings, in a membrane. Ions move through these pores in a predictable direction: from regions of high concentration to regions of low concentration and from areas of like charge to areas of unlike charge.

In **FIGURE 6.20**, for example, a large concentration gradient favors the movement of sodium ions from the outside of a membrane to the inside. But in addition, the inside of this cell has a net negative charge while the outside has a net positive charge. As a result, the combination of these two factors influences the final concentration of sodium ions inside the cell once equilibrium has been established.

**FIGURE 6.20 An Electrochemical Gradient Is a Combined Concentration and Electrical Gradient.** Electrochemical gradients are established when ions build up on one side of a membrane.

Ions move in response to a combined concentration and electrical gradient, or what biologists call an **electrochemical gradient.** ✔ If you understand this concept, you should be able to add an arrow to Figure 6.20 indicating the electrochemical gradient for chloride ions.

### Is an Ion Channel Involved in Cystic Fibrosis?

To understand the types of experiments that biologists do to confirm that a membrane protein is an ion channel, consider work on the cause of cystic fibrosis.

Cystic fibrosis (CF) is the most common genetic disease in humans of Northern European descent. It affects cells that produce mucus, sweat, and digestive juices. Normally these secretions are thin and slippery and act as lubricants. In individuals with CF, however, the secretions become abnormally concentrated and sticky and clog passageways in organs like the lungs.

Experiments published in 1983 suggested that cystic fibrosis is caused by defects in a membrane protein that allow chloride ions ($Cl^-$) to move across plasma membranes. It was proposed that reduced chloride ion transport would account for the thick mucus.

How is the transport of chloride ions involved in mucus consistency? Water movement across cell membranes is largely determined by the presence of extracellular ions like chloride. If a defective channel prevents chloride ions from leaving cells, water isn't pulled from cells by osmosis to maintain the proper mucus consistency. In effect, the disease results from the mismanagement of osmosis.

Using molecular techniques introduced in Unit 3 (see Chapter 20), biologists were able to (1) find the gene that is defective in people suffering from CF and (2) use the gene to produce copies of the normal protein, which was called CFTR (short for cystic fibrosis transmembrane conductance regulator).

Is CFTR a chloride channel? To answer this question, researchers inserted purified CFTR into planar bilayers and

**RESEARCH**

**QUESTION: Is CFTR a chloride channel?**

**HYPOTHESIS:** CFTR increases the flow of chloride ions across a membrane.

**NULL HYPOTHESIS:** CFTR has no effect on membrane permeability.

**EXPERIMENTAL SETUP:**

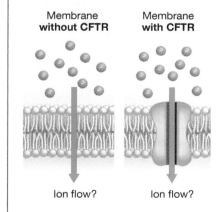

1. **Create planar bilayers** with and without CFTR.

2. **Add chloride ions** to one side of the planar bilayer to create an electrochemical gradient.

3. **Record electrical currents** to measure ion flow across the planar bilayers.

**PREDICTION:** Ion flow will be higher in membrane with CFTR.

**PREDICTION OF NULL HYPOTHESIS:** Ion flow will be the same in both membranes.

**RESULTS:**

**CONCLUSION:** CFTR facilitates diffusion of chloride ions along an electrochemical gradient. CFTR is a chloride channel.

**FIGURE 6.21 Electric Current Measurements Indicate that Chloride Flows through CFTR.**

SOURCE: Bear, C. A., et al. (1992). Purification and functional reconstitution of the cystic fibrosis transmembrane conductance regulator (CFTR). *Cell* 68: 809–818.

✔ **QUESTION** The researchers repeated the "with CFTR" treatment 45 times, but recorded a current in only 35 of the replicates. Does this observation negate the conclusion? Explain why or why not.

measured the flow of electric current across the membrane. Because ions carry a charge, ion movement across a membrane produces an electric current.

The graphs in **FIGURE 6.21**, which plot the amount of current flowing across the membrane over time, show the results from this experiment. Notice that when CFTR was absent, no electric current passed through the membrane. But when CFTR was

Key residues allow water to pass but block ions and larger molecules

Outside cell

H₂O

Inside cell

**FIGURE 6.22 Membrane Channels Are Highly Selective.** A cutaway view looking at the inside of a membrane channel, aquaporin. The key residues identified in the space-filling model selectively filter ions and other small molecules, allowing only water (red and white structures) to pass through.

inserted into the membrane, current began to flow. This was strong evidence that CFTR was indeed a chloride ion channel.

**Protein Structure Determines Channel Selectivity** Subsequent research has shown that cells have many different types of pore-like **channel proteins** in their membranes, including ion channels like CFTR. Channel proteins are selective. Each channel protein has a structure that permits only a particular type of ion or small molecule to pass through it.

For example, Peter Agre and co-workers discovered channels called **aquaporins** ("water-pores") that allow water to cross the plasma membrane over 10 times faster than it does in the absence of aquaporins. Aquaporins admit water but not other small molecules or ions.

**FIGURE 6.22** shows a cutaway view from the side of an aquaporin, indicating how it fits in a plasma membrane. Like other channels that have been studied in detail, aquaporins have a pore that is lined with polar functional groups—in this case, carbonyl groups that interact with water. A channel's pore is hydrophilic relative to the hydrophobic residues facing the phospholipid tails of the membrane.

But how can aquaporin be selective for water and not other polar molecules? The answer was found when researchers examined its structure. Key side chains in the interior of the pore function as a molecular filter. The distance between these groups across the channel allows only those substances capable of interacting with all of them to pass through to the other side.

**Movement Through Many Membrane Channels Is Regulated** Recent research has shown that many aquaporins and ion channels are **gated channels**—meaning that they open or close in response to a signal, such as the binding of a particular molecule or a change in the electrical voltage across the membrane.

As an example of how voltage-gated channels work, **FIGURE 6.23** shows a potassium channel in closed and open configurations. The electrical charge on the membrane is normally negative on the inside relative to the outside, which causes the channel to adopt a closed shape that prevents potassium ions from passing through. When this charge asymmetry is reversed, the shape changes in a way that opens the channel and allows potassium ions to cross. The key point here is that in almost all cases, the flow of ions and small molecules through membrane channels is carefully controlled.

In all cases, however, the movement of substances through channels is passive—meaning it does not require an input of energy. **Passive transport** is powered by diffusion along an electrochemical gradient. Channel proteins simply enable ions or polar molecules to move across lipid bilayers efficiently, in response to

When the inside of the membrane is negatively charged relative to the outside, channel is closed

Outside cell

+ + + +      + + + +

Inside cell

**Closed**

Gate blocks ions from entering channel

If membrane charge asymmetry is reversed, channel opens

Filter allows only K+ ions to pass

– – – –      – – – –

+ + + + +      + + + + +

**Open**

**FIGURE 6.23 Some Membrane Channels Are Highly Regulated.** A model of a voltage-gated K⁺ channel in the closed and open configurations. The channel filter displaces water molecules that normally surround the K⁺ ions in an aqueous solution.

an existing gradient. They are responsible for **facilitated diffusion:** the passive transport of substances that otherwise would not cross a membrane readily.

## Facilitated Diffusion via Carrier Proteins

Facilitated diffusion can also occur through **carrier proteins**—specialized membrane proteins that change shape during the transport process. Perhaps the best-studied carrier protein is one that is involved in transporting glucose into cells.

### The Search for a Glucose Carrier

Next to ribose, the six-carbon sugar glucose is the most prevalent sugar found in organisms. Virtually all cells alive today use glucose as a building block for important macromolecules and as a source of stored chemical energy (Chapter 5). But as Figure 6.8 shows, lipid bilayers are only moderately permeable to glucose. It is reasonable to expect, then, that plasma membranes have some mechanism for increasing their permeability to this sugar.

This prediction was supported in experiments on pure preparations of plasma membranes from human red blood cells. These plasma membranes turned out to be much more permeable to glucose than are pure lipid bilayers. Why?

After isolating and analyzing many proteins from red blood cell membranes, researchers found one protein that specifically increases membrane permeability to glucose. When they added this purified protein to liposomes, the artificial membrane transported glucose at the same rate as a membrane from a living cell. This experiment convinced biologists that the membrane protein—now called GLUT-1 (short for glucose transporter 1)—was indeed responsible for transporting glucose across plasma membranes.

### How Does GLUT-1 Work?

Recall that proteins frequently change shape when they bind to other molecules and that such conformational changes are often a critical step in their function (Chapter 3).

**FIGURE 6.24** illustrates the current hypothesis for how GLUT-1 works to facilitate the movement of glucose. The idea is that when glucose binds to GLUT-1, it changes the shape of the protein in a way that moves the sugar through the hydrophobic region of the membrane and releases it on the other side.

What powers the movement of molecules through carriers? The answer is diffusion. GLUT-1 facilitates diffusion by allowing glucose to enter the carrier from either side of the membrane. Glucose will pass through the carrier in the direction dictated by its concentration gradient. A large variety of molecules move across plasma membranes via specific carrier proteins.

## Pumps Perform Active Transport

Diffusion—whether it is facilitated by proteins or not—is a passive process that will move substances in either direction across a membrane to make the cell interior and exterior more similar. But it is also possible for cells to move molecules or ions in a directed manner, often *against* their electrochemical gradient. Accomplishing this task requires an input of energy, because the cell must counteract the decrease in entropy that occurs when molecules or ions are concentrated. It makes sense, then, that transport against an electrochemical gradient is called **active transport.**

In cells, ATP (adenosine triphosphate) often provides the energy for active transport by transferring a phosphate group ($HPO_4^{2-}$) to an active transport protein called a **pump.** Recall that ATP contains three phosphate groups (Chapter 4), and that phosphate groups carry two negative charges (Chapter 2). When a phosphate group leaves ATP and binds to a pump, its negative charges interact with charged amino acid residues in the protein. As a result, the protein's potential energy increases and its shape changes.

### The Sodium–Potassium Pump

A classic example of how structural change leads to active transport is provided in the **sodium–potassium pump,** or more formally, $Na^+/K^+$-ATPase. The $Na^+/K^+$ part of the name refers to the ions that are transported, ATP indicates that adenosine triphosphate is used, and *–ase* identifies the molecule as an enzyme.

**PROCESS: A HYPOTHESIS FOR HOW GLUT-1 FACILITATES GLUCOSE DIFFUSION**

Outside cell

Glucose

GLUT-1

Inside cell

**1. Unbound protein:** GLUT-1 is a transmembrane transport protein, shown with its binding site facing outside the cell.

**2. Glucose binding:** Glucose binds to GLUT-1 from outside the cell.

**3. Conformational change:** Glucose binding causes a conformational change, transporting glucose to the interior.

**4. Release:** Glucose moves inside the cell. Steps may repeat or reverse, depending on the concentration gradient.

**FIGURE 6.24 Carrier Proteins Undergo Structural Changes to Move Substances.** This model suggests that GLUT-1 binds a glucose molecule, undergoes a conformational change, and releases glucose on the other side of the membrane.

**1. Unbound protein:** Three binding sites within the protein have a high affinity for sodium ions.

**2. Sodium binding:** Three sodium ions from the inside of the cell bind to these sites.

**3. Shape change:** A phosphate group from ATP binds to the protein. In response, the protein changes shape.

**4. Release:** The sodium ions leave the protein and move to the exterior of the cell.

**FIGURE 6.25 The Sodium–Potassium Pump Depends on an Input of Chemical Energy Stored in ATP.**

As shown in **FIGURE 6.25**, sodium and potassium ions move in a multistep process:

**Step 1** When Na⁺/K⁺-ATPase is in the conformation shown here, binding sites with a high affinity for sodium ions are available.

**Step 2** Three sodium ions from the inside of the cell bind to these sites and activate the ATPase activity in the pump.

**Step 3** A phosphate group from ATP is transferred to the pump. When the phosphate group attaches, the pump changes its shape in a way that opens the ion-binding pocket to the external environment and reduces its affinity for sodium ions.

**Step 4** The sodium ions leave the protein and move to the exterior of the cell.

**Step 5** In this conformation, the pump has binding sites with a high affinity for potassium ions facing the external environment.

**Step 6** Two potassium ions from outside the cell bind to the pump.

**Step 7** When the potassium is bound, the phosphate group is cleaved from the protein and its structure changes in response—back to the original shape with the ion-binding pocket facing the interior of the cell.

**Step 8** In this conformation, the pump has low affinity for potassium ions. The potassium ions leave the protein and move to the interior of the cell. The cycle then repeats.

Other types of pumps move protons (H⁺), calcium ions (Ca²⁺), or other ions or molecules across membranes in a directed manner, regardless of the gradients. As a result, cells can import and concentrate valuable nutrients and ions inside the cell despite their relatively low external concentration. They can also expel molecules or ions, even when a concentration gradient favors diffusion of these substances into the cell.

**Secondary Active Transport** Approximately 30 percent of all the ATP generated in your body is used to drive the Na⁺/K⁺-ATPase cycle. Each cycle exports three Na⁺ ions for every two K⁺ ions it

imports. In this way, the sodium–potassium pump converts energy from ATP to an electrochemical gradient across the membrane. The outside of the membrane becomes positively charged relative to the inside. This gradient favors a flow of anions out of the cell and a flow of cations into the cell.

The electrochemical gradients established by the Na⁺/K⁺-ATPase represent a form of stored energy, much like the electrical energy stored in a battery. How do cells use this energy?

Gradients are crucial to the function of the cell, in part because they make it possible for cells to engage in **secondary active transport**—also known as cotransport. When cotransport occurs, a gradient set up by a pump provides the energy required to power the movement of a different molecule against its particular gradient.

Recall that GLUT-1 facilitates the movement of glucose into or out of cells in the direction of its gradient. Can glucose be moved against its gradient? The answer is yes—a cotransport protein in your gut cells uses the Na⁺ gradient created by Na⁺/K⁺-ATPases to import glucose against its chemical gradient. When Na⁺ ions bind to this cotransporter, its shape changes in a way that allows glucose to bind. Once glucose binds, another shape transports both the sodium and glucose to the inside of the cell. After dropping off sodium and glucose, the protein's original shape returns to repeat the cycle.

In this way, glucose present in the food you are digesting is actively transported into your body. The glucose molecules eventually diffuse into your bloodstream and are transported to your brain, where they provide the chemical energy you need to stay awake and learn some biology. (You will learn more about secondary active transport in Units 7 and 8.)

## Plasma Membranes and the Intracellular Environment

Taken together, the selective permeability of the lipid bilayer and the specificity of the proteins involved in passive transport and

**5. Unbound protein:** In this conformation, the protein has binding sites with a high affinity for potassium ions.

**6. Potassium binding:** Two potassium ions bind to the pump.

**7. Shape change:** The phosphate group is cleaved from the protein, allowing the pump to return to its original shape.

**8. Release:** The potassium ions leave the protein and diffuse to the interior of the cell. *These 8 steps repeat.*

active transport enable cells to create an internal environment that is much different from the external one (**FIGURE 6.26**).

With the evolution of membrane proteins, the early cells acquired the ability to create an internal environment that was conducive to life—one that contained the substances required for manufacturing ATP and copying ribozymes. Cells with particularly efficient and selective membrane proteins would be favored by natural selection and would come to dominate the population. Cellular life had begun.

Some 3.5 billion years later, cells continue to evolve. What do today's cells look like, and how do they produce and store the chemical energy that makes life possible? Answering these and related questions is the focus of the following unit.

## check your understanding

**C Y U**

### If you understand that . . .
- Membrane proteins allow substances that ordinarily do not readily cross lipid bilayers to enter or exit cells.
- Substances may move across a membrane along an electrochemical gradient, via facilitated diffusion through channel or carrier proteins. Or, they may move against a gradient in response to work done by pumps.

✔ **You should be able to . . .**
Explain what is passive about passive transport, active about active transport, and "co" about cotransport.

*Answers are available in Appendix A.*

**Diffusion**

**Facilitated diffusion**

**Active transport**

Outside cell

Inside cell

| **Description:** | Passive movement of small, uncharged molecules along an electrochemical gradient, through a membrane | Passive movement of ... | Active movement of ... |
|---|---|---|---|
| **Protein(s) involved:** | None | | |

**FIGURE 6.26 Summary of the Passive and Active Mechanisms of Membrane Transport.**

✔ **EXERCISE** Complete the chart.

## If you understand . . .

### 6.1 Lipid Structure and Function

- Lipids are largely hydrophobic compounds due to their high number of nonpolar C—H bonds.

- The three main types of lipids found in cells are fats, steroids, and phospholipids. These molecules vary considerably in structure and function.

- In hydrocarbon chains, the length and degree of saturation have a profound effect on their physical properties.

- Amphipathic lipids possess a distinct hydrophilic region containing polar or charged groups. Phospholipids have a polar head and a nonpolar tail. The nonpolar tail usually consists of fatty acids or isoprenoids.

✔ You should be able to explain how adding hydrogen ($H_2$) to vegetable oil, a process called hydrogenation, results in a butter-like solid called margarine.

### 6.2 Phospholipid Bilayers

- In solution, phospholipids spontaneously assemble into bilayers that can serve as a physical barrier between an internal and external environment.

- Small nonpolar molecules tend to move across lipid bilayers readily; ions cross rarely, if at all.

- The permeability and fluidity of lipid bilayers depend on temperature, on the concentration of steroids, and on the chemical structure of the lipids present, such as the saturation status and length of the hydrocarbon chains. Phospholipids with longer or saturated tails form a dense and highly hydrophobic interior that lowers bilayer permeability, relative to phospholipids containing shorter or unsaturated tails.

✔ You should be able to explain how the structure of a phospholipid bilayer that is highly permeable and fluid differs from one that is highly impermeable and lacking in fluidity.

### 6.3 How Molecules Move across Lipid Bilayers: Diffusion and Osmosis

- Diffusion is the random movement of ions or molecules owing to their kinetic energy.

- Diffusion can result in the net directional movement of solutes across a membrane, if the membrane separates solutions that differ in concentration, charge, or temperature. This is a spontaneous process driven by an increase in entropy.

- The diffusion of water across a membrane in response to a concentration gradient is called osmosis.

✔ You should be able to imagine a beaker with solutions separated by a planar membrane and then predict what will happen after addition of a solute to one side if the solute (1) crosses the membrane readily or (2) is incapable of crossing the membrane.

### 6.4 Membrane Proteins

- The permeability of lipid bilayers can be altered significantly by membrane proteins.

- Channel proteins provide pores in the membrane and facilitate the diffusion of specific solutes into and out of the cell.

- Carriers undergo conformational changes that facilitate the diffusion of specific molecules into and out of the cell.

- Pumps use energy to actively move ions or molecules in a single direction, often against the electrical or chemical gradient.

- In combination, the selective permeability of phospholipid bilayers and the specificity of transport proteins make it possible to create an environment inside a cell that is radically different from the exterior.

✔ You should be able to draw and label the membrane of a cell that is placed in a solution containing calcium ions and lactose and show the activity of the following membrane proteins: (1) an $H^+$ pump that exports protons; (2) a calcium channel; and (3) a lactose carrier. Your drawing should include arrows and labels indicating the direction of solute movement and the direction of the appropriate electrochemical gradients.

### MB MasteringBiology

1. **MasteringBiology Assignments**

   **Tutorials and Activities** Active Transport; Diffusion, Diffusion and Osmosis; Facilitated Diffusion Lipids; Membrane Structure; Membrane Transport: Diffusion and Passive Transport; Membrane Transport: The Sodium–Potassium Pump; Membrane Transport Proteins; Osmosis; Membrane Transport: Cotransport; Osmosis and Water Balance in Cells; Selective Permeability of Membranes

   **Questions** Reading Quizzes, Blue-Thread Questions, Test Bank

2. **eText** Read your book online, search, take notes, highlight text, and more.

3. **The Study Area** Practice Test, Cumulative Test, BioFlix® 3-D Animations, Videos, Activities, Audio Glossary, Word Study Tools, Art

## You should be able to . . .

1. How is the structure of saturated fats different from that of unsaturated fats?
   a. All of the carbons in the hydrocarbon tails of saturated fats are bonded to one another with double bonds.
   b. Saturated fats have three hydrocarbon tails bonded to the glycerol molecule instead of just two.
   c. The hydrocarbon tails in a saturated fat have the maximum number of hydrogens possible.
   d. Saturated fats have no oxygens present.

2. What distinguishes amphipathic lipids from other lipids?
   a. Amphipathic lipids have polar and nonpolar regions.
   b. Amphipathic lipids have saturated and unsaturated regions.
   c. Amphipathic lipids are steroids.
   d. Amphipathic lipids dissolve in water.

3. If a solution surrounding a cell is hypertonic relative to the inside of the cell, how will water move?
   a. It will move into the cell via osmosis.
   b. It will move out of the cell via osmosis.
   c. It will not move, because equilibrium exists.
   d. It will evaporate from the cell surface more rapidly.

4. When does a concentration gradient exist?
   a. when membranes rupture
   b. when solute concentrations are high
   c. when solute concentrations are low
   d. when solute concentrations differ on the two sides of a membrane

5. What two conditions must be present for the effects of osmosis to occur?

6. In terms of structure, how do channel proteins differ from carrier proteins?

7. If a cell were placed in a solution with a high potassium concentration and no sodium, what would happen to the sodium–potassium pump's activity?
   a. It would stop moving ions across the membrane.
   b. It would continue using ATP to pump sodium out of the cell and potassium into the cell.
   c. It would move sodium and potassium ions across the membrane, but no ATP would be used.
   d. It would reverse the direction of sodium and potassium ions to move them against their gradients.

8. Cooking oil lipids consist of long, unsaturated hydrocarbon chains. Would you expect these molecules to form membranes spontaneously? Why or why not? Describe, on a molecular level, how you would expect these lipids to interact with water.

9. Explain why phospholipids form a bilayer in solution, and why the process is spontaneous.

10. Ethanol ($C_2H_5OH$) is the active ingredient in alcoholic beverages. Would you predict that this molecule crosses lipid bilayers quickly, slowly, or not at all? Explain your reasoning.

11. Integral membrane proteins are anchored in lipid bilayers. Of the following four groups of amino acids—nonpolar, polar, charged/acidic, charged/basic (see Figure 3.2)—which would likely be found in the portion that crosses the lipid bilayer? Explain your reasoning.

12. Examine the experimental chamber in Figure 6.7a. If the lipid bilayer were to contain the CFTR molecule, what would pass through the membrane if you added a 1-molar solution of sodium chloride on the left side and a 1-molar solution of potassium ions on the right? Assume that there is an equal amount of water on each side at the start of the experiment.

13. In an experiment, you create two groups of liposomes—one made from red blood cell membranes and the other from frog egg cell membranes. When placed in water, those made with red blood cell membranes burst more rapidly than those made from frog membranes. What is the best explanation for these results?
    a. The red blood cell liposomes are more hypertonic relative to water than the frog egg liposomes.
    b. The red blood cell liposomes are more hypotonic relative to water than the frog egg liposomes.
    c. The red blood cell liposomes contain aquaporins, which are not abundant in the frog egg liposomes.
    d. The frog egg liposomes contain ion channels, which are not present in the red blood cell liposomes.

14. When phospholipids are arranged in a bilayer, it is theoretically possible for individual molecules in the bilayer to flip-flop. That is, a phospholipid could turn 180° and become part of the membrane's other surface. From what you know about the behavior of polar heads and nonpolar tails, predict whether flip-flops are frequent or rare. Then design an experiment, using a planar bilayer with one side made up of phospholipids that contain a dye molecule on their hydrophilic head, to test your prediction.

15. Unicellular organisms live in a wide range of habitats, from the hot springs in Yellowstone National Park to the freezing temperatures of the Antarctic. Make a prediction about the saturation status of membrane phospholipids in organisms that live in extremely cold environments versus those that live in extremely hot environments. Explain your reasoning.

16. When biomedical researchers design drugs, they sometimes add methyl ($CH_3$) groups or charged groups to the molecules. If these groups are not directly involved in the activity of the drug, predict the purpose of these modifications and explain why these strategies are necessary.

**BIG PICTURE**

The first spark of life ignited when simple chemical reactions began to convert small molecules into larger, more complex molecules with novel 3-D structures and activities. According to the theory of chemical evolution, these reactions eventually led to the formation of the four types of macromolecules characteristic of life—proteins, nucleic acids, carbohydrates, and lipids.

As you look through this concept map, consider how the functions of the four types of macromolecules are determined by their structures, and how these structures stem from the chemical properties of the atoms and bonds used to build them.

Note that each box in the concept map indicates the chapters and sections where you can go for review. Also, be sure to do the blue exercises in the Check Your Understanding box below.

is based on the reactivity of

**Atoms**
- Carbon (C)
- Hydrogen (H) } 96% of atoms in living matter
- Oxygen (O)
- Nitrogen (N)
- Phosphorus (P)
- Sulfur (S)
- Others

2.1, 2.4

differ in

**Electronegativity**

$O > N > C \cong H$

**Number of unpaired electrons:**
- Hydrogen: 1
- Oxygen: 2
- Nitrogen: 3
- Carbon: 4

2.1

combine to form

**Molecules** 2.1

notably

have specific

**3-D structure**
- (may possess primary, secondary, tertiary, quaternary structure)

2.1, 3.1–3, 4.1–3, 5.1–2, 6.1

determines function

determine type and number of

depends on

influence

**Polarity** 2.1

**Chemical bonds**
- Nonpolar covalent bonds
- Polar covalent bonds
- Ionic bonds
- Hydrogen bonds

$\delta^-$ $\delta^+$

2.1

including

affects

**Molecular function**
2.2, 3.1, 4.1, 5.1

formed and broken in

**Chemical reactions** 2.3

## check your understanding

**If you understand the big picture . . .**

✔ You should be able to . . .

1. Explain how the relative electronegativities of atoms affect the bonding within and among water molecules.

2. Describe the attributes of RNA that make it a candidate for the origin of life. Why isn't DNA considered a candidate?

3. Circle the atoms in amino acids and nucleotides that engage in creating bonds with other monomers.

4. Draw a protein in the lipid bilayer. What role might it play?

*Answers are available in Appendix A.*

as demonstrated by

**WATER**

is essential for life due to its

**Basic**

14

$H_2O$  7

**pH** 2.2

has neutral

0

**Acidic**

- Efficiency as a solvent
- Cohesion, adhesion and surface tension properties
- Higher density as a liquid than as a solid
- High capacity for energy absorption

2.2

## Biological macromolecules

**PROTEINS** — Ch 3

function in
- Catalysis of chemical reactions (enzymes)
- Defense
- Movement
- Signaling
- Structural support
- Transport

3.4

and are polymers of

**Amino acids**

3.1

linked by

**Peptide bonds** 3.1

**NUCLEIC ACIDS** — Ch 4

function in

**DNA**
- Long-term information storage

**RNA**
- Short-term information storage and transfer
- Catalysis of chemical reactions (ribozymes)

4.2, 4.3

and are polymers of

**Nucleotides**

4.1

linked by

**Phosphodiester bonds** 4.2

**CARBOHYDRATES** — Ch 5

function in

**Monosaccharides**
- Storage of chemical energy

**Polysaccharides**
- Storage of chemical energy
- Structural support
- Cellular identity

5.2, 5.3

and can be polymers of

**Sugars**

$CH_2OH$

5.1

linked by

**Glycosidic bonds** 5.2

**LIPIDS** — Ch 6

function in

**Fats**
- Storage of chemical energy

**Steroids**
- Signaling
- Membrane structure

**Phospholipids**
- Membrane structure

6.1

and can be organized by

**Hydrophobic interactions** 6.2

form via

such as

released by

**Condensation reactions** (dehydration reactions) 3.1

reversed by

used in

**Hydrolysis reactions** 3.1

**Lipid bilayers**

6.2

all four are key to the structure and function of

**Cells**

Ch 7

are a key component of

moves by

**Osmosis** 6.3

across

**Biological membranes** 6.2

are key to the structure and function of

is a solvent for

**Hydrophilic solutes** 6.3

move by

- Diffusion
- Facilitated diffusion
- Active transport

6.4

to form

# 7 Inside the Cell

**In this chapter you will learn that**

Life's properties emerge from the collaboration of internal structures in a cell

by asking

What are the parts of the cell?

examining

examining

Prokaryotic cell structures **7.1**

Eukaryotic cell structures **7.2**

How the parts fit into a whole **7.3**

looking closer at

Nuclear transport **7.4**

Endomembrane system **7.5**

Dynamic cytoskeleton **7.6**

This cell has been treated with fluorescing molecules that bind to its fibrous cytoskeleton. Microtubules (large protein fibers) are yellow; actin filaments (smaller fibers) are blue. The cell's nucleus has been stained green.

The cell theory states that all organisms consist of cells and all cells are derived from preexisting cells (Chapter 1). Since this theory was initially developed and tested in the 1850s, an enormous body of research has confirmed that the cell is the fundamental structural and functional unit of life. Life on Earth is cellular.

Previous chapters (Unit 1) delved into the fundamental attributes of life by looking at biologists' current understanding of how the cell evolved—from the early chemistry to the assembly and replication of a protocell. As the first cells left the hydrothermal vents, they took with them characteristics that are now shared among all known life-forms.

All cells have

1. nucleic acids that store and transmit information;
2. proteins that perform most of the cell's functions;

✔ When you see this checkmark, stop and test yourself. Answers are available in Appendix A.

**3.** carbohydrates that provide chemical energy, carbon, support, and identity; and

**4.** a plasma membrane, which serves as a selectively permeable membrane barrier.

Thanks to the selective permeability of phospholipid bilayers and the activity of membrane transport proteins, the plasma membrane creates an internal environment that differs from conditions outside the cell. Our task now is to explore the structures inside the cell to understand how the properties of life emerged from the combination of these characteristics.

Let's begin by analyzing how the parts inside a cell function individually and then exploring how they work as a unit. This approach is analogous to studying individual organs in the body and then analyzing how they work together to form the nervous system or digestive system. As you study this material, keep asking yourself some key questions: How does the structure of this part or group of parts correlate with its function? What problem does it solve?

## 7.1 Bacterial and Archaeal Cell Structures and Their Functions

Cells are divided into two fundamental types called eukaryotes and prokaryotes (see Chapter 1). This division is mostly based on cell **morphology** ("form-science")—eukaryotic cells have a membrane-bound compartment called a nucleus, and prokaryotic cells do not.

But according to **phylogeny** ("tribe-source"), or evolutionary history, organisms are divided into three broad domains called **(1)** Bacteria, **(2)** Archaea, and **(3)** Eukarya. Members of the Bacteria and Archaea are prokaryotic; members of the Eukarya—including algae, fungi, plants, and animals—are eukaryotic.

### A Revolutionary New View

For almost 200 years, biologists thought that prokaryotic cells were simple in terms of their morphology and that there was little structural diversity among species. This conclusion was valid at the time, given the resolution of the microscopes that were available and the number of species that had been studied.

Things have changed. Recent improvements in microscopy and other research tools have convinced biologists that prokaryotic cells, among which bacteria are the best understood, possess an array of distinctive structures and functions found among millions of species. This conclusion represents one of the most exciting discoveries in cell biology over the past 10 years.

To keep things simple at the start, though, **FIGURE 7.1** offers a low-magnification, stripped-down diagram of a bacterial cell.

### Prokaryotic Cell Structures: A Parts List

The labels in Figure 7.1 highlight the components common to all or most bacteria studied to date. Let's explore these elements one by one, and also look at more specialized structures found in particular species, starting from the inside and working out.

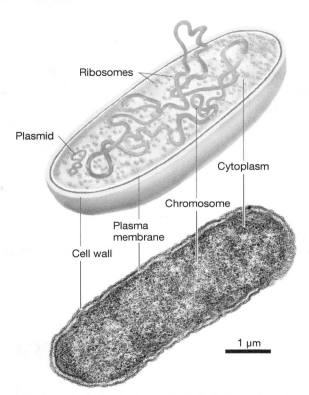

**FIGURE 7.1 Overview of a Prokaryotic Cell.** Prokaryotic cells are identified by a negative trait—the absence of a membrane-bound nucleus. Although there is wide variation in the size and shape of bacterial and archaeal cells, they all contain a plasma membrane, a chromosome, and protein-synthesizing ribosomes.

**The Chromosome Is Organized in a Nucleoid** The most prominent structure inside a bacterial cell is the **chromosome.** Most bacterial species have a single, circular chromosome that consists of a large DNA molecule associated with a small number of proteins. The DNA molecule contains information, and the proteins provide structural support for the DNA.

Recall that the information in DNA is encoded in its sequence of nitrogenous bases. Segments of DNA that contain information for building functional RNAs, some of which may be used to make polypeptides, are called **genes** (Chapter 4). Thus, chromosomes contain DNA, which contains genes.

In the well-studied bacterium *Escherichia coli*, the circular chromosome would be over 1 mm long if it were linear—500 times longer than the cell itself (**FIGURE 7.2a**; see page 108). This situation is typical in prokaryotes. To fit into the cell, the DNA double helix coils on itself with the aid of enzymes to form a compact, "supercoiled" structure. Supercoiled regions of DNA resemble a rubber band that has been held at either end and then twisted until it coils back upon itself.

The location and structural organization of the circular chromosome is called the **nucleoid** (pronounced *NEW-klee-oyd*). The genetic material in the nucleoid is often organized by clustering loops of DNA into distinct domains, but it is not separated from the rest of the cell interior by a membrane. The functional role of this organization of the bacterial chromosome and how it changes over time is currently the subject of intense research.

**(a)** Compared to the cell, chromosomal DNA is very long.

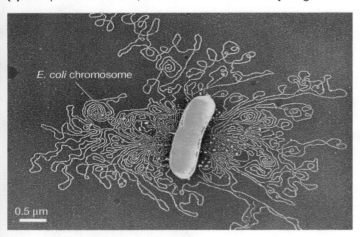

E. coli chromosome

0.5 µm

**(b)** DNA is packaged by supercoiling.

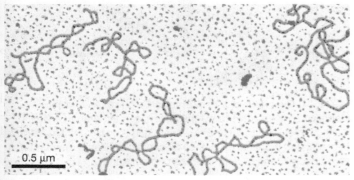

0.5 µm

**FIGURE 7.2 Bacterial DNA Is Supercoiled. (a)** The chromosomes of bacteria and archaea are often over 1000 times the length of the cell, as shown in this micrograph of E. coli that has been treated to release its DNA. To fit inside cells, this DNA must be highly compacted by supercoiling. **(b)** A colorized electron micrograph showing the effect of supercoiling on the DNA of isolated plasmids.

In addition to one or more chromosomes, bacterial cells may contain from one to about a hundred small, usually circular, supercoiled DNA molecules called **plasmids** (**FIGURE 7.2b**). Plasmids contain genes but are physically independent of the cellular chromosome. In many cases the genes carried by plasmids are not required under normal conditions; instead, they help cells adapt to unusual circumstances, such as the sudden presence of a poison in the environment. As a result, plasmids can be considered auxiliary genetic elements.

**Ribosomes Manufacture Proteins**  **Ribosomes** are observed in all prokaryotic cells and are found throughout the cell interior. It is not unusual for a single cell to contain 10,000 ribosomes, each functioning as a protein-manufacturing center.

Ribosomes are complex structures composed of large and small subunits, each of which contains RNA and protein molecules. Biologists often refer to ribosomes, along with other multicomponent complexes that perform specialized tasks, as "macromolecular machines." (Chapter 17 analyzes the structure and function of ribosomes in detail.)

**Photosynthetic Species Have Internal Membrane Complexes**  In addition to the nucleoid and ribosomes found in all bacteria and archaea studied to date, it is common to observe extensive internal membranes in prokaryotes that perform photosynthesis. Photosynthesis is the suite of chemical reactions responsible for converting the energy in sunlight into chemical energy stored in sugars.

The photosynthetic membranes observed in prokaryotes contain the enzymes and pigment molecules required for these reactions to occur and develop as infoldings of the plasma membrane. In some cases, vesicles pinch off as the plasma membrane folds in. In other cases, flattened stacks of photosynthetic membrane remain connected to the plasma membrane, like those shown in **FIGURE 7.3**. The extensive surface area provided by these internal membranes makes it possible for more photosynthetic reactions to occur and thus increases the cell's ability to make food.

**Organelles Perform Specialized Functions**  Recent research indicates that several bacterial species have internal compartments that qualify as **organelles** ("little organs"). An organelle is a membrane-bound compartment inside the cell that contains enzymes or structures specialized for a particular function.

Bacterial organelles perform an array of tasks, including

- storing calcium ions or other key molecules;

- holding crystals of the mineral magnetite, which function like a compass needle to help cells sense a magnetic field and swim in a directed way;

- organizing enzymes responsible for synthesizing complex carbon compounds from carbon dioxide; and

- sequestering enzymes that generate chemical energy from ammonium ions.

**The Cytoskeleton Structures the Cell Interior**  Recent research has also shown that bacteria and archaea contain long, thin fibers that serve a variety of roles inside the cell. All bacterial species,

Photosynthetic membranes

0.5 µm

**FIGURE 7.3 Photosynthetic Membranes in Bacteria.** The green stripes in this photosynthetic bacterium are membranes that contain the pigments and enzymes required for photosynthesis. This photo has been colorized to enhance the membranes.

for example, contain protein fibers that are essential for cell division to take place. Some species also have protein filaments that help maintain cell shape. Protein filaments such as these form the basis of the **cytoskeleton** ("cell skeleton").

The discovery of bacterial cytoskeletal elements is so new that much remains to be learned. Currently, researchers are working to understand how the different cytoskeletal elements enable cells to divide and if they play a role in organizing the cell interior into distinct regions.

**The Plasma Membrane Separates Life from Nonlife**   The plasma membrane consists of a phospholipid bilayer and proteins that either span the bilayer or attach to one side. Inside the membrane, all the contents of a cell, excluding the nucleus, are collectively termed the **cytoplasm** ("cell-formed").

Because all archaea and virtually all bacteria are unicellular, the plasma membrane creates an internal environment that is distinct from the outside, nonliving environment. The combined effect of a lipid bilayer and membrane proteins prohibits the entry of many substances that would be dangerous to life while allowing the passage of molecules and ions required for life (see Chapter 6).

**The Cell Wall Forms a Protective "Exoskeleton"**   Because the cytoplasm contains a high concentration of solutes, in most habitats it is hypertonic relative to the surrounding environment. When this is the case, water enters the cell via osmosis and makes the cell's volume expand. In virtually all bacteria and archaea, this pressure is resisted by a stiff **cell wall.**

Bacterial and archaeal cell walls are a tough, fibrous layer that surrounds the plasma membrane. In prokaryotes, the pressure of the plasma membrane against the cell wall is about the same as the pressure in an automobile tire.

The cell wall protects the organism and gives it shape and rigidity, much like the exoskeleton (external skeleton) of a crab or insect. In addition, many bacteria have another protective layer outside the cell wall that consists of lipids with polysaccharides attached. Lipids that contain carbohydrate groups are termed **glycolipids.**

**External Structures Enable Movement and Attachment**   Besides having a cell wall to provide protection, as just described, many bacteria also interact with their environment via structures that grow from the plasma membrane. The flagella and fimbriae shown in **FIGURE 7.4** are examples that are commonly found on bacterial surfaces.

Bacterial **flagella** (singular: **flagellum**) are assembled from over 40 different proteins at the cell surface of certain species. The base of this structure is embedded in the plasma membrane, and its rotation spins a long, helical filament that propels cells through water. At top speed, flagellar movement can drive a bacterial cell through water at 60 cell lengths per second. In contrast, the fastest animal in the ocean—the sailfish—can swim at a mere 10 body lengths per second.

**Fimbriae** (singular: **fimbria**) are needlelike projections that extend from the plasma membrane of some bacteria and promote attachment to other cells or surfaces. These structures are

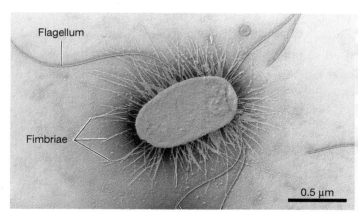

**FIGURE 7.4 Extracellular Appendages Found on Bacteria.** Some species of bacteria, such as the *E. coli* shown here, assemble large protein structures used for swimming through liquid (flagella) or adhering to surfaces (fimbriae).

more numerous than flagella and are often distributed over the entire surface of the cell. Fimbriae are crucial to the establishment of many infections based on their ability to glue bacteria to the surface of tissues.

The painting in **FIGURE 7.5** shows a cross section of a bacterial cell and provides a close-up view of the internal and external structures introduced in this section. One feature that prokaryotic and eukaryotic cells have in common: They are both packed with dynamic, highly integrated structures.

**FIGURE 7.5 Close-up View of a Prokaryotic Cell.** This painting is David Goodsell's representation of a cross section through part of a bacterial cell. It is based on electron micrographs of bacterial cells and is drawn to scale. Note that the cell is packed with proteins, DNA, ribosomes, and other molecular machinery.

**If you understand that . . .**

- Each structure in a prokaryotic cell performs a function vital to the cell.

✔ **You should be able to . . .**

Describe the structure and function of (1) the nucleoid, (2) photosynthetic membranes, (3) flagella, and (4) the cell wall.

*Answers are available in Appendix A.*

|  | Bacteria and Archaea | Eukaryotes |
|---|---|---|
| **Location of DNA** | In nucleoid (not membrane bound); plasmids also common | Inside nucleus (membrane bound); plasmids extremely rare |
| **Internal Membranes and Organelles** | Extensive internal membranes only in photosynthetic species; limited types and numbers of organelles | Large numbers of organelles; many types of organelles |
| **Cytoskeleton** | Limited in extent, relative to eukaryotes | Extensive—usually found throughout volume of cell |
| **Overall Size** | Usually small relative to eukaryotes | Most are larger than prokaryotes |

## 7.2 Eukaryotic Cell Structures and Their Functions

The Eukarya includes species that range from microscopic algae to 100-meter-tall redwood trees. Brown algae, red algae, fungi, amoebae, slime molds, green plants, and animals are all eukaryotic. Although multicellularity has evolved several times among eukaryotes (see Chapter 30), many species are unicellular.

The first thing that strikes biologists about eukaryotic cells is how much larger they are on average than bacteria and archaea. Most prokaryotic cells measure 1 to 10 μm in diameter, while most eukaryotic cells range from about 5 to 100 μm in diameter. A micrograph of an average eukaryotic cell, at the same scale as the bacterial cell in Figure 7.3, would fill this page. For many species of unicellular eukaryotes, this size difference allows them to make a living by ingesting bacteria and archaea whole.

Large size has a downside, however. As a cell increases in diameter, its volume increases more than its surface area. In other words, the relationship between them—the surface-area-to-volume ratio—changes. Since the surface is where the cell exchanges substances with its environment, the reduction in this ratio decreases the rate of exchange: Diffusion only allows for rapid movement across very small distances.

Prokaryotic cells tend to be small enough so that ions and small molecules arrive where they are needed via diffusion. The random movement of diffusion alone, however, is insufficient for this type of transport as the cell's diameter increases.

### The Benefits of Organelles

How do eukaryotic cells solve the problems that size can engender? The answer lies in their numerous organelles. In effect, the huge volume inside a eukaryotic cell is compartmentalized into many small bins. Because eukaryotic cells are subdivided, the cytosol—the fluid portion between the plasma membrane and these organelles—is only a fraction of the total cell volume. This relatively small volume of cytosol reduces the effect of the total cell surface-area-to-volume ratio with respect to the exchange of nutrients and waste products.

Compartmentalization also offers two key advantages:

1. Incompatible chemical reactions can be separated. For example, new fatty acids can be synthesized in one organelle while

excess or damaged fatty acids are degraded and recycled in a different organelle.

2. Chemical reactions become more efficient. First, the substrates required for particular reactions can be localized and maintained at high concentrations within organelles. Second, if substrates are used up in a particular part of the organelle, they can be replaced by substrates that have only a short distance to diffuse. Third, groups of enzymes that work together can be clustered within or on the membranes of organelles instead of floating free in the cytosol. When the product of one reaction is the substrate for a second reaction catalyzed by another enzyme, clustering the enzymes increases the speed and efficiency of both reaction sequences.

If bacteria and archaea can be compared to small, specialized machine shops, then eukaryotic cells resemble sprawling industrial complexes. The organelles and other structures found in eukaryotes are analogous to highly specialized buildings that act as administrative centers, factories, transportation corridors, waste and recycling facilities, warehouses, and power stations.

When typical prokaryotic and eukaryotic cells are compared, four key differences, identified in **TABLE 7.1**, stand out:

1. Eukaryotic chromosomes are found inside a membrane-bound compartment called the **nucleus.**

2. Eukaryotic cells are often much larger than prokaryotes.

3. Eukaryotic cells contain extensive amounts of internal membrane.

4. Eukaryotic cells feature a particularly diverse and dynamic cytoskeleton.

### Eukaryotic Cell Structures: A Parts List

**FIGURE 7.6** provides a simplified view of a typical animal cell and a plant cell. The artist has removed most of the cytoskeletal elements

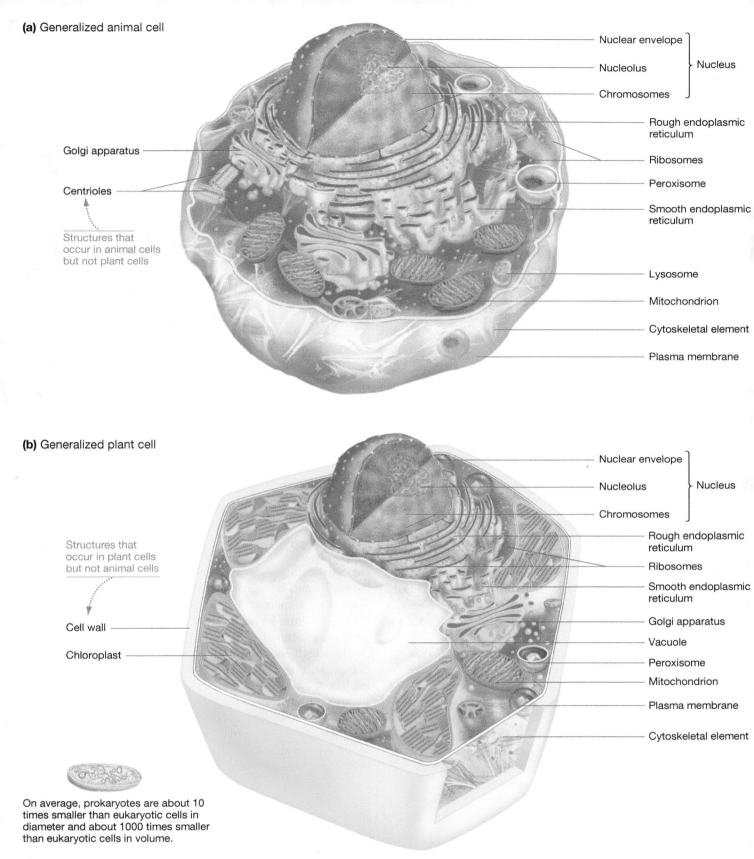

**(a) Generalized animal cell**

Nuclear envelope ⎫
Nucleolus ⎬ Nucleus
Chromosomes ⎭

Rough endoplasmic reticulum

Golgi apparatus

Ribosomes

Centrioles

Peroxisome

Smooth endoplasmic reticulum

Structures that occur in animal cells but not plant cells

Lysosome

Mitochondrion

Cytoskeletal element

Plasma membrane

**(b) Generalized plant cell**

Nuclear envelope ⎫
Nucleolus ⎬ Nucleus
Chromosomes ⎭

Structures that occur in plant cells but not animal cells

Rough endoplasmic reticulum

Ribosomes

Smooth endoplasmic reticulum

Golgi apparatus

Cell wall

Vacuole

Chloroplast

Peroxisome

Mitochondrion

Plasma membrane

Cytoskeletal element

On average, prokaryotes are about 10 times smaller than eukaryotic cells in diameter and about 1000 times smaller than eukaryotic cells in volume.

**FIGURE 7.6 Overview of Eukaryotic Cells.** Generalized images of **(a)** animal and **(b)** plant cells that illustrate the cellular structures in the "typical" eukaryote. The structures have been color-coded for clarity. Compare with the prokaryotic cell, shown at true relative size at bottom left.

Nucleus

Loosely packed sections of chromosomes

Densely packed sections of chromosomes

Nucleolus

Nuclear envelope

2 µm

**FIGURE 7.7 The Nucleus Stores and Transmits Information.** The genetic, or hereditary, information is encoded in DNA, which is a component of the chromosomes inside the nucleus.

Ribosomes

100 nm

**FIGURE 7.8 Ribosomes Are the Site of Protein Synthesis.** Eukaryotic ribosomes are larger than bacterial and archaeal ribosomes, but similar in overall structure.

to make the organelles and other cellular parts easier to see. As you read about each cell component in the pages that follow, focus on identifying how its structure correlates with its function. Then use **TABLE 7.2** (see page 117) as a study guide. As with bacterial cells, let's start from the inside and move to the outside.

**The Nucleus** The nucleus contains the chromosomes and functions as an administrative center for information storage and processing. Among the largest and most highly organized of all organelles (**FIGURE 7.7**), it is enclosed by a unique structure—a complex double membrane called the **nuclear envelope.** As Section 7.4 will detail, the nuclear envelope is studded with pore-like openings, and the inside surface is linked to fibrous proteins that form a lattice-like sheet called the **nuclear lamina.** The nuclear lamina stiffens the structure and maintains its shape.

Chromosomes do not float freely inside the nucleus—instead, each chromosome occupies a distinct area, which may vary in different cell types and over the course of cell replication. The nucleus also contains specific sites where gene products are processed and includes at least one distinctive region called the **nucleolus,** where the RNA molecules found in ribosomes are manufactured and the large and small ribosomal subunits are assembled.

**Ribosomes** In eukaryotes, the cytoplasm consists of everything inside the plasma membrane excluding the nucleus. Scattered throughout this cytoplasm are millions of ribosomes (**FIGURE 7.8**).

Like bacterial ribosomes, eukaryotic ribosomes are complex macromolecular machines that manufacture proteins. They are not classified as organelles because they are not surrounded by membranes.

**Endoplasmic Reticulum** The portions of the nuclear envelope extend into the cytoplasm to form an extensive membrane-enclosed factory called the **endoplasmic reticulum** (literally, "inside-formed-network"), or ER. As Figure 7.6 shows, the ER membrane is continuous with the nuclear envelope. Although the ER is a single structure, it has two regions that are distinct in structure and function. Let's consider each region in turn.

The **rough endoplasmic reticulum (RER),** or **rough ER,** is named for its appearance in transmission electron micrographs (see **FIGURE 7.9**, left). The knobby-looking structures in the rough ER are ribosomes that attach to the membrane.

The ribosomes associated with the rough ER synthesize proteins that will be inserted into the plasma membrane, secreted to the cell exterior, or shipped to an organelle. As they are being manufactured by ribosomes, these proteins move to the interior of the sac-like component of the rough ER. The interior of the rough ER, like the interior of any sac-like structure in a cell or body, is called the **lumen.** In the lumen of the rough ER, newly manufactured proteins undergo folding and other types of processing.

The proteins produced in the rough ER have a variety of functions. Some carry messages to other cells; some act as membrane

**Rough endoplasmic reticulum**

**Smooth endoplasmic reticulum**

Lumen of rough ER

Ribosomes on outside of rough ER

Free ribosomes in cytoplasm

200 nm

Lumen of smooth ER

200 nm

**FIGURE 7.9 The Endoplasmic Reticulum Is a Site of Synthesis, Processing, and Storage.** The ER is continuous with the nuclear envelope and possesses two distinct regions: on the left, the rough ER is a system of membrane-bound sacs and tubules with ribosomes attached; on the right, the smooth ER is a system of membrane-bound sacs and tubules that lacks ribosomes.

transport proteins or pumps; others are enzymes. The common theme is that many of the rough ER products are packaged into vesicles and transported to various distant destinations—often to the surface of the cell or beyond.

In electron micrographs, parts of the ER that are free of ribosomes appear smooth and even. Appropriately, these parts of the ER are called the **smooth endoplasmic reticulum (SER),** or **smooth ER** (see **FIGURE 7.9**, right).

The smooth ER contains enzymes that catalyze reactions involving lipids. Depending on the type of cell, these enzymes may synthesize lipids needed by the organism or break down lipids and other molecules that are poisonous. For example, the smooth ER is the manufacturing site for phospholipids used in plasma membranes. In addition, the smooth ER functions as a reservoir for calcium ions ($Ca^{2+}$) that act as a signal triggering a wide array of activities inside the cell.

The structure of the endoplasmic reticulum correlates closely with its function. The rough ER has ribosomes and functions primarily as a protein-manufacturing center; the smooth ER lacks ribosomes and functions primarily as a lipid-processing center.

**Golgi Apparatus** In many cases, the products of the rough ER pass through the Golgi apparatus before they reach their final destination. The **Golgi apparatus** consists of discrete flattened, membranous sacs called **cisternae** (singular: **cisterna**), which are stacked on top of one another (**FIGURE 7.10**). The organelle also

**Golgi apparatus**

cis

trans

Vesicle

cis side faces nucleus

Lumen of Golgi apparatus

Cisternae

trans side faces plasma membrane

Vesicles

100 nm

**FIGURE 7.10 The Golgi Apparatus Is a Site of Protein Processing, Sorting, and Shipping.** The Golgi apparatus is a collection of flattened vesicles called cisternae.

has a distinct polarity, or sidedness. The *cis* ("this side") surface is closest to the nucleus, and the *trans* ("across") surface is oriented toward the plasma membrane.

The *cis* side of a Golgi apparatus receives products from the rough ER, and the *trans* side ships them out to other organelles or the cell surface. In between, within the cisternae, the rough ER's products are processed and packaged for delivery. Micrographs often show "bubbles" on either side of the Golgi stack. These are membrane-bound vesicles that carry proteins or other products to and from the organelle. Section 7.5 analyzes the intracellular movement of molecules from the rough ER to the Golgi apparatus and beyond in more detail.

**Lysosomes** Animal cells contain organelles called **lysosomes** that function as recycling centers (**FIGURE 7.11**). Lysosomes contain about 40 different enzymes, each specialized for hydrolyzing different types of macromolecules—proteins, nucleic acids, lipids, or carbohydrates. The amino acids, nucleotides, sugars, and other molecules that result from acid hydrolysis leave the lysosome via transport proteins in the organelle's membrane. Once in the cytosol, they can be used as sources of energy or building blocks for new molecules.

These digestive enzymes are collectively called acid hydrolases because under acidic conditions (pH of 5.0), they use water to break monomers from macromolecules. In the cytosol, where the pH is about 7.2, acid hydrolases are less active. Proton pumps in the lysosomal membrane maintain an acidic pH in the lumen of the lysosome by importing hydrogen ions.

Even though lysosomes are physically separated from the Golgi apparatus and the endoplasmic reticulum, these various

**FIGURE 7.12 Vacuoles Are Generally Storage Centers in Plant and Fungal Cells.** Vacuoles vary in size and function. Some contain digestive enzymes and serve as recycling centers; most are large storage containers.

✓ **QUESTION** Why are toxins like nicotine, cocaine, and caffeine stored in vacuoles instead of the cytosol?

organelles jointly form a key functional grouping referred to as the **endomembrane system.** The endomembrane ("inner-membrane") system is a center for producing, processing, and transporting proteins and lipids in eukaryotic cells. For example, acid hydrolases are synthesized in the ER, processed in the Golgi, and then shipped to the lysosome.

**Vacuoles** The cells of plants, fungi, and certain other groups lack lysosomes. Instead, they contain a prominent organelle called a vacuole. Compared with the lysosomes of animal cells, the **vacuoles** of plant and fungal cells are large—sometimes taking up as much as 80 percent of a plant cell's volume (**FIGURE 7.12**).

Although some vacuoles contain enzymes that are specialized for digestion, most of the vacuoles observed in plant and fungal cells act as storage depots. In many cases, ions such as potassium ($K^+$) and chloride ($Cl^-$), among other solutes, are stored at such high concentrations they draw water in from the environment. As the vacuole expands in volume, the cytoplasm pushes the plasma membrane against the cell wall, which maintains the plant cell's shape. In other cells, vacuoles have more specialized storage functions:

- Inside seeds, cells may contain a large vacuole filled with proteins. When the embryonic plant inside the seed begins to grow, enzymes begin digesting these proteins to provide amino acids for the growing individual.

Material being digested within lysosomes

**FIGURE 7.11 Lysosomes Are Recycling Centers.** Lysosomes are usually oval or globular and have a single membrane.

- In cells that make up flower petals or fruits, vacuoles are filled with colorful pigments.

- Elsewhere, vacuoles may be packed with noxious compounds that protect leaves and stems from being eaten by predators. The type of chemical involved varies by species, ranging from bitter-tasting tannins to toxins such as nicotine, morphine, caffeine, or cocaine.

**Peroxisomes**   Virtually all eukaryotic cells contain globular organelles called **peroxisomes** (**FIGURE 7.13**). These organelles have a single membrane and originate as buds from the ER.

Although different types of cells from the same individual may have distinct types of peroxisomes, these organelles all share a common function: Peroxisomes are centers for reduction–oxidation (redox) reactions. (Chapter 8 explains in detail how redox reactions transfer electrons between atoms and molecules.) For example, the peroxisomes in your liver cells contain enzymes that remove electrons from, or oxidize, the ethanol in alcoholic beverages.

Different types of peroxisomes contain different suites of redox enzymes. In the leaves of plants, specialized peroxisomes called **glyoxysomes** are packed with enzymes that oxidize fats to form a compound that can be used to store energy for the cell. But plant seeds have a different type of peroxisome—one that is packed with enzymes responsible for releasing energy from stored fatty acids. The young plant uses this energy as it begins to grow.

In animals and plants, the products of these reactions often include hydrogen peroxide ($H_2O_2$), which is highly reactive.

If hydrogen peroxide escaped from the peroxisome, it would quickly react with and damage DNA, proteins, and cellular membranes. This event is rare, however, because inside the peroxisome, the enzyme catalase quickly "detoxifies" hydrogen peroxide by catalyzing its oxidation to form water and oxygen. The enzymes found inside the peroxisome make a specialized set of oxidation reactions possible and safe for the cell.

**Mitochondria**   The energy required to build these organelles and do other types of work comes from adenosine triphosphate (ATP), most of which is produced in the cell's **mitochondria** (singular: **mitochondrion**).

As **FIGURE 7.14** shows, each mitochondrion has two membranes. The outer membrane defines the organelle's surface, while the inner membrane is connected to a series of sac-like **cristae.** The solution enclosed within the inner membrane is called the **mitochondrial matrix.** In eukaryotes, most of the enzymes and molecular machines responsible for synthesizing ATP are embedded in the membranes of the cristae or suspended in the matrix (see Chapter 9). Depending on the type of cell, from 50 to more than a million mitochondria may be present.

Each mitochondrion has many copies of a small, circular chromosome that is independent of the nuclear chromosomes. This mitochondrial DNA contains only around 37 genes in most eukaryotes—most of the genes responsible for the function of the organelle reside in the nuclear DNA.

Among the genes present in mitochondrial DNA are those that encode RNAs for mitochondrial ribosomes. These ribosomes are

**FIGURE 7.13 Peroxisomes Are the Site of Oxidation Reactions.**
Peroxisomes are globular organelles that are defined by a single membrane.

Peroxisome membrane

Enzyme core

Peroxisome lumen

100 nm

**FIGURE 7.14 Mitochondria Are Power-Generating Stations.**
Mitochondria vary in size and shape, but all have a double membrane with sac-like cristae inside.

Outer and inner membranes

Matrix

Cristae

0.1 μm

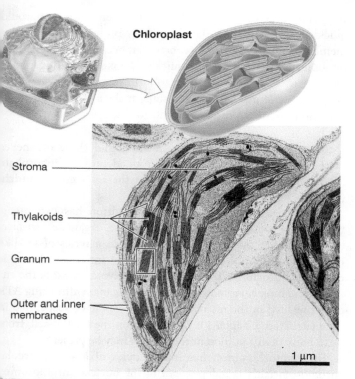

**Chloroplast**

Stroma

Thylakoids

Granum

Outer and inner membranes

1 µm

**FIGURE 7.15 Chloroplasts Are Sugar-Manufacturing Centers in Plants and Algae.** Many of the enzymes and other molecules required for photosynthesis are located in membranes inside the chloroplast. These membranes form thylakoids that consist of discs stacked into grana.

smaller than those found in the cytosol, yet they still function to produce some of the mitochondrial proteins. (Most of the proteins found in mitochondria are produced from ribosomes in the cytosol and imported into the organelle.)

**Chloroplasts** Most algal and plant cells possess an organelle called the **chloroplast,** in which sunlight is converted to chemical energy during photosynthesis (**FIGURE 7.15**). The number of chloroplasts per cell varies from none to several dozen.

The chloroplast has a double membrane around its exterior, analogous to the structure of a mitochondrion. Instead of featuring sac-like cristae that connect to the inner membrane, though, the interior of the chloroplast is dominated by a network of hundreds of membrane-bound, flattened, sac-like structures called **thylakoids,** which are independent of the inner membrane. Thylakoids have stacks, like pancakes, that are called **grana** (singular: **granum**). Many of the pigments, enzymes, and macromolecular machines responsible for converting light energy into chemical energy are embedded in the thylakoid membranes (see Chapter 10). The region outside the thylakoids, called the **stroma,** contains enzymes that use this chemical energy to produce sugars.

Like mitochondria, each chloroplast contains copies of a circular chromosome and small ribosomes that manufacture some, but not all, of the organelle's proteins. Both mitochondria

and chloroplasts also grow and divide independently of cell division through a process that resembles bacterial fission (see Chapter 12).

These attributes are odd compared with those of the other organelles and have led biologists to propose that mitochondria and chloroplasts were once free-living bacteria. According to the **endosymbiosis theory,** the ancestors of modern eukaryotes ingested these bacteria, but instead of destroying them, established a mutually beneficial relationship with them. (In Chapter 30, you will learn more about the origins of these eukaryotic organelles.)

**Cytoskeleton** The final major structural feature that is common to all eukaryotic cells is the cytoskeleton, an extensive system of protein fibers. In addition to giving the cell its shape and structural stability, cytoskeletal proteins are involved in moving the cell itself and moving materials within the cell. In essence, the cytoskeleton organizes all the organelles and other cellular structures into a cohesive whole. Section 7.6 will analyze the structure and functions of the cytoskeleton in detail.

**The Cell Wall** In fungi, algae, and plants, cells possess an outer cell wall in addition to their plasma membrane. The cell wall is located outside the plasma membrane and furnishes a durable, outer layer that provides structural support for the cell. The cells of animals, amoebae, and other groups lack a cell wall—their exterior surface consists of the plasma membrane only.

Although the composition of the cell wall varies among species and even among types of cells in the same individual, the general plan is similar: Rods or fibers composed of a carbohydrate run through a stiff matrix made of other polysaccharides and proteins (see Chapter 11 for details).

## check your understanding

**C Y U**

**If you understand that . . .**

- Each structure in a eukaryotic cell performs a function vital to the cell.
- In eukaryotes, many of the cellular functions are compartmentalized into organelles.

✔ **You should be able to . . .**

1. Explain how the structure of lysosomes and peroxisomes correlates with their function.

2. In Table 7.2, label each component with one of the following roles: administrative/information hub, power station, warehouse, large molecule manufacturing and shipping facility (with subtitles for lipid factory, protein finishing and shipping line, protein synthesis and folding center, waste processing and recycling center), support beams, perimeter fencing with secured gates, protein factory, food-manufacturing facility, and fatty-acid processing and detox center.

*Answers are available in Appendix A.*

**Eukaryotic Cell Components**

| Icons Not to Scale | | Structure | | |
| --- | --- | --- | --- | --- |
| | | **Membrane** | **Components** | **Function** |
| | **Nucleus** | Double ("envelope"); openings called nuclear pores | Chromosomes<br><br>Nucleolus<br>Nuclear lamina | Information storage and transmission<br>Ribosome subunit assembly<br>Structural support |
| | **Ribosomes** | None | Complex of RNA and proteins | Protein synthesis |
| | **Endomembrane system** | | | |
| | *Endoplasmic reticulum: rough* | Single; contains receptors for entry of selected proteins | Network of branching sacs<br>Ribosomes associated | Protein synthesis and processing |
| | *Endoplasmic reticulum: smooth* | Single; contains enzymes for synthesizing phospholipids | Network of branching sacs<br>Enzymes for synthesizing or breaking down lipids | Lipid synthesis and processing |
| | *Golgi apparatus* | Single; contains receptors for products of rough ER | Stack of flattened, distinct cisternae | Protein, lipid, and carbohydrate processing |
| | *Lysosomes* | Single; contains proton pumps | Acid hydrolases (catalyze hydrolysis reactions) | Digestion and recycling |
| | **Vacuoles** | Single; contains transporters for selected molecules | Varies—pigments, oils, carbohydrates, water, or toxins | Varies—coloration, storage of oils, carbohydrates, water, or toxins |
| | **Peroxisomes** | Single; contains transporters for selected macromolecules | Enzymes that catalyze oxidation reactions<br><br>Catalase (processes peroxide) | Oxidation of fatty acids, ethanol, or other compounds |
| | **Mitochondria** | Double; inner contains enzymes for ATP production | Enzymes that harvest energy from molecules to make ATP | ATP production |
| | **Chloroplasts** | Double; plus membrane-bound sacs in interior | Pigments<br>Enzymes that use light energy to make sugars | Production of sugars via photosynthesis |
| | **Cytoskeleton** | None | Actin filaments<br>Intermediate filaments<br>Microtubules | Structural support; movement of materials; in some species, movement of whole cell |
| | **Plasma membrane** | Single; contains transport and receptor proteins | Phospholipid bilayer with transport and receptor proteins | Selective permeability—maintains intracellular environment |
| | **Cell wall** | None | Carbohydrate fibers running through carbohydrate or protein matrix | Protection, structural support |

## 7.3 Putting the Parts into a Whole

Within a cell, the structure of each component correlates with its function. In the same way, the overall size, shape, and composition of a cell correlate with its function.

Cells might be analogous to machine shops or industrial complexes, but clothing manufacturing centers are very different in layout and composition from airplane production facilities. How does the physical and chemical makeup of a cell correlate with its function?

### Structure and Function at the Whole-Cell Level

Inside an individual plant or animal, cells are specialized for certain tasks and have a structure that correlates with those tasks. For example, the muscle cells in your upper leg are extremely long, tube-shaped structures. They are filled with protein fibers that slide past one another as the entire muscle flexes or relaxes. It is this sliding motion that allows your muscles to contract or extend as you run. Muscle cells are also packed with mitochondria, which produce the ATP required for the sliding motion to occur.

In contrast, nearby fat cells are rounded, globular structures that store fatty acids. They consist of little more than a plasma membrane, a nucleus, and a fat droplet. Neither cell bears a close resemblance to the generalized animal cell pictured in Figure 7.6a.

To drive home the correlation between the overall structure and function of a cell, examine the transmission electron micrographs in **FIGURE 7.16**.

The animal cell in Figure 7.16a, located in the pancreas, manufactures and exports digestive enzymes. It is packed with rough ER and Golgi, which make these functions possible.

The animal cell in Figure 7.16b, from the testis, synthesizes and exports the steroid hormone testosterone—a lipid-soluble signal. This cell is dominated by smooth ER, where processing of steroids and other lipids takes place.

The plant cell in Figure 7.16c, from the leaf of a potato, has hundreds of chloroplasts and is specialized for absorbing light and manufacturing sugar.

The animal cells in Figure 7.16d come from brown fat. The cells have numerous mitochondria that have been altered so they convert energy stored in fat into heat instead of ATP.

In each case, the types of organelles in each cell and their size and number correlate with the cell's specialized function.

### The Dynamic Cell

Biologists study the structure and function of organelles and cells with a combination of tools and approaches. For several decades, a technique called **differential centrifugation** was particularly important because it allowed researchers to isolate particular cell components and analyze their chemical composition. Differential centrifugation is based on breaking cells apart to create a complex mixture and separating components in a centrifuge (see **BioSkills 10** in Appendix B). The individual parts of the cell

**(a) Animal pancreatic cell:** Exports digestive enzymes.

0.5 μm

**(b) Animal testis cell:** Exports lipid-soluble signals.

0.5 μm

**(c) Plant leaf cell:** Manufactures ATP and sugar.

1 μm

**(d) Brown fat cells:** Burn fat to generate heat in lieu of ATP.

1 μm

**FIGURE 7.16 Cell Structure Correlates with Function.**

✔**EXERCISE** In part (a), label the rough ER and the dark, round secretory vesicles. In (b), label the smooth ER. In (c), label the chloroplasts, vacuole, and nucleus. In (d), label the mitochondria.

can then be purified and studied in detail, in isolation from other parts of the cell.

Historically and currently, however, the most important research in cell biology is based on imaging—simply looking at cells. Recent innovations allow biologists to put fluorescing tags or other types of markers on particular cell components and then look at them with increasingly sophisticated light microscopes and electron microscopes. Advances in microscopy provide increasingly high magnification and better resolution.

It's important to recognize, though, that some of these techniques have limitations. Differential centrifugation splits cells into parts that are analyzed independently, and electron microscopy gives a fixed "snapshot" of the cell or organisms being observed. Neither technique allows investigators to explore directly how things move from place to place in the cell or how parts interact. The information gleaned from these techniques can make cells seem static. In reality, cells are dynamic.

The amount of chemical activity and the speed of molecular movement inside cells are nothing short of fantastic. Bacterial ribosomes add up to 20 amino acids per second to a growing polypeptide, and eukaryotic ribosomes typically add 2 per second. Given that there are about 15,000 ribosomes in each bacterium and possibly a million in an average eukaryotic cell, hundreds or even thousands of new protein molecules can be produced each second in every cell. Here are some other remarkable cellular feats:

- In an average second, a typical cell in your body uses an average of 10 million ATP molecules and synthesizes just as many.

- It's not unusual for a cellular enzyme to catalyze 25,000 or more reactions per second; most cells contain hundreds or thousands of different enzymes.

- A minute is more than enough time for each membrane phospholipid in your body to travel the breadth of the organelle or cell where it resides.

- The hundreds of trillions of mitochondria inside you are completely replaced about every 10 days, for as long as you live.

Because humans are such large organisms, it's impossible for us to imagine what life is really like inside a cell. At the scale of a ribosome or an organelle or a cell, gravity is inconsequential. Instead, the dominant forces are the charge- or polarity-based electrostatic attractions between molecules and their energy of motion. At this level, events take nanoseconds, and speeds are measured in micrometers per second. This is the speed of life.

Contemporary methods for studying cells (including some of the imaging techniques featured in **BioSkills 11** in Appendix B) capture this dynamism by tracking how organelles and molecules move and interact over time. The ability to digitize video images of live cells, or take time-lapse photographs of living cells, is allowing researchers to see and study dynamic processes.

The rest of this chapter focuses on this theme of cellular dynamism and movement. Its goal is to put some of the individual pieces of a cell together and ask how they work as systems to accomplish key tasks.

To begin, let's first look at how molecules move into and out of the cell's control center—the nucleus—and then consider how proteins move from ribosomes into the lumen of the rough ER and then to the Golgi apparatus and beyond. The chapter closes by introducing the cytoskeletal elements and their associated motor proteins and how they are used to transport cargo inside the cell or move the cell itself.

## 7.4 Cell Systems I: Nuclear Transport

The nucleus is the information center of eukaryotic cells—a corporate headquarters, design center, and library all rolled into one. Appropriately enough, its interior is highly organized.

The organelle's overall shape and structure are defined by the mesh-like nuclear lamina. The nuclear lamina provides an attachment point for the chromosomes, each of which occupies a well-defined region in the nucleus.

In addition, specific centers exist where the genetic information in DNA is decoded and processed. At these locations, large suites of enzymes interact to produce RNA messages from specific genes at specific times. Meanwhile, the nucleolus functions as the site of ribosome assembly.

### Structure and Function of the Nuclear Envelope

The nuclear envelope separates the nucleus from the rest of the cell. Starting in the 1950s, transmission electron micrographs of cross sections through the nuclear envelope showed that the structure is supported by the fibrous nuclear lamina and bounded by two membranes, each consisting of a lipid bilayer. How does this administrative center communicate with the rest of the cell across the double membrane barrier?

Micrographs like the one in **FIGURE 7.17** (see page 120) show that the nuclear envelope is broken with openings, approximately 60 nanometers (nm) in diameter, called **nuclear pores**. Because these pores extend through both the inner and outer nuclear membranes, they connect the inside of the nucleus with the cytosol. Follow-up research showed that each pore consists of over 50 different proteins. As the diagram on the right side of Figure 7.17 shows, these protein molecules form an elaborate structure called the **nuclear pore complex.**

What substances traverse nuclear pores? Chromosomal DNA clearly does not—it remains in the nucleus as long as the nuclear envelope remains intact. But DNA is used to synthesize RNA inside the nucleus, most of which is exported through nuclear pores to the cytoplasm.

Several types of RNA molecules are produced, each distinguished by size and function. For example, **ribosomal RNAs** are manufactured in the nucleolus, where they bind to proteins to form ribosomes. Molecules called **messenger RNAs (mRNA)** carry the information required to manufacture proteins. Both the newly assembled ribosomes and the mRNAs must be transported from the nucleus to the cytoplasm, where protein synthesis takes place.

**Nuclear pore complex**

Cross-sectional view of nuclear envelope

Nuclear matrix

Ribosomes, mRNA

DNA in nucleus

Nuclear lamina

Inner membrane ⎤
Outer membrane ⎦ Nuclear envelope

Proteins and building blocks of DNA and RNA

Cytosol

0.1 μm

**FIGURE 7.17 Structure of the Nuclear Envelope and Nuclear Pore Complex.**

Inbound traffic is also impressive. Nucleoside triphosphates that act as building blocks for DNA and RNA enter the nucleus, as do a variety of proteins responsible for copying DNA, synthesizing RNAs, extending the nuclear lamina, or assembling ribosomes.

To summarize, ribosomal subunits and various types of RNAs exit the nucleus; nucleotides and certain proteins enter it. In a typical cell, over 500 molecules pass through each of the 3000–4000 nuclear pores every second. The scale of traffic through the nuclear pores is mind-boggling. How is it regulated and directed?

Experiments in the early 1960s showed that size matters in the passage of molecules through nuclear pores. This conclusion was based on the results from injecting tiny gold particles that varied in diameter and tracking their movement across the pores. In electron micrographs, gold particles show up as defined black dots that can be easily distinguished from cellular structures. Immediately after injection, most of the gold particles were observed in the cytoplasm, and only a few were closely associated with nuclear pores. Ten minutes after injection, only the small particles (< 12.5 nm in diameter) appeared to be distributed throughout both the nucleus and the cytoplasm, and the larger particles were excluded from entering the nucleus.

The fact that the pore opening is almost 5 times larger than this 12.5-nm size limit supports the hypothesis that the nuclear pore complex serves as a gate to control passage through the envelope. If this is the case, then what is required to open these gates so that proteins larger than the size limit, like those responsible for replicating DNA, may pass?

## How Do Large Molecules Enter the Nucleus?

It was clear to researchers that size was not the sole factor in selective transport across the nuclear envelope. Certain proteins were concentrated in the nucleus, while others were completely excluded—even if they were similar in size.

A series of experiments on a protein called nucleoplasmin helped researchers understand the nature of nuclear import. Nucleoplasmin is strictly found in the nucleus and plays an important role in the assembly of chromatin. When researchers labeled nucleoplasmin with a radioactive atom and injected it into the cytoplasm of living cells, they found that the radioactive protein was quickly concentrated into the nucleus. Is there a "send-to-nucleus" signal within the nucleoplasmin protein that is responsible for this directed transport?

As shown in **FIGURE 7.18**, the distinctive structure of nucleoplasmin was used to further investigate this process. First, researchers used enzymes called proteases to cleave the core sections of nucleoplasmin from the tails. After separating the tails from the core fragments, they labeled each component with radioactive atoms and injected them into the cytoplasm of different cells.

At various times after the injections, researchers examined the nuclei and cytoplasm of the cells to track down the radioactive label. The results were striking. They found that tail fragments were rapidly transported from the cytoplasm into the nucleus. Core fragments, in contrast, were not allowed to pass through the nuclear envelope and remained in the cytoplasm.

These data led to a key hypothesis: Nuclear proteins are synthesized by ribosomes in the cytosol and contain a "zip code"—a molecular address tag—that marks them for transport through the nuclear pore complex. This zip code allows the nuclear pore complex to open in some way that permits larger proteins and RNA molecules to pass through.

By analyzing different stretches of the tail, the biologists eventually found a 17-amino-acid-long section that had to be present to direct nucleoplasmin to the nucleus. Follow-up work confirmed that other proteins bound for the nucleus, even those expressed by some viruses, have similar amino acid sequences directing their transport. This common sequence came to be called the **nuclear localization signal (NLS).** Proteins that leave the nucleus have a different signal, required for nuclear export.

## RESEARCH

### QUESTION: Does the nucleoplasmin protein contain a "Send to nucleus" signal?

HYPOTHESIS: Nucleoplasmin contains a discrete "Send to nucleus" signal that resides in either the tail or core region.

NULL HYPOTHESIS: Nucleoplasmin does not require a signal to enter the nucleus, or the entire protein serves as the signal.

EXPERIMENTAL SETUP:

**Nucleoplasmin protein**

Core

"Tails"

Labeled tails        Labeled cores

1. Use protease to cleave tails off of nucleoplasmin protein core.

2. Attach radioactive labels to protein tails and cores.

3. Inject labeled tails and cores into cytoplasm of different cells.

4. Wait, then locate labeled fragments ....

PREDICTION:

PREDICTION OF NULL HYPOTHESIS:

RESULTS:

Labeled tail fragments **located in nucleus**

Labeled core fragments still **located in cytoplasm**

CONCLUSION:

**FIGURE 7.18 Does the Nucleoplasmin Protein Contain a "Send to Nucleus" Signal?**

SOURCES: Mills, A. D., R. A. Laskey, P. Black, et al. 1980. *Journal of Molecular Biology* 139: 561–568; Dingwall, C., S. V. Sharnick, and R. A. Laskey. 1982. *Cell* 30: 449–458.

✔**EXERCISE** Without looking at the text, fill in the prediction(s) and conclusion(s) in this experiment.

More recent research has shown that the movement of proteins and other large molecules into and out of the nucleus is an energy-demanding process that involves special transport proteins. These nuclear transport proteins function like trucks that haul cargo into or out of the nucleus through the nuclear pore complex, depending on whether they have an import or export zip code. Currently, biologists are trying to unravel how all this traffic in and out of the nucleus is regulated to avoid backups and head-on collisions.

✔ If you understand the process of nuclear transport, you should be able to compare and contrast the movement of (1) nucleotides and (2) large proteins through the nuclear pore complex. Which would you expect to require the input of energy?

## 7.5 Cell Systems II: The Endomembrane System Manufactures, Ships, and Recycles Cargo

The nuclear membrane is not the only place in cells where cargo moves in a regulated and energy-demanding fashion. Most of the proteins found in peroxisomes, mitochondria, and chloroplasts are also actively imported from the cytosol. These proteins contain special signal sequences, like the nuclear localization signal, that target them to the appropriate organelles.

If you think about it for a moment, the need to sort proteins and ship them to specific destinations should be clear. Proteins are produced by ribosomes that are either free in the cytosol or on the surface of the ER. Many of these proteins must be transported to a compartment inside the eukaryotic cell. Acid hydrolases must be shipped to lysosomes and catalase to peroxisomes. To get to the right location, each protein has to have an address tag and a transport and delivery system.

To get a better understanding of protein sorting and transport in eukaryotic cells, let's consider perhaps the most intricate of all manufacturing and shipping complexes: the endomembrane system. In this system, proteins that are synthesized in the rough ER move to the Golgi apparatus for processing, and from there they travel to the cell surface or other destinations.

### Studying the Pathway through the Endomembrane System

The idea that materials move through the endomembrane system in an orderly way was inspired by a simple observation. According to electron micrographs, cells that secrete digestive enzymes, hormones, or other products have particularly large amounts of rough ER and Golgi. This correlation led to the idea that these organelles may participate in a "secretory pathway" that starts in the rough ER and ends with products leaving the cell (**FIGURE 7.19**, see page 122). How does this hypothesized pathway work?

**Tracking Protein Movement via Pulse–Chase Assay** George Palade and colleagues did pioneering research on the secretory

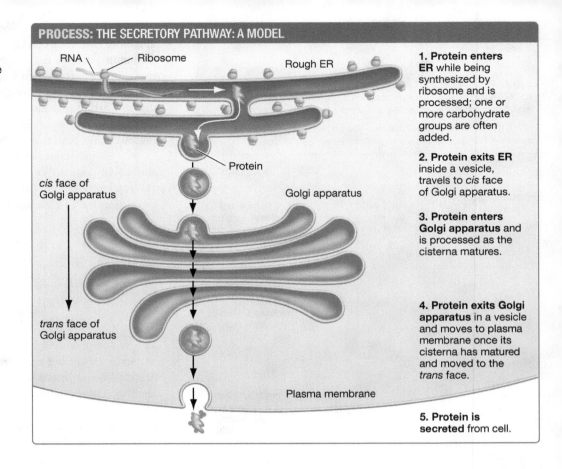

**PROCESS: THE SECRETORY PATHWAY: A MODEL**

RNA   Ribosome   Rough ER

Protein

cis face of Golgi apparatus

Golgi apparatus

trans face of Golgi apparatus

Plasma membrane

1. **Protein enters ER** while being synthesized by ribosome and is processed; one or more carbohydrate groups are often added.

2. **Protein exits ER** inside a vesicle, travels to *cis* face of Golgi apparatus.

3. **Protein enters Golgi apparatus** and is processed as the cisterna matures.

4. **Protein exits Golgi apparatus** in a vesicle and moves to plasma membrane once its cisterna has matured and moved to the *trans* face.

5. **Protein is secreted** from cell.

pathway using a **pulse–chase experiment** to track protein movement. This strategy is based on two steps:

1. *The "Pulse"* Expose experimental cells to a high concentration of a modified amino acid for a short time. For example, if a cell is briefly exposed to a large amount of radioactively labeled amino acid, virtually all the proteins synthesized during that interval will be radiolabeled.

2. *The "Chase"* The pulse ends by washing away the modified amino acid and replacing it with the normal version of the same molecule. The time following the end of the pulse is referred to as the chase. If the chase consists of unlabeled amino acid, then the proteins synthesized during the chase period will *not* be radiolabeled.

The idea is to mark a population of molecules at a particular interval and then follow their fate over time. This approach is analogous to adding a small amount of dye to a stream and then following the movement of the dye molecules.

To understand why the chase is necessary in these experiments, imagine what would happen if you added dye to a stream continuously. Soon the entire stream would be dyed—you could no longer tell where a specific population of dye molecules were moving.

In testing the secretory pathway hypothesis, Palade's team focused on pancreatic cells that were growing in **culture,** or in vitro.[1] These cells are specialized for secreting digestive enzymes into the small intestine and are packed with rough ER and Golgi.

The basic experimental approach was to pulse the cell culture for 3 minutes with a radiolabeled version of the amino acid leucine, followed by a long chase with nonradioactive leucine (**FIGURE 7.20a**). The pulse produced a population of proteins that were related to one another by the timing of their synthesis. At different points during the chase, the researchers tracked the movement of these proteins by preparing samples of the cells for autoradiography and electron microscopy (see **BioSkills 10 and 11** in Appendix B). The drawings in **FIGURE 7.20b** illustrate what the researchers would have seen in micrographs taken at different times before and after the start of the chase.

**Results of the Pulse–Chase Experiment** The graph in Figure 7.20b was based on the electron microscopy results, which showed that proteins are trafficked through the secretory pathway in a highly organized and directed manner. Track the movement of proteins through the cell during the chase by covering the graph with a piece of paper and then slowly sliding it off from

[1]The term in vitro is Latin for "in glass." Experiments that are performed outside living organisms are done in vitro. The term in vivo, in contrast, is Latin for "in life." Experiments performed with living organisms are done in vivo.

**(a)** Setup for a pulse-chase experiment

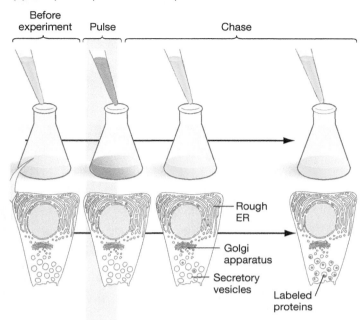

**(b)** Tracking pulse-labeled proteins during the chase

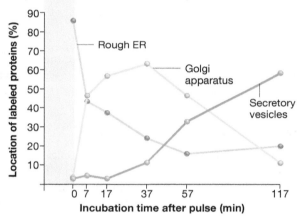

**FIGURE 7.20 Tracking Protein Movement in a Pulse–Chase Experiment.** Part **(a)** shows how investigators label newly synthesized proteins during the pulse with radioactive amino acids (red). At the start of the chase, this medium is replaced with non-radioactive amino acids (yellow) so only those proteins labeled in the pulse will be tracked. Part **(b)** provides the results of a pulse–chase experiment. The drawings represent micrographs taken that show the radiolabeled proteins (red dots) in the cells. The graph shows the relative abundance of radiolabeled proteins in three different organelles during the chase.

left to right. Notice what is happening to each line at the following three time points:

1. Immediately after the pulse, most of the newly synthesized proteins are inside this cell's rough ER.

2. At 37 minutes into the chase, the situation has changed. Most of the labeled proteins have left the rough ER and entered the

Golgi apparatus, and some of them have accumulated inside structures called secretory vesicles.

3. By the end of the chase, at 117 minutes, most of the labeled proteins have left the Golgi and are either in secretory vesicles or were secreted from the cells.

Over a period of two hours, the labeled population of proteins moved along a defined trail through the rough ER, Golgi apparatus, and secretory vesicles to reach the exterior of the cell. ✔ QUANTITATIVE If you understand how the pulse–chase experiment is used to track proteins, use the graph in Figure 7.20b to estimate the time it takes for proteins to pass through the Golgi apparatus.

The results support the hypotheses that a secretory pathway exists and that the rough ER and Golgi apparatus function together as an integrated endomembrane system. Next, let's break this secretory pathway down to examine four of the steps in more detail:

1. How do proteins enter the lumen of the ER?

2. How do the proteins move from the ER to the Golgi apparatus?

3. Once they're inside the Golgi, what happens to them?

4. And finally, how does the Golgi sort out the proteins so each will end up going to the appropriate place?

## Entering the Endomembrane System: The Signal Hypothesis

The synthesis of proteins destined to be secreted or embedded in membranes begins in ribosomes free in the cytosol. Günter Blobel and colleagues proposed that at some point these ribosomes become attached to the outside of the ER. But what directs these ribosomes to the ER? The signal hypothesis predicts that proteins bound for the endomembrane system have a molecular zip code analogous to the nuclear localization signal Blobel proposed that the first few amino acids in the growing polypeptide act as a signal that marks the ribosome for transport to the ER membrane.

This hypothesis received important support when researchers made a puzzling observation: When proteins that are normally synthesized in the rough ER are instead manufactured by isolated ribosomes in vitro—with *no* ER present—they are 20 amino acids longer, on average, than usual.

Blobel seized on these data. He claimed that the extra amino acids are the "send-to-ER" signal, and that the signal is removed inside the organelle. When the same protein is synthesized in vitro, the signal is not removed.

Blobel's group went on to produce convincing data that supported the hypothesis: They identified a sequence of amino acids that will move proteins into the ER lumen, called the **ER signal sequence.**

More recent work has documented the mechanisms responsible for receiving this send-to-ER signal and inserting the

1. Signal sequence is synthesized by ribosome.

2. Signal sequence binds to signal recognition particle (SRP) and halts synthesis.

3. SRP binds to receptor in ER membrane.

4. SRP is released. Protein synthesis continues. Protein enters ER.

5. Signal sequence is removed. Protein synthesis then proceeds to completion.

**FIGURE 7.21 The Signal Hypothesis Explains How Proteins Destined for Secretion Enter the Endomembrane System.** According to the signal hypothesis, proteins destined for secretion contain a short stretch of amino acids that interact with a signal recognition particle (SRP) in the cytoplasm. This interaction directs the synthesis of the remaining protein into the ER.

protein into the rough ER. **FIGURE 7.21** illustrates the key steps involved.

**Step 1** Protein synthesis begins on a free ribosome in the cytosol. The ribosome synthesizes the ER signal sequence.

**Step 2** The signal sequence binds to a **signal recognition particle (SRP)**—a complex of RNA and protein. The attached SRP causes protein synthesis to stop.

**Step 3** The ribosome + signal sequence + SRP complex moves to the ER membrane, where it attaches to the SRP receptor. Think of the SRP as a key that is activated by an ER signal sequence. The SRP receptor in the ER membrane is the lock.

**Step 4** Once the lock (the receptor) and key (the SRP) connect, the SRP is released and protein synthesis continues.

**Step 5** The growing protein is fed into the ER lumen through a channel, and the signal sequence is removed.

If the protein will eventually be shipped to the inside of an organelle or secreted from the cell, it is completely transferred into the lumen of the rough ER. If it is an integral membrane protein, part of it remains in the cytosol and rough ER membrane while it is being processed.

Once proteins are inside the rough ER or inserted into its membrane, they fold into their three-dimensional shape with the help of chaperone proteins (see Chapter 3). In addition, proteins that enter the ER lumen interact with enzymes that catalyze the addition of carbohydrate side chains (Figure 7.19). Because carbohydrates are polymers of sugar monomers, the addition of one or more carbohydrate groups is called **glycosylation** ("sugar-together"). The resulting molecule is a **glycoprotein**

("sugar-protein"; see Chapter 5). The number and arrangement of these sugars changes as the protein matures, serving as an indicator for shipment to the next destination.

## Moving from the ER to the Golgi

How do proteins travel from the ER to the Golgi apparatus? In Palade's pulse–chase experiment, labeled proteins found between the rough ER and the Golgi apparatus were inside membrane-bound structures. Based on these observations, Palade's group suggested that proteins are transported in vesicles that bud off from the ER, move away, fuse with the membrane on the *cis* face of the Golgi apparatus, and dump their cargo inside.

This hypothesis was supported when other researchers used differential centrifugation to isolate and characterize the vesicles that contained labeled proteins. They found that a distinctive type of vesicle carries proteins from the rough ER to the Golgi apparatus. Ensuring that only appropriate cargo is loaded into these vesicles and that the vesicles dock and fuse only with the *cis* face of the Golgi involves a complex series of events and is an area of active research.

## What Happens Inside the Golgi Apparatus?

Section 7.2 indicated that the Golgi apparatus consists of a stack of flattened vesicles called cisternae, and that cargo enters one side of the organelle and exits the other. Recent research has shown that the composition of the Golgi apparatus is dynamic. New cisternae constantly form at the *cis* face of the Golgi, while old cisternae break apart at the *trans* face, to be replaced by the cisternae behind it. In this way a new cisterna follows those formed earlier, advancing toward the *trans* face of the Golgi. As it does, it changes in composition and activity through a process called **cisternal maturation.**

By separating individual cisternae and analyzing their contents, researchers have found that cisternae at various stages of maturation contain different suites of enzymes. Many of these enzymes catalyze glycosylation reactions that further modify the oligosaccharides that were attached to the protein in the ER. As the cisternae slowly move from *cis* to *trans*, these enzymes are replaced with those representing more mature cisternae. The result is that proteins are modified in a stepwise manner as they slowly move through the Golgi.

If the rough ER is like a foundry and stamping plant where rough parts are manufactured, then the Golgi can be considered a finishing area where products are polished, painted, and readied for shipping.

## How Do Proteins Reach Their Destinations?

The rough ER and Golgi apparatus constitute an impressive assembly line. Certain proteins manufactured by this process remain in these organelles, replacing worn-out resident molecules. But those proteins that are simply passing through as cargo must be sorted and sent to their intended destination as the *trans* cisterna they are in breaks up into vesicles.

How are these finished products put into the right shipping containers, and how are the different containers addressed?

Studies on enzymes that are shipped to lysosomes have provided some answers to both questions. A key finding was that lysosome-bound proteins have a phosphate group attached to a specific sugar subunit on their surface, forming the compound mannose-6-phosphate. If mannose-6-phosphate is removed from these proteins, they are not transported to a lysosome.

This is strong evidence that the phosphorylated sugar serves as a zip code, analogous to the nuclear localization signal and ER signal sequence discussed earlier. Data indicate that mannose-6-phosphate binds to a receptor protein in the membrane of the *trans*-Golgi cisterna. Regions that are enriched with these receptor–cargo complexes will form vesicles that, in turn, have proteins on their cytosolic surfaces that direct their transport and fusion with pre-lysosomal compartments. In this way, the presence of mannose-6-phosphate targets proteins for vesicles that deliver their contents to organelles that eventually become lysosomes.

**FIGURE 7.22** presents a simplified model of how cargo is sorted and loaded into specific vesicles that are shipped to different destinations. Each cargo protein has a molecular tag that directs it to particular vesicle budding sites by interacting with receptors in the *trans* cisterna. These receptors, along with other cytosolic proteins that are not shown, direct the transport vesicles to the correct destinations.

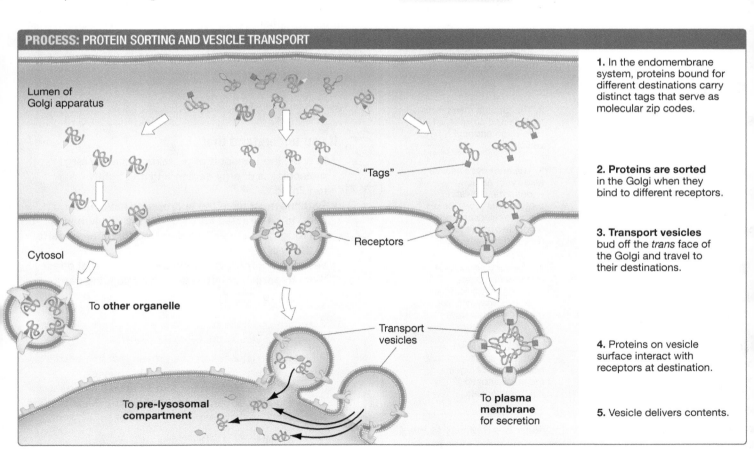

**PROCESS: PROTEIN SORTING AND VESICLE TRANSPORT**

Lumen of Golgi apparatus

"Tags"

Receptors

Cytosol

To **other organelle**

Transport vesicles

To **pre-lysosomal compartment**

To **plasma membrane** for secretion

1. In the endomembrane system, proteins bound for different destinations carry distinct tags that serve as molecular zip codes.

2. **Proteins are sorted** in the Golgi when they bind to different receptors.

3. **Transport vesicles** bud off the *trans* face of the Golgi and travel to their destinations.

4. Proteins on vesicle surface interact with receptors at destination.

5. Vesicle delivers contents.

**FIGURE 7.22 In the Golgi Apparatus, Proteins Are Sorted into Vesicles That Are Targeted to a Destination.**

In particular, notice that the transport vesicle shown on the right of Figure 7.22 is bound for the plasma membrane, where it will secrete its contents to the outside. This process is called **exocytosis** ("outside-cell-act"). When exocytosis occurs, the vesicle membrane and plasma membrane make contact. As the two membranes fuse, their lipid bilayers rearrange in a way that exposes the interior of the vesicle to the outside of the cell. The vesicle's contents then diffuse into the space outside the cell. This is how cells in your pancreas deliver digestive enzymes to the duct that leads to your small intestine—where food is digested.

## Recycling Material in the Lysosome

Now that you have seen how cargo moves out of the cell, let's look at how cargo is brought into the cell. Previously, you learned about how cells import small molecules across lipid bilayers (see Chapter 6), but this is not possible for large molecules like proteins and complex carbohydrates. For these molecules to be recycled and used by the cell, they must first be digested in the lysosome—but how do they get there?

**Endocytosis** ("inside-cell-act") refers to any pinching off of the plasma membrane that results in the uptake of material from outside the cell. **Receptor-mediated endocytosis** is illustrated in **FIGURE 7.23**. As its name implies, the sequence of events begins when macromolecules outside the cell bind to receptors on the plasma membrane. More than 25 distinct receptors have now been characterized, each specialized for binding to different cargo.

Once receptor binding occurs, the plasma membrane folds in and pinches off to form an endocytic vesicle. These vesicles then drop off their cargo in a transient organelle called the **early endosome** ("inside-body"). The activity of proton pumps in the membrane of this organelle acidifies its lumen, which causes the cargo to be released from their receptors. Many of these emptied cargo receptors are then repackaged into vesicles and returned to the plasma membrane.

As proton pumps continue to lower the early endosome's pH, it undergoes a series of processing steps that cause it to mature into a **late endosome.** The late endosome is the pre-lysosomal compartment introduced earlier (Figure 7.22), where the acid hydrolases from the Golgi apparatus are dropped off. As before, the emptied cargo receptors transported from the Golgi are removed from the late endosome as it matures into a fully active lysosome.

In addition to receptor-mediated endocytosis, the lysosome is involved in recycling material via autophagy and phagocytosis (see **FIGURE 7.24**). During **autophagy** (literally, "same-eating"), damaged organelles are enclosed within an internal membrane and delivered to a lysosome. There the components are digested and recycled. In **phagocytosis** ("eat-cell-act"), the plasma membrane of a cell surrounds a smaller cell or food particle and engulfs it, forming a structure called a phagosome. This structure is delivered to a lysosome, where it is taken in and digested.

Regardless of whether the materials in lysosomes originate via autophagy, phagocytosis, or receptor-mediated endocytosis, the result is similar: Molecules are hydrolyzed. ✔ If you understand the interaction between the endomembrane system

### PROCESS: RECEPTOR-MEDIATED ENDOCYTOSIS

**1.** Macromolecules outside the cell bind to membrane proteins that act as receptors.

**2.** The plasma membrane folds in and pinches off to form an endocytic vesicle.

**3.** The endocytic vesicle fuses with an early endosome, activating protons that lower its pH. Cargo is released and empty receptors are recycled to the surface.

**4.** The early endosome matures into a late endosome that receives digestive enzymes from the Golgi apparatus.

**5.** The late endosome matures into a functional lysosome and digests the endocytosed macromolecules.

*Labels in figure: Recycling of membrane proteins; Endocytic vesicle; Early endosome; Late endosome; Vesicle from Golgi apparatus; Lysosome*

**FIGURE 7.23 Receptor-Mediated Endocytosis Is a Pathway to the Lysosome.** Endosomes created by receptor-mediated endocytosis will mature into lysosomes.

check your understanding

**If you understand that . . .**

- In cells, the transport of proteins and other large molecules is energy demanding and tightly regulated.
- Proteins must have the appropriate molecular zip code to be directed into the nucleus, the lumen of the rough ER, or vesicles destined for different parts of the cell.
- Vesicles incorporate membrane proteins that direct them to particular target sites for unloading cargo.

**✔ You should be able to . . .**

1. Compare and contrast the movement of proteins into the nucleus versus the ER lumen.
2. Predict the final location of a protein that has been engineered to include an ER signal sequence, mannose-6-phosphate tag, and a nuclear localization signal. Justify your answer by addressing the impact of each signal on its transport.

*Answers are available in Appendix A.*

## (a) PROCESS: AUTOPHAGY

**Damaged organelle**

**Lysosome**

**1.** A damaged organelle is enclosed within a membrane (purple).

**2.** The membrane-bound organelle is delivered to a lysosome, which takes it in and begins digesting it.

**3.** Small molecules from the digested organelle are released into the cytosol.

## (b) PROCESS: PHAGOCYTOSIS

**Phagosome**

**Lysosome**

**1.** The plasma membrane detects a smaller cell or food particle and begins to engulf it.

**2.** The resulting membrane-bound vesicle is a phagosome.

**3.** The phagosome is delivered to a lysosome, which takes it in and begins digesting it.

**4.** Small molecules from the digested food particles are released into the cytosol.

**FIGURE 7.24 Two More Ways to Deliver Materials to Lysosomes.** Materials can be transported to lysosomes **(a)** via autophagy or **(b)** after phagocytosis.

and endocytosis, you should be able to predict how the loss of the mannose-6-phosphate receptor would affect receptor-mediated endocytosis.

It is important to note, however, that not all the materials that are surrounded by membrane and taken into a cell end up in lysosomes. In addition to receptor-mediated endocytosis and phagocytosis, small fluid-filled vesicles can be brought into a cell via **bulk-phase endocytosis.** There does not appear to be any cargo selection in bulk-phase endocytosis, and the vesicles are

not transported to lysosomes. These tiny vesicles are used elsewhere in the cell and are likely involved in recycling lipids deposited on the plasma membrane during exocytosis.

Throughout this section, vesicles have been key to the transport of cargo. If these transport steps depended on the random movement of diffusion alone, however, then the vesicles and their cargo might never reach their intended destinations. Are there instead defined tracks that direct the movement of these shipping containers? If so, what are these tracks, and what molecule or molecules function to transport the vesicles along them? Let's delve into these questions in the next section.

## 7.6 Cell Systems III: The Dynamic Cytoskeleton

The endomembrane system may be the best-studied example of how individual organelles work together in a dynamic, highly integrated way. This integration depends in part on the physical relationship of organelles, which is organized by the cytoskeletal system.

The cytoskeleton is a dense and complex network of fibers that helps maintain cell shape by providing structural support. However, the cytoskeleton is not a static structure like the scaffolding used at construction sites. Its fibrous proteins move and change to alter the cell's shape, shift its contents, and even move the cell itself. Like the rest of the cell, the cytoskeleton is dynamic.

As **TABLE 7.3** (see page 128) shows, there are three distinct cytoskeletal elements in eukaryotic cells: actin filaments, intermediate filaments, and microtubules. Recent research has shown structural and functional relationships between these three eukaryotic filaments and cytoskeletal elements in bacteria.

Each of the three cytoskeletal elements found in eukaryotes has a distinct size, structure, and function. Let's look at each one in turn.

### Actin Filaments

Sometimes called **microfilaments** because they are the cytoskeletal element with the smallest diameter, **actin filaments** are fibrous structures made of the globular protein actin (Table 7.3). In animal cells, actin is often the most abundant of all proteins—typically it represents 5–10 percent of the total protein in the cell. Each of your liver cells contains about half a billion of these molecules.

**Actin Filament Structure** A completed actin filament resembles two long strands that coil around each other. Actin filaments form when individual actin protein subunits assemble, or polymerize, from head to tail through the formation of noncovalent bonds.

Because the actin proteins are not symmetrical, this head-to-tail arrangement of actin subunits results in filaments that have two different ends, or polarity. The two distinct ends of an actin filament are referred to as plus and minus ends. The structural difference between these two ends results in different rates of

| Filament | Structure | Subunits | Functions |
|---|---|---|---|
| The three types of filaments that make up the cytoskeleton are distinguished by their size, structure, and type of protein subunit. | | | |
| Actin filaments (microfilaments) | Strands in double helix <br> 7 nm <br> − end    + end | Actin | • maintain cell shape by resisting tension (pull) <br> • move cells via muscle contraction or cell crawling <br> • divide animal cells in two <br> • move organelles and cytoplasm in plants, fungi, and animals |
| Intermediate filaments | Fibers wound into thicker cables <br> 10 nm | Keratins, lamins, or others | • maintain cell shape by resisting tension (pull) <br> • anchor nucleus and some other organelles |
| Microtubules | Hollow tube <br> 25 nm <br> − end    + end | α- and β-tubulin dimers | • maintain cell shape by resisting compression (push) <br> • move cells via flagella or cilia <br> • move chromosomes during cell division <br> • assist formation of cell plate during plant cell division <br> • move organelles <br> • provide tracks for intracellular transport |

sembling new actin subunits: The plus end grows faster than e minus end.

Each filament is generally unstable and will grow or shrink pending on the concentration of free actin subunits. In addi- n to controlling the availability of free actin, cells regulate the igth and longevity of microfilaments via actin-binding pro- ns that either stabilize or destabilize their structure.

In animal cells, actin filaments are particularly abundant just der the plasma membrane. They are organized into long, par- l bundles or dense, crisscrossing networks in which individ- actin filaments are linked to one another by other proteins. e reinforced bundles and networks of actin filaments help fen the cell and define its shape.

**in Filament Function** In addition to providing structural port, actin filaments are involved in movement. In several es, actin's role in movement depends on the protein myosin. osin is a **motor protein**: a protein that converts the potential rgy in ATP into the kinetic energy of mechanical work, just as ar's motor converts the chemical energy in gasoline into spin- g wheels.

The interaction between actin and myosin is frequently pre- ted in the context of how it produces muscle contraction and vement (Chapter 48). For now, it's enough to recognize that n myosin binds and hydrolyzes ATP to ADP, it undergoes a es of shape changes that extends the "head" region, attaches it ctin, and then contracts to pull itself along the actin filament. shape change of this protein causes the actin and myosin to e past each other. After repeated rounds of this contraction e, the myosin progressively moves toward the plus end of the n filament (**FIGURE 7.25a**). This type of movement is analogous n inchworm contracting its body as it moves along a stick.

**(a)** Actin and myosin interact to cause movement.

Myosin

ATP

ADP + P$_i$

"Head" region

+ end     Actin     − end

When myosin "head" attaches to actin and moves, the actin filament slides

**(b)** Examples of movement caused by actin–myosin interactions

**Cytokinesis in animals**

Actin–myosin interactions pinch membrane in two

**Cytoplasmic streaming in plants**

Actin–myosin interactions move cytoplasm around cell

Cell wall

**FIGURE 7.25 Many Cellular Movements Are Based on Actin–Myosin Interactions. (a)** ATP hydrolysis in the "head" region of myosin causes the protein to attach to actin and change shape. The movement slides the myosin toward the plus end of actin. **(b)** Actin–myosin interactions can divide cells and move organelles and cytoplasm.

As **FIGURE 7.25b** shows, the ATP-powered interaction between actin and myosin is the basis for array of cell movements:

- **Cytokinesis** ("cell-moving") is the process of cell division. In animals, this occurs by the use of actin filaments that are connected to the plasma membrane and arranged in a ring around the circumference of the cell. Myosin causes the filaments to slide past one another, drawing in the membrane and pinching the cell in two.

- **Cytoplasmic streaming** is the directed flow of cytosol and organelles within plant cells. The movement occurs along actin filaments and is powered by myosin. It is especially common in large cells, where the circulation of cytoplasm facilitates material transport.

In addition, the movement called **cell crawling** occurs when groups of actin filaments grow, creating bulges in the plasma membrane that extend and move the cell. Cell crawling occurs in a wide range of organisms and cell types, including amoebae, slime molds, and certain animal cells.

## Intermediate Filaments

Many types of **intermediate filament** exist, each consisting of a different—though similar in size and structure—type of protein (Table 7.3). Humans, for example, have 70 genes that code for intermediate filament proteins. This is in stark contrast to actin filaments and microtubules, which are made from the same protein subunits in all eukaryotic cells.

Moreover, intermediate filaments are not polar; instead, each end of these filaments is identical. They are not involved in directed movement driven by myosin or other motor proteins, but instead serve a purely structural role in eukaryotic cells.

The intermediate filaments that you are most familiar with belong to a family of molecules called the keratins. The cells that make up your skin and line surfaces inside your body contain about 20 types of keratin. These intermediate filaments provide the mechanical strength required for these cells to resist pressure and abrasion. Certain cells in the skin can also produce secreted forms of keratin. Depending on the location of the cell and keratins involved, the secreted filaments form fingernails, toenails, or hair.

**Nuclear lamins,** which make up the nuclear lamina layer introduced in Section 7.4, also qualify as intermediate filaments. Nuclear lamins form a dense mesh under the nuclear envelope. Recall that in addition to giving the nucleus its shape, they anchor the chromosomes. They are also involved in the breakup and reassembly of the nuclear envelope when cells divide.

Some intermediate filaments project from the nucleus through the cytoplasm to the plasma membrane, where they are linked to intermediate filaments that run parallel to the cell surface. In this way, intermediate filaments form a flexible skeleton that helps shape the cell surface and hold the nucleus in place.

## Microtubules

**Microtubules** are the largest cytoskeletal components in terms of diameter. As Table 7.3 shows, they are assembled from subunits

consisting of two polypeptides, called α-tubulin and β-tubulin that exist as stable protein **dimers** ("two-parts").

Tubulin dimers polymerize from head to tail to form filament that interact with one another to create relatively large, hollow tubes. Because of this polarity, these microtubules have α-tubulin polypeptides at one end (the minus end) and β-tubulins at th other end (the plus end). Like actin filaments, microtubules are dynamic and grow faster at their plus ends compared with thei minus ends.

Microtubules originate from a structure called the **microtubul organizing center (MTOC).** Their plus ends grow outward, ra diating throughout the cell. Although plant cells typically have hundreds of sites where microtubules start growing, most anima and fungal cells have just one site that is near the nucleus.

In animals, the microtubule organizing center has a distinc tive structure and is called a **centrosome.** As **FIGURE 7.26** shows animal centrosomes contain two bundles of microtubules calle **centrioles.** Although additional microtubules emanate from these structures in animals, they do not grow directly from th centrioles.

**(a)** In animals, microtubules originate from centrosomes.

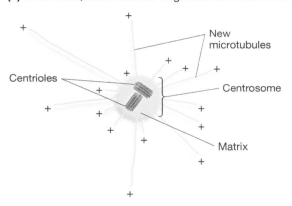

**(b)** Centrioles consist of microtubules.

**FIGURE 7.26 Centrosomes Are a Type of Microtubule-Organizing Center. (a)** Microtubule-organizing centers, such as the centrosomes of animal cells, are the sites where new microtubules are made. Microtubules grow from the matrix surrounding the centrioles, and their positive ends point away from the centrosomes. **(b)** The two centrioles inside a centrosome consist of microtubules as triplets arranged in a circle.

In function, microtubules are similar to actin filaments: They provide stability and are involved in movement. Like steel girders in a skyscraper, the microtubules that radiate from an organizing center stiffen the cell by resisting compression forces. Microtubules also provide a structural framework for organelles. If microtubules are prevented from forming, the network-like configuration of the ER collapses and the Golgi apparatus disappears into vesicles.

Microtubules are best known for their role in separating chromosomes during mitosis and meiosis (see Chapters 12 and 13). But microtubules are involved in many other types of cellular movement as well. Let's first consider their role in moving materials inside cells and then explore how microtubules can help cells to swim.

**Microtubules Serve as Tracks for Vesicle Transport** Recall from Section 7.5 that vesicles are used to transport materials to a wide array of destinations inside cells. To study how this movement happens, Ronald Vale and colleagues focused on the giant axon, an extremely large nerve cell in squid that runs the length of the animal's body. If the squid is disturbed, the cell signals muscles to contract so it can jet away to safety. The researchers decided to study this particular cell for three reasons.

1. The giant axon is so large that it is relatively easy to see and manipulate.

2. Large numbers of vesicles are transported down the length of the cell. As a result, a large amount of cargo moves a long distance.

3. The researchers found that if they gently squeezed the cytoplasm out of the cell, vesicle transport still occurred in the extracellular cytoplasmic material. This allowed them to do experiments on vesicle transport without the plasma membrane being in the way.

In short, the squid giant axon provided a system that could be observed and manipulated efficiently in the lab. To watch vesicle transport in action, the researchers mounted a video camera to a microscope. As **FIGURE 7.27** shows, this technique allowed them to document that vesicle transport occurred along filamentous tracks.

To identify the filament involved, the biologists measured the diameter of the tracks and analyzed their chemical composition. Both types of data indicated that the tracks consist of microtubules. Microtubules also appear to be required for movement of materials elsewhere in the cell. For instance, if experimental cells are treated with a drug that disrupts microtubules, the movement of vesicles from the rough ER to the Golgi apparatus is impaired.

The general message of these experiments is that transport vesicles move through the cell along microtubules. How? Do the tracks themselves move, like a conveyer belt, or are vesicles carried along on some sort of molecular vehicle?

**Motor Proteins Pull Vesicles Along the Tracks** To study the way vesicles move along microtubules, Vale's group took the squid axon's transport system apart and then determined what components were required to put it back together. A simple experiment convinced the group that this movement is an energy-dependent process: If they depleted the amount of ATP in the cytoplasm, vesicle transport stopped.

To examine this process further, they mixed purified microtubules and vesicles with ATP, but no transport occurred. Something had been left out—but what? To find the missing element or elements, the researchers purified one subcellular part after another and added it to the microtubule + vesicle + ATP system.

Through trial and error, and further purification steps, the researchers finally succeeded in isolating a protein that generated vesicle movement. They named the molecule **kinesin,** from the Greek word *kinein* ("to move").

Like myosin, kinesin is a motor protein. Kinesin converts the chemical energy in ATP into mechanical energy in the form of movement. More specifically, when ATP is hydrolyzed by kinesin, the protein moves along microtubules in a directional manner: toward the plus end.

Biologists began to understand how kinesin works when X-ray diffraction studies showed that it has three major regions: a head section with two globular pieces, a tail associated with small polypeptides, and a stalk that connects the head and tail (**FIGURE 7.28a**).

Follow-up studies confirmed that the head region binds to the microtubule while the tail region binds to the transport vesicle. Recent work has shown that kinesin uses these domains to "walk" along the microtubule through a series of conformational changes as it hydrolyzes ATP (**FIGURE 7.28b**). Amazingly, these motors have been found to "walk" up to 375 steps per second.

Cells contain several different versions of the kinesin motor, each specialized for a different role in the cell. If kinesins move

**a)** Electron micrograph

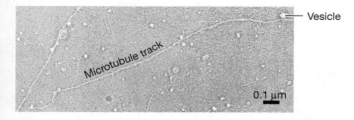

Vesicle

Microtubule track

0.1 μm

**b)** Video image

Vesicle

Microtubule track

0.1 μm

**FIGURE 7.27 Transport Vesicles Move along Microtubule Track.**
The images show extruded cytoplasm from a squid giant axon.
**a)** An electron micrograph that allowed researchers to measure the diameter of the filaments and confirm that they are microtubules. In the upper part of this image, you can see a vesicle on a "track."
**b)** A video microscope image using enhanced contrast that allowed researchers to watch vesicles move in real time.

**(a)** Structure of kinesin

Tail

Stalk

Head

5 nm

**(b)** Kinesin "walks" along a microtubule track.

Transport vesicle

Kinesin

Every step requires energy

ATP

ADP + P$_i$

Microtubule

− end

+ end

**FIGURE 7.28 Motor Proteins Move Vesicles along Microtubules. (a)** Kinesin has three distinct regions. **(b)** The current model depicting how kinesin "walks" along a microtubule track to transport vesicles. The two head segments act like feet that alternately attach, pivot, and release in response to the gain or loss of a phosphate group from ATP.

only toward the plus ends of microtubules, then what is responsible for moving the cargo in the opposite direction? By studying whole-cell locomotion, researchers discovered a motor that could move toward the minus end of microtubules.

## Flagella and Cilia: Moving the Entire Cell

Flagella are long, whiplike projections from the cell surface that function in movement. While many bacteria and eukaryotes have flagella, the structure is completely different in the two groups.

- Bacterial flagella are helical rods made of a protein called flagellin; eukaryotic flagella consist of several microtubules constructed from tubulin dimers.

- Bacterial flagella move the cell by rotating the rod like a ship's propeller; eukaryotic flagella move the cell by undulating—they whip back and forth.

- Eukaryotic flagella are surrounded by the plasma membrane and are considered organelles; bacterial flagella are not.

Based on these observations, biologists conclude that the two structures evolved independently, even though their function is similar.

To understand how some cells move, let's focus on eukaryotic flagella. Eukaryotic flagella are closely related to structures called **cilia** (singular: **cilium**), which are short, hairlike projections that are also found in some eukaryotic cells (**FIGURE 7.29**). Flagella are generally much longer than cilia, and the two structures differ in

Cilia

50 μm

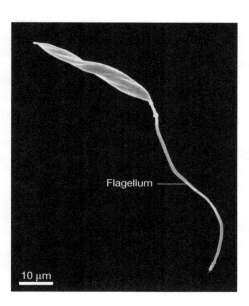

Flagellum

10 μm

**FIGURE 7.29 Cilia and Flagella Differ in Length and Number.** Cells typically only have 1–4 flagella but may have up to 14,000 cilia. The cells in these scanning electron micrographs have been colorized.

**(a)** Transmission electron micrograph of axoneme

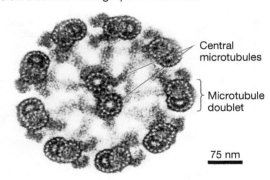

Central
microtubules

Microtubule
doublet

75 nm

**(b)** Structure of axoneme

Spoke

Plasma
membrane

Link

Dynein
arms

Central
microtubules

Microtubule
doublet

– end

**(c)** Mechanism of axoneme bending

Microtubule doublet

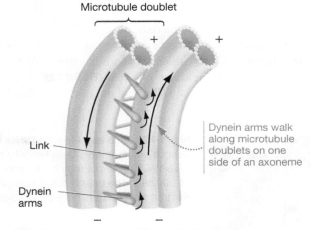

Link

Dynein
arms

Dynein arms walk
along microtubule
doublets on one
side of an axoneme

**+ ATP**: Causes dynein to walk toward minus end
and pull toward plus end

**FIGURE 7.30 The Structure and Function of Cilia and Flagella.**
**(a)** Transmission electron micrograph of a cross section through an
axoneme. **(b)** The microtubules in cilia and flagella are connected
by links and spokes, and the entire structure is surrounded by
the plasma membrane. **(c)** When dynein arms walk along the
microtubule doublets on one side of a flagellum, force is transmitted
to these links and spokes, causing the entire axoneme to bend.

✔**QUESTION** If the links and spokes were removed from the
microtubule doublets, what would happen to the axoneme after
adding ATP?

their abundance and pattern of movement. But when researchers
examined the two structures with an electron microscope, they
found that their underlying organization is identical.

**How are Cilia and Flagella Constructed?**   In the 1950s, anatomical studies established that most cilia and flagella have a characteristic "9 + 2" arrangement of microtubules. As **FIGURE 7.30a**
shows, nine microtubule pairs, or doublets, surround two central
microtubules. The doublets consist of one complete and one incomplete microtubule and are arranged around the periphery of
the structure.

The entire 9 + 2 structure is called the **axoneme** ("axle-
thread"). The nine doublets of the axoneme originate from a
structure called the **basal body.** The basal body is identical in
structure with a centriole and plays a central role in the growth
of the axoneme.

Through further study, biologists gained a more detailed view
of the axoneme's structure. Spoke-like proteins connect each doublet to the central pair of microtubules, and molecular links connect the nine doublets to one another (**FIGURE 7.30b**). Each doublet
also has a set of arms that project toward an adjacent doublet.

Axonemes are complex. How do their components interact to
generate motion?

**What Provides the Force Required for Movement?**   In the 1960s
Ian Gibbons began studying the cilia of a common unicellular
eukaryote called *Tetrahymena*. Gibbons found that he could isolate axonemes by using a detergent to remove the plasma membrane that surrounds cilia and then subjecting the resulting
solution to differential centrifugation. These steps gave Gibbons
a cell-free system for studying how the axonemes in cilia and flagella work. He found that the isolated structures would beat only
if he supplied them with ATP, confirming that the beating of cilia
is an energy-demanding process.

In another experiment, Gibbons treated the isolated axonemes with a molecule that disrupts interactions between proteins. The resulting axonemes could not beat even after being supplied with ATP. When Gibbons examined them in the electron microscope, he found that the treatment had removed the arms from the doublets. This result suggested that the arms are required for movement. Follow-up work showed that the arms are made of a large protein that Gibbons named **dynein** (from the Greek word *dyne*, meaning "force").

Like myosin and kinesin, dynein is a motor protein that uses ATP to undergo conformational changes. These shape changes move dynein along microtubules toward the minus end. Note that dynein moves in the opposite direction from the kinesin motor, which moves toward the plus end. In the cytoplasm, dynein motors are known to play various roles similar to the other motors, including the transport of vesicles. In the context of the axoneme, however, the outcome of dynein walking in the axoneme is very different.

So what is special about the axoneme? Remember that each of the nine doublets in the axoneme is connected to the central pair of microtubules by a spoke, and all the doublets are connected to each other by molecular links (Figure 7.30b). As a result, the sliding motion produced by dynein walking is constrained—if one doublet slides, it transmits force to the rest of the axoneme via the links and spokes (**FIGURE 7.30c**). If the dynein arms on just one side of the axoneme are activated, then the localized movement results in bending. The bending of cilia or flagella results in a swimming motion.

Scaled for size, flagella-powered swimming can be rapid. In terms of the number of body or cell lengths traveled per second, a sperm cell from a bull moves faster than a human world-record-holder does when swimming freestyle. At the cellular level, life is fast paced.

Taken together, the data reviewed in this chapter can be summed up in six words: Cells are dynamic, highly integrated structures. To maintain the level of organization that is required for life, chemical reactions must take place at mind-boggling speeds. How cells accomplish this feat is taken up elsewhere (see Chapter 8).

## If you understand . . .

### 7.1 Bacterial and Archaeal Cell Structures and Their Functions

- There are two basic cellular designs: prokaryotic and eukaryotic. The single defining characteristic that differentiates prokaryotes from eukaryotes is the absence of a nucleus.

- Structures common to most, if not all, prokaryotes are ribosomes, a cell wall, a plasma membrane, an interior cytoskeleton, and a nucleoid.

- Many prokaryotes also possess flagella, fimbriae, and internal membrane structures, some of which are considered organelles.

✔ You should be able to predict what would happen to cells that are exposed to (1) a drug that prevents ribosomes from functioning, (2) an enzyme that degrades the cell wall, or (3) a drug that prevents the assembly of the cytoskeleton.

### 7.2 Eukaryotic Cell Structures and Their Functions

- Eukaryotic cells are usually much larger and more structurally complex than prokaryotic cells.

- Eukaryotic cells contain numerous specialized organelles, which allow eukaryotic cells to compartmentalize functions and grow to a large size. Organelles common to most, if not all, eukaryotes are as follows:

  1. The nucleus, which contains the cell's chromosomes and serves as its control center.

  2. The endomembrane system, which consists of a diverse group of interrelated organelles, including the endoplasmic reticulum, Golgi apparatus, lysosomes or vacuoles, and endosomes. These organelles work together to synthesize, process, sort, transport, and recycle material.

  3. Peroxisomes, which are organelles where key reactions take place that often result in the generation of toxic by-products. Specialized enzymes are included that safely disarm these by-products soon after they are generated.

  4. Mitochondria and chloroplasts, which have extensive internal membrane systems where the enzymes responsible for ATP generation and photosynthesis reside.

✔ You should be able to predict what would happen to a plant cell that is exposed to (1) a drug that poisons mitochondria, (2) a drug that inhibits catalase in the peroxisome, or (3) a drug that inhibits the formation of centrioles.

### 7.3 Putting the Parts into a Whole

- Cells have a tightly organized interior, where the presence and quantity of organelles often reflect the function of the cell.

- The activity in a cell illustrates the dynamic nature of life. Organelles and cytosolic proteins continually bustle about with a seemingly nonstop rush hour.

- Much of what is known about cellular activity has come from advances in cell imaging and techniques for isolating cellular components.

You should be able to predict how a liver cell would differ compared with a salivary gland cell in terms of organelles.

## 7.4 Cell Systems I: Nuclear Transport

Cells have sophisticated systems for making sure that proteins and other products end up in the right place.

Traffic across the nuclear envelope occurs through nuclear pores, which contain a multiprotein nuclear pore complex that serves as gatekeeper.

Small molecules can passively diffuse through the nuclear pore. Larger molecules enter the nucleus only if they contain a specific molecular signal that directs them through the pore via nuclear transport proteins.

✓ You should be able to propose a hypothesis that would address how certain cytoplasmic proteins can be induced to enter the nucleus by either the addition or the removal of phosphates.

## Cell Systems II: The Endomembrane System Manufactures, Ships, and Recycles Cargo

Molecules synthesized in the ER may be transported as cargo to the Golgi apparatus and then to a number of different sites, depending on the cargo.

Before products leave the Golgi, they are sorted by their molecular "zip codes" that direct them to specific vesicles. The vesicles interact with receptor proteins at the target location so that the contents are delivered correctly.

The lysosome is built from enzymes and membranes that are made and processed through the endomembrane system. These organelles are involved in recycling products via autophagy, phagocytosis, and receptor-mediated endocytosis.

✓ You should be able to justify why proteins (see Chapter 3)—and not RNA, DNA, carbohydrates, or lipids—are the molecules responsible for "reading" the array of molecular zip codes in cells.

## 7.6 Cell Systems III: The Dynamic Cytoskeleton

The cytoskeleton is an extensive system of fibers that provides (1) structural support and a framework for arranging and organizing organelles and other cell components; (2) paths for moving vesicles inside cells; and (3) machinery for moving the cell as a whole through the beating of flagella or cilia, or through cell crawling.

- Subunits are constantly being added to or removed from cytoskeletal filaments. Actin filaments and microtubules are polarized, meaning different ends of the filaments are designated as plus or minus ends. The plus ends have a higher growth rate than the minus ends.

- Movement often depends on motor proteins, which use chemical energy stored in ATP to change shape and position. Myosin motors move toward the plus ends of actin filaments. Kinesin and dynein motors move along microtubules toward the plus and minus ends, respectively.

- A specific type of dynein is found in the axonemes of eukaryotic cilia and flagella. These motors move microtubules to generate forces that bend the structures and enable cells to swim or generate water currents.

✓ You should be able to predict which of the three motors presented in this section would be responsible for transporting vesicles from the Golgi to the plasma membrane.

# You should be able to . . .

1. Which of the following accurately describes a difference between prokaryotic and eukaryotic cells?
   a. Prokaryotic cells have fimbriae that allow the cell to swim whereas eukaryotic cells have flagella.
   b. Eukaryotic cells are generally larger than prokaryotic cells.
   c. Eukaryotic cells have organelles.
   d. Prokaryotic cells have nuclei and eukaryotic cells have nucleoids.

2. What are three attributes of mitochondria and chloroplasts that suggest they were once free-living bacteria?

3. Which of the following is *not* true of secreted proteins?
   a. They are synthesized using ribosomes.
   b. They enter the ER lumen during translation.
   c. They contain a signal that directs them into the lysosome.
   d. They are transported between organelles in membrane-bound vesicles.

4. Which of the following results provided evidence of a nuclear localization signal in the nucleoplasmin protein?
   a. The protein was small and easily slipped through the nuclear pore complex.
   b. After cleavage of the protein, only the tail segments appeared in the nucleus.
   c. Removing the tail allowed the core segment to enter the nucleus.
   d. The SRP bound only to the tail, not the core segment.

5. Molecular zip codes direct molecules to particular destinations in the cell. How are these signals read?
   a. They bind to receptor proteins.
   b. They enter transport vesicles.
   c. They bind to motor proteins.
   d. They are glycosylated by enzymes in the Golgi apparatus.

6. How does the hydrolysis of ATP result in the movement of a motor protein along a cytoskeletal filament?

7. Compare and contrast the structure of a generalized plant cell, animal cell, and prokaryotic cell. Which features are common to all cells? Which are specific to just prokaryotes, or just plants, or just animals?

8. Cells that line your intestines are known to possess a large number of membrane proteins that transport small molecules and ions across the plasma membrane. Which of the following cell structures would you expect to be required for this function of the cells?
   a. the endoplasmic reticulum
   b. peroxisomes
   c. lysosomes
   d. the cell wall

9. Most of the proteins that reside in the nucleus possess a nuclear localization signal (NLS), even if they are small enough to pass through the pore complex unhindered. Why would a small protein have an NLS, when it naturally diffuses across the pore without one?

10. Make a flowchart that traces the movement of a secreted protein from its site of synthesis to the outside of a eukaryotic cell. Identify all the organelles that the protein passes through. Add notes indicating what happens to the protein at each step.

11. Although all three cytoskeletal fibers constantly replace their subunits, only actin filaments and microtubules demonstrate differences in the rate of growth between the two ends. What is responsible for this difference, and why is this not observed in intermediate filaments?

12. Describe how vesicles move in a directed manner between organelles of the endomembrane system. Explain why this movement requires ATP.

13. Which of the following cell structures would you expect to be most important in the growth of bacteria on the surface of your teeth?
   a. cell wall
   b. fimbriae
   c. flagella
   d. cilia

14. The enzymes found in peroxisomes are synthesized by cytosolic ribosomes. Suggest a hypothesis for how these proteins find their way to the peroxisomes.

15. Propose an experiment that would determine if the NLS in nucleoplasmin is limited to this protein only or if it could direct other structures into the nucleus.

16. George Palade's research group used the pulse–chase assay to dissect the secretory pathway in pancreatic cells. If they had instead performed this assay on muscle cells, which have high energy demands and primarily consist of actin and myosin filaments, where would you expect the labeled proteins to go during the chase?

# 8 Energy and Enzymes: An Introduction to Metabolic Pathways

**In this chapter you will learn how**

Enzymes use energy to drive the chemistry of life

looking at energy, asking

What happens to energy in chemical reactions? **8.1**

Can chemical energy drive nonspontaneous reactions? **8.2**

looking at enzymes, asking

How do enzymes help speed chemical reaction rates? **8.3**

What factors affect enzyme function? **8.4**

How do enzymes work together in metabolic pathways? **8.5**

When table sugar is heated in the presence of oxygen, it undergoes the uncontrolled oxidation reaction known as burning. The heat energy in the flame is released as electrons are transferred from sugar to oxygen. Cells use the energy released from this type of reaction to drive the energy-demanding processes required for life.

## BIG PICTURE

This chapter is part of the Big Picture. See how on pages 198–199.

Cells are dynamic. Vesicles move cargo from the Golgi apparatus to the plasma membrane and other destinations, enzymes catalyze the synthesis of a complex array of macromolecules, and millions of proteins transport ions and molecules across cellular membranes. These activities change constantly in response to signals from other cells or the environment.

What drives all this action? The answer is twofold—energy and enzymes. Because staying alive takes work, there is no life without energy. Life, at its most basic level, consists of chemical reactions catalyzed by enzymes. By using enzymes to direct which reactions occur and which do not, life possesses the distinguishing feature of creating order from a naturally disordered environment.

✔ When you see this checkmark, stop and test yourself. Answers are available in Appendix A.

This chapter is about how enzymes work to help cells acquire and use energy. It is also your introduction to metabolic pathways—the ordered series of chemical reactions that build up or break down a particular molecule.

Let's begin by reviewing some fundamental concepts about energy and how it is used in cells.

## 8.1 What Happens to Energy in Chemical Reactions?

When biologists consider energy in chemical reactions, they often use the term **free energy** to describe the amount of energy that is available to do work. Recall that two types of energy exist: kinetic energy or potential energy (Chapter 2). **Kinetic energy** is energy of motion. There are several different forms of kinetic energy—at the molecular level, the energy of motion is called thermal energy. **Potential energy** is energy that is associated with position or configuration. In molecules, this is referred to as chemical energy and is stored in the position of electrons.

### Chemical Reactions Involve Energy Transformations

The existence of two types of energy does not mean that energy is locked into either the kinetic or the potential type. Energy is often transformed from one type to the other. To drive this point home, consider a water molecule sitting at the top of a waterfall, as in **FIGURE 8.1**.

***Step 1*** The molecule has potential energy ($E_p$) because of its position.

***Step 2*** As the molecule passes over the waterfall, its potential energy is converted to the kinetic energy ($E_k$) of motion.

***Step 3*** When the molecule reaches the rocks below, it undergoes a change in potential energy because it has changed position. The difference in potential energy is transformed into an equal amount of kinetic energy that is manifested in a variety of forms: mechanical energy, which tends to break up the rocks; heat (thermal energy), which raises the temperature of the rocks and the water itself; and sound.

The amount of potential energy in an electron is based on its position relative to other electrons and the protons in the nuclei of nearby atoms (see **FIGURE 8.2a** on page 138). If an electron is close to negative charges on other electrons and far from the positive charges in nuclei, it has high potential energy. In general, the potential energy of a molecule is a function of the way its electrons are configured or positioned.

An electron in an outer electron shell is analogous to the water molecule at the top of a waterfall (**FIGURE 8.2b**). If the electron falls to a lower shell, its potential energy is converted to the kinetic energy of motion. After the electron occupies the lower electron shell, it undergoes a change in potential energy. As panel 3 in Figure 8.1b shows, the change in potential energy is transformed

### PROCESS: ENERGY TRANSFORMATION IN A WATERFALL

$E_p$ (higher)

**1. Potential energy**
A water molecule sitting at the top of a waterfall has a defined amount of potential energy, $E_p$.

$E_k$

**2. Kinetic energy**
As the molecule falls, some of this stored energy is converted to kinetic energy (the energy of motion), $E_k$.

Mechanical energy   Heat   Sound
$E_p$ (lower)

**3. Other forms of kinetic energy**
When the molecule strikes the rocks below, its energy of motion is converted to thermal, mechanical, and sound energy. The molecule's potential energy is now much lower. The change in potential energy has been transformed into an equal amount of other forms of kinetic energy.

**Conclusion:** Energy is neither created nor destroyed; it simply changes form.

**FIGURE 8.1 Energy Transformations.** During an energy transformation, the total amount of energy in the system remains constant.

into an equal amount of kinetic energy—usually thermal energy, but sometimes light.

These examples illustrate the **first law of thermodynamics**, which states that energy is conserved. Energy cannot be created or destroyed, but only transferred and transformed.

The total energy in a molecule is referred to as its **enthalpy** (represented by $H$). Enthalpy includes the potential energy of the molecule, often referred to as heat content, plus the effect of the molecule on its surroundings in terms of pressure and volume.

**(a)** The potential energy of an electron is related to its position.

Electrons have the greatest potential energy in the outermost electron shells

Nucleus    1st    2nd    3rd    Electron shells

---

**(b) PROCESS: ENERGY TRANSFORMATION IN AN ATOM**

$E_p$ (higher)

**1. Potential energy**
An electron in an outer shell has a defined amount of potential energy, $E_p$.

$E_k$

**2. Kinetic energy**
As the electron falls to a lower energy shell, its potential energy is converted to kinetic energy, $E_k$.

Heat or light

$E_p$ (lower)

**3. Other forms of kinetic energy**
Once the electron arrives at a lower electron shell, the energy is converted to light or heat. The energy in the light or heat released is equal to the difference in potential energy between the outermost and inner shells.

**Conclusion:** Energy is neither created nor destroyed; it simply changes form.

**FIGURE 8.2 Chemical energy transformations** Potential energy energy stored in atoms or molecules may be transformed into kinetic energy by changes in electron position.

---

The contributions of heat, pressure, and volume to the enthalpy of a molecule are best understood by observing the changes in enthalpy in a chemical reaction. For example, let's examine the reaction responsible for the explosive bursts of scalding hot liquid a bombardier beetle can produce when provoked, as seen in **FIGURE 8.3**:

$$2\ H_2O_2(aq) \longrightarrow 2\ H_2O(l) + O_2(g)$$

In this reaction, hydrogen peroxide ($H_2O_2$) is broken down into water and $O_2$ gas, which expands to over 500 times the original volume of the $H_2O_2$. Heat given off from the reaction also increases the temperature of the liquid dramatically. These massive increases in temperature and volume generate the pressure that propels the boiling liquid out of an opening at the tip of the beetle's abdomen.

Changes in enthalpy in chemical reactions can be measured and are represented by $\Delta H$. (The uppercase Greek letter delta, $\Delta$, is often used in chemical and mathematical notation to represent change.) The value of $\Delta H$ is primarily based on the difference in heat content, since—apart from the reaction in the bombardier beetle—most biological reactions do not result in substantial changes in pressure and volume. When a reaction releases heat energy (products have less potential energy than the reactants), it is **exothermic** and the $\Delta H$ is negative. If heat energy is taken up during the reaction, generating products that have higher potential energy than the reactants, the reaction is **endothermic** and $\Delta H$ is positive.

Another factor that changes during a chemical reaction is the amount of disorder or **entropy** (symbolized by $\Delta S$). When the products of a chemical reaction become less ordered than the reactant molecules were, entropy increases and $\Delta S$ is positive. The **second law of thermodynamics,** in fact, states that total entropy always increases in an isolated system. Keep in mind that the isolated system in this case is the universe, which includes the surroundings as well as the products of the reaction.

To determine whether a chemical reaction is spontaneous, it's necessary to assess the combined contributions of changes in heat and disorder. Chemists do this with a quantity called the **Gibbs free-energy change,** symbolized by $\Delta G$.

$$\Delta G = \Delta H - T\Delta S$$

Here, $T$ stands for temperature measured on the Kelvin scale (see **BioSkills 1,** in Appendix B). Water freezes at 273.15 K and boils at 373.15 K.

In words, the free-energy change in a reaction is equal to the change in enthalpy minus the change in entropy multiplied by the temperature. The $T\Delta S$ term simply means that entropy becomes more important in determining free-energy change as the temperature of the molecules increases. Thermal energy increases the amount of disorder in the system, so the faster molecules are moving, the more important entropy becomes in determining the overall free-energy change.

Chemical reactions are spontaneous when $\Delta G$ is less than zero. Such reactions are said to be **exergonic.** Reactions are

**FIGURE 8.3 Reactions May Be Explosive due to Changes in Enthalpy.** When provoked, the bombardier beetle mixes reactants with enzymes in a special chamber near the tip of its abdomen. The enzyme-catalyzed reaction releases heat energy and oxygen gas. The result is the projection of boiling hot liquid at a predator.

nonspontaneous when $\Delta G$ is greater than zero. Such reactions are termed **endergonic.** When $\Delta G$ is equal to zero, reactions are at equilibrium. ✔ If you understand these concepts, you should be able to explain (1) why the same reaction can be nonspontaneous at low temperature but spontaneous at high temperature, and (2) why some exothermic reactions are nonspontaneous.

Free energy changes when the potential energy and/or entropy of substances change. Spontaneous chemical reactions run in the direction that lowers the free energy of the system. Exergonic reactions are spontaneous and release energy; endergonic reactions are nonspontaneous and require an input of energy to proceed.

## Temperature and Concentration Affect Reaction Rates

Even if a chemical reaction occurs spontaneously, it may not happen quickly. The reactions that convert iron to rust or sugar molecules to carbon dioxide and water are spontaneous, but at room temperature they occur very slowly, if at all.

For most reactions to proceed, one or more chemical bonds have to break and others have to form. For this to happen, the substances involved must collide in a specific orientation that brings the electrons involved near each other. (See Chapter 2 to review the forces involved in bond formation.)

The number of collisions occurring between the substances in a mixture depends on their temperature and concentration:

- When the concentration of reactants is high, more collisions should occur and reactions should proceed more quickly.

- When their temperature is high, reactants should move faster and collide more frequently.

Higher concentrations and higher temperatures should speed up chemical reactions. To test this hypothesis, students at Parkland College in Champaign, Illinois, performed the experiments shown in **FIGURE 8.4** (see page 140). Pay special attention to the two graphs in the "Results" section:

- *Temperature versus reaction rate* The graph on the left is based on experiments where the concentration of the reactants was the same, but the temperature varied. Each data point represents one experiment. Notice that the points represent a trend that rises from left to right—meaning, in this case, that the reaction rate speeded up when the temperature of the reaction mixture was higher.

- *Concentration versus reaction rate* The graph on the right is based on experiments where the temperature was constant, but the concentration of reactants varied. Each bar represents the average reaction rate over many replicates of each treatment, or set of concentrations. The thin lines at the top of each bar indicate the standard error of the mean—a measure of variability (see **BioSkills 4** in Appendix B). The take-home message of this graph is that reaction rates are higher when reactant concentrations are higher.

The reactions shown in Figure 8.4 were exergonic, meaning that the products had lower free energy than the reactants, so no input of energy was required. But, what drives nonspontaneous endergonic reactions? Let's take a closer look.

## 8.2 Nonspontaneous Reactions May Be Driven Using Chemical Energy

By definition, endergonic reactions require an input of energy to proceed. Recall that radiation from the Sun and electricity from lightning could have driven nonspontaneous reactions during

**QUESTION:** Do chemical reaction rates increase with increased temperature and concentration?

**RATE INCREASE HYPOTHESIS:** Chemical reaction rates increase with increased temperature. They also increase with increased concentration of reactants.

**NULL HYPOTHESIS:** Chemical reaction rates are not affected by increases in temperature or concentration of reactants.

**EXPERIMENTAL SETUP:**

Experimental reaction: $3\ HSO_3^-(aq) + IO_3^-(aq) \rightleftharpoons 3\ HSO_4^-(aq) + I^-(aq)$

**Reactant concentrations constant**
**Temperature increases**

Almost continuous variation in temperature

−1°C  3°C  9°C  12°C  21°C  22°C  35°C  38°C  50°C

**Reactant concentrations vary**
**Temperature constant**

Many replicates at each concentration

Treatment 1  Treatment 2  Treatment 3

| | Temperature increases | | Treatment 1 | Treatment 2 | Treatment 3 |
|---|---|---|---|---|---|
| Concentration of 3 $HSO_3^-$ (M): | 0.167 ⟶ 0.167 | | 0.167 | 0.167 | 0.333 |
| Concentration of $IO_3^-$ (M): | 0.167 ⟶ 0.167 | | 0.167 | 0.333 | 0.333 |
| Temperature (°C): | −1 ⟶ 50 | | 23 | 23 | 23 |

**PREDICTION:** Reaction rate, measured as 1/(time for reaction to go to completion), will increase with increased concentrations of reactants and increased temperature of reaction mix.

**PREDICTION OF NULL HYPOTHESIS:** There will be no difference in reaction rates among treatments in each setup.

**RESULTS:**

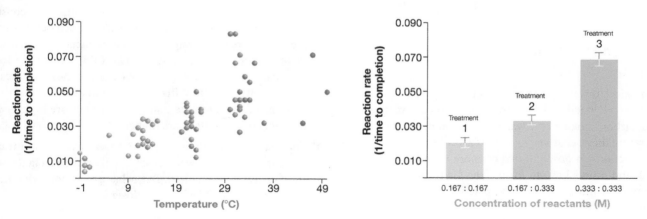

**CONCLUSION:** Chemical reaction rates increase with increased temperature or concentration.

**FIGURE 8.4 Testing the Hypothesis that Reaction Rates Are Sensitive to Changes in Temperature and Concentration.**

**QUESTION** Use **BioSkills 4** in Appendix B to explain why no error bars are used for the points shown on the graph on the left side of the "Results" section.

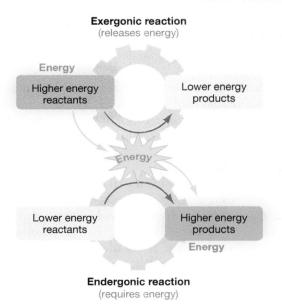

**Exergonic reaction**
(releases energy)

Energy

Higher energy
reactants

Lower energy
products

Energy

Lower energy
reactants

Higher energy
products

Energy

**Endergonic reaction**
(requires energy)

**FIGURE 8.5 Energetic Coupling Allows Endergonic Reactions to Proceed Using the Energy Released from Exergonic Reactions.**

chemical evolution (Chapter 2). What source of energy drives these reactions inside cells?

Exergonic reactions release free energy. **FIGURE 8.5** shows how **energetic coupling** between exergonic and endergonic reactions allows chemical energy released from one reaction to drive another. In cells, this process generally occurs in one of two ways, either through the transfer of high-energy electrons or the transfer of a phosphate group.

## Redox Reactions Transfer Energy via Electrons

Chemical reactions that involve the loss or gain of one or more electrons are called **reduction–oxidation reactions,** or **redox reactions.** When an atom or molecule loses one or more electrons, it is oxidized. This makes sense if you notice that the term

oxidized sounds as if oxygen has done something to an atom or molecule. Recall that oxygen is highly electronegative and often pulls electrons from other atoms (Chapter 2). On the other hand, when an atom or molecule gains one or more electrons, it is reduced. To keep these terms straight, students often use the mnemonic "OIL RIG"—**Oxidation** Is Loss of electrons; **Reduction** Is Gain of electrons.

Oxidation events are always paired with a reduction; if one atom loses an electron, another has to gain it, and vice versa. Since electron position is related to energy levels, redox reactions represent the energetic coupling of two half-reactions, one exergonic and one endergonic. Oxidation is the exergonic half-reaction, and reduction is the endergonic half-reaction. Some of the energy that is lost by the oxidized molecule is used to increase potential energy of the reduced molecule. In cases where more free energy is released by the oxidation step than is necessary for the reduction step, the overall reaction is exergonic.

The gain or loss of an electron can be relative, however. During a redox reaction, an electron can be transferred completely from one atom to another, or an electron can simply shift its position in a covalent bond.

**An Example of Redox in Action** To see how redox reactions work, consider the spontaneous reaction that occurs when reduced carbons in glucose ($C_6H_{12}O_6$) are oxidized as the sugar is burned in the presence of oxygen ($O_2$) (**FIGURE 8.6**). The orange dots in the illustration represent the positions of the electrons involved in covalent bonds.

Now compare the position of the electrons in the first reactant, glucose, with their position in the first product, carbon dioxide. Notice that many of the electrons have moved farther from the carbon nucleus in carbon dioxide. This means that carbon has been oxidized: it has "lost" electrons. The change occurred because the carbon and hydrogen atoms in glucose share electrons equally, while the carbon and oxygen atoms in $CO_2$ don't. In $CO_2$, the high electronegativity of the oxygen atoms pulled electrons away from the carbon atom.

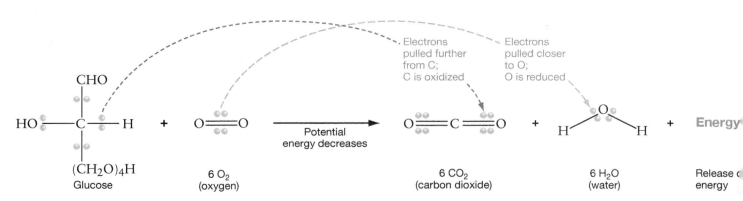

**FIGURE 8.6 Redox Reactions Involve the Gain or Loss of One or More Electrons.** This diagram shows how the position of electrons changes when glucose reacts with oxygen. The carbons of glucose are oxidized while the oxygen atoms of $O_2$ are reduced.

Now compare the position of the electrons in the reactant $O_2$ molecules with their position in the product water molecules. In water, the electrons have moved closer to the oxygen nuclei than they were in the $O_2$ molecules, meaning that the oxygen atoms have been reduced. Oxygen has "gained" electrons. Thus, when glucose burns, carbon atoms are oxidized while oxygen atoms are reduced.

These shifts in electron position change the amount of chemical energy in the reactants and products. When glucose reacts with oxygen, electrons are held much tighter in the product molecules than in the reactant molecules. This means their potential energy has decreased. The entropy of the products is also much higher than that of the reactants, as indicated by the increase in the number of molecules. As a result, this reaction is exergonic. It releases energy in the form of heat and light.

**Another Approach to Understanding Redox** During the redox reactions that occur in cells, electrons ($e^-$) may also be transferred from an atom in one molecule, called the **electron donor,** to an atom in a different molecule, the **electron acceptor.** When this occurs, the electron may be accompanied by a proton ($H^+$), which would result in the addition of a neutral hydrogen (H) atom to the electron acceptor.

Molecules that obtain hydrogens via redox reactions tend to gain potential energy because the electrons in C−H bonds are equally shared and hence relatively far from the positive charges in the C and H nuclei. This observation should sound familiar,

from what you have learned about carbohydrates (see Chapter 5). Molecules that have a large number of C−H bonds, such as carbohydrates and fats, store a great deal of potential energy.

Conversely, molecules that are oxidized in cells often lose a proton along with an electron. Instead of having many C−H bonds, oxidized molecules in cells tend to have an increased number of C−O bonds (see Figure 8.6). Oxidized molecules tend to lose potential energy. To understand why, remember that oxygen atoms have extremely high electronegativity. Because oxygen atoms hold electrons so tightly, the electrons involved in bonds with oxygen atoms have low potential energy.

In many redox reactions in biology, understanding where oxidation and reduction have occurred is a matter of following hydrogen atoms—reduction often "adds Hs" and oxidation often "removes Hs." For example, **flavin adenine dinucleotide (FAD)** is a cellular electron acceptor that is reduced by two electrons accompanied by two protons to form $FADH_2$ (**FIGURE 8.7a**). $FADH_2$ readily donates these high-energy electrons to other molecules. As a result, it is called an **electron carrier** and is said to have "reducing power."

Another common electron carrier is **nicotinamide adenine dinucleotide ($NAD^+$),** which is reduced to form **NADH.** Like FAD, two electrons reduce $NAD^+$. These two carriers differ, however, in the number of hydrogen atoms transferred. $NAD^+$ acquires only one of the two hydrogens and releases the second into the environment as $H^+$ (**FIGURE 8.7b**).

**(a)** Flavin adenine dinucleotide

$$AH_2 + FAD \longrightarrow A + FADH_2$$

**(b)** Nicotinamide adenine dinucleotide

$$BH_2 + NAD^+ \longrightarrow B + NADH + H^+$$

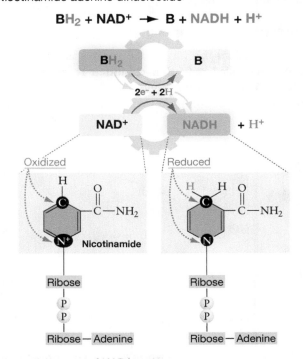

**FIGURE 8.7 Redox Reactions May Transfer Protons Along with Electrons.** The potential energy of $NAD^+$ and FAD is increased by redox reactions that transfer high-energy electrons, which may or may not be accompanied by protons. The products $FADH_2$ and NADH are important electron carriers.

The two examples in Figure 8.6 illustrate an important point—all redox reactions involve the transfer of electrons, but they do not always involve the transfer of hydrogens. Redox reactions are central in biology—they transfer energy via electrons. The energy released from certain key redox reactions (see Chapters 9 and 10) is used to drive the endergonic formation of the nucleotide ATP from ADP and $P_i$. How is the energy stored in ATP used by the cell?

## ATP Transfers Energy via Phosphate Groups

**Adenosine triphosphate (ATP)** (introduced in Chapter 4) makes things happen in cells because it has a great deal of potential energy. As **FIGURE 8.8a** shows, four negative charges are confined to a small area in the three phosphate groups in ATP. In part because these negative charges repel each other, the potential energy of the electrons in the phosphate groups is extraordinarily high.

**ATP Hydrolysis Releases Free Energy**   When ATP reacts with water during a hydrolysis reaction, the bond between ATP's outermost phosphate group and its neighbor is broken, resulting in the formation of ADP and inorganic phosphate, $P_i$, which has the formula $H_2PO_4^-$ (**FIGURE 8.8b**). This reaction is highly exergonic. Under standard conditions of temperature and pressure in the laboratory, a total of 7.3 kilocalories of energy per mole of ATP (or 7.3 kcal/mol), is released during the reaction. A **kilocalorie (kcal)** of energy raises 1 kilogram (kg) of water 1°C.

ATP hydrolysis is exergonic because the entropy of the product molecules is higher than that of the reactants, and because there is a large drop in potential energy when ATP breaks down into ADP and $P_i$. The change in potential energy occurs in part because the electrons from ATP's phosphate groups are now spread across two molecules instead of being clustered on one molecule—meaning that there is now less electrical repulsion.

In addition, the destabilizing effect of the negative charges is reduced in ADP and $P_i$ since these products interact with the partial positive charges on surrounding water molecules more efficiently than the clustered negative charges on ATP did.

**How Does ATP Drive Endergonic Reactions?**   In the time it takes to read this sentence, millions of endergonic reactions have occurred in your cells. This chemical activity is possible, in part, because cells are able to use the energy released from the exergonic hydrolysis of ATP.

If the reaction diagrammed in Figure 8.8b occurred in a test tube, the energy released would be lost as heat. But cells don't lose that 7.3 kcal/mole as heat. Instead, they use it to make things happen. Specifically, the energy that is released when ATP is hydrolyzed may be used to transfer the cleaved phosphate to a target molecule, called a **substrate.**

The addition of a phosphate group to a substrate is called **phosphorylation.** When ATP is used as the phosphate donor, phosphorylation is exergonic because the electrons in ADP and the phosphate added to the substrate have much less potential energy than they did in ATP.

To see how this process works, consider an endergonic reaction between two reactant molecules—compound A and compound B—that results in a product AB needed by your cells. For this reaction to proceed, an input of energy is required.

When a phosphate group from ATP is added to one or both of the reactant molecules, the potential energy of the reactant is increased. This phosphorylated intermediate is referred to as an activated substrate. This is the critical point: Activated substrates have high enough potential energy that the reaction between compound A and, for example, the activated form of compound B is now exergonic. The two compounds then go on to react and form the product molecule AB.

**(a)** ATP stores a large amount of potential energy.

**FIGURE 8.8 Adenosine Triphosphate (ATP) Has High Potential Energy. (a)** ATP's high potential energy results, in part, from the four negative charges clustered in its three phosphate groups. The negative charges repel each other, raising the potential energy of the electrons. **(b)** When ATP is hydrolyzed to ADP and inorganic phosphate, a large free-energy change occurs.

**(b)** Energy is released when ATP is hydrolyzed.

**FIGURE 8.9 Exergonic Phosphorylation Reactions Are Coupled to Endergonic Reactions.** In cells, many reactions only occur if one reactant is activated by phosphorylation. The phosphorylated reactant molecule has high enough free energy that the subsequent reaction is exergonic. In this graph, the free energy being tracked on the *y*-axis represents A, B, and the 7.3 kcal/mol that is released when ATP is hydrolyzed. For simplicity, the free energy in ADP and P$_i$ is not shown. $\Delta G$ represents the change in free energy between the reactants and products for each indicated step.

✔**EXERCISE** Label the $\Delta G$ in the uncoupled reaction and the two steps of the coupled reaction to indicate if the change is representing a positive ($>0$) or negative ($<0$) value.

**FIGURE 8.9** graphs how phosphorylation can couple exergonic and endergonic reactions. Note that the reaction between A and B to produce the product AB is endergonic—the $\Delta G$ is positive. But after the exergonic transfer of a phosphate group from ATP to B occurs, the free energy of the reactants A and BP is high enough to make the reaction that forms AB exergonic. When reactant molecules in an endergonic reaction are phosphorylated, the free energy released during phosphorylation is coupled to the endergonic reaction to make the combined overall reaction exergonic.

## check your understanding

### If you understand that . . .

- When redox reactions occur, electrons change position. Chemical energy is based on the positions of electrons in chemical bonds, so redox reactions usually involve a change in potential energy.
- ATP contains a cluster of three negatively charged phosphate groups.
- When ATP or phosphate groups from ATP bind to substrates, they gain a great deal of potential energy.

### ✔ You should be able to . . .

1. Explain why reduced molecules with many C—H bonds store more potential energy than oxidized molecules with many C—O bonds.
2. Explain why ATP has such high potential energy.

*Answers are available in Appendix A.*

✔ If you understand the principles of energetic coupling, you should be able to compare and contrast how energy is transferred via redox reactions and ATP hydrolysis.

It is hard to overstate the importance of energetic coupling: Without it, life is impossible. If the cells in your body could no longer drive endergonic reactions by coupling them to exergonic reactions, you would die within minutes.

Now the question is, What role do enzymes play in these reactions?

## 8.3 How Enzymes Work

Regardless of whether reactions in cells are spontaneous or not, none would occur at the speed required for life without the support of enzymes. How do they do it?

Recall that the initial hypothesis for how enzymes speed up reactions—the "lock-and-key" model—was first proposed in 1894 by Emil Fischer (introduced in Chapter 3). In this model, the substrates would fit into enzymes and react in a manner analogous to a key being inserted into a lock. In other words, enzymes are **catalysts**—they bring substrates together in a precise orientation that makes reactions more likely. Fischer's model also explained why many enzymes are specific for a single reaction—specificity is a product of the geometry and chemical properties of the sites where substrates bind.

### Enzymes Help Reactions Clear Two Hurdles

Recall that two hurdles must be cleared before reactions can take place: Reactants need to (1) collide in a precise orientation and

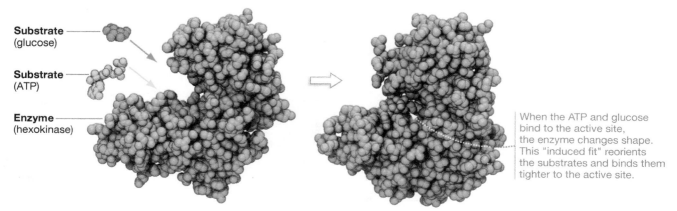

Substrate
(glucose)

Substrate
(ATP)

Enzyme
(hexokinase)

When the ATP and glucose bind to the active site, the enzyme changes shape. This "induced fit" reorients the substrates and binds them tighter to the active site.

**FIGURE 8.10 Reactant Molecules Bind to Specific Locations in an Enzyme.** The reactant molecules, shown in red and yellow, fit into a precise location, called the active site, in the green enzyme. In this enzyme and in many others, the binding event causes the protein to change shape.

**(2)** have enough kinetic energy to overcome repulsion between electrons that come into contact as a bond forms (Chapter 2). To appreciate how enzymes work, let's consider each hurdle in turn.

**Enzymes Bring Substrates Together**   Part of the reason enzymes are such effective catalysts is that they bring substrate molecules together in a substrate binding site known as the enzyme's **active site** (Chapter 3). In this way, enzymes help substrates collide in a precise orientation so that the electrons involved in the reaction can interact.

Enzymes generally are very large relative to substrates and roughly globular. The active site is in a cleft or cavity within the globular shape. A good example can be seen in the enzyme glucokinase, which catalyzes the phosphorylation of the sugar glucose. (Many enzymes have names that hint at the identity of the substrate and end with -*ase*.) As the left side of **FIGURE 8.10** shows, the active site in glucokinase is a small notch in an otherwise large, crescent-shaped enzyme.

In Fischer's original lock-and-key model, enzymes were conceived of as being rigid—almost literally as rigid as a lock. As research on enzyme action progressed, however, Fischer's model had to be modified. Perhaps the most important realization was that enzymes are not rigid and static, but flexible and dynamic. In fact, many enzymes undergo a significant change in shape, or conformation, when reactant molecules bind to the active site. You can see this conformational change, called an **induced fit,** in the glucokinase molecule on the right side of Figure 8.10. Once glucokinase binds its substrates—ATP and glucose—the enzyme rocks forward over the active site to bring the two substrates together.

In addition, recent research has clarified the nature of Fischer's key. When one or more substrate molecules enter the active site, they are held in place through hydrogen bonding or other weak interactions with amino acids in the active site. Once the substrate is bound, one or more R-groups in the active site come into play. The degree of interaction between the substrate and enzyme increases and reaches a maximum when a temporary,

unstable, intermediate condition called the **transition state** is formed. When Fischer's key is in its lock, it represents the transition state of the substrate.

There is more to achieving this transition state than simply an enzyme binding to its substrates, however. Even if the reaction is spontaneous, a certain amount of kinetic energy is required to strain the chemical bonds in substrates so they can achieve this transition state—called the **activation energy.** How do enzymes help clear the activation energy hurdle?

**Enzymes Lower the Activation Energy**   Reactions happen when reactants have enough kinetic energy to reach the transition state. The kinetic energy of molecules, in turn, is a function of their temperature. (This is why reactions tend to proceed faster at higher temperatures.)

**FIGURE 8.11** (see page 146) graphs the changes in free energy that take place during the course of a chemical reaction. As you read along the *x*-axis from left to right, note that a dramatic rise in free energy occurs when the reactants combine to form the transition state—followed by a dramatic drop in free energy when products form. The free energy of the transition state is high because the bonds that existed in the substrates are destabilized—it is the transition point between breaking old bonds and forming new ones.

The $\Delta G$ label on the graph indicates the overall change in free energy in the reaction—that is, the energy of the products minus the energy of the reactants. In this particular case, the products have lower free energy than the reactants, meaning that the reaction is exergonic. But because the activation energy for this reaction, symbolized by $E_a$, is high, the reaction would proceed slowly—even at high temperature.

This is an important point: The more unstable the transition state, the higher the activation energy and the less likely a reaction is to proceed quickly.

Reaction rates, then, depend on both the kinetic energy of the reactants and the activation energy of the particular reaction—meaning the free energy of the transition state. If the kinetic

**IGURE 8.11 Changes in Free Energy during a Chemical Reaction.** he energy profile shows changes in free energy that occur over he course of a hypothetical reaction between a molecule A and molecule containing parts B and C. The overall reaction would e written as A + BC → AB + C. $E_a$ is the activation energy of the eaction.

**FIGURE 8.12 A Catalyst Changes the Activation Energy of a Reaction.** The energy profile for the same reaction diagrammed in Figure 8.11, but now with a catalyst present. Even though the energy barrier to the reaction, $E_a$, is much lower, $\Delta G$ does not change.

✔**QUESTION** Can a catalyst make a nonspontaneous reaction occur spontaneously? Explain why or why not.

nergy of the participating molecules is high, such as at high emperatures, then molecular collisions are more likely to over-ome the activation energy barrier. At this point, the transition tate is formed and the reaction takes place.

Enzymes don't change the temperature of a solution, though. Iow do they fit in?

Interactions with amino acid R-groups at the enzyme active ite stabilize the transition state and thus lower the activation nergy required for the reaction to proceed. At the atomic level, R-groups that line the active site may form short-lived covalent onds that assist with the transfer of atoms or groups of atoms rom one reactant to another. More commonly, the presence of cidic or basic R-groups allows the reactants to lose or gain a roton more readily.

**FIGURE 8.12** diagrams how enzymes lower the activation energy or a reaction by lowering the free energy of the transition state. Note that the presence of an enzyme does not affect the overall energy change, $\Delta G$, or change the energy of the reactants or the products. An enzyme changes only the free energy of the transition state.

Most enzymes are specific in their activity—they catalyze just a single reaction by lowering the activation energy that is required—and many are astonishingly efficient. Most of the important reactions in biology would not occur at all, or else proceed at imperceptible rates, without a catalyst. It's not unusual for enzymes to speed up reactions by a factor of a million; some enzymes make reactions go many *trillions* of times faster than they would without a catalyst.

It's also important to note that an enzyme is not consumed in a chemical reaction, even though it participates in the reaction. The composition of an enzyme is exactly the same after the reaction as it was before.

Enzyme catalysis can be analyzed as a three-step process. **FIGURE 8.13** summarizes this model:

**PROCESS: A MODEL OF ENZYME ACTION**

**1. Initiation:** Reactants bind to the active site in a specific orientation, forming an enzyme-substrate complex.

**2. Transition state facilitation:** Interactions between enzyme and substrate lower the activation energy required.

**3. Termination:** Products have lower affinity for active site and are released. Enzyme is unchanged after the reaction.

**FIGURE 8.13 Enzyme Action Can Be Analyzed as a Three-Step Process.**

1. **Initiation** Instead of reactants occasionally colliding in a random fashion, enzymes orient reactants precisely as they bind at specific locations within the active site.

2. **Transition state facilitation** Inside a catalyst's active site, reactant molecules are more likely to reach their transition state. In some cases the transition state is stabilized by a change in the enzyme's shape. Interactions between the substrate and R-groups in the enzyme's active site lower the activation energy required for the reaction. Thus, the catalyzed reaction proceeds much more rapidly than the uncatalyzed reaction.

3. **Termination** The reaction products have less affinity for the active site than the transition state does. Binding ends, the enzyme returns to its original conformation, and the products are released.

✔ If you understand the basic principles of enzyme catalysis, you should be able to complete the following sentences: (1) Enzymes speed reaction rates by _____ and lowering activation energy. (2) Activation energies drop because enzymes destabilize bonds in the substrates, forming the _____. (3) Enzyme specificity is a function of the active site's shape and the chemical properties of the _____ at the active site. (4) In enzymes, as in many molecules, function follows from _____.

## What Limits the Rate of Catalysis?

For several decades after Fischer's model was published, most research on enzymes focused on rates of enzyme action, or what biologists call enzyme kinetics. Researchers observed that, when the amount of product produced per second—indicating the speed of the reaction—is plotted as a function of substrate concentration, a graph like that shown in **FIGURE 8.14** results.

**FIGURE 8.14 Enzyme-Catalyzed Reactions Can Be Saturated.** At high substrate concentration, enzyme-catalyzed reactions reach a maximum rate. Uncatalyzed reactions slowly increase as substrate concentration increases.

✔**EXERCISE** Label the parts of the *catalyzed reaction curve* that represent where (1) the reaction rate is most sensitive to changes in substrate concentration and (2) most or all of the active sites present are occupied.

In this graph, each data point represents an experiment where reaction rate was measured when substrates were at various concentrations. The two lines represent two series of experiments one with the reactions catalyzed by an enzyme and the other uncatalyzed. As you read the curve for the catalyzed reaction from left to right, note that it has three basic sections:

1. When substrate concentrations are low, the speed of an enzyme-catalyzed reaction increases in a steep, linear fashion.

2. At intermediate substrate concentrations, the increase in speed begins to slow.

3. At high substrate concentration, the reaction rate plateaus at a maximum speed.

This pattern is in striking contrast to the situation for the uncatalyzed reactions, where the reaction speed is far slower, but tends to show a continuing linear increase with substrate concentration. The "saturation kinetics" of enzyme-catalyzed reactions were taken as strong evidence that the enzyme–substrate complex proposed by Fischer actually exists. The idea was that at some point, active sites cannot accept substrates any faster, no matter how large the concentration of substrates gets. Stated another way, reaction rates level off because all available enzyme molecules are being used.

## Do Enzymes Work Alone?

The answer to this question, in many cases, is no. Atoms or molecules that are not part of an enzyme's primary structure are often required for an enzyme to function normally. These enzyme "helpers" can be divided into three different types:

1. **Cofactors:** Inorganic ions, such as the metal ions $Zn^{2+}$ (zinc), $Mg^{2+}$ (magnesium), and $Fe^{2+}$ (iron), which reversibly interact with enzymes. Cofactors that now participate in key reactions in virtually all living cells are thought to have been involved in catalysis early on in chemical evolution (see Chapter 2).

2. **Coenzymes:** Organic molecules that reversibly interact with enzymes, such as the electron carriers NADH or $FADH_2$.

3. **Prosthetic groups:** Non-amino acid atoms or molecules that are permanently attached to proteins, such as the molecule retinal. Retinal is involved in converting light energy into chemical energy (see Chapter 47).

In many cases, these enzyme helpers are part of the active site and play a key role in stabilizing the transition state. Their presence is therefore essential for the catalytic activity of many enzymes.

To appreciate why this is important, consider that many of the vitamins in your diet are required for the production of coenzymes. Vitamin deficiencies result in coenzyme deficiencies. Lack of coenzymes, in turn, disrupts normal enzyme function and causes disease. For example, thiamine (vitamin $B_1$) is required for the production of a coenzyme called thiamine pyrophosphate, which is required by three different enzymes. Lack of thiamine in the diet dramatically reduces the activity of these enzymes and causes an array of nervous system and heart disorders collectively known as beriberi.

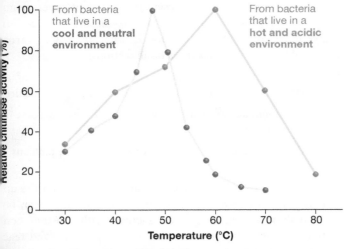

**(a)** Enzymes from different organisms may function best at different temperatures.

From bacteria that live in a **cool and neutral environment**

From bacteria that live in a **hot and acidic environment**

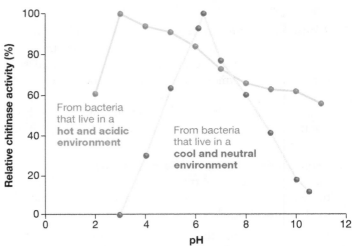

**(b)** Enzymes from different organisms may function best at different pHs.

From bacteria that live in a **hot and acidic environment**

From bacteria that live in a **cool and neutral environment**

**FIGURE 8.15 Enzymes Have an Optimal Temperature and pH.** The activity of enzymes is sensitive to changes in temperature **(a)** and pH **(b)**.

DATA: Nawani, N., B. P. Kapadnis, A. D. Das, et al. 2002. *Journal of Applied Microbiology* 93: 865–975. Also Nawani, N., and B. P. Kapadnis. 2001. *Journal of Applied Microbiology* 90: 803–808.

## 8.4 What Factors Affect Enzyme Function?

Given that an enzyme's structure is critical to its function, it's not surprising that an enzyme's activity is sensitive to conditions that alter protein shape. Recall that protein structure is dependent on the sequence of amino acids and a variety of chemical bonds and interactions that fold the polypeptide into its functional form (Chapter 3).

In particular, the activity of an enzyme often changes drastically as a function of temperature, pH, interactions with other molecules, and modifications of its primary structure. Let's take a look at how enzyme function is affected by, and sometimes even regulated by, each of these factors.

### Enzymes Are Optimized for Particular Environments

Temperature affects the folding and movement of an enzyme as well as the kinetic energy of its substrates. The concentration of protons in a solution, as measured by pH, also affects enzyme structure and function. pH affects the charge on carboxyl and amino groups in residue side chains, and also the active site's ability to participate in reactions that involve the transfer of protons or electrons.

Do data support these assertions? **FIGURE 8.15a** shows how the activity of an enzyme, plotted on the *y*-axis, changes as a function of temperature, plotted on the *x*-axis. These data were collected for an enzyme called chitinase, which is used by bacteria to digest cell walls of fungi. In this graph, each data point represents the enzyme's relative activity—meaning the rate of the enzyme-catalyzed reaction, scaled relative to the highest rate observed—in

experiments conducted under conditions that differed only in temperature. Results are shown for two types of bacteria.

Note that, in both bacterial species, the enzyme has a distinct optimum or peak—a temperature at which it functions best. One of the bacterial species lives in the cool soil under palm trees, where the temperature is about 25°C, while the other lives in hot springs, where temperatures can be close to 100°C. The temperature optimum for the enzyme reflects these environments.

The two types of bacteria have different versions of the enzyme that differ in primary structure. Natural selection (introduced in Chapter 1) has favored a structure in each species that is best suited for its distinct environment. The two versions are adaptations that allow each species to thrive at different temperatures.

**FIGURE 8.15b** makes the same point for pH. The effect of pH on enzyme activity was tested on the same chitinases used in Figure 8.15a, but this time using conditions that varied only in pH. The soil-dwelling bacteria described earlier grow in a neutral pH environment, but the species that lives in hot springs is also exposed to acidic conditions.

Note that the organism that thrives in a hot, acidic environment has a version of the enzyme that performs best at high temperatures and low pH; the organism that lives in the cool soil has a version of the enzyme that functions best at cooler temperatures and nearly neutral pH. Each enzyme is sensitive to changes in temperature and pH, but each species' version of the enzyme has a structure that allows it to function best in its particular environment.

To summarize, the rate of an enzyme-catalyzed reaction depends not only on substrate concentration and the enzyme's intrinsic affinity for the substrate but also on temperature and pH (among other factors). Temperature affects the movement of the substrates and enzyme; pH affects the enzyme's shape and reactivity.

**(a)** Competitive inhibition      **(b)** Allosteric regulation

Substrates

Enzyme

*or*

**Enzyme in absence of regulation**

Regulatory molecule

**Competitive inhibition**
The substrates cannot bind when a regulatory molecule binds to the enzyme's active site.

*or*

Shape changes

Regulatory molecule

**Allosteric activation**
The active site becomes available to the substrates when a regulatory molecule binds to a different site on the enzyme.

*or*

Shape changes

Regulatory molecule

**Allosteric inhibition**
The active site becomes unavailable to the substrates when a regulatory molecule binds to a different site on the enzyme.

**FIGURE 8.16 An Enzyme's Activity Is Precisely Regulated.** Enzymes are turned on or off when specific regulatory molecules bind to them.

## Most Enzymes Are Regulated

Controlling when and where enzymes will function is vital to the work of a cell. While temperature and pH affect the activity of enzymes, they are not often used as a means of regulating enzyme function. Instead, other molecules, in some cases other enzymes, regulate most of the cell's enzymatic activity. These regulatory molecules often change the enzyme's structure in some way, and their activity either activates or inactivates the enzyme.

**Regulating Enzymes via Noncovalent Modifications** Many molecules that regulate enzyme activity bind non-covalently to the enzyme to either activate or inactivate it. Since the interaction does not alter the enzyme's primary structure, it is often referred to as a "reversible" modification.

Reversible modifications affect enzyme function in one of two ways:

1. The regulatory molecule is similar in size and shape to the enzyme's natural substrate and inhibits catalysis by binding to the enzyme's active site. This event is called **competitive inhibition** because the molecule involved competes with the substrate for access to the enzyme's active site (**FIGURE 8.16a**).

2. The regulatory molecule binds at a location other than the active site and changes the shape of the enzyme. This type of regulation is called **allosteric** ("different-structure") **regulation** because the binding event changes the shape of the enzyme in a way that makes the active site available or unavailable (**FIGURE 8.16b**).

Both strategies depend on the concentration of the regulatory molecule—the more regulatory molecule present, the more likely it will be to bind to the enzyme and affect its activity. The amount of regulatory molecule is often tightly controlled and, as you'll see in Section 8.5, the regulatory molecules themselves often manage the enzymes that produce them.

**Regulating Enzymes via Covalent Modifications** In some cases, the function of an enzyme is altered by a chemical change in its primary structure. This change may be reversible or irreversible, depending on the type of modification.

Irreversible changes often result from the cleavage of peptide bonds that make up the primary structure of the enzyme. The enzyme trypsin, for example, is not functional until a small section of the protein is removed by a specific protease.

The most common modification of enzymes is the addition of one or more phosphate groups, similar to what was described for activated substrates in Section 8.2. In this case, however, the enzyme is phosphorylated instead of the substrate molecule. The transfer of a phosphate from ATP to the enzyme may be catalyzed by the enzyme itself or by a different enzyme.

When phosphorylation adds a negative charge to one or more amino acid residues in a protein, the electrons in that part of the protein change configuration. The enzyme's conformation

**check your understanding**

**If you understand that . . .**

- An enzyme's function is dependent on its folded structure.
- Enzymes have been optimized to fold into functional structures at particular environmental conditions, such as temperature and pH.
- An enzyme's activity is often regulated by an alteration to its structure.

✔ **You should be able to . . .**

1. Explain why the relative activity appears to drop off in Figure 8.15b, when it has been shown that reaction rates tend to increase at higher temperatures (Figure 8.4).

2. Predict how the shape change that occurs when an enzyme is phosphorylated would affect its catalytic activity.

*Answers are available in Appendix A.*

| Unphosphorylated form (inactive) | Phosphorylated form (active) |
|---|---|

Sites of phosphorylation

Phosphate groups cause green loop to move

**FIGURE 8.17 Phosphorylation Changes the Shape and Activity of Proteins.** When proteins are phosphorylated, they often change shape in a way that alters their activity. The figure shows the subtle structural change that occurs when mitogen-activated protein kinase (MAPK) is activated by adding two phosphate groups (yellow) to the enzyme.

usually changes as well, which may activate or inactivate its function. Note that although a substrate or an enzyme may be "activated" via phosphorylation, this activation does not represent the same effect. When a substrate is activated, its potential energy has increased, and this energy is used to convert an endergonic reaction to one that is exergonic. When an enzyme is activated, its catalytic function has been turned on—any change in the potential energy of the enzyme is not directly used in driving the reaction.

To see how phosphorylation affects the shape and activity of an enzyme, let's look at an enzyme called mitogen-activated protein kinase (MAPK), which is involved in cell signaling (see Chapter 11). As shown in **FIGURE 8.17**, phosphorylation of amino acid residues in a particular loop of the primary sequence causes a shape change, which functions like a switch to activate the enzyme.

Phosphorylation of an enzyme is a reversible modification to the protein's structure. Dephosphorylation—removal of phosphates—can quickly return the protein to its previous shape. The relative abundance of enzymes that catalyze phosphorylation and dephosphorylation, then, regulates the function of the protein.

## 8.5 Enzymes Can Work Together in Metabolic Pathways

The eukaryotic cell has been compared to an industrial complex, where distinct organelles are functionally integrated into a cooperative network with a common goal—life (see Chapter 7). Similarly, enzymes often work together in a manner resembling an

assembly line in a factory. Each of the molecules of life presented in this book is built by a series of reactions, each catalyzed by a different enzyme. These multistep processes are referred to as **metabolic pathways.**

The following is an example of this type of teamwork, where an initial substrate A is sequentially modified by enzymes 1–3 to produce product D:

$$A \xrightarrow{\text{enzyme 1}} B \xrightarrow{\text{enzyme 2}} C \xrightarrow{\text{enzyme 3}} D$$

The B and C molecules are referred to as intermediates in the pathway—they serve as both a product and a reactant. For example, molecule B is the product of reaction 1 and the reactant for reaction 2.

Although these reactions have been written in a single direction, from left to right, the directionality is dependent on the relative concentrations of the reactants and products. At equilibrium, however, the concentration of the product for each reaction will be higher than the concentration of its respective reactant. Since D is the overall product for this pathway, it will have the highest concentration at equilibrium.

## Metabolic Pathways Are Regulated

Since enzymes catalyze the reactions in metabolic pathways, the mechanisms that regulate enzyme function introduced in Section 8.4 also apply to the individual steps in a pathway. For example, to understand how blocking an individual reaction can affect an entire pathway, go back to the three-step model presented earlier and inactivate enzyme 2 by crossing it out. ✔ If you understand the assembly-line behavior of enzymes in a metabolic pathway, you should be able to predict how inactivating enzyme 2 would affect the concentration of molecules A, B, C, and D relative to what they would be if the pathway were fully functional.

When an enzyme in a pathway is inhibited by the product of the reaction sequence, **feedback inhibition** occurs. This is a convenient way for pathways to shut themselves down when their activity is no longer needed. As the concentration of the product molecule becomes abundant, it "feeds back" to stop the reaction sequence (**FIGURE 8.18**). By inhibiting a step early in the pathway, the amount of the initial substrate is not depleted unnecessarily, allowing it to be stored or used for other reactions.

## Metabolic Pathways Evolve

While many enzymes are extraordinarily specific, some can catalyze a range of reactions and are able to interact with a family of related substrates. Research suggests that this flexibility allowed new enzymes to evolve and that enzymes specialized for catalyzing key reactions provided cells with a selective advantage. Could the same flexibility also help explain the evolution of the stepwise series of reactions seen in metabolic pathways?

In 1945, Norman Horowitz proposed a simple, stepwise process that could have directed pathway evolution. In Horowitz's model, enzymes first would have evolved to make the building blocks of life from readily available substrates, such as small organic compounds (see Chapter 2).

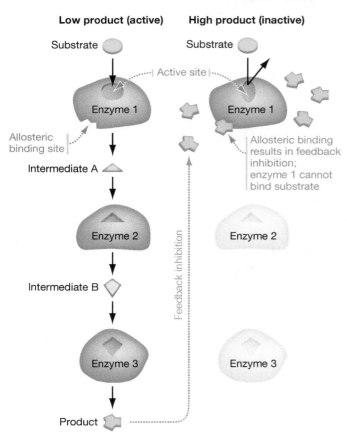

**Low product (active)**   **High product (inactive)**

Substrate

Active site

Enzyme 1

Allosteric
binding site

Intermediate A

Enzyme 2

Intermediate B

Feedback inhibition

Enzyme 3

Product

Substrate

Enzyme 1

Allosteric binding
results in feedback
inhibition;
enzyme 1 cannot
bind substrate

Enzyme 2

Enzyme 3

**FIGURE 8.18 Feedback Inhibition May Regulate Metabolic Pathways.** Feedback inhibition occurs when the product of a metabolic pathway inhibits an enzyme that functions early in the pathway.

If an original substrate were depleted, natural selection would next favor the evolution of a new enzyme to make more of it from other existing molecules. By evolving a new reaction step to produce the original substrate—now serving as an intermediate in a two-step pathway—the original enzyme would have been able to continue its work. **FIGURE 8.19** illustrates this model—referred to as retro-evolution—in which repetition of this backward process produces a multistep metabolic pathway.

Researchers also speculate that as early pathways emerged, early enzymes may have been recruited to new pathways, where they evolved new catalytic activities that performed new tasks. This hypothesis is called patchwork evolution, since the new reaction series would consist of enzymes brought together from different pathways.

Evidence of patchwork evolution has been observed in modern organisms, where new metabolic activities have emerged in response to human-made chemicals. For example, a novel pathway has recently evolved in one species of bacterium to break down the pesticide pentachlorophenol, for use as a source of energy and carbon building blocks. Pentachlorophenol was first introduced into the environment in the 1930s as a timber preservative. The new pathway uses enzymes from two preexisting pathways, which had evolved the ability to work together. The metabolic activity of microbes is now being scrutinized and engineered to clean up a variety of human-made pollutants—giving rise to a new technology called **bioremediation** (see Chapter 29).

Regardless of how they evolved, metabolic pathways are now vital to the function of all cells. Those that break down molecules for sources of energy and carbon building blocks are called **catabolic pathways;** those that use energy and carbon building blocks to synthesize molecules are called **anabolic pathways.**

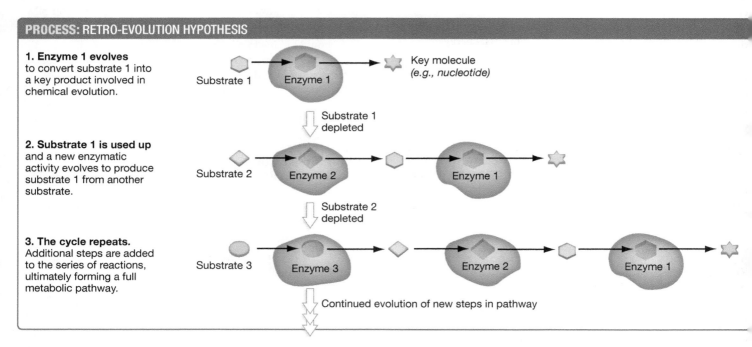

**PROCESS: RETRO-EVOLUTION HYPOTHESIS**

**1. Enzyme 1 evolves** to convert substrate 1 into a key product involved in chemical evolution.

Substrate 1    Enzyme 1    Key molecule *(e.g., nucleotide)*

Substrate 1 depleted

**2. Substrate 1 is used up** and a new enzymatic activity evolves to produce substrate 1 from another substrate.

Substrate 2    Enzyme 2    Enzyme 1

Substrate 2 depleted

**3. The cycle repeats.** Additional steps are added to the series of reactions, ultimately forming a full metabolic pathway.

Substrate 3    Enzyme 3    Enzyme 2    Enzyme 1

Continued evolution of new steps in pathway

**FIGURE 8.19 A Hypothetical Model for Metabolic Pathway Evolution.**

You are being kept alive by key catabolic and anabolic athways. The catabolic pathways of cellular respiration (in- oduced in Chapter 9) harvest high-energy electrons from re- uced carbons (from foods such as starch and sugar) and pass em through redox reactions to generate ATP. These reduced

carbons are produced by the anabolic pathways of photosynthe- sis that are driven by light energy (introduced in Chapter 10). The reactions involved in cellular respiration and photosynthe- sis perform the most important energy transformations to life on Earth.

# CHAPTER 8 REVIEW

For media, go to MasteringBiology

## f you understand . . .

### 8.1 What Happens to Energy in Chemical Reactions?

Spontaneous reactions do not require an input of energy to occur.

The Gibbs free energy change, $\Delta G$, summarizes the combined ef- fects of changes in enthalpy and entropy during a chemical reaction.

Spontaneous reactions have a negative $\Delta G$ and are said to be exer- gonic; nonspontaneous reactions have a positive $\Delta G$ and are said to be endergonic.

You should be able to explain why changes in enthalpy and en- tropy are used to determine whether a reaction is spontaneous.

### 8.2 Nonspontaneous Reactions May Be Driven Using Chemical Energy

Redox reactions transfer energy by coupling exergonic oxidation reactions to endergonic reduction reactions.

High-energy C—H bonds may be formed during the reduction step of a redox reaction when an $H^+$ is combined with a trans- ferred electron.

The hydrolysis of ATP is an exergonic reaction and may be used to drive a variety of cellular processes.

When a phosphate group from ATP is added to a substrate that participates in an endergonic reaction, the potential energy of the substrate is raised enough to make the reaction exergonic and thus spontaneous.

You should be able to explain what energetic coupling means, and why life would not exist without it.

### 8.3 How Enzymes Work

Enzymes are protein catalysts. They speed reaction rates but do not affect the change in free energy of the reaction.

The structure of an enzyme has an active site that brings sub- strates together. After binding to substrates, the structure of the enzyme changes to stabilize the transition state.

Activation energy is the amount of kinetic energy required to reach the transition state of a reaction. Enzymes speed up a reac- tion by lowering the activation energy.

Many enzymes function only with the help of cofactors, coen- zymes, or prosthetic groups.

You should be able to explain how an enzyme's active site can reduce the activation energy of a reaction.

### 8.4 What Factors Affect Enzyme Function?

- Enzymes are proteins, and thus their activity can be directly in- fluenced by modifications or environmental factors, such as tem- perature and pH, that alter their three-dimensional structure.

- Most enzymes are regulated by molecules that either compete with substrates to occupy the active site, or alter enzyme shape.

- Protein cleavage and phosphorylation are examples of how en- zymes may be regulated by modifying their primary structure.

✔ You should be able to compare and contrast the effect of alloste- ric regulation versus phosphorylation on enzyme function.

### 8.5 Enzymes Can Work Together in Metabolic Pathways

- In cells, enzymes often work together in metabolic pathways that sequentially modify a substrate to make a product.

- A pathway may be regulated by controlling the activity of one en- zyme, often the first in the series of reactions. Feedback inhibition results from the accumulation of a product that binds to an en- zyme in the pathway and inactivates it.

- Metabolic pathways were vital to the evolution of life, and new pathways continue to evolve in cells.

✔ You should be able to predict how the removal of the intermedi- ate in a two-step metabolic pathway would affect the enzymatic rates of the first and last.

### MasteringBiology

1. **MasteringBiology Assignments**

   **Tutorials and Activities** ATP and Energy; Chemical Reactions and ATP; Energy Transformations; Enzyme and Substrate Concentrations; Enzyme Inhibition; Factors That Affect Reaction Rate; How Enzymes Function; Regulating Enzyme Action; Redox Reactions

   **Questions** Reading Quizzes, Blue-Thread Questions, Test Bank

2. **eText** Read your book online, search, take notes, highlight text, and more.

3. **The Study Area** Practice Test, Cumulative Test, BioFlix® 3-D Animations, Videos, Activities, Audio Glossary, Word Study Tools, Art

# You should be able to . . .

**1.** The first law of thermodynamics states which of the following?
   **a.** Energy exists in two forms: kinetic and potential.
   **b.** Reactions will take place only if energy is released.
   **c.** Energy is conserved: it cannot be created or destroyed.
   **d.** Disorder always increases in the universe.

**2.** If a reaction is exergonic, then which of these statements is true?
   **a.** The products have lower free energy than the reactants.
   **b.** Energy must be added for the reaction to proceed.
   **c.** The products have lower entropy (are more ordered) than the reactants.
   **d.** The reaction occurs extremely quickly.

**3.** What is a transition state?
   **a.** the complex formed as covalent bonds are being broken and re-formed during a reaction
   **b.** the place where an allosteric regulatory molecule binds to an enzyme
   **c.** an interaction between reactants with high kinetic energy, due to high temperature
   **d.** the shape adopted by an enzyme that has an inhibitory molecule bound at its active site

**4.** What often happens to an enzyme after it binds to its substrate? Is this a permanent change?

**5.** How does pH affect enzyme-catalyzed reactions?
   **a.** Protons serve as substrates for most reactions.
   **b.** Energy stored in protons is used to drive endergonic reactions.
   **c.** Proton concentration increases the kinetic energy of the reactants, allowing them to reach their transition state.
   **d.** The concentration of protons affects the folded structure of the enzyme.

**6.** When does feedback inhibition occur?

**7.** Explain the lock-and-key model of enzyme activity. What was incorrect about this model?

**8.** If you were to expose glucose to oxygen on your lab bench, why would you not expect to see it burn as shown in Figure 8.6?
   **a.** The reaction is endergonic and requires an input of energy.
   **b.** The reaction is not spontaneous unless an enzyme is added to the substrates.
   **c.** The sugar must first be phosphorylated to increase its potential energy.
   **d.** Energy is required for the sugar and oxygen to reach their transition state.

**9.** Explain why substrate phosphorylation using ATP is an exergonic reaction. How does the phosphorylation of reactants result in driving reactions that would normally be endergonic?

**10.** QUANTITATIVE In Figure 8.9, the energetic coupling of ATP hydrolysis and an endergonic reaction are shown. If the hydrolysis of ATP releases 7.3 kcal of free energy, use the graph in this figure to estimate what you would expect the $\Delta G$ values to be for the uncoupled reaction and the two steps in the coupled reaction.

**11.** Compare and contrast competitive inhibition and allosteric regulation.

**12.** Using what you have learned about changes in free energy, would you predict the $\Delta G$ value of catabolic reactions to be positive or negative? What about anabolic reactions? Justify your answers using the terms enthalpy and entropy.

**13.** Draw a redox reaction that occurs between compounds $AH_2$ and $B^+$ to form A, BH, and $H^+$. On the drawing, connect the reactant and product forms of each compound and state if it is the reduction or oxidation step and how many electrons are transferred. If this represents an exergonic reaction, identify which of the five substances would have the highest-energy electrons.

**14.** Researchers can analyze the atomic structure of enzymes during catalysis. In one recent study, investigators found that the transition state included the formation of a free radical (see Chapter 2) and that a coenzyme bound to the active site donated an electron to help stabilize the free radical. How would the reaction rate and the stability of the transition state change if the coenzyme were not available?

**15.** Recently, researchers were able to measure movement that occurred in a single amino acid in an enzyme as reactions were taking place in its active site. The amino acid that moved was located in the active site, and the rate of movement correlated closely with the rate at which the reaction was taking place. Discuss the significance of these findings, using the information in Figures 8.10 and 8.13.

**16.** You have discovered an enzyme that appears to function only when a particular sugar accumulates. Which of the following scenarios would you predict to be responsible for activating this enzyme?
   **a.** The sugar cleaves the enzyme so it is now in an active conformation.
   **b.** The sugar binds to the enzyme and changes the conformation of the active site.
   **c.** The sugar binds to the active site and competes with the normal substrate.
   **d.** The sugar phosphorylates the enzyme, triggering a conformational change.

# 9 Cellular Respiration and Fermentation

This chapter is part of the Big Picture. See how on pages 198–199.

In this chapter you will learn how

Cells make ATP starting from sugars and other high potential energy compounds

by examining

How cells produce ATP when oxygen is present   **9.1**

by examining

How cells produce ATP when oxygen is absent

looking closer at

Glycolysis   **9.2**

Pyruvate oxidation **9.3**

Citric acid cycle **9.4**

Electron transport and chemiosmosis   **9.5**

focusing on

Fermentation   **9.6**

This hydroelectric dam on the Duero river between Spain and Portugal uses pumps to move water from the lower reservoir to the upper reservoir. During periods of high energy demand, the potential energy stored by this activity is used to generate electricity. A similar process is used by cells to produce ATP during cellular respiration.

ife requires energy. From the very start, chemical evolution was driven by energy from chemicals, radiation, heat, or other sources (see Chapter 2). Harnessing energy and controlling its flow has been the single most important step in the evolution of life.

What fuels life in cells? The answer is the nucleotide adenosine triphosphate (ATP). ATP has high potential energy and allows cells to overcome life's energy barriers (see Chapter 8).

This chapter investigates how cells make ATP, starting with an introduction to the metabolic pathways that harvest energy from high-energy molecules like **glucose**—the most common source of chemical energy used by organisms. The four central pathways of cellular respiration will be

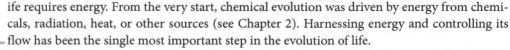

✔ When you see this checkmark, stop and test yourself. Answers are available in Appendix A.

presented with emphasis on how the oxidation of glucose leads to ATP production. Fermentation will also be introduced as an alternative pathway used to make ATP when key reactions in cellular respiration are either shut down or not available.

As cells process sugar, the energy that is released is used to transfer a phosphate group to adenosine diphosphate (ADP), generating ATP. (You can see the Big Picture of how the production of glucose in photosynthesis is related to its catabolism in cellular respiration on pages 198–199.)

## 9.1 An Overview of Cellular Respiration

In general, a cell contains only enough ATP to last from 30 seconds to a few minutes. Because it has such high potential energy, ATP is unstable and is not stored. Like many other cellular processes, the production and use of ATP is fast. Most cells are making ATP all the time.

Most of the glucose that is used to make ATP is produced by plants and other photosynthetic species. These organisms use the energy in sunlight to reduce carbon dioxide ($CO_2$) to glucose and other carbohydrates. While they are alive, photosynthetic species use the glucose that they produce to make ATP for themselves. When photosynthetic species decompose or are eaten, they provide glucose to animals, fungi, and many bacteria and archaea.

All organisms use glucose in the synthesis of complex carbohydrates, fats, and other energy-rich compounds. Storage carbohydrates, such as starch and glycogen, act like savings accounts for chemical energy. ATP, in contrast, is like cash. To withdraw chemical energy from the accounts to get cash, storage carbohydrates are first hydrolyzed into their glucose monomers. The glucose is then used to produce ATP through one of two general processes: cellular respiration or fermentation (**FIGURE 9.1**). The primary difference between these two processes lies in the degree to which glucose is oxidized.

### What Happens When Glucose Is Oxidized?

When glucose undergoes the uncontrolled oxidation reaction called burning, some of the potential energy stored in its chemical bonds is converted to kinetic energy in the form of heat:

$$C_6H_{12}O_2 + 6\,O_2 \longrightarrow 6\,CO_2 + 6\,H_2O + \text{Heat}$$
$$\text{glucose} \quad \text{oxygen} \quad \text{carbon dioxide} \quad \text{water}$$

More specifically, a total of about 685 kilocalories (kcal) of heat is released when one mole of glucose is oxidized. To put this in perspective, if you burned this amount of glucose, it would give off enough heat to bring almost 2.5 gallons of room-temperature water to a boil.

Glucose does not burn in cells, however. Instead, the glucose in cells is oxidized through a long series of carefully controlled redox reactions. These reactions are occurring, millions of

**FIGURE 9.1 Glucose Is the Hub of Energy Processing in Cells.** Glucose is a product of photosynthesis. Both plants and animals store glucose and oxidize it to provide chemical energy in the form of ATP.

times per minute, in your cells right now. Instead of releasing all of this energy as heat, much of it is being used to make the ATP you need to read, think, move, and stay alive. In cells, the change in free energy (Chapter 8) that occurs during the oxidation of glucose is used to synthesize ATP from ADP and $P_i$.

So how does fermentation differ from cellular respiration? Respiration, like burning, results in the complete oxidation of glucose into $CO_2$ and water. Fermentation, on the other hand, does not fully oxidize glucose. Instead, small, reduced organic molecules are produced as waste. As a result, cellular respiration releases more energy from glucose than fermentation.

The complete oxidation of glucose via cellular respiration can be thought of as a four-step process used to convert the chemical energy in glucose to chemical energy in ATP. Each of the four steps consists of a series of chemical reactions, and each step has a distinctive starting molecule and a characteristic set of products.

1. **Glycolysis** During **glycolysis,** one 6-carbon molecule of glucose is broken into two molecules of the three-carbon compound pyruvate. During this process, ATP is produced from ADP, and nicotinamide adenine dinucleotide ($NAD^+$) is reduced to form NADH.

2. **Pyruvate processing** Pyruvate is processed to release one molecule of $CO_2$, and the remaining two carbons are used to form the compound acetyl CoA. The oxidation of pyruvate results in more $NAD^+$ being reduced to NADH.

3. **Citric acid cycle** Acetyl CoA is oxidized to two molecules of $CO_2$. During this sequence of reactions, more ATP and NADH are produced, and flavin adenine dinucleotide (FAD) is reduced to form $FADH_2$.

4. **Electron transport and oxidative phosphorylation** Electrons from NADH and $FADH_2$ move through a series of proteins called an electron transport chain (ETC). The energy released in this chain of redox reactions is used to create a proton gradient across a membrane; the ensuing flow of protons back across the membrane is used to make ATP. Because this mode of ATP production links the phosphorylation of ADP with the oxidation of NADH and $FADH_2$, it is called **oxidative phosphorylation.**

FIGURE 9.2 summarizes the four steps in cellular respiration. Formally, **cellular respiration** is defined as any suite of reactions that uses electrons harvested from high-energy molecules to produce ATP via an electron transport chain.

The enzymes, products, and intermediates involved in cellular respiration and fermentation do not exist in isolation. Instead, they are part of a huge and dynamic inventory of chemicals inside the cell.

This complexity can be boiled down to a simple essence, however. Two of the most fundamental requirements of a cell are energy and carbon. They need a source of high-energy electrons for generating chemical energy in the form of ATP, and a source of carbon-containing molecules that can be used to synthesize DNA, RNA, proteins, fatty acids, and other molecules. Let's take a closer look at the central role cellular respiration plays in metabolic pathways as a whole.

## Cellular Respiration Plays a Central Role in Metabolism

Recall that sets of reactions that break down molecules are called catabolic pathways (Chapter 8). These reactions often harvest stored chemical energy to produce ATP. On the other hand, sets of reactions that synthesize larger molecules from smaller components are called anabolic pathways. Anabolic reactions often use energy in the form of ATP.

How does the process of cellular respiration interact with other catabolic and anabolic pathways? Let's first consider how

FIGURE 9.2 **Cellular Respiration Oxidizes Glucose to Make ATP.** Cells produce ATP from glucose via a series of processes: (1) glycolysis, (2) pyruvate processing, (3) the citric acid cycle, and (4) electron transport and oxidative phosphorylation. Each component produces high-energy molecules in the form of nucleotides (ATP or GTP) or electron carriers (NADH or $FADH_2$). Because the four components are connected, glucose oxidation is an integrated metabolic pathway. The first three steps oxidize glucose to produce NADH and $FADH_2$, which then feed the electron transport chain.

✔**EXERCISE** Fill in the chart along the bottom.

eukaryotes extract energy from molecules other than glucose and then examine how intermediates produced in glycolysis and the citric acid cycle are used as building blocks to synthesize cell components.

### Catabolic Pathways Break Down a Variety of Molecules

Most organisms ingest, absorb, or synthesize many different carbohydrates. These molecules range from sucrose, maltose, and other simple sugars to large polymers such as glycogen and starch (see Chapter 5).

Recall that both glycogen and starch are polymers of glucose, but differ in the way their long chains of glucose branch. Using enzyme-catalyzed reactions, cells can produce glucose from glycogen, starch, and most simple sugars. Glucose and fructose can then be processed in glycolysis.

Carbohydrates are not the only important source of carbon compounds used in catabolic pathways, however. Fats are highly reduced macromolecules consisting of glycerol bonded to chains of fatty acids (see Chapter 6). In cells, enzymes routinely break down fats to release the glycerol and convert the fatty acids into acetyl CoA molecules. Glycerol can be further processed and enter glycolysis. Acetyl CoA enters the citric acid cycle.

Proteins can also be catabolized, meaning that they can be broken down and used to produce ATP. Once they are hydrolyzed to their constituent amino acids, enzyme-catalyzed reactions remove the amino ($-NH_2$) groups. The amino groups are excreted in urine as waste. The carbon compounds that remain are converted to pyruvate, acetyl CoA, and other intermediates in glycolysis and the citric acid cycle.

The top half of **FIGURE 9.3** summarizes the catabolic pathways of carbohydrates, fats, and proteins and shows how their breakdown products feed an array of steps in glucose oxidation and cellular respiration. When all three types of molecules are available in the cell to generate ATP, carbohydrates are used up first, then fats, and finally proteins.

### Catabolic Intermediates Are Used in Anabolic Pathways

Where do cells get the precursor molecules required to synthesize amino acids, RNA, DNA, phospholipids, and other cell components? Not surprisingly, the answer often involves intermediates in carbohydrate metabolism. For example,

- In humans, about half the required amino acids can be synthesized from molecules siphoned from the citric acid cycle.

- Acetyl CoA is the starting point for anabolic pathways that result in the synthesis of fatty acids. Fatty acids can then be used to build phospholipid membranes or fats.

- Intermediates in glycolysis can be oxidized to start the synthesis of the sugars in ribonucleotides and deoxyribonucleotides. Nucleotides, in turn, are building blocks used in RNA and DNA synthesis.

- If ATP is abundant, pyruvate and lactate (from fermentation) can be used in the synthesis of glucose. Excess glucose may be converted to glycogen or starch and stored.

The bottom half of Figure 9.3 summarizes how intermediates in carbohydrate metabolism are drawn off to synthesize macromolecules. The take-home message is that the same molecule can serve many different functions in the cell. As a result, catabolic and anabolic pathways are closely intertwined.

Metabolism comprises thousands of different chemical reactions, yet the amounts and identities of molecules inside cells are relatively constant. By regulating key reactions involved in catabolic and anabolic pathways, the cell is able to maintain its internal environment even under different environmental conditions—a process referred to as **homeostasis.** Cellular respiration and

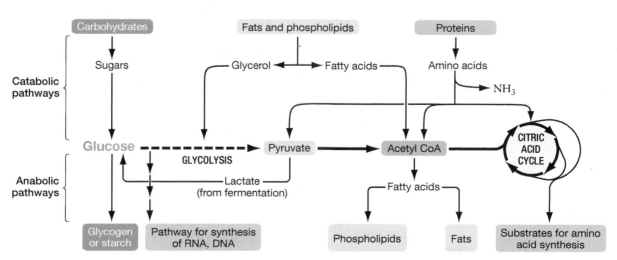

**FIGURE 9.3 Cellular Respiration Interacts with Other Catabolic and Anabolic Pathways.** A variety of high-energy compounds from carbohydrates, fats, or proteins can be broken down in catabolic reactions and used by cellular respiration for ATP production. Several of the intermediates in carbohydrate metabolism act as precursor molecules in anabolic reactions leading to the synthesis of glycogen or starch, RNA, DNA, fatty acids, and amino acids.

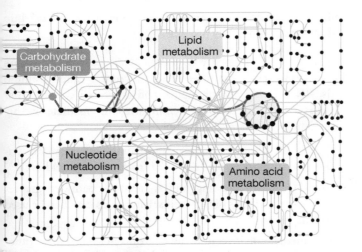

**FIGURE 9.4 Pathways of Cellular Respiration Play a Central Role in the Metabolic Activity of Cells.** A representation of a few of the thousands of chemical reactions that occur in cells. The dots represent molecules, and the lines represent enzyme-catalyzed reactions. At the center of all this, the first three steps of cellular respiration are emphasized by bold dots and thick lines. For reference, glucose, pyruvate, and acetyl CoA are represented by the distinctive colors used in Figure 9.3.

Fermentation pathways may be crucial to the life of a cell, but they also have to be seen as central parts of a whole (**FIGURE 9.4**).

Once you've filled in the chart at the bottom of Figure 9.2, you'll ready to analyze each of the four steps of cellular respiration in detail. As you delve in, keep asking yourself the same key questions: What goes in and what comes out? What happens to the potential energy that is released? Where does each step occur, and how is it regulated? Then take a look in the mirror. All these processes are occurring right now, in virtually all your cells.

## 9.2 Glycolysis: Processing Glucose to Pyruvate

Because the enzymes responsible for glycolysis have been observed in nearly every bacterium, archaean, and eukaryote, it is logical to infer that the ancestor of all organisms living today made ATP by glycolysis. It's ironic, then, that the process was discovered by accident.

In the 1890s Hans and Edward Buchner were working out techniques for breaking open baker's yeast cells and extracting the contents for commercial and medicinal use. (Yeast extracts are still added to some foods as a flavor enhancer or nutritional supplement.) In one set of experiments, the Buchners added sucrose to their extracts. At the time, sucrose was commonly used as a preservative—a substance used to preserve food from decay.

Instead of preserving the yeast extracts, though, the sucrose was quickly broken down and fermented, and alcohol appeared as a by-product. This was a key finding: It showed that metabolic pathways like fermentation could be studied in vitro—outside the organism. Until then, researchers thought that metabolism could take place only in intact organisms.

When researchers studied how the sugar was being processed, they found that the reactions could go on much longer than normal if inorganic phosphate were added to the mixture. This result implied that some of the compounds involved were being phosphorylated. Soon after, a molecule called fructose bisphosphate was isolated. (The prefix *bis*– means that the phosphate groups are attached to the fructose molecule at two different locations.) Subsequent work showed that all but the starting

**FIGURE 9.5 Glycolysis Pathway.** This sequence of 10 reactions oxidizes glucose to pyruvate. Each reaction is catalyzed by a different enzyme to produce two net ATP (4 ATP are produced, but 2 are invested), two molecules of NADH, and two molecules of pyruvate. In step 4, fructose-1,6-bisphosphate is divided into two products that both proceed through steps 6–10. The amounts for "What goes in" and "What goes out" are the combined totals for both molecules.

and ending molecules in glycolysis—glucose and pyruvate—are phosphorylated.

In 1905 researchers found that the processing of sugar by yeast extracts stopped if they boiled the reaction mix. Because it was known that enzymes could be inactivated by heat, their discovery suggested that enzymes were involved in at least some of the processing steps. Years later, investigators realized that each step in glycolysis is catalyzed by a different enzyme. Eventually, each of the reactions and enzymes involved was worked out.

## Glycolysis Is a Sequence of 10 Reactions

In both eukaryotes and prokaryotes, all 10 reactions of glycolysis occur in the cytosol (**FIGURE 9.5**). Note three key points about this reaction sequence:

1. Glycolysis starts by *using* ATP, not producing it. In the initial step, glucose is phosphorylated to form glucose-6-phosphate. After the second reaction rearranges the sugar to form fructose-6-phosphate, the third reaction adds a second phosphate group, forming the fructose-1,6-bisphosphate observed by early researchers. Thus, two ATP molecules are used up before any ATP is produced.

2. Once the energy-investment phase of glycolysis is complete, the subsequent reactions represent an energy-payoff phase. The sixth reaction in the sequence results in the reduction of two molecules of NAD$^+$; the seventh produces two molecules of ATP. This is where the energy "debt"—of two molecules of ATP invested early in glycolysis—is paid off. The final reaction in the sequence produces another two ATPs. For each molecule of glucose processed, the net yield is two molecules of NADH, two of ATP, and two of pyruvate.

3. In reactions 7 and 10 of Figure 9.5, an enzyme catalyzes the transfer of a phosphate group from a phosphorylated substrate to ADP, forming ATP. Enzyme-catalyzed reactions that result in

**FIGURE 9.6 Substrate-Level Phosphorylation Involves an Enzyme and a Phosphorylated Substrate.** Substrate-level phosphorylation occurs when an enzyme catalyzes the transfer of a phosphate group from a phosphorylated substrate to ADP, forming ATP.

ATP production are termed **substrate-level phosphorylation** (**FIGURE 9.6**). The key idea to note here is that the energy to produce the ATP comes from the phosphorylated substrate—not from a proton gradient, as it does when ATP is produced by oxidative phosphorylation.

The discovery and elucidation of the glycolytic pathway ranks as one of the great achievements in the history of biochemistry. For more detail concerning the enzymes that catalyze each step, see **TABLE 9.1** (on page 160). While the catabolism of glucose can occur via other pathways, this set of reactions is among the most ancient and fundamental of all life processes.

## How Is Glycolysis Regulated?

An important advance in understanding how glycolysis is regulated occurred when biologists observed that high levels of ATP inhibit a key glycolytic enzyme called phosphofructokinase. **Phosphofructokinase** catalyzes reaction 3 in Figure 9.5—the synthesis of fructose-1,6-bisphosphate from fructose-6-phosphate. This is a crucial step in the sequence.

The "2" indicates that fructose-1,6-bisphosphate has been split into two 3-carbon sugars (only one is shown)

During the energy-payoff phase, 4 ATP are produced for a net gain of 2 ATP

2 NAD$^+$   2 ADP   2 ADP

2 P$_i$

6 → 2   1,3-Bisphosphoglycerate → 7 → 2   3-Phosphoglycerate → 8 → 2   2-Phosphoglycerate → 9 (2 H$_2$O) → 2   Phosphoenolpyruvate → 10 → 2   **Pyruvate**

2 NADH + 2 H$^+$   2 ATP   2 ATP

| Step | Enzyme | Reaction |
|------|--------|----------|
| 1 | Hexokinase | Transfers a phosphate from **ATP** to glucose, increasing its potential energy. |
| 2 | Phosphoglucose isomerase | Converts glucose-6-phosphate to fructose-6-phosphate; referred to as an isomer of glucose-6-phosphate. |
| 3 | Phosphofructokinase | Transfers a phosphate from **ATP** to the opposite end of fructose-6-phosphate, increasing its potential energy. |
| 4 | Fructose-bis-phosphate aldolase | Cleaves fructose-1,6-bisphosphate into two different 3-carbon sugars. |
| 5 | Triose phosphate isomerase | Converts dihydroxyacetone phosphate (DAP) to glyceraldehyde-3-phosphate (G3P). Although the reaction is fully reversible, the DAP-to-G3P reaction is favored because G3P is immediately used as a substrate for step 6. |
| 6 | Glyceraldehyde-3-phosphate dehydrogenase | A two-step reaction that first oxidizes G3P using the **NAD$^+$** coenzyme to produce **NADH**. Energy from this reaction is used to attach a $P_i$ to the oxidized product to form 1,3-bisphosphoglycerate. |
| 7 | Phosphoglycerate kinase | Transfers a phosphate from 1,3-bisphosphoglycerate to **ADP** to make 3-phosphoglycerate and **ATP**. |
| 8 | Phosphoglycerate mutase | Rearranges the phosphate in 3-phosphoglycerate to make 2-phosphoglycerate. |
| 9 | Enolase | Removes a water molecule from 2-phosphoglycerate to form a C=C double bond and produce phosphoenolpyruvate. |
| 10 | Pyruvate kinase | Transfers a phosphate from phosphoenolpyruvate to **ADP** to make pyruvate and **ATP**. |

After reactions 1 and 2 occur, an array of enzymes can reverse the process and regenerate glucose for use in other pathways. Before step 3, then, the sequence is not committed to glycolysis. But once fructose-1,6-bisphosphate is synthesized, there is no point in stopping the process. Based on these observations, it makes sense that the pathway is regulated at step 3. How do cells do it?

As shown in Figure 9.5, ATP serves as a substrate for the addition of a phosphate to fructose-6-phosphate. In the vast majority of cases, increasing the concentration of a substrate would *speed* the rate of a chemical reaction, but in this case, it inhibits it. Why would ATP—a substrate that is required for the reaction—also serve as an inhibitor of the reaction? The answer lies in the fact that ATP is also the end product of the overall catabolic pathway.

Recall that when an enzyme in a pathway is inhibited by the product of the reaction sequence, feedback inhibition occurs (see Chapter 8). When the product molecule is abundant, it can inhibit its own production by interfering with the reaction sequence used to create it.

Feedback inhibition increases efficiency. Cells that are able to stop glycolytic reactions when ATP is abundant can conserve their stores of glucose for times when ATP is scarce. As a result, natural selection should favor individuals who have phosphofructokinase molecules that are inhibited by high concentrations of ATP.

How do high levels of the substrate inhibit the enzyme? As **IGURE 9.7** shows, phosphofructokinase has two distinct binding ites for ATP. ATP can bind at the enzyme's active site, where it is used to phosphorylate fructose-6-phosphate, or at a regulatory site, where it turns off the enzyme's activity.

The key to feedback inhibition lies in the ability of the two sites to bind to ATP. When concentrations are low, ATP binds

ATP at regulatory site

When ATP binds here, the reaction rate slows dramatically

Fructose-6-phosphate at active site

ATP at active site

**FIGURE 9.7 Phosphofructokinase Has Two Binding Sites for ATP.** A model of one of the four identical subunits of phosphofructokinase. In the active site, ATP is used as a substrate to transfer one of its phosphate groups to fructose-6-phosphate. In the regulatory site, ATP binding inhibits the reaction by changing the shape of the enzyme.

only to the active site, which has a greater affinity for ATP than does the regulatory site. As ATP concentrations increase, however, it also binds at the regulatory site on phosphofructokinase. When ATP binds at this second location, the enzyme's conformation changes in a way that dramatically lowers the reaction rate at the active site. In phosphofructokinase, ATP acts as an allosteric regulator (see Chapter 8). ✔ **If you understand the principle behind the difference in affinity between the two ATP binding sites, you should be able to predict the consequences if the regulatory site had higher affinity for ATP than the active site did.**

To summarize, glycolysis starts with one 6-carbon glucose molecule and ends with two 3-carbon pyruvate molecules. The reactions occur in the cytoplasm, and the energy that is released is used to produce a net total of two ATP and two NADH. Now the question is, what happens to the pyruvate?

## 9.3 Processing Pyruvate to Acetyl CoA

In eukaryotes, the pyruvate produced by glycolysis is transported from the cytosol to mitochondria. Mitochondria are organelles found in virtually all eukaryotes (see Chapter 7).

As shown in **FIGURE 9.8**, mitochondria have two membranes, called the inner membrane and outer membrane. The interior of the organelle is filled with layers of sac-like structures called **cristae.** Short tubes connect the cristae to the main part of the inner membrane. The region inside the inner membrane but outside the cristae is the **mitochondrial matrix.**

Pyruvate moves across the mitochondrion's outer membrane through small pores, but how it is transported across the inner membrane is still unclear. Current research suggests that either pyruvate is transported directly into the matrix using an unknown

transporter, or it is converted first into lactate, transported across the membrane, and then converted back into pyruvate.

Inside the mitochondrion, pyruvate reacts with a compound called **coenzyme A (CoA).** Coenzyme A is sometimes abbreviated as CoA-SH to call attention to its key sulfhydryl functional group. In this and many other reactions, CoA acts as a coenzyme by accepting and then transferring an acetyl group ($-COCH_3$) to a substrate (the A stands for acetylation). Pyruvate reacts with CoA, through a series of steps, to produce **acetyl CoA.**

The reaction sequence occurs inside an enormous and intricate enzyme complex called **pyruvate dehydrogenase.** In eukaryotes, pyruvate dehydrogenase is located in the mitochondrial matrix. In bacteria and archaea, pyruvate dehydrogenase is located in the cytosol.

As pyruvate is being processed, one of the carbons in the pyruvate is oxidized to $CO_2$ and $NAD^+$ is reduced to NADH. The remaining two-carbon acetyl unit is transferred to CoA (**FIGURE 9.9**).

**FIGURE 9.9 Pyruvate Is Oxidized to Acetyl CoA.** The reaction shown here is catalyzed by pyruvate dehydrogenase.

✔**EXERCISE** Above the reaction arrow, list three molecules whose presence speeds up the reaction. Label them "Positive control." Below the reaction arrow, list three molecules whose presence slows down the reaction. Label them "Negative control by feedback inhibition."

**FIGURE 9.8 The Structure of the Mitochondrion.** Mitochondria have outer and inner membranes that define the intermembrane space and matrix. Pyruvate processing occurs within the mitochondrial matrix. Recent research using cryo-electron tomography (the colorized micrograph on the right) shows the inner membrane is connected by short tubes to sac-like cristae.

Acetyl CoA is the final product of the pyruvate-processing step in glucose oxidation. Pyruvate, $NAD^+$, and CoA go in; $CO_2$, NADH, and acetyl CoA come out.

When supplies of ATP are abundant, however, the process shuts down. Pyruvate processing stops when the pyruvate dehydrogenase complex becomes phosphorylated and changes shape. The rate of phosphorylation increases when other products—specifically acetyl CoA and NADH—are at high concentration.

These regulatory changes are more examples of feedback inhibition. Reaction products feed back to stop or slow down the pathway.

On the contrary, high concentrations of $NAD^+$, CoA, or adenosine monophosphate (AMP)—which indicates low ATP supplies—*speed up* the reactions catalyzed by the pyruvate dehydrogenase complex.

Pyruvate processing is under both positive and negative control. Large supplies of products inhibit the enzyme complex; large supplies of reactants and low supplies of products stimulate it.

To summarize, pyruvate processing starts with the three-carbon pyruvate molecule and ends with one carbon released as $CO_2$ and the remaining two carbons in the form of acetyl CoA. The reactions occur in the mitochondrial matrix, and the potential energy that is released is used to produce one NADH for each pyruvate that is processed. Now the question is, what happens to the acetyl CoA?

# 9.4 The Citric Acid Cycle: Oxidizing Acetyl CoA to $CO_2$

While researchers were working out the sequence of reactions in glycolysis, biologists in other laboratories were focusing on redox reactions that oxidize small organic acids called **carboxylic acids.** Note that carboxylic acids all have carboxyl functional groups (R-COOH), hence the name.

A key finding emerged from their studies: Redox reactions that involve carboxylic acids such as citrate, malate, and succinate produce carbon dioxide. Recall from Section 9.1 that carbon dioxide is the endpoint of glucose oxidation via cellular respiration. Thus, it was logical for researchers to propose that the oxidation of small carboxylic acids could be an important component of glucose catabolism.

Early researchers identified eight small carboxylic acids that are rapidly oxidized in sequence, from least to most oxidized. What they found next was puzzling. When they added one of the eight carboxylic acids to cells, the rate of glucose oxidation increased, suggesting that the reactions are somehow connected to pathways involved in glucose catabolism. But, the added molecules did not appear to be used up. Instead, virtually all the carboxylic acids added were recovered later. How is this possible?

Hans Krebs solved the mystery when he proposed that the reaction sequence occurs in a cycle instead of a linear pathway. Krebs had another crucial insight when he suggested that the reaction sequence was directly tied to the processing of pyruvate—the endpoint of the glycolytic pathway.

To test these hypotheses, Krebs and a colleague set out to determine if adding pyruvate could link the two ends of the sequence

of eight carboxylic acids. If pyruvate is the key link in forming a cycle, it would need to be involved in the conversion of oxaloacetate, the most oxidized of the eight carboxylic acids, to citrate, the most reduced carboxylic acid. When Krebs added pyruvate, the series of redox reactions occurred. The conclusion? The sequence of eight carboxylic acids is indeed arranged in a cycle (**FIGURE 9.10**).

Many biologists now refer to the cycle as the **citric acid cycle** because it starts with citrate, which is the salt of citric acid after the protons are released. The citric acid cycle is also known as the tricarboxylic acid (TCA) cycle, because citrate has three carboxyl groups, and also as the Krebs cycle, after its discoverer.

When radioactive isotopes of carbon became available in the early 1940s, researchers showed that carbon atoms cycle through the reactions just as Krebs had proposed. For more detail concerning the enzymes that catalyze each step, see **TABLE 9.2** (on page 164). In each cycle, the energy released by the oxidation of one molecule of acetyl CoA is used to produce three molecules of NADH, one of $FADH_2$, and one of **guanosine triphosphate (GTP),** or ATP, through substrate-level phosphorylation. Whether GTP or ATP is produced depends on the type of cell being considered.[1] For example, GTP appears to be produced in the liver cells of mammals, while ATP is produced in muscle cells.

In bacteria and archaea, the enzymes responsible for the citric acid cycle are located in the cytosol. In eukaryotes, most of the enzymes responsible for the citric acid cycle are located in the mitochondrial matrix. Because glycolysis produces two molecules of pyruvate, the cycle turns twice for each molecule of glucose processed in cellular respiration.

## How Is the Citric Acid Cycle Regulated?

By now, it shouldn't surprise you to learn that the citric acid cycle is carefully regulated. The citric acid cycle can be turned off at multiple points, via several different mechanisms of feedback inhibition. Reaction rates are high when ATP is scarce; reaction rates are low when ATP is abundant.

**FIGURE 9.11** highlights the major control points. Notice that in step 1, the enzyme that combines acetyl CoA and oxaloacetate to form citrate is shut down when ATP binds to it. This is another example of feedback inhibition, which also regulates enzymes at two additional points in the cycle. In step 3, NADH interferes with the reaction by binding to the enzyme's active site. This is an example of competitive inhibition (see Chapter 8). In step 4, ATP binds to the enzyme at an allosteric regulatory site.

To summarize, the citric acid cycle starts with the two-carbon acetyl molecule in the form of acetyl CoA and ends with the release of two $CO_2$. The reactions occur in the mitochondrial matrix, and the potential energy that is released is used to produce three NADH, one $FADH_2$, and one ATP or GTP for each acetyl oxidized. But a major question remains.

---

[1]Traditionally it was thought that the citric acid cycle produced GTP, which was later converted to ATP in the same cell. Recent work suggests that ATP is produced directly in some cell types, while GTP is produced in other cells. See C. O. Lambeth, Reconsideration of the significance of substrate-level phosphorylation in the citric acid cycle. *Biochemistry and Molecular Biology Education* 34 (2006): 21–29.

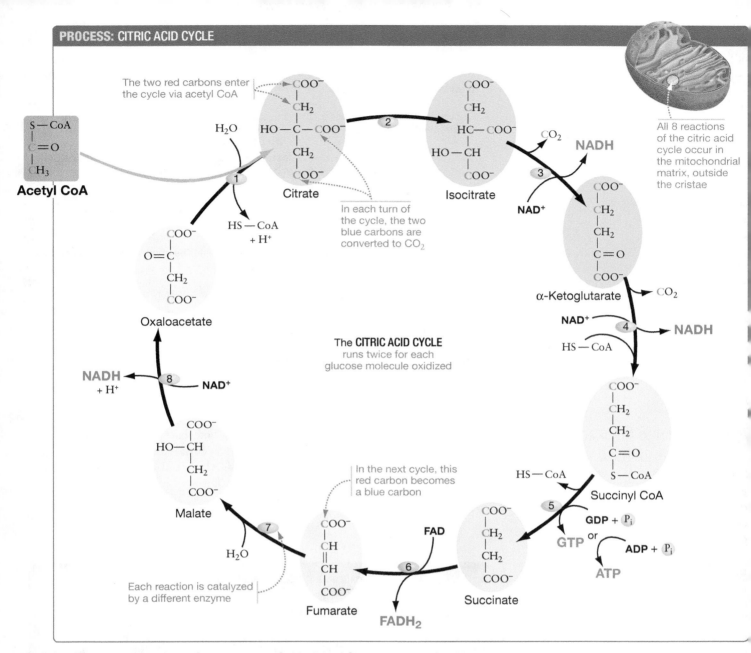

The two red carbons enter the cycle via acetyl CoA

In each turn of the cycle, the two blue carbons are converted to $CO_2$

All 8 reactions of the citric acid cycle occur in the mitochondrial matrix, outside the cristae

The **CITRIC ACID CYCLE** runs twice for each glucose molecule oxidized

In the next cycle, this red carbon becomes a blue carbon

Each reaction is catalyzed by a different enzyme

**Acetyl CoA**

Citrate

Isocitrate

α-Ketoglutarate

Succinyl CoA

Succinate

Fumarate

Malate

Oxaloacetate

**FIGURE 9.10 The Citric Acid Cycle Completes the Oxidation of Glucose.** Acetyl CoA goes into the citric acid cycle, and carbon dioxide, NADH, $FADH_2$, and GTP or ATP come out. GTP or ATP is produced by substrate-level phosphorylation. If you follow individual carbon atoms around the cycle several times, you'll come to an important conclusion: each of the carbons in the cycle is eventually a "blue carbon" that is released as $CO_2$.

**FIGURE 9.11 The Citric Acid Cycle Is Regulated by Feedback Inhibition.** The citric acid cycle slows down when ATP and NADH are plentiful. ATP acts as an allosteric regulator, while NADH acts as a competitive inhibitor.

This step is regulated by **ATP**

These steps are also regulated via feedback inhibition by **NADH** and **ATP**

| Step | Enzyme | Reaction |
|---|---|---|
| 1 | Citrate synthase | Transfers the 2-carbon acetyl group from acetyl CoA to the 4-carbon oxaloacetate to produce the 6-carbon citrate. |
| 2 | Aconitase | Converts citrate to isocitrate by the removal of one water molecule and the addition of another water molecule. |
| 3 | Isocitrate dehydrogenase | Oxidizes isocitrate using the **NAD$^+$** coenzyme to produce **NADH** and release one $CO_2$, resulting in the formation of the 5-carbon molecule α-ketoglutarate. |
| 4 | α-Ketoglutarate dehydrogenase | Oxidizes α-ketoglutarate using the **NAD$^+$** coenzyme to produce **NADH** and release one $CO_2$. The remaining 4-carbon molecule is added to coenzyme A (CoA) to form succinyl CoA. |
| 5 | Succinyl-CoA synthetase | CoA is removed, converting succinyl CoA to succinate. The energy released is used to transfer $P_i$ to GDP to form **GTP**, or to ADP to form **ATP**. |
| 6 | Succinate dehydrogenase | Oxidizes succinate by transferring two hydrogens to the coenzyme **FAD** to produce **FADH$_2$**, resulting in the formation of fumarate. |
| 7 | Fumarase | Converts fumarate to malate by the addition of one water molecule. |
| 8 | Malate dehydrogenase | Oxidizes malate by using the **NAD$^+$** coenzyme to produce **NADH**, resulting in the regeneration of the oxaloacetate that will be used in step 1 of the cycle. |

## What Happens to the NADH and FADH$_2$?

**FIGURE 9.12** reviews the relationships of glycolysis, pyruvate processing, and the citric acid cycle and identifies where each process takes place in eukaryotic cells. As the carbons in glucose are oxidized in these steps, the relative changes in free energy are shown in **FIGURE 9.13**.

As you study these figures, note that for each molecule of glucose that is fully oxidized to 6 carbon dioxide molecules, the cell produces 10 molecules of NADH, 2 of FADH$_2$, and 4 of ATP. The overall reaction for glycolysis and the citric acid cycle can be written as

$$C_6H_{12}O_6 + 10\ NAD^+ + 2\ FAD + 4\ ADP + 4\ P_i \longrightarrow$$
$$6\ CO_2 + 10\ NADH + 2\ FADH_2 + 4\ ATP$$

**PROCESS: SUMMARY OF GLUCOSE OXIDATION**

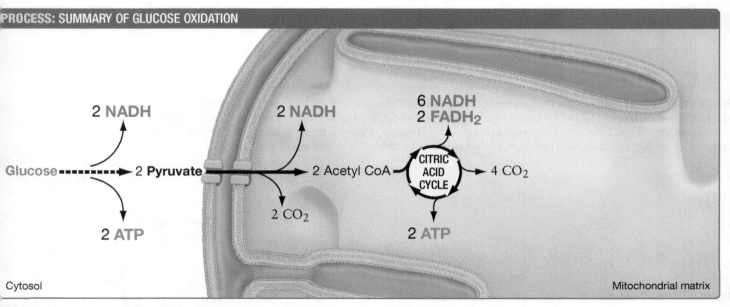

**FIGURE 9.12 Glucose Oxidation Produces ATP, NADH, FADH$_2$, and CO$_2$.** Glucose is completely oxidized to carbon dioxide via glycolysis, pyruvate processing, and the citric acid cycle. In eukaryotes, glycolysis occurs in the cytosol; pyruvate oxidation and the citric acid cycle take place in the mitochondrial matrix.

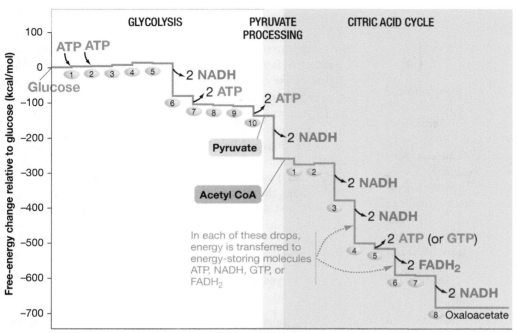

FIGURE 9.13 Free Energy Changes as Glucose Is Oxidized. If you read the vertical axis of this graph carefully, it should convince you that about 685 kcal/mol of free energy is released from the oxidation of glucose. Much of the energy is harnessed in the form of ATP, NADH, and $FADH_2$. The numbered green ovals identify the reaction steps in glycolysis and the citric acid cycle (see Tables 9.1 and 9.2).

DATA: Li, X., R. K. Dash, R. K. Pradhan, et al. 2010. *Journal of Physical Chemistry B*. 114: 16068–16082.

✔ QUANTITATIVE Based on the data in this graph, which of the three high-energy molecules produced during glucose oxidation would you expect to carry the highest amount of chemical energy? Justify your answer.

The ATP molecules are produced by substrate-level phosphorylation and can be used to drive endergonic reactions. The $CO_2$ molecules are a gas that is disposed of as waste—you exhale it; plants release it or use it as a reactant in photosynthesis.

What happens to the NADH and $FADH_2$ produced by glycolysis, pyruvate processing, and the citric acid cycle? Recall that the overall reaction for glucose oxidation is

$$C_6H_{12}O_6 + 6\,O_2 \longrightarrow 6\,CO_2 + 6\,H_2O + Energy$$

These three steps account for the glucose, the $CO_2$, and—because ATP is produced—some of the chemical energy that results from the overall reaction. But the $O_2$ and the $H_2O$ are still unaccounted for. As it turns out, so is much of the chemical energy. The reaction that has yet to occur is

$$NADH + FADH_2 + O_2 + ADP + P_i \longrightarrow$$
$$NAD^+ + FAD + 2\,H_2O + ATP$$

In the above reaction, the electrons from NADH and $FADH_2$ are transferred to oxygen. NADH and $FADH_2$ are oxidized to $NAD^+$ and FAD, and oxygen is reduced to form water.

In effect, glycolysis, pyruvate processing, and the citric acid cycle transfer electrons from glucose to $NAD^+$ and FAD to form NADH and $FADH_2$. When oxygen accepts electrons from these reduced molecules, water is produced.

At this point, all the components of the overall reaction for glucose oxidation are accounted for, except for the energy. What happens to the energy that is released as electrons are transferred from NADH and $FADH_2$ to the highly electronegative oxygen atoms?

Specifically, how is the transfer of electrons linked to the production of ATP? In the 1960s—decades after the details of glycolysis and the citric acid cycle had been worked out—a startling answer to these questions emerged.

check your understanding

**If you understand that . . .**

- During glycolysis, glucose is oxidized to pyruvate, in the cytosol.
- During pyruvate processing, pyruvate is oxidized to acetyl CoA, in the mitochondrial matrix.
- In the citric acid cycle, the acetyl from acetyl CoA is oxidized to carbon dioxide ($CO_2$), in the mitochondrial matrix.
- Glycolysis, pyruvate processing, and the citric acid cycle are all regulated processes. The cell produces ATP only when ATP is needed.

**✔ You should be able to . . .**

Model the following components of cellular respiration by pretending that a large piece of paper is a cell. Draw a large mitochondrion inside it. Cut out small circles of paper and label them glucose, pyruvate, acetyl CoA, $CO_2$, ADP → ATP, $NAD^+$ → NADH, and FAD → $FADH_2$. Cut out small squares of paper and label them as glycolytic reactions, citric acid cycle reactions, and pyruvate dehydrogenase complex.

1. Put each of the squares in the appropriate location in the cell.
2. Add the circles and draw arrows to connect the appropriate molecules and reactions.
3. Using 12 paper triangles for pairs of electrons, show how electrons from glucose are transferred to NADH or $FADH_2$ (one pair should go to each NADH or $FADH_2$ formed) as glucose is oxidized to $CO_2$.
4. Label points where regulation occurs.

*Answers are available in Appendix A.*

# Electron Transport and Chemiosmosis: Building a Proton Gradient to Produce ATP

The answer to one fundamental question about the oxidation of NADH and FADH$_2$ turned out to be relatively straightforward. By isolating different parts of mitochondria, researchers determined that NADH is oxidized by components in the inner membrane of the mitochondria, including the cristae. In prokaryotes, the oxidation of NADH occurs in the plasma membrane.

Biologists made a key discovery when they isolated membrane components—they were found to cycle between oxidized and reduced states after the addition of NADH and FADH$_2$. The membrane-associated molecules were hypothesized to be the key to processing NADH and FADH$_2$. What are these molecules, and how do they work?

## The Electron Transport Chain

Collectively, the molecules responsible for the oxidation of NADH and FADH$_2$ are designated the **electron transport chain (ETC).** As electrons are passed from one molecule to another in the chain, the energy released by the redox reactions is used to move protons across the inner membrane of mitochondria.

Several points are fundamental to understanding how the ETC works:

Most of the molecules are proteins that contain distinctive cofactors and prosthetic groups where the redox events take place (see Chapter 8). They include iron–sulfur complexes, ring-containing structures called flavins, or iron-containing heme groups called cytochromes. Each of these groups is readily reduced or oxidized.

The inner membrane of the mitochondrion also contains a molecule called **ubiquinone,** which is not a protein. Ubiquinone got its name because it is nearly ubiquitous in organisms and belongs to a family of compounds called quinones. Also called **coenzyme Q** or simply Q, ubiquinone is lipid soluble and moves efficiently throughout the hydrophobic interior of the inner mitochondrial membrane.

The molecules involved in processing NADH and FADH$_2$ differ in electronegativity, or their tendency to hold electrons. Some of the molecules pick up a proton with each electron, forming hydrogen atoms, while others obtain only electrons.

Because Q and the ETC proteins can cycle between a reduced state and an oxidized state, and because they differ in electronegativity, investigators realized that it should be possible to arrange them into a logical sequence. The idea was that electrons would pass from a molecule with lower electronegativity to one with higher electronegativity, via a redox reaction.

As electrons moved through the chain, they would be held more and more tightly. A small amount of energy would be released in each reaction, and the potential energy in each successive bond would lessen.

**Organization of the Electron Transport Chain** Researchers worked out the sequence of compounds in the ETC by experimenting with poisons that inhibit particular proteins in the inner membrane. It was expected that if part of the chain were inhibited, then the components upstream of the block would become reduced, but those downstream would remain oxidized.

Experiments with various poisons showed that NADH donates an electron to a flavin-containing protein (FMN) at the top of the chain, while FADH$_2$ donates electrons to an iron- and sulfur-containing protein (Fe·S) that then passes them directly to Q. After passing through each of the remaining components in the chain, the electrons are finally accepted by oxygen.

**FIGURE 9.14** shows how electrons step down in potential energy from the electron carriers NADH and FADH$_2$ to O$_2$. The *x*-axis

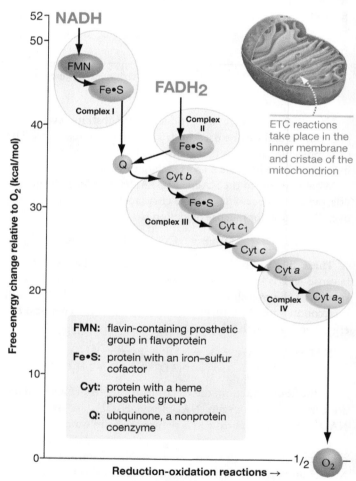

**FIGURE 9.14 A Series of Reduction–Oxidation Reactions Occur in an Electron Transport Chain.** Electrons step down in potential energy from the electron carriers NADH and FADH$_2$ through an electron transport chain to a final electron acceptor. When oxygen is the final electron acceptor, water is formed. The overall free-energy change of 52 kcal/mol (from NADH to oxygen) is broken into small steps.

DATA: Wilson D. F., M. Erecinska, and P. L. Dutton. 1974. *Annual Review of Biophysics and Bioengineering* 3: 203–230. Also Sled, V. D., N. I. Rudnitzky, Y. Hatefi, et al. 1994. *Biochemistry* 33: 10069–10075.

plots the sequence of redox reactions in the ETC; the *y*-axis plots the free-energy changes that occur.

The components of the electron transport chain are organized into four large complexes of proteins, often referred to as simply complexes I–IV. Q and the protein **cytochrome *c*** act as shuttles that transfer electrons between these complexes. Once the electrons at the bottom of the ETC are accepted by oxygen to form water, the oxidation of glucose is complete. Details on the names of the complexes and their role in the electron transport chain are provided in **TABLE 9.3** (on page 168).

Under controlled conditions in the laboratory, the total potential energy difference from NADH to oxygen is a whopping 53 kilocalories/mole (kcal/mol). Oxidation of the 10 molecules of NADH produced from each glucose accounts for almost 80 percent of the total energy released from the sugar. What does the ETC do with all this energy?

**Role of the Electron Transport Chain**  Throughout the 1950s most biologists working on cellular respiration assumed that electron transport chains include enzymes that catalyze substrate-level phosphorylation. Recall that when substrate-level phosphorylation occurs, a phosphate group is transferred from a phosphorylated substrate to ADP, forming ATP. Despite intense efforts, however, no one was able to find an enzyme among the components of the ETC that would catalyze the phosphorylation of ADP to produce ATP.

What researchers did find, however, is that the movement of electrons through the ETC actively transports protons from the matrix, across the inner membrane, and into the intermembrane space (see **FIGURE 9.15**). The exact route and mechanism used to pump protons is still being worked out. In some cases, it is not clear how the redox reactions taking place inside each complex result in the movement of protons.

The best-understood interaction between electron transport and proton transport takes place in complex III. Research has shown that when Q accepts electrons from complex I or complex II, it picks up protons from the matrix side of the inner membrane. The reduced form of Q then diffuses through the inner

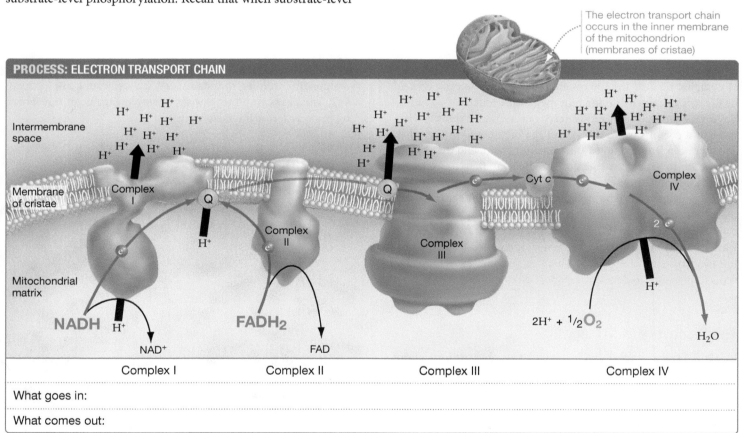

**PROCESS: ELECTRON TRANSPORT CHAIN**

The electron transport chain occurs in the inner membrane of the mitochondrion (membranes of cristae)

| | Complex I | Complex II | Complex III | Complex IV |
|---|---|---|---|---|
| What goes in: | | | | |
| What comes out: | | | | |

**FIGURE 9.15 How Does the Electron Transport Chain Work?** The individual components of the electron transport chain diagrammed in Figure 9.14 are found in the inner membrane of mitochondria. Electrons are carried from one complex to another by Q and by cytochrome *c*; Q also shuttles protons across the membrane. The orange arrow indicates Q moving back and forth. Complexes I and IV use the potential energy released by the redox reactions to pump protons from the mitochondrial matrix to the intermembrane space.

✔**EXERCISE** Add an arrow across the membrane and label it "Proton gradient." In the boxes at the bottom, list "What goes in" and "What comes out" for each complex.

| ETC Component | Descriptive Name | Reaction |
|---|---|---|
| **Complex I** | NADH dehydrogenase | Oxidizes **NADH** and transfers the two electrons through proteins containing FMN prosthetic groups and Fe·S cofactors to reduce an oxidized form of ubiquinone (Q). Four **H$^+$** are pumped out of the matrix to the intermembrane space. |
| **Complex II** | Succinate dehydrogenase | Oxidizes **FADH$_2$** and transfers the two electrons through proteins containing Fe·S cofactors to reduce an oxidized form of Q. This complex is also used in step 6 of the citric acid cycle. |
| **Q** | Ubiquinone | Reduced by complexes I and II and moves throughout the hydrophobic interior of the ETC membrane, where it is oxidized by complex III. |
| **Complex III** | Cytochrome *c* reductase | Oxidizes Q and transfers one electron at a time through proteins containing heme prosthetic groups and Fe·S cofactors to reduce an oxidized form of cytochrome *c* (cyt *c*). A total of four **H$^+$** for each pair of electrons is transported from the matrix to the intermembrane space. |
| **Cyt *c*** | Cytochrome *c* | Reduced by accepting a single electron from complex III and moves along the surface of ETC membrane, where it is oxidized by complex IV. |
| **Complex IV** | Cytochrome *c* oxidase | Oxidizes cyt *c* and transfers each electron through proteins containing heme prosthetic groups to reduce oxygen gas (O$_2$), which picks up two **H$^+$** from the matrix to produce water. Two additional **H$^+$** are pumped out of the matrix to the intermembrane space. |

membrane, where its electrons are used to reduce a component of complex III near the intermembrane space. The protons held by Q are then released to the intermembrane space.

In this way, through redox reactions alone, Q shuttles electrons and protons from one side of the membrane to the other. The electrons proceed down the transport chain, and the protons contribute to an electrochemical gradient as they are released into the intermembrane space.

Once the nature of the electron transport chain became clear, biologists understood the fate of the electrons and the energy carried by NADH and FADH$_2$. Much of the chemical energy that was originally present in glucose is now accounted for in the proton electrochemical gradient. This is satisfying, except for one crucial question: If electron transport does not make ATP, what does?

## The Discovery of ATP Synthase

In 1960 Efraim Racker made several key observations about how ATP is synthesized in mitochondria. When he used mitochondrial membranes to make vesicles, Racker noticed that some vesicles formed with their membrane inside out. Electron microscopy revealed that the inside-out membranes had many large proteins studded along their surfaces. Each protein appeared to have a base in the membrane, from which a lollipop-shaped stalk and a knob project (**FIGURE 9.16**). If the solution was vibrated or treated with a compound called urea, the stalks and knobs fell off.

Racker seized on this technique to isolate the stalks and knobs and do experiments with them. For example, he found that isolated stalks and knobs could hydrolyze ATP, forming ADP and inorganic phosphate. The vesicles that contained just the base component, without the stalks and knobs, could not process ATP. The base components were, however, capable of transporting protons across the membrane.

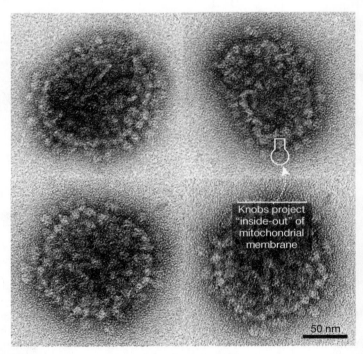

Knobs project "inside-out" of mitochondrial membrane

50 nm

**FIGURE 9.16 The Discovery of ATP Synthase.** When patches of mitochondrial membrane turn inside out and form vesicles, the lollipop-shaped stalk-and-knob structures of ATP synthase proteins face outward. Normally, the stalk and knob face inward, toward the mitochondrial matrix.

Based on these observations, Racker proposed that the stalk-and-knob component of the protein was an enzyme that both hydrolyzes and synthesizes ATP. To test his idea, Racker added the stalk-and-knob components back to vesicles that had been stripped of them and confirmed that the vesicles regained the ability to synthesize ATP. The entire complex is known as **ATP synthase.** Follow-up work also confirmed his hypothesis that the membrane-bound base component of ATP synthase is a proton channel. Is there a connection between proton transport and ATP synthesis?

## The Chemiosmosis Hypothesis

In 1961 Peter Mitchell broke with the prevailing ideas that electron transport produces ATP via substrate phosphorylation. Instead, he proposed something completely new—an indirect connection between electron transport and ATP production. Mitchell's novel hypothesis? The real job of the electron transport chain is to pump protons across the inner membrane of mitochondria from the matrix to the intermembrane space. After a proton gradient is established, an enzyme in the inner membrane, like Racker's ATP synthase, would synthesize ATP from ADP and $P_i$.

Mitchell introduced the term **chemiosmosis** to describe the use of a proton gradient to drive energy-requiring processes, like the production of ATP. Here, osmosis refers to the force generated from the proton gradient rather than the transport of water. Although proponents of a direct link between electron transport and substrate-level phosphorylation objected vigorously to Mitchell's idea, several key experiments supported it.

**FIGURE 9.17** illustrates how the existence of a key element in Mitchell's hypothesis was confirmed: A proton gradient alone can be used to synthesize ATP via ATP synthase. The researchers made vesicles from artificial membranes that contained Racker's ATP synthase isolated from mitochondria. Along with this enzyme, they inserted bacteriorhodopsin, a well-studied membrane protein that acts as a light-activated proton pump.

When light strikes bacteriorhodopsin, it absorbs some of the light energy and changes conformation in a way that pumps protons from the interior of a membrane to the exterior. As a result, the experimental vesicles established a strong electrochemical gradient favoring proton movement to the interior. When the vesicles were illuminated to initiate proton pumping, ATP began to be produced from ADP and $P_i$ inside the vesicles.

Mitchell's prediction was correct: In this situation, ATP production depended solely on the existence of a **proton-motive force,** which is based on a proton electrochemical gradient. It could occur in the *absence* of an electron transport chain. This result, along with many others, has provided strong support for the hypothesis of chemiosmosis. Most of the ATP produced by cellular respiration is made by a flow of protons.

✔ If you understand chemiosmosis, you should be able to explain why ATP production during cellular respiration is characterized as indirect. More specifically, you should be able to explain the relationship between glucose oxidation, the proton gradient, and ATP synthase.

**RESEARCH**

**QUESTION: How are the electron transport chain and ATP production linked?**

CHEMIOSMOTIC HYPOTHESIS: The linkage is indirect. The ETC creates a proton-motive force that drives ATP synthesis by the mitochondrial ATP synthase.

ALTERNATIVE HYPOTHESIS: The linkage is direct. The ETC is associated with enzymes that perform substrate-level phosphorylation.

EXPERIMENTAL SETUP:

Vesicle

**1. Produce vesicles from artificial membranes**; add ATP synthase, an enzyme found in mitochondria.

ATP synthase

Bacterio-rhodopsin

**2. Add bacteriorhodopsin**, a protein that acts as a light-activated proton pump.

Light   Light

$H^+$

**3. Illuminate vesicle** so that bacteriorhodopsin pumps protons out of vesicle, creating a proton gradient.

PREDICTION OF CHEMIOSMOTIC HYPOTHESIS: ATP will be produced within the vesicle.

PREDICTION OF ALTERNATIVE HYPOTHESIS: No ATP will be produced.

RESULTS:

ATP is produced within the vesicle, in the absence of the electron transport chain.

CONCLUSION: The linkage between electron transport and ATP synthesis is indirect; the movement of protons drives the synthesis of ATP.

**FIGURE 9.17 Evidence for the Chemiosmotic Hypothesis.**

Racker, E., and W. Stoeckenius. 1974. Reconstitution of purple membrane vesicles catalyzing light-driven proton uptake and adenosine triphosphate formation. *Journal of Biological Chemistry.* 249: 662–663.

✔ QUESTION If bacteriorhodopsin were not available, what could the researchers have done with the ATP synthase vesicles to test their hypothesis?

Electron transport chains and ATP synthases are used by organisms throughout the tree of life. They are humming away in our cells now. Let's look in more detail at how they function.

### The Proton-Motive Force Couples Electron Transport to ATP Synthesis

As **FIGURE 9.18** shows, the structure of ATP synthase is now well understood. The ATP synthase "knob" component is called the $F_1$ unit; the membrane-bound, proton-transporting base component is the $F_0$ unit. The $F_1$ and $F_0$ units are connected by a shaft, as well as by a stator, which holds the two units in place.

The $F_0$ unit serves as a rotor, whose turning is conveyed to the $F_1$ unit via the shaft. A flow of protons through the $F_0$ unit causes the rotor and shaft to spin. By attaching long actin filaments to the shaft and examining them with a videomicroscope, researchers have been able to see the rotation, which can reach speeds of 350 revolutions per second. As the shaft spins within the $F_1$ unit, it is thought to change the conformation of the $F_1$ subunits in a way that catalyzes the phosphorylation of ADP to ATP.

Chemiosmosis is like the process of generating electricity in a hydroelectric dam (like the one pictured on page 154). The ETC is analogous to a series of gigantic pumps that force water up and behind the dam. The inner mitochondrial membrane functions as the dam, with ATP synthase spinning and generating electricity inside as water passes through—like a turbine. In a mitochondrion, protons are pumped instead of water. When protons move through ATP synthase, the protein spins and generates ATP.

It has been determined that the ETC transports enough protons to produce approximately three ATP for each NADH and two for each $FADH_2$, depending on the type of ATP synthase used. These yields, however, are not observed in cells, since the proton-motive force is also used to drive other processes, such as the import of phosphates into the mitochondrial matrix.

Unlike the turbines in a hydroelectric dam, however, ATP synthase can reverse its direction and hydrolyze ATP to build a proton gradient. If the proton gradient dissipates, the direction of the spin is reversed and ATP is hydrolyzed to pump protons from the matrix to the intermembrane space. Understanding how these reactions occur is currently the focus of intense research. ATP synthase makes most of the ATP that keeps you alive.

### The Proton-Motive Force and Chemical Evolution

How was energy first transformed into a usable form during the evolution of life? Since chemiosmosis is responsible for most of the ATP produced by cells throughout the tree of life, it is likely to have arisen early in evolution. But how could a complex electron transport chain evolve to produce the proton-motive force without a proton-motive force to supply the energy?

This apparent conundrum left many of the chemical evolution theorists perplexed until a key discovery was made deep in the ocean along the Mid-Atlantic Ridge—the Lost City hydrothermal vents (see Chapter 2). Researchers propose that the alkaline fluid (low proton concentration) released from these vents in the acidic oceans (high proton concentration) of early Earth may have provided such a gradient.

While there is still considerable debate concerning the role hydrothermal vents may have played in chemical evolution, their discovery has generated much excitement. By harnessing the natural electrochemical gradient deep in the early oceans, the proton-motive force of life may have evolved to mimic the environment of its origin.

## Organisms Use a Diversity of Electron Acceptors

**FIGURE 9.19** summarizes glucose oxidation and cellular respiration by tracing the fate of the carbon atoms and electrons in glucose. Notice that electrons from glucose are transferred to NADH and $FADH_2$, passed through the electron transport chain, and accepted by oxygen. Proton pumping during electron transport creates the proton-motive force that drives ATP synthesis.

The diagram also indicates the approximate yield of ATP from each component of the process. Recent research shows that about 29 ATP molecules are produced from each molecule of glucose.[2] Of these, 25 ATP molecules are produced by ATP synthase. The fundamental message here? The vast majority of the "payoff" from the oxidation of glucose occurs via oxidative phosphorylation.

### Aerobic Versus Anaerobic Respiration

During cellular respiration, oxygen is the electron acceptor used by all eukaryotes and

**FIGURE 9.18 ATP Synthase Is a Motor.** ATP synthase has two major components, designated $F_0$ and $F_1$, connected by a shaft. The $F_0$ unit spins as protons pass through. The shaft transmits the rotation to the $F_1$ unit, causing it to make ATP from ADP and $P_i$.

[2]Traditionally, biologists thought that 36 ATP would be synthesized for every molecule of glucose oxidized in eukaryotic cells. More recent work has shown that actual yield is only about 29 ATP [see M. Brand, Approximate yield of ATP from glucose, designed by Donald Nicholson. *Biochemistry and Molecular Biology Education* 31 (2003): 2–4]. Also, it's important to note that yield varies with conditions in the cell.

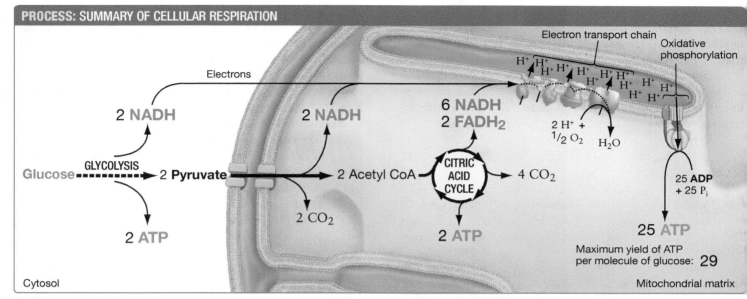

**FIGURE 9.19 ATP Yield during Cellular Respiration.** The actual yield of ATP per glucose (29 ATP) is lower than the theoretical calculation (38 ATP) because of energy required for the import of NADH from the cytoplasm and the use of the proton-motive force to actively transport $P_i$ into the mitochondrial matrix.

a wide diversity of bacteria and archaea. Species that depend on oxygen as an electron acceptor for the ETC use **aerobic** respiration and are called aerobic organisms. (The Latin root *aero* means "air.")

It is important to recognize, though, that cellular respiration can occur without oxygen. Many thousands of bacterial and archaeal species rely on electron acceptors other than oxygen, and electron donors other than glucose. For example, nitrate ($NO_3^-$) and sulfate ($SO_4^{2-}$) are particularly common electron acceptors in species that live in oxygen-poor environments (see Chapter 29). In addition, many bacteria and archaea use $H_2$, $H_2S$, $CH_4$, or other inorganic compounds as electron donors—not glucose.

Cells that depend on electron acceptors other than oxygen are said to use **anaerobic** ("no air") respiration. Even though the starting and ending points of cellular respiration differ, aerobic and anaerobic cells still use electron transport chains to create a proton-motive force that drives the synthesis of ATP. In bacteria and archaea, the ETC and ATP synthase are located in the plasma membrane.

**Aerobic Respiration Is Most Efficient** Even though an array of compounds can serve as the final electron acceptor in cellular respiration, oxygen is the most efficient. Because oxygen holds electrons so tightly, the potential energy of electrons in a bond between an oxygen atom and a non-oxygenic atom, such as hydrogen, is low. As a result, there is a large difference between the potential energy of electrons in NADH and the potential energy of electrons bonded to an oxygen atom, such as found in water (see Figure 9.14). The large differential in potential energy means that the electron transport chain can generate a large proton-motive force.

Cells that do not use oxygen as an electron acceptor cannot generate such a large potential energy difference. As a result, they make less ATP from each glucose molecule than cells that use aerobic respiration. This finding is important: It means that anaerobic organisms tend to grow much more slowly than aerobic organisms. If cells that use anaerobic respiration compete with cells using aerobic respiration, those that use oxygen as an electron acceptor almost always grow faster and reproduce more.

What happens when oxygen or other electron acceptors get used up? When there is no terminal electron acceptor, the electrons in

## check your understanding

 **If you understand that . . .**

- As electrons from NADH and $FADH_2$ move through the electron transport chain, protons are pumped into the intermembrane space of mitochondria.
- The electrochemical gradient across the inner mitochondrial membrane drives protons through ATP synthase, resulting in the production of ATP from ADP.

 ✔ **You should be able to . . .**

Add paper squares labeled ETC and ATP synthase and a paper circle labeled ½ $O_2$ → $H_2O$ to the model you made in Section 9.4. Explain the steps in electron transport and chemiosmosis using paper triangles to represent electron pairs and dimes to represent protons.

*Answers are available in Appendix A.*

each of the complexes of the electron transport chain have no place to go and the electron transport chain stops. Without an oxidized complex I, NADH remains reduced. The concentration of $NAD^+$ drops rapidly as cells continue to convert $NAD^+$ to NADH.

This situation is life threatening. When there is no longer any $NAD^+$ to drive glycolysis, pyruvate processing, and the citric acid cycle, then no ATP can be produced. If $NAD^+$ cannot be regenerated somehow, the cell will die. How do cells cope?

## 9.6 Fermentation

**Fermentation** is a metabolic pathway that regenerates $NAD^+$ by oxidizing stockpiles of NADH. The electrons removed from NADH are transferred to pyruvate, or a molecule derived from pyruvate, instead of an electron transport chain (**FIGURE 9.20**).

In respiring cells, fermentation serves as an emergency back-up that allows glycolysis to continue producing ATP even when the ETC is shut down. It allows the cell to survive and even grow in the absence of electron transport chains.

In many cases, the cell cannot use the molecule that is formed when pyruvate (or another electron acceptor) accepts electrons from NADH. This by-product may even be toxic and excreted from the cell as waste even though it has not been fully oxidized.

**Many Different Fermentation Pathways Exist** When you run up a long flight of stairs, your muscles begin metabolizing glucose so fast that the supply of oxygen is rapidly used up by their mitochondria. When oxygen is absent, the electron transport chains shut down and NADH cannot donate its electrons there. The pyruvate produced by glycolysis then begins to accept electrons from NADH, and fermentation takes place. This process, called **lactic acid fermentation**, regenerates $NAD^+$ by forming a product molecule called lactate: a deprotonated form of lactic acid (**FIGURE 9.21a**). Your body reacts by making you breathe faster and increasing your heart rate. By getting more oxygen to your muscle cells, the electron transport chain is revived.

**FIGURE 9.21b** illustrates a different fermentation pathway, **alcohol fermentation,** which occurs in the fungus *Saccharomyces*

*cerevisiae*—baker's and brewer's yeast. When yeast cells are placed in an environment such as bread dough or a bottle of grape juice and begin growing, they quickly use up all the available oxygen. Instead of depositing the electrons from NADH into pyruvate, yeast first convert pyruvate to the two-carbon compound acetaldehyde. This reaction gives off carbon dioxide, which causes bread to rise and produces the bubbles in champagne and beer.

Acetaldehyde then accepts electrons from NADH, forming the $NAD^+$ required to keep glycolysis going. The addition of electrons to acetaldehyde forms ethanol as a waste product. The yeast cells excrete ethanol as waste. In essence, the active ingredient in alcoholic beverages is like yeast urine.

Cells that employ other types of fermentation are used commercially in the production of soy sauce, tofu, yogurt, cheese, vinegar, and other products.

Bacteria and archaea that exist exclusively through fermentation are present in phenomenal numbers in the oxygen-free environment of your small intestine and in the first compartment of a cow's stomach, called the rumen. The rumen is a specialized digestive organ that contains over $10^{10}$ (10 billion) bacterial and archaeal cells per *milliliter* of fluid. The fermentations that occur in these cells produce an array of fatty acids. Cattle don't actually live off grass directly—they eat it to feed their bacteria and archaea and then use the fermentation by-products from these organisms as a source of energy.

**Fermentation as an Alternative to Cellular Respiration** Even though fermentation is a widespread type of metabolism, it is extremely inefficient compared with aerobic cellular respiration. Fermentation produces just 2 molecules of ATP for each molecule of glucose metabolized, while cellular respiration produces about 29—almost 15 times more energy per glucose molecule than fermentation. The reason for the disparity is that oxygen has much higher electronegativity than electron acceptors such as pyruvate and acetaldehyde. As a result, the potential energy drop between the start and end of fermentation is a tiny fraction of the potential energy change that occurs during cellular respiration.

Based on these observations, it is not surprising that organisms capable of both processes almost never use fermentation

**FIGURE 9.20 Cellular Respiration and Fermentation Are Alternative Pathways for Producing Energy.** When oxygen or another electron acceptor used by the ETC is present in a cell, the pyruvate produced by glycolysis enters the citric acid cycle and the electron transport system is active. But if no electron acceptor is available to keep the ETC running, the pyruvate undergoes reactions known as fermentation.

**(a)** Lactic acid fermentation occurs in humans.

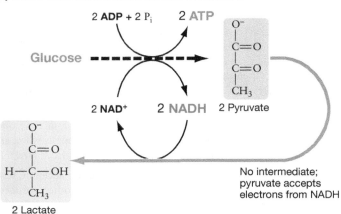

2 Lactate

No intermediate; pyruvate accepts electrons from NADH

**(b)** Alcohol fermentation occurs in yeast.

2 Ethanol          2 Acetylaldehyde          $2 CO_2$

**FIGURE 9.21 Fermentation Regenerates NAD⁺ So That Glycolysis Can Continue.** These are just two examples of the many types of fermentation that occur among bacteria, archaea, and eukaryotes.

when an appropriate electron acceptor is available for cellular respiration. In organisms that usually use oxygen as an electron acceptor, fermentation is an alternative mode of ATP production when oxygen supplies temporarily run out.

Organisms that can switch between fermentation and cellular respiration that uses oxygen as an electron acceptor are called **facultative anaerobes.** The adjective facultative reflects the ability to use cellular respiration when oxygen is present and fermentation when it is absent (anaerobic). Many of your cells can function as facultative anaerobes to a certain extent; however, you cannot survive for long without oxygen. To make this point clear, try holding your breath—it should take only a minute for you to realize how important electron transport is to your cells.

check your understanding

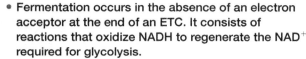

**If you understand that . . .**
- Fermentation occurs in the absence of an electron acceptor at the end of an ETC. It consists of reactions that oxidize NADH to regenerate the $NAD^+$ required for glycolysis.

✔ **You should be able to . . .**
Explain why organisms that have an ETC as well as fermentation pathways seldom ferment pyruvate if an electron acceptor at the end of the ETC is readily available.

*Answers are available in Appendix A.*

---

## If you understand . . .

### 9.1 An Overview of Cellular Respiration

- Cellular respiration is based on redox reactions that transfer electrons from a compound with high free energy, such as glucose, to a molecule with lower free energy, such as oxygen, through an electron transport chain.

- In eukaryotes, cellular respiration consists of four steps: glycolysis, pyruvate processing, the citric acid cycle, and electron transport coupled to oxidative phosphorylation.

- Glycolysis, pyruvate processing, and the citric acid cycle are central to the metabolism of most cells. Other catabolic pathways feed into them, and the intermediates of the central pathways are used in the synthesis of many key molecules.

✔ You should be able to explain why many different molecules—including lipids, amino acids, and $CO_2$—are radiolabeled when cells are fed glucose with $^{14}C$ radioactive carbons.

### 9.2 Glycolysis: Processing Glucose to Pyruvate

- The glycolytic pathway is a 10-step reaction sequence in which glucose is broken down into two molecules of pyruvate. It takes place in the cytosol, where ATP and NADH are produced.

- Glycolysis slows when ATP binds to phosphofructokinase.

✔ **QUANTITATIVE** You should be able to draw a graph predicting how the rate of ATP production in glycolysis changes as a function of ATP concentration. (Write "ATP concentration" on the $x$-axis and "ATP production" on the $y$-axis.)

## 9.3 Processing Pyruvate to Acetyl CoA

- During pyruvate processing, a series of reactions convert pyruvate to acetyl CoA. NADH is produced and $CO_2$ is released.

- The pyruvate dehydrogenase complex is inhibited when it is phosphorylated by ATP. It speeds up in the presence of substrates like NAD and ADP.

✓ You should be able to explain why it is not surprising that pyruvate dehydrogenase consists of a large, multi-enzyme complex.

## 9.4 The Citric Acid Cycle: Oxidizing Acetyl CoA to $CO_2$

- The citric acid cycle is an eight-step reaction cycle that begins with acetyl CoA. $FADH_2$, NADH, and GTP or ATP are produced; $CO_2$ is released. By the end of the citric acid cycle, glucose is completely oxidized to $CO_2$.

- Certain enzymes in the citric acid cycle are inhibited when NADH or ATP binds to them.

✓ You should be able to describe what would happen to NADH levels in a cell in the first few seconds after a drug has poisoned the enzyme that combines acetyl CoA and oxaloacetate to form citrate.

## 9.5 Electron Transport and Chemiosmosis: Building a Proton Gradient to Produce ATP

- NADH and $FADH_2$ donate electrons to an electron transport chain that resides in the inner membrane of mitochondria and the plasma membrane of many bacteria. The series of redox reactions in these chains gradually steps the electrons down in potential energy until they are transferred to a final electron acceptor (often $O_2$).

- The energy released from redox reactions in the electron transport chain is used to move protons across the inner mitochondrial membrane, creating an electrochemical gradient. ATP synthase uses the energy stored in this gradient to produce ATP via chemiosmosis—a process called oxidative phosphorylation.

✓ You should be able to predict the effect of a drug that inhibits ATP synthase on the pH in the mitochondrial matrix.

## 9.6 Fermentation

- In many eukaryotes and bacteria, fermentation occurs when cellular respiration slows down or stops due to an insufficient amount of the final electron acceptor. If the final electron acceptor is absent, then the electron transport chain would no longer oxidize NADH to $NAD^+$ and ATP could no longer be produced by glycolysis, the citric acid cycle, or oxidative phosphorylation.

- Fermentation pathways regenerate $NAD^+$, so glycolysis can continue to make ATP and keep the cell alive. This happens when an organic molecule such as pyruvate accepts electrons from NADH.

- Depending on the molecule that acts as an electron acceptor, fermentation pathways produce lactate, ethanol, or other reduced organic compounds as a by-product.

✓ You should be able to explain why you would expect organisms that produce ATP only via fermentation to grow much more slowly than organisms that produce ATP via cellular respiration.

### (MB) MasteringBiology

**1. MasteringBiology Assignments**

**Tutorials and Activities** Build a Chemical Cycling System; Cellular Respiration (1 of 5): Inputs and Outputs; Cellular Respiration (2 of 5): Glycolysis; Cellular Respiration (3 of 5): Acetyl CoA Formation and the Citric Acid Cycle; Cellular Respiration (4 of 5): Oxidative Phosphorylation; Cellular Respiration (5 of 5): Summary; Citric Acid Cycle; Electron Transport; Fermentation; Glucose Metabolism; Glycolysis; Overview of Cellular Respiration; Pathways for Pyruvate

**Questions** Reading Quizzes, Blue-Thread Questions, Test Bank

**2. eText** Read your book online, search, take notes, highlight text, and more.

**3. The Study Area** Practice Test, Cumulative Test, BioFlix® 3-D animations, Videos, Activities, Audio Glossary, Word Study Tools, Art

## You should be able to . . .

### ✓ TEST YOUR KNOWLEDGE
*Answers are available in Appendix A*

1. Make a flowchart indicating the relationships among the four steps of cellular respiration. Which steps are responsible for glucose oxidation? Which produce the most ATP?

2. Where does the citric acid cycle occur in eukaryotes?
   a. in the cytosol
   b. in the matrix of mitochondria
   c. in the inner membrane of mitochondria
   d. in the intermembrane space of mitochondria

3. What does the chemiosmotic hypothesis claim?
   a. Substrate-level phosphorylation occurs in the electron transport chain.
   b. Substrate-level phosphorylation occurs in glycolysis and the citric acid cycle.
   c. The electron transport chain is located in the inner membrane of mitochondria.
   d. Electron transport chains generate ATP indirectly, by the creation of a proton-motive force.

**4.** After glucose is fully oxidized by glycolysis, pyruvate processing, and the citric acid cycle, where is most of the energy stored?

**5.** What is the function of the reactions in a fermentation pathway?
  **a.** to generate NADH from $NAD^+$, so electrons can be donated to the electron transport chain
  **b.** to synthesize pyruvate from lactate
  **c.** to generate $NAD^+$ from NADH, so glycolysis can continue
  **d.** to synthesize electron acceptors, so that cellular respiration can continue

**6.** Which of the following would cause cells to switch from cellular respiration to fermentation?
  **a.** The final electron acceptor in the ETC is not available.
  **b.** The proton-motive force runs down.
  **c.** NADH and $FADH_2$ supplies are low.
  **d.** Pyruvate is not available.

**7.** Describe the relationship between carbohydrate metabolism, the catabolism of proteins and fats, and anabolic pathways.

**8.** Compare and contrast substrate-level phosphorylation and oxidative phosphorylation.

**9.** Why does aerobic respiration produce much more ATP than anaerobic respiration?

**10.** If you were to expose cells that are undergoing cellular respiration to a radioactive oxygen isotope in the form of $O_2$, which of the following molecules would you expect to be radiolabeled?
  **a.** pyruvate
  **b.** water

  **c.** NADH
  **d.** $CO_2$

**11.** In step 3 of the citric acid cycle, the enzyme isocitrate dehydrogenase is regulated by NADH. Compare and contrast the regulation of this enzyme with what you have learned about phosphofructokinase in glycolysis.

**12.** Explain the relationship between electron transport and oxidative phosphorylation. What does ATP synthase look like, and how does it work?

**13.** Cyanide ($C \equiv N^-$) blocks complex IV of the electron transport chain. Suggest a hypothesis for what happens to the ETC when complex IV stops working. Your hypothesis should explain why cyanide poisoning in humans is fatal.

**14.** The presence of many sac-like cristae results in a large amount of membrane inside mitochondria. Suppose that some mitochondria had few cristae. How would their output of ATP compare with that of mitochondria with many cristae? Justify your answer.

**15.** QUANTITATIVE Early estimates suggested that the oxidation of glucose via aerobic respiration would produce 38 ATP. Based on what you know of the theoretical yields of ATP from each step, show how this total was determined. Why do biologists now think this amount of ATP/glucose is not achieved in cells?

**16.** Suppose a drug were added to mitochondria that allowed protons to freely pass through the inner membrane. Which of the following mitochondrial activities would most likely be inhibited?
  **a.** the citric acid cycle
  **b.** oxidative phosphorylation
  **c.** substrate-level phosphorylation
  **d.** the electron transport chain

# 11 Cell–Cell Interactions

**In this chapter you will learn how**

Cells modify their environment and interact with one another via social networks

*by exploring*

The cell surface
**11.1**

*then asking*

How do adjacent cells connect and communicate?
**11.2**

How do distant cells connect and communicate?

*finally exploring*

*looking closer at*

Cell-cell attachments and gaps

Signaling in multicellular organisms **11.3**

Signaling between unicellular organisms **11.4**

In this micrograph of cardiac tissue, muscle cells are stained red and their nuclei are stained blue. The green dye highlights a protein called dystrophin, which links the cytoskeleton of muscle cells to proteins that attach to the extracellular matrix. Deficiency in dystrophin leads to muscular dystrophy.

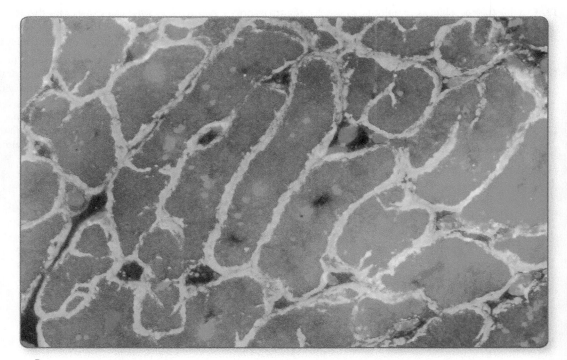

A diversity of events takes place at the cellular level. The plasma membrane surrounds a bustling enterprise consisting of organelles, molecular machines, and cytoskeletal elements (see Chapters 6 and 7). Molecular motors transport cargo throughout the cell at breathtaking speed. It would be a mistake, however, to think that cells are self-contained—that they are worlds in and of themselves. Instead, cells are dependent on interactions with other cells and the surrounding environment.

✔ When you see this checkmark, stop and test yourself. Answers are available in Appendix A.

For most unicellular species, the outside environment is teeming with other organisms. Inside your gut, for example, hundreds of billions of bacterial cells are jostling for space and resources. In addition to interacting with these individuals, every unicellular organism must contend with constant shifts in the physical environment, such as heat, light, ion concentrations, and food supplies. If unicellular organisms are unable to sense these conditions and respond appropriately, they die.

In multicellular species, the environment outside the cell is made up of other cells, both neighboring and distant. The cells that make up a redwood tree, a mushroom, or your body are intensely social. Although biologists often study cells in isolation, an individual tree, fungus, or person is actually an interdependent community of cells. If those cells do not communicate and cooperate, the whole will break into dysfunctional parts and die.

To understand the life of a cell, then, it is critical to analyze how the cell interacts with the world outside its membrane. How do cells obtain information about the world and respond to that information? In particular, how do cells interact with other cells? To answer these questions, let's begin with the cell surface—with the molecules that separate the cell from its environment.

# 11.1 The Cell Surface

The line between life and nonlife is drawn by the plasma membrane that surrounds every cell. Recall that the structure of this membrane consists of a phospholipid bilayer studded with membrane proteins that are integral, meaning that they are embedded in the bilayer, or peripheral, meaning that they are attached to one surface (see Chapter 6). These proteins participate in the primary function of the plasma membrane: to create an environment inside the cell that is different from conditions outside by regulating the transport of substances.

The plasma membrane does not exist in isolation, however. Cytoskeletal elements attach to the interior face of the bilayer (see Chapter 7), and a complex array of extracellular structures interacts with the membrane's exterior surface. Let's consider the nature of the material outside the cell and then analyze how the cell interacts with it and other cells.

## The Structure and Function of an Extracellular Layer

It is actually extremely rare for cells to be bounded simply by a plasma membrane. Most cells secrete products that are assembled into a layer or wall just beyond the membrane. This extracellular material helps define the cell's shape and either attaches it to another cell or acts as a first line of defense against the outside world.

Virtually all types of extracellular structures—from the cell walls of bacteria, algae, fungi, and plants to the extracellular material that surrounds most animal cells—follow the same fundamental design principle. Like reinforced concrete, they are "fiber composites": They consist of a cross-linked network of long

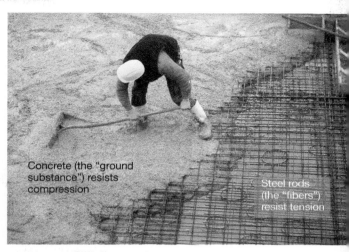

**FIGURE 11.1 Fiber Composites Resist Tension and Compression.** Fiber composites, such as reinforced concrete, consist of ground substance that fills spaces between cross-linked rods.

Concrete (the "ground substance") resists compression

Steel rods (the "fibers") resist tension

filaments embedded in a stiff surrounding material, or ground substance (**FIGURE 11.1**). The molecules that make up the filaments and the encasing material vary from group to group, but the engineering principle is the same. Why?

- The rods or filaments in a fiber composite are extremely effective at withstanding stretching and straining forces, or tension. The fibers present in extracellular material of most cells are functionally similar to the steel rods in reinforced concrete—they resist being pulled or pushed lengthwise.

- The stiff surrounding substance is effective at withstanding the pressing forces called compression. Concrete performs this function in highways, and a gel-forming mixture of polysaccharides achieves the same end in extracellular material.

Thanks to the combination of tension- and compression-resisting elements, fiber composites are particularly rugged. And in many living cells, the fiber and composite elements are flexible as well as strong.

What molecules make up the rods and ground substance found on the surface of plant and animal cells? How are these extracellular layers synthesized, and what do they do?

## The Cell Wall in Plants

Virtually all plant cells are surrounded by a cell wall—a fiber composite that is the basis of major industries. The paper in this book, the threads in your cotton clothing, and the wood in your neighborhood's houses are made up primarily of plant cell walls.

Before analyzing the structure of plant cell walls in detail, it's important to note that these structures are dynamic. If they are damaged by attacking insects, they may release signaling molecules that trigger the reinforcement of walls in nearby cells. Cell walls are also degraded in a controlled way as fruits ripen, making the fruits softer and more digestible for the animals that disperse the seeds inside.

Side view                                    Top view

Primary
cell wall

Cellulose
microfibrils

Cross-links

Pectin

Plasma
membrane

50 nm

**FIGURE 11.2 Primary Cell Walls of Plants Are Fiber Composites.** In a plant's primary cell wall, cellulose microfibrils are cross-linked by polysaccharide chains. The spaces between the microfibrils are filled with pectin molecules, which form a gelatinous solid.

**Primary Cell Walls**   When plant cells first form, they secrete an initial fiber composite called a **primary cell wall.**

The fibrous component of the primary cell wall consists of long strands of cellulose, which are bundled into stout, cable-like structures termed **microfibrils** and then cross-linked by other polysaccharide filaments. The microfibrils are synthesized by a complex of enzymes in the plasma membrane, forming a crisscrossed network (**FIGURE 11.2**).

The space between microfibrils is filled with gelatinous polysaccharides such as **pectins**—the molecules that are used to thicken jams and jellies. Because the polysaccharides in pectin are hydrophilic, they attract and hold large amounts of water to keep the cell wall moist. The gelatinous components of the cell wall are synthesized in the rough endoplasmic reticulum and Golgi apparatus and secreted to the extracellular space.

The primary cell wall defines the shape of a plant cell. Under normal conditions, the nucleus and cytoplasm fill the entire volume of the cell and push the plasma membrane up against the wall. Because the concentration of solutes is higher inside the cell than outside, water tends to enter the cell via osmosis. The incoming water increases the cell's volume, exerting a force against the wall that is known as **turgor pressure.**

Although plant cells experience turgor pressure throughout their lives, it is particularly important in young cells that are actively growing. Young plant cells secrete proteins named expansins into their cell wall. **Expansins** disrupt hydrogen bonds that cross-link the microfibrils in the wall, allowing them to slide past one another. Turgor pressure then forces the wall to elongate and expand. The result is cell growth (see Chapter 40).

**Secondary Cell Walls**   As plant cells mature and stop growing, they may secrete an additional layer of material—a **secondary cell wall**—between the plasma membrane and the primary cell wall. The structure of the secondary cell wall varies from cell to cell in the plant and correlates with that cell's function. Cells on the surface of a leaf have secondary cell walls that are impregnated with waxes that form a waterproof coating; the cells that support the plant's stem have secondary cell walls that contain a great deal of cellulose.

In cells that form wood, the secondary cell wall also includes **lignin,** a complex polymer that forms an exceptionally rigid network. Cells that have thick secondary cell walls of cellulose and lignin help plants withstand the forces of gravity and wind.

Although animal cells do not make a cell wall, they do form a fiber composite outside their plasma membrane. What is this substance, and what does it do?

## The Extracellular Matrix in Animals

Most animal cells secrete a fiber composite called the **extracellular matrix (ECM).** Like the extracellular materials found in other organisms, structural support is one of the ECM's most important functions.

ECM design follows the same principles observed in the cell walls of bacteria, archaea, algae, fungi, and plants. There is a key difference, however: The animal ECM contains much more protein relative to carbohydrate than does a cell wall.

- The fibrous component of animal ECM is dominated by a cable-like protein termed **collagen** (**FIGURE 11.3a**).

- The matrix that surrounds collagen and other fibrous components contains gel-forming **proteoglycans** that consist of protein cores with many large polysaccharides attached to them. In some tissues, complexes of proteoglycans may also be produced (**FIGURE 11.3b**).

Most ECM components are synthesized in the rough endoplasmic reticulum (ER), processed in the Golgi apparatus, and

**(a)** Collagen proteins consist of three polypeptide chains that wind around one another to form the fibrous component of the animal ECM.

3 chains

1.5-nm collagen protein

**(b)** Complexes of gelatinous proteoglycans form the ground substance of the animal ECM.

Proteoglycan complex

Proteoglycan

Proteoglycan

Polysaccharides    Core protein

0.5 μm

**FIGURE 11.3 The Extracellular Matrix Is a Fiber Composite.**
**(a)** Although several types of fibrous proteins are found in the ECM of animal cells, the most abundant is collagen. Groups of collagen proteins coalesce to form collagen fibrils, and bundles of fibrils link to form collagen fibers. **(b)** The spaces between the collagen fibers are filled with complexes of gelatinous proteoglycans. The proteoglycan subunits consist of a protein core attached to many polysaccharides.

secreted from the cell via exocytosis. After secretion, however, proteins like collagen may then assemble into larger structures, such as the fibrils shown in **FIGURE 11.4**. In addition, the secreted proteoglycans may be attached to long polysaccharides synthesized by cellular enzymes in the extracellular space. These huge complexes, such as the one shown in Figure 11.3b, are responsible for the rubber-like consistency of cartilage.

Even in the same organism, the amount of ECM varies among different types of **tissues,** which consist of similar cells that function as a unit. Bone and cartilage, for example, have relatively few cells surrounded by a large amount of ECM. Skin cells, in contrast, are packed together with a minimal amount of ECM.

The composition of the ECM also varies among tissue types. For example, the ECM surrounding cells in lung tissue contains large amounts of a rubber-like protein called elastin, which allows the ECM to expand and contract during breathing. The structure of a cell's ECM correlates with the function of the tissue.

Although collagen and the other common ECM proteins are much more elastic and bendable than the stiff cell walls of plants, they support cell structure via attachments to the cell surface. As

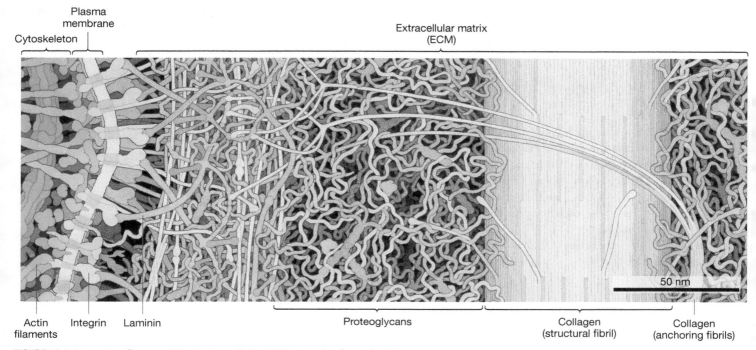

Cytoskeleton

Plasma membrane

Extracellular matrix (ECM)

Actin filaments    Integrin    Laminin

Proteoglycans

Collagen (structural fibril)

Collagen (anchoring fibrils)

50 nm

**FIGURE 11.4 Integrins Connect the Extracellular Matrix to the Cytoskeleton.**

Figure 11.4 shows, membrane proteins called **integrins** bind to extracellular proteins, including laminins, which in turn bind to other components of the ECM. **Laminins** are ECM crosslinking proteins—not to be confused with lamins, which are intermediate filaments found in the nucleus (see Chapter 7).

The intracellular portions of the integrins also bind to proteins that are connected to the cytoskeleton, effectively forming a bridge between the two support systems. This linkage between the cytoskeleton and ECM is critical. Besides keeping individual cells in place, it helps adjacent cells adhere to each other via their common connection to the ECM.

Cells monitor this cytoskeleton–ECM linkage via signaling pathways that will be introduced in Section 11.3. When integrins bind to the ECM, they transmit signals that inform the cell it is in the right place and properly anchored. If these linkages break down, the signals are not transmitted and cells normally die as a result. For most of the cells in your body, anchorage to the ECM is a matter of life and death.

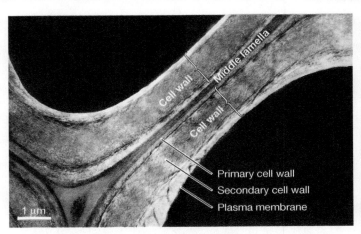

**FIGURE 11.5 The Middle Lamella Connects Adjacent Plant Cells.** The middle lamella contains gelatinous polysaccharides, called pectins, that help glue together the walls of adjacent cells.

## check your understanding

**If you understand that . . .**

- Most cells secrete a layer of structural material that supports the cell and helps define its shape. The extracellular material is usually a fiber composite—a combination of cross-linked filaments surrounded by a ground substance.

✔ **You should be able to . . .**

Compare and contrast the molecular composition of a plant cell wall and the ECM of animal cells.

*Answers are available in Appendix A.*

# 11.2 How Do Adjacent Cells Connect and Communicate?

Intercellular connections are the basis of **multicellularity.** These physical connections between cells—either direct, or indirect via the ECM—are particularly important in the structure and function of tissues. The muscle tissue in your heart, for example, depends on these attachments to support the structure of the cells as they contract and relax with each beat (see the micrograph on the opening page of this chapter).

Let's look first at the structures that attach cells to each other and then examine how they allow adjacent cells to exchange materials and information.

## Cell–Cell Attachments in Multicellular Eukaryotes

Materials and structures that bind cells together are particularly important in the **epithelium** (plural: **epithelia**)—a tissue that forms external and internal surfaces. These epithelial layers function as a barrier between the external and internal environments of plants and animals. In animals, epithelial cells also form layers that separate organs to prevent mixing of solutions from adjacent organs or structures.

The adhesive structures that hold cells together vary among multicellular organisms. To illustrate this diversity, consider the intercellular connections observed in the best-studied groups of organisms: plants and animals.

**Indirect Intercellular Attachments** The extracellular space between adjacent plant cells comprises three layers (**FIGURE 11.5**). The primary cell walls of adjacent plant cells sandwich a central layer designated the middle lamella, which consists primarily of gelatinous pectins. Because this gel layer is continuous with the primary cell walls of the adjacent cells, it serves to glue them together. The two cell walls are like slices of bread; the middle lamella is like a layer of peanut butter. If enzymes degrade the middle lamella, as they do when flower petals and leaves detach and fall, the surrounding cells separate.

In many animal tissues, integrins connect the cytoskeleton of each cell to the extracellular matrix (see Section 11.1). A middle-lamella-like layer of gelatinous polysaccharides and proteoglycans runs between adjacent animal cells. Along with the cytoskeleton–ECM connections, the polysaccharide glue helps hold cells together in tissues. In addition, in certain animal tissues the polysaccharide glue is reinforced by collagen fibrils that span the ECM to connect adjacent cells.

In animals, where cell walls do not exist, a variety of membrane proteins allow for direct cell–cell attachments in epithelia and other tissues (**FIGURE 11.6**). Let's start by looking at the tight junctions and desmosomes that hold cells together and then examine the role of gap junctions in intercellular communication.

Tight junctions
seal cells
together.

Desmosomes
connect the
cytoskeletons
of cells.

Gap junctions
act as channels
between cells.

Space between cells

**FIGURE 11.6 An Array of Structures Are Involved in Cell–Cell Adhesion and Communication between Animal Cells.**

**Tight Junctions Form a Seal between Cells** A **tight junction** is a cell–cell attachment composed of specialized proteins in the plasma membranes of adjacent animal cells (**FIGURE 11.7a**). As the drawing in **FIGURE 11.7b** indicates, these proteins line up and bind to one another. The resulting structure resembles quilting, where the proteins "stitch" the membranes of two cells together to form a watertight seal. In this way, tight junctions prevent solutions from flowing through the space between the two cells.

Because tight junctions form a watertight seal, this type of junction is commonly found in cells that form a barrier, such as the epithelial cells lining your stomach and intestines. There, they restrict the passive movement of substances between the contents of your gut and the rest of your body. Instead, only selected nutrients enter and leave the epithelia via specialized transport proteins and channels in the plasma membrane (Chapter 6).

Although tight junctions are indeed tight, they are variable. The tight junctions between the cells lining your bladder draw the cells closer together than those between the cells lining your small intestine, because they consist of different proteins. As a result, small ions can pass between the cells lining the surface of the small intestine more easily than between those lining the bladder—helping you absorb ions in your food and eliminate them in your waste.

Tight junctions are also dynamic. For example, they loosen to permit more transport between epithelial cells lining the small intestine after a meal and then "retighten" later. In this way, tight junctions can open and close in response to changes in environmental conditions.

Although tight junctions are very good at holding cells close together, they are weak adhesions that can be easily broken. Since epithelial cells often experience pulling and shearing forces, other intercellular adhesions are required to help hold cells together in a tissue. What are these other adhesions, and how do they resist being pulled apart?

**(a)** Electron micrograph of a tight junction in longitudinal section

A tight junction forms a
watertight seal between
epithelial cells

Tight junction

0.1 μm

**(b)** Three-dimensional view of a tight junction

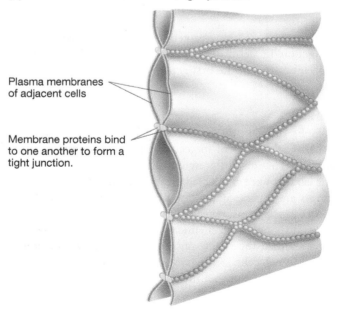

Plasma membranes
of adjacent cells

Membrane proteins bind
to one another to form a
tight junction.

**FIGURE 11.7 In Animals, Tight Junctions Form a Seal between Adjacent Cells.**

**(a)** Micrograph of desmosome in longitudinal section

Desmosome —

0.1 μm

**(b)** Three-dimensional view of desmosome

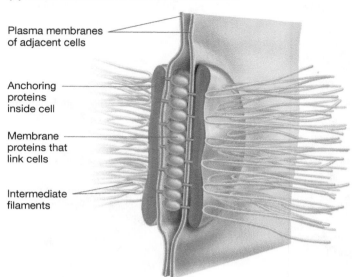

Plasma membranes of adjacent cells

Anchoring proteins inside cell

Membrane proteins that link cells

Intermediate filaments

**FIGURE 11.8 Adjacent Animal Cells Are Linked by Desmosomes, Which Bind Cytoskeletons Together.**

**Desmosomes Form Secure Adhesions** **FIGURE 11.8a** illustrates **desmosomes,** cell–cell attachments particularly common in animal epithelial cells and certain muscle cells. The structure and function of a desmosome are analogous to the rivets that hold pieces of sheet metal together.

As **FIGURE 11.8b** indicates, desmosomes are extremely sophisticated cell–cell connections. At their heart are integral membrane attachment proteins that form bridges between anchoring proteins inside adjacent cells. Intermediate filaments help reinforce these connections by attaching to the anchoring proteins in the cytoplasm. In this way, desmosomes help form a continuous structural support system between all the cells in the tissue (see Figure 11.6).

What are the membrane proteins that serve this cell attachment function in desmosomes? The answer to this question traces back to some of the first experiments conducted on cell–cell interactions.

**Intercellular Adhesions Are Selective** Long before electron micrographs revealed the presence of desmosomes, biologists realized that some sort of molecule must bind animal cells to one another. This insight grew out of experiments from H. V. Wilson's lab that were conducted on sponges in the early 1900s.

Sponges are aquatic animals, and the sponge species used in this study consists of just two basic types of tissues. When Wilson treated adult sponges with chemicals that made the cells separate from one another, the result was a jumbled mass of individual and unconnected cells. But when normal chemical conditions were restored, he noted that the cells gradually began to move and stick together.

As the experiment continued, cells began to aggregate based on their origin—adhering to other cells of the same tissue type.

This phenomenon is now called **selective adhesion.** Eventually the experimental sponge cells re-formed functional adult sponges with two distinct tissues. How could this happen?

**The Discovery of Cell–Cell Adhesion Proteins** What is the molecular basis of selective adhesion? The initial hypothesis, proposed in the 1970s, was that specialized membrane proteins were involved. The idea was that different types of cells have different types of adhesion proteins in their membranes, and only those with the same or complementary adhesion proteins are able to attach to one another.

This hypothesis was tested through experiments that relied on molecules called antibodies. An **antibody** is a protein produced by an immune response that binds specifically to a unique molecule type, often another protein (see Chapter 51). When an antibody binds to a protein, it can change the target protein's structure or interfere with its ability to interact with other molecules. This property of antibodies was crucial to these experiments.

**FIGURE 11.9** shows how researchers tested the hypothesis that cell–cell adhesion takes place via interactions between membrane proteins:

**Step 1** Isolate the membrane proteins from a certain cell type. Produce pure preparations of each protein.

**Step 2** Inject one of the membrane proteins into a rabbit. The rabbit's immune system cells respond by creating antibodies to the membrane protein, which is recognized as being foreign. Purify those antibodies. Repeat this procedure for the other membrane proteins that were isolated. In this way, obtain a large collection of antibodies—each of which binds specifically to one (and only one) type of membrane protein.

**QUESTION:** Do animal cells have adhesion proteins on their surfaces?

**HYPOTHESIS:** Selective adhesion is due to specific membrane proteins.

**NULL HYPOTHESIS:** Selective adhesion is not due to specific membrane proteins.

**EXPERIMENTAL SETUP:**

Membrane proteins

Antibodies

Experiment 1:    Experiment 2:

1. **Isolate the membrane proteins** from a certain cell type that adheres to other cells of the same type. (There are many membrane proteins; only two are shown here.)

2. **Produce antibodies** that bind to specific membrane proteins. Purify the antibodies.

3. **Treat cells with an antibody**, one type at a time. Wait; then observe whether cells adhere normally.

**PREDICTION:**

**PREDICTION OF NULL HYPOTHESIS:**

**RESULTS:**

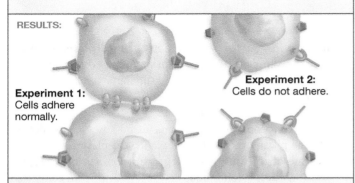

**Experiment 1:** Cells adhere normally.

**Experiment 2:** Cells do not adhere.

**CONCLUSION:** The protein that was blocked in experiment 2 (called a cadherin) is involved in cell–cell adhesion.

**FIGURE 11.9 Evidence for Adhesion Proteins on Animal Cells.**

SOURCES: Hatta, K., and M. Takeichi. 1986. Expression of N-cadherin adhesion molecules associated with early morphogenetic events in chick development. *Nature* 320: 447–449. Also Takeichi, M. 1988. The cadherins: Cell–cell adhesion molecules controlling animal morphogenesis. *Development* 102: 639–655.

✔ **EXERCISE** Fill in the prediction made by each hypothesis.

---

***Step 3*** Add one antibody type to a mixture of dissociated cells from a tissue and observe whether the cells reaggregate normally. Repeat this experiment with each of the other antibody types, one type at a time.

If treatment with a particular antibody prevents the cells from attaching to one another, the antibody is probably bound to an adhesion protein. The logic is that if the antibody "shakes hands" with the adhesion protein, the adhesion protein can't shake hands with other adhesion proteins and attach the cells to one another.

This approach allowed biologists to identify several major classes of cell adhesion proteins, including **cadherins**—the attachment molecules in desmosomes. There are various types of cadherins, and cells from different tissues have different forms of cadherin in their plasma membranes. Each cadherin can bind only to cadherins of the same type. In this way, cells of the same tissue type attach specifically to one another.

To summarize: Animal cells attach to one another in a selective manner because different types of cell adhesion proteins can bind and rivet certain cells together. Cadherins provide the physical basis for selective adhesion in many cells and are a critical component of the desmosomes that join mature cells.

✔ If you understand cell–cell attachments, you should be able to predict what would happen if you treated cells in a developing frog embryo with a molecule that blocked a cadherin present in muscle tissue.

In addition to providing structural support to tissues, intercellular connections can direct cell–cell communication. But how can cellular connections pass information between cells?

## Cells Communicate via Cell–Cell Gaps

In both plants and animals, direct connections between cells in the same tissue help them to work in a coordinated fashion. One way of accomplishing this is to generate channels in the membranes of adjacent cells, allowing them to communicate via the diffusion of cytosolic ions and small molecules from cell to cell.

How cells respond to this exchange of information varies from signal to signal and from cell to cell, but the result falls into two general categories:

1. Signals may alter which proteins are produced and which are not, by regulating gene expression; or

2. Signals may activate or deactivate particular proteins that already exist in the cell—often those involved in metabolism, membrane transport, secretion, and the cytoskeleton.

Whatever the mechanism, the activity of the cell often changes dramatically after the signal arrives. Let's take a closer look at how these signals are able to travel between adjacent cells connected by gap junctions and plasmodesmata.

**Gap Junctions Connect Cells via Protein Channels**  In most animal tissues, structures called **gap junctions** connect adjacent cells. The key feature of gap junctions is the specialized proteins that assemble in the membranes of adjacent cells, creating

**(a)** Gap junctions create gaps that connect animal cells.

Gap junctions

Membrane proteins from adjacent cells line up to form a channel.

20 μm

**(b)** Plasmodesmata create gaps that connect plant cells.

Plasmodesma with a tubule of endoplasmic reticulum passing through

Cell walls

0.1 μm

Cell wall of cell 1   Cell wall of cell 2

Membrane of cell 1

Membrane of cell 2

Smooth endoplasmic reticulum

**FIGURE 11.10 Adjacent Animal Cells and Adjacent Plant Cells Communicate Directly.**

interconnected pores between the cells (**FIGURE 11.10a**). These channels allow water, ions, and small molecules such as amino acids, sugars, and nucleotides to move between adjacent cells.

Gap junctions are communication portals. The flow of small molecules through gap junctions can help adjacent cells coordinate their activities by allowing the rapid passage of regulatory ions or molecules. In the muscle cells of your heart, for example, a flow of ions through gap junctions acts as a signal that coordinates contractions. Without this cell–cell communication, a normal heartbeat would be impossible.

In plants, direct interactions between membrane proteins are impossible due to the presence of cell walls. How do adjacent plant cells communicate?

**Plasmodesmata Connect Cells via Membrane Channels** In plants, gaps in cell walls create direct connections between the cytoplasm

of adjacent cells. At these connections, named **plasmodesmata** (singular: **plasmodesma**), the plasma membrane and the cytoplasm of the two cells are continuous. Tubular extensions from the smooth endoplasmic reticulum (smooth ER) run through these membrane-lined portals (**FIGURE 11.10b**).

Like gap junctions, plasmodesmata are communication portals through the plasma membrane. In plants, the plasma membrane separates most tissues into two independent compartments: (1) the **symplast,** which is a continuous network of cytoplasm connected by plasmodesmata, and (2) the **apoplast,** which is the region outside the plasma membrane (**FIGURE 11.11**). The apoplast consists of cell walls, the middle lamella, and air spaces. Small molecules can move through plant tissues in either of these compartments without ever crossing a membrane (see Chapter 38).

Gap junctions and plasmodesmata allow for adjacent cells to transmit information, like a conversation between neighbors.

**If you understand that . . .**

- In plants and animals, adjacent cells are either directly physically connected or, via the ECM, indirectly connected.
- Adjacent cells may communicate with each other through openings in their plasma membranes.

✓ **You should be able to . . .**

1. Compare and contrast the structure and function of the middle lamella of plants and the tight junctions and desmosomes of animals.

2. Describe the structure and function of plasmodesmata and gap junctions.

*Answers are available in Appendix A.*

But how do multicellular organisms send messages between different tissues, where in most cases there is no direct contact? For example, suppose that the muscle cells in your arm are exercising so hard they run low on sugar or that leaf cells in a maple tree are attacked by caterpillars. How do these cells signal tissues or organs elsewhere in the organism to release materials that are needed to fend off exhaustion or caterpillars? Distant cell communication is the subject of Section 11.3.

## 11.3 How Do Distant Cells Communicate?

Cells that are not in physical contact communicate with one another. This is true for unicellular organisms, where hundreds or thousands of cells may live in close proximity, as well as for multicellular organisms like humans and maple trees, which typically contain trillions of cells and dozens of tissue types.

Cell–cell communication qualifies as one of the most dynamic and important research areas in biology. Let's begin by analyzing how distant cells in humans and other multicellular eukaryotes exchange information, and then in Section 11.4 explore how unicellular organisms communicate.

### Cell–Cell Signaling in Multicellular Organisms

Suppose that cells in your brain sense that you are becoming dehydrated. Brain cells can't do much about the water you lose during urination, but kidney cells can. In response to dehydration, certain brain cells release a signaling molecule that travels to the kidneys. The arrival of this molecule activates specialized membrane channels that prevent water from being lost in urine—an important aspect of fighting dehydration.

Thanks to cell–cell signals, the activities of cells in different parts of a multicellular body are coordinated.

Biologists have classified many different types of signaling molecules that keep distant tissues in touch. For example, neurotransmitters activate membrane channel receptors that open to allow a flow of ions into the cytosol of the cell, changing the electrical properties of the membrane. This type of signal is responsible for the transmission of information along neurons, allowing your brain to control the movements of the rest of your body (see Chapters 46 and 48). The best-studied means of distant signaling, however, may be via **hormones**—information-carrying molecules that can act on distant target cells because they are secreted by plant and animal cells into bodily fluids.

Hormones are usually small molecules and are typically present in minute concentrations. Even so, they have a large impact on the activity of target cells and the condition of the body as a whole. Hormones are like a scent or whispered phrase from someone you are attracted to—a tiny signal, but one that makes your cheeks flush and your heart pound.

As **TABLE 11.1** (see page 210) indicates, hormones have a wide array of chemical structures and effects. The important point about a signaling molecule, though, is not whether it is a gas or peptide or steroid, but whether it is lipid soluble or not. The ability of a signaling molecule to pass through lipid bilayers is crucial in determining how a target cell recognizes it. Where does this recognition occur—inside the cell or outside?

- Most lipid-soluble signaling molecules are able to diffuse across the hydrophobic region of the plasma membrane and enter the cytoplasm of their target cells.

- Large or hydrophilic signaling molecules are lipid insoluble and do not cross the plasma membrane. To affect a target cell, they have to be recognized at the cell surface.

How do cells receive and process signals from distant cells? The basic steps are common to all cell–cell signaling systems. Let's consider each step in turn.

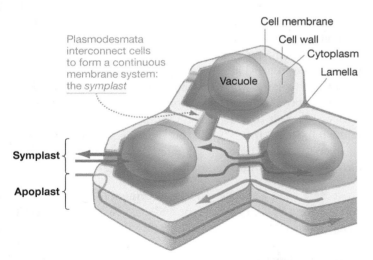

Plasmodesmata interconnect cells to form a continuous membrane system: the *symplast*

Cell membrane
Cell wall
Cytoplasm
Lamella
Vacuole

Symplast
Apoplast

**FIGURE 11.11 Most Plant Tissues Are Divided into Two Compartments—Symplast and Apoplast.** Small molecules may be transported through plant tissues either within the shared cytoplasm (symplast) or through the extracellular space (apoplast).

## TABLE 11.1 Hormones Have Diverse Structures and Functions

| Hormone Name | Chemical Structure | Where Is Signal Received? | Function of Signal |
|---|---|---|---|
| Auxin | Small organic compound | At plasma membrane | Signals changes in long axis of plant body |
| Brassinosteroids | Steroid | At plasma membrane | Stimulate plant cell elongation |
| Estrogens | Steroid | Inside cell | Stimulate development of female characteristics in animals |
| Ethylene | $C_2H_4$ (a gas) | At plasma membrane | Stimulates fruit ripening; regulates aging |
| FSH | Glycoprotein | At plasma membrane | Stimulates egg maturation, sperm production in animals |
| Insulin | Protein, 51 amino acids | At plasma membrane | Stimulates glucose uptake in animal bloodstream |
| Prostaglandins | Modified fatty acid | At plasma membrane | Perform a variety of functions in animal cells |
| Systemin | Peptide, 111 amino acids | At plasma membrane | Stimulates plant defenses against herbivores |
| Thyroxine (T4) | Modified amino acid | Inside cell | Regulates metabolism in animals |

## Signal Reception

Hormones and other types of cell–cell signaling molecules deliver their message by binding to receptor molecules. Even though the molecule that carries the message "We're getting dehydrated—conserve water" is broadcast throughout the body, only certain kidney cells respond because only they have the appropriate receptor. The presence of an appropriate receptor dictates which cells will respond to a particular hormone. Bone and muscle cells don't respond to the "conserve water" message, because they don't have a receptor for it.

Cells in a wide array of tissues may respond to the same signaling molecule, though, if they have the appropriate receptor. If you are startled by a loud noise, cells in your adrenal glands secrete a hormone called adrenaline (also called epinephrine) that carries the message "Get ready to fight or run." In response, your heart rate increases, your breathing rate increases, and cells in your liver release sugars that your muscles can use to power rapid movement. This is the basis of an "adrenaline rush." Heart, lung, and liver cells respond to adrenaline because they each have the receptor that binds to it. Identical receptors in diverse cells and tissues allow long-distance signals to coordinate the activities of cells throughout a multicellular organism.

No matter where signal receptors are located, it's critical to note two important points about these proteins:

1. *Receptors are dynamic.* The number of receptors in a particular cell may decline if hormonal stimulation occurs at high levels over a long period of time. The ability of a receptor molecule to bind tightly to a signaling molecule may also decline in response to intensive stimulation. As a result, the sensitivity of a cell to a particular hormone may change over time.

2. *Receptors can be blocked.* The drugs called beta-blockers, for example, bind to certain receptors for the hormone adrenaline. When adrenaline binds to receptors in heart cells, it stimulates more rapid and forceful contractions. So if a physician wants to reduce a patient's heart cell contraction as a way to lower pressure, she is likely to prescribe a beta-blocker.

Most signal receptors are located in the plasma membrane, where they can bind to signaling molecules that cannot or do not cross the membrane. Other signal receptors exist inside the cell, where they respond to lipid-soluble signaling molecules that readily diffuse through the plasma membrane.

The most important general characteristic of signal receptors, though, is that their conformation—meaning, overall shape—changes when a hormone binds to them. A **signal receptor** is a protein that changes its shape and activity after binding to a signaling molecule.

This is a critical event in cell–cell signaling. The change in receptor structure means that the signal has been received. It's like throwing an "on" switch. What happens next?

## Signal Processing

Once a cell receives a signal, something has to happen to initiate the cell's response. This signal processing step happens in one of two ways, depending on whether the signal is received inside the cell or at the membrane surface.

**Processing Lipid-Soluble Signals** When lipid-soluble signals enter a cell, the information they carry is processed directly—without any intermediate steps. For example, steroid hormones such as testosterone and estradiol (one of a group commonly referred to as estrogens) diffuse through the plasma membrane and enter the cytoplasm, where they bind to a cytosolic receptor protein. The hormone–receptor complex is then transported to the nucleus, where it triggers changes in the genes being expressed in the cell (**FIGURE 11.12**). By altering the expression of genes (see Chapter 17), the cell produces different proteins that will have a direct effect on the function or shape of the cell.

**Processing Lipid-Insoluble Signals** Hormones that *cannot* diffuse across the plasma membrane and enter the cytoplasm can't change the activity of genes or pumps directly. Instead, the signal that arrives at the surface of the cell has to initiate an intracellular signal—the signal processing step is indirect.

When a signaling molecule binds at the cell surface, it triggers **signal transduction**—the conversion of a signal from one form to another. A long and often complex series of events ensues, collectively called a signal transduction pathway.

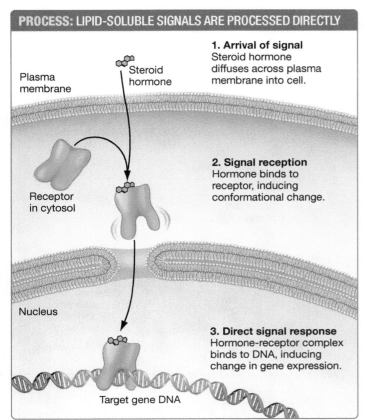

**PROCESS: LIPID-SOLUBLE SIGNALS ARE PROCESSED DIRECTLY**

Plasma membrane

Steroid hormone

**1. Arrival of signal** Steroid hormone diffuses across plasma membrane into cell.

Receptor in cytosol

**2. Signal reception** Hormone binds to receptor, inducing conformational change.

Nucleus

**3. Direct signal response** Hormone-receptor complex binds to DNA, inducing change in gene expression.

Target gene DNA

**FIGURE 11.12 Some Cell–Cell Signaling Molecules Enter the Cell and Bind to Receptors in the Cytoplasm.** Because they are lipids, steroid hormones can diffuse across the plasma membrane and bind to signal receptors inside the cell. The hormone–receptor complex is transported to the nucleus and binds to genes, changing their activity.

✔ **QUESTION** Based on what you have learned about nuclear transport (see Chapter 7), what type of signal would you expect to be exposed on the cytosolic receptor after the steroid hormone changes the receptor's conformation?

Signal transduction is a common occurrence in everyday life. For example, the e-mail messages you receive are transmitted from one computer to another over cables or wireless transmissions. These electronic signals can be transmitted efficiently over long distances but would be meaningless to you. Software in your computer has to transduce, or convert, the signals into a form that you can understand and respond to, such as words on the screen.

Signal transduction pathways work the same way (**FIGURE 11.13**). In a cell, signal transduction converts an extracellular signal to an intracellular signal. As in an e-mail transmission, a signal that is easy to transmit is converted to a signal that is easily understood and that triggers a response.

**Intracellular Signals May Be Amplified** Recall that hormones are present in minuscule concentrations but trigger a large response from cells. Signal amplification is one reason this is possible. When a hormone arrives at the cell surface, the message it transmits may be amplified as it changes form. The amplifier

in your portable music player performs an analogous function. Once it is amplified, a tiny sound signal can get a whole roomful of people dancing.

In cells, signal transduction begins at the plasma membrane; amplification occurs inside. Amplification may occur in a variety of ways. In general, the mechanism of amplification correlates with the mechanism of signal transduction. But the general observation is that the arrival of a single signaling molecule may result in a secondary signal that involves many ions or molecules.

For example, one major type of signal transduction system consists of membrane channel receptors that open to allow a flow of ions into the cytosol of the cell. In muscle cells, this type of amplification occurs when calcium ions flood into the cytosol, activating all the myosin filaments so the entire cell contracts as a whole (see Chapter 48).

Here let's focus on two other major types of signal transduction and amplification systems that are distinguished based on how they are initiated:

1. G-protein-coupled receptors initiate the production of intracellular or "second" messengers that then amplify the signal.

2. Enzyme-linked receptors amplify the signal by triggering the activation of a series of proteins inside the cell, through the addition of phosphate groups.

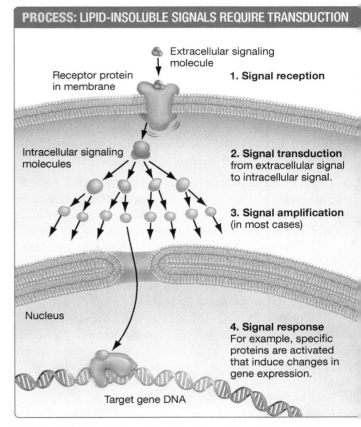

**PROCESS: LIPID-INSOLUBLE SIGNALS REQUIRE TRANSDUCTION**

Extracellular signaling molecule

Receptor protein in membrane

**1. Signal reception**

Intracellular signaling molecules

**2. Signal transduction** from extracellular signal to intracellular signal.

**3. Signal amplification** (in most cases)

Nucleus

**4. Signal response** For example, specific proteins are activated that induce changes in gene expression.

Target gene DNA

**FIGURE 11.13 Signal Transduction Converts an Extracellular Signal to an Intracellular Signal.** Signal transduction is a multistep process.

Although there are many variations in the signaling pathways that l within these two categories, the common features are emphasized re. Let's look at these two signal transduction systems in turn.

**gnal Transduction via G-Protein-Coupled Receptors** Many gnal receptors span the plasma membrane and are closely as-ciated with membrane-anchored proteins inside the cell called **proteins.** When G proteins are activated by a signal receptor, ey trigger a key step in signal transduction: the production of a essenger inside the cell. They link the receipt of an extracellular gnal to the production of an intracellular signal.

G proteins got their name because the type of guanine nucleo-le they are bound to regulates their activity: either guanosine phosphate (GTP) or guanosine diphosphate (GDP). GTP is a icleoside triphosphate that is similar in structure to adenosine phosphate (ATP; introduced in Chapter 4). Recall that nucleo-le triphosphates have high potential energy because their three osphate groups have four negative charges close together.

When GTP binds to a G protein, the addition of the nega-ve charges alters the protein's shape. Changes in shape produce anges in activity. G proteins are turned on or activated when ey bind GTP; they are turned off or inactivated when a phos-ate group, and thus a negative charge, is removed to form GDP. ie G protein will remain in this off position until the GDP is moved and the protein binds to a new GTP.

To understand how G proteins fit into an overall signal trans-ction pathway, follow the events in **FIGURE 11.14**.

**ep 1** A hormone arrives and binds to a receptor in the plasma membrane. Notice that the receptor is a transmembrane pro-tein with the intracellular portion coupled to a G protein that is composed of multiple subunits.

**ep 2** In response to hormone binding, the receptor changes shape and activates its G protein. Specifically, the receptor kicks out the GDP from the inactive G protein, allowing it to bind to a new GTP. When GTP is bound, the G protein changes shape radically: the active GTP-binding subunit splits off.

**ep 3** The active G protein subunit interacts with a nearby enzyme that is embedded in the plasma membrane. This in-teraction stimulates the enzyme to catalyze production of a **second messenger**—a small, nonprotein signaling molecule that elicits an intracellular response to the first messenger (the signaling molecule that arrived at the cell surface).

Second messengers are effective because they are small and dif-se rapidly to spread the signal throughout the cell. In addition, ey can be produced quickly in large quantities. This characteris-c is important. Because the arrival of a single hormone molecule n stimulate the production of many second messenger mol-ules, the signal transduction event amplifies the original signal.

Several types of small molecules act as second messengers in lls. **TABLE 11.2** lists some of the best-studied second messengers d provides an example of how cells respond to each of them. ote that several second messengers activate **protein kinases**— izymes that activate or inactivate other proteins by adding a iosphate group to them.

**PROCESS: HOW DO G-PROTEIN-COUPLED RECEPTORS WORK?**

1. G protein is "off" (bound to GDP). Signal arrives and binds to receptor.

2. Signal–receptor complex changes conformation. G protein binds GTP and splits into two parts.

3. Activated G protein binds to an enzyme and induces the production of second messenger, which triggers a response.

**FIGURE 11.14 G-Protein-Coupled Receptors Trigger the Production of a Second Messenger.**

It's also important to note two things:

1. Second messengers aren't restricted to a single role or single cell type—the same second messenger can initiate dramati-cally different events in different cell types; and

2. It is common for more than one second messenger to be in-volved in triggering a cell's response to the same extracellular signaling molecule.

To make sure that you understand how G proteins and second messengers work, imagine the following movie scene: A spy ar-rives at a castle gate. The guard receives a note from the spy, but

### TABLE 11.2 Examples of Second Messengers

| Name | Type of Response |
|------|------------------|
| Cyclic guanosine monophosphate (cGMP) | Opens ion channels; activates certain protein kinases |
| Diacylglycerol (DAG) | Activates certain protein kinases |
| Inositol trisphosphate ($IP_3$) | Opens calcium channels to transport stored calcium ions |
| Cyclic adenosine monophosphate (cAMP) | Activates certain protein kinases |
| Calcium ions ($Ca^{2+}$) | Binds to a receptor called calmodulin; $Ca^{2+}$/calmodulin complex then activates proteins |

he cannot read the coded message. Instead, the guard turns to the queen. She reads the note and summons the commander of the guard, who sends soldiers throughout the castle to warn everyone of approaching danger. ✔ You should be able to identify which characters in the scene correspond to the second messenger, G protein, hormone, receptor, and enzyme activated by the G protein.

It's difficult to overstate the importance of signal transduction by G-protein-coupled receptors. Biomedical researchers estimate that half of human drugs target signal receptors that are associated with G proteins.

**Signal Transduction via Enzyme-Linked Receptors** Enzyme-linked receptors transduce hormonal signals by directly catalyzing a reaction inside the cell. **FIGURE 11.15** focuses on the best-studied group of enzyme-linked receptors: the **receptor tyrosine kinases (RTKs).**

*Step 1* A hormone binds to an RTK.

*Step 2* The protein forms a dimer. In this conformation, the catalytic activity of the receptor is turned on, allowing it to phosphorylate itself using ATP inside the cell.

*Step 3* Proteins inside the cell bind to the phosphorylated RTK to form a bridge between the receptor and a peripheral membrane protein called **Ras,** which is a G protein. The formation of the RTK bridge activates Ras by causing it to exchange its GDP for a GTP.

*Step 4* When Ras is activated, it triggers the phosphorylation and activation of another protein.

*Step 5* The phosphorylated protein is a protein kinase, which then catalyzes the phosphorylation and activation of other kinases, which phosphorylate yet another population of proteins.

This sequence of events is termed a **phosphorylation cascade,** and it culminates in a response by the cell. The enzymes involved are called **mitogen-activated protein kinases (MAPK).** They are so named because many of the signaling molecules that start

**PROCESS: HOW DO ENZYME-LINKED RECEPTORS WORK?**

Signaling molecule

GDP
Ras protein
Receptor tyrosine kinase (RTK)

1. Signaling molecule arrives and binds to receptor monomers, causing them to dimerize.

GDP
P   P   ATP
ADP

2. Activated receptor complex turns on the receptor's kinase activity, which phosphorylates itself at tyrosine residues.

GTP
GDP
Ras   Bridging proteins
P   P

3. Binding proteins bind to the phosphorylated receptor and one of them activates Ras by causing it to exchange GDP for GTP.

GTP
P   P
ATP
ADP
Inactive kinase 1
P   Active kinase 1

4. Activated Ras triggers phosphorylation and activation of a protein kinase.

ATP
ADP
Inactive kinase 2
P   Active kinase 2

5. A phosphorylation cascade results, where each kinase phosphorylates a different kinase until a response is triggered in the cell.

ATP
ADP
Inactive kinase 3
**Triggers response**

**FIGURE 11.15 Enzyme-Linked Receptors Trigger a Phosphorylation Cascade.**

hese pathways are substances called mitogens, which activate cell division. (The *mito–* in mitogen stands for mitosis, a process involved in eukaryotic cell division.)

In some cases, each copy of an enzyme in the cascade catalyzes the phosphorylation of many copies of the next "downstream" protein, and so on. When this occurs, activated enzymes at a given stage in the cascade exist in greater numbers than the activated enzymes that preceded them, and the original signal is amplified many times over.

To make sure you understand how RTKs and phosphorylation cascades work, imagine that you have two red dominos, one black domino, and a large supply of green, blue, and yellow dominos. The red dominos represent the two subunits of an RTK dimer, and the black domino represents Ras. Each of the other colors represents a different protein kinase in a phosphorylation cascade. ✔ QUANTITATIVE You should be able to (1) explain how you would set up the dominos to simulate a phosphorylation cascade, and (2) state how many green, blue, and yellow dominos would be required to model the pathway if Ras and each protein kinase in the cascade were to activate 10 proteins.

In many cases, the proteins that take part in a phosphorylation cascade are held in close physical proximity by scaffolding proteins. Although this organization limits the amplification of the response, it increases the speed and efficiency of the reaction sequence.

In general, intracellular signals initiated by G-protein-coupled receptors result in the production of second messengers, while enzyme-linked receptors drive phosphorylation cascades. It's important to recognize, however, that these pathways overlap significantly. Some G-protein-coupled receptors trigger phosphorylation cascades, and some enzyme-linked receptors result in the production of second messengers.

To summarize: Many of the key signal transduction events observed in cells occur via G-protein-coupled receptors or enzyme-linked receptors. The signal transduction event has two results: (1) It converts an easily transmitted extracellular message into an intracellular message, and (2) in some cases it amplifies the original message many times over.

## Signal Response

What is the ultimate response to the messages carried by hormones? Recall that when adjacent cells share information through cell–cell gaps, two general categories of response may occur (see Section 11.2). Likewise, second messengers or a cascade of protein phosphorylation events also may alter gene expression, or activate or deactivate existing proteins in the target cell.

For example, when plants experience drought, the tissues in the root system are the first to respond by secreting the hormone abscisic acid. This hormone travels huge distances to reach the leaves and eventually bind to its receptors in guard cells that control the stomatal pores that allow for gas exchange (see Chapter 10). When abscisic acid binds to these receptors, a signal transduction pathway ensues that increases the concentration of calcium inside the guard cells. In response, potassium ions ($K^+$) move out of the guard cells, creating an osmotic

gradient that leads to the movement of water out of the guard cells. The guard cells deflate and close the pore, which prevents water loss from the plant.

At this point, you've analyzed the first three steps of cell–cell communication: signal reception, signal processing, and the response. Now the question is, how is the signal turned off? Consider the flush of testosterone and estrogens that you experienced during puberty, and the morphological changes these hormones induced. Abnormalities would result if these changes continued indefinitely. What limits the response to a cell–cell signal?

## Signal Deactivation

Cells have built-in systems for turning off intracellular signals. For example, once activated G proteins turn on downstream enzymes, the GTP is hydrolyzed to GDP and $P_i$. When this reaction occurs, the G protein's conformation changes and it returns to an inactive state. Activation of its downstream target stops, and production of the second messenger ceases.

The presence of second messengers in the cytosol is also short lived. For example, pumps in the membrane of the smooth ER return calcium ions to storage, and enzymes called phosphodiesterases convert active cAMP and cGMP (see Table 11.2) to inactive AMP and GMP. When second messengers are cleared from the cytosol, the response stops.

To continue the response from G-protein-coupled receptors, the G proteins must be reactivated by the activated signal receptor to start the process again. Otherwise, the signal transduction system quickly shuts down.

Phosphorylation cascades are also sensitive to the presence of the external signal. Enzymes, called **phosphatases,** that remove phosphate groups from cascade proteins are always present in the cell. If hormone stimulation of a receptor tyrosine kinase ends, phosphatases will dephosphorylate enough components of the phosphorylation cascade that the response ceases.

Although an array of specific mechanisms are involved, here is the general observation: Signal transduction systems trigger a rapid response and can be shut down quickly. As a result, they are exquisitely sensitive to small changes in the concentration of hormones or in the number and activity of signal receptors.

It is critical, though, to appreciate what happens when a signal transduction system does not shut down properly. For example, recall that Ras is active when it binds GTP, but is deactivated once it has hydrolyzed GTP to GDP and $P_i$. If this hydrolysis activity were defective, however, Ras would stay in the GTP-bound "on" position and continue stimulating a phosphorylation cascade even when the external signal is absent.

Why is continuously active Ras a problem? Recall that the phosphorylation cascade that is activated by Ras involves mitogen-activated protein kinases, many of which induce cell replication. If cells express this type of defective Ras, they would receive a never-ending "divide now" signal that may lead to the development of cancer. An estimated 25–30 percent of all human cancers express this type of defective Ras. (To learn more about the family of diseases called cancer, see Chapters 12 and 19.)

## Crosstalk: Synthesizing Input from Many Signals

Although the preceding discussion focused on how cells respond to individual signals, it's crucial to realize that every cell has an array of signal receptors on its plasma membrane and in its cytoplasm, and many cells receive an almost constant stream of different signals. Just as you receive information about your environment via text messages, e-mails, phone calls, and snail mail, cells get an array of chemical signals about changes in their environment.

The signal transduction pathways that are triggered by these signals and receptors intersect and connect. In reality, they are not strictly linear like the pathways illustrated in Figures 11.12 through 11.15. Signal transduction pathways form a network. This complexity is important: It allows cells to respond to many different signals in an integrated way.

The diverse signals that a cell receives are integrated by what biologists call **crosstalk**—meaning, the signals from different pathways interact to modify the cell response (**FIGURE 11.16**). This would be like getting advice from multiple people before making a decision. Here are three key things to note:

1. Elements or products from one pathway may inhibit steps in a different pathway—reducing the cell's response, even though the appropriate signal is present.

2. A response from one pathway may stimulate a greater response by a protein in a different pathway, increasing the cell's response to the other signal.

3. The presence of multiple steps in each signaling pathway provides a series of points where crosstalk can regulate the flow of information. These interactions are important, because they allow the cell to respond appropriately to many signals at the same time.

check your understanding

**C Y U**

**If you understand that . . .**
- Intercellular signals coordinate the activities of cells throughout the body of a multicellular organism in response to changes in internal or external conditions.
- If intercellular signaling molecules do not enter the cell, they bind to a receptor on the plasma membrane. In response, the intercellular signal is transduced to an intracellular signal that the cell responds to.

✔ **You should be able to . . .**
1. Explain how only certain cells respond to particular signaling molecules that may be sent throughout the body.
2. Explain how some signals are amplified.

*Answers are available in Appendix A.*

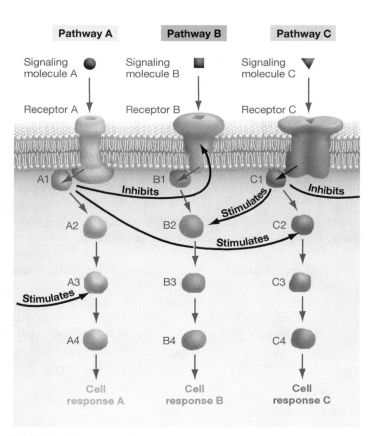

**Pathway A**   **Pathway B**   **Pathway C**

Signaling molecule A   Signaling molecule B   Signaling molecule C

Receptor A   Receptor B   Receptor C

A1   B1   C1
Inhibits   Inhibits
Stimulates
A2   B2   C2
Stimulates
A3   B3   C3
Stimulates
A4   B4   C4

Cell response A   Cell response B   Cell response C

**FIGURE 11.16 Signaling Pathways Interact via "Crosstalk."**

✔ **EXERCISE** Predict which response would occur in cells exposed to the following signaling molecules: (1) A + B; (2) A + C; (3) C alone.

## 11.4 Signaling between Unicellular Organisms

Cell–cell signaling has been one of the hottest research areas in biological science over the past two decades. Surprisingly, much of what we know about signal transduction in multicellular organisms has come from the study of unicellular organisms. While single-cell microbes communicate with one another in a manner similar to what is observed in multicellular organisms, the topic of conversation often differs. Rather than asking for help, as when a dehydrated brain asks the kidney to conserve water, the conversations between unicellular microbes are often about sex and environmental change.

### Responding to Sex Pheromones

While unicellular eukaryotes generally reproduce by cell division, some also are known to undergo sexual reproduction (see Chapters 12 and 13 to learn more about cellular reproduction). At its most basic level, sex involves the fusion of two cells such that genetic material of the two individuals is combined into one nucleus. What attracts individuals of the opposite sex to each other?

In *Saccharomyces cerevisiae*, or baker's yeast, there are two sexes, or mating types, referred to as "**a**" cells and "**α**" cells. By

**(a)** Yeast cells alter their growth in response to pheromones of the opposite mating type.

Red stain shows new cell growth

5 μm

**(b)** Slime mold amoebae aggregate in response to sensing a quorum.

100 μm

Cells migrate toward a central point

**FIGURE 11.17 Unicellular Organisms Interact and Respond in a Variety of Ways. (a)** Yeast cells respond to pheromone signals from the opposite mating type by growing toward the source of the signal during sexual reproduction. **(b)** Signals secreted by free-living slime mold protists stimulate them to aggregate under high population densities.

studying this eukaryotic model organism, biologists have figured out the cell signaling events that bring yeast of the opposite sex together (to learn more about model organisms, see **BioSkills 13** in Appendix B).

Although the yeast cells are visually indistinguishable, opposite mating types recognize one another via chemical signaling molecules called **pheromones.** The **a** mating type secretes the pheromone **a** factor, and the **α** type secretes the pheromone **α** factor. Receptors on the surface of these cells will bind only to the opposite mating type factor, so when an **a** cell detects the **α** factor, it recognizes that a suitable mate is nearby.

Since yeast cells are not motile, part of the cellular response to the pheromone is to direct new growth toward the signal (**FIGURE 11.17a**). The signaling pathway that is responsible for this morphological change uses both G-protein-coupled receptors and phosphorylation cascades that were presented in Section 11.3. One of the proteins affected by this signaling pathway is actin, which is used to construct new microfilaments at the site where the G proteins have been activated. These new filaments push out new growth toward the highest concentration of the pheromone to allow the cell to find, and eventually fuse with, its mate.

## Responding to Population Density

Within a population of unicellular organisms, widespread communication can occur that closely monitors the environment—in particular, the density of the population. Signaling pathways that respond to population density in microbes are collectively referred to as **quorum sensing.** The name was inspired by the observation that cells of the same species may undergo dramatic changes in activity when their numbers reach a threshold, or quorum.

Quorum sensing is based on signaling molecules that are secreted by cells and diffuse through the environment. The response to these molecules varies dramatically between species and ranges from bacterial bioluminescence—or light emission—in the light organs of squid to the secretion of molecules that help glue a community of microbes to a surface in biofilms (see Chapter 29).

In effect, quorum sensing allows unicellular organisms to communicate and coordinate activity. When it occurs, these single-celled organisms take on some of the characteristics of multicellular organisms. For example, quorum sensing via a G-protein-coupled receptor recruits the free-living amoebae of the cellular slime mold *Dictyostelium* to aggregate into multicellular mounds (**FIGURE 11.17b**). Amazingly, the slug-like bodies that are formed from these aggregates can crawl across a surface and eventually organize themselves into a fruiting body that releases spores into the air (see **BioSkills 13** in Appendix B).

This brief introduction to cell–cell signaling brings us to the frontier of biological research. It has taken decades of painstaking research to work out each step in individual signaling pathways. Biologists are now investigating cell signaling at a whole system level—examining how the major pathways interact and how they are integrated at the tissue level within multicellular organisms.

The number of molecules involved and the complexity of their interactions can seem overwhelming, but the punch line is simple: In organisms ranging from bacteria to blue whales, cell–cell signaling helps organisms receive information about their environment and respond to changing conditions in an appropriate way.

## If you understand . . .

### 11.1 The Cell Surface

- The vast majority of cells secrete an extracellular layer.

- In bacteria, archaea, algae, and plants, the extracellular material is stiff and is called a cell wall. In animals, the secreted layer is flexible and is called the extracellular matrix (ECM).

- Extracellular layers are fiber composites. They consist of cross-linked filaments that provide tensile strength and a ground substance that fills space and resists compression.

- In plants, the extracellular filaments are cellulose microfibrils; in animals, the most abundant filaments are made of the protein collagen. In both plants and animals, the ground substance is composed of gel-forming polysaccharides.

✓ You should be able to predict what happens to animal cells when they are treated with an enzyme that (1) cuts integrin molecules, or (2) digests collagen fibrils.

### 11.2 How Do Adjacent Cells Connect and Communicate?

- In multicellular organisms, molecules in the extracellular layer and plasma membrane mediate interactions between adjacent cells.

- Adjacent cells may be physically bound to one another by glue-like middle lamellae in plants or by tight junctions and desmosomes in animals.

- The cytoplasm of adjacent cells is in direct communication through openings called plasmodesmata in plants and gap junctions in animals.

- Cells may respond to signals by activating certain enzymes, releasing or taking up specific ions or molecules, or changing the activity of target genes. As a result, cells and tissues throughout the body can alter their activity in response to changing conditions, and do so in a coordinated way.

✓ You should be able to predict the consequences of removing the gap junctions between the cells in the cardiac muscle in your heart.

### 11.3 How Do Distant Cells Communicate?

- Distant cells in multicellular organisms communicate through signaling molecules that bind to receptors found in or on specific target cells.

- Cell–cell signaling molecules that are not lipid soluble bind to receptors in the plasma membrane. The receptor then changes conformation and triggers production of a new type of intracellular signal—a second messenger or phosphorylation cascade.

- Because enzymes inside the cell quickly deactivate the signal and signaling pathways often interact, the cell's response is tightly regulated.

✓ You should be able to explain how the hormone adrenalin can stimulate cells in both the heart and the liver, yet trigger different responses (increasing heart rate versus releasing glucose).

### 11.4 Signaling between Unicellular Organisms

- Unicellular organisms use chemical signals to sense the pheromones of opposite mating types and population density. Quorum sensing allows closely related cells to coordinate changes in their activity when population density is high.

✓ You should be able to compare and contrast the role of intercellular signaling between unicellular organisms and the cells in a multicellular organism.

(MB) **MasteringBiology**

1. **MasteringBiology Assignments**

   **Tutorials and Activities** Build a Signaling Pathway; Cell Junctions; Cell Signaling: Reception; Cell Signaling: Transduction and Response; Cellular Responses; Overview of Cell Signaling; Reception; Signal Transduction Pathways

   **Questions** Reading Quizzes, Blue-Thread Questions, Test Bank

2. eText Read your book online, search, take notes, highlight text, and more.

3. The Study Area Practice Test, Cumulative Test, BioFlix® 3-D Animations, Videos, Activities, Audio Glossary, Word Study Tools, Art

# You should be able to . . .

1. What is a fiber composite? How do cellular fiber composites resemble reinforced concrete?

2. In animals, where are most components of the extracellular material synthesized?
   a. smooth ER
   b. the rough ER
   c. in the extracellular layer itself
   d. in the plasma membrane

3. Treating dissociated cells with certain antibodies makes the cells unable to reaggregate. Why?
   a. The antibodies bind to cell adhesion proteins.
   b. The antibodies bind to the fiber component of the extracellular matrix.
   c. The antibodies bind to the cell surface and inhibit motility.
   d. The antibodies act as enzymes that break down desmosomes.

4. What does it mean to say that a signal is transduced?
   a. The signaling molecule enters the cell directly and binds to a receptor inside.
   b. The physical form of the signal changes between the outside of the cell and the inside.
   c. The signal is amplified, such that even a single molecule evokes a large response.
   d. The signal triggers a sequence of phosphorylation events inside the cell.

5. What characteristics do tight junctions bestow on tissues that use these adhesions to connect adjacent cells?
   a. They allow communication between adjacent cells.
   b. They provide strong connections to resist pulling forces.
   c. They use the extracellular matrix to indirectly connect adjacent cells.
   d. They form a watertight barrier between the cells.

6. What are the two general categories of cellular responses to an intercellular signal?

7. Which of the following statements represents a fundamental difference between the fibers found in the extracellular layers of plants and those of animals?
   a. Plant fibers resist compression forces; animal fibers resist pulling forces.
   b. Animal fibers consist of proteins; plant fibers consist of polysaccharides instead.
   c. Plant extracellular fibers never move; animal fibers can slide past one another.
   d. Cellulose microfibrils run parallel to one another; collagen filaments crisscross.

8. Explain how it is possible for a phosphorylation cascade to amplify an intercellular signal.

9. Compare and contrast the structure and function of tight junctions, desmosomes, and gap junctions.

10. Animal cells adhere to each other selectively. Summarize experimental evidence that supports this statement. Explain the molecular basis of selective adhesion.

11. Make a flowchart summarizing the reception, processing, response, and deactivation steps for a signaling molecule that binds to an intracellular receptor.

12. What is the significance of the observation that many signal transduction pathways create a network, where they intersect or overlap?

13. What would be the impact on the structure of a plant tissue if the cells lacked the ability to modify the extracellular environment?
    a. Cells would swell and burst if placed in a hypotonic environment.
    b. Cells would not be able to adhere to one another.
    c. No defined tissues, consisting of similar cells with coordinated activities, would be possible.
    d. All of the above.

14. Suppose that a particular cell–cell signaling molecule induces a cellular response without requiring signal transduction (i.e., no second messengers or phosphorylation cascades). Compared to the signal transduction pathways you learned about in this chapter, how would an event like this affect (a) the types of responses that are possible, (b) amplification, and (c) regulation?

15. In most species of fungi, chitin is a major polysaccharide found in cell walls. Review the structure of chitin (see Chapter 5), and then describe what would have to take place for the directional growth that occurs when yeast, a type of fungi, respond to sex pheromones.

16. Suppose you created an antibody that bound to the receptor tyrosine kinase illustrated in Figure 11.15. You expected this antibody to inhibit the cell response, but instead it resulted in activating the response, even when no signal was present. Explain this result.

# 12 The Cell Cycle

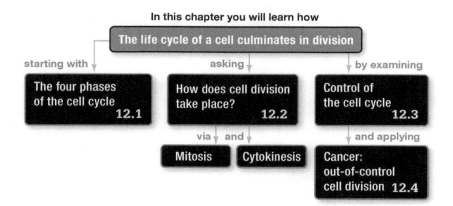

**In this chapter you will learn how**

**The life cycle of a cell culminates in division**

starting with → | asking → | by examining →

**The four phases of the cell cycle** 12.1

**How does cell division take place?** 12.2

**Control of the cell cycle** 12.3

via ↓ and ↓

**Mitosis** | **Cytokinesis**

and applying ↓

**Cancer: out-of-control cell division** 12.4

This cell, from a hyacinth plant, is undergoing a type of nuclear division called mitosis. Understanding how mitosis occurs is a major focus of this chapter.

This chapter is part of the Big Picture. See how on pages 366–367.

The cell theory maintains that all organisms are made of cells and all cells arise from preexisting cells (Chapter 1). Although the cell theory was widely accepted among biologists by the 1860s, most believed that new cells arose within preexisting cells by a process that resembled the growth of mineral crystals. But Rudolf Virchow proposed that new cells arise by splitting preexisting cells—that is, by **cell division.**

In the late 1800s, microscopic observations of newly developing organisms, or **embryos,** confirmed Virchow's hypothesis. Multicellular eukaryotes start life as single-celled embryos and grow through a series of cell divisions.

Early studies revealed two fundamentally different ways that nuclei divide before cell division: meiosis and mitosis. In animals, **meiosis** leads to the production of sperm and eggs, which are the male and female reproductive cells termed **gametes. Mitosis** leads to the production of all other cell types, referred to as **somatic** (literally, "body-belonging") **cells.** (You can see the Big Picture of

✔ When you see this checkmark, stop and test yourself. Answers are available in Appendix A.

21

how these two nuclear divisions are related to each other and the transmission of genetic information on pages 366–367.)

Mitosis and meiosis are usually accompanied by **cytokinesis** ("cell movement")—the division of the cytoplasm into two distinct cells. When cytokinesis is complete, a so-called parent cell has given rise to two daughter cells.

Mitotic and meiotic cell divisions are responsible for one of the five fundamental attributes of life: reproduction (see Chapter 1). But even though mitosis and meiosis share many characteristics, they are fundamentally different. During mitosis, the genetic material is copied and then divided equally between two cells. This is referred to as cellular *replication*, since these daughter cells are genetically identical with the original parent cell. In contrast, meiosis results in daughter cells that are genetically different from each other and that have half the amount of hereditary material as the parent cell.

This chapter focuses on mitotic cell division; meiotic cell division is the subject of the next chapter (Chapter 13). Let's begin with a look at the key events in a cell's life cycle, continue with an in-depth analysis of mitosis and the regulation of the cell cycle, and end by examining how uncontrolled cell division can lead to cancer.

## 12.1 How Do Cells Replicate?

For life on Earth to exist, cells must replicate. The general requirements for cellular replication are to (1) copy the DNA (deoxyribonucleic acid), (2) separate the copies, and (3) divide the cytoplasm to create two complete cells.

This chapter focuses on eukaryotic cell replication, which is responsible for three key events:

1. *Growth*   The trillions of genetically identical cells that make up your body are the product of mitotic divisions that started in a single fertilized egg.

2. *Wound repair*   When you suffer a scrape, cellular replication generates the cells that repair your skin.

3. *Reproduction*   When yeast cells grow in bread dough or in a vat of beer, they are reproducing by cellular replication. In yeasts and other single-cell eukaryotes, mitotic division is the basis of asexual reproduction. **Asexual reproduction** produces offspring that are genetically identical with the parent.

These events are so basic to life that cell replication has been studied for well over a century. Like much work in biology, the research on how cells divide began by simply observing the process.

### What Is a Chromosome?

As studies of cell division in eukaryotes began, biologists found that certain chemical dyes made threadlike structures visible within nuclei. In 1879, Walther Flemming used a dye made from a coal tar to observe these threadlike structures and how they changed in the dividing cells of salamander embryos. The threads

first appeared in pairs just before division and then split to produce single, unpaired threads in the daughter cells. Flemming introduced the term mitosis, from the Greek *mitos* ("thread"), to describe this process.

Others studied the roundworm *Ascaris* and noted that the total number of threads in a cell was the same before and after mitosis. All the cells in a roundworm had the same number of threads.

In 1888 Wilhelm Waldeyer coined the term **chromosome** ("colored-body") to refer to these threadlike structures (visible in the chapter-opening photo). A chromosome consists of a single, long DNA double helix that is wrapped around proteins, called **histones,** in a highly organized manner. DNA encodes the cell's hereditary information, or genetic material. A gene is a length of DNA that codes for a particular protein or ribonucleic acid (RNA) found in the cell.

Before mitosis, each chromosome is replicated. As mitosis starts, the chromosomes condense into compact structures that can be moved around the cell efficiently. Then one of the chromosome copies is distributed to each of two daughter cells.

**FIGURE 12.1** illustrates unreplicated chromosomes, replicated chromosomes before they have condensed prior to mitosis, and replicated chromosomes that have condensed at the start of mitosis. Each of the DNA copies in a replicated chromosome is called a **chromatid.** Before mitosis, the two chromatids are joined along their entire length by proteins called cohesins. Once mitosis begins, however, many of these connections are removed except for those at a specialized region of the chromosome called the **centromere.** Chromatid copies that remain attached at their centromere are referred to as **sister chromatids.** Even though a replicated chromosome consists of two chromatids, it is still considered a single chromosome.

### Cells Alternate between M Phase and Interphase

The division of eukaryotic cells is like a well-choreographed stage performance. The most visually stimulating part of the show occurs when cells are in their dividing phase, called the **M** (*mitotic* or *meiotic*) **phase.** With a light microscope, chromosomes can be stained and observed as discrete units only during M phase, when they condense into compact structures.

The rest of the time, the cell is in **interphase** ("between-phase"). No dramatic changes in the nucleus are visible by light microscopy during interphase. The chromosomes uncoil into the extremely long, thin structures shown in Figure 12.1 and are no longer stained as individual threads. However, this does not mean that the cell is idle. Interphase is an active time: The cell is either growing and preparing to divide or fulfilling its specialized function in a multicellular individual. Cells actually spend most of their time in interphase.

### The Discovery of S Phase

Once M phase and interphase were identified by microscopy, researchers could start assigning roles to these distinct phases. They could see that the separation of chromosomes and cytokinesis

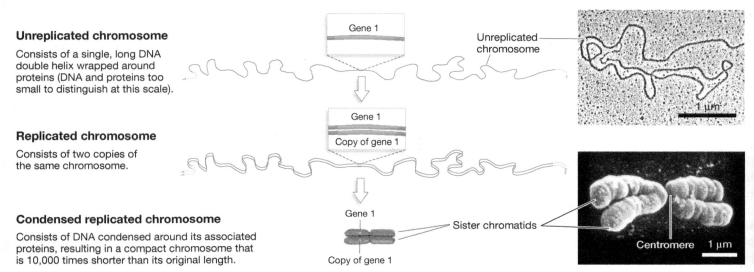

**Unreplicated chromosome**

Consists of a single, long DNA double helix wrapped around proteins (DNA and proteins too small to distinguish at this scale).

**Replicated chromosome**

Consists of two copies of the same chromosome.

**Condensed replicated chromosome**

Consists of DNA condensed around its associated proteins, resulting in a compact chromosome that is 10,000 times shorter than its original length.

Gene 1

Gene 1
Copy of gene 1

Gene 1
Copy of gene 1

Unreplicated chromosome

Sister chromatids

Centromere    1 µm

1 µm

**FIGURE 12.1 Changes in Chromosome Morphology.** After chromosomes replicate, the two identical copies are attached to each other along their entire length. Early in mitosis, replicated chromosomes condense and sister chromatids remain attached at a region called the centromere.

took place during the M phase, but when are the chromosomes copied?

To answer this question, researchers needed to distinguish cells that were replicating their DNA from those that were not. They were able to do this by adding radioactive phosphorus, in the form of phosphates, to cells. Those cells that were synthesizing DNA would incorporate the radioactive isotope into nucleotides (see Chapter 4 to review where phosphates are in DNA).

The idea was to:

1. label DNA as chromosomes were being copied;

2. wash away any radioactive isotope that hadn't been incorporated and remove RNA, which would also incorporate phosphorus; and then

3. visualize the labeled, newly synthesized DNA by exposing the treated cells to X-ray film. Emissions from radioactive phosphorus create a black dot in the film. This is the technique called autoradiography (see **BioSkills 9** in Appendix B).

In 1951, Alma Howard and Stephen Pelc performed this experiment and looked for cells with black dots—indicating active DNA synthesis—immediately after the exposure to a radioactive isotope ended. They found black dots in some of the interphase cells, but none in M-phase cells. Several years later, these results were verified using radioactive thymidine, which is incorporated into DNA but not RNA. These results were strong evidence that DNA replication occurs during interphase.

Thus, biologists had identified a new stage in the life of a cell. They called it **synthesis** (or **S**) **phase.** S phase is part of interphase. Replication of the genetic material is separated, in time, from the partitioning of chromosome copies during M phase.

Howard and Pelc coined the term **cell cycle** to describe the orderly sequence of events that leads a eukaryotic cell through the duplication of its chromosomes to the time it divides.

## The Discovery of the Gap Phases

In addition to discovering the S phase, Howard and Pelc made another key observation—not all the interphase cells were labeled. This meant that there was at least one "gap" in interphase when DNA was not being copied.

Howard and Pelc, along with researchers in other labs, followed up on these early results by asking where S phase was positioned in interphase. There were three possible scenarios:

1. The S phase is immediately before M phase, with a single gap between the end of M and start of S phase;

2. the S phase is immediately after M phase, with a gap between the end of S and the start of M phase; or

3. two gaps exist, one before and one after the S phase.

To address which of these models, if any, is correct, many experiments were done using cells in culture. Cultured cells are powerful experimental tools because they can be manipulated much more easily than cells in an intact organism (see **BioSkills 12** in Appendix B). In most of these studies, researchers used cultures that were asynchronous, meaning that the cells were randomly distributed in the cycle.

To understand the value of these asynchronous cultures, imagine the cell cycle were a clock. Every complete rotation around the clock would represent one cell division, and each tick would represent a different point in the cycle. At any given time, an asynchronous culture would have at least one cell present at each of the ticks on the clock. As time passes, these cells would move around this cell-cycle clock at the same rate and in the same direction.

**FIGURE 12.2 The Pulse–Chase Assay Reveals a Gap Phase.** Cells labeled with radioactive thymidine during the pulse can be tracked during the chase to identify when they enter M phase. In this assay, a gap between the end of S phase and start of M phase was identified based on the delay observed between the pulse and the presence of labeled mitotic cells.

Indicates direction of progression through the cell cycle

Red tracks progress of labeled cells through cell cycle

In one experiment, researchers marked the S-phase cells in a human cell culture by exposing it to radioactively labeled thymidine. A short time later, they stopped the labeling by flooding the solution surrounding the cultured cells with nonradioactive thymidine. This pulse–chase approach (introduced in Chapter 7) labeled only those cells that were in S phase during the radioactive pulse. Imagine these marked cells moving like a hand on the clock that could be tracked as they progressed through the cell cycle.

Once the pulse ended, the researchers analyzed samples of the culture at different times during the chase. For each batch of cells, they recorded how many labeled cells were undergoing mitosis, meaning that the cells that were in S phase during the pulse had entered M phase.

One striking result emerged early on: None of the labeled cells started mitosis immediately. Because the cultures were asynchronous, at least some of the cells must have been at the very end of their S phase when exposed to the pulse. If the S phase had been immediately followed by the M phase, some of these labeled cells would have entered M just as the chase began. Instead, it took several hours before any of the labeled cells began mitosis.

The time lag between the end of the pulse and the appearance of the first labeled mitotic nuclei corresponds to a period between the end of S phase and the beginning of M phase. This gap represents the time when chromosome replication is complete, but mitosis has not yet begun. **FIGURE 12.2** shows how cells labeled with radioactive thymidine can be tracked as they progress through the M phase.

After this result, the possibilities for the organization of the cell cycle were narrowed to either one gap between the end of S and start of M phase, or two gaps that flank the S phase. Which of the models best represents the eukaryotic cell cycle? Once researchers determined the lengths of the S and M phases, they found that the combined time, including the gap between these phases, was still short compared with the length of the cell cycle. This discrepancy represents an additional gap phase that is between the end of M and the start of S phase.

The cell cycle was thus finally mapped out. The gap between the end of M and start of S phase is called the **G$_1$ phase.** The second gap, between the end of S and start of M phase, is called the **G$_2$ phase.**

## The Cell Cycle

**FIGURE 12.3** pulls these results together into a comprehensive view of the cell cycle. The cell cycle involves four phases: M phase and an interphase consisting of the G$_1$, S, and G$_2$ phases. In the cycle diagrammed here, the G$_1$ phase is about twice as long as G$_2$, but the timing of these phases varies depending on the cell type and growth conditions.

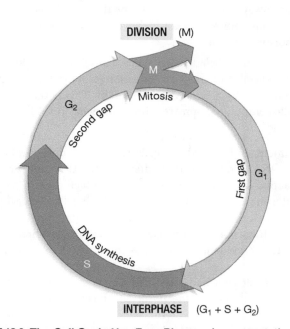

**FIGURE 12.3 The Cell Cycle Has Four Phases.** A representative cell cycle. The time required for the G$_1$ and G$_2$ phases varies dramatically among cells and organisms.

Why do the gap phases exist? Besides needing to copy their chromosomes during interphase, cells also must prepare for division by replicating organelles and increasing in size. Before mitosis can take place, the parent cell must grow large enough to divide into two cells that will be normal in size and function. The two gap phases provide the time required to accomplish these tasks. They allow the cell to complete all the requirements for cell division other than chromosome replication.

Now let's turn to the M phase. Once the genetic material has been copied, how do cells divide it between daughter cells?

## 12.2 What Happens during M Phase?

The M phase typically consists of two distinct events: the division of the nucleus and the division of the cytoplasm. During cell replication, mitosis divides the replicated chromosomes to form two daughter nuclei with identical chromosomes and genes. Mitosis is usually accompanied by cytokinesis—cytoplasmic division that results in two daughter cells.

**FIGURE 12.4** provides an overview of how chromosomes change before, during, and after mitosis and cytokinesis, beginning with a hypothetical plant cell or animal cell in $G_1$ phase. The first drawing shows a total of four chromosomes in the cell, but chromosome number varies widely among species—chimpanzees and potato plants have a total of 48 chromosomes in each cell; a maize (corn) plant has 20, dogs have 78, and fruit flies have 8.

Eukaryotic chromosomes consist of DNA wrapped around the globular histone proteins. In eukaryotes this DNA–protein material is called **chromatin.** During interphase, the chromatin of each chromosome is in a "relaxed" or uncondensed state, forming long, thin strands (see Figure 12.1, top).

The second drawing in Figure 12.4 shows chromosomes that have been copied before mitosis. Each chromosome now consists of two sister chromatids. Each chromatid contains one long DNA double helix, and sister chromatids represent exact copies of the same genetic information.

At the start of mitosis, then, each chromosome consists of two sister chromatids that are attached to each other at the centromere.

✔ You should be able to explain the relationship between chromosomes and (1) genes, (2) chromatin, and (3) sister chromatids.

### Events in Mitosis

As the third drawing in Figure 12.4 indicates, mitosis begins when chromatin condenses to form a much more compact structure. Replicated, condensed chromosomes correspond to the paired threads observed by early biologists.

During mitosis, the two sister chromatids separate to form independent daughter chromosomes. One copy of each chromosome goes to each of the two daughter cells. (See the final drawing in Figure 12.4.) As a result, each cell receives an identical copy of the genetic information that was contained in the parent cell.

Biologists have identified five subphases within M phase based on distinctive events that occur. Interphase is followed by the mitotic subphases of prophase, prometaphase, metaphase, anaphase, and telophase.

Recall that before mitosis begins, chromosomes have already replicated during the S phase of interphase. Now let's look at how cells separate the chromatids in these replicated chromosomes by investigating each subphase of mitosis in turn (**FIGURE 12.5**, on page 224).

INTERPHASE

G₁ PHASE — S PHASE — G₂ PHASE

Parent cell

Parent cell

M PHASE    Daughter cells

Parent cell

Sister chromatids

4 unreplicated chromosomes (chromosomes are shown partially condensed to make them visible)

4 replicated chromosomes, each consisting of two sister chromatids

At start of mitosis, replicated chromosomes condense.

During mitosis, sister chromatids separate. Two daughter cells are formed by cytokinesis.

**FIGURE 12.4 An Overview of the Cell Cycle.** Chromosomes are replicated during S phase to produce the $G_2$ cell. During M phase, the replicated chromosomes are partitioned to the two daughter cells. Each daughter cell contains the same complement of chromosomes as the parent cell.

## PROCESS: MITOSIS

Sister chromatids separate; one chromosome copy goes to each daughter nucleus.

Centrioles
Centrosomes    Chromosomes

Sister chromatids

Early spindle apparatus

Kinetochore

Polar microtubules    Kinetochore microtubules    Astral microtubules

**1. Interphase:** After chromosome replication, each chromosome is composed of two sister chromatids. Centrosomes have replicated.

**2. Prophase:** Chromosomes condense, and spindle apparatus begins to form.

**3. Prometaphase:** Nuclear envelope breaks down. Microtubules contact chromosomes at kinetochores.

**4. Metaphase:** Chromosomes complete migration to middle of cell.

**FIGURE 12.5 Mitosis and Cytokinesis.** In the micrographs, under the drawings, chromosomes are stained blue, microtubules are yellow/green, and intermediate filaments are red.

**QUANTITATIVE:** If the model cell in this figure has $x$ amount of DNA and four chromosomes in its $G_1$ phase, then what is the amount of DNA and number of chromosomes in **(1)** prophase; **(2)** anaphase; **(3)** each daughter cell after division is complete?

**Prophase**    Mitosis begins with the events of **prophase** ("before-phase," Figure 12.5, step 2), when chromosomes condense into compact structures. Chromosomes first become visible in the light microscope during prophase.

Prophase is also marked by the formation of the spindle apparatus. The **spindle apparatus** is a structure that produces mechanical forces that **(1)** move replicated chromosomes during early mitosis and **(2)** pull chromatids apart in late mitosis.

The spindle consists of microtubules—components of the cytoskeleton (see Chapter 7). In all eukaryotes, microtubules originate from microtubule-organizing centers (MTOCs). MTOCs define the two poles of the spindle and produce large numbers of microtubules. During prophase, some of these microtubules extend from each spindle pole and overlap with one another—these are called **polar microtubules.**

Although the nature of this MTOC varies among plants, animals, fungi, and other eukaryotic groups, the spindle apparatus has the same function. Figure 12.5 illustrates an animal cell undergoing mitosis, where the MTOC is a **centrosome**—a structure that contains a pair of **centrioles** (see Chapter 7). During prophase in animal cells, the spindle begins to form around the chromosomes by moving centrosomes to opposite sides of the nucleus.

**Prometaphase**    In many eukaryotes, once chromosomes have condensed, the nuclear envelope disintegrates. Once the envelope has been removed, microtubules are able to attach to chromosomes at specialized structures called **kinetochores.** These events occur during **prometaphase** ("before middle-phase"; see Figure 12.5, step 3). (Organisms that maintain their nuclear envelope use different strategies for separating chromosomes, which will not be discussed here.)

Each sister chromatid has its own kinetochore, which is assembled at the centromere. Since the centromere is also the attachment site for chromatids, the result is two kinetochores on opposite sides of each replicated chromosome. The microtubules that are attached to these structures are called **kinetochore microtubules.**

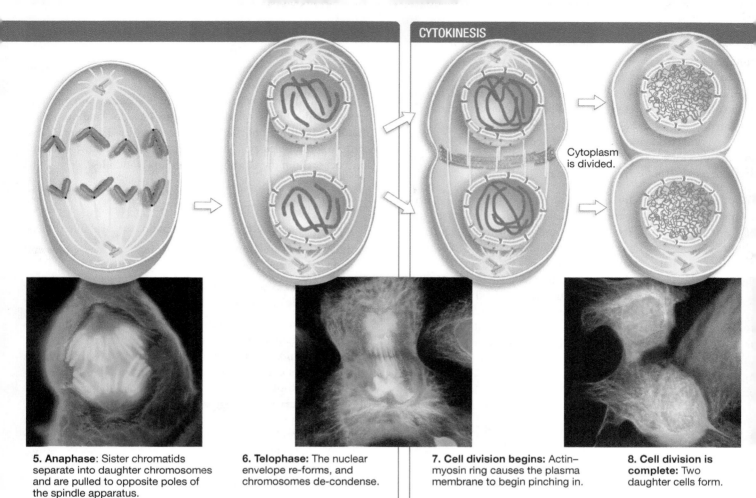

Cytoplasm is divided.

**5. Anaphase**: Sister chromatids separate into daughter chromosomes and are pulled to opposite poles of the spindle apparatus.

**6. Telophase:** The nuclear envelope re-forms, and chromosomes de-condense.

**7. Cell division begins:** Actin–myosin ring causes the plasma membrane to begin pinching in.

**8. Cell division is complete:** Two daughter cells form.

Early in mitosis, kinesin and dynein motors are recruited to the kinetochore, where they can "walk" the chromosome up and down microtubules. These motors are thought to be very important in the initial attachment of the kinetochore to the plus end of the microtubule. If these ideas are correct, then the process is similar to the way these motors walk along microtubules during vesicle transport (see Chapter 7).

In all eukaryotes, after the kinetochores have attached to microtubules, chromosomes begin to move to the middle of the cell during prometaphase.

**Metaphase**   Once the kinetochore microtubules have moved all the chromosomes to the middle of the spindle (Figure 12.5, step 4), the mitotic cells enter **metaphase** ("middle-phase"). At this point, the chromosomes are lined up along an imaginary plane between the two spindle poles called the **metaphase plate.**

The formation of the spindle apparatus is now complete. The polar microtubules that extend from each spindle pole overlap in the middle of the cell, thereby forming a pole-to-pole connection. Each chromosome is held by kinetochore microtubules reaching out from opposite poles and exerting the same amount of tension, or pull. The spindle poles are held in place partly because of

**astral microtubules** that extend from the MTOCs and interac with proteins on the cell membrane.

The alignment of these chromosomes results from the growth and shrinkage of the attached kinetochore microtubules. When chromosomes reach the metaphase plate, the shrinkage of these microtubules at the MTOCs is balanced by slow growth of mi crotubules at the kinetochores. Since the sister chromatids o each chromosome are connected to opposite poles, a tug of wa occurs during metaphase that pulls them in opposite directions.

**Anaphase**   At the start of **anaphase** ("against-phase"), the cohes ins that are holding sister chromatids together at the centromere split (Figure 12.5, step 5). Because the chromatids are under ten sion, each replicated chromosome is pulled apart to create two in dependent daughter chromosomes. By definition, this separation of chromatids instantly doubles the number of chromosomes in the cell.

Two types of movement occur during anaphase. First, the daughter chromosomes move to opposite poles via the attach ment of kinetochore proteins to the shrinking kinetochore mi crotubules. Second, the two poles of the spindle are pushed and pulled farther apart. The motor proteins in overlapping polar microtubules push the poles away from each other. Different motors on the membrane walk along on the astral microtubules to pull the poles to opposite sides of the cell.

During anaphase, then, replicated chromosomes split into two identical sets of daughter chromosomes. Their separation to opposite poles is a critical step in mitosis because it ensures that each daughter cell receives the same complement of chromosomes.

When anaphase is complete, two complete collections of chromosomes are fully separated, each being identical with those of the parent cell before chromosome replication.

**Telophase** During **telophase** ("end-phase"), the nuclear envelope that dissolved in prometaphase reforms around each set of chromosomes, and the chromosomes begin to de-condense (Figure 12.5, step 6). Once two independent nuclei have formed, mitosis is complete. At this point, most cells will go on to divide their cytoplasm via cytokinesis to form two daughter cells.

**TABLE 12.1** summarizes the key structures involved in mitosis.

✔ After you've studied the table and reviewed Figure 12.5, you should be able to make a table with rows titled (1) spindle apparatus, (2) nuclear envelope, and (3) chromosomes, and columns titled with the five phases of mitosis. Fill in the table by summarizing what happens to each structure during each phase of mitosis.

SUMMARY TABLE 12.1    **Structures Involved in Mitosis**

| Structure | Definition |
|-----------|------------|
| Chromosome | A structure composed of a DNA molecule and associated proteins |
| Chromatin | The material that makes up eukaryotic chromosomes; consists of a DNA molecule complexed with histone proteins (see Chapter 19) |
| Chromatid | One strand of a replicated chromosome, with its associated proteins |
| Sister chromatids | The two strands of a replicated chromosome. When chromosomes are replicated, they consist of two sister chromatids. The genetic material in sister chromatids is identical. When sister chromatids separate during mitosis, they become independent chromosomes. |
| Centromere | The structure that joins sister chromatids |
| Kinetochores | The structures on sister chromatids where microtubules attach |
| Microtubule-organizing center | Any structure that organizes microtubules (see Chapter 7) |
| Centrosome | The microtubule-organizing center in animals and some plants |
| Centrioles | Cylindrical structures that comprise microtubules, located inside animal centrosomes |

## How Do Chromosomes Move during Anaphase?

The exact and equal partitioning of genetic material to the two daughter nuclei is the most fundamental aspect of mitosis. How does this process occur?

To understand how sister chromatids separate and move to opposite sides of the spindle, biologists have focused on understanding the function of spindle microtubules. How do kinetochore microtubules pull chromatids apart? And how does the kinetochore join the chromosome and microtubules?

**Mitotic Spindle Forces**    The spindle apparatus is composed of microtubules (see Chapter 7). Recall that:

- microtubules are composed of α-tubulin and β-tubulin dimers,

- microtubules are asymmetric—meaning they have a plus end and a minus end, and

- the plus end is the site where microtubule growth normally occurs while disassembly is more frequent at the minus end.

During mitosis, the microtubules originating from the poles are highly dynamic. Rapid growth and shrinkage ensures that some of the microtubules will be able to attach to kinetochores with their plus ends. Others will be stabilized by different proteins in the cytoplasm and become polar or astral microtubules.

These observations suggest two possible mechanisms for the movement of chromosomes during anaphase. The simplest mechanism would be for microtubules to stop growing at the plus ends, but remain attached to the kinetochore. As the minus ends disassemble at the spindle pole, the chromosome would be reeled in like a hooked fish. An alternative model would have the chromosomes moving along microtubules that are being disassembled at the plus ends at the kinetochore. In this case, the chromosome is like a yo-yo running up a string into your hand.

To test these hypotheses, biologists introduced fluorescently labeled tubulin subunits into prophase or metaphase cells. This treatment made the kinetochore microtubules visible (**FIGURE 12.6**, step 1). Once anaphase began, the researchers marked a region of these microtubules with a bar-shaped beam of laser light. The laser permanently bleached a section of the fluorescently labeled structures, darkening them—although they were still functional (Figure 12.6, step 2).

As anaphase progressed, two things happened: (**1**) The darkened region appeared to remain stationary, and (**2**) the chromosomes moved closer to the darkened regions of the microtubules, eventually overtaking them.

This result suggested that the kinetochore microtubules remain stationary during anaphase, but shorten because tubulin subunits are lost from their plus ends. As microtubule ends shrink back to the spindle poles, the chromosomes are pulled along. But if the microtubule is disassembling at the kinetochore, how does the chromosome remain attached?

**Kinetochores Are Linked to Retreating Microtubule Ends**    The kinetochore is a complex of many proteins that build a base on the centromere region of the chromosome and a "crown" of fibrous proteins projecting outward. **FIGURE 12.7** shows a current

## RESEARCH

QUESTION: How do kinetochore microtubules shorten to pull daughter chromosomes apart during anaphase?

HYPOTHESIS: Microtubules shorten at the spindle pole.

ALTERNATIVE HYPOTHESIS: Microtubules shorten at the kinetochore.

EXPERIMENTAL SETUP:

**1. Label targets:** Use fluorescent labels to make the metaphase chromosomes fluoresce blue and the microtubules fluoresce yellow.

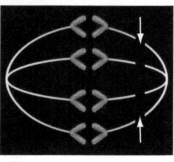

**2. Mark microtubules:** At the start of anaphase, darken a section of microtubules to mark them without changing their function.

PREDICTION:

PREDICTION OF ALTERNATIVE HYPOTHESIS: Daughter chromosomes will move toward the pole faster than the darkened section.

RESULTS:

The darkened areas of the microtubules remained stationary as the chromosomes moved through them toward the pole.

CONCLUSION: Kinetochore microtubules shorten at the kinetochore to pull daughter chromosomes apart during anaphase.

**FIGURE 12.6 During Anaphase, Microtubules Shorten at the Kinetochore.**

SOURCE: Gorbsky, G. J., et al. 1987. Chromosomes move poleward during anaphase along stationary microtubules that coordinately disassemble from their kinetochore ends. *Journal of Cellular Biology* 104: 9–18.

✔**EXERCISE** Complete the prediction for what would occur if chromosome movement were based on microtubules shortening at the spindle pole.

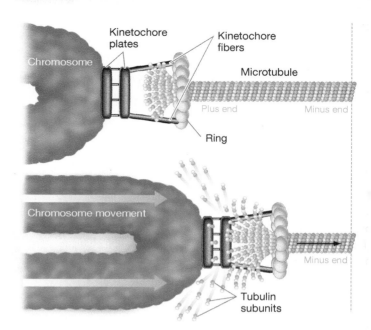

**FIGURE 12.7 How Do Microtubules Move Chromosomes during Anaphase?** Microtubules are disassembled at the kinetochore during anaphase. In yeast, kinetochore proteins tether the chromosome to a ring that is pushed toward the spindle pole by the fraying plus end of the microtubule.

model for kinetochore structure and function during chromosome movement in anaphase. For simplicity, a yeast kinetochore is shown, which attaches to only one microtubule. (Other eukaryotes can have as many as 30 microtubules attached to each kinetochore.)

Biologists have found that as anaphase gets under way, the plus ends of the kinetochore microtubules begin to fray and disassemble. Fibers that extend from the yeast kinetochore are tethered to this retreating end by attaching to a ring that surrounds the kinetochore microtubule (Figure 12.7, top). As the fraying end widens, its expansion forces the ring, and the attached chromosome, toward the minus end of the microtubule (see Figure 12.7, bottom). The result is that the chromosome is pulled to the spindle pole by the depolymerization of the kinetochore microtubule.

## Cytokinesis Results in Two Daughter Cells

At this point, the chromosomes have been replicated in S phase and partitioned to opposite sides of the spindle via mitosis. Now it's time to divide the cell into two daughters that contain identical copies of each chromosome. If these cells are to be viable, however, the parent cell must also ensure that more than just chromosomes make it into each daughter cell.

While the cell is in interphase, the cytoplasmic contents, including the organelles, have increased in number or volume. During cytokinesis (Figure 12.5, steps 7 and 8), the cytoplasm divides to form two daughter cells, each with its own nucleus and complete set of organelles. In most types of cells, cytokinesis directly follows mitosis.

**(a)** Cytokinesis in plants

**(b)** Cytokinesis in animals

Microtubules direct vesicles to center of spindle where they fuse to divide the cell in two

Microtubule    Cell plate

5 μm

Actin–myosin interactions pinch the membrane in two

Cleavage furrow

100 μm

**FIGURE 12.8 The Mechanism of Cytokinesis Varies among Eukaryotes. (a)** In plants, the cytoplasm is divided by a cell plate that forms in the middle of the parent cell. **(b)** In animals, the cytoplasm is divided by a cleavage furrow. (The cells in both micrographs have been stained or colorized.)

In plants, polar microtubules left over from the spindle help define and organize the region where the new plasma membranes and cell walls will form. Vesicles from the Golgi apparatus carry components to build a new cell wall to the middle of the dividing cell. These vesicles are moved along the polar microtubules via motor proteins. In the middle of what was the spindle, the vesicles start to fuse together to form a flattened sac-like structure called the **cell plate** (**FIGURE 12.8a**). The cell plate continues to grow as new vesicles fuse with it, eventually contacting the existing plasma membrane. When the cell plate fuses with the existing plasma membrane, it divides the cell into two new daughter cells.

In animals and many other eukaryotes, cytokinesis begins with the formation of a **cleavage furrow** (**FIGURE 12.8b**). The furrow appears because a ring of actin filaments forms just inside the plasma membrane, in the middle of what used to be the spindle. Myosin motor proteins bind to these actin filaments and use adenosine triphosphate (ATP) to contract in a way that causes actin filaments to slide (see Chapter 7).

As myosin moves the ring of actin filaments on the inside of the plasma membrane, the ring shrinks in size and tightens. Because the ring is attached to the plasma membrane, the shrinking ring pulls the membrane with it. As a result, the plasma membrane pinches inward. The actin and myosin filaments continue to slide past each other, tightening the ring further, until the original membrane pinches in two and cell division is complete.

The overall process involved in chromosome separation and cytoplasmic division is a common requirement for all living organisms. The mechanisms involved in accomplishing these events, however, vary depending on the type of cell. What about

bacterial cells? How does chromosomal segregation and cytokinesis compare between prokaryotes and eukaryotes?

**Bacterial Cell Replication**   Many bacteria divide using a process called **binary fission**. Recent research has shown that chromosome segregation and cytokinesis in bacterial division is strikingly similar to what occurs in the eukaryotic M phase (**FIGURE 12.9**). As the bacterial chromosome is being replicated, protein filaments attach to the copies and separate them to opposite sides of the cell.

**PROCESS: BACTERIAL CELL DIVISION**

New DNA
Original DNA    Replication enzymes

**1.** DNA is copied and protein filaments attach.

**2.** DNA copies are separated; ring of protein forms.

**3.** Ring of protein draws in membrane.

**4.** Fission complete.

**FIGURE 12.9 Bacterial Cells Divide but Do Not Undergo Mitosis.**

Once the copies of the chromosome have been partitioned to opposite sides of the cell, other filaments, made up of proteins that are similar to eukaryotic tubulin, are responsible for dividing the cytoplasm. These filaments attach to the cell membrane to form a ring between the chromosome copies. A signal from the cell causes the filaments to constrict, drawing in the membrane and eventually cleaving the parent into two genetically identical cells.

Having explored what occurs during cell division, let's focus on how it is controlled in eukaryotes. When does a eukaryotic cell divide, and when does it stop dividing?

## 12.3 Control of the Cell Cycle

Although the events of mitosis are virtually identical in all eukaryotes, other aspects of the cell cycle vary. In humans, for example, intestinal cells routinely divide more than twice a day to replace tissue that is lost during digestion; mature human nerve and muscle cells do not divide at all.

Most of these differences are due to variation in the length of the $G_1$ phase. In rapidly dividing cells, $G_1$ is essentially eliminated. Most nondividing cells, in contrast, are permanently stuck in $G_1$. Researchers refer to this arrested stage as the $G_0$ state, or simply "G zero." Cells that are in $G_0$ have effectively exited the cell cycle and are sometimes referred to as post-mitotic. Nerve cells, muscle cells, and many other cell types enter $G_0$ once they have matured.

A cell's division rate can also vary in response to changing conditions. For example, human liver cells normally replicate about once per year. But if part of the liver is damaged or lost, the remaining cells divide every one or two days until repair is accomplished. Cells of unicellular organisms such as yeasts, bacteria, or archaeans divide rapidly only if the environment is rich in nutrients; otherwise, they enter a quiescent (inactive) state.

To explain these differences, biologists hypothesized that the cell cycle must be regulated in some way. Cell-cycle control is now the most prominent issue in research on cell division—partly because defects in control can lead to uncontrolled, cancerous growth.

### The Discovery of Cell-Cycle Regulatory Molecules

The first solid evidence for cell-cycle control molecules came to light in 1970. Researchers found that certain chemicals, viruses, or an electric shock could fuse the membranes of two mammalian cells that were growing in culture, forming a single cell with two nuclei.

How did cell-fusion experiments relate to cell-cycle regulation? When investigators fused cells that were in different stages of the cell cycle, certain nuclei changed phases. For example, when a cell in M phase was fused with one in interphase, the nucleus of the interphase cell immediately initiated mitosis, even if the chromosomes had not been replicated. The biologists hypothesized that the cytoplasm of M-phase cells contains a regulatory molecule that induces interphase cells to enter M phase.

But cell-fusion experiments were difficult to control and left researchers wondering if it was the nucleus or the cytoplasm that was responsible for the induction. To address this issue, they turned to the South African clawed frog, *Xenopus laevis*.

As an egg of these frogs matures, it changes from a cell called an oocyte, which is arrested in a phase similar to $G_2$, to a mature egg that is arrested in M phase. The large size of these cells—more than 1 mm in diameter—makes them relatively easy to manipulate. Using instruments with extremely fine needles, researchers could specifically examine the effects of the cytoplasm by pulling a sample from a mature egg or an oocyte and injecting it into another.

When biologists purified cytoplasm from M-phase frog eggs and injected it into the cytoplasm of frog oocytes arrested in $G_2$, the immature oocytes immediately entered M phase (**FIGURE 12.10**, see page 230). But when cytoplasm from interphase cells was injected into $G_2$ oocytes, the cells remained in the $G_2$ phase. The researchers concluded that the cytoplasm of M-phase cells—but not the cytoplasm of interphase cells—contains a factor that drives immature oocytes into M phase to complete their maturation.

The factor that initiates M-phase in oocytes was purified and is now called **M phase–promoting factor,** or **MPF.** Subsequent experiments showed that MPF induces M phase in all eukaryotes. For example, injecting M-phase cytoplasm from mammalian cells into immature frog oocytes results in egg maturation, and human MPF can also trigger M phase in yeast cells.

MPF appears to be a general signal that says "Start M phase." How does it work?

**QUESTION:** Is M phase controlled by regulatory molecules in the cytoplasm?

**HYPOTHESIS:** Cytoplasmic regulatory molecules control entry into M phase.

**NULL HYPOTHESIS:** M-phase regulatory molecules are not in the cytoplasm or do not exist.

**EXPERIMENTAL SETUP:**

M-phase cytoplasm

Interphase cytoplasm

Microinject cytoplasm from M-phase cell into one frog oocyte and cytoplasm from interphase cell into another frog oocyte.

**PREDICTION:** Only the oocyte injected with M-phase cytoplasm will begin M phase.

**PREDICTION OF NULL HYPOTHESIS:** Neither of the frog oocytes will begin M phase.

**RESULTS:**

Oocyte is driven into M phase (nuclear envelope begins to break down, spindle apparatus forms).

Oocyte remains in $G_2$ phase.

**CONCLUSION:** M-phase cytoplasm contains a regulatory molecule that induces M phase in interphase cells.

**FIGURE 12.10 Experimental Evidence for Cell-Cycle Control Molecules.** When the cytoplasm from M-phase cells is microinjected into cells in interphase, the interphase chromosomes condense and begin M phase.

SOURCE: Masui, Y., and C. L. Markert. 1971. Cytoplasmic control of nuclear behavior during meiotic maturation of frog oocytes. *Journal of Experimental Zoology* 177: 129–145.

✔**QUESTION** This experiment was done using cells that were undergoing meiosis. What could the investigators do to show that the factor used in meiotic division is the same as used for mitotic division?

**MPF Contains a Protein Kinase and a Cyclin** MPF is made up of two distinct polypeptide subunits. One subunit is a protein kinase—an enzyme that catalyzes the transfer of a phosphate group from ATP to a target protein. Recall that phosphorylation may activate or inactivate the function of proteins by changing their shape (Chapter 8). As a result, kinases frequently act as regulatory proteins in the cell.

These observations suggested that MPF phosphorylates proteins that trigger the onset of M phase. But research showed that

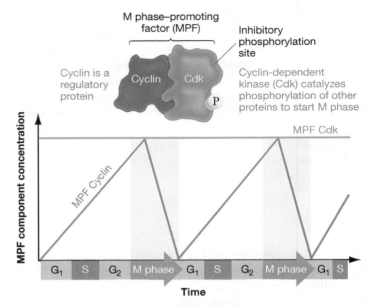

**FIGURE 12.11 Cyclin Concentration Regulates the Concentration of the MPF Dimer.** Cyclin concentrations cycle in dividing cells, reaching a peak in M phase. The activity of MPF, shown in the blue shaded area, requires both cyclin and Cdk components.

✔**QUESTION** Proteins that degrade cyclin are activated by events that MPF initiates. Why is this important?

the concentration of the protein kinase is more or less constant throughout the cell cycle. How can MPF trigger M phase if the protein kinase subunit is always present?

The answer lies in the second MPF subunit, which belongs to a family of proteins called **cyclins.** Cyclins got their name because their concentrations fluctuate throughout the cell cycle.

As **FIGURE 12.11** shows, the concentration of the cyclin associated with MPF builds during interphase and peaks in M phase. The timing of this increase is important because the protein kinase subunit in MPF is functional only when it is bound to the cyclin subunit. As a result, the protein kinase subunit of MPF is called a **cyclin-dependent kinase,** or **Cdk.**

To summarize, MPF is a dimer consisting of a cyclin and a cyclin-dependent kinase. The cyclin subunit regulates the formation of the MPF dimer; the kinase subunit catalyzes the phosphorylation of other proteins to start M phase.

**How Is MPF Turned On?** According to Figure 12.11, the number of cyclins builds up steadily during interphase. Why doesn't this increasing concentration of MPF trigger the onset of M phase?

The answer is that the activity of MPF's Cdk subunit is further regulated by two phosphorylation events. The phosphorylation of one site in Cdk activates the kinase, but when the second site is phosphorylated, it is inactivated. Both these sites are phosphorylated after cyclin binds to the Cdk. This allows the concentration of the dimer to increase without prematurely starting M phase. Late in $G_2$ phase, however, an enzyme removes the inhibitory phosphate. This dephosphorylation reaction, coupled with the addition of the activating phosphate, changes the Cdk's shape in a way that turns on its kinase activity.

Once MPF is active, it triggers a chain of events. Although the exact mechanisms involved are still under investigation, the result is that chromosomes begin to condense and the spindle apparatus starts to form. In this way, MPF triggers the onset of M phase.

**How Is MPF Turned Off?**   During anaphase, an enzyme complex begins degrading MPF's cyclin subunit. In this way, MPF triggers a chain of events that leads to its own destruction.

MPF deactivation illustrates two key concepts about regulatory systems in cells:

- **Negative feedback** occurs when a process is slowed or shut down by one of its products. Thermostats shut down furnaces when temperatures are high; phosphofructokinase is inhibited by ATP (see Chapter 9); MPF is turned off by an enzyme complex that is activated by events in mitosis.

- Destroying specific proteins is a common way to control cell processes. In this case, the enzyme complex that is activated in anaphase attaches small proteins called ubiquitins to MPF's cyclin subunit. This marks the subunit for destruction by a protein complex called the proteasome.

In response to MPF activity, then, the concentration of cyclin declines rapidly. Slowly, it builds up again during interphase. This sets up an oscillation in cyclin concentration.

✔ If you understand this aspect of cell-cycle regulation, you should be able to explain the relationship between MPF and (1) cyclin, (2) Cdk, and (3) the enzymes that phosphorylate MPF, dephosphorylate MPF, and degrade cyclin.

## Cell-Cycle Checkpoints Can Arrest the Cell Cycle

The dramatic changes in cyclin concentrations and Cdk activity drive the ordered events of the cell cycle. These events are occurring in your body right now. Over a 24-hour period, you swallow millions of cheek cells and lose millions of cells from your intestinal lining as waste. To replace them, cells in your cheek and intestinal tissue are making and degrading cyclin and pushing themselves through the cell cycle.

MPF is only one of many protein complexes involved in regulating the cell cycle, however. A different cyclin complex triggers the passage from $G_1$ phase into S phase, and several regulatory proteins maintain the $G_0$ state of quiescent cells. An array of regulatory molecules holds cells in particular stages or stimulates passage to the next phase.

To make sense of these observations, Leland Hartwell and Ted Weinert introduced the concept of a **cell-cycle checkpoint.** A cell-cycle checkpoint is a critical point in the cell cycle that is regulated.

Hartwell and Weinert identified checkpoints by analyzing yeast cells with defects in the cell cycle. The defective cells kept dividing under culture conditions when normal cells stopped growing, because the defective cells lacked a specific checkpoint. In multicellular organisms, cells that keep dividing in this way may form a mass of cells called a **tumor.**

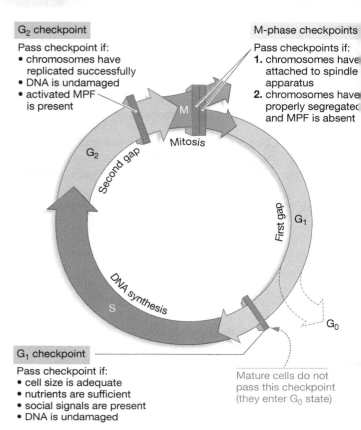

**G2 checkpoint**

Pass checkpoint if:
- chromosomes have replicated successfully
- DNA is undamaged
- activated MPF is present

**M-phase checkpoints**

Pass checkpoints if:
1. chromosomes have attached to spindle apparatus
2. chromosomes have properly segregated and MPF is absent

**G1 checkpoint**

Pass checkpoint if:
- cell size is adequate
- nutrients are sufficient
- social signals are present
- DNA is undamaged

Mature cells do not pass this checkpoint (they enter $G_0$ state)

**FIGURE 12.12 The Four Cell-Cycle Checkpoints.**

There are distinct checkpoints in three of the four phases of the cell cycle (**FIGURE 12.12**). In effect, interactions among regulatory molecules at each checkpoint allow a cell to "decide" whether to proceed with division or not. If these regulatory molecules are defective, the checkpoint may fail and cells may start dividing in an uncontrolled fashion.

**G1 Checkpoint**   The first cell-cycle checkpoint occurs late in $G_1$. For most cells, this checkpoint is the most important in establishing whether the cell will continue through the cycle and divide, or exit the cycle and enter $G_0$. What determines whether a cell passes the $G_1$ checkpoint?

- *Size*   Because a cell must reach a certain size before its daughter cells will be large enough to function normally, biologists hypothesize that some mechanism exists to arrest the cell cycle if the cell is too small.

- *Availability of nutrients*   Unicellular organisms arrest at the $G_1$ checkpoint if nutrient conditions are poor.

- *Social signals*   Cells in multicellular organisms pass (or do not pass) through the $G_1$ checkpoint in response to signaling molecules from other cells, which are termed social signals.

- *Damage to DNA*   If DNA is physically damaged, the protein p53 activates genes that either stop the cell cycle until the damage can be repaired or cause the cell's programmed controlled destruction—a phenomenon known as **apoptosis.** In this way, p53 acts as a brake on the cell cycle.

If "brake" molecules such as p53 are defective, damaged DNA remains unrepaired. Damage in genes that regulate cell growth can lead to uncontrolled cell division. Consequently, regulatory proteins like p53 are called **tumor suppressors.**

**G$_2$ Checkpoint** The second checkpoint occurs after S phase, at the boundary between the G$_2$ and M phases. Because MPF is the key signal triggering the onset of M phase, investigators were not surprised to find that it is involved in the G$_2$ checkpoint.

Data suggest that if DNA is damaged or if chromosomes are not replicated correctly, removal of the inactivating phosphate is blocked. When MPF is not turned on, cells remain in G$_2$ phase. Cells at this checkpoint may also respond to signals from other cells and to internal signals relating to their size.

**M-Phase Checkpoints** The final two checkpoints occur during mitosis. The first regulates the onset of anaphase. Cells in M phase will not split the chromatids until all kinetochores attach properly to the spindle apparatus. If the metaphase checkpoint did not exist, some chromosomes might not separate correctly, and daughter cells would receive either too many or too few chromosomes.

The second checkpoint regulates the progression through M phase into G$_1$. If chromosomes do not fully separate during anaphase, MPF will not decline and the cell will be arrested in M phase. The enzymes that are responsible for cyclin destruction are activated only when all the chromosomes have been properly separated. The presence of MPF activity prevents the cell from undergoing cytokinesis and exiting the M phase.

To summarize, the four cell-cycle checkpoints have the same purpose: They prevent the division of cells that are damaged or that have other problems. The G$_1$ checkpoint also prevents mature cells that are in the G$_0$ state from dividing.

Understanding cell-cycle regulation is fundamental. If one of the checkpoints fails, the affected cells may begin dividing in an uncontrolled fashion. For the organism as a whole, the consequences of uncontrolled cell division may be dire: cancer.

## check your understanding

### If you understand that . . .

• The cell cycle consists of four carefully controlled phases.

✔ **You should be able to . . .**

1. List the phases of the cell cycle, noting where checkpoints occur.

2. Summarize how levels of Cdk and cyclin change over time and how this is related to MPF activity, noting the particular phases that are involved.

*Answers are available in Appendix A.*

## 12.4 Cancer: Out-of-Control Cell Division

Fifty percent of American men and 33 percent of American women will develop cancer during their lifetime. In the United States, one in four of all deaths is from cancer. It is the second leading cause of death, exceeded only by heart disease.

**Cancer** is a general term for disease caused by cells that divide in an uncontrolled fashion, invade nearby tissues, and spread to other sites in the body. Cancerous cells cause disease because they use nutrients and space needed by normal cells and disrupt the function of normal tissues.

Humans suffer from at least 200 types of cancer. Stated another way, cancer is not a single illness but a complex family of diseases that affect an array of organs, including the breast, colon, brain, lung, and skin (**FIGURE 12.13**). In addition, several types of cancer can affect the same organ. Skin cancers, for example, come in multiple forms.

Although cancers vary in time of onset, growth rate, seriousness, and cause, they have a unifying feature: Cancers arise from cells in which cell-cycle checkpoints have failed.

Cancerous cells have two types of defects related to cell division: (**1**) defects that make the proteins required for cell growth active when they shouldn't be, and (**2**) defects that prevent tumor suppressor genes from shutting down the cell cycle.

For example, the protein Ras is a key component in signal transduction systems—including phosphorylation cascades that trigger cell growth (see Chapter 11). Many cancers have defective forms of Ras that do not become inactivated. Instead, the defective Ras constantly sends signals that trigger mitosis and cell division.

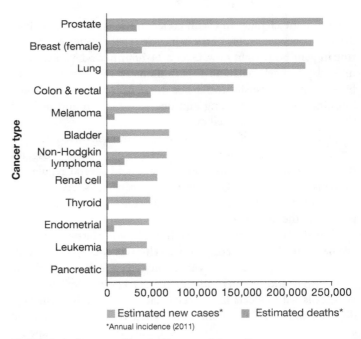

**FIGURE 12.13 Cancers Vary in Type and Severity.**
DATA: The website of the National Cancer Institute (http://www.cancer.gov), Common Cancer Types, November 2010.

Likewise, a large percentage of cancers have defective forms of the tumor suppressor p53. Instead of being arrested or destroyed, cells with damaged DNA are allowed to continue growing.

Let's review the general characteristics of cancer and then explore how regulatory mechanisms become defective.

## Properties of Cancer Cells

When even a single cell in a multicellular organism begins to divide in an uncontrolled fashion, a mass of cells called a tumor may result. If a tumor can be surgically removed without damage to the affected organ, a cure might be achieved. Often, though, surgery doesn't cure cancer. Why?

In addition to uncontrolled replication, cancer cells are invasive—meaning that they are able to spread to adjacent tissues and throughout the body via the bloodstream or the lymphatic vessels (introduced in Chapter 51), which collect excess fluid from tissues and return it to the bloodstream.

Invasiveness is a defining feature of a **malignant tumor**—one that is cancerous. Masses of noninvasive cells are noncancerous and form **benign tumors.** Some benign tumors are largely harmless. Others grow quickly and can cause problems if they are located in the brain or other sensitive parts of the body.

Cells become malignant and cancerous if they gain the ability to detach from the original tumor and invade other tissues. By spreading from the primary tumor site, cancer cells can establish secondary tumors elsewhere in the body (**FIGURE 12.14**). This process is called **metastasis.**

If metastasis has occurred by the time the original tumor is detected, secondary tumors have already formed and surgical removal of the primary tumor will not lead to a cure. This is why early detection is the key to treating cancer most effectively.

## Cancer Involves Loss of Cell-Cycle Control

What causes cancer at the molecular level? Recall that when many cells mature, they enter the $G_0$ phase—meaning their cell cycle is arrested at the $G_1$ checkpoint. In contrast, cells that do pass through the $G_1$ checkpoint are irreversibly committed to replicating their DNA and entering $G_2$.

Based on this observation, biologists hypothesize that many types of cancer involve defects in the $G_1$ checkpoint. To understand the molecular nature of the disease, then, researchers have focused on understanding the normal mechanisms that operate at that checkpoint. Cancer research and research on the normal cell cycle have become two sides of the same coin.

**Social Control**  In unicellular organisms, passage through the $G_1$ checkpoint is thought to depend primarily on cell size and the availability of nutrients. If nutrients are plentiful, cells pass through the checkpoint and divide rapidly.

In multicellular organisms, however, cells divide in response to signals from other cells. Biologists refer to this as *social control* over cell division. The general idea is that individual cells should be allowed to divide only when their growth is in the best interests of the organism as a whole.

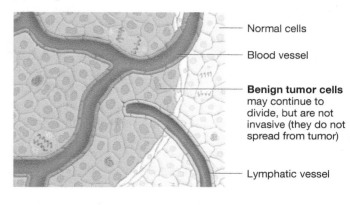

**(a)** Benign tumor

— Normal cells

— Blood vessel

**Benign tumor cells** may continue to divide, but are not invasive (they do not spread from tumor)

— Lymphatic vessel

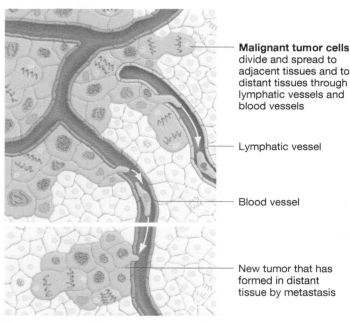

**(b)** Malignant tumor

**Malignant tumor cells** divide and spread to adjacent tissues and to distant tissues through lymphatic vessels and blood vessels

— Lymphatic vessel

— Blood vessel

— New tumor that has formed in distant tissue by metastasis

**FIGURE 12.14 Cancers Spread to New Locations in the Body.** **(a)** Benign tumors grow in a single location. **(b)** Malignant tumors are metastatic—meaning that their cells can spread to distant parts of the body and initiate new tumors. Malignant tumors cause cancer.

Social control of the cell cycle is based on **growth factors**—polypeptides or small proteins that stimulate cell division. Many growth factors were discovered by researchers who were trying to grow cells in culture. When isolated mammalian cells were placed in a culture flask and provided with adequate nutrients, they arrested in $G_1$ phase. The cells began to grow again only when biologists added **serum**—the liquid portion of blood that remains after blood cells and cell fragments have been removed. Researchers identified growth factors as the components in the serum that were responsible for allowing cells to pass through the $G_1$ checkpoint.

Cancer cells are an exception. They can often be cultured successfully without externally supplied growth factors. This observation suggests that the normal social controls on the $G_1$ checkpoint have broken down in cancer cells.

**How Does the G₁ Checkpoint Work?** In $G_0$ cells, the arrival of growth factors stimulates the production of a key regulatory protein called E2F. When E2F is activated, it triggers the expression of genes required for S phase.

When E2F is first produced, however, its activity is blocked by a tumor suppressor protein called Rb. **Rb protein** is one of the key molecules that enforces the $G_1$ checkpoint. It is called Rb because a nonfunctional version was first discovered in children with retinoblastoma, a cancer in the light-sensing tissue, or retina, of the eye.

When E2F is bound to Rb, it is in the "off" position—it can't activate the genes required for S phase. As long as Rb stays bound to E2F, the cell remains in $G_0$. But as **FIGURE 12.15** shows, the situation changes dramatically if growth factors continue to arrive. To understand how growth factors affect E2F activity, think back to how cells progress from $G_2$ to M phase. As in passage from $G_2$ to M phase, phosphorylation of other proteins catalyzed by an activated cyclin–Cdk dimer permits passage from $G_1$ to S.

**Step 1** Growth factors arrive from other cells.

**Step 2** The growth factors stimulate the production of E2F and of $G_1$ cyclins, which are different from those used in MPF.

**Step 3** Rb binds to E2F, inactivating it. The $G_1$ cyclins begin forming cyclin–Cdk dimers. Initially, the Cdk component is phosphorylated and inactive.

**Step 4** When dephosphorylation turns on the $G_1$ cyclin–Cdk complexes, they catalyze the phosphorylation of Rb.

**Step 5** The phosphorylated Rb changes shape and releases E2F.

**Step 6** The unbound E2F is free to activate its target genes. Production of S-phase proteins gets S phase under way.

In this way, growth factors function as a social signal that says, "It's OK to override Rb. Go ahead and pass the $G_1$ checkpoint and divide."

**How Do Social Controls and Cell-Cycle Checkpoints Fail?** Cells can become cancerous when social controls fail—meaning, when cells begin dividing in the absence of the go-ahead signal from growth factors. One of two things can go wrong: The $G_1$ cyclin is overproduced, or Rb is defective.

When cyclins are overproduced and stay at high concentrations, the Cdk that binds to cyclin phosphorylates Rb continuously. This activates E2F and sends the cell into S phase.

Cyclin overproduction results from (1) excessive amounts of growth factors or (2) cyclin production in the absence of growth signals. Cyclins are produced continuously when a signaling pathway is defective. Because this pathway includes the Ras protein (highlighted in Chapter 11), it is common to find overactive Ras proteins in cancerous cells.

What happens if Rb is defective? When Rb is missing or does not bind normally to E2F, any E2F that is present pushes the cell through the $G_1$ checkpoint and into S phase, leading to uncontrolled cell division.

Because cancer is actually a family of diseases with a complex and highly variable molecular basis, there will be no "magic bullet," or single therapy, that cures all forms of the illness. Still, recent progress in understanding the cell cycle and the molecular basis of cancer has been dramatic, and cancer prevention and early detection programs are increasingly effective. The prognosis for many cancer patients is remarkably better now than it was even a few years ago. Thanks to research, almost all of us know someone who is a cancer survivor.

**PROCESS: THE G₁ CHECKPOINT IS SUBJECT TO SOCIAL CONTROL**

1. Growth factors arrive from other cells.

2. Growth factors cause increase in cyclin and E2F concentrations.

3. Cyclin binds to Cdk; Cdk is phosphorylated. Rb inactivates E2F by binding to it.

4. Inactivating phosphate is removed, and active Cdk phosphorylates Rb.

5. Phosphorylated Rb releases E2F.

6. E2F triggers production of S-phase proteins.

**FIGURE 12.15 Growth Factors Move Cells through the G₁ Checkpoint.**

## If you understand . . .

### 12.1 How Do Cells Replicate?

- When a cell divides, it must copy its chromosomes, separate the copies, and divide the cytoplasm to generate daughter cells such that each carries the same chromosomal complement as the parent.
- Eukaryotic cells divide by alternating between interphase and M phase.
- Interphase consists of S phase, when chromosomes are replicated, and gap phases called $G_1$ and $G_2$, when cells grow and prepare for division.
- Eukaryotic cells divide by cycling through four phases: $G_1$, S, $G_2$, and M. Mature cells arrest at $G_1$ and enter a nonreplicating phase called $G_0$.

✓ You should be able to explain the roles of each of the four stages of the cell cycle.

### 12.2 What Happens during M Phase?

- Mitosis and cytokinesis are responsible for the partitioning of chromosomes and division of the parent cell into two daughter cells.
- Mitosis can be described as a sequence of five phases:
  1. *Prophase*  Chromosomes condense. The spindle apparatus begins to form, and polar microtubules overlap each other.
  2. *Prometaphase*  In cells of many organisms, the nuclear envelope disintegrates. Microtubules attach to the kinetochores of chromosomes and begin moving them to the middle of the spindle.
  3. *Metaphase*  All the chromosomes are positioned in the middle of the spindle. The spindle is anchored to the cell membrane by astral microtubules.
  4. *Anaphase*  Sister chromatids are pulled apart by the disassembly of kinetochore microtubules at the kinetochore. The separated chromatids are now daughter chromosomes. The spindle poles are moved farther apart to fully separate the replicated chromosomes.
  5. *Telophase*  Daughter chromosomes are fully separated and are clustered at opposite poles of the spindle. A nuclear envelope forms around each set and the chromosomes de-condense.
- In most cells, mitosis is followed by cytokinesis—division of all cell contents.

✓ You should be able to predict how mitosis would be different in cells where the nuclear envelope remains intact (e.g., yeast).

### 12.3 Control of the Cell Cycle

- The onset of S and M phases is primarily determined by the activity of protein dimers consisting of cyclin and cyclin-dependent kinases (Cdks).

- Cyclin concentrations oscillate during the cell cycle, regulating the formation of the dimer. The activity of the Cdk is further regulated by addition of a phosphate in its activating site and removal of one from its inhibitory site.
- Progression through the cell cycle is controlled by checkpoints in three phases.
  1. The $G_1$ checkpoint regulates progress based on nutrient availability, cell size, DNA damage, and social signals.
  2. The $G_2$ checkpoint delays progress until chromosome replication is complete and any damaged DNA that is present is repaired.
  3. The two M-phase checkpoints will (1) delay anaphase until all chromosomes are correctly attached to the spindle apparatus and (2) delay the onset of cytokinesis and $G_1$ until all the chromosomes have been properly partitioned.

✓ You should be able to predict what would happen if the kinase that adds the inhibitory phosphates to Cdk were defective.

### 12.4 Cancer: Out-of-Control Cell Division

- Cancer is characterized by (1) loss of control at the $G_1$ checkpoint resulting in cells that divide in an uncontrolled fashion; and (2) metastasis, or the ability of tumor cells to spread throughout the body.
- The $G_1$ checkpoint depends in part on Rb, which prevents progression to S phase, and $G_1$ cyclin–Cdk complexes that trigger progression to S phase. Defects in Rb and $G_1$ cyclin are common in human cancer cells.

✓ You should be able to compare and contrast the effect of removing growth factors from asynchronous cultures of human cells that are normal versus those that are cancerous.

(MB) **MasteringBiology**

**1. MasteringBiology Assignments**

**Tutorials and Activities** Causes of Cancer; Cell Culture Methods; Four Phases of the Cell Cycle; Mitosis (1 of 3): Mitosis and the Cell Cycle; Mitosis (2 of 3): Mechanism of Mitosis; Mitosis (3 of 3): Comparing Cell Division in Animals, Plants, and Bacteria; Mitosis and Cytokinesis Animation; Roles of Cell Division; The Cell Cycle; The Phases of Mitosis

**Questions** Reading Quizzes, Blue-Thread Questions, Test Bank

**2. eText** Read your book online, search, take notes, highlight text, and more.

**3. The Study Area** Practice Test, Cumulative Test, BioFlix® 3-D Animations, Videos, Activities, Audio Glossary, Word Study Tools, Art

## ✔ TEST YOUR KNOWLEDGE

1. Which statement about the daughter cells following mitosis and cytokinesis is correct?
   a. They are genetically different from each other and from the parent cell.
   b. They are genetically identical with each other and with the parent cell.
   c. They are genetically identical with each other but different from the parent cell.
   d. Only one of the two daughter cells is genetically identical with the parent cell.

2. Progression through the cell cycle is regulated by oscillations in the concentration of which type of molecule?
   a. p53, Rb, and other tumor suppressors
   b. receptor tyrosine kinases
   c. cyclin-dependent kinases
   d. cyclins

3. After the S phase, what comprises a single chromosome?
   a. two daughter chromosomes
   b. a double-stranded DNA molecule
   c. two single-stranded molecules of DNA
   d. two sister chromatids

4. What major events occur during anaphase of mitosis?
   a. Chromosomes replicate, so each chromosome consists of two identical sister chromatids.
   b. Chromosomes condense and the nuclear envelope disappears.
   c. Sister chromatids separate, and the spindle poles are pushed farther apart.
   d. The chromosomes end up at opposite ends of the cell, and two nuclear envelopes form around them.

5. What evidence suggests that during anaphase, kinetochore microtubules shorten at the kinetochore?

6. Under normal conditions, what happens to the cell cycle if the chromosomes fail to separate properly at anaphase?

## ✔ TEST YOUR UNDERSTANDING

7. Identify at least two events in the cell cycle that must be completed successfully for daughter cells to share an identical complement of chromosomes.

8. Make a concept map illustrating normal events at the $G_1$ checkpoint. Your diagram should include p53, DNA damage, Rb, E2F, social signals, $G_1$ Cdk, $G_1$ cyclin, S-phase proteins, phosphorylated (inactivated) cyclin–Cdk, dephosphorylated (activated) cyclin–Cdk, phosphorylated (inactivated) Rb.

9. Explain how microinjection experiments supported the hypothesis that specific molecules in the cytoplasm are involved in the transition from interphase to M phase. What was the control for this experiment?

0. Why are most protein kinases considered regulatory proteins?

11. Why are cyclins called cyclins? Explain their relationship to MPF activity.

12. In multicellular organisms, nondividing cells stay in $G_0$ phase. For the cell, why is it better to be held in $G_1$ rather than S, $G_2$, or M phase?
    a. $G_1$ cells are larger and more likely to perform the normal functions of the cell.
    b. $G_1$ cells have not replicated their DNA in preparation for division.
    c. $G_1$ cells are the only ones that do not have their chromatin in a highly condensed state.
    d. MPF is required to enter S phase, so the cell is committed to entering M phase if the cycle moves beyond $G_1$.

## ✔ TEST YOUR PROBLEM-SOLVING SKILLS

3. QUANTITATIVE A particular cell spends 4 hours in $G_1$ phase, 2 hours in S phase, 2 hours in $G_2$ phase, and 30 minutes in M phase. If a pulse–chase assay were performed with radioactive thymidine on an asynchronous culture, what percentage of mitotic cells would be radiolabeled after 9 hours?
   a. 0%
   b. 50%
   c. 75%
   d. 100%

4. When fruit fly embryos first begin to develop, a large cell is generated that contains over 8000 nuclei that are genetically identical with one another. What is most likely responsible for this result?

15. What is most likely responsible for the reduction in death rates over the past several years in cancers of the breast and prostate? How is this related to the development of cancer?

16. Cancer is primarily a disease of older people. Further, a group of individuals may share a genetic predisposition to developing certain types of cancer, yet vary a great deal in time of onset—or not get the disease at all. What conclusion could be drawn based on these observations? How does this relate to the requirements for a cell to become cancerous?

# 13 Meiosis

U

**In this chapter you will learn how**

**Meiosis promotes genetic diversity and allows the benefits of sex**

starting with → | by examining → | by asking →

**How does meiosis occur?** 13.1

**How meiosis produces genetic variation**

**Why does meiosis exist?** 13.4

and comparing to ↓

**Mitosis** Ch. 12

looking at ↓

**Independent assortment, crossing over, and fertilization** 13.2

**Purifying-selection hypothesis**

**Changing-environment hypothesis**

then asking ↓

**What happens when things go wrong?** 13.3

Scanning electron micrograph (with color added) showing human sperm attempting to enter a human egg. This chapter introduces the type of nuclear division called meiosis, which in animals occurs before the formation of sperm and eggs.

This chapter is part of the Big Picture. See how on pages 366–367.

W hy sex?

Simple questions—such as why sexual reproduction exists—are sometimes the best. This chapter asks what sexual reproduction is and why some organisms employ it. The focus here is on how organisms reproduce, or replicate—one of the five fundamental attributes of life introduced in Chapter 1.

For centuries people have known that during sexual reproduction, a male reproductive cell—a **sperm**—and a female reproductive cell—an **egg**—unite to form a new individual. The process of uniting sperm and egg is called **fertilization.** The first biologists to observe fertilization studied the large, translucent eggs of sea urchins. Owing to the semitransparency of the sea urchin egg cell, researchers were able to see the nuclei of a sperm and an egg fuse.

✔ When you see this checkmark, stop and test yourself. Answers are available in Appendix A.

When these observations were published in 1876, they raised an important question, because biologists had already established that the number of chromosomes is constant from cell to cell within a multicellular organism. The question is, How can the chromosomes from a sperm cell and an egg cell combine, but form an offspring that has the same chromosome number as its mother and its father?

A hint at the answer came in 1883, with the observation that cells in the body of roundworms of the genus *Ascaris* have four chromosomes, while their sperm and egg nuclei have only two chromosomes apiece.

Four years later, August Weismann formally proposed a hypothesis to explain the riddle: During the formation of **gametes**—reproductive cells such as sperm and eggs—there must be a distinctive type of cell division that leads to a reduction in chromosome number. Specifically, if the sperm and egg contribute an equal number of chromosomes to the fertilized egg, Weismann reasoned, they must each contain half of the usual number of chromosomes. Then, when sperm and egg combine, the resulting cell has the same chromosome number as its mother's cells and its father's cells have.

In the decades that followed, biologists confirmed this hypothesis by observing gamete formation in a wide variety of plant and animal species. Eventually this form of cell division came to be called meiosis (literally, "lessening-act").

**Meiosis** is nuclear division that leads to a halving of chromosome number and ultimately to the production of sperm and egg. (Meiosis is an important part of The Big Picture of Genetic Information on pages 366-367). To a biologist, asking "Why sex?" is equivalent to asking "Why meiosis?" Let's delve in by first looking at how meiosis happens.

# 13.1  How Does Meiosis Occur?

To understand meiosis, it is critical to grasp some key ideas about chromosomes. For example, when cell biologists began to study the cell divisions that lead to gamete formation, they made an important observation: Each organism has a characteristic number of chromosomes.

Consider the drawings in **FIGURE 13.1**, based on a paper published by Nettie Maria Stevens in 1908. They show the chromosomes of the fruit fly *Drosophila melanogaster*, or *Drosophila* for short. This model organism has been a focus of biological research for more than 100 years (see **BioSkills 13** in Appendix B). Stevens was studying the cell divisions leading up to the formation of egg and sperm. In total, she found eight chromosomes in *Drosophila* cells. Your cells have 46 chromosomes, and some ferns have over 1000.

## Chromosomes Come in Distinct Sizes and Shapes

Stevens found that each *Drosophila* cell has eight chromosomes, but just five distinct types, distinguished by their size and shape. Three of these chromosomes always occurred in pairs and are labeled chromosomes 2–4 in Figure 13.1. In males, Stevens

*Drosophila* chromosomes drawn by Nettie Stevens in 1908 ... ... and photographed through a modern microscope.

**FIGURE 13.1 Cells Contain Different Types of Chromosomes, and in Diploid Organisms, Chromosomes Come in Pairs.** Numbers and letters designate the types of *Drosophila* chromosomes. These chromosomes are from the cell of a male, so there is an X and a Y chromosome plus three homologous pairs of autosomes.

observed an unpaired set of chromosomes, which came to be known as the X and the Y chromosomes. Stevens found that females lack a Y chromosome but contain a pair of X chromosomes. This is the same situation in some other insects and in mammals. The X and Y chromosomes are called **sex chromosomes** and are associated with an individual's sex. Non-sex chromosomes, such as chromosomes 2–4 in *Drosophila*, are **autosomes.**

Chromosomes that are the same size and shape are called **homologous** ("same-proportion") **chromosomes,** or **homologs,** and the pair is called a homologous pair. Later work showed that homologous chromosomes are similar in content as well as in size and shape. Homologous chromosomes carry the same genes. A **gene** is a section of DNA that influences some hereditary trait in an individual. For example, each copy of chromosome 2 found in *Drosophila* carries genes that influence eye color, wing size and shape, and bristle size.

The versions of a gene found on homologous chromosomes may differ, however. Biologists use the term **allele** to denote different versions of the same gene. For example, the allele for an eye-color gene on one homolog of chromosome 2 may be associated with red eyes, the normal color in *Drosophila*, whereas the allele of the same eye-color gene on the other homolog may be associated with purple eyes (**FIGURE 13.2**); the particular alleles of the bristle-size gene will influence whether the fly's bristles are long or short, and so on.

Homologous chromosomes carry the same genes, but each homolog may contain different alleles.

## The Concept of Ploidy

At this point in her study, Stevens had determined the *Drosophila* **karyotype**—meaning the number and types of chromosomes present. As karyotyping studies became more common, cell biologists realized that, like *Drosophila*, the vast majority of plants and animals have more than one of each type of chromosome.

Homologous
chromosomes
(replicated)

**Gene** for eye color
(allele for red eyes)

**Gene** for eye color
(allele for purple eyes)

*Drosophila* autosome 2

**FIGURE 13.2 Homologous Chromosomes May Contain Different Alleles of the Same Gene.** The homologs of *Drosophila* chromosome 2 are shown; the location of only one of many genes is indicated.

Insects, humans, oak trees, and other organisms that have two versions of each type of chromosome are called **diploid** ("double-form"). Diploid organisms have two alleles of each gene. One allele is carried on each of the homologous pairs of chromosomes. Although a diploid individual can carry only two different alleles of a gene, there can be many different alleles in a population.

Organisms whose cells contain just one of each type of chromosome—for example, bacteria, archaea, and many algae and fungi—are called **haploid** ("single-form"). Haploid organisms have only one copy of each chromosome and just one allele of each gene.

Biologists use a compact notation to indicate the number of chromosomes and chromosome sets in a particular organism or type of cell:

- By convention, the letter $n$ stands for the number of distinct types of chromosomes in a given cell and is called the **haploid number.** If sex chromosomes are present, they are counted as a single type in the haploid number. In humans, $n$ is 23.

- To indicate the number of complete chromosome sets observed, a number is placed before the $n$. Thus, a cell can be $n$, or $2n$, or $3n$, and so on.

The combination of the number of sets and $n$ is termed the cell's **ploidy.** Diploid cells or species are designated $2n$, because two chromosomes of each type are present—one from each parent. A **maternal chromosome** comes from the mother, and a **paternal chromosome** comes from the father.

Humans are diploid; $2n$ is 46. Haploid cells or species are labeled simply $n$, because they have just one set of chromosomes—no homologs are present. In haploid cells, the number 1 in front of $n$ is implied and is not written out.

To summarize, the haploid number $n$ indicates the number of distinct types of chromosomes present. In contrast, a cell's ploidy ($n$, $2n$, $3n$, etc.) indicates the number of each type of chromosome present. Stating a cell's ploidy is the same as stating the number of haploid chromosome sets present. ✔ If you understand how these terms relate, you should be able to state the haploid number, ploidy, and total number of chromosomes present in a male *Drosophila.*

Later work revealed that it is common for species in some lineages—particularly certain land plants, such as ferns—to contain more than two of each type of chromosome. Instead of having two homologous chromosomes per cell, **polyploid** ("many-form") species have three or more of each type of chromosome in each cell.

Depending on the number of homologs present, polyploid species are called triploid ($3n$), tetraploid ($4n$), hexaploid ($6n$), octoploid ($8n$), and so on.

Stevens and other early cell biologists did more than just describe the karyotypes observed in their study organisms. Through careful examination, they were able to track how chromosome numbers change during meiosis. These studies confirmed Weismann's hypothesis that a special type of cell division occurs during gamete formation.

## An Overview of Meiosis

Cells replicate each of their chromosomes before undergoing meiosis. At the start of meiosis, chromosomes are in the same state they are in before mitosis.

Recall that an unreplicated eukaryotic chromosome consists of a single, long DNA double helix organized around proteins called histones (see Chapter 12). When chromosome replication is complete, each chromosome will consist of two identical **sister chromatids.** Sister chromatids contain identical copies of the DNA double helix present in the unreplicated chromosome and therefore the same genetic information. They remain physically joined along their entire length during much of meiosis (**FIGURE 13.3**).

To understand meiosis, it is critical to understand the relationship between chromosomes and sister chromatids. The trick is to recognize that unreplicated and replicated chromosomes are both considered *single* chromosomes—even though the replicated chromosome contains *two* sister chromatids. This makes sense if you consider that a chromosome carries a particular set of genetic information in its DNA and that the amount of *unique* information is the same whether there is one copy of it present or two.

Maternal chromosome

Paternal chromosome

Nuclear envelope

Replication

Replicated chromosome

Centromere

Sister chromatids

Homologous pair of replicated chromosomes

**FIGURE 13.3 Each Chromosome Replicates before Undergoing Meiosis.**

| Term | Definition | Example or Comment |
|---|---|---|
| **Chromosome** | Structure made up of DNA and proteins; carries the cell's hereditary information (genes) | Eukaryotes have linear chromosomes; most bacteria and archaea have just one, circular, chromosome |
| • **Sex chromosome** | Chromosome associated with an individual's sex | X and Y chromosomes of humans (males are XY, females XX); Z and W chromosomes of birds and butterflies (males are ZZ, females ZW) |
| • **Autosome** | A non-sex chromosome | Chromosomes 1–22 in humans |
| **Unreplicated chromosome** | A chromosome that consists of one double-helical molecule of DNA packaged with proteins | |
| **Replicated chromosome** | A chromosome that has been copied; consists of two identical chromatids, each containing one double-helical DNA molecule | Centromere |
| **Sister chromatids** | The two identical chromatid copies in a replicated chromosome | Sister chromatids |
| **Homologous chromosomes (homologs)** | In a diploid organism, chromosomes that are similar in size, shape, and gene content | You have a chromosome 22 from each parent — Homologous chromosomes |
| **Non-sister chromatids** | Chromatids belonging to homologous chromosomes | Non-sister chromatids |
| **Bivalent (or tetrad)** | Homologous replicated chromosomes that are joined together during prophase I and metaphase I of meiosis | Bivalent |
| **Haploid number** | The number of different types of chromosomes in a cell; symbolized $n$ | Humans have 23 different types of chromosomes ($n = 23$) |
| **Diploid number** | The number of chromosomes present in a diploid cell (see below); symbolized $2n$ | In humans all cells except gametes are diploid and contain 46 chromosomes ($2n = 46$) |
| **Ploidy** | The number of each type of chromosome present | The number of haploid chromosome sets present |
| • **Haploid** | Having one of each type of chromosome ($n$) | Bacteria and archaea are haploid, as are many algae; plant and animal gametes are haploid |
| • **Diploid** | Having two of each type of chromosome ($2n$) | Most familiar plants and animals are diploid |
| • **Polyploid** | Having more than two of each type of chromosome; cells may be triploid ($3n$), tetraploid ($4n$), hexaploid ($6n$), and so on | Seedless bananas are triploid; many ferns are tetraploid; bread wheat is hexaploid |

Note that an unreplicated chromosome is never called a chromatid; you can refer to chromatids only as the structures in a replicated chromosome.

**TABLE 13.1** summarizes the vocabulary that biologists use to describe chromosomes and illustrates the relationship between chromosomes and chromatids. ✔ If you understand this relationship, you should be able to draw the same chromosome in the unreplicated and replicated state, label the sister chromatids, indicate the number of DNA molecules present in each structure, and explain why both structures represent a single chromosome.

**Meiosis Comprises Two Cell Divisions** Meiosis consists of two cell divisions, called **meiosis I** and **meiosis II**. As **FIGURE 13.4** shows, the two divisions occur consecutively but differ sharply.

During meiosis I, the homologs in each chromosome pair separate from each other. One homolog goes to one daughter cell; the other homolog goes to the other daughter cell. It is a matter of chance which daughter cell receives which homolog.

At the end of meiosis I, each of the two daughter cells has one of each type of chromosome instead of two, and thus half as many chromosomes as the parent cell had. Put another way: During meiosis I, the diploid ($2n$) parent cell produces two haploid ($n$)

**FIGURE 13.5 Fertilization Restores a Full Complement of Chromosomes.**

Parent cell is diploid (2n) and contains a homologous pair of replicated chromosomes

Homologs separate

Sister chromatids separate

Daughter cells are haploid (n) and contain just one homolog

MEIOSIS I

MEIOSIS II

Four daughter cells contain one chromosome each (n). In animals, these cells become gametes.

**FIGURE 13.4 The Major Events in Meiosis.** Before undergoing meiosis, chromosomes are replicated so there are two chromatids per chromosome. Meiosis reduces chromosome number by half. In diploid organisms, the products of meiosis are haploid. Maternal chromosomes are shown in red; paternal chromosomes, blue. Note that in this cell, 2n = 2.

daughter cells. Notice, however, that each chromosome still consists of two sister chromatids—meaning that chromosomes are still replicated at the end of meiosis I.

During meiosis II, sister chromatids from each chromosome separate. One sister chromatid (now called a daughter chromosome) goes to one daughter cell; the other sister chromatid goes to the other daughter cell as a daughter chromosome. Remember that the cell that started meiosis II had one of each type of chromosome, but each chromosome was still replicated (meaning still consisting of two sister chromatids). The cells produced by meiosis II also have one of each type of chromosome, but now the daughter chromosomes are no longer replicated.

To reiterate, sister chromatids separate into daughter chromosomes during meiosis II. This is just what happens during mitosis. Meiosis II is actually equivalent to mitosis occurring in a haploid cell. In meiosis I, on the other hand, sister chromatids stay together. This sets meiosis I apart from both mitosis and meiosis II.

As in mitosis, chromosome movements during meiosis I and II are coordinated by microtubules of the **spindle apparatus** that attach to **kinetochores** located at the **centromere** of each chromosome. Recall that the centromere is a region on the chromosome; kinetochores are structures in that region (see Chapter 12). Chromosome movement is driven by fraying of the ends of microtubules at each kinetochore, just as it is in mitosis (see Figure 12.7).

**Meiosis I is a Reduction Division** A host of early cell biologists worked out this sequence of events through careful observation of cells with the light microscope. Based on these studies, they came to a key realization: The outcome of meiosis I is a reduction

in chromosome number. For this reason, meiosis I is known as a reduction division. Reduction is another important way in which meiosis I differs from meiosis II and mitosis.

In most plants and animals, the original cell entering meiosis is diploid and the four final daughter cells are haploid. In animals, the haploid daughter cells, each containing one of each homologous chromosome, eventually go on to form egg cells or sperm cells via a process called **gametogenesis** ("gamete-origin").

When two haploid gametes fuse during fertilization, a full complement of chromosomes is restored (**FIGURE 13.5**). The cell that results from fertilization is diploid and is called a **zygote**. In this way, each diploid individual receives a haploid chromosome set from its mother and a haploid set from its father.

**FIGURE 13.6** puts these events into the context of an animal's **life cycle**—the sequence of events that occurs over the life span of an individual, from fertilization to the production of offspring. As you study the figure, note how ploidy changes as the result of

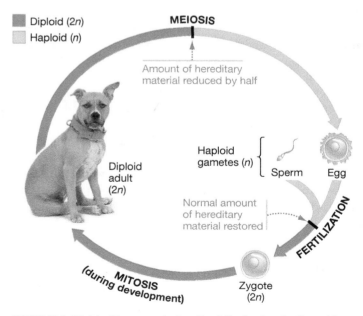

**FIGURE 13.6 Ploidy Changes during the Life Cycle of a Dog.** Most of the dog life cycle involves diploid cells.

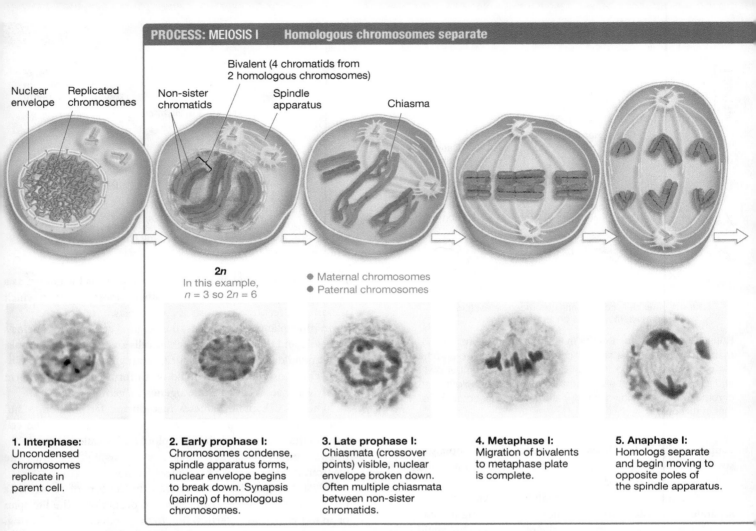

Nuclear envelope
Replicated chromosomes
Non-sister chromatids
Bivalent (4 chromatids from 2 homologous chromosomes)
Spindle apparatus
Chiasma

**2n**
In this example, $n = 3$ so $2n = 6$

● Maternal chromosomes
● Paternal chromosomes

**1. Interphase:** Uncondensed chromosomes replicate in parent cell.

**2. Early prophase I:** Chromosomes condense, spindle apparatus forms, nuclear envelope begins to break down. Synapsis (pairing) of homologous chromosomes.

**3. Late prophase I:** Chiasmata (crossover points) visible, nuclear envelope broken down. Often multiple chiasmata between non-sister chromatids.

**4. Metaphase I:** Migration of bivalents to metaphase plate is complete.

**5. Anaphase I:** Homologs separate and begin moving to opposite poles of the spindle apparatus.

**FIGURE 13.7 The Phases of Meiosis.** The micrographs of each phase are from a species of salamander.

meiosis and fertilization. In the case of the dog illustrated here, meiosis in a diploid adult results in the formation of haploid gametes, which combine to form a diploid zygote. The zygote marks the start of a new generation, and through mitotic divisions during development, the zygote goes on to form an adult dog.

✔ If you understand the events of meiosis, you should be able to predict how many DNA molecules will be present in the gametes of the fruit fly *Drosophila*, a diploid organism that has eight replicated chromosomes in each cell that enters meiosis.

Once Stevens and others had published their work on meiosis and the accompanying changes in ploidy, the mystery of fertilization was finally solved. To appreciate the consequences of meiosis fully, let's analyze the events in more detail.

## The Phases of Meiosis I

Meiosis begins after chromosomes have been replicated during S phase (see Chapter 12). Before the start of meiosis, chromosomes are extremely long structures, just as they are during interphase of the normal cell cycle. The major steps that occur once meiosis begins are shown in **FIGURE 13.7**.

**Early Prophase I**    During early prophase I, the nuclear envelope begins to break down, chromosomes condense and the spindle apparatus begins to form. Then a crucial event occurs: Homologous chromosome pairs come together. The end result of this process is called **synapsis** and is illustrated in step 2 of Figure 13.7. Synapsis is possible because regions of homologous chromosomes that are similar at the molecular level come together. In most organisms, synapsis requires breaking and then connecting together DNA of the two homologs at one or more spots along their length.

The structure that results from synapsis is called a **bivalent** (*bi* means "two" in Latin) or **tetrad** (*tetra* means "four" in Greek). A bivalent consists of paired homologous chromosomes, with each homolog consisting of two sister chromatids. Chromatids from different homologs are referred to as **non-sister chromatids.** In the figure, the red-colored chromatids are non-sister chromatids with respect to the blue-colored chromatids.

**Late Prophase I**    During late prophase I, the nuclear envelope breaks down and microtubules of the spindle apparatus attach to

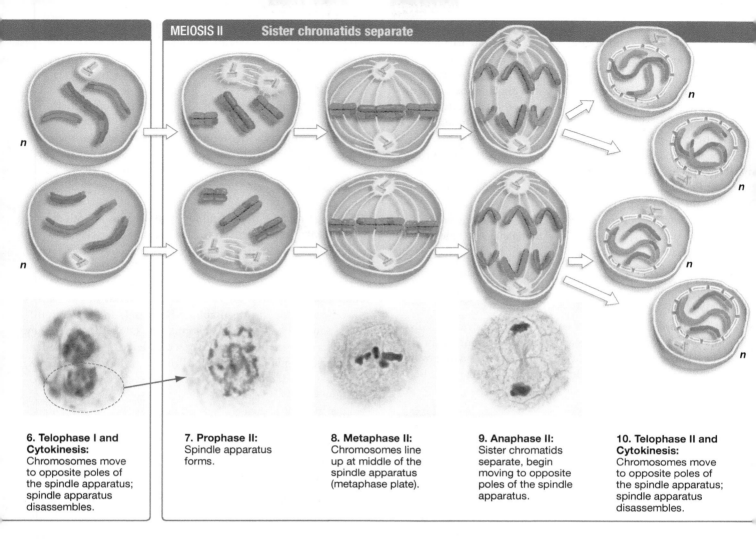

**6. Telophase I and Cytokinesis:** Chromosomes move to opposite poles of the spindle apparatus; spindle apparatus disassembles.

**7. Prophase II:** Spindle apparatus forms.

**8. Metaphase II:** Chromosomes line up at middle of the spindle apparatus (metaphase plate).

**9. Anaphase II:** Sister chromatids separate, begin moving to opposite poles of the spindle apparatus.

**10. Telophase II and Cytokinesis:** Chromosomes move to opposite poles of the spindle apparatus; spindle apparatus disassembles.

kinetochores. Non-sister chromatids begin to separate at many points along their length. They stay joined at certain locations, however, each of which forms an X-shaped structure called a **chiasma** (plural: **chiasmata**). (In the Greek alphabet, the letter X is called "chi.") Normally, at least one chiasma forms in every pair of homologous chromosomes; often there are several chiasmata. The chiasmata mark sites where DNA was broken and rejoined between homologs early in prophase I.

As step 3 of Figure 13.7 shows, the chromatids that meet to form a chiasma are non-sister chromatids. At each chiasma there is an exchange of parts of chromosomes between paternal and maternal homologs. These reciprocal exchanges between different homologs create non-sister chromatids that have both paternal and maternal segments. This process of chromosome exchange is called **crossing over.**

In step 4 of Figure 13.7, the result of crossing over is illustrated by chromosomes with a combination of red and blue segments. When crossing over occurs, the chromosomes that result have a mixture of maternal and paternal alleles. Crossing over is a major way that meiosis creates genetic diversity.

**Metaphase I**   The next major stage in meiosis I is metaphase I. This is when kinetochore microtubules move the pairs of homologous chromosomes (bivalents) to a region called the **metaphase plate** in the middle of the spindle apparatus (step 4). The metaphase plate is not a physical structure but an imaginary plane dividing the spindle apparatus.

Here are two key points about chromosome movement: Each bivalent moves to the metaphase plate independently of the other bivalents, and the alignment on one side or the other of the metaphase plate is random for maternal and paternal homologs from each chromosome. This movement explains the most basic principles of genetics (see Chapter 14).

**Anaphase and Telophase I**   Sister chromatids of each chromosome remain together. During anaphase I, the homologous chromosomes in each bivalent separate and begin moving to opposite poles of the spindle apparatus (step 5). Meiosis I concludes with telophase I, when the homologs finish moving to opposite sides of the spindle (step 6). When meiosis I is complete, **cytokinesis** (division of cytoplasm) occurs and two haploid daughter cells form.

**Meiosis I: A Recap** The end result of meiosis I is that one chromosome of each homologous pair is distributed to a different daughter cell. A reduction division has occurred: The daughter cells of meiosis I are haploid, having only one copy of each type of chromosome. The sister chromatids remain attached in each chromosome, however, meaning that the haploid daughter cells produced by meiosis I still contain replicated chromosomes.

The chromosomes in each cell are a random assortment of maternal and paternal chromosomes as a result of (1) crossing over and (2) the random distribution of maternal and paternal homologs during metaphase.

The preceding discussion shows that although meiosis I is a continuous process, biologists summarize the events by identifying distinct phases:

- *Early Prophase I* Replicated chromosomes condense and the spindle apparatus forms. Synapsis of homologs forms pairs of homologous chromosomes, or bivalents.

- *Late Prophase I* Breakdown of the nuclear envelope. Microtubules of the spindle apparatus attach to kinetochores. Chiasmata become visible, marking sites where crossing over occurs. Crossing over results in an exchange of segments between maternal and paternal chromosomes.

- *Metaphase I* Bivalents move to the metaphase plate and line up. One homolog is on one side of the plate and the other homolog is on the other.

- *Anaphase I* Homologs separate and begin moving to opposite spindle poles.

- *Telophase I* Homologs finish moving to opposite spindle poles. Spindle apparatus disassembles. In some species, a nuclear envelope re-forms around each set of chromosomes.

Throughout, chromosome movement takes place as microtubules that are attached to the kinetochore dynamically assemble and disassemble. When meiosis I is complete, the cell divides and two haploid daughter cells are produced.

## The Phases of Meiosis II

Recall that chromosome replication occurred before meiosis I. Throughout meiosis I, sister chromatids remained attached. Because no chromosome replication occurs between meiosis I and meiosis II, each chromosome consists of two sister chromatids at the start of meiosis II. And because only one member of each homologous pair of chromosomes is present, the cell is haploid.

During prophase II, a spindle apparatus forms in both daughter cells. Microtubules attach to kinetochores on each side of every chromosome and begin moving the chromosomes toward the middle of each cell (step 7 of Figure 13.7).

In metaphase II, the chromosomes are lined up at the metaphase plate (step 8). The sister chromatids of each chromosome separate during anaphase II (step 9) and move to different daughter cells during telophase II (step 10). Once they are separated, each chromatid is considered an independent daughter chromosome. Meiosis II results in four haploid cells, each with one daughter chromosome of each type in the chromosome set.

Like meiosis I, meiosis II is continuous, but biologists routinely divide it into distinct phases. These stages are essentially those of mitosis. To summarize,

- *Prophase II* The spindle apparatus forms. If a nuclear envelope formed at the end of meiosis I, it breaks apart.

- *Metaphase II* Replicated chromosomes, consisting of two sister chromatids, are lined up at the metaphase plate.

- *Anaphase II* Sister chromatids separate. The daughter chromosomes that result begin moving to opposite poles of the spindle apparatus.

**SUMMARY TABLE 13.2 Key Differences between Mitosis and Meiosis**

| Feature | Mitosis | Meiosis |
|---|---|---|
| **Number of cell divisions** | One | Two |
| **Number of chromosomes in daughter cells compared with parent cell** | Same | Half |
| **Synapsis of homologs** | No | Yes |
| **Number of crossing-over events** | None | One or more per pair of homologous chromosomes |
| **Makeup of chromosomes in daughter cells** | Identical | Different—various combinations of maternal and paternal chromosomes, paternal and maternal segments mixed within chromosomes |
| **Role in organism life cycle** | Asexual reproduction in some eukaryotes; cell division for growth | Halving of chromosome number in cells that will produce gametes |

- *Telophase II* Chromosomes finish moving to opposite poles of the spindle apparatus. A nuclear envelope forms around each haploid set of chromosomes.

When meiosis II is complete, each cell divides to form two daughter cells. Because meiosis II occurs in both daughter cells of meiosis I, the process results in a total of four daughter cells from each original, parent cell. To describe meiosis in a nutshell, one diploid cell with replicated chromosomes gives rise to four haploid cells with unreplicated chromosomes.

**TABLE 13.2** and **FIGURE 13.8** provide a comparison of mitosis and meiosis. A key difference between the two processes is that homologous chromosomes pair early in meiosis but do not pair at all during mitosis. Because homologs pair through synapsis in prophase of meiosis I, they can migrate to the metaphase plate together and then separate during anaphase of meiosis I, resulting in a reduction division. ✔ If you understand this key distinction between meiosis and mitosis, you should be able to describe the consequences for meiosis if homologs do not pair.

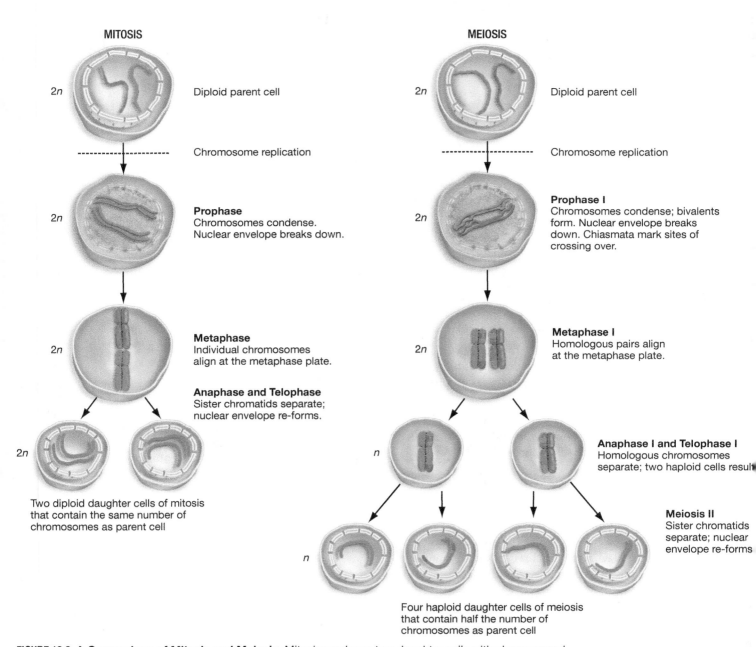

**FIGURE 13.8 A Comparison of Mitosis and Meiosis.** Mitosis produces two daughter cells with chromosomal complements identical to the parent cell. Meiosis produces four haploid cells with chromosomal complements unlike one another and unlike the diploid parent cell.

**FIGURE 13.9 A Closer Look at Key Events in Prophase of Meiosis I.**

## A Closer Look at Synapsis and Crossing Over

The pairing of homologs and crossing over in prophase I are important events unique to meiosis. **FIGURE 13.9** takes a closer look at how chromosomes come together and exchange parts during meiosis I.

**Step 1** Sister chromatids are held together along their full length by proteins known as cohesins. At the entry to prophase I, chromosomes begin to condense.

**Step 2** Homologs pair. In many organisms, pairing begins when a break is made in the DNA of one chromatid. This break initiates a crossover between non-sister chromatids.

**Step 3** A network of proteins forms the **synaptonemal complex**, which holds the two homologs tightly together.

**Step 4** The synaptonemal complex disassembles in late prophase I. The two homologs partially separate and are held together only at chiasmata. Attachments at chiasmata are eventually broken to restore individual, unconnected chromosomes.

At a chiasma the non-sister chromatids from each homolog have been physically broken at the same point and *attached to each other*. As a result, corresponding segments of maternal and paternal chromosomes are exchanged.

Crossing over can occur at many locations along the length of paired homologs, and it routinely occurs at least once between each pair of non-sister chromatids. In humans, each chromosome undergoes an average of 1½ crossovers during meiosis.

Why does meiosis exist at all? What are its consequences?

check your understanding

**If you understand that . . .**

- Meiosis is called a reduction division because the total number of chromosomes present is cut in half.
- During meiosis, a single diploid parent cell with replicated chromosomes gives rise to four haploid daughter cells, with unreplicated chromosomes.

✔ **You should be able to . . .**

1. Demonstrate the phases of meiosis I illustrated in Figure 13.7 by using pipe cleaners or pieces of cooked spaghetti.

2. Identify the event that makes meiosis a reduction division, unlike mitosis, and explain why it is responsible for reduction division.

3. Explain how meiosis generates cells with one of every kind of chromosome rather than random mixtures of different chromosomes.

*Answers are available in Appendix A.*

## 13.2 Meiosis Promotes Genetic Variation

The cell biologists who worked out the details of meiosis in the late 1800s and early 1900s realized that the process solved the riddle of fertilization. Weismann's hypothesis—that a reduction division precedes gamete formation in animals—was confirmed.

By now, having come to appreciate that meiosis is an intricate, tightly regulated process, you shouldn't be surprised to learn that it involves dozens, if not hundreds, of different proteins. Given this complexity, it is logical to hypothesize that meiosis accomplishes something extremely important: Thanks to the independent shuffling of maternal and paternal chromosomes and crossing over during meiosis I, the chromosomes in one gamete are different from the chromosomes in another gamete and different from the chromosomes in parental cells. Subsequently, fertilization brings haploid sets of chromosomes from a mother and father together to form a diploid offspring. The chromosome complement of this offspring is unlike that of either parent. It is a random combination of genetic material from each parent.

This change in chromosomal complement is crucial. The critical factor here is that changes in chromosome sets occur only during sexual reproduction—*not* during asexual reproduction.

- **Asexual reproduction** is any mechanism of producing offspring that does not involve the production and fusion of gametes. Asexual reproduction in eukaryotes is based on mitosis. The chromosomes in cells produced by mitosis are identical to the chromosomes in the parental cell.

- **Sexual reproduction** is the production of offspring through the production and fusion of gametes. Sexual reproduction results in offspring that have chromosome complements unlike those of their siblings or their parents.

Why is this difference important?

### Chromosomes and Heredity

The changes in chromosomes produced by meiosis and fertilization are significant because chromosomes contain the cell's hereditary material. Stated another way, chromosomes contain the instructions for specifying particular traits. These inherited traits range from eye color and height in humans to the number or shape of the bristles on a fruit fly's leg to the color or shape of the seeds found in pea plants.

In the early 1900s, biologists began using the term gene to refer to the inherited instructions for a particular trait. Recall that the term allele refers to a particular version of a gene and that homologous chromosomes may carry different alleles.

Chromosomes are the repositories of genes, and identical copies of chromosomes are distributed to daughter cells during mitosis. Thus, cells that are produced by mitosis are genetically identical to the parent cell, and offspring produced during asexual reproduction are genetically identical to one another as well as to their parent. Offspring produced by asexual reproduction are **clones**—or exact copies—of their parent. A familiar example of asexual reproduction is growing a new plant from a cutting.

In contrast, the offspring produced by sexual reproduction are genetically different from one another and unlike either their mother or their father.

Let's begin by analyzing two aspects of meiosis that create variation among chromosomes: (1) separation and distribution of homologous chromosomes and (2) crossing over. We'll then look at how these processes interact with fertilization to produce genetically variable offspring.

### The Role of Independent Assortment

Each somatic cell in your body contains 23 homologous pairs of chromosomes and 46 chromosomes in total. Half of these chromosomes came from your mother, and half came from your father. Each chromosome contains genes, and genes influence particular traits. For example, one gene that affects your eye color might be located on one chromosome, while one of the genes that affects your hair color might be located on a different chromosome (**FIGURE 13.10a**).

**(a)** Example: Individual with different alleles of two genes

Maternal chromosome    Paternal chromosome

Maternal chromosome    Paternal chromosome

Allele that contributes to brown eyes    Allele that contributes to green eyes

**An eye-color gene**

Allele that contributes to black hair    Allele that contributes to red hair

**A hair-color gene**

**(b)** During meiosis I, bivalents can line up two different ways before the homologs separate.

— OR —

Brown eyes Black hair    Green eyes Red hair    Brown eyes Red hair    Green eyes Black hair

**FIGURE 13.10 Independent Assortment of Homologous Chromosomes Results in Varied Combinations of Genes.**

Suppose that the chromosomes you inherited from your mother contain alleles associated with brown eyes and black hair, but the chromosomes you inherited from your father include alleles associated with green eyes and red hair. (This is a simplification for the purpose of explanation. In reality, several genes with various alleles interact in complex ways to produce human eye color and hair color.)

Will any particular gamete you produce contain the genetic instructions inherited from your mother or the instructions inherited from your father? To answer this question, study the diagram of meiosis in **FIGURE 13.10b**. It shows that when pairs of homologous chromosomes line up during meiosis I and the homologs separate, a variety of combinations of maternal and paternal chromosomes can result. Each daughter cell gets a random assortment of maternal and paternal chromosomes.

This phenomenon is known as the principle of independent assortment. In the example given here, meiosis results in gametes with alleles for brown eyes and black hair, the traits from your mother, and green eyes and red hair, the traits from your father. But two additional combinations also occur: brown eyes and red hair, or green eyes and black hair. The appearance of new combinations of alleles is called **genetic recombination.** Four different combinations of paternal and maternal chromosomes are possible when two chromosomes are distributed to daughter cells during meiosis I.

✔ If you understand how independent assortment produces genetic variation in the daughter cells of meiosis, you should be able to explain how genetic variation would be affected if maternal chromosomes always lined up together on one side of the metaphase plate during meiosis I and paternal chromosomes always lined up on the other side.

How many different combinations of maternal and paternal homologs are possible when more chromosomes are involved? With each additional pair of chromosomes, the number of combinations doubles. In general, a diploid organism can produce $2^n$ combinations of maternal and paternal chromosomes, where $n$ is the haploid chromosome number. This means that you ($n = 23$) can produce $2^{23}$, or about 8.4 million, gametes that differ in their combination of maternal and paternal chromosome sets. The random assortment of whole chromosomes generates an impressive amount of genetic variation among gametes.

### The Role of Crossing Over

Recall from Section 13.1 that segments of paternal and maternal chromatids exchange when crossing over occurs during meiosis I. Thus, crossing over produces new combinations of alleles within a chromosome—combinations that did not exist in either parent. This phenomenon is known as recombination. Crossing over is an important source of genetic recombination.

Genetic recombination is important because it dramatically increases the genetic variability of gametes produced by meiosis. The independent assortment of homologous chromosomes during meiosis generates varied combinations of chromosomes in gametes; genetic recombination due to crossing over varies the combinations of alleles along each chromosome that is involved

in a crossover. With crossing over, the number of genetically different gametes that you can produce is much more than the 8.4 million—it is virtually limitless.

## How Does Fertilization Affect Genetic Variation?

Crossing over and the independent assortment of maternal and paternal chromosomes ensure that each gamete is genetically unique. Even if two gametes produced by the same individual fuse to form a diploid offspring—in which case **self-fertilization,** or "selfing," is taking place—the offspring are very likely to be genetically different from the parent (**FIGURE 13.11**). Selfing is common in many plant species, and it also occurs in animal species in which single individuals—called hermaphrodites—contain both male and female sex organs.

Self-fertilization, however, is rare or nonexistent in many sexually reproducing species. Instead, gametes from different individuals combine to form offspring. This process is called **outcrossing.** Outcrossing increases the genetic diversity of offspring even further because it combines chromosomes from different individuals. These chromosomes are likely to contain different alleles.

How many genetically distinct offspring can be produced when outcrossing occurs? Let's answer this question using humans as an example. Recall that a single human can produce about 8.4 million different gametes by independent assortment alone. When a sperm and egg come together at fertilization, the number of possible genetic combinations that can result is equal to the product of the numbers of different gametes produced by each parent. (To understand this logic, see **BioSkills 5** in Appendix B.) In humans this means that two parents can potentially produce 8.4 million $\times$ 8.4 million $= 70.6 \times 10^{12}$ genetically distinct offspring, even without crossing over. This number is far greater than the total number of people who have ever lived.

## check your understanding

**If you understand that . . .**

• The daughter cells produced by meiosis are genetically different from the parent cell because (1) maternal and paternal homologs align randomly at metaphase of meiosis I and (2) crossing over leads to recombination within chromosomes.

✔ **You should be able to . . .**

1. Draw a diploid parent cell with $2n = 6$ (three types of chromosomes) and then sketch the genetically distinct types of daughter cells that may result by independent assortment of these chromosomes at meiosis.

2. Discuss how crossing over would influence the genetic diversity of these gametes.

3. Compare and contrast the degree of genetic variation that results from asexual reproduction, selfing, and outcrossing.

*Answers are available in Appendix A.*

The red and blue chromosomes can line up in different ways during metaphase

OR

2n = 4

**1. Parent cell** with four chromosomes.

**2. Crossing over** during meiosis I.

**3. Independent assortment** of homologous chromosomes during meiosis I.

**4. Gametes** produced by meiosis II.

**5. Fertilization** of random pairs of gametes (only some possibilities shown).

**FIGURE 13.11 Crossing Over, Independent Assortment, and the Random Pairing of Gametes during Fertilization Increase Genetic Variation, Even in Offspring Produced by Self-Fertilization.**

✔**EXERCISE** In step 5, only a few of the many types of offspring that could be produced are shown. Sketch two additional types that are different from those shown.

In any complicated process such as meiosis, things can and do go wrong. What happens if there is a mistake, and the chromosomes are not properly distributed?

## 13.3 What Happens When Things Go Wrong in Meiosis?

Errors in meiosis are surprisingly common. If this were like a spelling mistake, it might be only an annoyance. But in humans, a conservative estimate is that 25 percent of conceptions are spontaneously terminated because of problems in meiosis. What are the consequences for offspring if gametes contain an abnormal set of chromosomes?

In 1866 Langdon Down described a distinctive set of co-occurring conditions observed in some people. The syndrome was characterized by mental retardation, a high risk for heart problems and leukemia, and a degenerative brain disorder similar to Alzheimer's disease. **Down syndrome,** as the disorder came to be called, is observed in about 0.15 percent of live births (1 infant in every 666).

For over 80 years the cause of the syndrome was unknown. Then, in the late 1950s, a study of the chromosome sets of nine Down syndrome children suggested that the condition is associated with the presence of an extra copy of chromosome 21. This situation is called **trisomy** ("three-bodies")—in this case trisomy-21—because each cell has three copies of the chromosome. The explanation proposed for the trisomy was that a mistake had occurred during meiosis in either the mother or the father.

### How Do Mistakes Occur?

For a gamete to get one complete set of chromosomes, two steps in meiosis must be perfectly executed.

1. The chromosomes in each homologous pair must separate from each other during the first meiotic division, so that only one homolog ends up in each daughter cell.

2. Sister chromatids must separate from each other and move to opposite poles of the dividing cell during meiosis II.

If both homologs in meiosis I or both sister chromatids in meiosis II move to the same pole of the parent cell, the products of meiosis will be abnormal. This sort of meiotic error is referred to as **nondisjunction,** because the homologs or sister chromatids fail to separate, or disjoin.

**FIGURE 13.12** shows what happens when homologs do not separate correctly during meiosis I. Notice that at the end of meiosis, two daughter cells have two copies of the same chromosome—the smaller one in Figure 13.12—while the other two lack that chromosome entirely. Gametes that contain an extra chromosome are symbolized as $n + 1$; gametes that lack one chromosome are symbolized as $n - 1$.

If an $n + 1$ gamete is fertilized by a normal $n$ gamete, the resulting zygote will be $2n + 1$. This situation is trisomy. If the $n - 1$ gamete is fertilized by a normal $n$ gamete, the resulting zygote will be $2n - 1$. This situation is called **monosomy**. Cells that have too many or too few chromosomes of a particular type are said to be **aneuploid** ("without-form").

Meiotic mistakes occur often. Researchers estimate that 25 percent of all human conceptions produce a zygote that is aneuploid. Most of these errors result from the failure of a homologous pair to separate in anaphase of meiosis I; less often, sister chromatids stay together during anaphase of meiosis II.

The consequences of meiotic mistakes are almost always severe. Trisomy-21 is unusual in allowing development to proceed when there are three copies of chromosome 21. Even for this chromosome, live births are not seen when there is only one copy.

In one study of human pregnancies that ended in early embryonic or fetal death, 38 percent involved abnormal chromosome sets that resulted from mistakes in meiosis. Trisomy accounted for about one-third of the abnormal karyotypes. Three copies of every chromosome ($3n$), a condition called triploidy, was also common. Monosomy and abnormally sized or shaped chromosomes were also seen. Mistakes in meiosis are common and are the leading cause of spontaneous abortion (miscarriage) in humans.

## Why Do Mistakes Occur?

Trisomy and other meiotic mistakes are random errors that occur during meiosis. Recent research indicates that problems are especially common in attaching microtubules to kinetochores early in meiosis I and in separating chromosomes that have a single chiasma near their ends or near centromeres.

Researchers see strong patterns in occurrence of human trisomies at birth. Here are some of the patterns that emerge:

- Trisomy is much more common with the smaller chromosomes (numbers 13–22) than it is with the larger chromosomes (numbers 1–12), and trisomy-21 is far and away the most common type of trisomy observed. Chromosome 21 is the smallest human autosome.

- With the exception of trisomy-21, most trisomies and monosomies observed in humans involve the sex chromosomes.

- Errors in meiosis leading to eggs are more common than errors in meiosis leading to sperm.

- Maternal age is an important factor in the occurrence of trisomy. For example, in the case of Down syndrome, as **FIGURE 13.13** shows, the incidence increases dramatically in babies born to mothers over 35 years old.

Why do these patterns occur? One important point to remember is that these observations are made at birth, not fertilization. The frequency of nondisjunction is about equal among chromosomes, but aneuploidy tends to be lethal to embryos if it involves chromosomes that contain a large number of genes. Trisomy-21 is common most likely because it involves a small chromosome with a correspondingly small number of genes.

**PROCESS: NONDISJUNCTION**

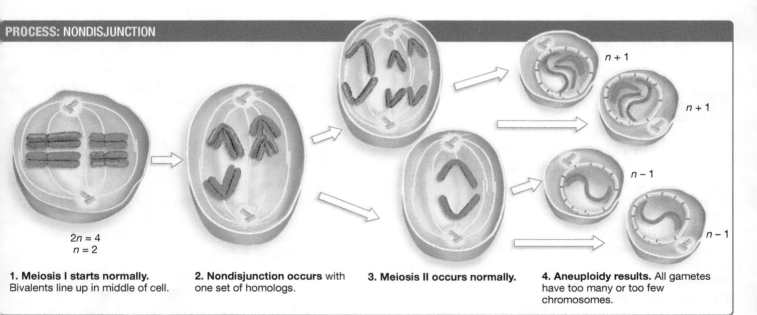

$2n = 4$
$n = 2$

**1. Meiosis I starts normally.** Bivalents line up in middle of cell.

**2. Nondisjunction occurs** with one set of homologs.

**3. Meiosis II occurs normally.**

**4. Aneuploidy results.** All gametes have too many or too few chromosomes.

$n + 1$
$n + 1$
$n - 1$
$n - 1$

**FIGURE 13.12 Nondisjunction Leads to Gametes with Abnormal Chromosome Numbers.** If homologous chromosomes fail to separate during meiosis I, the gametes that result will have an extra chromosome or will lack a chromosome. Nondisjunction can also occur during meiosis II if sister chromatids fail to separate.

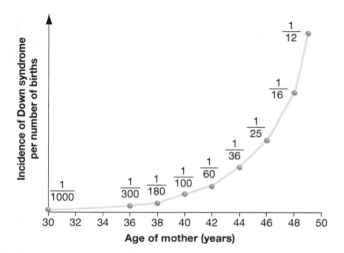

**FIGURE 13.13 The Frequency of Down Syndrome Increases as a Function of a Mother's Age.**

DATA: National Down Syndrome Society. 2012. www.ndss.org/index.php?option=com_content&view=article&id=61&Itemid=78

There are more questions than answers. Why are there more errors in women than men? Why is there such a strong correlation between maternal age and frequency of trisomy-21?

In part, the answers lie with an unusual feature of human egg development (oogenesis). Diploid precursors to eggs enter meiosis I before birth and arrest in prophase I until ovulation. For some eggs, this is 40 years or more later. Spindle apparatus function and the ability to separate chromosomes properly appear to decline after this long wait. Much remains to be discovered, but one thing is clear: Successful meiosis is critical to the health of offspring.

## 13.4 Why Does Meiosis Exist?

Why sex and meiosis? Although it seems obvious that sex and meiosis are needed universally for reproduction, that's not the case. Meiosis and sexual reproduction occur in only a small fraction of the lineages on the tree of life. Bacteria and archaea normally undergo only asexual reproduction; most algae, all fungi, and some animals and land plants reproduce asexually as well as sexually. Asexual reproduction is even observed in some vertebrates. Several species of guppy in the genus *Poeciliopsis*, for example, reproduce exclusively by mitosis.

Although sexual reproduction plays a central role in the life of most familiar organisms—including us—until recently, scientists had no clear idea of why it occurs. In fact, on the basis of theory, biologists had good reason to think that sexual reproduction should *not* exist.

### The Paradox of Sex

In 1978 John Maynard Smith pointed out that the existence of sexual reproduction presents a paradox. Maynard Smith developed a mathematical model showing that because asexually reproducing individuals do not have to produce male offspring, their progeny on average can produce twice as many offspring as individuals that reproduce sexually. **FIGURE 13.14** diagrams this result by showing the number of females (♀), males (♂), and asexually reproducing organisms (O) produced over several generations by asexual versus sexual reproduction.

In this example, each asexually reproducing individual and each sexually reproducing couple produces four offspring over the course of their lifetimes. Note that in the sexual population, it takes two individuals—one male and one female—to produce

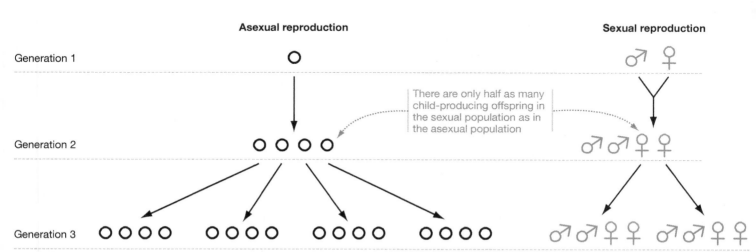

**FIGURE 13.14 Asexual Reproduction Produces More Offspring.** Each female (♀), male (♂), and asexual (O) symbol represents an individual. This hypothetical example assumes that (1) every asexual individual or sexually reproducing couple produces four offspring over the course of a lifetime, (2) sexually reproducing individuals produce half males and half females, and (3) all offspring survive to breed.

✔**QUANTITATIVE** How many asexually produced offspring would be present in generation 4? How many sexually produced offspring?

four offspring. Two out of every four children that each female produces sexually are males who cannot have children of their own. As a result, after one generation (generation 2 in Figure 13.14) the sexual population has just half as many child-producing individuals as the asexual population. Maynard Smith referred to this as the "two-fold cost of males." Asexual reproduction is much more efficient than sexual reproduction because no males are produced.

Based on this analysis, what will happen when asexual and sexual individuals exist in the same population and compete with one another? If all other things are equal, individuals that reproduce asexually should increase in frequency in the population while individuals that reproduce sexually should decline in frequency. In fact, Maynard Smith's model predicts that sexual reproduction is so inefficient that it should be completely eliminated.

To resolve this paradox, biologists began examining the assumption "If all other things are equal." Stated another way, biologists began looking for ways that meiosis and outcrossing could lead to the production of offspring that reproduce more than asexually produced individuals do. After decades of debate and analysis, two solid hypotheses to explain the paradox of sex are beginning to emerge.

## The Purifying Selection Hypothesis

The first clue to unraveling the paradox of sex is a simple observation: If a gene is damaged or altered in a way that causes it to function poorly, it will be inherited by *all* of that individual's offspring when asexual reproduction occurs. Suppose the altered gene arose in generation 1 of Figure 13.14. If this gene is important, its alteration might cause the four asexual females present in generation 2 to produce fewer than four offspring apiece—perhaps because the members of generation 2 die young. If so, then generation 3 will not have twice as many individuals in the asexual lineage compared with the sexual lineage.

An allele that functions poorly and lowers the fitness of an individual is said to be deleterious. Asexual individuals are doomed to transmitting all their deleterious alleles to all of their offspring.

Suppose, however, that the same deleterious allele arose in the sexually reproducing female in generation 1 of Figure 13.14. If the female also has a normal copy of the gene, and if she mates with a male that has normal copies of the gene, then on average half her offspring will lack the deleterious allele. Sexual individuals are likely to have some offspring that lack the deleterious alleles that are present in a parent.

Natural selection against deleterious alleles is called purifying selection. Purifying selection should reduce the numerical advantage of asexual reproduction.

To test this hypothesis, researchers recently compared the same genes in two closely related species of *Daphnia*, a tiny crustacean that is a common inhabitant of ponds and lakes (see Chapter 50). One of these species reproduces asexually and the other reproduces sexually. As predicted, the researchers found that individuals in the asexual species contained many more deleterious alleles than individuals in the sexual species. Results like

**QUESTION: Does exposure to evolving pathogens favor outcrossing?**

**HYPOTHESIS:** In environments where evolving pathogens are present, sexual reproduction by outcrosing will be favored.

**NULL HYPOTHESIS:** The presence of evolving pathogens will not favor outcrossing.

**EXPERIMENTAL SETUP:**

Grow without pathogen    Grow with pathogen

1. **Start with a pathogen free population of roundworms** with a 20% rate of outcrossing.

2. **Divide the population;** grow one subgroup in the absence of a pathogen and another subgroup in the presence of an evolving pathogen.

3. **Assess the rate of outcrossing** over many generations.

**PREDICTION:** The rate of outcrossing will increase in response to exposure by a pathogen.

**PREDICTION OF NULL HYPOTHESIS:** The rate of outcrossing will not be influenced by a pathogen.

**RESULTS:**

**CONCLUSION:** Exposure to evolving pathogens favors outcrossing.

**FIGURE 13.15 Does Exposure to Pathogens Favor Sexual Reproduction through Outcrossing?** Each point in the graph shows the average percentage of reproduction by outcrossing for five populations. The bars indicate the degree of variation in the data (see **BioSkills 4** in Appendix B for a description of error bars).

Morran, L. T., et al. 2011. Running with the red queen: Host-parasite coevolution selects for biparental sex. *Science* 333: 216–218.

✔ **QUESTION** What would you predict if a non-evolving pathogen were used?

these have convinced biologists that purifying selection is an important factor promoting the success of sexual reproduction.

## The Changing-Environment Hypothesis

The second hypothesis to explain sexual reproduction also focuses on the benefits of producing genetically diverse offspring. Here's the key idea: Offspring that are genetic clones of their parents are unlikely to thrive if the environment changes.

What type of environmental change might favor genetically diverse offspring? The leading hypothesis points to pressure put on hosts by rapidly changing pathogens and parasites—bacteria, viruses, fungi, and other entities that cause disease. In your own lifetime, for example, several new disease-causing agents have emerged that afflict humans. These include the SARS virus, HIV, and new strains of the tuberculosis bacterium. Hundreds of genes help defend you against these types of invaders. Certain alleles help you fight off particular strains of disease-causing bacteria, eukaryotes, or viruses. In this evolutionary arms race, pathogens and parasites constantly evolve new ways to infect the most common types of host.

What happens if all the offspring produced by an individual are genetically identical? If a new strain of disease-causing agent evolves, then all the asexually produced offspring are likely to be susceptible to that new strain. But if the offspring are genetically varied, then it is likely that at least some offspring will have combinations of alleles that enable them to fight off the new strain of pathogen or parasite and produce offspring of their own.

Recall from Section 13.2 that over multiple generations, outcrossing—mating between two different individuals—increases the amount of genetic diversity relative to self-fertilization. A logical question to ask is: Does exposure to evolving pathogens favor outcrossing in sexually reproducing organisms? To address this question, Levi Morran, Curtis Lively, and colleagues carried out a pivotal study on a tiny (only about 1 mm long) roundworm named *Caenorhabditis elegans*.

*C. elegans* is an important model organism (see **BioSkills 13** in Appendix B) that was chosen for this study because it leads an unusual sex life. There are no females, only males and hermaphrodites. Because hermaphrodites have both male and female sex organs, this means that *C. elegans* can reproduce either by self-fertilization or by outcrossing with males. The proportion of roundworms that reproduce by self-fertilization versus outcrossing can vary in different strains or in different environments over time. So, the research team was able to test whether the rate of outcrossing increased in response to intense selection by a pathogen.

The setup of Morran, Lively, and colleagues' experiment is shown in **FIGURE 13.15**. The team began with a population of roundworms that had not been exposed to the pathogen and that reproduced predominantly by self-fertilization. The researchers then split the starting population into different groups. Half the groups were grown in the presence of a pathogen—a deadly bacterium—and the other half were grown without it. Once ingested by a roundworm, the bacterial pathogen could kill a susceptible individual within 24 hours.

At each generation, bacteria were collected from the carcasses of roundworms killed in the previous generation. Companion experiments showed that the pathogen evolved to become even more infectious over the course of the study.

The results are shown at the bottom of Figure 13.15. The rate of outcrossing stayed low over 32 generations in populations that did not encounter the pathogen. In contrast, populations that were exposed to the evolving pathogen showed a rapid increase in the rate of outcrossing.

At the end of the experiment, the roundworms in the pathogen-exposed population were significantly more resistant to the evolved pathogen than their ancestors. In other words, the roundworms in the predominantly outcrossing population had evolved along with the pathogen. In striking contrast, when a parallel experiment was done with a strain of roundworms that could reproduce only by self-fertilization, those populations were unable to evolve resistance to the pathogen. In fact, they became extinct.

These results and many others support the changing-environment hypothesis. Although the paradox of sex remains an active area of research, more biologists are becoming convinced that sexual reproduction is helpful for two reasons: (1) Offspring are not doomed to inherit harmful alleles, and (2) the production of genetically varied offspring means that at least some may be able to resist rapidly evolving pathogens and parasites.

---

## CHAPTER 13   REVIEW

For media, go to MasteringBiology

### If you understand . . .

### 13.1   How Does Meiosis Occur?

- Meiosis is a nuclear division resulting in cells that have only one of each type of chromosome and half as many chromosomes as the parent cell. In animals it leads to the formation of eggs and sperm.

- In diploid ($2n$) organisms, individuals have two versions of each type of chromosome. The two versions are called homologs. One homolog is inherited from the mother and one from the father. Haploid organisms ($n$) have just one of each type of chromosome.

- Each chromosome is replicated before meiosis begins. At the start of meiosis I, each chromosome consists of a pair of sister chromatids.

Homologous pairs of chromosomes synapse early in meiosis I, forming a bivalent—two closely paired homologous chromosomes. Non-sister chromatids undergo crossing over.

When crossing over is complete, the pair of homologous chromosomes is moved to the metaphase plate.

At the end of meiosis I, the homologous chromosomes are separated and distributed to two daughter cells. The daughter cells are haploid, because each receives one of each type of chromosome.

During meiosis II, sister chromatids separate and are distributed to two daughter cells.

From one diploid cell with replicated chromosomes, meiosis produces four haploid daughter cells with unreplicated chromosomes.

✓ You should be able to diagram a diploid cell with a homologous pair of chromosomes and show when in meiosis this cell produces haploid daughter cells. Be sure to show all chromatids.

## 13.2 Meiosis Promotes Genetic Variation

Each cell produced by meiosis receives a different combination of chromosomes. Because genes are located on chromosomes, each cell produced by meiosis receives a different complement of genes. The resulting offspring are genetically distinct from one another and from their parents.

When meiosis and outcrossing occur, the chromosome complements of offspring differ from one another and from their parents for three reasons:

1. Gametes receive a random assortment of maternal and paternal chromosomes when homologs separate in meiosis I. This is independent assortment.
2. Because of crossing over, each chromosome contains a random assortment of paternal and maternal alleles.
3. Outcrossing results in a combination of chromosome sets from different individuals.

✓ You should be able to draw a diploid cell with four chromosomes entering meiosis and illustrate (a) how different combinations of chromosomes can result from independent assortment; and (b) focusing on a single homologous pair, show how many recombinant chromosomes (chromosomes with mixtures of maternal and paternal segments) are produced when crossing over occurs once along this homologous pair.

## 13.3 What Happens When Things Go Wrong in Meiosis?

If mistakes occur during meiosis, the resulting egg and sperm cells may contain the wrong number of chromosomes. It is rare for offspring with an incorrect number of chromosomes to develop normally.

- Mistakes during meiosis lead to gametes and offspring with an abnormal number of chromosomes. Children with Down syndrome, for example, have an extra copy of chromosome 21.
- The leading hypothesis to explain meiotic mistakes is that they are accidental failures of homologous chromosomes or sister chromatids to separate properly during meiosis.

✓ Using pipe cleaners or spaghetti to model a homologous pair of chromosomes, you should be able to demonstrate (a) what happens if one pair of homologous chromosomes fails to separate at anaphase of meiosis I and (b) what happens if sister chromatids of one chromosome fail to separate at anaphase of meiosis II but later separate in a daughter cell.

## 13.4 Why Does Meiosis Exist?

- Asexual reproduction is much more efficient than sexual reproduction because all individuals produced asexually are capable of bearing progeny. With sexual reproduction, half the offspring (the males) are unable to bear progeny.
- The leading hypotheses to explain the existence of meiosis and sexual reproduction are that:

  1. parents can produce offspring that lack harmful alleles; and
  2. genetically diverse offspring are likely to include some that are better able to resist evolving pathogens and parasites.

✓ You should be able to predict whether, in species that alternate between asexual and sexual reproduction, sexual reproduction occurs during times when environmental conditions are stable or times when conditions change rapidly.

### MB MasteringBiology

1. **MasteringBiology Assignments**

**Tutorials and Activities** Asexual and Sexual Life Cycles; Genetic Variation from Sexual Recombination; Meiosis; Meiosis (1 of 3): Genes, Chromosomes, and Sexual Reproduction; Meiosis (2 of 3): The Mechanism; Meiosis (3 of 3): Determinants of Heredity and Genetic Variation; Meiosis Animation; Mistakes in Meiosis; Origins of Genetic Variation

**Questions** Reading Quizzes, Blue-Thread Questions, Test Bank

2. **eText** Read your book online, search, take notes, highlight text, and more.

3. **The Study Area** Practice Test, Cumulative Test, BioFlix® 3-D Animations, Videos, Activities, Audio Glossary, Word Study Tools, Art

## You should be able to . . .

1. In the roundworm *Ascaris*, eggs and sperm have two chromosomes, but all other cells have four. Observations such as this inspired which important hypothesis?
   a. Before gamete formation, a special type of cell division leads to a quartering of chromosome number.
   b. Before gamete formation, a special type of cell division leads to a halving of chromosome number.
   c. After gamete formation, half the chromosomes are destroyed.
   d. After gamete formation, either the maternal or the paternal set of chromosomes disintegrates.

2. What are homologous chromosomes?
   a. chromosomes that are similar in their size, shape, and gene content
   b. similar chromosomes that are found in different individuals of the same species
   c. the two "threads" in a replicated chromosome (they are identical copies)
   d. the products of crossing over, which contain a combination of segments from maternal chromosomes and segments from paternal chromosomes

3. What is a bivalent?
   a. the X that forms when chromatids from homologous chromosomes cross over
   b. a group of four chromatids produced when homologs synapse
   c. the four points where homologous chromosomes touch as they synapse
   d. the group of four genetically identical daughter cells produced by mitosis

4. What is an outcome of genetic recombination?
   a. the synapsing of homologs during prophase of meiosis I
   b. the new combination of maternal and paternal chromosome segments that results when homologs cross over
   c. the new combinations of chromosome segments that result when self-fertilization occurs
   d. the combination of a haploid phase *and* a diploid phase in a life cycle

5. What proportion of chromosomes in a human skin cell are paternal chromosomes?

6. Meiosis II is similar to _____.

7. Explain the relationship between homologous chromosomes and the relationship between sister chromatids.

8. Lay four pens and four pencils on a tabletop, and imagine that they represent replicated chromosomes in a diploid cell where $n = 2$. Explain the phases of meiosis II by moving the pens and pencils around. (If you don't have enough pens and pencils, use strips of paper or fabric.)

9. Meiosis is called a reduction division, but all the reduction occurs during meiosis I—no reduction occurs during meiosis II. Explain why meiosis I is a reduction division but meiosis II is not.

10. Dogs have 78 chromosomes in their diploid cells. If a diploid dog cell enters meiosis, how many chromosomes and chromatids will be present in each daughter cell at the end of meiosis I?

   a. 39 chromosomes and 39 chromatids
   b. 39 chromosomes and 78 chromatids
   c. 78 chromosomes and 78 chromatids
   d. 78 chromosomes and 156 chromatids

11. Triploid ($3n$) watermelons are produced by crossing a tetraploid ($4n$) strain with a diploid ($2n$) plant. Briefly explain why this mating produces a triploid individual. Why can mitosis proceed normally in triploid cells, but meiosis cannot?

12. Some plant breeders are concerned about the susceptibility of asexually cultivated plants, such as seedless bananas, to new strains of disease-causing bacteria, viruses, or fungi. Briefly explain their concern by discussing the differences in the genetic "outcomes" of asexual and sexual reproduction.

13. The gibbon has 44 chromosomes per diploid set, and the siamang has 50 chromosomes per diploid set. In the 1970s a chance mating between a male gibbon and a female siamang produced an offspring. Predict how many chromosomes were observed in the somatic cells of the offspring. Do you predict that this individual would be able to form viable gametes? Why or why not?

14. Meiosis results in a reassortment of maternal and paternal chromosomes. If $n = 3$ for a given organism, there are eight different combinations of paternal and maternal chromosomes. If no crossing over occurs, what is the probability that a gamete will receive *only* paternal chromosomes?
   a. 0; b. 1/16; c. 1/8; d. 1/3

15. Some researchers hypothesize that older women are less responsive to triggers of spontaneous abortion than younger women. How could the data shown in Figure 13.13, which graphs a mother's age versus the incidence of Down syndrome, be used to support this hypothesis?

16. A species of rotifer, a small freshwater invertebrate, abandoned sexual reproduction millions of years ago. A remarkable feature of the rotifer's life cycle is its ability to withstand extreme drying. When the rotifer's watery environment dries out, so does the rotifer, and it can be blown in the wind to a new environment. Once blown to water, the rotifer rehydrates and resumes an active life. A major pathogen of these rotifers is a species of fungus. Some scientists hypothesize that fungus-infected rotifers rid themselves of the pathogen when they dry.
   a. Design an experimental study to test this hypothesis.
   b. Provide an explanation for how these asexually reproducing rotifers are able to evade pathogens even though they are genetically identical.

# 14 Mendel and the Gene

**In this chapter you will learn how**

Mendel's principles can predict patterns of inheritance

*starting with* ↓

**Mendel's experimental system** 14.1

*then examining* ↓

**Experiments with a single trait** 14.2

**Experiments with two traits** 14.3

*explained by* ↓

**The principle of segregation**

*explained by* ↓

**The principle of independent assortment**

*expanding to* ↓

**The chromosome theory of inheritance** 14.4

*exploring* ↓

**Extensions to Mendel's principles** 14.5

*applied to* ↓

**Human inheritance** 14.6

Experiments on garden peas and sweet peas (shown here) helped launch the science of genetics.

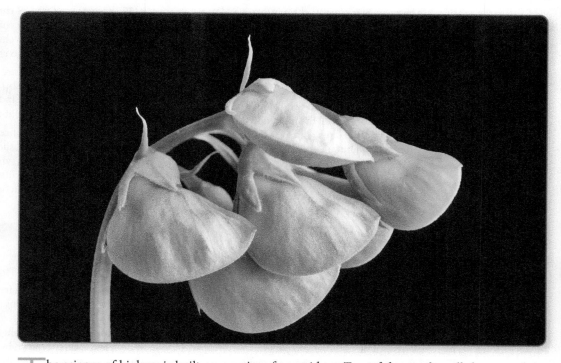

The science of biology is built on a series of great ideas. Two of these—the cell theory and the theory of evolution—were introduced in Chapter 1. The cell theory describes the basic structure of organisms; the theory of evolution by natural selection clarifies why species change through time. Life is cellular; populations evolve. These are two of the five fundamental attributes of life.

This chapter introduces a third great idea in biology: the chromosome theory of inheritance. The chromosome theory explained how genetic information is transmitted from one generation to the next. It shed light on a third fundamental attribute of life: Organisms process information.

**BIG PICTURE**

This chapter is part of the Big Picture. See how on pages 366–367.

✔ When you see this checkmark, stop and test yourself. Answers are available in Appendix A.

An Austrian monk named Gregor Mendel laid the groundwork for the theory in 1865, when he announced that he had worked out the rules of inheritance through a series of experiments on garden peas. Another key insight emerged during the final decades of the nineteenth century, when biologists described the details of meiosis (see Chapter 13).

The chromosome theory of inheritance, formulated in 1902 by Walter Sutton and Theodor Boveri, linked these two insights. This theory contends that meiosis causes the patterns of inheritance that Mendel observed. It also asserts that the hereditary factors called genes are located on chromosomes. (Genes determine inherited traits and are center stage in the Big Picture on pages 366–367.)

The chromosome theory launched the study of **genetics**, the branch of biology that focuses on the inheritance of traits. Let's start at the beginning: What are the rules of inheritance that Mendel discovered?

# 14.1 Mendel's Experimental System

When biological science began to emerge as an important discipline, questions about **heredity**—meaning inheritance, or the transmission of traits from parents to offspring—were primarily the concern of animal breeders and horticulturists. A **trait** is any characteristic of an individual, ranging from height to the primary structure of a particular membrane protein.

In the city where Gregor Mendel lived, there was particular interest in how selective breeding could result in hardier and more productive varieties of sheep, fruit trees, and vines; and an agricultural society had been formed there to promote research into making selective breeding more efficient. Mendel was an active member of this society, and the monastery he belonged to was also devoted to scientific teaching and research.

## What Questions Was Mendel Trying to Answer?

Mendel set out to address the most fundamental of all issues concerning heredity: What are the basic patterns in the transmission of traits from parents to offspring?

At the time, two hypotheses had been formulated to answer this question:

1. *Blending inheritance* claimed that the traits observed in a mother and father blend together to form the traits observed in their offspring. As a result, an offspring's traits are intermediate between the mother's and father's traits.

2. *Inheritance of acquired characters* claimed that traits present in parents are modified, through use, and passed on to their offspring in the modified form.

Each of these hypotheses made predictions. Blending inheritance contended that when black sheep and white sheep mate, their hereditary determinants will blend to form a new hereditary determinant for gray wool. Therefore, their offspring should be gray. Inheritance of acquired characters predicts that if giraffes extend their necks by straining to reach leaves high in the tops of trees, they subsequently produce longer-necked offspring.

These hypotheses were being promoted by the greatest scientists of Mendel's time. Are they correct?

## The Garden Pea Served as the First Model Organism in Genetics

After investigating and discarding several candidate species to study, Mendel chose the garden pea, *Pisum sativum*. His reasons were practical: Peas are inexpensive and easy to grow from seed, have a relatively short generation time, and produce reasonably large numbers of seeds. These features made it possible for him to continue experiments over several generations and collect data from large numbers of individuals.

Peas served as a **model organism:** a species that is used for research because it is practical and because conclusions drawn from studying it turn out to apply to many other species as well. **BioSkills 13** in Appendix B introduces some of the important model organisms used in biological science today.

Two additional features of the pea made it possible for Mendel to design his experiments: Individuals were available that differed in easily recognizable traits, such as flower color or seed shape, and he could control which parents were involved in a mating.

**How Did Mendel Control Matings?** **FIGURE 14.1a** shows the male and female reproductive organs of a garden pea flower. Sperm cells are produced in pollen grains, which are small sacs that

**(a)** Self-pollination

Female organ (receives pollen)

Male organs (produce pollen grains, which produce sperm cells)

Eggs

**(b)** Cross-pollination

Collect pollen from one individual and transfer it ...

... to the female organs of an individual whose male organs have been removed.

**FIGURE 14.1 Peas Can Be Self-Pollinated or Cross-Pollinated.**
**(a)** Under normal conditions, garden peas pollinate themselves.
**(b)** Mendel developed a method of controlling the matings of his model organism.

mature in the male reproductive structure of the plant. Eggs are produced in the female reproductive structure.

Under normal conditions, garden peas **self-fertilize:** a flower's pollen falls on the female reproductive organ of that same flower. As **FIGURE 14.1b** shows, however, Mendel could prevent self-fertilization by removing the male reproductive organs from a flower before any pollen formed. Later he could transfer pollen from another pea plant to the target flower's female reproductive organ with a brush. This type of mating is referred to as a cross-fertilization, or simply a **cross.** Using this technique, Mendel could control the matings of his model organism.

**What Traits Did Mendel Study?** Mendel conducted his experiments on varieties of peas that differed in seven traits: seed shape, seed color, pod shape, pod color, flower color, flower and pod position, and stem length. Biologists refer to the observable traits of an individual, such as the shape of a pea seed or the eye color of a person, as its **phenotype** (literally, "show-type"). Phenotype is just one term in the rich vocabulary of genetics. You

can review many of these terms in **TABLE 14.1**. In the first pea populations that Mendel studied, two distinct phenotypes existed for each of the seven traits.

Mendel began his work by obtaining individuals from what breeders called pure lines or true-breeding lines. A **pure line** consists of individuals that produce offspring identical to themselves when they are self-pollinated or crossed to another member of the pure-line population. For example, earlier breeders had developed pure lines for wrinkled seeds and round seeds. During two years of trial experiments, Mendel confirmed that individuals that germinated from his wrinkled seeds produced only wrinkled-seeded offspring when they were mated to themselves or to another pure-line individual that germinated from a wrinkled seed, and he confirmed that the same was true for round seeds.

Why is this important? Remember that Mendel wanted to find out how traits are transmitted from parents to offspring. Once he had confirmed that he was working with pure lines, he could compare the results of crosses within a pure line with crosses between individuals from different pure lines.

SUMMARY TABLE 14.1 **Vocabulary Used in Mendelian Genetics**

| Term | Definition | Example or Comment |
|---|---|---|
| Gene | A hereditary factor that influences a particular trait. | This definition will become more precise in later chapters. |
| Allele | A particular form of a gene. | The two alleles in a diploid may be the same or different. |
| Genotype | A listing of the alleles in an individual. | In diploids, the genotype lists two alleles of each gene; in haploids, the genotype lists one allele of each gene. |
| Phenotype | An individual's observable traits. | Can be observed at levels from molecules to the whole organism; influenced, not dictated, by the genotype. |
| Homozygous | Having two of the same allele. | Refers to a particular gene. |
| Heterozygous | Having two different alleles. | Refers to a particular gene. |
| Dominant allele | An allele that produces its phenotype in heterozygous and homozygous form. | Dominance does not imply high frequency or high fitness. |
| Recessive allele | An allele that produces its phenotype only in homozygous form. | Phenotype "recedes" or disappears in heterozygous individuals. |
| Pure line | Individuals of the same phenotype that, when crossed, always produce offspring with the same phenotype. | Pure-line individuals are homozygous for the gene in question. |
| Hybrid | Offspring from crosses between homozygous parents with different genotypes. | Hybrids are heterozygous. |
| Reciprocal cross | A cross in which the phenotypes of the male and female are reversed compared with a prior cross. | If reciprocal crosses give identical results, the sex of the parent does not influence transmission of the trait. |
| Testcross | A cross between a homozygous recessive individual and an individual with the dominant phenotype but an unknown genotype. | Usually used to determine whether a parent with a dominant phenotype is homozygous or heterozygous. |
| X-linked | Referring to a gene located on the X chromosome. | X-linked genes and traits show different patterns of inheritance in males and females. |
| Y-linked | Referring to a gene located on the Y chromosome. | In humans, Y-linked genes determine male-specific development. |
| Autosomal | Referring to a gene located on any non-sex chromosome (an autosome) or a trait determined by an autosomal gene. | Mendel studied only autosomal genes and traits. |

Suppose that Mendel arranged matings between a pure-line individual with round seeds and a pure-line individual with wrinkled seeds. He knew that one parent carried a hereditary determinant for round seeds, while the other carried a hereditary determinant for wrinkled seeds. But each offspring from this mating would contain both types of hereditary determinants. They would be **hybrids**—offspring from matings between true-breeding parents that differ in one or more traits.

Would these hybrid offspring have wrinkled seeds, round seeds, or a blended combination of wrinkled and round? What would the seed shape in subsequent generations be when hybrid individuals self-pollinated or were crossed with members of the pure lines?

## 14.2 Mendel's Experiments with a Single Trait

Mendel's first set of experiments consisted of crossing pure lines that differed in just one trait. This is an important research strategy in biological science: Start with a simple situation. Once you understand what's going on, you can consider more complex questions, such as, What happens in crosses between individuals that differ in two traits?

Mendel began his single-trait crosses by crossing individuals from round-seeded and wrinkled-seeded pure lines. The adults used in an initial experimental cross are the **parental generation**. Their progeny (that is, offspring) are the $F_1$ **generation**. $F_1$ stands for "first filial"; the Latin roots *filius* and *filia* mean "son" and "daughter," respectively. Subsequent generations are called the $F_2$ generation, $F_3$ generation, and so on.

### The Monohybrid Cross

In his first set of crosses, Mendel took pollen from round-seeded plants and placed it on the female reproductive organs of plants from the wrinkled-seeded line. As **FIGURE 14.2a** shows, all the seeds produced by progeny from this cross were round.

This was a remarkable result, for two reasons:

1. The traits did not blend together to form an intermediate phenotype. Instead, the round-seeded form appeared intact. This result was in stark contrast to the predictions of the blending-inheritance hypothesis shown in **FIGURE 14.2b**.

2. The genetic determinant for wrinkled seeds seemed to have disappeared. Where did it go?

**Dominant and Recessive Traits** To figure out what was going on, Mendel did something that turned out to be brilliant: He planted the $F_1$ seeds and allowed the individuals to self-pollinate when they matured.

Remember that he knew that each of these individuals had inherited a genetic determinant for round seeds and a genetic determinant for wrinkled seeds. A mating like this—between parents that each carry two different genetic determinants for the same trait—is called a **monohybrid cross**.

When he collected the seeds that were produced by many plants in the resulting $F_2$ generation, he observed that 5474 were round and 1850 were wrinkled (see Figure 14.2a). This observation was astonishing. The wrinkled seed shape had reappeared in the $F_2$ generation after disappearing completely in the $F_1$ generation. No one had observed the phenomenon before, simply because it had been customary for biologists to stop their breeding experiments with $F_1$ offspring.

Mendel invented some important terms to describe this result.

- He designated wrinkled shape as a **recessive** trait relative to the round-seed trait. This was an appropriate term because none of the $F_1$ individuals had wrinkled seeds—meaning the wrinkled-seed phenotype appeared to recede or temporarily become latent or hidden.

- He referred to round seeds as **dominant** to the wrinkled-seed trait. This term was apt because the round-seed phenotype appeared to dominate over the wrinkled-seed determinant when both were present.

It's important to note, though, that in genetics the term dominant has nothing to do with its everyday English usage as powerful

**(a)** Results of Mendel's single-trait (monohybrid) cross

Male parents
(produce round seeds)

× Female parents
(produce wrinkled seeds)

$F_1$ generation — All produce round seeds

Plant, grow, and allow to self-fertilize

$F_2$ generation

5474 : 1850
3 : 1

**(b)** Prediction of blending-inheritance hypothesis

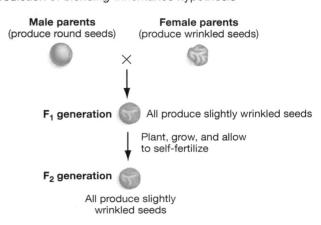

Male parents
(produce round seeds)

× Female parents
(produce wrinkled seeds)

$F_1$ generation — All produce slightly wrinkled seeds

Plant, grow, and allow to self-fertilize

$F_2$ generation — All produce slightly wrinkled seeds

**FIGURE 14.2 A Monohybrid Cross.** The results of Mendel's crosses involving a single trait **(a)** contrasted strongly with the predictions of the blending-inheritance hypothesis **(b)**.

superior. Subsequent research has shown that individuals with the dominant phenotype do not necessarily have higher fitness than individuals with the recessive phenotype. Nor are genetic determinants associated with a dominant phenotype necessarily more common than recessive ones. For example, a fatal illness—a type of brain degeneration called Huntington's disease—is caused by a rare, dominant genetic determinant. In genetics, the terms dominant and recessive identify *only* which phenotype is observed in individuals carrying two different genetic determinants for a given trait.

Mendel also noticed that the round and wrinkled seeds of the $F_2$ generation were present in a ratio of 2.96 : 1, or essentially 3 : 1. The 3 : 1 ratio means that for every four individuals, on average three had the dominant phenotype and one had the recessive phenotype. The results can also be stated in terms of frequencies or proportions: In this case, about ¾ of the $F_2$ seeds were round and ¼ were wrinkled.

**Reciprocal Cross** Mendel wanted to test the hypothesis that it mattered which parent and gamete type had a particular genetic determinant—that gender influenced the inheritance of seed shape. To do this, he performed a second set of crosses between two pure-breeding lines—this time with pollen taken from an individual from a pure line of wrinkled-seeded peas (**FIGURE 14.3**).

These experiments completed a **reciprocal cross**—a set of matings where the mother's phenotype in the initial cross is the father's phenotype in a subsequent cross, and the father's phenotype in the initial cross is the mother's phenotype in a subsequent cross.

In this case the results of the reciprocal crosses were identical: All the $F_1$ progeny had round seeds, just as in the initial cross. The reciprocal cross established that it does not matter whether the genetic determinants for seed shape are located in the male or female parent.

**Do Mendel's Results Hold for Other Traits?** Before he tried to interpret this pattern, it was important for Mendel to establish that the results were not restricted to inheritance of seed shape. So he repeated the experiments with each of the six other traits listed earlier. As **TABLE 14.2** shows, in each case, he obtained similar results:

---

**RESEARCH**

**QUESTION:** Is the inheritance of seed shape in peas affected by whether the genetic determinant is in a male or female gamete?

**HYPOTHESIS:** The type of gamete *does* affect the inheritance of seed shape.

**NULL HYPOTHESIS:** The type of gamete does *not* affect the inheritance of seed shape.

**EXPERIMENTAL SETUP:**

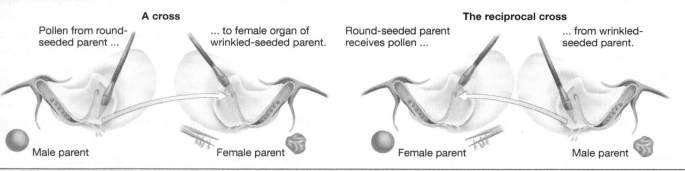

A cross

Pollen from round-seeded parent ...        ... to female organ of wrinkled-seeded parent.

Male parent        Female parent

The reciprocal cross

Round-seeded parent receives pollen ...        ... from wrinkled-seeded parent.

Female parent        Male parent

**PREDICTION OF "SEX MATTERS" HYPOTHESIS:** Offspring phenotypes will be different in the two crosses.

**PREDICTION OF NULL HYPOTHESIS:** Offspring phenotypes will be identical in the two crosses.

**RESULTS:**

Results are identical

**First cross:** All progeny have round seeds.        **Reciprocal cross:** All progeny have round seeds.

**CONCLUSION:** It makes no difference whether the genetic determinant for seed shape comes from the male gamete or from the female gamete.

**FIGURE 14.3 A Reciprocal Cross.**

SOURCE: Mendel, G. 1866. Versuche über Pflanzen-hybriden. *Verhandlungen des naturforschenden Vereines in Brünn.* 4: 3–47. English translation available from ESP: Electronic Scholarly Publishing (www.esp.org).

**✶QUESTION** Some people think that experiments are failures if the hypothesis being tested is not supported. What does it mean to say that an experiment failed? Was this experiment a failure?

**TABLE 14.2  F₂ Results from Mendel's Monohybrid Reciprocal Cross Experiments***

| Trait | Dominant Phenotype | Recessive Phenotype | Ratio |
|---|---|---|---|
| Seed shape | 5474 round | 1850 wrinkled | 2.96 : 1 |
| Seed color | 6022 yellow | 2001 green | 3.01 : 1 |
| Pod shape | 882 inflated | 299 constricted | 2.95 : 1 |
| Pod color | 428 green | 152 yellow | 2.82 : 1 |
| Flower color | 705 purple | 224 white | 3.15 : 1 |
| Flower and pod position | 651 axial | 207 terminal | ____ : ___ |
| Stem length | 787 tall | ____ dwarf | 2.96 : 1 |

*Mendel pooled the results from the reciprocal crosses for each trait because the results were the same whether the dominant trait originated from the male parent or the female parent.
DATA: Mendel, G. 1866. *Verhandlungen des naturforschenden Vereines in Brünn*. 4: 3–47.

✔**EXERCISE** Two entries in the last rows are left blank. Fill in these entries with the correct values calculated from the available data.

- The F₁ progeny showed only the dominant trait and did not exhibit an intermediate phenotype.
- Reciprocal crosses produced the same results.
- The ratio of F₂ generation individuals with dominant and recessive phenotypes was about 3 to 1.

How could these patterns be explained? Mendel answered this question with a series of propositions about the nature and behavior of the hereditary determinants. These hypotheses are considered some of the most brilliant insights in the history of biological science.

## Particulate Inheritance

Mendel's results were clearly inconsistent with either the hypothesis of blending inheritance or the hypothesis of acquired characters. To explain the patterns that he observed, Mendel proposed a competing hypothesis called **particulate inheritance.** He maintained that the hereditary determinants for traits do not blend together or become modified through use. In fact, hereditary determinants maintain their integrity from generation to generation. Instead of blending together, they act as discrete entities or particles.

Mendel's hypothesis was the only way to explain the observation that phenotypes disappeared in one generation and reappeared intact in the next. It also represented a fundamental break with ideas that had prevailed for hundreds of years.

**Genes, Alleles, and Genotypes**   Today, geneticists use the word **gene** to indicate the hereditary determinant for a trait. For example, the hereditary factor that determines whether the seeds of garden peas are round or wrinkled is referred to as the gene for seed shape.

Mendel also proposed that each individual can have two versions of any gene. Today different versions of the same gene are called **alleles.** Different alleles are responsible for the variation in the traits that Mendel studied. In the case of the gene for seed shape, one allele of this gene is responsible for the round form of the seed while another allele is responsible for the wrinkled form.

The alleles found in a particular individual are called the **genotype.** An individual's genotype has a profound effect on the phenotype—the observable physical traits.

The hypothesis that pea plants have two copies of each gene—either two of the same allele or two different alleles—was important because it gave Mendel a framework for explaining dominance and recessiveness. He proposed that some alleles are dominant and others are recessive. Recall that dominance and recessiveness determine which phenotype appears in an individual when two different alleles are present. In garden peas, the allele for round seeds is dominant; the allele for wrinkled seeds is recessive. Therefore, so long as one allele for round seeds is present, seeds are round. When both alleles present are for wrinkled seeds (thus no allele for round seeds is present), seeds are wrinkled.

These hypotheses explain why the wrinkled-seed phenotype disappeared in the F₁ generation. But why did wrinkled seeds reappear in the F₂, and why was there a 3:1 ratio of round and wrinkled seeds in the F₂ generation?

**The Principle of Segregation**   To explain the reappearance of the recessive phenotype and the characteristic 3:1 ratio of phenotypes in F₂ individuals, Mendel reasoned that the two members of each gene pair must segregate—that is, separate—into different gamete cells during the formation of eggs and sperm. As a result, each gamete contains one allele of each gene. This idea is called the **principle of segregation.**

To show how this principle works, Mendel used a letter to indicate the gene for a particular trait. For example, he used uppercase *R* to symbolize a dominant allele for seed shape and lowercase *r* to symbolize a recessive allele for seed shape. (Notice that the symbols for genes are always italicized.)

Using this notation, Mendel described the genotype of the individuals in the round-seed pure line as *RR* (having two of the dominant allele). The genotype of the wrinkled-seed pure line is *rr* (two of the recessive allele). Because *RR* and *rr* individuals have two copies of the same allele, they are said to be **homozygous** for the seed-shape gene (*homo* is the Greek root for "same," while *zygo* means "yoked"). Crosses of individuals from the same pure line always produce offspring with the same phenotype because they are homozygous—no other allele is present.

**FIGURE 14.4a** uses a diagram called a Punnett square to show what happened to these alleles when Mendel crossed the *RR* and *rr* pure lines. R. C. Punnett invented this straightforward technique for predicting the genotypes and phenotypes of different crosses years after Mendel published his work. According to Mendel's hypothesis, *RR* parents produce eggs and sperm that all carry the *R* allele, while *rr* parents produce gametes with the *r* allele only. When two gametes—one from each parent—come together at fertilization, they create offspring with the *Rr* genotype. Such individuals, with two different alleles for the same gene, are said to be **heterozygous** (*hetero* is the Greek root for "different"). Heterozygous individuals, or heterozygotes, show that the *R* allele is dominant because only the round phenotype is expressed even though the wrinkled allele is present.

Why do the two phenotypes appear in a 3 : 1 ratio in the $F_2$ generation? Mendel proposed that during gamete formation in the $F_1$ heterozygotes, the paired *Rr* alleles separate into different gamete cells. As a result, and as shown in the Punnett square of FIGURE 14.4b, half the gametes should carry the *R* allele and half should carry the *r* allele. A given sperm has an equal chance of fertilizing either an *R*-bearing egg or an *r*-bearing egg.

**Predicting Offspring Genotypes and Phenotypes with a Punnett Square** The box you've just studied in Figure 14.4b is an example of a simple Punnett square. To produce a Punnett square, follow these steps:

1. Write each of the *unique* gamete genotypes produced by one parent in a horizontal row along the top of the diagram.

2. Write each of the *unique* gamete genotypes produced by the other parent in a vertical column down the left side of the diagram.

3. Create a table under the horizontal row of gametes and to the right of the vertical column of gametes.

4. Fill in the table with the entries for the parental gamete genotypes that are written at the top and at the left side. This step represents fertilization and produces the offspring genotypes.

**(a) A cross between two homozygotes**

*R* = Dominant allele for seed shape (**round**)

*r* = Recessive allele for seed shape (**wrinkled**)

Offspring genotypes: All *Rr* (heterozygous)
Offspring phenotypes: All round seeds

**(b) A cross between two heterozygotes**

*R* = Dominant allele for seed shape (**round**)

*r* = Recessive allele for seed shape (**wrinkled**)

Offspring genotypes: ¼ *RR* : ½ *Rr* : ¼ *rr*
Offspring phenotypes: ¾ round : ¼ wrinkled

**FIGURE 14.4 Mendel Analyzed the $F_1$ and $F_2$ Offspring of a Cross between Pure Lines.** Notice that when you construct a Punnett square, you only need to list each unique type of gamete once at the head of a row or column. For example, even though the *RR* alleles segregate in the male parent of part (a), you have to list just one *R* gamete to represent the male's contribution, not two.

✔**QUESTION** In constructing a Punnett square, does it matter whether the male or female gametes go on the left or across the top? Why or why not?

5. Tally the proportions or ratios of each offspring genotype and phenotype.

✔ If you understand these concepts, you should be able to state how filling in the top and side of the Punnett square is related to the principle of segregation and predict the phenotype and genotype ratios for a cross between *Rr* and *rr* peas.

## SUMMARY TABLE 14.3 Mendel's Model to Explain the Results of a Cross between Pure Lines*

| Mendel's Claims | Comments |
|---|---|
| 1. Peas have two copies of each gene and thus may have two different alleles of the gene. | This also turns out to be true for many other organisms. |
| 2. Genes are particles of inheritance that do not blend together. | Genes maintain their integrity from generation to generation. |
| 3. Each gamete contains one copy of each gene (one allele). | This is because of the principle of segregation—the members of each gene pair segregate during the formation of gametes. |
| 4. Males and females contribute equally to the genotype of their offspring. | When gametes fuse, offspring acquire a total of two of each gene—one from each parent. |
| 5. Some alleles are dominant to other alleles. | When a dominant and a recessive allele for the same gene are found in the same individual (a heterozygote), that individual has the dominant phenotype. |

*Mendel did not use these modern terms. He expressed these ideas in different words.

## check your understanding

**If you understand that . . .**

- Mendel discovered that individuals have two alleles of each gene and that these alleles separate (segregate) into gametes. This is the principle of segregation.
- The alleles that Mendel analyzed were either dominant or recessive, meaning heterozygous individuals had the dominant phenotype.

✔ **You should be able to . . .**

Use the genetic problems at the end of this chapter to practice the following skills:

1. Starting with parents of known genotypes, create and analyze Punnett squares of crosses involving a single trait to predict the genotypes and phenotypes that will occur in their $F_1$ and $F_2$ offspring; then use the Punnett square to determine the expected frequency of each genotype and phenotype. (Do Problem 13 in Test Your Problem-Solving Skills.)

2. Given the outcome of a cross, infer the genotypes and phenotypes of the parents. (Do Problem 15 in Test Your Problem-Solving Skills.)

*Answers are available in Appendix A.*

As an example of the concluding step in analyzing a cross, the Punnett square in Figure 14.4b predicts that ¼ of the $F_2$ offspring will be $RR$, ½ will be $Rr$, and ¼ will be $rr$. Because the $R$ allele is dominant to the $r$ allele, ¾ of the offspring should be round-seeded (the sum of the $RR$ and the $Rr$ offspring) and ¼ should be wrinkled-seeded (the $rr$ offspring). These results are what Mendel found in his experiments with peas. In the simplest and most elegant fashion possible, Mendel's interpretation explains the 3 : 1 ratio of round to wrinkled seeds observed in the $F_2$ offspring and the mysterious reappearance of the wrinkled seeds.

The term genetic model refers to a set of hypotheses that explains how a particular trait is inherited. **TABLE 14.3** summarizes Mendel's model for explaining the basic patterns in the transmission of traits from parents to offspring; these hypotheses are sometimes referred to as Mendel's rules. They represent a radical break from the ideas of blending inheritance and the inheritance of acquired characters that had dominated scientific thinking about heredity.

## 14.3 Mendel's Experiments with Two Traits

Working with one trait at a time allowed Mendel to establish that blending inheritance does not occur. It also allowed him to infer that each pea plant had two copies of each gene and to recognize the principle of segregation.

Mendel's next step extended these results. The important question now was whether the principle of segregation holds true if individuals differ with respect to two traits, instead of just one. Do different genes segregate together, or independently?

### The Dihybrid Cross

Mendel crossed a pure-line parent that produced round, yellow seeds with a pure-line parent that produced wrinkled, green seeds. According to his model, the $F_1$ offspring of this cross should be heterozygous for both genes. A mating between two such individuals—both heterozygous for two traits—is called a **dihybrid cross.**

Mendel's earlier experiments had established that the allele for yellow seeds was dominant to the allele for green seeds; these alleles were designated $Y$ for yellow and $y$ for green. As **FIGURE 14.5** (see page 264) indicates, two distinct possibilities existed for how the alleles of these two different genes—the gene for seed shape and the gene for seed color—would be transmitted to offspring.

- The first possibility was that the allele for seed shape and the allele for seed color originally present in each parent would separate from each other and be transmitted independently. This hypothesis is called independent assortment because the two alleles would be sorted into gametes independently of each other (Figure 14.5a).

- The second possibility was that the allele for seed shape and the allele for seed color originally present in each parent

**(a) Hypothesis of independent assortment:**
Alleles of different genes don't stay together when gametes form.

**(b) Hypothesis of dependent assortment:**
Alleles of different genes stay together when gametes form.

*r* = Recessive allele for seed shape (**wrinkled**)

*y* = Recessive allele for seed color (**green**)

*R* = Dominant allele for seed shape (**round**)

*Y* = Dominant allele for seed color (**yellow**)

Female parent
*rryy*

Female gametes
*ry*

F₁

Male parent
*RRYY*

Male gametes
*RY*

*RrYy*

F₁ offspring all *RrYy*

Female parent
*rryy*

Female gametes
*ry*

F₁

Male parent
*RRYY*

Male gametes
*RY*

*RrYy*

F₁ offspring all *RrYy*

F₂ female parent
*RrYy*

Female gametes

F₂   ¼ *RY*   ¼ *Ry*   ¼ *rY*   ¼ *ry*

F₂ male parent
*RrYy*

Male gametes

| | ¼ RY | ¼ Ry | ¼ rY | ¼ ry |
|---|---|---|---|---|
| ¼ RY | *RRYY* | *RRYy* | *RrYY* | *RrYy* |
| ¼ Ry | *RRYy* | *RRyy* | *RrYy* | *Rryy* |
| ¼ rY | *RrYY* | *RrYy* | *rrYY* | *rrYy* |
| ¼ ry | *RrYy* | *Rryy* | *rrYy* | *rryy* |

F₂ female parent
*RrYy*

Female gametes

F₂   ½ *RY*   ½ *ry*

F₂ male parent

*RrYy*

Male gametes   ½ *RY*   ½ *ry*

| | ½ RY | ½ ry |
|---|---|---|
| ½ RY | *RRYY* | *RrYy* |
| ½ ry | *RrYy* | *rryy* |

F₂ offspring genotypes: ¼ *RRYY* : ½ *RrYy* : ¼ *rryy*
F₂ offspring phenotypes: ¾ ⬤ : ¼ ⬡

F₂ offspring genotypes:   ⁹⁄₁₆ *R–Y–* :   ³⁄₁₆ *R–yy* :   ³⁄₁₆ *rrY–* :   ¹⁄₁₆ *rryy*   — Dashes in a genotype mean that either allele can be present
F₂ offspring phenotypes:   ⁹⁄₁₆ ⬤ :   ³⁄₁₆ ⬤ :   ³⁄₁₆ ⬡ :   ¹⁄₁₆ ⬡

**(c) Mendel's results**

| **F₂ phenotypes** | ⬤ | ⬤ | ⬡ | ⬡ | 556 total |
|---|---|---|---|---|---|
| Number | 315 | 108 | 101 | 32 | |
| Fraction of offspring | ⁹⁄₁₆ | ³⁄₁₆ | ³⁄₁₆ | ¹⁄₁₆ | |

Data are consistent with the predictions of independent assortment.

**FIGURE 14.5 Mendel Analyzed the F₁ and F₂ Offspring of a Cross between Pure Lines for Two Traits.** Each of two hypotheses predicted a different pattern for the outcome when alleles of different genes are transmitted to offspring: **(a)** The alleles could be sorted into gametes independently of each other, or **(b)** particular alleles could always be transmitted together. **(c)** Mendel's results supported independent assortment.

would be transmitted to gametes together. This hypothesis can be called dependent assortment because the transmission of one allele would depend on the transmission of another (Figure 14.5b).

As Figure 14.5 shows, the $F_1$ offspring of Mendel's mating are expected to have the dominant round and yellow phenotypes whether the different genes are transmitted together or independently. When Mendel did the cross and observed the $F_1$ individuals, this is exactly what he found. All the $F_1$ offspring had round, yellow seeds.

The two hypotheses make radically different predictions, however, about what will be observed when the $F_1$ individuals are allowed to self-fertilize and produce an $F_2$ generation. If the alleles of different genes assort independently to form gametes, then each heterozygous parent should produce four different gamete genotypes, as shown in Figure 14.5a. A 4-row-by-4-column Punnett square results, and it predicts that there should be 9 different offspring genotypes and 4 phenotypes. Further, the yellow-round, green-round, yellow-wrinkled, and green-wrinkled phenotypes should be present in frequencies of $9/16$, $3/16$, $3/16$, and $1/16$, respectively. This is a ratio of $9:3:3:1$.

On the other hand, if the alleles from each parent stay together, then the prediction is for only three possible offspring genotypes and a $3:1$ ratio of two phenotypes—yellow-round or green-wrinkled—in the $F_2$, as Figure 14.5b shows.

When Mendel examined the phenotypes of the $F_2$ offspring, he found that they conformed to the predictions of the hypothesis of independent assortment. Four phenotypes were present in proportions that closely approximated the predicted ratio of $9:3:3:1$ (Figure 14.5c). On the basis of these data, Mendel accepted the hypothesis that alleles of different genes are transmitted independently of one another. This result became known as the **principle of independent assortment.**

✔ If you understand the principle of independent assortment, it should make sense to you that an individual with the genotype *AaBb* produces gametes with the genotypes *AB*, *Ab*, *aB*, and *ab*. You should be able to predict the genotypes of the gametes produced by individuals with the genotypes *AABb*, *PpRr*, and *AaPpRr*.

## Using a Testcross to Confirm Predictions

Mendel did experiments with combinations of traits other than seed shape and color and obtained results similar to those in Figure 14.5c. Each paired set of traits produced a $9:3:3:1$ ratio of progeny phenotypes in the $F_2$ generation. He even did a limited set of crosses examining three traits at a time. Although all these data were consistent with the principle of independent assortment, his most powerful support for the hypothesis came from a different type of experiment.

In designing this study, Mendel's goal was to test the prediction that an *RrYy* plant produces four different types of gametes in equal proportions. To accomplish this, Mendel invented a technique called a testcross. A **testcross** uses a parent that contributes only recessive alleles to its offspring and helps to determine the unknown genotype of the second parent.

Testcrosses are useful because the genetic contribution of the homozygous recessive parent is known. As a result, a testcross allows experimenters to test the genetic contribution of the other parent. If the other parent has the dominant phenotype but an unknown genotype, the results of the testcross allow researchers to infer whether that parent is homozygous or heterozygous for the dominant allele.

In this case, Mendel performed a cross between a parent that was homozygous for the recessive green and wrinkled phenotypes (*rryy*) and a parent that had an unknown genotype but was known from its yellow- and round-seeded phenotype to possess the dominant *R* and *Y* alleles. Two (of four) possible genotypes for this yellow- and round-seeded parent are *RrYy* and *RRYY*. The types and proportions of offspring that could result from a testcross involving *RrYy* or *RRYY* pea plants can be predicted with the Punnett square shown in **FIGURE 14.6** (see page 266). If the principle of independent assortment is valid, the testcross should produce four types of offspring in equal proportions if the tested parent is *RrYy*, and only one type of offspring if the tested parent is *RRYY*.

What were the actual proportions observed? Mendel did a testcross using the $F_1$ offspring of a pure line yellow-, round-seeded parent and a green-, wrinkled-seeded parent. These $F_1$ offspring were expected to have an *RrYy* genotype as shown in Figure 14.5a. When he examined the seeds produced by the testcross, Mendel found that among the 110 progeny, 31 were round

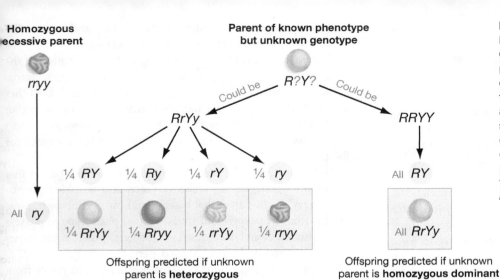

**FIGURE 14.6 The Predictions Made by the Principle of Independent Assortment Can Be Evaluated in a Testcross.** If the principle of independent assortment is correct, and *RrYy* parents produce four types of gametes in equal proportions, then a mating between *RrYy* and *rryy* parents should produce four types of offspring in equal proportions, as shown on the left. Test crosses can also reveal the genotype of a parent with dominant phenotypes, as seen in the example of different results obtained from *RrYy* and *RRYY* parental genotypes.

and yellow, 26 were round and green, 27 were wrinkled and yellow, and 26 were wrinkled and green. This is almost exactly ¼ of each type, which matched the predicted proportions for offspring of an *RrYy* parent. The testcross had confirmed the principle of independent assortment.

Mendel's work provided a powerful conceptual framework for thinking about transmission genetics—the patterns that occur as alleles pass from one generation to the next. This framework was based on (**1**) the segregation of discrete, paired genes into separate gametes, and (**2**) the independent assortment of genes that affect different traits.

The experiments you've just reviewed were brilliant in design, execution, and interpretation. Unfortunately, they were ignored for 34 years.

## 14.4 The Chromosome Theory of Inheritance

Historians of science debate why Mendel's work was overlooked for so long. It is probably true that his use of ratios and proportions were difficult for biologists of that time to understand and absorb. It may also be true that the theory of blending inheritance was so well entrenched that his results were dismissed as peculiar or unbelievable.

Whatever the reason, Mendel's work was not appreciated until 1900, when three biologists, working with a variety of plants and animals, independently "discovered" Mendel's work and reached the same main conclusions.

The rediscovery of Mendel's work more than three decades after its publication ignited the young field of genetics. Mendel's experiments had established the basic patterns of inheritance, but what process is responsible for these patterns? Two biologists, working independently, came up with the answer. Walter Sutton and Theodor Boveri each realized that meiosis could account for

Mendel's rules. When this hypothesis was published in 1902, research in genetics exploded.

## Meiosis Explains Mendel's Principles

What Sutton and Boveri grasped is that meiosis explains the principle of segregation and the principle of independent assortment. The cell at the top of **FIGURE 14.7** illustrates Sutton and Boveri's central insight: Mendel's hereditary determinants, or genes, are located on chromosomes. In this example, the gene for seed shape is shown at a particular position along a certain chromosome. This location is known as a **locus** ("place"; plural, **loci**).

The paternal and maternal chromosomes shown in Figure 14.7 happen to possess different alleles at the seed shape gene locus: One allele specifies round seeds (*R*) and the other specifies wrinkled seeds (*r*).

The subsequent steps in Figure 14.7 show how these alleles segregate into different daughter cells during meiosis I, when homologous chromosomes separate. The physical separation of alleles during anaphase of meiosis I is responsible for Mendel's principle of segregation.

**FIGURE 14.8** follows the segregation of two different gene pairs—in this case, for seed shape and seed color—as meiosis proceeds. If the alleles for different genes are located on different chromosomes, they assort independently of one another at meiosis I. This is the physical basis of Mendel's principle of independent assortment. Over many meiotic divisions, four types of gametes will be produced in equal proportions.

Sutton and Boveri formalized these observations in the **chromosome theory of inheritance.** Like other theories in biology, the chromosome theory describes a predictable pattern—a set of observations about the natural world—and a process that explains the pattern. The chromosome theory states that Mendel's rules can be explained by the independent alignment and separation of homologous chromosomes at meiosis I.

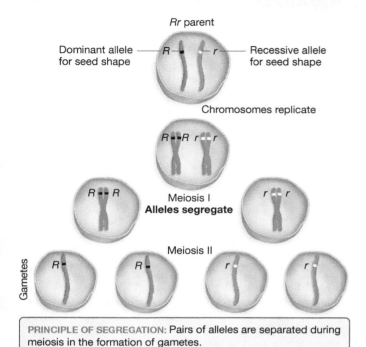

Rr parent

Dominant allele for seed shape — R ··· r — Recessive allele for seed shape

Chromosomes replicate

Meiosis I
**Alleles segregate**

Meiosis II

Gametes

PRINCIPLE OF SEGREGATION: Pairs of alleles are separated during meiosis in the formation of gametes.

**FIGURE 14.7 Meiosis Explains the Principle of Segregation.**
The two members of a parent's gene pair segregate into different gametes because homologous chromosomes separate during meiosis I.

When Sutton and Boveri published their ideas, however, the hypothesis that genes are located on chromosomes was untested. What experiments confirmed that chromosomes contain genes?

## Testing the Chromosome Theory

During the first decade of the twentieth century, an unassuming insect rose to prominence as a model organism for testing the chromosome theory of inheritance. This organism—the fruit fly *Drosophila melanogaster*—has been at the center of genetic studies ever since (see **BioSkills 13** in Appendix B).

*Drosophila melanogaster* has all the attributes of a useful model organism for studies in genetics: small size, ease of rearing in the lab, a short generation time (about 10 days), and abundant offspring (up to a few hundred per mating). The elaborate external anatomy of this insect also makes it possible to identify interesting phenotypic variation among individuals (**FIGURE 14.9a;** see page 268).

*Drosophila* was adopted as a model organism by Thomas Hunt Morgan and his students. But because *Drosophila* is not a domesticated species like the garden pea, common phenotypic variants such as Mendel's round and wrinkled seeds were not available to Morgan. Instead, he had access only to flies with the most common phenotype for each trait, phenotypes referred to as **wild type.** Consequently, an early goal of Morgan's research

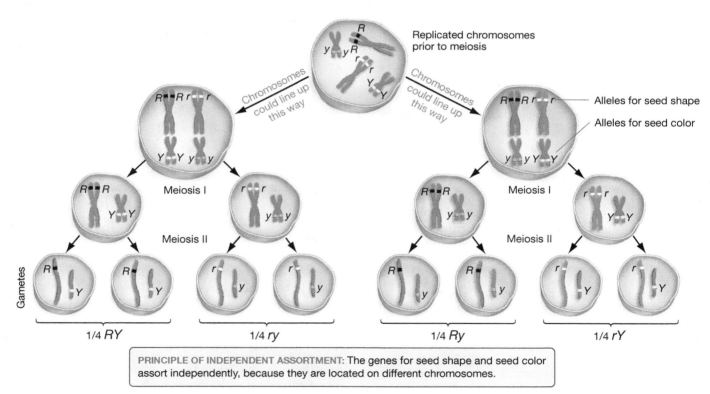

Replicated chromosomes prior to meiosis

Chromosomes could line up this way

Chromosomes could line up this way

Alleles for seed shape
Alleles for seed color

Meiosis I

Meiosis I

Meiosis II

Meiosis II

Gametes

1/4 *RY*          1/4 *ry*          1/4 *Ry*          1/4 *rY*

PRINCIPLE OF INDEPENDENT ASSORTMENT: The genes for seed shape and seed color assort independently, because they are located on different chromosomes.

**FIGURE 14.8 Meiosis Is Responsible for the Principle of Independent Assortment.** The genes for different traits assort independently because nonhomologous chromosomes assort independently during meiosis.

**(a)** The fruit fly *Drosophila melanogaster*

1 mm

**(b)** Eye color is a variable trait.

Wild type · Mutant

**FIGURE 14.9 The Fruit Fly *Drosophila melanogaster* Is an Important Model Organism in Genetics.**

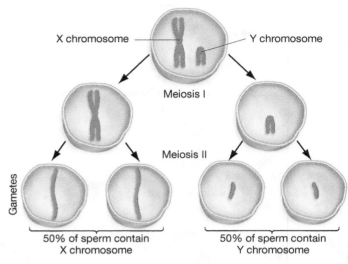

X chromosome · Y chromosome

Meiosis I

Meiosis II

Gametes

50% of sperm contain X chromosome · 50% of sperm contain Y chromosome

**FIGURE 14.10 Sex Chromosomes Pair during Meiosis I, Then Segregate in Males to Form X-Bearing and Y-Bearing Gametes.** Sex chromosomes synapse at meiosis I in male fruit flies because of a small, gene-free region shared by the X and Y chromosomes. This allows normal segregation, so half the sperm cells bear an X chromosome and half have a Y chromosome.

was simply to find and characterize individuals with different phenotypes to use in genetic studies.

**The White-Eyed Mutant** At one point, Morgan discovered a male fly that had white eyes rather than the wild-type red eyes (**FIGURE 14.9b**). Morgan inferred that the white-eyed phenotype resulted from a **mutation**—a heritable change in a gene. An individual with a phenotype due to a mutation is referred to as a **mutant.**

With his first mutant in hand, Morgan set out to explore how the eye-color trait was inherited. He mated a red-eyed female fly with the mutant white-eyed male fly. All the $F_1$ progeny had red eyes. By continued crosses, Morgan obtained white-eyed female flies. When he performed a reciprocal cross between a white-eyed female and a red-eyed male, he found something puzzling: All the $F_1$ females had red eyes, but all $F_1$ males had white eyes.

Recall that Mendel's reciprocal crosses had always given results that were similar to each other. But Morgan's reciprocal crosses did not. The experiment suggested a definite relationship between the sex of the progeny and the inheritance of eye color. What was going on?

**The Discovery of Sex Chromosomes** Nettie Stevens began studying the karyotypes of insects about the time that Morgan began his work with *Drosophila*. First, in the beetle *Tenebrio*

*molitor,* and later in other insects, including *Drosophila,* she noticed a striking difference in the chromosome complements of males and females.

Recall that Stevens and others discovered that there were sex chromosomes (the X and the Y) and autosomes (see Chapter 13). Female flies have a pair of X chromosomes and male flies have an X and a Y chromosome. Morgan's knowledge of Stevens' findings was the key to explaining his puzzling results and in providing support for the chromosome theory.

**Sex Linkage and the Chromosome Theory** Morgan realized that the transmission pattern of the X chromosome in males and females explained the results of his reciprocal crosses. He reasoned that half the gametes produced by males would contain an X chromosome and half a Y chromosome (**FIGURE 14.10**). Morgan proposed that the gene for eye color in fruit flies is located on the X chromosome and that the Y chromosome does not carry this gene.

This situation is described as **X-linked inheritance,** or simply **X-linkage.** Correspondingly, a gene residing on the Y chromosome is said to have **Y-linked inheritance,** or Y-linkage. The general term for inheritance of genes on either sex chromosome is **sex-linked inheritance,** or sex-linkage.

According to the hypothesis of X-linkage, a female fruit fly has two copies of the gene that specifies eye color because she has two X chromosomes. One of these chromosomes came from her female parent, the other from her male parent. A male, in contrast, has only one copy of the eye-color gene because he has only one X chromosome, inherited from his mother.

The Punnett squares in **FIGURE 14.11** show that Morgan's experimental results can be explained if the gene for eye color is located

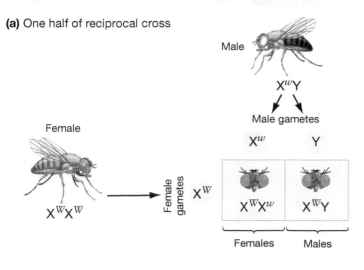

**(a)** One half of reciprocal cross

Male

$X^wY$

Male gametes

$X^w$    Y

Female

$X^WX^W$

Female gametes

$X^W$

|  | $X^w$ | Y |
|---|---|---|
|  | $X^WX^w$ | $X^WY$ |
|  | Females | Males |

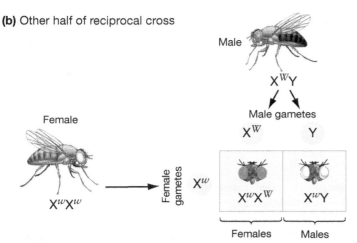

**(b)** Other half of reciprocal cross

Male

$X^WY$

Male gametes

$X^W$    Y

Female

$X^wX^w$

Female gametes

$X^w$

|  | $X^W$ | Y |
|---|---|---|
|  | $X^wX^W$ | $X^wY$ |
|  | Females | Males |

**FIGURE 14.11 Reciprocal Crosses Confirm that Eye Color in _Drosophila_ Is an X-Linked Trait.** When Morgan crossed red-eyed females with white-eyed males **(a)** and then crossed white-eyed females with red-eyed males **(b)**, he observed strikingly different results.

on the X chromosome, and if the allele for red color is dominant to the allele for white color. In this figure, the allele for red eyes is denoted $X^W$ while the allele for white eyes is denoted $X^w$. The Y chromosome present in males is simply designated by Y. Using this notation,[1] the genotypes used in the experiment are written as $X^WX^W$ for red-eyed females; $X^wY$ for white-eyed males; $X^wX^w$ for white-eyed females; and $X^WY$ for red-eyed males.

Notice how the symbol for _Drosophila_ alleles represents the mutant phenotype. Instead of showing alleles for the eye color gene with an _R_ for wild-type red eyes and an _r_ for mutant white eyes, the alleles are shown with a _W_ (red eyes) or a _w_ (white eyes).

---

[1]Scientific papers on fruit fly genetics use a different notation. The wild-type allele is designated with a superscript +, and no X is used for X-linked traits. The red-eye allele, for example, is denoted $w^+$; the white-eye allele _w_. The notation used here is simplified and conforms to conventions used in human genetics.

By applying the principles of segregation and random fertilization, you should see that the results predicted by the hypothesis of X-linkage match the observed results.

When reciprocal crosses give different results, such as those illustrated in Figure 14.11, it is likely that the gene in question is located on a sex chromosome—it is sex-linked. Recall that non-sex chromosomes are called autosomes (see Chapter 13). Genes on non-sex chromosomes are said to show **autosomal inheritance.**

Morgan's discovery of X-linked inheritance carried an even more fundamental message. In _Drosophila_, the gene for white eye color is clearly correlated with inheritance of the X chromosome. This correlation was important evidence in support of the hypothesis that chromosomes contain genes. The discovery of X-linked inheritance convinced most biologists that the chromosome theory of inheritance was correct.

## check your understanding

**(C)(Y)(U)**

**If you understand that . . .**

• Meiosis is the process responsible for Mendel's principle of segregation. It occurs because alleles on homologous chromosomes separate at anaphase of meiosis I.

• Meiosis is the process responsible for Mendel's principle of independent assortment. Alleles of different genes go to gametes independently because pairs of homologous chromosomes line up randomly at metaphase of meiosis I.

✔ **You should be able to . . .**

1. Draw the chromosomes involved in a cross between _Pp_ and _Pp_ peas, and use your diagram to explain the segregation of alleles.

2. Draw the chromosomes involved in a cross between _YyRr_ and _YyRr_ peas, and use your diagram to explain the independent assortment of alleles.

_Answers are available in Appendix A._

## 14.5 Extending Mendel's Rules

Biologists point out that Mendel analyzed the simplest possible genetic system. The traits that he was studying were not sex-linked. Moreover, they were influenced by just two alleles of each gene, and each allele was completely dominant or recessive.

With this well-chosen model system, Mendel was able to discover the most fundamental rules of inheritance. Mendel probably would have failed, as so many others had done before him, had he been trying to analyze more complex patterns of inheritance.

Once Mendel's work was rediscovered, researchers began to analyze traits and alleles whose inheritance was more complicated.

If experimental crosses produced $F_2$ progeny that did not conform to the expected 3:1 or 9:3:3:1 ratios, researchers had a strong hint that something interesting was going on. The discovery of sex-linkage is a prominent example. How can other traits that don't appear to follow Mendel's rules contribute to a more complete understanding of heredity?

## Linkage: What Happens When Genes Are Located on the Same Chromosome?

Once the chromosome theory had been tested and supported, biologists began to reevaluate Mendel's principle of independent assortment. It seemed unlikely that genes on the same chromosome would assort independently.

**Linkage** is the tendency of particular alleles of different genes to be inherited together. Linkage is seen when genes are on the same chromosome. Notice that the terms linkage and sex-linkage have different meanings. If genes are linked, it means that they are located on the same chromosome. If a gene is sex-linked, it means that it is located on a sex chromosome but says nothing about its location relative to other genes.

The first examples of linked genes were those on the X chromosome of fruit flies. After Morgan established that the *white-eye* gene was located on *Drosophila*'s X chromosome, he and colleagues established that one of the several genes that affects body color is also located on the X. Red eyes and gray body are the wild-type phenotypes; white eyes and a yellow body occur as rare mutant phenotypes. The alleles for red eyes ($X^W$) and gray body ($X^Y$) are dominant to the alleles for white eyes ($X^w$) and yellow body ($X^y$). (Be sure not to confuse the notation for the Y chromosome in males, Y, with the gray body allele, $X^Y$.)

**Linked Genes Do Not Assort Independently** Because linked genes are located on the same chromosome, it is logical to predict that they should always be transmitted together during gamete formation. Stated another way, linked genes should violate the principle of independent assortment.

Recall from Section 14.4 that genes on different chromosomes show independent assortment because different chromosomes assort independently during meiosis I. How will the X-linked body-color and eye-color genes be inherited? **FIGURE 14.12** shows a cell of a female fruit fly with one X chromosome carrying the white eye and gray body alleles, written $X^{wY}$, and the homologous X chromosome carrying the red eye and yellow body alleles, written $X^{Wy}$. This female would be expected to generate just two classes of gametes in equal numbers during meiosis, instead of the four classes that are predicted under the principle of independent assortment. Is this what actually occurs?

**The Role of Crossing Over** To determine whether linked traits always stay linked, Morgan performed crosses like the one described in the "Experimental Setup" section of **FIGURE 14.13**. In this case, $X^{wY}X^{Wy}$ females mated with $X^{wY}Y$ males.

The "Results" table in Figure 14.13 summarizes the phenotypes and genotypes observed in this experimental cross.

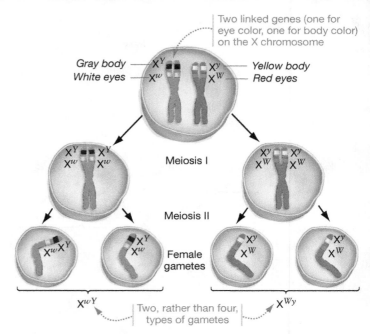

**FIGURE 14.12 Linked Genes Are Often Inherited Together.** If the eye-color and body-color genes were found on different chromosomes, then this female would generate four different types of gametes instead of just two types as shown here.

✔ **EXERCISE** List the four genotypes that would be generated if the white-eye and yellow-body genes were not linked.

Morgan recorded results only from male offspring. By doing this he could figure out which X-linked alleles were present on the chromosomes produced during meiosis in the mother. Since there is a single X chromosome in the male offspring, the phenotype associated with any X-linked allele, dominant or recessive, is expressed:

- Most of these males carried an X chromosome with one of the two combinations of alleles found in the chromosomes of their mothers: $X^{wY}$ or $X^{Wy}$.

- A small percentage of males had novel combinations of phenotypes and genotypes: $X^{wy}$ and $X^{WY}$. Morgan referred to these individuals as **recombinant** because the combination of alleles on their X chromosome was different from the combinations of alleles present in their mother.

Morgan concluded that alleles on the same chromosome don't always stay together. To explain the recombinant phenotypes, Morgan proposed that gametes with new combinations of alleles were generated when crossing over occurred during prophase of meiosis I in the females.

Recall that crossing over involves a physical exchange of segments of non-sister chromatids between homologous chromosomes (see Chapter 13). Crossing over typically occurs at least once in every synapsed pair of homologous chromosomes, and usually multiple times. (Male fruit flies are an exception to this rule. For unknown reasons, no crossing over occurs in male fruit flies.)

**QUESTION:** Will genes undergo independent assortment if they are on the same chromosome?

**LINKAGE HYPOTHESIS:** Linked genes will violate the principle of independent assortment.

**NULL HYPOTHESIS:** Linked genes will adhere to the principle of independent assortment.

**EXPERIMENTAL SETUP:**

Red-eyed gray-bodied female
$X^{wY}X^{Wy}$

White-eyed gray-bodied male
$X^{wY}Y$

**PREDICTION:** Because these two genes are X-linked, male offspring will have only one copy of each gene, from their mother; the two possible male offspring genotypes are $X^{wY}Y$ and $X^{Wy}Y$.

**PREDICTION OF NULL HYPOTHESIS:** Four male genotypes are possible ($X^{wY}Y : X^{Wy}Y : X^{wy}Y : X^{WY}Y$) and will occur with equal frequency.

**RESULTS:**

**Male offspring**

| | Phenotype | Genotype | Number | |
|---|---|---|---|---|
| | | $X^{wY}Y$ | 4292 | Four male genotypes were observed (rather than two), but not the equal frequencies predicted by independent assortment |
| | | $X^{Wy}Y$ | 4605 | |
| Recombinant genotypes | | $X^{wy}Y$ | 86 | |
| | | $X^{WY}Y$ | 44 | |

**CONCLUSION:** Neither hypothesis is fully supported. Independent assortment does not apply to linked genes—linked genes segregate together except when crossing over and genetic recombination have occurred.

**FIGURE 14.13 Linked Genes Are Inherited Together Unless Recombination Occurs.**

SOURCE: Morgan, T. H. 1911. An attempt to analyze the constitution of the chromosomes on the basis of sex-limited inheritance in *Drosophila*. *Journal of Experimental Zoology* 11: 365–414.

✔**QUESTION** Why didn't Morgan observe equal numbers of white-eyed, yellow-bodied males and red-eyed, gray-bodied males?

As **FIGURE 14.14** shows, a crossover between the eye-color and body-color genes in the $X^{wY}X^{Wy}$ females can explain the recombinant gametes. Male progeny produced from fertilization with these gametes are predicted to have either yellow bodies and white eyes or gray bodies and red eyes. This is what Morgan observed.

Notice, however, that the results of Figure 14.14 don't fit either the model of independent assortment or complete linkage. Independent assortment predicts a 1:1:1:1 ratio of all four

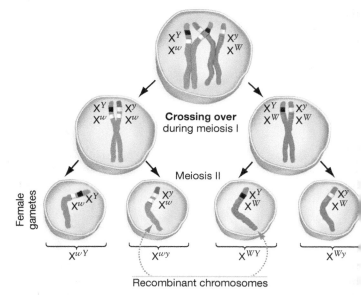

**Crossing over** during meiosis I

Meiosis II

Female gametes

$X^{wY}$   $X^{wy}$   $X^{WY}$   $X^{Wy}$

Recombinant chromosomes

**FIGURE 14.14 Genetic Recombination Results from Crossing Over.** To explain the results in Figure 14.13, Morgan proposed that crossing over occurred between the body color (*y*) and eye color (*w*) genes in a small percentage of meiotic divisions in the female parent. The recombinant chromosomes that resulted would produce the recombinant phenotypes observed in the male offspring.

combinations of phenotypes, while complete linkage would give only the two phenotypes associated with the nonrecombinant or parental chromosomes. Instead, most flies have parental phenotypes and a smaller number have recombinant phenotypes.

As **Quantitative Methods 14.1** (see page 274) explains, the percentage of recombinant offspring that occur in crosses like the one diagrammed in Figure 14.14 can be used to estimate the relative distance between genes. The reasoning is that the farther genes are apart on the same chromosome, the more likely it is that a crossover will occur someplace between these genes. Data on the frequency of crossing over between many genes on the same chromosome can be used to create a **genetic map**—a diagram showing the relative positions of genes along a particular chromosome.

Knowing a gene's locus relative to others can be very useful. An important example is genes involved in human genetic diseases. Most of these genes have been identified on the basis of mapping their location relative to other known genes.

The take-home message of Morgan's experiments is simple: Linked genes are inherited together unless crossing over occurs between them. When crossing over takes place, genetic recombination occurs. Linkage is an important exception to Mendel's rules.

## How Many Alleles Can a Gene Have?

Mendel worked with genes that each had two alleles. In most populations, however, it's not unusual to find dozens of alleles of a single gene. The existence of more than two alleles of the same gene is known as **multiple allelism**. When you consider that

| Product of $I^A$ allele | Product of $I^B$ allele | Product of $i$ allele |

ycoproteins
plasma
embrane of
d blood cells

enotype    $I^AI^A$    $I^AI^B$    $I^BI^B$       $I^Ai$   $I^Bi$   $ii$

ood type        A       AB        B           A      B     O

GURE 14.15 Phenotypes Produced by Alleles Responsible for
3O Blood Types. Alleles $I^A$ and $I^B$ produce a phenotype called
3 when paired with each other in heterozygotes. Both $I^A$ and
produce a dominant phenotype when paired with allele $i$. The
fferent colored hexagons on the products of the $I^A$ and $I^B$ alleles
present related but distinct sugars.

nes are made of DNA sequences that can change over time, the
ea of multiple alleles isn't surprising.

The ABO blood group types in humans are coded for by a
ne with three common alleles. The gene is known as $I$, and it
is $I^A$, $I^B$, and $i$ alleles. As the number of alleles for a gene in-
eases, the number of possible genotypes rises sharply. When
ore than two distinct phenotypes are present in a population
ving to multiple allelism, the trait is **polymorphic** ("many-
rmed"). ABO blood type is a polymorphic trait.

Each $I$ gene allele controls the production of a different poly-
ccharide attached to a glycoprotein (see Chapter 5) found in
e plasma membrane of red blood cells. The $I^A$ and $I^B$ alleles
de for different forms of an enzyme that adds a different sugar
the end of a core polysaccharide. The $i$ allele codes for a non-
nctional form of this enzyme, so no sugar is added to the core
lysaccharide. ABO blood group types are important in blood
ansfusions. Some mismatches of blood type between a donor
d recipient are tolerated, but others can cause fatal reactions.

The type of polysaccharide associated with each allele is
own in **FIGURE 14.15** along with all possible genotypes and phe-
otypes. As you can see, there are six possible genotypes for the
ree alleles of the $I$ gene. The $I^A$ allele codes for the type A poly-
ccharide, and the $I^B$ allele codes for the type B polysaccharide.
/hat happens in a person with both alleles?

## re Alleles Always Dominant or Recessive?

he terms dominant and recessive describe which phenotype is ob-
erved when two different alleles of a gene occur in a heterozygous
dividual. In all traits that Mendel studied, only the phenotype as-
ociated with one allele—the "dominant" one—appeared in hetero-
gotes. However, not all combinations of alleles work this way.

**Codominance** Many alleles show a relationship that is called
**codominance.** The type AB blood group shown in Figure 14.15
is an example of codominance. In this case, an AB heterozygote
expresses both the A and the B polysaccharides together on the
surface of red blood cells. This is the essence of codominance—
the simultaneous expression of the phenotype associated with
each allele in a heterozygote. An AB individual expresses both
the A and the B phenotypes.

The three alleles of the ABO blood group system illustrate another interesting point—alleles of one gene can show more than
one form of dominance. Notice in Figure 14.15 that the $I^A$ and $I^B$
alleles are both completely dominant to the $i$ allele while the $I^A$
and $I^B$ alleles are codominant with each other.

**Incomplete Dominance** Complete dominance and codominance are not the end of the story. Consider the flowers called
four-o'clocks, pictured in **FIGURE 14.16a**. Plant breeders have developed a pure line that has red flowers and a pure line that has
white flowers. When individuals from these strains are mated, all
their offspring are pink (**FIGURE 14.16b**). In Mendel's peas, crosses
between dominant and recessive parents produced only offspring
with the dominant phenotype. Why the difference?

Biologists answered this question by allowing the pink flow-
ered $F_1$ plants to self-fertilize and examining the phenotypes of
$F_2$ four-o'clocks. Of the $F_2$ plants, ¼ have red flowers, ½ have
pink flowers, and ¼ have white flowers. This 1:2:1 ratio of
phenotypes exactly matches the 1:2:1 ratio of genotypes that
is produced when flower color is controlled by one gene with
two alleles.

To convince yourself that this explanation is sound, study
the genetic model shown in Figure 14.16b. According to the
diagram, the pattern of inheritance of flower color genotypes
in four-o'clocks and peas is identical, but the four-o'clock alleles show a different form of dominance known as **incomplete
dominance.**

When incomplete dominance occurs, heterozygotes have a
phenotype that is between the two different homozygous parents. In the case of four-o'clocks, neither red nor white alleles
dominate. Instead, the heterozygous $F_1$ progeny show a phenotype in between the two parental strains.

By this point, it should be clear that the answer to the question of whether alleles are always dominant or recessive is a
resounding no. Instead, there are three possible dominance relationships between different alleles: complete, incomplete, and
codominance.

## Does Each Gene Affect Just One Trait?

Mendel's results led him to hypothesize that one gene influences
one trait. The gene for seed color in garden peas, for example, did
not appear to affect other aspects of the individual's phenotype.
In reality, however, many genes influence more than one trait.

A gene that influences many traits is said to be **pleiotropic**
("more-turning"). For example, mutations in one gene, *FBN1*,
cause Marfan syndrome in humans. In this case the mutant

**(a)** Flower color is variable in four-o'clocks.

**(b)** Incomplete dominance in flower color

**FIGURE 14.16 When Incomplete Dominance Occurs, Heterozygotes Have Intermediate Phenotypes.** The cross in part (b) is explained by hypothesizing that a single gene influences flower color and that alleles *R* and *r* exhibit incomplete dominance.

*FBN1* allele is dominant to the wild-type allele. What is the phenotype of an individual with a mutant *FBN1* allele?

People with a mutant *FBN1* allele are tall, have disproportionately long limbs and fingers and an abnormally shaped chest, and often have severe heart problems. Therefore, the gene associated with Marfan syndrome influences many traits and is pleiotropic. On the basis of this set of phenotypes, many medical scientists believe Abraham Lincoln had Marfan syndrome.

## Is There More to Phenotype than Genotype?

After analyzing the results of Mendel's experiments, it would be tempting to conclude that *R* alleles dictate that seeds are round and *T* alleles dictate that individual plants are tall—that there is a strict correspondence between alleles and phenotypes.

It's important to recognize, though, that when Mendel analyzed height in his experiments, he ensured that each plant received a similar amount of sunlight and grew in similar soil. This was critical because even individuals with alleles for tallness will be stunted if they are deprived of nutrients, sunlight, or water—so much so that they look similar to individuals with alleles for dwarfing. Mendel also worked with pure lines that had been inbred for many generations. This breeding method reduces the genetic variation in each line.

For Mendel to analyze the hereditary determinants of height, he had to control the environmental determinants of height. Let's consider how the environment and alleles at other gene loci affect phenotype.

**The Environment Affects Phenotypes** The phenotypes produced by most genes are strongly affected by the individual's environment. Consequently, an individual's phenotype is often as much a product of the environment as it is a product of the genotype. Environmental influences include temperature, sunlight, nutrient availability, competition, and even a mother's hormone levels during development of an embryo. To capture this point, biologists refer to the combined effect of genes and environment as gene-by-environment interaction.

Gene-by-environment interactions have a profound effect on how physicians treat people with the genetic disease phenylketonuria (PKU). These individuals are homozygous for a recessive allele of an enzyme-coding gene. The enzyme helps convert the amino acid phenylalanine to the amino acid tyrosine. In PKU this enzyme is absent and, as a result, phenylalanine and a related molecule, phenylpyruvic acid, accumulate. These compounds interfere with the development of the nervous system and produce severe mental retardation.

But are people without the ability to metabolize phenylalanine genetically fated to mental retardation?

In many countries, newborns are routinely tested for the defect. If identified at birth, individuals with PKU can be placed on a low-phenylalanine diet. The change in environment—reduced phenylalanine in the diet—has a dramatic influence on phenotype. Treated individuals develop normally. PKU is a genetic disease, but by controlling the environment, it is neither inevitable nor invariant.

**Interactions Between Genes Affect Phenotypes** In Mendel's pea plants, there was a one-to-one correspondence between genes and traits. The pea seeds he analyzed were round or wrinkled regardless of the types of alleles present at other loci. Only one gene influenced each trait.

In many cases, however, different genes work together to control a single trait. Consider a classic experiment published in 1905 on comb shape in chickens. William Bateson and R. C. Punnett crossed parents from pure lines with comb shapes called rose and pea and found that the F₁ offspring had a new phenotype called walnut combs, a new phenotype not seen in either parent. When these individuals bred, their offspring had walnut, rose

**FIGURE 14.17 The Physical Distance between Genes Determines the Frequency of Crossing Over.** The arrows show that crossing over is possible at any point between the genes, but the chance of a crossover between a pair of genes increases when the distance between the genes is large.

In experiments like the one diagrammed in Figure 14.13, researchers calculate the recombination frequency as the number of offspring with recombinant phenotypes divided by the total number of offspring. With crosses involving the X-linked traits of white eyes and yellow bodies, 1.4 percent of offspring have recombinant phenotypes and genotypes.

But in crosses with different pairs of X-linked traits, the fraction of recombinant offspring varies, and this variation provides information on the relative distance separating linked genes. For example, in crosses of fruit flies with X-linked genes for white eyes and another mutant phenotype called singed bristles, recombinant phenotypes are seen 19.6 percent of the time.

To explain these observations, Alfred Sturtevant, an undergraduate student working with Morgan, proposed that the physical distance between genes determines how frequently crossing over occurs between them. His idea was that crossing over occurs at random and can take place at any location along a chromosome. The shorter the distance between a pair of genes, the lower the probability that crossing over will take place between them (**FIGURE 14.17**). Using this reasoning, he set out to create a genetic map.

To define the unit of distance on his genetic map, Sturtevant used the percentage of offspring that have recombinant phenotypes with respect to two genes. One map unit (later called 1 centiMorgan [cM]) is the physical distance that produces 1 percent recombinant offspring.

The eye-color and bristle-shape genes of fruit flies are 19.6 cM apart on the X chromosome, because recombination between these genes results in 19.6 percent recombinant offspring, on average. The genes for yellow body and white eye color, in contrast, are just 1.4 cM apart.

Where is the *yellow-body* gene relative to the *singed-bristles* gene? Twenty-one percent of the offspring were recombinant for these traits, meaning that the *yellow-body* and *singed-bristles* genes are 21.0 cM apart. Sturtevant inferred that the gene for white eyes must be located *between* the genes for yellow body and singed bristles, as shown in **FIGURE 14.18a**.

Mapping genes relative to one another is like fitting pieces into a puzzle: Placing *white* between *yellow* and *singed bristles* is the only way to make the distances between each pair sum correctly. The key observation is that 21.0 cM—the distance between *yellow* and *singed bristles*—is equal to 1.4 cM + 19.6 cM, or the sum of the distances between *yellow* and *white* and *white* and *singed bristles*.

**FIGURE 14.18b** provides a partial genetic map of the X chromosome in *Drosophila melanogaster*, along with the data used to establish the map positions. Using this logic and similar data, Sturtevant assembled the first genetic map.

---

**(a) Mapping genetic distance**

Frequency of recombinant offspring correlates directly with the distance between two genes; 19.6% recombinant offspring, for example, translates to 19.6 map units (centiMorgans, cM).

**(b) Constructing a genetic map**

| % Frequency of crossing over between some genes on the X chromosome of fruit flies | | |
|---|---|---|
| | Miniature Wings | Ruby Eyes |
| Yellow body | 36.1 | 7.5 |
| White eyes | 34.7 | 6.1 |
| Singed bristles | 15.1 | 13.5 |
| Miniature wings | — | 28.6 |

These distances are in cM

**FIGURE 14.18 The Locations of Genes Can Be Mapped by Analyzing the Frequency of Recombination. (a)** The *yellow body* gene is on the end of the fruit fly X chromosome. To explain the recombination frequencies observed in experimental crosses, the *yellow body, white eyes,* and *singed bristles* genes must be in the locations shown here. **(b)** A partial genetic map of the X chromosome in fruit flies.

✔**EXERCISE** In part (b), label the orange and blue genes. (Which is *ruby* and which is *miniature wings?*)

pea, and a fourth phenotype called single combs in a 9:3:3:1 ratio (**FIGURE 14.19a**).

The genetic model in **FIGURE 14.19b** shows how the interaction between two different genes that control one trait (comb shape) can account for the results. If comb morphology results from interactions between two genes (symbolized R and P), if a dominant and a recessive allele exist for each gene, and if the four comb phenotypes are associated with the genotypes indicated at the bottom of the figure, then a cross between *RRpp* and *rrPP* parents would give the results that Bateson and Punnett observed.

When gene-by-gene interactions occur, one trait is influenced by the alleles of two or more different genes. If a chicken has an *R* allele, its phenotype depends on the allele present at the *P* gene.

Gene-by-gene interaction is very common and has important implications in human genetics. Imagine that two people have the same genotype at one locus that increases risk for a heart disease. If there is gene-by-gene interaction, then the risk of developing heart disease also depends on the genotype at other loci. Even if they experience identical environments, these two people may have very different overall risks from genetic factors alone.

## Can Mendel's Principles Explain Traits That Don't Fall into Distinct Categories?

Mendel worked with **discrete traits**—traits that are clearly different from each other. In garden peas, seed color is either yellow or green—no intermediate phenotypes exist. But many traits in peas and other organisms don't fall into discrete categories. In humans, for example, height, weight, and skin color vary continuously. People are not limited to being either 160 cm tall or 180 cm tall—countless other heights are possible.

For height and many other characteristics, individuals differ by degree. These types of continuously varying traits that don't fall into discrete categories are called **quantitative traits.** Like discrete traits, quantitative traits are greatly influenced by the environment. The effects of nutrition on human height, intelligence, and disease resistance, for example, have been well documented.

Many quantitative traits share a common characteristic: When the frequencies of different trait values observed in a population are plotted on a histogram, or frequency distribution (see **BioSkills 3** in Appendix B), they often form a bell-shaped curve, or normal distribution (**FIGURE 14.20**).

In 1909 Herman Nilsson-Ehle had an important insight: If many genes each contribute a small amount to the value of a quantitative trait, then a normal distribution results for the population as a whole.

**(a)** Crosses between chickens with different comb phenotypes give odd results.

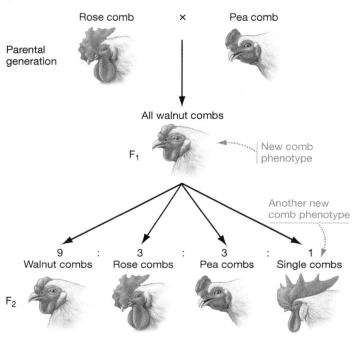

**(b)** A genetic model based on gene-by-gene interactions can explain the results.

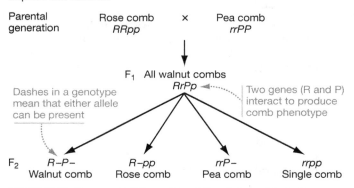

**FIGURE 14.19 Genes at Different Loci Can Interact to Influence a Trait. (a)** This cross is notable because new phenotypes show up in the F$_1$ and the F$_2$ generation. **(b)** To explain the results, researchers hypothesized that comb shape depends on two genes that interact. The phenotype associated with any one allele of one gene depends on the alleles at a second gene.

✔ **EXERCISE** What is different about the 9:3:3:1 ratio in the F$_2$ of this cross compared with the ratio observed in a standard dihybrid cross?

**FIGURE 14.20 Quantitative Traits Have a Normal Distribution.** A histogram showing the heights of first-grade schoolchildren in Guatemala in 2001.

DATA: Pan American Health Organization/WHO. 2004. *Epidemiological Bulletin* 25: 9-13, Graph 1.

**(a)** Wheat kernel color is a quantitative trait.

**(b)** Hypothesis to explain inheritance of kernel color

**FIGURE 14.21 Quantitative Traits Result from the Action of Many Genes. (a)** When wheat plants with white kernels were crossed with wheat plants with red kernels, the F₂ offspring showed a range of kernel colors. The frequency of these phenotypes approximates a normal distribution. **(b)** This model can explain the results of part (a). The bold numbers above each genotype match the numbers shown in part (a) and indicate the relative number of plants with each phenotype.

✓**QUESTION** Why are there fewer very dark or very light wheat kernels compared with kernels of intermediate coloration?

Nilsson-Ehle established this finding using strains of wheat that differed in kernel color. **FIGURE 14.21a** includes a histogram showing the distribution of F₂ phenotypes from a cross he performed between pure lines of white wheat and dark-red wheat. Notice that the frequency of colors in F₂ progeny approximates a bell-shaped curve. To explain these results, Nilsson-Ehle proposed the hypotheses illustrated in **FIGURE 14.21b**:

- The parental strains differ with respect to three genes that control kernel color: *AABBCC* produces dark-red kernels, and *aabbcc* produces white kernels.

- The three genes assort independently.

- The *a, b,* and *c* alleles do not contribute to pigment production, but the *A, B,* and *C* alleles contribute to pigment production in an equal and additive way. This is a form of incomplete dominance. As a result, the degree of red pigmentation is determined by the number of *A, B,* or *C* alleles present. Each uppercase (dominant) allele that is present makes a wheat kernel slightly darker red.

Later work supported Nilsson-Ehle's model. He did not have to propose any new genetic principles to explain the inheritance of a quantitative trait. All that was needed was extension of Mendel's hypotheses about segregation and independent assortment.

Quantitative traits are produced by the independent actions of many genes, although it is now clear that some genes have much greater effects on the trait in question than other genes do. As a result, the transmission of quantitative traits is said to result from polygenic ("many-genes") inheritance. In **polygenic inheritance,** each gene adds a small amount to the value of the phenotype.

In the decades immediately after the rediscovery of Mendel's work, the question of why offspring resemble their parents could be answered in more satisfying ways. **TABLE 14.4** summarizes some of the key exceptions and extensions to Mendel's rules and gives you a chance to compare and contrast their effects on patterns of inheritance.

check your understanding

(C)(Y)(U)

**If you understand that . . .**

- Genes near each other on the same chromosome violate the principle of independent assortment. They are not transmitted to gametes independently of each other unless crossing over occurs between them.
- Sex linkage, linkage, incomplete dominance, codominance, multiple allelism, pleiotropy, environmental effects, gene interactions, and polygenic inheritance are aspects of inheritance that Mendel did not study. When they occur, crosses do not result in classical Mendelian monohybrid or dihybrid ratios of offspring phenotypes.

✓ **You should be able to . . .**

Explain why the following crosses don't produce a 3 : 1 phenotype ratio in F₂ offspring:

1. Rose-comb × pea-comb chickens
2. Red-kernel × white-kernel wheat plants

*Answers are available in Appendix A.*

| Type of Inheritance | Definition | Consequences or Comments |
|---|---|---|
| Sex linkage | Genes located on sex chromosomes. | Patterns of inheritance in males and females differ. |
| Linkage | Two genes found on same chromosome. | Linked genes violate principle of independent assortment. |
| Incomplete dominance | Heterozygotes have intermediate phenotype. | Polymorphism—heterozygotes have unique phenotype. |
| Codominance | Heterozygotes have phenotype of both alleles. | Polymorphism is possible—heterozygotes have unique phenotype. |
| Multiple allelism | In a population, more than two alleles present at a locus. | Polymorphism is possible. |
| Polymorphism | In a population, more than two phenotypes associated with a single gene are present. | Can result from actions of multiple alleles, incomplete dominance, and codominance. |
| Pleiotropy | A single gene affects many traits. | This is common. |
| Gene-by-gene interaction | In discrete traits, the phenotype associated with an allele depends on which alleles are present at another gene. | One allele can be associated with different phenotypes. |
| Gene-by-environment interaction | Phenotype influenced by environment experienced by individual. | Same genotypes can be associated with different phenotypes. |
| Polygenic inheritance of quantitative traits | Many genes are involved in specifying traits that exhibit continuous variation. | Unlike alleles that determine discrete traits, each allele adds a small amount to phenotype. |

## 14.6 Applying Mendel's Rules to Human Inheritance

When researchers set out to study how a particular gene is transmitted in wheat or fruit flies or garden peas, they begin by making a series of controlled experimental crosses. For obvious reasons, this strategy is not possible with humans. But suppose you are concerned about an illness that runs in your family and go to a genetic counselor to find out how likely your children are to have the disease. To advise you, the counselor needs to know how the trait is transmitted, including whether the gene involved is autosomal or sex-linked and what type of dominance is associated with the disease allele.

To understand the transmission of human traits, investigators have to analyze human genotypes and phenotypes that already exist. A **mode of transmission** describes a trait as autosomal or sex-linked and gives the type of dominance of the allele. To learn the mode of transmission, scientists construct a **pedigree,** or family tree, of affected and unaffected individuals. By analyzing pedigrees, biomedical researchers have been able to discover how more than 2000 human genetic diseases are inherited.

A pedigree records the genetic relationships between the individuals in a family along with each person's sex and phenotype with respect to the trait in question. If the trait is governed by a single gene, then analyzing the pedigree may reveal whether a given phenotype is due to a dominant or recessive allele and whether the gene responsible is located on a sex chromosome or

on an autosome. Let's look at a series of specific case histories to see how this work is done.

### Identifying Human Alleles as Recessive or Dominant

To analyze the inheritance of a discrete trait, biologists begin by assuming that a single autosomal gene is responsible and that the alleles present in the population have a simple dominant–recessive relationship.

This is the simplest possible situation. If the pattern of inheritance fits this model, then the assumptions—of inheritance by a single autosomal gene and simple dominance—are supported. Let's first analyze the pattern of inheritance that is typical of autosomal recessive traits and then examine patterns that emerge in pedigrees for autosomal dominant traits.

**Patterns of Inheritance: Autosomal Recessive Traits** If a phenotype is due to an autosomal recessive allele, then

- Individuals with the trait must be homozygous.
- If the parents of an affected individual do not have the trait, then the parents are heterozygous for the trait.

Heterozygous individuals who carry a recessive allele for an inherited disease are referred to as **carriers** of the disease. These individuals carry the allele and may transmit it even though they do not exhibit signs of the disease. When two carriers mate,

**(a)** Autosomal recessive trait (e.g., sickle-cell disease)

**(b)** Autosomal dominant trait (e.g., Huntington's disease)

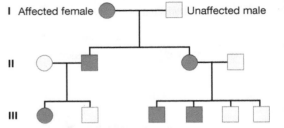

**CHARACTERISTICS:**
- Males and females are equally likely to be affected
- Affected offspring often have unaffected parents
- Unaffected parents of affected offspring are heterozygous (carriers)
- Affected offspring are homozygous
- If both parents are heterozygous, about ¼ of the offspring will be affected
- Trait often skips generations

**CHARACTERISTICS:**
- Males and females are equally likely to be affected
- Affected offspring have at least one affected parent
- Affected offspring are heterozygous if only one parent is affected
- Unaffected offspring are homozygous recessive
- If one parent is heterozygous, about ½ of the offspring will be affected
- Trait does not skip generations

**FIGURE 14.22 Pedigrees of Families with Autosomal Recessive and Autosomal Dominant Traits.** Pedigrees use standard symbols: squares = males, circles = females; unfilled symbols = unaffected individuals (those without the trait), filled symbols = affected individuals, half-filled symbols = heterozygotes for a recessive trait (carriers); horizontal lines connect parents, vertical lines connect parents to children.

about ¼ of their offspring are expected to express the recessive phenotype.

**FIGURE 14.22a** is a pedigree from a family in which an autosomal recessive trait, such as sickle-cell disease, occurs. The key feature to notice in this pedigree is that both boys and girls can exhibit the trait even though their parents do not. This is the pattern you would expect when the parents of an individual with the trait are heterozygous. It is also logical to observe that when an affected (homozygous) individual has children, those children do not necessarily have the trait. This pattern is predicted if affected people marry individuals who are homozygous for the dominant allele. This is likely to occur if the recessive allele is rare in the population.

In general, a recessive phenotype should show up in offspring only when both parents have that recessive allele and pass it on to their offspring. By definition, a recessive allele produces a given phenotype only when the individual is homozygous for that allele.

**Patterns of Inheritance: Autosomal Dominant Traits** When a trait is autosomal dominant, individuals who are homozygous or heterozygous for it must have the dominant phenotype. Even if one parent is heterozygous and the other is homozygous recessive, on average half their children should show the dominant phenotype. And unless a new mutation has occurred in a gamete, any child with the trait must have a parent with this trait. The latter observation is in strong contrast to the pattern seen in autosomal recessive traits.

**FIGURE 14.22b** shows the inheritance of the degenerative brain disorder called Huntington's disease (see Section 14.2). This pedigree has two features that indicate Huntington's disease is passed to the next generation through an autosomal dominant allele.

First, if a child shows the trait, then one of its parents shows the trait as well. Second, if families have a large number of children, the trait usually shows up in every generation—owing to the high probability of heterozygous parents having affected children.

## Identifying Human Traits as Autosomal or Sex-Linked

When it is not possible to arrange reciprocal crosses, can data in a pedigree indicate whether a trait is autosomal or sex-linked? The answer is based on a simple premise. If a trait appears about equally often in males and females, then it is likely to be autosomal. But if males express the trait in question more often than females, then the allele responsible is likely to be recessive and found on the X chromosome.

**X-linked Recessive Traits** X-linked recessive traits are relatively common. They include the form of red–green color blindness that affects about 10 percent of males and the devastating blood clotting disorder hemophilia. A pedigree for red–green color blindness is shown in **FIGURE 14.23a**.

A key characteristic of X-linked recessive traits is that males express the trait more often than females. This is because males have only one copy of the X chromosome. Therefore, any X-linked allele will be expressed in a male.

Because human females have two X chromosomes, they have two copies of each X-linked gene and a recessive allele will not be expressed in heterozygotes. In the pedigree of Figure 14.23a the fact that only males are affected gives an immediate clue that this is an X-linked recessive trait.

Further, the appearance of an X-linked recessive trait usually skips a generation in the pedigree. Notice how on the right-hand

**(a)** X-linked recessive trait (e.g., red–green color blindness)

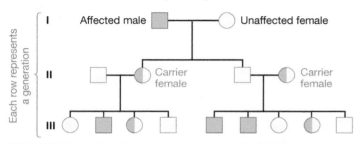

**(b)** X-linked dominant trait (e.g., hypophosphatemia)

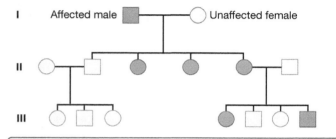

**CHARACTERISTICS:**
- Males are affected more frequently than females
- Trait is never passed from father to son
- Affected sons are usually born to carrier mothers
- About ½ of the sons of a carrier mother will be affected
- All daughters of affected males and unaffected non-carrier females are carriers
- Trait often skips generations

**CHARACTERISTICS:**
- Males and females are equally likely to be affected
- All daughters of an affected father are affected, but no sons
- Affected sons always have affected mothers
- About ½ of the offspring of an affected mother will be affected
- Affected daughters can have an affected mother or father
- Trait does not skip generations

**FIGURE 14.23 Pedigrees of Families with X-linked Recessive (a) and X-linked Dominant (b) Traits.**
✔**QUESTION** What genotype in a mother and a father would be predicted to produce a 1 : 1 ratio of normal : color-blind offspring? What would the ratio of color-blind male : female be from this mating?

side of the pedigree the trait appears in generations I and III but not in generation II. This pattern occurs because an affected male passes his only X chromosome on to his daughters. But because his daughters almost always receive a wild-type allele from their mother, the daughters don't show the trait. They will pass the defective allele on to about half their sons, however.

Most X-linked traits are recessive. There are only a few rare examples of X-linked dominant traits.

**X-linked Dominant Traits**   One example of an X-linked dominant trait is a bone disorder known as hypophosphatemia, or vitamin D–resistant rickets. What can be predicted about the inheritance of an X-linked dominant trait? As the pedigree in **FIGURE 14.23b** shows, the most telling feature is that an affected male will pass the trait to all his daughters and none of his sons.

This is because daughters receive their father's only X chromosome. In contrast, a heterozygous female will pass the trait to half her daughters and half her sons. This occurs because there is an equal chance that a heterozygous mother will pass on an X chromosome with either the dominant or the recessive trait.

What about Y-linked traits? Although the patterns for Y-linked inheritance can easily be predicted, the reality is that very few genes occur on the Y chromosome. These genes are involved with male-specific sexual development. Except for maleness, there are no known human Y-linked traits.

Within a few decades of the rediscovery of Mendel's work, the burning question in genetics was no longer the nature of inheritance but the nature of the gene. What are genes made of, and how are they copied so that parents pass their alleles on to their offspring? These are the questions turned to in Chapter 15.

# CHAPTER 14   REVIEW

For media, go to MasteringBiology

## If you understand . . .

### 14.1  Mendel's Experimental System

- When Mendel began his work, there were two leading hypotheses of inheritance: blending inheritance and the inheritance of acquired characteristics.
- Mendel chose pea plants as a model organism and began his work with pure lines that he crossed to produce hybrids.
- Mendel sought to discover rules of heredity that explained how phenotypes were transmitted from parent to offspring.

✔ You should be able explain why pure lines are homozygous.

### 14.2  Mendel's Experiments with a Single Trait

- From analysis of the trait expressed in hybrids, Mendel concluded that one trait was dominant and the other recessive.
- From the results of monohybrid crosses, Mendel concluded that inheritance is particulate—genes do not blend together.
- The traits that Mendel studied are specified by paired hereditary determinants (genes) that separate from each other during gamete formation.

- Analysis of monohybrid crosses led to the principle of segregation: Before the formation of gametes, the alleles of each gene separate so that each egg or sperm cell receives only one of them.

✓ You should be able to predict the gamete genotypes generated by a parent with the genotype *Bb*.

## 14.3 Mendel's Experiments with Two Traits

- Analysis of dihybrid crosses led to the principle of independent assortment: alleles of different genes are transmitted to egg cells and sperm cells independently of each other.

- Testcrosses allow an investigator to determine whether an individual of dominant phenotype is homozygous or heterozygous.

✓ You should be able to predict the gamete genotypes generated by a parent with the genotype *BbRr*.

## 14.4 The Chromosome Theory of Inheritance

- The chromosome theory states that chromosomes contain genes and that Mendel's rules can be explained by the segregation and independent assortment of homologous chromosomes at meiosis I.

- The chromosome theory was supported by the discovery of sex linkage. Crosses with X-linked traits supported the theory's contention that genes are found on chromosomes.

- X-linked traits give different results in reciprocal crosses.

✓ You should be able to use a Punnett square to show why reciprocal crosses involving an X-linked recessive gene give different results.

## 14.5 Extending Mendel's Rules

- There are important exceptions and extensions to the basic patterns of inheritance that Mendel discovered.

- All genes follow the principle of segregation, but genes close together on the same chromosome do not follow the principle of independent assortment.

- Crossing over between homologous chromosomes creates new combinations of alleles along each homolog.

- The frequency of crossing over can be used to create genetic maps that show the position and spacing of genes along chromosomes.

- Many genes have more than two alleles; this is multiple allelism. When more than two phenotypes are due to multiple allelism, the trait is polymorphic.

- Not all heterozygotes show a dominant phenotype. In addition to complete dominance, incomplete dominance and codominance are also common.

- Many genes are pleiotropic, meaning that they influence more than one trait.

- The phenotype associated with an allele is influenced by the environment that the individual experiences, and by the actions of alleles of other genes.

- Traits are often influenced by the action of many genes. These polygenic traits show quantitative instead of discrete variation. The frequency of different phenotypes is distributed normally (a plot produces a "bell curve" or normal distribution).

✓ You should be able to explain why crossing over is said to break up linkage between alleles.

## 14.6 Applying Mendel's Rules to Human Inheritance

- Pedigrees map out the transmission of human traits.

- Applying Mendel's rules to pedigrees can reveal the mode of transmission—whether a trait is dominant or recessive, autosomal or X-linked.

✓ You should be able to draw a pedigree that shows two sons and two daughters produced by a red–green color-blind father and a homozygous mother with normal color vision and explain why all the daughters are expected to be carriers of color blindness and none of the sons are expected to be color-blind.

### (MB) MasteringBiology

**1. MasteringBiology Assignments**

**Tutorials and Activities** Determining Genotype: Pea Pod Color; What Is the Inheritance Pattern of Sex-Linked Traits? Gregor's Garden; Incomplete Dominance; Inheritance of Fur Color in Mice; Linked Genes and Crossing Over; Linked Genes and Linkage Mapping; Mendel's Experiments; Mendel's Law of Independent Assortment; Mendel's Law of Segregation; Pedigree Analysis: Dominant and Recessive Autosomal Conditions; Pedigree Analysis: Galactosemia, Sex Linkage, Sex-Linked Genes

**Questions** Reading Quizzes, Blue-Thread Questions, Test Bank

**2. eText** Read your book online, search, take notes, highlight text, and more.

**3. The Study Area** Practice Test, Cumulative Test, BioFlix® 3-D Animations, Videos, Activities, Audio Glossary, Word Study Tools, Art

## You should be able to . . .

## ✓ TEST YOUR KNOWLEDGE

Answers are available in Appendix A

1. In studies of how traits are inherited, what makes certain species candidates for model organisms?
   a. They are the first organisms to be used in a particular type of experiment, so they are a historical "model" of what researchers expect to find.
   b. They are easy to study because a great deal is already known about them.
   c. They are the best or most fit of their type.
   d. They are easy to maintain, have a short life cycle, produce many offspring, and yield data that are relevant to many other organisms.

2. Why is the allele for wrinkled seed shape in garden peas considered recessive?
   a. It "recedes" in the $F_2$ generation when homozygous parents are crossed.
   b. The trait associated with the allele is not expressed in heterozygotes.
   c. Individuals with the allele have lower fitness than that of individuals with the dominant allele.
   d. The allele is less common than the dominant allele. (The wrinkled allele is a rare mutant.)

3. The alleles found in haploid organisms cannot be dominant or recessive. Why?
   a. Dominance and recessiveness describe which allele is expressed in phenotype when different alleles occur in the same individual.
   b. Because only one allele is present, alleles in haploid organisms are always dominant.
   c. Alleles in haploid individuals are transmitted like mitochondrial DNA or chloroplast DNA.
   d. Most haploid individuals are bacteria, and bacterial genetics is completely different from eukaryotic genetics.

4. Why can you infer that individuals that are "pure line" are homozygous for the gene in question?
   a. Because they are highly inbred.
   b. Because only two alleles are present at each gene in the populations to which these individuals belong.
   c. Because in a pure line, phenotypes are not affected by environmental conditions or gene interactions.
   d. Because no other phenotype is ever observed in a pure-line population, this implies that only one allele is present.

5. The genes for the traits that Mendel worked with are either located on different chromosomes or so far apart on the same chromosome that crossing over almost always occurs between them. How did this circumstance help Mendel recognize the principle of independent assortment?
   a. Otherwise, his dihybrid crosses would not have produced a 9:3:3:1 ratio of $F_2$ phenotypes.
   b. The occurrence of individuals with unexpected phenotypes led him to the discovery of recombination.
   c. It led him to the realization that the behavior of chromosomes during meiosis explained his results.
   d. It meant that the alleles involved were either dominant or recessive, which gave 3:1 ratios in the $F_1$ generation.

6. What is meant by the claim that Mendel worked with the simplest possible genetic system?
   a. Discrete traits, two alleles, simple dominance and recessiveness, no sex chromosomes, and unlinked genes are the simplest situation known.
   b. The ability to self-fertilize or cross-pollinate made it simple for Mendel to set up controlled crosses.
   c. Mendel was aware of meiosis and the chromosome theory of inheritance, so it was easy to reach the conclusions he did.
   d. Mendel's experimental designs and his rules of inheritance are actually neither complex nor sophisticated.

7. Mendel's rules do not correctly predict patterns of inheritance for tightly linked genes or the inheritance of alleles that show incomplete dominance. Does this mean that his hypotheses are incorrect?
   a. Yes, because they are relevant to only a small number of organisms and traits.

b. Yes, because not all data support his hypotheses.
   c. No, because he was not aware of meiosis or the chromosome theory of inheritance.
   d. No, it just means that his hypotheses are limited to certain conditions.

8. The artificial sweetener NutraSweet consists of a phenylalanine molecule linked to aspartic acid. The labels of diet sodas that contain NutraSweet include a warning to people with PKU. Why?
   a. NutraSweet stimulates the same taste receptors that natural sugars do.
   b. People with PKU have to avoid phenylalanine in their diet.
   c. In people with PKU, phenylalanine reacts with aspartic acid to form a toxic compound.
   d. People with PKU cannot lead normal lives, even if their environment is carefully controlled.

9. When Sutton and Boveri published the chromosome theory of inheritance, research on meiosis had not yet established that paternal and maternal homologs of different chromosomes assort independently. Then, in 1913, Elinor Carothers published a paper about a grasshopper species with an unusual karyotype: One chromosome had no homolog (meaning no pairing partner at meiosis I); another chromosome had homologs that could be distinguished under the light microscope. If chromosomes assort independently, how often should Carothers have observed each of the four products of meiosis shown in the following figure?

Grasshopper chromosomes at meiosis I — No pairing partner — Maternal and paternal homologs look different

Four types of gametes possible
(each meiotic division can produce only two of the four)

a. Only the gametes with one of each type of chromosome would occur.
   b. The four types of gametes should be observed to occur at equal frequencies.
   c. The chromosome with no pairing partner would disintegrate, so only gametes with one copy of the other chromosome would be observed.
   d. Gametes with one of each type of chromosome would occur twice as often as gametes with just one chromosome.

10. Which of the following is the strongest evidence that a trait might be influenced by polygenic inheritance?
   a. $F_1$ offspring of parents with different phenotypes have an intermediate phenotype.
   b. $F_1$ offspring of parents with different phenotypes have the dominant phenotype.
   c. The trait shows qualitative (discrete) variation.
   d. The trait shows quantitative variation.

The best way to test and extend your knowledge of transmission genetics is to work problems. Most genetics problems are set up as follows: You are given some information about the genotypes or phenotypes of one or both parents, along with data on the phenotypes of $F_1$ or $F_2$ offspring. Your task is to generate a set of hypotheses—a genetic model—to explain the results. Your hypotheses should address each of the following questions:

- Is the trait under study discrete or quantitative?
- Is the phenotype a product of one gene or many genes?
- For each gene involved, how many alleles are present—one, two, or many?
- Do the alleles involved show complete dominance, incomplete dominance, or codominance?
- Are the genes involved sex-linked or autosomal?
- If more than one gene is involved, are they linked or unlinked? If they are linked, does crossing over occur frequently?

It's also helpful to ask yourself whether gene interactions or pleiotropy might be occurring and whether it is safe to assume that the experimental design carefully controlled for effects of variation in other genes and in the environment.

In working the problem, be sure to start with the simplest possible explanation. For example, if you are dealing with a discrete trait, you might hypothesize that the cross involves a single autosomal gene with two alleles that show complete dominance. Your next step is to infer what the parental genotypes would be (according to your hypothesis), if they are not already given, and then do a Punnett square to predict what the offspring phenotypes and their frequencies should be based on your hypothesis. Next, check whether these predictions match the observed results given in the problem. If the

answer is yes, you have a valid solution. But if the answer is no, you need to go back and change one of your hypotheses, redo the Punnett square, and check to see if the predictions and observations match. Keep repeating these steps until you have a model that fits the data.

11. Example Problem *Plectritis congesta* plants produce fruits that either have or do not have prominent structures called wings. The alleles involved are $W^+$ = winged fruit; $W^-$ = wingless fruit. Researchers collected an array of individuals from the field and performed a series of crosses. The results are given in the following table. Complete the table by writing down the genotype of the parent or parents involved in each cross.

| Parental Phenotype(s) | Number of Offspring with Winged Fruits | Number of Offspring with Wingless Fruits | Parental Genotype(s) |
|---|---|---|---|
| Wingless (self-fertilized) | 0 | 80 | |
| Winged (self-fertilized) | 90 | 30 | |
| Winged × wingless | 46 | 0 | |
| Winged × winged | 44 | 0 | |

A worked solution is available in Appendix A.

12. Example Problem Two black female mice are crossed with a brown male. In several litters, female I produced 9 blacks and 7 browns; female II produced 57 blacks. What deductions can you make concerning the inheritance of black and brown coat color in mice? What are the genotypes of the parents in this case?

A worked solution is available in Appendix A.

13. In peas, purple flowers are dominant to white. If a purple-flowered, heterozygous plant were crossed with a white-flowered plant, what is the expected ratio of genotypes and phenotypes among the $F_1$ offspring? If two of the purple-flowered $F_1$ offspring were randomly selected and crossed, what is the expected ratio of genotypes and phenotypes among the $F_2$ offspring?

14. In garden peas, yellow seeds ($Y$) are dominant to green seeds ($y$), and inflated pods ($I$) are dominant to constricted pods ($i$). Suppose you have crossed $YYII$ parents with $yyii$ parents.
- Draw the $F_1$ Punnett square and predict the expected $F_1$ phenotype(s).
- List the genotype(s) of gametes produced by $F_1$ individuals.
- Draw the $F_2$ Punnett square. Based on this Punnett square, predict the expected phenotype(s) in the $F_2$ generation and the expected frequency of each phenotype.

15. The smooth feathers on the back of the neck in pigeons can be reversed by a mutation to produce a "crested" appearance in which feathers form a distinctive spike at the back of the head. A pigeon breeder examined offspring produced by a single pair of non-crested birds and recorded the following: 22 non-crested and 7 crested. She then made a series of crosses using offspring from the first cross. When she crossed two of the crested birds, all 20 of the offspring were crested. When she crossed a non-crested bird with a crested bird, 7 offspring were non-crested and 6 were crested.

- For these three crosses, provide genotypes for parents and offspring that are consistent with these results.
- Which allele is dominant?

16. A plant with orange, spotted flowers was grown in the greenhouse from a seed collected in the wild. The plant was self-pollinated and gave rise to the following progeny: 88 orange with spots, 34 yellow with spots, 32 orange with no spots, and 8 yellow with no spots. What can you conclude about the dominance relationships of the alleles responsible for the spotted and unspotted phenotypes? For the orange and yellow phenotypes? What can you conclude about the genotype of the original plant that had orange, spotted flowers?

17. As a genetic counselor, you routinely advise couples about the possibility of genetic disease in their offspring based on their family histories. This morning you met with an engaged couple, both of whom are phenotypically normal. The man, however, has a brother who died of Duchenne-type muscular dystrophy, an X-linked condition that results in death before the age of 20. The allele responsible for this disease is recessive. His prospective bride, whose family has no history of the disease, is worried that the couple's sons or daughters might be afflicted.
- How would you advise this couple?
- The sister of this man is planning to marry his fiancée's brother. How would you advise this second couple?

18. Suppose you are heterozygous for two genes that are located on different chromosomes. You carry alleles *A* and *a* for one gene and alleles *B* and *b* for the other. Draw a diagram illustrating what happens to these genes and alleles when meiosis occurs in your reproductive tissues. Label the stages of meiosis, the homologous chromosomes, sister chromatids, nonhomologous chromosomes, genes, and alleles. Be sure to list all the genetically different gametes that could form and indicate how frequently each type should be observed. On the diagram, identify the events responsible for the principle of segregation and the principle of independent assortment.

19. Review the text's description of ABO blood types. Suppose a woman with blood type O married a man with blood type AB. What phenotypes and genotypes would you expect to observe in their offspring, and in what proportions? Answer the same question for a heterozygous mother with blood type A and a heterozygous father with blood type B.

20. An alien friend named Tukan has two sets of eyes, one set forward-looking and one set backward-looking, and smooth skin. His mate, Valco, lacks eyes but has skin covered with tiny hooks that attract all sorts of debris. Tukan and Valco have thrived on earth and have had four children, all with no eyes and smooth skin. Typical of their ways, the children interbred and produced 32 children of their own.
   - Under the models of inheritance proposed by Mendel, identify which alleles are dominant and which are recessive.
   - Provide gene symbols that would reflect the dominant–recessive allelic relationships.
   - Of the 32 children, how many would you expect to have two sets of eyes and smooth skin?

21. Phenylketonuria (PKU) is a genetic disease caused by homozygosity for a recessive mutation in the enzyme that converts the amino acid phenylalanine to tyrosine. In the absence of this enzyme, phenylalanine and some of its derivatives accumulate in the body and cause mental retardation. If individuals are identified soon enough after birth, they can be treated by a low-phenylalanine diet for the early years of their lives. As adults, though, homozygous recessive individuals are allowed to adopt a diet with normal amounts of phenylalanine. Not long after such treatments were initiated, a troubling phenomenon was observed. A high number of children born to treated mothers were mentally retarded even though the children were heterozygous for the PKU gene. Children born of treated PKU males suffered no ill effects.
   - Can you offer an explanation as to why genetically heterozygous children of treated PKU mothers might be prone to mental retardation?
   - Propose a solution to reduce the likelihood of mental retardation in children of treated PKU mothers.

22. The blending-inheritance hypothesis proposed that the genetic material from parents is unavoidably and irreversibly mixed in the offspring. As a result, offspring and later descendants should always appear intermediate in phenotype to their forebears. Mendel, in contrast, proposed that genes are discrete and that their integrity is maintained in the offspring and in subsequent generations. Suppose the year is 1890. You are a horse breeder and have just read Mendel's paper. You don't believe his results, however, because you often work with cremello (very light-colored) and chestnut (reddish-brown) horses. You know that if you cross a cremello individual from a pure-breeding line with a chestnut individual from a pure-breeding line, the offspring will be palomino—meaning they have an intermediate (golden-yellow) body color. What additional crosses would you do to test whether Mendel's model is valid in the case of genes for horse color? List the crosses and the offspring genotypes and phenotypes you'd expect to obtain. Explain why these experimental crosses would provide a test of Mendel's model.

23. Two mothers give birth to sons at the same time in a busy hospital. The son of couple 1 is afflicted with hemophilia A, which is a recessive X-linked disease. Neither parent has the disease. Couple 2 has a normal son even though the father has hemophilia A. The two couples sue the hospital in court, claiming that a careless staff member swapped their babies at birth. You appear in court as an expert witness. What do you tell the jury? Make a diagram that you can submit to the jury.

24. You have crossed two *Drosophila melanogaster* individuals that have long wings and red eyes—the wild-type phenotype. In the progeny, the mutant phenotypes called curved wings and lozenge eyes appear as follows:

| Females | Males |
|---|---|
| 600 long wings, red eyes | 300 long wings, red eyes |
| 200 curved wings, red eyes | 100 curved wings, red eyes |
| | 300 long wings, lozenge eyes |
| | 100 curved wings, lozenge eyes |

   - According to these data, is the curved-wing allele autosomal recessive, autosomal dominant, sex-linked recessive, or sex-linked dominant?
   - Is the lozenge-eyed allele autosomal recessive, autosomal dominant, sex-linked recessive, or sex-linked dominant?
   - What is the genotype of the female parent?
   - What is the genotype of the male parent?

25. In parakeets, two autosomal genes that are located on different chromosomes control the production of feather pigment. Gene *B* codes for an enzyme that is required for the synthesis of a blue pigment, and gene *Y* codes for an enzyme required for the synthesis of a yellow pigment. Recessive mutations that result in no production of the affected pigment are known for both genes. Suppose that a bird breeder has two green parakeets and mates them. The offspring are green, blue, yellow, and albino (unpigmented).
   - Based on this observation, what are the genotypes of the green parents? What is the genotype of each type of offspring? What fraction of the total progeny should exhibit each type of color?
   - Suppose that the parents were the progeny of a cross between two true-breeding strains. What two types of crosses between true-breeding strains could have produced the green parents? Indicate the genotypes and phenotypes for each cross.

26. Recall that hemophilia is an X-linked recessive disease. If a woman with hemophilia had children with a man without hemophilia, what is the chance that their first child will have the disease? What is the chance that their first child will be a carrier?

# 15 DNA and the Gene: Synthesis and Repair

In this chapter you will learn how

**DNA replication and repair preserve genetic information**

by asking
↓

**What are genes made of? 15.1**

by analyzing
↓

**DNA synthesis: early hypotheses 15.2**

expanding to
↓

**Steps in replication: a model for faithful DNA synthesis 15.3**

and ways to

**Replicate ends of linear chromosomes 15.4**

**Correct DNA errors; repair DNA damage 15.5**

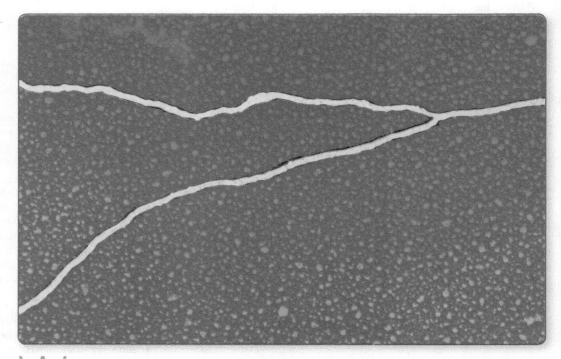

Electron micrograph (with color added) showing DNA in the process of replication. The original DNA double helix (far right) is being replicated into two DNA double helices (on the left). The two helices diverge at the replication fork, which is where DNA synthesis is taking place.

**BIG PICTURE**

This chapter is part of the Big Picture. See how on pages 366–367.

What are genes made of, and how are they copied so that they are faithfully passed on to offspring? These questions dominated biology during the middle of the twentieth century.

Since Mendel's time, the predominant research strategy in genetics had been to conduct a series of experimental crosses, create a genetic model to explain the types and proportions of phenotypes that resulted, and then test the model's predictions through reciprocal crosses, testcrosses, or other techniques. This strategy led to virtually all the discoveries of classical genetics, including Mendel's rules, sex linkage, linkage, and quantitative inheritance (see Chapter 14).

The chemical composition and molecular structure of Mendel's hereditary factors—which came to be called genes—remained a mystery for the first half of the twentieth century. Although biologists knew that genes and chromosomes were replicated during the cell cycle, with copies distributed

✔ When you see this checkmark, stop and test yourself. Answers are available in Appendix A.

to daughter cells during mitosis and meiosis (see Chapters 12 and 13), no one had the slightest clue about how the copying occurred.

The goal of this chapter is to explore how researchers solved these mysteries. The results provided a link between two of the five attributes of life (introduced in Chapter 1): processing genetic information and replication. (You can see how DNA synthesis and repair fits into the Big Picture of Genetic Information on pages 366–367.)

How are genes copied, so they can be passed on to succeeding generations? Let's begin with studies that identified the nature of the genetic material, then explore how genes are copied during the synthesis phase of the cell cycle, and conclude by analyzing how incorrectly copied or damaged genes are repaired. Once the molecular nature of the gene was known, the nature of biological science changed forever.

## 15.1 What Are Genes Made Of?

The chromosome theory of inheritance (Chapter 14) proposed that chromosomes contain genes. It had been known since the late 1800s that chromosomes are a complex of DNA and proteins. The question, then, of what genes are made of came down to a simple choice: DNA or protein?

Initially, most biologists backed the hypothesis that genes are made of proteins. The arguments in favor of this hypothesis were compelling. Hundreds, if not thousands, of complex and highly regulated chemical reactions occur in even the simplest living cells. The amount of information required to specify and coordinate these reactions is mind-boggling. With their almost limitless variation in structure and function, proteins are complex enough to contain this much information.

In contrast, DNA was known to be composed of just four types of deoxyribonucleotides (Chapter 4). Early but incorrect evidence suggested that DNA was a simple molecule with some sort of repetitive and uninteresting structure. It seemed impossible that such a simple compound could hold complex information.

DNA or protein? The experiment that settled the question is considered a classic in biological science.

### The Hershey–Chase Experiment

In 1952 Alfred Hershey and Martha Chase took up the question of whether genes were made of protein or DNA by studying how a virus called T2 infects and replicates within the bacterium *Escherichia coli*. Nearly 10 years before Hershey and Chase began their study, Oswald Avery and colleagues showed in 1944 that DNA could serve as genetic material, but many scientists remained unconvinced of the finding or its generality. Hershey and Chase knew that T2 infections begin when the virus attaches to the cell wall of *E. coli* and injects its genes into the cell's interior (**FIGURE 15.1a**). These genes then direct the production of a new generation of

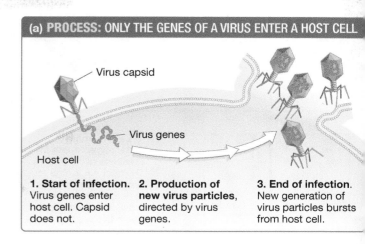

**(a) PROCESS: ONLY THE GENES OF A VIRUS ENTER A HOST CELL**

Virus capsid

Virus genes

Host cell

**1. Start of infection.** Virus genes enter host cell. Capsid does not.

**2. Production of new virus particles,** directed by virus genes.

**3. End of infection.** New generation of virus particles bursts from host cell.

**(b)** The virus's capsid stays outside the cell.

Virus capsid

Virus genes

100 nm

**FIGURE 15.1 Viruses Inject Genes into Bacterial Cells and Leave a Capsid Behind.** Color has been added to the transmission electron micrograph in (b) to make key structures more visible.

virus particles inside the infected cell, which acts as a host for the virus. (For more information on viruses, see Chapter 36.)

During the infection, the exterior protein coat, or **capsid,** of the original, parent virus is left behind. The capsid remains attached to the exterior of the host cell (**FIGURE 15.1b**). Hershey and Chase also knew that T2 is made up almost exclusively of protein and DNA. Was it protein or DNA that entered the host cell and directed the production of new viruses?

Hershey and Chase's strategy for determining the composition of the viral substance that enters the cell and acts as the hereditary material was based on two biochemical facts: (1) Proteins contain sulfur but not phosphorus, and (2) DNA contains phosphorus but not sulfur.

As **FIGURE 15.2** (see page 286) shows, the researchers began their work by growing viruses in the presence of either a radioactive isotope of sulfur ($^{35}$S) or a radioactive isotope of phosphorus ($^{32}$P). Because these isotopes were incorporated into newly synthesized proteins and DNA, this step produced a population of viruses with radioactive proteins and a population with radioactive DNA.

## QUESTION: Do viral genes consist of DNA or protein?

**DNA HYPOTHESIS:** Viral genes consist of DNA.

**PROTEIN HYPOTHESIS:** Viral genes consist of protein.

**EXPERIMENTAL SETUP:**

Viral DNA is radioactive.

Viral protein is radioactive.

**1. Label viruses.**
Grow some viruses in presence of $^{32}P$ (P is in DNA but not in viral protein) and some viruses in presence of $^{35}S$ (S is in protein but not in DNA).

E. coli

E. coli

**2. Infect bacteria.**
Allow viruses with labeled DNA to infect one culture of *E. coli* cells and viruses with labeled protein to infect another.

Viral capsids outside

Genes inside

**3. Agitate cultures**
in kitchen blender to separate empty viral capsids from bacterial cells in each culture.

Viral capsids in solution

Viral genes in cells in pellet

**4. Centrifuge solutions**
of bacterial cells from each culture to force cells into a pellet. Record location of radioactive labels.

**PREDICTION OF DNA HYPOTHESIS:** Radioactive DNA will be located within pellet.

**PREDICTION OF PROTEIN HYPOTHESIS:** Radioactive protein will be located within pellet.

**RESULTS:**

Radioactive protein is in solution

Radioactive DNA is in pellet

DNA

Protein

**CONCLUSION:** Viral genes consist of DNA.

**FIGURE 15.2 Experimental Evidence that DNA Is the Hereditary Material.**

SOURCE: Hershey, A. D., and M. Chase. 1952. Independent functions of viral protein and nucleic id in growth of bacteriophage. *Journal of General Physiology* 36: 39–56.

**QUESTION** What evidence would these investigators have to oduce to convince you that the viral capsids were shaken off the acterial cells by the agitation step?

Hershey and Chase allowed each set of radioactive viruses to infect *E. coli* cells. If genes consist of DNA, then radioactive protein should be found only in the capsids outside the infected host cells, while radioactive DNA should be located inside the cells. But if genes consist of proteins, then radioactive protein—and no radioactive DNA—should be inside the cells.

To test these predictions, Hershey and Chase sheared the capsids off the cells by vigorously agitating each of the cultures in kitchen blenders. When the researchers spun the samples in a centrifuge, the small phage capsids remained in the solution while the cells formed a pellet at the bottom of the centrifuge tube (see **BioSkills 10** in Appendix B to review how centrifugation works).

As predicted by the DNA hypothesis, the biologists found that virtually all the radioactive protein was outside cells in the emptied capsids, while virtually all the radioactive DNA was inside the host cells. Because the injected component of the virus directs the production of a new generation of virus particles, this component must represent the virus's genes.

After these results were published, proponents of the protein hypothesis accepted that DNA, not protein, must be the hereditary material. An astonishing claim—that DNA contained all the information for life's complexity—was correct.

## The Secondary Structure of DNA

In 1953, one year after Hershey and Chase's landmark results were published, Watson and Crick proposed a model for the secondary structure of DNA. Recall that DNA is typically double-stranded with each strand consisting of a long, linear polymer made up of monomers called deoxyribonucleotides (Chapter 4).

Each deoxyribonucleotide consists of a deoxyribose sugar, a phosphate group, and a nitrogenous base (**FIGURE 15.3a**). Deoxyribonucleotides link together into a polymer when a phosphodiester bond forms between a hydroxyl group on the 3′ carbon of one deoxyribose and the phosphate group attached to the 5′ carbon of another deoxyribose. The two strands together make up one DNA molecule that functions as the genetic information storage molecule of cells.

As **FIGURE 15.3b** shows, the primary structure of each strand of DNA has two major features: (1) a "backbone" made up of the sugar and phosphate groups of deoxyribonucleotides and (2) a series of bases that project from the backbone. Each strand of DNA has a directionality, or polarity: One end has an exposed hydroxyl group on the 3′ carbon of a deoxyribose, while the other has an exposed phosphate group on a 5′ carbon. Thus, the molecule has distinctly different 3′ and 5′ ends.

As they explored different models for the secondary structure of DNA, Watson and Crick hit on the idea of lining up two of these long strands in opposite directions, or in what is called antiparallel fashion (**FIGURE 15.4a**). They realized that antiparallel strands will twist around each other into a spiral or helix because certain bases fit together snugly in pairs inside the spiral and form hydrogen bonds (**FIGURE 15.4b**). The double-stranded molecule that results is called a **double helix.**

**(a) Structure of a deoxyribonucleotide**

Phosphate group attached to 5′ carbon of the sugar

P

5′ CH₂  O

Sugar (deoxyribose)

Base — Could be adenine (A), thymine (T), guanine (G), cytosine (C)

3′

Hydroxyl (OH) group on 3′ carbon of the sugar → OH

**(b) Primary structure of DNA**

5′ end of strand

P

5′ CH₂  O

T — Nitrogen-containing bases project from the backbone

Sugar-phosphate backbone of DNA strand

P

CH₂  O

A

Phosphodiester bond links deoxyribonucleotides

P

CH₂  O

G

3′

OH

3′ end of strand

**FIGURE 15.3 DNA's Primary Structure. (a)** Deoxyribonucleotides are monomers that polymerize to form DNA. **(b)** DNA's primary structure is made up of a sequence of deoxyribonucleotides. Notice that the structure has a sugar–phosphate "backbone" with nitrogen-containing bases attached.

✔**EXERCISE** Write the base sequence of the DNA in part (b), in the 5′ → 3′ direction.

The double-helical DNA is stabilized by hydrogen bonds that form between the bases adenine (A) and thymine (T) and between the bases guanine (G) and cytosine (C), along with hydrophobic interactions that the bases experience inside the helix. Hydrogen bonding of particular base pairs is **complementary base pairing**.

# 15.2 Testing Early Hypotheses about DNA Synthesis

Watson and Crick realized that the A-T and G-C pairing rules suggested a way for DNA to be copied when chromosomes are replicated during S phase of the cell cycle, before mitosis and meiosis. They suggested that the existing strands of DNA served as a template (pattern) for the production of new strands and that deoxyribonucleotides were added to the new strands according to complementary base pairing. For example, if the template

**(a) Complementary base pairing**     **(b) The double helix**

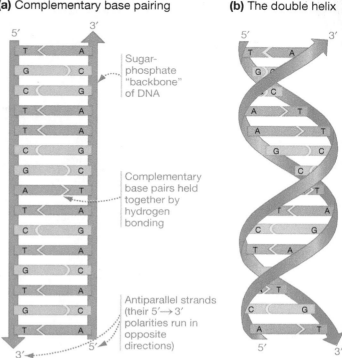

**FIGURE 15.4 DNA's Secondary Structure: The Double Helix. (a)** DNA normally consists of two strands, each with a sugar–phosphate backbone. Nitrogen-containing bases project from each strand and form hydrogen bonds. Only A-T and G-C pairs fit together in a way that allows hydrogen bonding to occur between the strands. **(b)** Bonding between complementary bases twists the molecule into a double helix.

strand contained a T, then an A would be added to the new strand to pair with that T. Similarly, a G on the template strand would dictate the addition of a C on the new strand.

Complementary base pairing provided a mechanism for DNA to be copied. But many questions remained about how the copying was done.

## Three Alternative Hypotheses

Biologists at the time proposed three alternative hypotheses about how the old and new strands might interact during replication:

1. *Semiconservative replication* If the old, **parental strands** of DNA separated, each could then be used as a template for the synthesis of a new, **daughter strand.** This hypothesis is called **semiconservative replication** because each new daughter DNA molecule would consist of one old strand and one new strand.

2. *Conservative replication* If the bases temporarily turned outward so that complementary strands no longer faced each other, they could serve as a template for the synthesis of an entirely new double helix all at once. This hypothesis, called conservative replication, would result in an intact parental

**QUESTION:** Is replication semiconservative, conservative, or dispersive?

| HYPOTHESIS 1: | HYPOTHESIS 2: | HYPOTHESIS 3: |
|---|---|---|
| Replication is semiconservative. | Replication is conservative. | Replication is dispersive. |

**EXPERIMENTAL SETUP:**

Generation 0 DNA sample

Generation 1 DNA sample

Generation 2 DNA sample

Cell transfer

**1.** Grow *E. coli* cells in medium with $^{15}N$ as sole source of nitrogen for many generations. Collect sample and purify DNA.

**2.** Transfer cells to medium containing $^{14}N$. After cells divide once, collect sample and purify DNA.

**3.** After cells have divided a second time in $^{14}N$ medium, collect sample and purify DNA.

**4.** Centrifuge the three samples separately. Compare the locations of the DNA bands in each sample.

**PREDICTIONS:**

| Semiconservative replication | Conservative replication | Dispersive replication |
|---|---|---|

Generation 0 — $^{15}N$ / $^{15}N$ / $^{15}N$

Generation 1 — Hybrid  Hybrid / $^{15}N$  $^{14}N$ / Hybrid  Hybrid

Generation 2 — Hybrid $^{14}N$ Hybrid $^{14}N$ / $^{15}N$ $^{14}N$ / Hybrid

After 2 generations:
**1/2 low-density DNA ($^{14}N$)**
**1/2 intermediate-density DNA (hybrid)**

After 2 generations:
**1/4 high-density DNA ($^{15}N$)**
**3/4 low-density DNA ($^{14}N$)**

After 2 generations:
**All intermediate-density DNA (hybrid)**

**RESULTS:**

Top of centrifuge tube (lower density)

$^{14}N$
Hybrid
$^{15}N$

Bottom of centrifuge tube (higher density)

After 2 generations:
1/2 low-density DNA
1/2 intermediate-density DNA

0   1   2
**Generation**

**CONCLUSION:** Data from generation 1 conflict with conservative replication hypothesis. Data from generation 2 conflict with dispersive replication hypothesis. Replication is semiconservative.

**FIGURE 15.5 The Meselson–Stahl Experiment.**

SOURCE: Meselson, M., and F. W. Stahl. 1958. The replication of DNA in *Escherichia coli*. *Proceedings of the National Academy of Sciences USA* 44: 671–682.

✔**EXERCISE** Meselson and Stahl actually let their experiment run for a fourth generation with cultures growing in the presence of $^{14}N$. Explain what data from third- and fourth-generation DNA should look like—that is, where the DNA band(s) should be.

molecule and a daughter DNA molecule consisting entirely of newly synthesized strands.

3. **Dispersive replication** If the parental double helix were cut wherever one strand crossed over another and DNA was synthesized in short sections by extending each of the cut parental strands to the next strand crossover, then there would be a mix of new and old segments along each replicated molecule. This possibility is called dispersive replication—stretches of old DNA would be interspersed with new DNA down the length of each daughter strand.

Matthew Meselson and Franklin Stahl realized that if they could tag or mark parental and daughter strands of DNA in a way that would make them distinguishable from each other, they could determine whether replication was conservative, semiconservative, or dispersive.

## The Meselson–Stahl Experiment

Before Meselson and Stahl could do any tagging to distinguish old DNA from new DNA, they needed to choose an organism to study. They decided to work with the bacterium *Escherichia coli*—the same inhabitant of the human gastrointestinal tract that Hershey and Chase used. Because *E. coli* is small and grows quickly and readily in the laboratory, it had become a favored model organism in studies of biochemistry and molecular genetics. (See **BioSkills 13** in Appendix B for more on *E. coli*.)

Like all organisms, bacterial cells copy their entire complement of DNA, or their **genome,** before every cell division. To distinguish parental strands of DNA from daughter strands when *E. coli* replicated, Meselson and Stahl grew the cells for successive generations in the presence of different isotopes of nitrogen: first $^{15}N$ and later $^{14}N$. Because $^{15}N$ contains an extra neutron, it is heavier than the normal isotope, $^{14}N$.

This difference in mass, which creates a difference in density between $^{14}N$-containing and $^{15}N$-containing DNA, was the key to the experiment summarized in **FIGURE 15.5**. The logic ran as follows:

- If different nitrogen isotopes were available in the growth medium when different generations of DNA were produced, then the parental and daughter strands would have different densities.

- The technique called density-gradient centrifugation separates molecules based on their density (**BioSkills 10** in Appendix B). Low-density molecules cluster in bands high in the centrifuge tube; higher-density molecules cluster in bands lower in the centrifuge tube.

- When intact, double-stranded DNA molecules are subjected to density-gradient centrifugation, DNA that contains $^{14}N$ should form a band higher in the centrifuge tube; DNA that contains $^{15}N$ should form a band lower in the centrifuge tube.

In short, DNA containing $^{14}N$ and DNA containing $^{15}N$ should form separate bands. How could this tagging system be used to test whether replication is semiconservative, conservative, or dispersive?

Meselson and Stahl began by growing *E. coli* cells with nutrients that contained only $^{15}N$. They purified DNA from a sample of these cells and transferred the rest of the culture to a growth medium containing only the $^{14}N$ isotope. After enough time had elapsed for these cells to divide once—meaning that the DNA had been copied once—they removed a sample and isolated the DNA. After the remainder of the culture had divided again, they removed another sample and isolated its DNA.

As Figure 15.5 shows, the conservative, semiconservative, and dispersive models make distinct predictions about the makeup of the DNA molecules after replication occurs in the first and second generation. Examine the figure carefully to understand these distinct predictions.

The photograph at the bottom of Figure 15.5 shows the experiment's results. After one generation, the density of the DNA molecules was intermediate. These data suggested that the hypothesis of conservative replication was wrong, since it predicted two different densities in the first generation.

After two generations, a lower-density band appeared in addition to the intermediate-density band. This result offered strong support for the hypothesis that DNA replication is semiconservative. Had dispersive replication occurred, the second generation would have produced only a single, intermediate density band. Each newly made DNA molecule comprises one old strand and one new strand—replication is semiconservative.

## 15.3 A Model for DNA Synthesis

The DNA inside a cell is like an ancient text that has been painstakingly copied and handed down, generation after generation. But while the most ancient of all human texts contain messages that are thousands of years old, the DNA in living cells has been copied and passed down for billions of years. And instead of being copied by monks or clerks, DNA is replicated by molecular scribes. What molecules are responsible for copying DNA, and how do they work?

Meselson and Stahl showed that each strand of DNA is copied in its entirety each time replication occurs, but how does DNA synthesis proceed? Does it require an input of energy in the form of ATP, or it is spontaneous? Is it catalyzed by an enzyme, or does it occur quickly on its own?

The initial breakthrough on DNA replication came with the discovery of an enzyme called **DNA polymerase,** so named because it polymerizes deoxyribonucleotides into DNA. This protein catalyzes DNA synthesis. Follow-up work showed that there are several types of DNA polymerase. DNA polymerase III, for example, is the enzyme that is primarily responsible for copying *E. coli*'s chromosome before cell division.

**FIGURE 15.6** (see page 290) illustrates a critical characteristic of DNA polymerases: They can work in only one direction. DNA polymerases can add deoxyribonucleotides only to the 3′ end of a growing DNA chain. As a result, DNA synthesis always proceeds in the 5′ → 3′ direction. ✔ If you understand this

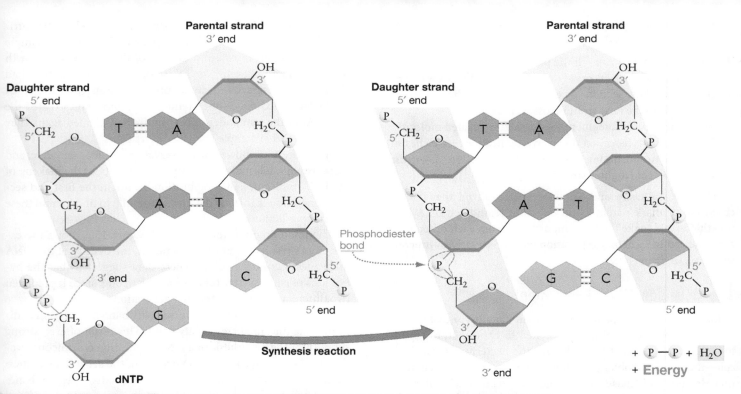

**FIGURE 15.6 The DNA Synthesis Reaction.** A condensation reaction results in formation of a phosphodiester bond between the 3′ carbon on the end of a DNA strand and the 5′ carbon on an incoming deoxyribonucleoside triphosphate (dNTP) monomer.

concept, you should be able to draw two lines representing a DNA molecule, assign the 3′-to-5′ polarity of each strand, and then label the direction in which DNA synthesis will proceed for each strand.

Figure 15.6 makes another important point about DNA synthesis. You might recall from earlier chapters that polymerization reactions generally are endergonic, meaning they require an input of energy. But for DNA synthesis, the reaction is exergonic (it releases energy) because the monomers that are used in the DNA synthesis reaction are **deoxyribonucleoside triphosphates (dNTPs).** (The N in dNTP stands for any of the four bases found in DNA: adenine, thymine, guanine, or cytosine). Because they have three closely spaced phosphate groups, dNTPs have high potential energy—high enough to make the formation of phosphodiester bonds in a growing DNA strand exergonic as two of the phosphates are cleaved off (see Chapter 8).

## How Does Replication Get Started?

Another major insight into the mechanism of DNA synthesis emerged when electron microscopy caught DNA replication in action. As **FIGURE 15.7a** shows, a "bubble" forms when DNA is being synthesized. Initially, the replication bubble forms at a specific sequence of bases called the **origin of replication** (**FIGURE 15.7b**). Bacterial chromosomes have only one origin of replication, and thus a single replication bubble forms. Eukaryotes have multiple origins of replication along each chromosome, and thus multiple replication bubbles (**FIGURE 15.7c**).

DNA synthesis is bidirectional—that is, it occurs in both directions at the same time. Therefore, replication bubbles grow in two directions as DNA replication proceeds.

A specific set of proteins are responsible for recognizing sites where replication begins and opening the double helix at those points. These proteins are activated by the proteins that initiate S phase in the cell cycle (see Chapter 12).

Once a replication bubble opens at the origin of replication, a different set of enzymes takes over to start DNA synthesis. Active DNA synthesis takes place at the replication forks of each replication bubble (shown in Figure 15.7c). The **replication fork** is the Y-shaped region where the parent–DNA double helix is split into two single strands and copied.

## How Is the Helix Opened and Stabilized?

A large group of enzymes and specialized proteins converge on the point where the double helix opens. The enzyme called **DNA helicase** breaks the hydrogen bonds between the base pairs. This reaction causes the two strands of DNA to separate. **Single-strand DNA-binding proteins (SSBPs)** attach to the separated strands and prevent them from snapping back into a double helix. Working together, DNA helicase and single-strand DNA-binding proteins open up the double helix and maintain the separation of both strands during copying (**FIGURE 15.8**, step 1).

The "unzipping" process that occurs at the replication fork creates tension farther down the helix. To understand why, imagine what would happen if you started to pull apart the twisted

**(a)** DNA being replicated

0.25 μm

**(b)** Bacterial chromosomes have a single origin of replication.

Old DNA

New DNA

3′
5′
5′  3′

Origin of replication

Replication proceeds in both directions

**(c)** Eukaryotic chromosomes have multiple origins of replication.

5′
3′       3′
5′

5′
3′       3′
5′

Old DNA
New DNA

Replication bubble

Replication fork

5′
3′
5′

Replication proceeds in both directions from each starting point

**FIGURE 15.7 DNA Synthesis Proceeds in Two Directions from an Origin of Replication.** Color has been added to the micrograph in part (a).

strands of a rope. The untwisting movements at one end would force the intact section to rotate in response. If the intact end of the rope were fixed in place, it would coil on itself in response to the twisting forces. DNA does not become tightly coiled ahead of the replication fork, because the twisting induced by helicase is relaxed by proteins called topoisomerases. A **topoisomerase** is an enzyme that cuts DNA, allows it to unwind, and rejoins it ahead of the advancing replication fork.

Now, what happens once the DNA helix is open?

## How Is the Leading Strand Synthesized?

The keys to understanding what happens at the start of DNA synthesis are to recall that DNA polymerase (**1**) works only in the 5′ → 3′ direction and (**2**) requires both a 3′ end to extend from and a single-stranded template. Both of these properties control how synthesis occurs on both template strands of DNA, and as you'll soon see, they significantly complicate copying one of these. The single-stranded template dictates which

**PROCESS: SYNTHESIS OF LEADING STRAND**

**1. DNA is opened,** unwound, and primed.

**Primase** synthesizes RNA primer

**Topoisomerase** relieves twisting forces

3′    5′

5′

5′
3′

**Helicase** opens double helix

**Single-strand DNA-binding proteins (SSBPs)** stabilize single strands

**2. Synthesis** of leading strand begins.

**Sliding clamp** holds DNA polymerase in place

**DNA polymerase** works in 5′ → 3′ direction, synthesizing leading strand

3′
5′
RNA primer
Leading strand

5′

5′
3′

**FIGURE 15.8 Leading-Strand Synthesis.**

deoxyribonucleotide should be added next. A **primer**—a strand a few nucleotides long that is bonded to the template strand—provides DNA polymerase with a free 3′ hydroxyl (−OH) group that can combine with an incoming deoxyribonucleotide to form a phosphodiester bond. As shown in the figure below and in Figure 15.8, step 2, primers used during cellular DNA synthesis are short RNA strands, not DNA strands.

But what adds the primer? Before DNA synthesis can get under way, an enzyme called **primase** synthesizes a short stretch of RNA that acts as a primer for DNA polymerase. The primer is about 10 nucleotides long in *E. coli*. Primase is a type of **RNA polymerase**—an enzyme that catalyzes the polymerization of ribonucleotides into RNA (see Chapter 4 to review RNA's structure). Unlike DNA polymerases, primase and other RNA polymerases do not require a primer to begin synthesis.

Once a primer is present on a single-stranded template, DNA polymerase begins working in the 5′ → 3′ direction and adds deoxyribonucleotides to complete the complementary strand. As Figure 15.8, step 2, shows, DNA polymerase has a shape that grips the DNA strand during synthesis, similar to your hand clasping a rope. Deoxyribonucleotide addition is catalyzed at an active site in a groove between the enzyme's "thumb" and "fingers." As DNA polymerase moves along the DNA molecule, a doughnut-shaped structure behind it, called the sliding clamp, holds the enzyme in place on the template strand.

The enzyme's product is called the **leading strand,** or **continuous strand,** because it leads into the replication fork and is synthesized continuously. ✔ If you understand leading-strand synthesis, you should be able to list the enzymes involved and predict the consequences if any of them are defective.

## How Is the Lagging Strand Synthesized?

Synthesis of the leading strand is straightforward. After an RNA primer is in place, DNA polymerase moves along, adding deoxyribonucleotides to the 3′ end of that strand. The enzyme moves into the replication fork, which "unzips" ahead of it. By comparison, events on the opposite strand are more involved.

Recall that the two strands of the DNA double helix are antiparallel—meaning they lie parallel to one another but oriented in opposite directions. The fact that DNA polymerases can synthesize DNA only in the 5′ → 3′ direction creates a paradox. Only one strand of DNA at the replication fork—the leading strand—can be synthesized in a direction that follows the moving replication fork.

The other strand must be synthesized in a direction that runs *away* from the moving replication fork, as illustrated in **FIGURE 15.9**. The strand of DNA that extends in the direction away from the

**FIGURE 15.9 The Lagging Strand Is Synthesized in a Direction Moving Away from the Replication Fork.** This occurs because the DNA strands are antiparallel and DNA polymerase can work only in the 5′ → 3′ direction.

replication fork is called the **lagging strand,** or **discontinuous strand,** because it lags behind the synthesis occurring at the fork. As the replication fork moves, it exposes gaps of single-stranded template DNA (Time 2 in Figure 15.9). How are the growing gaps filled in?

**The Discontinuous Replication Hypothesis**   The puzzle posed by lagging-strand synthesis was resolved when Reiji Okazaki and colleagues tested a hypothesis called discontinuous replication. This hypothesis held that primase synthesizes new RNA primers for lagging strands as the moving replication fork opens single-stranded regions of DNA, and that DNA polymerase uses these primers to synthesize short lagging-strand DNA fragments that are linked together into a continuous strand. These ideas are illustrated in **FIGURE 15.10**.

Note that Figure 15.10 shows details of how lagging-strand synthesis occurs in *E. coli*. The overall process, however, applies to all groups of organisms—bacteria, archaea, and eukaryotes. The basic reactions of lagging-strand synthesis are universal. The differences lie in the names or specific properties of the key proteins and enzymes.

To explore the discontinuous replication hypothesis, Okazaki's group set out to test a key prediction: Could they find short DNA fragments produced during replication? Their critical experiment was based on the pulse–chase strategy (see Chapter 7). They added a brief "pulse" of radioactive deoxyribonucleotides to *E. coli* cells, followed by a "chase" of nonradioactive deoxyribonucleotides. According to the discontinuous replication model, some of these radioactive deoxyribonucleotides should first appear in short, fragments of DNA.

**The Discovery of Okazaki Fragments**   As predicted, the researchers succeeded in finding short DNA fragments when they purified DNA from the experimental cells, separated the two strands of DNA, and analyzed the size of the molecules

**1. Primer added.** Primase synthesizes RNA primer.

**2. First fragment synthesized.** DNA polymerase III works in 5′→ 3′ direction, synthesizing first Okazaki fragment of lagging strand.

**3. Second fragment synthesized.** Primase and DNA polymerase III synthesize another Okazaki fragment.

**4. Primer replaced.** DNA polymerase I removes ribonucleotides of primer, replaces them with deoxyribonucleotides in 5′→ 3′ direction.

**5. Gap closed.** DNA ligase closes gap in sugar–phosphate backbone.

**FIGURE 15.10 Lagging-Strand Synthesis.**

by centrifugation. A small number of labeled DNA fragments about 1000 base pairs long were present immediately after the pulse. These short DNAs came to be known as **Okazaki fragments** and are shown in steps 2 and 3 of Figure 15.10. These small DNAs became larger during the chase as they were linked together into longer pieces. Subsequent work showed that Okazaki fragments in eukaryotes are even smaller—just 100 to 200 base pairs long.

How are Okazaki fragments connected? First, as step 4 of Figure 15.10 shows, in *E. coli* a specialized DNA polymerase called DNA polymerase I attaches to the 3′ end of an Okazaki fragment. As DNA polymerase I moves along in the 5′ → 3′ direction, it removes that RNA primer ahead of it and replaces the ribonucleotides with the appropriate deoxyribonucleotides.

Once the RNA primer is removed and replaced by DNA, an enzyme called **DNA ligase** catalyzes the formation of a phosphodiester bond between the adjacent fragments (Figure 15.10, step 5). ✔ If you understand lagging-strand synthesis, you should be able to draw what the two newly synthesized molecules of DNA at a single replication fork would look like if DNA ligase were defective.

In eukaryotes, the mechanism for primer removal is different, but the mechanism of synthesizing short Okazaki fragments that are later joined into an unbroken chain of DNA is the same.

Working together, the enzymes that open the replication fork and manage the synthesis of the leading and lagging strands (**TABLE 15.1**) produce faithful copies of DNA before cell division. Although separate enzymes are drawn at different locations around the replication fork in Figures 15.8 and 15.10, in reality, all these enzymes are joined into the **replisome,** a large macromolecular machine. In *E. coli*, the replisome contains two copies of DNA polymerase III that are actively engaged in DNA synthesis. As shown in **FIGURE 15.11**, the lagging strand loops out and

**SUMMARY TABLE 15.1**    **Proteins Required for DNA Synthesis in Bacteria**

| Name | Structure | Function |
|---|---|---|
| ***Opening the helix*** | | |
| Helicase | | Catalyzes the breaking of hydrogen bonds between base pairs to open the double helix |
| Single-strand DNA-binding proteins (SSBPs) | | Stabilizes single-stranded DNA |
| Topoisomerase | | Breaks and rejoins the DNA double helix to relieve twisting forces caused by the opening of the helix |
| ***Leading strand synthesis*** | | |
| Primase | | Catalyzes the synthesis of the RNA primer |
| DNA polymerase III | | Extends the leading strand |
| Sliding clamp | | Holds DNA polymerase in place during strand extension |
| ***Lagging strand synthesis*** | | |
| Primase | | Catalyzes the synthesis of the RNA primer on an Okazaki fragment |
| DNA polymerase III | | Extends an Okazaki fragment |
| Sliding clamp | | Holds DNA polymerase in place during strand extension |
| DNA polymerase I | | Removes the RNA primer and replaces it with DNA |
| DNA ligase | | Catalyzes the joining of Okazaki fragments into a continuous strand |

**FIGURE 15.11 The Replisome.** The enzymes required for DNA synthesis are organized into a macromolecular machine. Note how the lagging strand loops out as the leading strand is being synthesized.

check your understanding

**C Y U**

**If you understand that . . .**
- DNA synthesis begins at specific origins of replication on the chromosome and then proceeds in both directions.
- Synthesis at the replication fork occurs in three steps: (1) Helicase opens the double helix, SSBPs stabilize the exposed single strands, and topoisomerase prevents twists downstream of the fork; (2) DNA polymerase synthesizes the leading strand after primase has added an RNA primer; and (3) A series of enzymes synthesize the lagging strand.
- Lagging-strand synthesis cannot be continuous, because it moves away from the replication fork. In bacteria, enzymes called primase, DNA polymerase III, DNA polymerase I, and ligase work in sequence to synthesize Okazaki fragments and link them into a continuous whole.

✔ **You should be able to . . .**
1. Explain the function of primase.
2. Explain why DNA polymerase I is used predominantly on the lagging strand.

*Answers are available in Appendix A.*

around the complex, allowing the replisome to move as a single unit as it follows the replication fork. After the DNA polymerase on the lagging strand completes synthesis of an Okazaki fragment, it is released from the DNA and reassembles on the most recently synthesized primer.

## 15.4 Replicating the Ends of Linear Chromosomes

The circular DNA molecules in bacteria and archaea can be synthesized by the enzymes introduced in Section 15.3, and so can most of the linear DNA molecules found in eukaryotes. But replication at the very ends of linear eukaryotic chromosomes is another story altogether. Replication of chromosome ends requires a specialized DNA replication enzyme that has been the subject of intense research.

### The End Replication Problem

The region at the end of a eukaryotic chromosome is called a **telomere** (literally, "end-part"). **FIGURE 15.12** illustrates the problem that arises during the replication of telomeres.

- When the replication fork reaches the end of a linear chromosome, a eukaryotic DNA polymerase synthesizes the leading strand all the way to the end of the parent DNA template (step 1 and step 2, top strand). As a result, leading-strand synthesis results in a double-stranded copy of the DNA molecule.

- On the lagging strand, primase adds an RNA primer close to the tip of the chromosome (see step 2, bottom strand).

- DNA polymerase synthesizes the final Okazaki fragment on the lagging strand (step 3). An enzyme that degrades ribonucleotides removes the primer.

**PROCESS: PROBLEMS WITH COPYING THE ENDS OF LINEAR CHROMOSOMES**

Leading strand · DNA polymerase Sliding clamp · End of chromosome · Lagging strand · Helicase

**1. DNA unwinding completed.** Helicase unwinds end of DNA helix (at end of chromosome).

RNA primer · Primase

**2. Leading strand completed.** DNA polymerase completes the leading strand. Primase synthesizes RNA primer near the end of the template for the lagging strand.

DNA polymerase · Last Okazaki fragment

**3. Lagging strand completed.** DNA polymerase synthesizes the last Okazaki fragment in lagging strand.

**4. Lagging strand too short.** No DNA synthesis occurs after primer is removed.

No primer for DNA polymerase; unreplicated end will degrade, shortening chromosome

Unreplicated end

**FIGURE 15.12 Chromosomes Shorten during Normal DNA Replication.** An RNA primer is added to the lagging strand near the end of the chromosome. Once the primer is removed, it cannot be replaced with DNA. As a result, the chromosome shortens.

DNA polymerase is unable to add DNA near the tip of the chromosome, because it cannot synthesize DNA without a primer (step 4). As a result, the single-stranded DNA that is left stays single stranded.

The single-stranded DNA at the end of the lagging strand is eventually degraded, which results in the shortening of the chromosome. If this process were to continue unabated, every chromosome would shorten by about 50 to 100 deoxyribonucleotides each time DNA replication occurred. Over time, linear chromosomes would vanish.

## Telomerase Solves the End Replication Problem

How do eukaryotes maintain their chromosomes? One answer emerged after Elizabeth Blackburn, Carol Greider, and Jack Zostak reported two striking discoveries:

1. Telomeres do not contain genes but are made of short stretches of bases that are repeated over and over. In human telomeres, for example, the base sequence TTAGGG is repeated thousands of times.

2. A remarkable enzyme called telomerase that carries its own template is involved in replicating telomeres.

**Telomerase** is extraordinary because it catalyzes the synthesis of DNA from an RNA template that it contains. Telomerase adds DNA onto the end of a chromosome to prevent it from getting shorter.

**FIGURE 15.13** shows one model for how telomerase works to maintain the ends of eukaryotic chromosomes.

**Step 1** The unreplicated segment of the telomere at the 3′ end of the template for the lagging strand forms a single-stranded "overhang".

**Step 2** Telomerase binds to the overhanging single-stranded DNA and begins DNA synthesis. The template for this reaction is a portion of the RNA held within telomerase.

**Step 3** Telomerase synthesizes DNA in the 5′ → 3′ direction and catalyzes repeated additions of the same short DNA sequence to the end of the growing single strand.

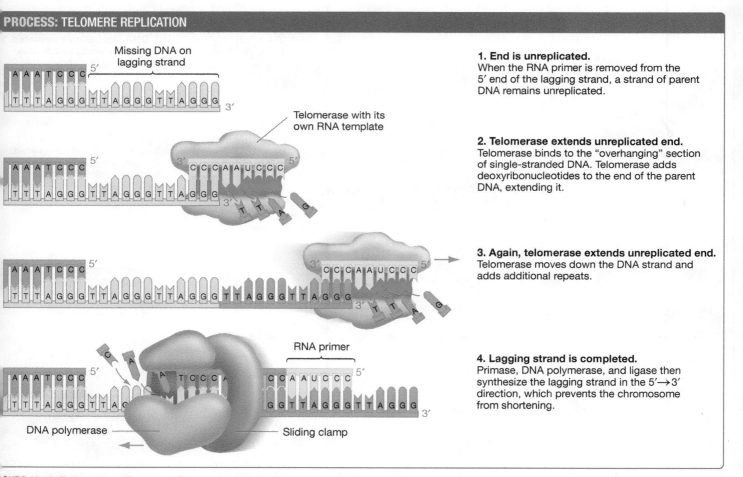

**PROCESS: TELOMERE REPLICATION**

Missing DNA on lagging strand

**1. End is unreplicated.**
When the RNA primer is removed from the 5′ end of the lagging strand, a strand of parent DNA remains unreplicated.

Telomerase with its own RNA template

**2. Telomerase extends unreplicated end.**
Telomerase binds to the "overhanging" section of single-stranded DNA. Telomerase adds deoxyribonucleotides to the end of the parent DNA, extending it.

**3. Again, telomerase extends unreplicated end.**
Telomerase moves down the DNA strand and adds additional repeats.

RNA primer

**4. Lagging strand is completed.**
Primase, DNA polymerase, and ligase then synthesize the lagging strand in the 5′→3′ direction, which prevents the chromosome from shortening.

DNA polymerase — Sliding clamp

**FIGURE 15.13 Telomerase Prevents Shortening of Telomeres during Replication.** By extending the number of repeated sequences in the 5′ → 3′ direction, telomerase provides room for enzymes to add an RNA primer to the lagging-strand template. Normal DNA replication enzymes can then fill in the missing section of the lagging strand.

**QUESTION** Would this telomerase work as well if its RNA template had a different sequence?

**Step 4** Once the single-stranded overhang on the parent strand is lengthened, the normal enzymes of DNA synthesis use this strand as a template to synthesize a complementary strand. The result is that the lagging strand becomes slightly longer than it was originally.

## Telomerase Regulation

The way telomerase is regulated is just as remarkable as the enzyme itself. Telomerase is active in only a limited number of cell types. In humans, for example, active telomerase is found primarily in the cells that produce gametes. Most **somatic cells,** meaning cells that are not involved in gamete formation, lack telomerase activity. As predicted, the chromosomes of somatic cells gradually shorten with each mitotic division, becoming progressively smaller as an individual ages.

These observations led to the hypothesis that the number of cell divisions possible for a somatic cell would be limited by the initial length of its telomeres. Carol Greider and colleagues tested this hypothesis by obtaining cells with a variety of telomere lengths from donors aged newborn to 90 years old and growing these cells in culture. (For an introduction to cell culture, see **BioSkills 12** in Appendix B.) Results of their study are shown in **FIGURE 15.14**. As predicted, there was a positive relationship between initial telomere length and the number of cell divisions before cells stop dividing—longer initial telomere length allowed a greater number of cell divisions, regardless of the donor's age.

You've probably noticed that the data points in Figure 15.14 do not fall perfectly on a line. This scatter or noise is typical in many studies. In interpreting results like these, researchers must consider what might account for the scatter and use statistical tests (see **BioSkills 4** in Appendix B) to determine how reliable the results are likely to be.

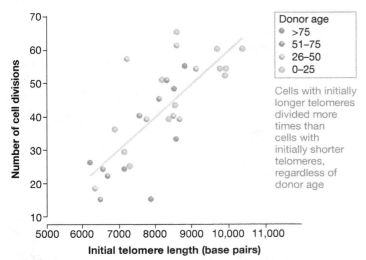

**FIGURE 15.14 Telomere Length Predicts the Number of Divisions before Cells Stop Dividing.**
DATA: Allsopp, R. C., et al. 1992. *Proceedings of the National Academy of Sciences*, 82: 10114–10118.

If telomere shortening controls the number of divisions possible for a cell, then a related prediction is that by restoring telomerase in somatic cells, these cells should be freed from growth limitations. As predicted, when researchers added telomerase to human cells growing in culture, the cells continued dividing long past the age when otherwise identical cells stop growing. Most biologists are convinced that telomere shortening has a role in limiting the number of cell divisions for somatic cells.

There is a dark side of telomerase activity, however. Unlike the somatic cells they derive from, most cancer cells have active telomerase. Many cancer biologists have proposed that telomerase activity allows the unlimited divisions of cancer cells. A simple prediction is that by inhibiting telomerase, the progression of cancer can be slowed or stopped. When combined with other approaches, could drugs that knock out telomerase be an effective way to fight cancer? Unfortunately, the complexity of cancer often thwarts such simple predictions. So far, answers to this question are unclear. Research continues.

## 15.5 Repairing Mistakes and DNA Damage

DNA polymerases work fast. In *E. coli*, for example, each replication fork advances about 500 nucleotides per second. But the replication process is also astonishingly accurate. In organisms ranging from *E. coli* to animals, the error rate during DNA replication averages about one mistake per *billion* deoxyribonucleotides.

This level of accuracy is critical. Humans, for example, develop from a fertilized egg that has roughly 12 billion deoxyribonucleotides in its DNA. This DNA is replicated over and over to create the trillions of cells that eventually make up the adult body. If more than one or two mutations occurred during each cell division cycle as a person developed, genes would be riddled with errors by the time the individual reached maturity. Genes that contain errors are often defective.

Based on these observations, it is no exaggeration to claim that the accurate replication of DNA is a matter of life and death. Natural selection favors individuals with enzymes that copy DNA quickly and accurately.

These observations raise a key question. How can the enzymes of DNA replication be as precise as they are?

## Correcting Mistakes in DNA Synthesis

As DNA polymerase marches along a DNA template, hydrogen bonding occurs between incoming deoxyribonucleotides and the deoxyribonucleotides on the template strand. DNA polymerases are selective about the bases they add to a growing strand because (1) the correct base pairings (A-T and G-C) are energetically the most favorable, and (2) these correct pairings have a distinct shape. As a result, DNA polymerase inserts an incorrect deoxyribonucleotide (**FIGURE 15.15a**) only about once in every 100,000 bases added.

An error rate of one in 100,000 seems low, but it is much higher than the rate of one in a billion listed at the start of this section. What happens when DNA polymerase makes a mistake?

**DNA Polymerase Proofreads** Biologists learned more about how DNA synthesis could be so accurate when they found mutant cells in which DNA synthesis was *in*accurate.

Specifically, researchers found *E. coli* mutants with error rates that were 100 times greater than normal. Recall that a mutant is an individual with a novel trait caused by a mutation (see Chapter 14). In the case of *E. coli* mutants with high error rates

**a)** DNA polymerase adds a mismatched base...

**b)** ...but detects the mistake and corrects it.

**FIGURE 15.15 DNA Polymerase Can Proofread.** If a mismatch such as the pairing of A with C occurs **(a)**, DNA polymerase can act as a $3' \rightarrow 5'$ exonuclease, meaning that it can remove bases in that direction **(b)**. The DNA polymerase then adds the correct base.

in DNA replication, biologists found a defect in a portion of the DNA polymerase III enzyme called the ε (epsilon) subunit. Further analyses showed that the ε subunit acts as an exonuclease—meaning an enzyme that removes deoxyribonucleotides from the ends of DNA strands (**FIGURE 15.15b**).

If a newly added deoxyribonucleotide is not correctly paired with a base on the complementary strand, the positioning of the incorrect deoxyribonucleotide provides a poor substrate for DNA polymerase to extend. This is because the geometry of incorrect base pairs differs from that of the correct A-T and G-C pairs. DNA polymerase's active site can detect these shapes and will add a new deoxyribonucleotide only when the previous base pair is correct. In wild-type *E. coli*, the polymerase pauses when it detects the wrong shape, and the exonuclease activity of the ε subunit removes the mismatched deoxyribonucleotide.

These findings led to the conclusion that DNA polymerase III can **proofread.** If the wrong base is added during DNA synthesis, the enzyme pauses, removes the mismatched deoxyribonucleotide that was just added, and then proceeds again with synthesis.

Eukaryotic DNA polymerases have the same type of proofreading ability. Typically, proofreading reduces the overall error rate of DNA synthesis to about one mistake in 10 million bases added. Is this accurate enough? The answer remains no.

**Mismatch Repair** If—despite its proofreading ability—DNA polymerase leaves a mismatched base behind in the newly synthesized strand, a battery of enzymes springs into action to correct the problem. **Mismatch repair** occurs when mismatched bases are corrected after DNA synthesis is complete.

The proteins responsible for mismatch repair were discovered in the same way proofreading was—by analyzing *E. coli* mutants. In this case, the mutants had normal DNA polymerase III but abnormally high mutation rates.

The first mutation that caused a deficiency in mismatch repair was identified in the late 1960s and was called *mutS*. (The *mut* is short for "mutator.") Twenty years later, researchers had identified 10 proteins involved in the identification and repair of base-pair mismatches in *E. coli*.

These proteins recognize the mismatched base, remove a section containing the incorrect base from the newly synthesized strand, and fill in the correct bases using the older strand as a template. In *E. coli*, chemical marks on the older strand allow the enzymes to distinguish the original strand from the newly synthesized strand. Eukaryotes use a different scheme to recognize the old and new strands of DNA.

This final layer of error detection and correction brings the overall error rate of DNA synthesis down to roughly one mistake per billion deoxyribonucleotides. The mismatch-repair enzymes are like a copy editor who corrects the errors that a writer—DNA polymerase—did not catch.

The importance of mismatch repair is revealed by grim discoveries: Mutations in components of the mismatch repair system are observed in many common human cancers, where they play an important role in cancer development and progression.

## Repairing Damaged DNA

Even after DNA is synthesized and proofread and mismatches repaired, the job of ensuring accuracy doesn't end. Genes are under constant assault. DNA is damaged by sunlight, X-rays, and many chemicals like the hydroxyl (OH) radicals produced during aerobic metabolism, aflatoxin B1 found in moldy peanuts and corn, and benzo[α]pyrene in cigarette smoke. If this damage were ignored, mutations would quickly accumulate to lethal levels. To fix problems caused by chemical attack, radiation, or other events, organisms have evolved a wide array of DNA damage-repair systems. As an example, consider the **nucleotide excision repair** system that works on DNA damage caused by ultraviolet light and many different chemicals.

Ultraviolet (UV) light in sunlight—and tanning booths—can cause a covalent bond to form between adjacent pyrimidine bases within the same DNA strand. The thymine-thymine pair illustrated in **FIGURE 15.16** is a common example. This defect, called a thymine dimer, creates a kink in the structure of DNA. The kink stalls standard DNA polymerases, blocking DNA replication. If the damage is not repaired, the cell may die.

Nucleotide excision repair fixes thymine dimers and many other types of damage that distort the DNA helix. In the first step of excision repair, an enzyme recognizes the kink in the DNA helix (step 1 in **FIGURE 15.17**). Once a damaged region is recognized, another enzyme removes a segment of single-stranded DNA containing the defective sequence (step 2). The intact DNA strand provides a template for synthesis of a corrected strand, and the 3′ hydroxyl of the DNA strand next to the gap serves as a primer (step 3). DNA ligase links the newly synthesized DNA to

the original undamaged DNA (step 4). As with mismatch repair, multiple enzymes work together and DNA synthesis plays a central role in repair.

What happens when a human DNA repair system is defective?

## Xeroderma Pigmentosum: A Case Study

**Xeroderma pigmentosum (XP)** is a rare autosomal recessive disease in humans. Individuals with this condition are extremely sensitive to ultraviolet (UV) light. Their skin develops lesions including rough, scaly patches and irregular dark spots after even slight exposure to sunlight.

In 1968 James Cleaver proposed a connection between XP and DNA nucleotide excision repair. He knew that mutants of *E. coli* had defects in nucleotide excision repair that caused an increased sensitivity to radiation. Cleaver's hypothesis was that people with XP have similar mutations. He proposed that they are extremely sensitive to sunlight because they are unable to repair damage induced by UV light.

Cleaver and other researchers made extensive use of cell cultures (**BioSkills 12**, see Appendix B) to study the hypothesized connection between DNA damage, faulty nucleotide excision repair, and XP. They collected skin cells from people with XP and from people with normal UV light sensitivity. When these cells were grown in culture, the biologists exposed them to increasing amounts of UV radiation and recorded how many survived.

**FIGURE 15.16 UV Light Damages DNA.** When UV light strikes a section of DNA that has adjacent thymines, the energy can break bonds within each base and lead to the formation of bonds *between* them. The thymine dimer that is produced causes a kink in the DNA.

✓**QUESTION** Why are infrared wavelengths much less likely than UV to damage DNA? (Hint: See Figure 10.4.)

**FIGURE 15.17 In Nucleotide Excision Repair, Defective Bases Are Removed and Replaced.**

**(a) Vulnerability of cells to UV light damage**

**(b) Ability of cells to repair UV light damage**

**FIGURE 15.18 DNA Damage from UV Light Is Not Repaired Properly in Individuals with XP. (a)** When cell cultures from unaffected individuals and XP patients are irradiated with various doses of UV light (expressed here as ergs/mm²), the percentage of cells that survive is strikingly different. **(b)** When cell cultures from unaffected individuals and XP patients are irradiated with various doses of UV light and then provided with a radioactive deoxyribonucleotide, only cells from unaffected individuals incorporate the labeled deoxyribonucleotide into their DNA.

DATA: (a) Cleaver, J. E. 1970. *Int. J. Rad. Biol.* 18: 577–565, Fig 3. (b) Cleaver, J. E. 1972. *J. Invest. Dermatol.* 58: 124–128, Fig 1.

✔**QUESTION** Why are people who cultivate a sun tan increasing their risk of developing cancer? (Hint: Tanning is a response to UV light.)

**FIGURE 15.18a** shows the results of one such study by Cleaver. Note that the intensity of the radiation is graphed on the *x*-axis, and the percentage of cells surviving is graphed on the *y*-axis. Note, too, that the *y*-axis is logarithmic. (For help with reading graphs, see **BioSkills 3** and for help with logarithms, see **BioSkills 6**, both in Appendix B.) Cell survival declined with increasing radiation dose in both types of cells, but XP cells died off much more rapidly.

The connection to nucleotide excision repair systems was confirmed in a separate study when Cleaver exposed cells from unaffected and XP individuals to various amounts of UV light and then incubated the cells with a radioactive deoxyribonucleotide to label DNA synthesized during DNA repair. If repair is defective in XP individuals, then their cells should incorporate little radioactive deoxyribonucleotide into their DNA. Cells from unaffected individuals, in contrast, should incorporate large amounts of labeled deoxyribonucleotide into their DNA as it is repaired.

As **FIGURE 15.18b** shows, this is exactly what happens. Here the amount of radioactive deoxyribonucleotides incorporated into DNA is graphed against radiation dose. Increasingly large amounts of radioactivity are found in the DNA of healthy cells as UV dose increases, but almost no such increase occurs in XP cells. These data are consistent with the hypothesis that nucleotide excision repair is virtually nonexistent in XP individuals.

Genetic analyses of XP patients have shown that the condition can result from mutations in any of eight genes. This discovery is not surprising in light of the large number of enzymes involved in repairing damaged DNA.

As you saw for mismatch repair, defects in DNA repair genes are frequently associated with cancer. Individuals with xeroderma pigmentosum, for example, are 1000 to 2000 times more likely to get skin cancer than are individuals with intact excision repair systems. To explain this pattern, biologists suggest that if DNA damage in the genes involved in the cell cycle goes unrepaired, mutations will result that may allow the cell to grow in an uncontrolled manner. Tumor formation could result. Recall

**check your understanding**

**If you understand that . . .**

- DNA polymerases occasionally add the wrong base during DNA synthesis.
- Proofreading by DNA polymerase and mismatch repair of misincorporated bases sharply reduces the number of errors.
- DNA is damaged frequently, and most of this damage can be fixed by DNA repair systems such as nucleotide excision repair.

✔ **You should be able to . . .**

1. Predict how the mutation rate would be affected if there were no differences in stability and shape between all possible base pairs.
2. Predict the effect on mutation rate of a failure in the system for distinguishing old and newly synthesized DNA.
3. State which nucleotide excision repair enzymes are specific for DNA repair and which work in both normal DNA replication and in DNA repair.

*Answers are available in Appendix A.*

that most cancers develop only after several genes have been damaged (see Chapter 12). If the overall mutation rate in a cell is elevated because of defects in DNA repair, then mutations that trigger cancer become more likely.

At this point, it's clear that genes are made of DNA and that DNA is accurately copied and passed on to offspring. How can information be stored in DNA, and how can this information be used? (These are the topics of the next two chapters.)

## If you understand . . .

### 15.1  What Are Genes Made Of?

- Experiments on viruses that had labeled proteins or DNA showed that DNA is the hereditary material.
- DNA's primary structure consists of a sugar–phosphate backbone and a sequence of nitrogen-containing bases.
- DNA's secondary structure consists of two strands in an antiparallel orientation. The strands twist into a helix and are held together by complementary pairing between bases.

✓ You should be able to interpret an imaginary experiment like the one done by Hershey and Chase that shows that $^{32}$P is found only in the pellet and that $^{35}$S is found in both the pellet and the solution.

### 15.2  Testing Early Hypotheses about DNA Synthesis

- By labeling DNA with $^{15}$N or $^{14}$N, researchers were able to validate the hypothesis that DNA replication is semiconservative.
- In semiconservative replication, each strand of a parent DNA molecule provides a template for the synthesis of a daughter strand, resulting in two complete DNA double helices.

✓ You should be able to write a sequence of double-stranded DNA that is 10 base pairs long, separate the strands, and, without comparing them, write in the bases that are added during DNA replication.

### 15.3  A Model for DNA Synthesis

- DNA synthesis requires many different enzymes, and it occurs in one direction only.
- DNA synthesis requires both a template and a primer sequence. It takes place at the replication fork where the double helix is opened.
- Synthesis of the leading strand in the $5' \rightarrow 3'$ direction is continuous, but synthesis of the lagging strand is discontinuous because on that strand, the DNA polymerase moves away from the replication fork.

- On the lagging strand, short DNA fragments called Okazaki fragments form and are joined together. Okazaki fragments are primed by a short strand of RNA.

✓ You should be able to draw and label a diagram of a replication bubble that shows (1) the $5' \rightarrow 3'$ polarity of the two parental DNA strands and (2) the leading and lagging daughter strands at each replication fork.

### 15.4  Replicating the Ends of Linear Chromosomes

- At the ends of linear chromosomes in eukaryotes, the enzyme telomerase adds short, repeated sections of DNA so that the lagging strand can be synthesized without shortening the chromosome.
- Telomerase is active in reproductive cells that eventually undergo meiosis. As a result, gametes contain chromosomes of normal length.
- Chromosomes in cells without telomerase shorten with continued cell division until their telomeres reach a critical length at which cell division no longer occurs.

✓ You should be able to explain the significance of telomerase reactivation in cancer cells.

### 15.5  Repairing Mistakes and DNA Damage

- DNA replication is remarkably accurate because (1) DNA polymerase selectively adds a deoxyribonucleotide that correctly pairs with the template strand; (2) DNA proofreads each added deoxyribonucleotide; and (3) mismatch repair enzymes remove incorrect bases once synthesis is complete and replace them with the correct base.
- DNA repair occurs after DNA has been damaged by chemicals or radiation.
- Nucleotide excision repair cuts out damaged portions of DNA and replaces them with correct sequences.
- If DNA repair enzymes are defective, mutation rate increases. Because of this, several types of human cancers are associated with defects in the genes responsible for DNA repair.

✓ You should be able to explain the logical connections between failure of repair systems, increases in mutation rate, and high likelihood of cancer developing.

# MasteringBiology

**1. MasteringBiology Assignments**

**Tutorials and Activities** DNA and RNA Structure; DNA Double Helix; DNA Replication; DNA Replication: A Closer Look; DNA Replication: A Review; DNA Replication: An Overview; DNA Synthesis; Experimental Inquiry: Does DNA Replication Follow the Conservative, Semiconservative, or Dispersive Model; Hershey–Chase Experiment

**Questions** Reading Quizzes, Blue-Thread Questions, Test Bank

**2. eText** Read your book online, search, take notes, highlight text, and more.

**3. The Study Area** Practice Test, Cumulative Test, BioFlix® 3-D Animations, Videos, Activities, Audio Glossary, Word Study Tools, Art

## You should be able to . . .

### ✓ TEST YOUR KNOWLEDGE
Answers are available in Appendix A

1. What does it mean to say that strands in a double helix are antiparallel?
   a. Their primary sequences consist of a sequence of *complementary* bases.
   b. They each have a sugar–phosphate backbone.
   c. They each have a 5′ → 3′ directionality.
   d. They have opposite directionality, or polarity.

2. Which of the following is *not* a property of DNA polymerase?
   a. It adds dNTPs only in the 5′ → 3′ direction.
   b. It requires a primer to work.
   c. It is associated with a sliding clamp only on the leading strand.
   d. Its exonuclease activity is involved in proofreading.

3. The enzyme that removes twists in DNA ahead of the replication fork is _____.

4. What is the function of primase?
   a. synthesis of the short section of double-stranded DNA required by DNA polymerase
   b. synthesis of a short RNA, complementary to single-stranded DNA
   c. closing the gap at the 3′ end of DNA after excision repair
   d. removing primers and synthesizing a short section of DNA to replace them

5. How are Okazaki fragments synthesized?
   a. using the leading strand template, and synthesizing 5′ → 3′
   b. using the leading strand template, and synthesizing 3′ → 5′
   c. using the lagging strand template, and synthesizing 5′ → 3′
   d. using the lagging strand template, and synthesizing 3′ → 5′

6. An enzyme that uses an internal RNA template to synthesize DNA is _____.

### ✓ TEST YOUR UNDERSTANDING
Answers are available in Appendix A

7. Researchers design experiments so that only one thing is different between the treatments that are being compared. In the Hershey–Chase experiment, what was this single difference?

8. What is the relationship between defective DNA repair and cancer?

9. Why is the synthesis of the lagging strand of DNA discontinuous? How is it possible for the synthesis of the leading strand to be continuous?

10. Explain how telomerase prevents linear chromosomes from shortening during replication.

11. Predict what would occur in a bacterial mutant that lost the ability to chemically mark the template strand of DNA.
   a. The mutation rate would increase.
   b. The ability of DNA polymerase to discriminate between correct and incorrect base pairs would decrease.
   c. The energy differences between correct and incorrect base pairs would decrease.
   d. The energy differences between correct and incorrect base pairs would increase.

12. What aspect of DNA structure makes it possible for the enzymes of nucleotide excision repair to recognize many different types of DNA damage?
   a. the polarity of each DNA strand
   b. the antiparallel orientation of strands in the double helix
   c. the energy differences between correct and incorrect base pairs
   d. the regularity of DNA's overall structure

**13.** If you could engineer an activity into DNA polymerase to allow both strands to follow the replication fork, what would this additional activity be?
**a.** the ability to begin DNA synthesis without a primer
**b.** the ability to proofread in the $5' \to 3'$ direction
**c.** the ability to synthesize DNA in the $3' \to 5'$ direction
**d.** the ability to synthesize DNA without using a template

**14.** In the late 1950s, Herbert Taylor grew bean root-tip cells in a solution of radioactive thymidine and allowed them to undergo one round of DNA replication. He then transferred the cells to a solution without the radioactive deoxyribonucleotide, allowed them to replicate again, and examined their chromosomes for the presence of radioactivity. His results are shown in the following figure, where red indicates a radioactive chromatid.

Nonradioactive chromosome    Radioactive chromatids

**1.** DNA replication in radioactive solution  **2.** Mitosis  **3.** DNA replication in nonradioactive solution

**a.** Draw diagrams explaining the pattern of radioactivity observed in the sister chromatids after the first and second rounds of replication.
**b.** What would the results of Taylor's experiment be if eukaryotes used a conservative mode of DNA replication?

**15.** The graph that follows shows the survival of four different *E. coli* strains after exposure to increasing doses of ultraviolet light. The wild-type strain is normal, but the other strains have a mutation in either a gene called *uvrA*, a gene called *recA*, or both.

DATA: Howard-Flanders, P., and R. P. Boyce. 1966. *Radiation Research Supplement* 6: 156–184, Fig. 8.

**a.** Which strains are most sensitive to UV light? Which strains are least sensitive?
**b.** What are the relative contributions of these genes to the repair of UV damage?

**16.** **QUANTITATIVE** Assuming that each replication fork moves at a rate of 500 base pairs per second, how long would it take to replicate the *E. coli* chromosome (with 4.6 million base pairs) from a single origin of replication?

# 16 How Genes Work

In this chapter you will learn how

Genetic information flows from DNA → RNA → proteins

by asking ↓

**What do genes do?** 16.1

then examining ↓

**The central dogma of molecular biology** 16.2

and analyzing ↓

**The genetic code, with its 3-letter "words"** 16.3

which together explain ↓

**How mutations can modify genes and genomes** 16.4

This image shows a normal human male spectral karyotype—a micrograph of metaphase chromosomes stained to show different homologous chromosome pairs. This chapter explores how DNA sequences in chromosomes are related to phenotypes.

This chapter is part of the Big Picture. See how on pages 366–367.

DNA has been called the blueprint of life. If an organism's DNA is like a set of blueprints, then its cells are like construction sites, and the enzymes inside a cell are like construction workers. But how does the DNA inside each cell assemble this team of skilled laborers and specify the materials needed to build and maintain the cell, and remodel it when conditions change?

Mendel provided insights that made the study of these questions possible. He discovered that particular alleles are associated with certain phenotypes and that alleles do not change when transmitted from parent to offspring. Later, the chromosome theory of inheritance established that genes are found in chromosomes, whose movement during meiosis explains Mendel's results.

The science of molecular biology began with the discovery that DNA is the hereditary material and that DNA is a double-helical structure containing sequences of four bases. From these early advances, it was clear that genes are made of DNA and that genes carry the instructions for making and maintaining an individual.

✔ When you see this checkmark, stop and test yourself. Answers are available in Appendix A.

But biologists still didn't know how the information in DNA is translated into action. How does **gene expression**—the process of converting archived information into molecules that actually do things in the cell—occur?

This chapter introduces some of the most pivotal ideas in all of biology—ideas that connect genotypes to phenotypes by revealing how genes work at the molecular level. They also speak to the heart of a key attribute of life: processing genetic information to produce a living organism. (You can see how these concepts fit into the Big Picture of Genetic Information on pages 366–367.)

Understanding how genes work triggered a major transition in biological science. Instead of thinking about genes solely in relation to their effects on eye color in fruit flies or on seed shape in garden peas, biologists could begin analyzing the molecular composition of genes and their products. The molecular revolution in biology took flight.

# 16.1 What Do Genes Do?

Although biologists of the early twentieth century made tremendous progress in understanding how genes are inherited, an explicit hypothesis explaining what genes do did not appear until 1941. That year George Beadle and Edward Tatum published a series of breakthrough experiments on a bread mold called *Neurospora crassa*.

Beadle and Tatum's research was inspired by an idea that was brilliant in its simplicity. As Beadle said: "One ought to be able to discover what genes do by making them defective." The idea was to knock out a gene by damaging it and then infer what the gene does by observing the phenotype of the mutant individual.

Today, alleles that do not function at all are called **knock-out, null,** or **loss-of-function alleles.** Creating knock-out mutant alleles and analyzing their effects is still one of the most common research strategies in studies of gene function. But Beadle and Tatum were the pioneers.

## The One-Gene, One-Enzyme Hypothesis

To start their work, Beadle and Tatum exposed a large number of *N. crassa* cells to radiation. As described earlier (Chapter 15), radiation can damage the double-helical structure of DNA—often in a way that makes the affected gene nonfunctional.

Their next step was to examine the mutant cells. Eventually they succeeded in finding *N. crassa* mutants that could not make specific compounds. For example, one of the mutants could not make pyridoxine, also called vitamin B$_6$, even though normal individuals can. Further, Beadle and Tatum showed that the inability to synthesize pyridoxine was due to a defect in a single gene, and that the inability to synthesize other molecules was due to defects in other genes.

These results inspired their **one-gene, one-enzyme hypothesis.** Beadle and Tatum proposed that the mutant *N. crassa* could not make pyridoxine because it lacked an enzyme required to synthesize the compound. They further proposed that the lack of the enzyme was due to a genetic defect. Based on analyses of knock-out mutants, the one-gene, one-enzyme hypothesis claimed that each gene contains the information needed to make an enzyme.

## An Experimental Test of the Hypothesis

Three years later, Adrian Srb and Norman Horowitz published a rigorous test of the one-gene, one-enzyme hypothesis. These biologists focused on the ability of *N. crassa* to synthesize the amino acid arginine. In the lab, normal cells of this bread mold grow well on a laboratory culture medium that lacks arginine. This is possible because *N. crassa* cells are able to synthesize their own arginine.

Previous work had shown that organisms synthesize arginine in a series of steps called a **metabolic pathway.** As **FIGURE 16.1** shows, compounds called ornithine and citrulline are intermediate products in the metabolic pathway leading to arginine. Specific enzymes are required to synthesize ornithine, convert ornithine to citrulline, and change citrulline to arginine. Srb and Horowitz hypothesized that specific *N. crassa* genes are responsible for producing each of the three enzymes involved.

To test this idea, Srb and Horowitz used radiation to create a large number of mutant cells. However, radiation is equally likely to damage DNA and mutate genes in any part of the organism's genome, and most organisms have thousands or tens of thousands of genes. Of the many mutants the biologists created, how could they find the handful that specifically knocked out a step in the pathway for arginine synthesis?

To find the mutants they were looking for, the researchers performed what is now known as a genetic screen. A **genetic screen** is any technique for picking certain types of mutants out of many randomly generated mutants.

Srb and Horowitz began their screen by raising colonies of irradiated cells on a medium that included arginine. Then they transferred a sample of each colony to a medium that *lacked* arginine. If an individual could grow in the presence of arginine but failed to grow without arginine, they concluded that it couldn't make its own arginine.

**Metabolic pathway for arginine synthesis:** Precursor → (Enzyme 1) → Ornithine → (Enzyme 2) → Citrulline → (Enzyme 3) → Arginine

**FIGURE 16.1 Different Enzymes Catalyze Each Step in the Metabolic Pathway for Arginine.**

✔**QUESTION** If a cell lacked enzyme 2 but was placed in growth medium with ornithine, could it grow? Could it grow if it received citrulline instead?

The biologists followed up by confirming that the offspring of these cells also had this defect. Based on these data, they were confident that they had isolated individuals with mutations in one or more of the genes for the enzymes shown in Figure 16.1.

To test the one-gene, one-enzyme hypothesis, the biologists grew each mutant under four different conditions: on normal media without added arginine, and on normal medium supplemented with ornithine, citrulline, or arginine.

As **FIGURE 16.2** shows, the results from these growth experiments were dramatic. Some of the mutant cells were able to grow on some of these media but not on others. More specifically, the mutants fell into three distinct classes, which the researchers called *arg1*, *arg2*, and *arg3*.

As the "Interpretation" section of the figure shows, the data make sense if each type of mutant lacked a different, specific step in a metabolic pathway because of a defect in a particular gene. In short, Srb and Horowitz had documented a correlation between a specific genetic defect and a defect at a specific point in a metabolic pathway. This experiment convinced most investigators that the one-gene, one-enzyme hypothesis was correct.

---

## RESEARCH

### QUESTION: What do genes do?

**HYPOTHESIS:** Each gene contains the information required to make one enzyme.

**NULL HYPOTHESIS:** Genes do not have a one-to-one correspondence with enzymes.

**EXPERIMENTAL STRATEGY:** Mutate specific genes. Test to see if each mutant also lacks one of the enzymes required for different steps in the pathway for synthesizing arginine.

**EXPERIMENTAL SETUP:** Isolate mutant *N. crassa* that cannot synthesize arginine. Grow each type of mutant on normal medium that is:

The slanted surface provides adequate room for growth

*Neurospora crassa*

Growth medium

**Not supplemented** (no ornithine, citrulline, or arginine)

**Supplemented with ornithine only** (no citrulline or arginine)

**Supplemented with citrulline only** (no ornithine or arginine)

**Supplemented with arginine only** (no ornithine or citrulline)

**PREDICTION:** There will be three distinct types of mutants, corresponding to defects in enzyme 1, enzyme 2, and enzyme 3 in the pathway for synthesizing arginine. Each type of mutant will be able to grow on different combinations of the four types of media.

**PREDICTION OF NULL HYPOTHESIS:** There will not be a simple correspondence between a particular mutation and a particular enzyme.

**RESULTS:** There are three distinct types of mutants, called *arg1*, *arg2*, and *arg3,* each defective in one enzyme.

| | | Supplement type | | | |
|---|---|---|---|---|---|
| | | None | Ornithine only | Citrulline only | Arginine only |
| Mutant type | *arg1* | no growth | GROWTH | GROWTH | GROWTH |
| | *arg2* | no growth | no growth | GROWTH | GROWTH |
| | *arg3* | no growth | no growth | no growth | GROWTH |

**INTERPRETATION:**

Precursor → Ornithine → Citrulline → Arginine

*arg1* cells lack enzyme 1

*arg2* cells lack enzyme 2

*arg3* cells lack enzyme 3

**CONCLUSION:** The one-gene, one-enzyme hypothesis is supported.

**FIGURE 16.2 Experimental Support for the One-Gene, One-Enzyme Hypothesis.** The association between specific genetic defects in *N. crassa* and specific defects in the metabolic pathway for arginine synthesis provided evidence that supported the one-gene, one-enzyme hypothesis.

SOURCE: Srb, A. M., and N. H. Horowitz. 1944. The ornithine cycle in *Neurospora* and its genetic control. *Journal of Biological Chemistry* 154: 129–139.

✔**QUESTION** Experimental designs must be repeatable so that other investigators can try the experiment themselves to check the results. Name three things that these researchers would need to describe so that others could repeat this experiment.

Follow-up work showed that genes contain the information for all the proteins produced by an organism—not just enzymes. Biologists finally understood what most genes do: They contain the instructions for making proteins.

In many cases, though, a protein is made up of several different polypeptides, each of which is a product of a different gene. Consequently, for greater accuracy, the one-gene, one-enzyme hypothesis is best called the one-gene, one-polypeptide hypothesis.

# 16.2 The Central Dogma of Molecular Biology

*How* does a gene specify the production of a protein? As soon as Beadle and Tatum's hypothesis had been supported in *N. crassa* and a variety of other organisms, this question became a central one.

Part of the answer lay in the molecular structure of the gene. Biochemists knew that the primary components of DNA were four nitrogen-containing bases: the pyrimidines thymine (abbreviated T) and cytosine (C), and the purines adenine (A) and guanine (G). They also knew that these bases were connected in a linear sequence by a sugar–phosphate backbone. Watson and Crick's model for the secondary structure of the DNA molecule (see Chapters 4 and 15) revealed that two strands of DNA are wound into a double helix, held together by hydrogen bonds between the complementary base pairs A-T and G-C.

Given DNA's structure, it appeared extremely unlikely that DNA directly catalyzed the reactions that produce proteins. Its shape was too regular to suggest that it could bind a wide variety of substrate molecules and lower the activation energy for chemical reactions. So how, then, did information translate into action?

## The Genetic Code Hypothesis

Crick proposed that the sequence of bases in DNA might act as a code. His idea was that DNA was *only* an information-storage molecule. The instructions it contained would have to be read and then translated into proteins.

Crick offered Morse code as an analogy. Morse code is a message-transmission system using dots and dashes to represent the letters of the alphabet, and in that way it can convey all the complex information of human language. Crick proposed that different combinations of bases could specify the 20 amino acids, just as different combinations of dots and dashes specify the 26 letters of the alphabet. A particular stretch of DNA, then, could contain the information needed to produce the amino acid sequence of a particular polypeptide.

In code form, the tremendous quantity of information required to build and operate a cell could be stored compactly. This information could also be copied through complementary base pairing and transmitted efficiently from one generation to the next.

It soon became apparent, however, that the information encoded in the base sequence of DNA is not translated into the amino acid sequence of proteins directly. Instead, the link between DNA as information repository and proteins as cellular machines is indirect.

## RNA as the Intermediary between Genes and Proteins

The first clue that the biological information in DNA must go through an intermediary in order to produce proteins came from knowledge of cell structure. In eukaryotic cells, DNA is enclosed within a membrane-bound organelle called the nucleus (see Chapter 7). But the cells' ribosomes, where protein synthesis takes place, are outside the nucleus, in the cytoplasm.

To make sense of this observation, François Jacob and Jacques Monod suggested that RNA molecules act as a link between genes and the protein-manufacturing centers. Jacob and Monod's hypothesis is illustrated in **FIGURE 16.3**. They predicted that short-lived molecules of RNA, which they called **messenger RNA,** or **mRNA** for short, carry information out of the nucleus from DNA to the site of protein synthesis. Messenger RNA is one of several distinct types of RNA in cells.

Follow-up research confirmed that the messenger RNA hypothesis is correct. One particularly important piece of evidence was the discovery of an enzyme that catalyzes the synthesis of RNA. This protein is called **RNA polymerase** because it polymerizes ribonucleotides into strands of RNA.

RNA polymerase synthesizes RNA molecules according to the information provided by the sequence of bases in a particular stretch of DNA. Unlike DNA polymerase, RNA polymerase

**FIGURE 16.3 The Messenger RNA Hypothesis.** In cells of eukaryotes such as plants, animals, and fungi, most DNA is found in the nucleus, but proteins are manufactured using ribosomes in the cytoplasm outside the nucleus. Biologists proposed that the information coded in DNA is carried from inside the nucleus out to the ribosomes by messenger RNA (mRNA).

oes not require a primer to begin connecting ribonucleotides ogether to produce a strand of RNA.

To test the mRNA hypothesis, researchers created a reaction ix containing three critical elements: (1) the enzyme RNA olymerase; (2) ribonucleotides containing the bases adenine A), uracil (U), guanine (G), and cytosine (C); and (3) strands f synthetic DNA that contained deoxyribonucleotides in which he only base was thymine (T).

After allowing the polymerization reaction to proceed, the iologists isolated RNA molecules that contained only the base denine.

This result supported the hypothesis that RNA polymerase ynthesizes RNA according to the rules of complementary base airing (introduced in Chapter 4), because thymine pairs with denine. Similar experiments showed that synthetic DNAs con-aining only cytosine result in the production of RNA molecules ontaining only guanine.

## issecting the Central Dogma

nce the mRNA hypothesis was accepted, Francis Crick articu-ted what became known as the central dogma of molecular bi-logy. The **central dogma** summarizes the flow of information cells. It simply states that DNA codes for RNA, which codes r proteins:

$$DNA \longrightarrow RNA \longrightarrow proteins$$

rick's simple statement encapsulates much of the research re-ewed in this chapter and the preceding one. DNA is the he-editary material. Genes consist of specific stretches of DNA that de for products used in the cell. The sequence of bases in DNA ecifies the sequence of bases in an RNA molecule, which speci-es the sequence of amino acids in a protein. In this way, genes ltimately code for proteins.

Proteins are the workers of cells, functioning not only as en-ymes but also as motors, structural elements, transporters, and olecular signals.

**he Roles of Transcription and Translation**   Biologists use spe-alized vocabulary to summarize the sequence of events cap-red in the central dogma.

. DNA is transcribed to RNA by RNA polymerase. **Transcrip-tion** is the process of copying hereditary information in DNA to RNA.

. Messenger RNA is translated to proteins in ribosomes. **Translation** is the process of using the information in nu-cleic acids to synthesize proteins.

The term transcription is appropriate. In everyday English, anscription simply means making a copy of information. The ientific use is similar because it conveys the idea that DNA acts a permanent record—an information archive or blueprint. his permanent record is copied, during transcription, to pro-ce the short-lived form called mRNA.

Translation is also an appropriate term. In everyday English, anslation refers to converting information from one language

to another. In biology, translation is the transfer of information from one type of molecule to another—from the "language" of nucleic acids to the "language" of proteins. Translation is also re-ferred to simply as protein synthesis.

The following equation summarizes the relationship between transcription and translation as well as the relationships between DNA, RNA, and proteins:

Gene expression occurs via transcription and translation.

**Linking Genotypes and Phenotypes**   An organism's genotype is determined by the sequence of bases in its DNA, while its pheno-type is a product of the proteins it produces.

To appreciate this point, consider that the proteins encoded by genes are what make the "stuff" of the cell and dictate which chemical reactions occur inside. For example, in populations of the oldfield mouse native to southeastern North America, indi-viduals have a gene for a protein called the melanocortin recep-tor. Melanocortin is a hormone—an important type of molecular signal (discussed in Chapter 11)—that works through the mela-nocortin receptor to influence how much dark pigment is depos-ited in fur. An important aspect of a mouse's phenotype—its coat color—is determined in part by the DNA sequence at the gene for this receptor (**FIGURE 16.4a**).

Later work revealed that alleles of a gene differ in their DNA sequence. As a result, the proteins produced by different alleles of the gene may differ in their amino acid sequence. If the primary structures of proteins vary, their functions are likely to vary as well.

To drive this point home, look at the DNA sequence in the portion of the melanocortin receptor gene shown in **FIGURE 16.4b**, and compare it with the sequence in Figure 16.4a. The sequences differ—meaning that they are different alleles. Now look at the protein products of each allele, and note that one of the amino acids in the protein's primary structure differs—one allele speci-fies an arginine residue; the other specifies a cysteine residue.

At the protein level, the phenotypes associated with these al-leles differ. The consequences for the mouse are striking: Mela-nocortin receptors that have arginine in this location deposit a large amount of pigment, but receptors that have cysteine in this location deposit small amounts of pigment. Whether a mouse is dark or light depends, largely, on a single base change in its DNA sequence. In this case, a tiny difference in genotype produces a large change in phenotype. The central dogma links genotypes to phenotypes.

**Exceptions to the Central Dogma**   The central dogma provided an important conceptual framework for the burgeoning field of molecular genetics and inspired a series of fundamental ques-tions about how genes and cells work. But important modifica-tions to the central dogma have occurred in the decades since Frances Crick first proposed it:

**(a)** Genetic information flows from DNA to RNA to proteins.

**DNA** (information storage)

3′ G C G T T G G A C 5′

↓ TRANSCRIPTION

**mRNA** (information carrier)

5′ C G C A A C C U G 3′

↓ TRANSLATION

**Proteins** (melanocortin receptor)

[ Arg ]—[ Asn ]—[ Leu ]

Forest mouse

Mice with this DNA sequence have **dark** coats.

**(b)** Differences in genotype may cause differences in phenotype

3′ A C G T T G G A C 5′ **GENOTYPE**

↓ TRANSCRIPTION

5′ U G C A A C C U G 3′

↓ TRANSLATION

[ Cys ]—[ Asn ]—[ Leu ]

Beach mouse

Mice with this DNA sequence have **light** coats.

**PHENOTYPE**

Physical traits that are a product of the proteins produced.

**FIGURE 16.4 The Relationship between Genotype and Phenotype.** The central dogma revealed the flow of information within the cell. The DNA sequences given in parts **(a)** and **(b)** are from different alleles (genotypes) that influence coat color (phenotypes) in oldfield mice. Forest-dwelling mice are dark, which camouflages them in their forested habitats. Beach-dwelling mice are light, which camouflages them in their sandy habitat.

- Many genes code for RNA molecules that do not function as mRNAs—they are not translated into proteins.

- In some cases, information flows from RNA back to DNA.

The discovery of a wide array of different RNA types ranks among the most profound advances in the past decade of biological science. Some RNAs form major parts of the ribosome, others help to form mRNA from a much longer precursor RNA (Chapter 17), and yet others regulate which genes are expressed (see Chapter 19). New types of RNA are still being discovered. For the genes coding for these types of RNA, information flow would be diagrammed as simply DNA → RNA.

In the early 1970s, the discovery of "reverse" information flow created the kind of excitement now being generated by the discovery of so many kinds of RNA. Some viruses, for example, have genes consisting of RNA. When some RNA viruses infect a cell, a specialized viral polymerase called **reverse transcriptase** synthesizes a DNA version of the RNA genes. In these viruses, information flows from RNA to DNA.

The human immunodeficiency virus (HIV), which causes AIDS, is an RNA virus that uses reverse transcriptase. Several of the most commonly prescribed drugs for AIDS patients fight the infection by poisoning the HIV reverse transcriptase. The drugs prevent viruses from replicating efficiently by disrupting reverse information flow.

The punch line? Crick's hypothesis is a central concept in biology, but cells, viruses, and researchers aren't dogmatic about it.

## check your understanding

**If you understand that . . .**

- Genes code for proteins, but they do so indirectly.
- The sequence of bases in DNA is used to produce RNA, including messenger RNA (mRNA), via transcription. The sequence of bases in an RNA molecule is complementary to one of the DNA strands of a gene.
- Messenger RNAs are translated into proteins.
- Differences in DNA sequence can lead to differences in the amino acid sequence of proteins.

✔ **You should be able to . . .**

List the steps that link a change in the base sequence of a gene to a change in the phenotype of an organism.

*Answers are available in Appendix A.*

## 16.3 The Genetic Code

Once biologists understood the general pattern of information flow in the cell, the next challenge was to understand the final link between DNA and proteins. Exactly how does the sequence of bases in a strand of mRNA code for the sequence of amino acids in a protein?

If this question could be answered, biologists would have cracked the **genetic code**—the rules that specify the relationship between a sequence of nucleotides in DNA or RNA and the sequence of amino acids in a protein. Researchers from all over the world took up the challenge. A race was on.

### How Long Is a Word in the Genetic Code?

The first step in cracking the genetic code was to determine how many bases make up a "word." In a sequence of mRNA, how long is a message that specifies one amino acid?

Based on some simple logic, George Gamow suggested that each code word contains three bases. His reasoning derived from the observation that 20 amino acids are commonly used in cells and from the hypothesis that each amino acid must be specified by a particular sequence of mRNA. **FIGURE 16.5** illustrates Gamow's reasoning:

- There are only four different bases in ribonucleotides (A, U, G, and C), so a one-base code could specify only four different amino acids.

- A two-base code could represent just 4 × 4, or 16, different amino acids.

- A three-base code could specify 4 × 4 × 4, or 64, different amino acids.

A three-base code provides more than enough words to code for all 20 amino acids. A three-base code is known as a **triplet code.**

Gamow's hypothesis suggested that the genetic code could be redundant. That is, more than one triplet of bases might specify the same amino acid. As a result, different three-base sequences in an mRNA—say, AAA and AAG—might code for the same amino acid—say, lysine.

The group of three bases that specifies a particular amino acid is called a **codon.** According to the triplet code hypothesis, many of the 64 codons that are possible might specify the same amino acids.

Work by Francis Crick and Sydney Brenner confirmed that codons are three bases long. Their experiments used chemicals that caused an occasional addition or deletion of a base in DNA. As predicted for a triplet code, a one-base addition or deletion in the base sequence led to a loss of function in the gene being studied. This is because a single addition or deletion mutation throws the sequence of codons, or the **reading frame,** out of register. To understand how a reading frame works, consider the sentence

"The fat cat ate the rat."

The reading frame of this sentence is a three-letter word and a space. If the fourth letter in this sentence—the *f* in *fat*—were deleted, the reading frame would transform the sentence into

"The atc ata tet her at."

This is gibberish.

When the reading frame in a DNA sequence is thrown out of register by the addition or deletion of a base, the composition of each codon changes just like the letters in each word of the example sentence above. The protein produced from the altered DNA sequence has a completely different sequence of amino acids. In terms of its normal function, this protein is gibberish.

Crick and Brenner were also able to produce DNA sequences that had deletions or additions of two base pairs or three base

**FIGURE 16.5 How Many Bases Form a "Word" in the Genetic Code?**

pairs. The only time functional proteins were produced was when three bases were added or removed. In the sentence

"The fat cat ate the rat."

the combination of removing one letter from each of the first three words might result in

"Tha tca ate the rat."

Just as the altered sentence still conveys some meaning, genes with three deletion mutations were able to produce a functional protein.

The researchers interpreted these results as strong evidence in favor of the triplet code hypothesis. Most other biologists agreed.

The confirmation of the triplet code launched an effort to determine which amino acid is specified by each of the 64 codons. Ultimately, it was successful.

## How Did Researchers Crack the Code?

The initial advance in deciphering the genetic code came in 1961, when Marshall Nirenberg and Heinrich Matthaei developed a method for synthesizing RNAs of known sequence. They began by creating a long polymer of uracil-containing ribonucleotides. These synthetic RNAs were added to an in vitro system for synthesizing proteins. The researchers analyzed the resulting amino acid chain and determined that it was polyphenylalanine—a polymer consisting of the amino acid phenylalanine.

This result provided evidence that the RNA triplet UUU codes for the amino acid phenylalanine. By complementary base pairing, it was clear that the corresponding DNA sequence would be AAA. This initial work was followed by experiments using RNAs consisting of only A or C. RNAs with only AAAAA . . . produced polypeptides composed of only lysine; poly-C RNAs (RNAs consisting of only CCCCC . . .) produced polypeptides composed entirely of proline.

Nirenberg and Philip Leder later devised a system for synthesizing specific codons. With these they performed a series of experiments in which they added each codon to a cell extract containing the 20 different amino acids, ribosomes, and other molecules required for protein synthesis. Recall that ribosomes are macromolecular machines that synthesize proteins (Chapter 7). Then the researchers determined which amino acid became bound to the ribosomes when a particular codon was present. For example, when the codon CAC was in the reaction mix, the amino acid histidine would bind to the ribosomes. This result indicated that CAC codes for histidine.

These ribosome-binding experiments allowed Nirenberg and Leder to determine which of the 64 codons coded for each of the 20 amino acids.

Researchers also discovered that certain codons are punctuation marks signaling "start of message" or "end of message." These codons indicate that protein synthesis should start at a given codon or that the protein chain is complete.

- There is one **start codon** (AUG), which signals that protein synthesis should begin at that point on the mRNA molecule. The start codon specifies the amino acid methionine.

- There are three **stop codons,** also called termination codons (UAA, UAG, and UGA). The stop codons signal that the protein is complete, they do not code for any amino acid, and they end translation.

The complete genetic code is given in **FIGURE 16.6**. Deciphering it was a tremendous achievement, requiring more than five years of work by several teams of researchers.

**FIGURE 16.6 The Genetic Code.** To read a codon in mRNA, locate its first base in the red band on the left; then move rightward to the box under the codon's second base in the blue band along the top. Finally, locate the codon's third base in the green band on the right side to learn the amino acid. By convention, codons are always written in the 5′ → 3′ direction.

**(a) Using the genetic code to predict an amino acid sequence**

The bottom strand of the DNA sequence...

5′ [ATG][GCC][AAT][GAC][TTT][CAA][TAA] 3′

3′ [TAC][CGG][TTA][CTG][AAA][GTT][ATT] 5′

...would be transcribed as

5′ [AUG][GCC][AAU][GAC][UUU][CAA][UAA] 3′

...and translated as

| Met (start) | Ala | Asn | Asp | Phe | Gln | (stop) |

**(b) Your turn—a chance to practice using the genetic code**

The bottom strand of the DNA sequence...

5′ [ATG][CTG][GAG][GGG][GTT][AGA][CAT] 3′

3′ [TAC][GAC][CTC][CCC][CAA][TCT][GTA] 5′

...would be transcribed as

5′ [ ][ ][ ][ ][ ][ ][ ] 3′

...and translated as

| | | | | | | |

Remember that RNA contains U (uracil) instead of T (thymine), and that U forms a complementary base pair with A (adenine)

**FIGURE 16.7 Using the Genetic Code.**

✔ **EXERCISE** Fill in the mRNA and amino acid sequences in part (b).

**Analyzing the Code** Once biologists had cracked the genetic code, they realized that it has a series of important properties.

- *The code is redundant.* All amino acids except methionine and tryptophan are coded by more than one codon.

- *The code is unambiguous.* A single codon never codes for more than one amino acid.

- *The code is non-overlapping.* Once the ribosome locks onto the first codon, it then reads each separate codon one after another.

- *The code is nearly universal.* With a few minor exceptions, all codons specify the same amino acids in all organisms.

- *The code is conservative.* When several codons specify the same amino acid, the first two bases in those codons are almost always identical.

The last point is subtle, but important. Here's the key: If a mutation in DNA or an error in transcription or translation affects the third position in a codon, it is less likely to change the amino acid in the final protein. This feature makes individuals less vulnerable to small, random changes or errors in their DNA sequences. Compared with randomly generated codes, the existing genetic code minimizes the phenotypic effects of small changes in DNA sequence and errors during translation. Stated another way, the genetic code does not represent a random assemblage of bases, like letters drawn from a hat. It has been honed by natural selection and is remarkably efficient.

**Using the Code** Using the genetic code and the central dogma, biologists can:

1. Predict the codons and amino acid sequence encoded by a particular DNA sequence (see **FIGURE 16.7a**).

2. Determine the set of mRNA and DNA sequences that would code for a particular sequence of amino acids.

Why is a *set* of mRNA or DNA sequences predicted from a given amino acid sequence? The answer lies in the code's redundancy. If a polypeptide contains phenylalanine, you don't know if the codon responsible is UUU or UUC.

✔ If you understand how to read the genetic code, you should be able to do the following tasks: (1) Identify the codons in Figure 16.4 and decide whether they are translated correctly. (2) Complete the exercise for **FIGURE 16.7b**. (3) Write an mRNA that codes for the amino acid sequence Ala-Asn-Asp-Phe-Gln yet is different from the one given in Figure 16.7a. Indicate the mRNA's 5′ → 3′ polarity. Then write the double-stranded DNA that corresponds to this mRNA. Indicate the 5′ → 3′ polarity of both DNA strands.

Once they understood the central dogma and genetic code, biologists were able to explore and eventually understand the molecular basis of mutation. How do novel traits—such as dwarfing in garden peas and white eye color in fruit flies—come to be?

## 16.4 How Can Mutation Modify Genes and Chromosomes?

This chapter has explored how the information archived in DNA is put into action in the form of working RNAs and proteins. Now the questions are, what happens if the information in DNA changes? In what ways can this information be changed? What are the consequences for the cell and organism?

A **mutation** is any permanent change in an organism's DNA. It is a modification in a cell's information archive—a change in its genotype. Mutations create new alleles.

Mutations can alter DNA sequences that range in size from a single base pair in DNA to whole sets of chromosomes. Let's look at these different types of mutation and their consequences.

### Point Mutation

**FIGURE 16.8** shows how a common type of mutation occurs. If a mistake is made during DNA synthesis or DNA repair, a change in the sequence of bases in DNA results. A single-base change such as this is called a **point mutation.**

What happens when point mutations occur in regions of DNA that code for proteins? To answer this question, look back at Figure 16.4 and recall that a change in a single base in DNA is associated with a difference in coat color in populations of oldfield mice. The DNA sequence in Figure 16.4a is found in dark-colored mice that live in forest habitats; the sequence in Figure 16.4b is found in light-colored mice that live in beach habitats.

Because beach-dwelling populations are evolutionarily younger than the nearby forest-dwelling populations, researchers hypothesize the following sequence of events:

1. Forest mice colonized beach habitats.

2. Either before or after the colonization event, a random point mutation occurred in a mouse that altered the melanocortin receptor gene and resulted in some offspring with light coats.

3. Light-colored mice are camouflaged in beach habitats; in sandy environments, they suffer lower predation than dark-colored mice.

4. Over time, the allele created by the point mutation increased in frequency in beach-dwelling populations.

Point mutations that cause these types of changes in the amino acid sequence of proteins are called **missense mutations.** But note that if the same G-to-A change had occurred in the third position of the same DNA codon, instead of the first position, there would have been no change in the protein produced. The mRNA codons CGC and CGU both code for arginine. A point mutation that does not change the amino acid sequence of the gene product is called a **silent mutation.**

Some point mutations disrupt major portions of a protein. Recall that a single addition or deletion mutation throws the sequence of codons out of register and alters the meaning of all subsequent codons. Such mutations are called **frameshift mutations.** Another type of point mutation with a large effect is a **nonsense mutation.** Nonsense mutations occur when a codon that specifies an amino acid is changed by mutation to one that specifies a stop codon. This causes early termination of the polypeptide chain and often results in a non-functional protein.

In terms of the impact on organisms, biologists divide mutations into three categories:

1. **Beneficial** Some mutations increase the fitness of the organism—meaning, its ability to survive and reproduce—in certain environments. The G-to-A mutation is beneficial in beach habitats because it camouflages mice.

2. **Neutral** If a mutation has no effect on fitness, it is termed neutral. Silent mutations are usually neutral.

3. **Deleterious** Because organisms tend to be well adapted to their current habitat, and because mutations are random changes in the genotype, many mutations lower fitness. These mutations are termed harmful or deleterious. The G-to-A mutation would be deleterious in the forest habitat.

Recent studies indicate that the majority of point mutations are slightly deleterious or neutral. **TABLE 16.1** (see page 314) summarizes the types of point mutations that occur in protein-coding sequences of a gene and reviews their consequences for the amino acid sequences of proteins and for fitness.

Point mutations can and do occur in DNA sequences that do not code for proteins. These mutations, however, are not referred to as missense, silent, frameshift, or nonsense mutations

**FIGURE 16.8 Unrepaired Mistakes in DNA Synthesis Lead to Point Mutations.**

**MUTANT**

**Point Mutations That Alter Codons**

| Name | Definition | Example | Consequence |
|------|-----------|---------|-------------|
| | | Original DNA sequence —— TAT TGG CTA GTA CAT | |
| | | Original mRNA transcript —— UAU UGG CUA GUA CAU | |
| | | Tyr – Trp – Leu – Val – His —— Original polypeptide | |
| **Silent** | Change in nucleotide sequence that does not change the amino acid specified by a codon | TAC TGG CTA GTA CAT<br>UAC UGG CUA GUA CAU<br>Tyr – Trp – Leu – Val – His | No change in phenotype; neutral with respect to fitness |
| **Missense** | Change in nucleotide sequence that changes the amino acid specified by codon | TAT TGT CTA GTA CAT<br>UAU UGU CUA GUA CAU<br>Tyr – Cys – Leu – Val – His | Change in primary structure of protein; may be beneficial, neutral, or deleterious |
| **Nonsense** | Change in nucleotide sequence that results in an early stop codon | TAT TGA CTA GTA CAT<br>UAU UGA CUA GUA CAU<br>Tyr – STOP | Leads to mRNA breakdown or a shortened polypeptide; usually deleterious |
| **Frameshift** | Addition or deletion of a nucleotide | TAT TCG GCT AGT ACA T<br>UAU UCG GCU AGU ACA U<br>Tyr – Ser – Ala – Ser – Thr | Reading frame is shifted, altering the meaning of all subsequent codons; almost always deleterious |

because these terms apply only to mutations that can change the protein-coding potential of a gene. If point mutations alter DNA sequences that are important for *gene expression*, they can have important effects on phenotype even though they do not change the amino acid sequence of a protein.

## Chromosome Mutations

Besides documenting various types of point mutations, biologists study larger-scale mutations that change chromosomes. You might recall, for example, that polyploidy is an increase in the number of each type of chromosome, while aneuploidy is the addition or deletion of individual chromosomes (Chapter 13).

Polyploidy, aneuploidy, and other changes in chromosome number result from chance mistakes in moving chromosomes into daughter cells during meiosis or mitosis. Polyploidy and aneuploidy are forms of mutation that don't change DNA sequences, but alter the number of chromosome copies.

In addition to changes in overall chromosome number, the composition of individual chromosomes can change in important ways. For example, chromosome segments can become detached when accidental breaks in chromosomes occur. The segments may be flipped and rejoined—a phenomenon known as a chromosome **inversion**—or become attached to a different chromosome, an event called chromosome **translocation**. When a segment of chromosome is lost, this is a **deletion,** and when additional copies of a segment are present, this is a **duplication.**

Like point mutations, chromosome mutations can be beneficial, neutral, or deleterious. For example, more than 200 different inverted sections of chromosomes were found in comparisons

of the DNA from eight phenotypically normal people. These mutations appear to be neutral. Not all chromosome mutations are so harmless, however. Chromosomes of cancer cells exhibit deleterious chromosome mutations that include aneuploidy, inversions, translocations, deletions, and duplications. **FIGURE 16.9**

**FIGURE 16.9 Chromosome-Level Mutations.** A spectral karyotype of a breast cancer cell from a female that shows chromosome rearrangements and aneuploidy typical of cancer. In a normal spectral karyotype, each chromosome is stained a single, solid color, which varies for each chromosome pair.

✔**EXERCISE** Compare this karyotype to the one shown in the chapter-opening image. Remember that females normally have two X chromosomes and males normally have one X chromosome. Which chromosomes show evidence of aneuploidy? Which chromosomes show evidence of rearrangements?

drives this point home by showing the **karyotype**—the complete set of chromosomes in a cell—of a cancerous human cell.

To summarize, point mutations and chromosome mutations are random changes in DNA that can produce new genes, new alleles, and new traits. At the level of individuals, mutations can cause disease or death or lead to increases in fitness. At the level of populations, mutations furnish the heritable variation that Mendel and Morgan analyzed and that makes evolution possible. The central role of mutation in evolution is explored in depth in Unit 5.

---

# CHAPTER 16 REVIEW

*For media, go to MasteringBiology*

## If you understand . . .

### 16.1 What Do Genes Do?

- Experiments with mutants of the bread mold *N. crassa* led to the one-gene, one-enzyme hypothesis.

- The original one-gene, one-enzyme hypothesis has been broadened to account for genes that code for proteins other than enzymes and for genes that have RNA as a final product.

✓ You should be able to use Figure 16.1 to explain what compounds could be added to the medium to allow the growth of a mutant unable to synthesize citrulline because of a mutation in the gene for enzyme 1.

### 16.2 The Central Dogma of Molecular Biology

- DNA is transcribed to messenger RNA (mRNA) by RNA polymerase, and then mRNA is translated to proteins by ribosomes. In this way, genetic information is converted from DNA to RNA to protein.

- The flow of information from DNA to RNA to protein is called the central dogma of molecular biology.

- Many RNAs do not code for proteins. Instead, these RNAs perform other important functions in the cell.

- Reverse transcriptase reverses information flow by copying RNA into DNA. Some viruses with an RNA genome use this enzyme during their replication.

✓ You should be able to explain how a compound that blocks RNA synthesis will affect protein synthesis.

### 16.3 The Genetic Code

- Each amino acid in a protein is specified by a codon—a group of three bases in mRNA.

- By synthesizing RNAs of known base composition and then observing the results of translation, researchers were able to decipher the genetic code.

- The genetic code is redundant—meaning that most of the 20 amino acids are specified by more than one codon.

- Certain codons signal where translation starts and stops.

✓ Using the genetic code shown in Figure 16.6, you should be able to write all possible mRNA sequences that would produce the following sequence of amino acids: Met-Trp-Lys-Gln.

### 16.4 How Can Mutation Modify Genes and Chromosomes?

- Mutations are random, heritable changes in DNA that range from changes in a single base to changes in the structure and number of chromosomes.

- Point mutations in protein-coding regions may have no effect on the protein (silent mutation), may change a single amino acid (missense mutation), may shorten the protein (nonsense mutation), or may shift the reading frame and cause many amino acids to be wrong (frameshift mutation).

- Mutations can have beneficial, neutral, or harmful effects on organisms.

✓ You should be able to explain how redundancy in the genetic code allows for silent mutations and whether a silent mutation is likely to be beneficial, neutral, or harmful.

### MasteringBiology

**1. MasteringBiology Assignments**

**Tutorials and Activities** Genetic Code; One-Gene One-Enzyme Hypothesis; Overview of Protein Synthesis; Role of the Nucleus and Ribosomes in Protein Synthesis; Triplet Nature of the Genetic Code

**Questions** Reading Quizzes, Blue-Thread Questions, Test Bank

**2. eText** Read your book online, search, take notes, highlight text, and more.

**3. The Study Area** Practice Test, Cumulative Test, BioFlix® 3-D Animations, Videos, Activities, Audio Glossary, Word Study Tools, Art

# You should be able to . . .

1. What does the one-gene, one-enzyme hypothesis state?
   a. Genes are composed of stretches of DNA.
   b. Genes are made of protein.
   c. Genes code for ribozymes.
   d. A single gene codes for a single protein.

2. Which of the following is an important exception to the central dogma of molecular biology?
   a. Many genes code for RNAs that function directly in the cell.
   b. DNA is the repository of genetic information in all cells.
   c. Messenger RNA is a short-lived "information carrier."
   d. Proteins are responsible for most aspects of the phenotype.

3. DNA's primary structure is made up of just four different bases, and its secondary structure is regular and highly stable. How can a molecule with these characteristics hold all the information required to build and maintain a cell?
   a. The information is first transcribed, then translated.
   b. The messenger RNA produced from DNA has much more complex secondary structures, allowing mRNA to hold much more information.

   c. A protein coded for in DNA has much more complex primary and secondary structures, allowing it to hold much more information.
   d. The information in DNA is in a code form that is based on the sequence of bases.

4. Why did researchers suspect that DNA does not code for proteins directly?

5. Which of the following describes an important experimental strategy in deciphering the genetic code?
   a. comparing the amino acid sequences of proteins with the base sequence of their genes
   b. analyzing the sequence of RNAs produced from known DNA sequences
   c. analyzing mutants that changed the code
   d. examining the polypeptides produced when RNAs of known sequence were translated

6. What is a stop codon?

7. Explain why Morse code is an appropriate analogy for the genetic code.

8. Draw a hypothetical metabolic pathway in *Neurospora crassa* composed of five substrates, five enzymes, and a product called Biological Sciazine. Number the substrates 1–5, and label the enzymes A–E, in order. (For instance, enzyme A catalyzes the reaction between substrates 1 and 2.)
   • Suppose a mutation made the gene for enzyme C nonfunctional. What molecule would accumulate in the affected cells?
   • Suppose a mutant strain can survive if substrate 5 is added to the growth medium but it cannot grow if substrates 1, 2, 3, or 4 are added. Which enzyme in the pathway is affected in this mutant?

9. How did experiments with *Neurospora crassa* mutants support the one-gene, one-enzyme hypothesis?

10. Why does a single-base deletion mutation within a protein-coding sequence usually have a more severe effect than a deletion of three adjacent bases?
    a. because single-base deletions prevent the ribosome from binding to mRNA
    b. because single-base deletions stabilize mRNA
    c. because single-base deletions change the reading frame
    d. because single-base deletions alter the meaning of individual codons

11. When researchers discovered that a combination of three deletion mutations or three addition mutations would restore the function of a gene, most biologists were convinced that the genetic code was read in triplets. Explain the logic behind this conclusion.

12. Explain why all point mutations change the genotype, but why only some point mutations change the phenotype.

13. Recall that DNA and RNA are synthesized only in the $5' \rightarrow 3'$ direction and that DNA and RNA sequences are written in the $5' \rightarrow 3'$ direction, unless otherwise noted. Consider the following DNA sequence:

    5′ TTGAAATGCCCGTTTGGAGATCGGGTTACAGCTAGTCAAAG 3′

    3′ AACTTTACGGGCAAACCTCTAGCCCAATGTCGATCAGTTTC 5′

    • Identify bases in the bottom strand that can be transcribed into start and stop codons.
    • Write the mRNA sequence that would be transcribed between start and stop codons if the bottom strand served as the template for RNA polymerase.
    • Write the amino acid sequence that would be translated from the mRNA sequence you just wrote.

14. What problems would arise if the genetic code contained only 22 codons—one for each amino acid, a start signal, and a stop signal?

15. Scientists say that a phenomenon is a "black box" if they can describe it and study its effects but don't know the underlying mechanism that causes it. In what sense was genetics—meaning the transmission of heritable traits—a black box before the central dogma of molecular biology was understood?

16. **QUANTITATIVE** One of the possibilities that researchers interested in the genetic code considered was that the code was overlapping, meaning that a single base could be part of up to three codons. How many amino acids would be encoded in the sequence 5′ AUGUUACGGAAU 3′ by a non-overlapping and maximally overlapping code?
    a. 4 (non-overlapping) and 16 (overlapping)
    b. 4 and 12
    c. 4 and 10
    d. 12 and 4

# 17 Transcription, RNA Processing, and Translation

**In this chapter you will learn how**

Information in genes directs the synthesis of RNAs and proteins

by looking at

then asking

How DNA is transcribed into RNA **17.1**

and

How eukaryotes process RNA **17.2**

How is messenger RNA translated into proteins? **17.3**

and looking closer at

The structure and function of transfer RNA **17.4**

The structure and function of ribosomes **17.5**

Extensive transcription is occurring along this gene within a frog cell. The horizontal strand in the middle of this micrograph is DNA; the strands that have been colored yellow and red, and that are coming off on either side, are RNA molecules.

Proteins are the stuff of life. They give shape to our cells, control the chemical reactions that go on inside them, and regulate how materials move into, out of, and through them. Some of these proteins may not be produced at all in some types of cells; others may be present in quantities ranging from millions of copies to fewer than a dozen.

A cell builds the proteins it needs from instructions encoded in its DNA. The central dogma of molecular biology states that the flow of information in cells is from DNA to mRNA to protein (Chapter 16). Once this pattern of information flow had been established, biologists puzzled over how cells actually accomplish the two major steps of the central dogma: transcription and

**BIG PICTURE**

This chapter is part of the Big Picture. See how on pages 366–367.

✔ When you see this checkmark, stop and test yourself. Answers are available in Appendix A.

translation. Specifically, how does RNA polymerase know where to start transcribing a gene, and where to end? And once an RNA message is produced, how is the linear sequence of ribonucleotides translated into the linear sequence of amino acids in a protein?

This chapter delves into the molecular mechanisms of gene expression—the blood and guts of the central dogma. It starts with the monomers that build RNA and ends with a protein.

# 17.1 An Overview of Transcription

The first step in converting genetic information into proteins is to synthesize an RNA version of the instructions archived in DNA. Enzymes called **RNA polymerases** are responsible for synthesizing mRNA (see Chapter 15).

**FIGURE 17.1** shows how the polymerization reaction occurs. Note the incoming monomer—a ribonucleoside triphosphate, or NTP—at the far right of the diagram. NTPs are like dNTPs (introduced in Chapter 15), except that they have a hydroxyl (—OH) group on the 2′ carbon. This makes the sugar in an NTP a ribose instead of the deoxyribose sugar of DNA.

Once an NTP that matches a base on the DNA template is in place, RNA polymerase cleaves off two phosphates and catalyzes the formation of a phosphodiester linkage between the 3′ end of the growing mRNA chain and the new ribonucleoside monophosphate. As this 5′ → 3′ matching-and-catalysis process continues, an RNA that is complementary to the gene is synthesized. This is transcription.

Notice that only one of the two DNA strands is used as a template and transcribed, or "read," by RNA polymerase.

- The strand that is read by the enzyme is the **template strand.**
- The other strand is called the **non-template strand** or **coding strand.** Coding strand is an appropriate name, because, with one exception, its sequence matches the sequence of the RNA that is transcribed from the template strand and codes for a polypeptide.

The coding strand and the RNA don't match exactly, because RNA has uracil (U) rather than the thymine (T) found in the coding strand. Likewise, an adenine (A) in the DNA template strand specifies a U in the complementary RNA strand.

Like DNA polymerases (see Chapter 15), an RNA polymerase performs a template-directed synthesis in the 5′ → 3′ direction. But unlike DNA polymerases, RNA polymerases do not require a primer to begin transcription.

Bacteria have a single RNA polymerase. In contrast, eukaryotes, have at least three distinct types. Let's first take a look at general principles of transcription using bacteria as an example and then examine things that differ in eukaryotes.

## Initiation: How Does Transcription Begin in Bacteria?

How does RNA polymerase know where and in which direction to start transcription on the DNA template? The answer to this question defined what biologists call the **initiation** phase of transcription.

**FIGURE 17.1 Transcription Is the Synthesis of RNA from a DNA Template.** The reaction catalyzed by RNA polymerase (not shown) results in the formation of a phosphodiester linkage between ribonucleotides. RNA polymerase produces an RNA strand whose sequence is complementary to the bases in the DNA template.

✓**QUESTION** In which direction is RNA synthesized, 5′ → 3′ or 3′ → 5′? In which direction is the DNA template "read"?

Soon after the discovery of bacterial RNA polymerase, researchers found that the enzyme cannot initiate transcription on its own. Instead, a detachable protein subunit called **sigma** must bind to the polymerase before transcription can begin.

Bacterial RNA polymerase and sigma form a **holoenzyme** (literally, "whole enzyme"; **FIGURE 17.2a**). A holoenzyme consists of a **core enzyme** (RNA polymerase, in this case), which contains the active site for catalysis, and other required proteins (such as sigma).

What does sigma do? When researchers mixed the polymerase and DNA together, they found that the core enzyme could bind to any sequence of DNA. When sigma was added to this mixture, the holoenzyme formed and bound only to specific sections of DNA. These binding sites were named **promoters,** because they are sections of DNA that promote the start of transcription.

Most bacteria have alternative sigma proteins that bind to promoters with slightly different DNA base sequences, and may activate a group of genes in response to environmental change. For example, one type of sigma initiates the transcription of genes that help the cell cope with high temperatures. Controlling which sigma proteins are used is one of the ways that bacterial cells regulate which groups of genes are expressed.

The discovery of promoters suggested that sigma was responsible for guiding RNA polymerase to specific locations where transcription should begin. What is the nature of these specific locations? What do promoters look like, and what do they do?

**Bacterial Promoters** David Pribnow offered an initial answer to these questions in the mid-1970s. When Pribnow analyzed the base sequence of promoters from various bacteria and from viruses that infect bacteria, he found that the promoters were 40–50 base pairs long and had a particular section in common: a series of bases identical or similar to TATAAT. This six-base-pair sequence is now known as the −10 box, because it is centered about 10 bases from the point where bacterial RNA polymerase starts transcription (**FIGURE 17.2b**).

DNA that is located in the direction RNA polymerase moves during transcription is said to be **downstream** from the point of reference; DNA located in the opposite direction is said to be **upstream.** Thus, the −10 box is centered about 10 bases upstream from the transcription start site. The place where transcription begins is called the +1 site.

Soon after the discovery of the −10 box, researchers recognized that the sequence TTGACA also occurred in promoters and was about 35 bases upstream from the +1 site. This second key sequence is called the −35 box. Although all bacterial promoters have a −10 box and a −35 box, the sequences within the promoter but outside these boxes vary.

**Events inside the Holoenzyme** In bacteria, transcription begins when sigma, as part of the holoenzyme complex, binds to the −35 and −10 boxes. Sigma, and not RNA polymerase, makes the initial contact with DNA of the promoter. Sigma's binding to a promoter determines where and in which direction RNA polymerase will start synthesizing RNA.

Once the holoenzyme is bound to a promoter for a bacterial gene, the DNA helix is opened by RNA polymerase, creating two

**(a)** RNA polymerase and sigma form a holoenzyme.

**(b)** Sigma recognizes and binds to the promoter.

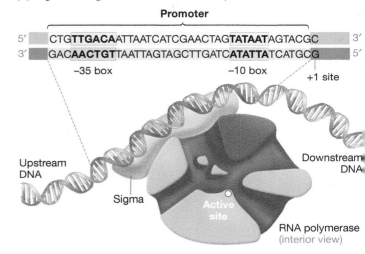

**FIGURE 17.2 Sigma Is the Promoter-Recognizing Subunit of Bacterial RNA Polymerase Holoenzyme. (a)** A space-filling model of bacterial RNA polymerase holoenzyme. **(b)** A cartoon of bacterial RNA polymerase, showing that sigma binds to the −35 box and −10 box of the promoter.

separated strands of DNA as shown in **FIGURE 17.3** (see page 320), steps 1 and 2. As step 2 shows, the template strand is threaded through a channel that leads to the active site inside RNA polymerase. Ribonucleoside triphosphates (NTPs)—the RNA building blocks—enter a channel in the enzyme and diffuse to the active site.

When an incoming NTP pairs with a complementary base on the template strand of DNA, RNA polymerization begins. The reaction catalyzed by RNA polymerase is exergonic and spontaneous because NTPs have significant potential energy, owing to their three phosphate groups. As step 3 of Figure 17.3 shows, the initiation phase of transcription is complete as RNA polymerase extends the mRNA from the +1 site.

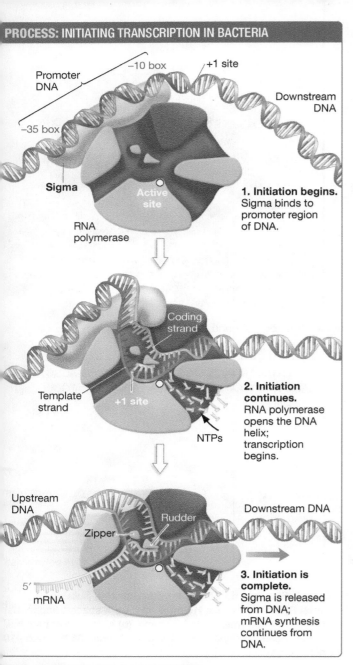

**1. Initiation begins.** Sigma binds to promoter region of DNA.

**2. Initiation continues.** RNA polymerase opens the DNA helix; transcription begins.

**3. Initiation is complete.** Sigma is released from DNA; mRNA synthesis continues from DNA.

**FIGURE 17.3 Sigma Orients the DNA Template inside RNA Polymerase.** Sigma binds to the promoter, and RNA polymerase opens the DNA helix and threads the template strand through the active site.

## Elongation and Termination

Once RNA polymerase begins moving along the DNA template synthesizing RNA, the **elongation** phase of transcription is under way. RNA polymerase is a macromolecular machine with different parts. In the interior of the enzyme, a group of amino acids forms a rudder to help steer the template and non-template strands through channels inside the enzyme (see Figure 17.3, step 3). Meanwhile, the enzyme's active site catalyzes the addition of nucleotides to the 3′ end of the growing RNA molecule at the rate of about 50 nucleotides per second. A group of projecting amino acids forms a region called the zipper to help separate the newly synthesized RNA from the DNA template.

During the elongation phase of transcription, all the prominent channels and grooves in the enzyme are filled (Figure 17.3, step 3). Double-stranded DNA goes into and out of one groove, ribonucleoside triphosphates enter another, and the growing RNA strand exits to the rear. The enzyme's structure is critical for its function.

**Termination** ends transcription. In bacteria, transcription stops when RNA polymerase transcribes a DNA sequence that functions as a transcription-termination signal.

The bases that make up the termination signal in bacteria are transcribed into a stretch of RNA with an important property: As soon as it is synthesized, this portion of the RNA folds back on itself and forms a short double helix that is held together by complementary base pairing (**FIGURE 17.4**). Recall that this type of RNA secondary structure is called a hairpin (Chapter 4). The hairpin structure disrupts the interaction between RNA polymerase and the RNA transcript, resulting in the physical separation of the enzyme and its product.

## Transcription in Eukaryotes

Fundamental features of transcription are the same in bacteria and eukaryotes. In fact, these similarities provide compelling evidence for a common ancestor of all cells. There are, however, some differences that are worth noting:

- Eukaryotes have three polymerases—RNA polymerase I, II, and III—that are often referred to as pol I, pol II, and pol III. Each polymerase transcribes only certain types of RNA in eukaryotes. RNA pol II is the only polymerase that transcribes protein-coding genes.

- Promoters in eukaryotic DNA are more diverse than bacterial promoters. Most eukaryotic promoters include a sequence called the **TATA box,** centered about 30 base pairs upstream of the transcription start site, and other important sequences that vary more widely.

- Instead of using a sigma protein, eukaryotic RNA polymerases recognize promoters using a group of proteins called **basal transcription factors.** Basal transcription factors assemble at the promoter, and RNA polymerase follows. (This idea, as well as the extensive use of other types of transcription factors to regulate transcription, will be covered in Chapter 19.)

- Termination of eukaryotic protein-coding genes involves a short sequence called the polyadenylation signal or **poly(A) signal.** Soon after the signal is transcribed, the RNA is cut by an enzyme downstream of the poly(A) signal as the polymerase continues to transcribe the DNA template. Eventually RNA polymerase falls off the DNA template and terminates transcription. Bacteria end transcription at a distinct site for each gene, but in eukaryotes, transcription ends variable distances from the poly(A) signal.

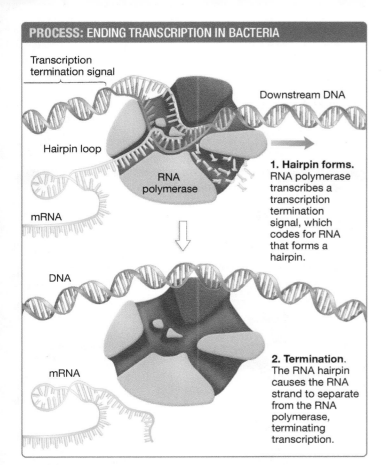

## PROCESS: ENDING TRANSCRIPTION IN BACTERIA

Transcription termination signal

Downstream DNA

Hairpin loop

RNA polymerase

mRNA

**1. Hairpin forms.** RNA polymerase transcribes a transcription termination signal, which codes for RNA that forms a hairpin.

DNA

mRNA

**2. Termination.** The RNA hairpin causes the RNA strand to separate from the RNA polymerase, terminating transcription.

**FIGURE 17.4 Transcription Terminates When an RNA Hairpin Forms.**

## 17.2 RNA Processing in Eukaryotes

The molecular machinery required for transcription is much more complex in eukaryotes than in bacteria. But these differences are minor when compared with what happens to the eukaryotic RNA after transcription. In bacteria, when transcription terminates, the result is a mature mRNA that's ready to be translated into a protein. In fact, translation often begins while the mRNA is still being transcribed.

The fate of the transcript in eukaryotes is more complicated. When eukaryotic genes of any type are transcribed, the initial product is termed a **primary transcript.** This RNA must undergo multistep processing before it is functional. For protein-coding genes, the primary transcript is called a **pre-mRNA.**

The processing of primary transcripts has important consequences for gene expression in eukaryotes. Let's delve in to see how and why.

### The Startling Discovery of Split Eukaryotic Genes

Eukaryotic genes do not consist of one continuous DNA sequence that codes for a product, as do bacterial genes. Instead, the regions in a eukaryotic gene that code for proteins are intermittently interrupted by stretches of hundreds or even thousands of intervening bases.

Although these intervening bases are part of the gene, they do not code for a product. To make a functional RNA, eukaryotic cells must dispose of certain sequences inside the primary transcript and then combine the separated sections into an integrated whole.

What sort of data would provoke such a startling claim? The first evidence came from work that Phillip Sharp and colleagues carried out in the late 1970s to determine the location of genes within the DNA of a virus that infects mammalian cells. Viruses are often used as tools to provide insights into fundamental processes of the cells they infect.

They began one of their experiments by heating the virus DNA sufficiently to break the hydrogen bonds between complementary bases. This treatment separated the two strands. The single-stranded DNA was then incubated with the mRNA encoded by the virus. The team's intention was to promote base pairing between the mRNA and the single-stranded DNA.

The researchers expected that the mRNA would form base pairs with the DNA sequence that acted as the template for its synthesis—that the mRNA and DNA would match up exactly

**(a)** Micrograph of DNA-RNA hybrid

**(b)** Interpretation of micrograph

Single-stranded DNA only

Single-stranded DNA base paired with mRNA

**FIGURE 17.5 The Discovery of Introns.** The loops in the micrograph and drawing represent regions of DNA that are transcribed but are not found in the final mRNA. These regions are introns.

**✓QUESTION** If the noncoding regions of the gene did not exist, what would the micrograph in part (a) look like?

But when the team examined the DNA–RNA hybrid molecules using an electron microscope, they observed the structure shown in **FIGURE 17.5a**. Instead of matching up exactly, parts of the DNA formed loops.

What was going on? As **FIGURE 17.5b** shows, Sharp's group interpreted these loops as stretches of DNA that are present in the template strand but are *not* in the corresponding mRNA.

Sharp's group and a team headed by Richard Roberts then carried out similar studies on eukaryotic genes. The results were the same as for the viral genes. They went on to propose that there is not a one-to-one correspondence between the nucleotide sequence of a eukaryotic gene and its mRNA. As an analogy, it could be said that eukaryotic genes do not carry messages such as "Biology is my favorite course of all time." Instead, they carry messages that read something like:

BIOLτηεπροτεινχοδινγρεγιονσοφγενεσOGY IS MY
FAVORαρειντερρθπτεθβυνονψοδινγθITE COURSE
OF ανθηαωετοβεσπλιχεθτογετηερ ALL TIME

Here the sections of noncoding sequence are represented with Greek letters. They must be removed from the mRNA before it can carry an intelligible message to the translation machinery.

When it became clear that the genes-in-pieces hypothesis was correct, Walter Gilbert suggested that regions of eukaryotic genes that are part of the final mRNA be referred to as **exons** (because they are *ex*pressed) and the sections of primary transcript not in mRNA be referred to as **introns** (because they are *int*ervening). Introns are sections of genes that are not represented in the final RNA product. Because of introns, eukaryotic genes are much larger than their corresponding mature RNAs. Introns were first discovered in genes that produce mRNA, but researchers later found that genes for other types of RNA also could be split.

## RNA Splicing

The transcription of eukaryotic genes by RNA polymerase generates a primary transcript (**FIGURE 17.6a**) that contains both exons and introns. As transcription proceeds, the introns are removed

**(a)** Introns must be removed from eukaryotic RNA transcripts.

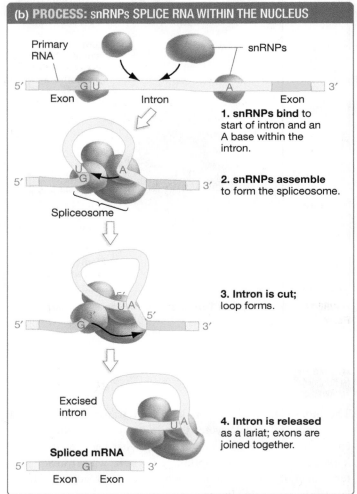

**(b) PROCESS: snRNPs SPLICE RNA WITHIN THE NUCLEUS**

1. **snRNPs bind** to start of intron and an A base within the intron.

2. **snRNPs assemble** to form the spliceosome.

3. **Intron is cut;** loop forms.

4. **Intron is released** as a lariat; exons are joined together.

**FIGURE 17.6 Introns Are Spliced Out of the Primary Transcript.**

from the growing RNA strand by a process known as **splicing.** In this phase of information processing, pieces of the primary transcript are removed and the remaining segments are joined together. Splicing occurs within the nucleus while transcription is still under way and results in an RNA that contains an uninterrupted genetic message.

**FIGURE 17.6b** provides more detail about how introns are removed from primary transcripts to form mRNA. Splicing of primary transcripts is catalyzed by RNAs called small nuclear RNAs (snRNAs) working with a complex of proteins. These protein-plus-RNA macromolecular machines are known as **small nuclear ribonucleoproteins,** or **snRNPs** (pronounced "snurps").

5′ cap
Poly(A) signal   Poly(A) tail
5′ untranslated region
**Coding region**
3′ untranslated region

**FIGURE 17.7 In Eukaryotes, a Cap and a Tail Are Added to mRNAs.** As part of eukaryotic pre-mRNA processing, a cap consisting of a modified guanine (G) nucleotide (symbolized as m⁷G) bonded to three phosphate groups is added to the 5′ end, and a tail made up of a long series of adenine (A) residues is added to the 3′ end after cleavage of the primary transcript.

The snRNAs of the snRNPs recognize RNA sequences critical for splicing. Splicing can be broken into four steps:

1. The process begins when snRNPs bind to the 5′ exon–intron boundary, which is marked by the bases GU, and to a key adenine ribonucleotide (A) near the end the intron.

2. Once the initial snRNPs are in place, other snRNPs arrive to form a multipart complex called a **spliceosome.** The spliceosomes found in human cells contain about 145 different proteins and RNAs, making them the most complex macromolecular machines known.

3. The intron forms a loop plus a single-stranded stem (a lariat) with the adenine at its connecting point.

4. The lariat is cut out, and a phosphodiester linkage links the exons on either side, producing a continuous coding sequence—the mRNA.

Splicing is now complete. In most cases, the excised intron is degraded to ribonucleoside monophosphates.

As you'll see later (Chapter 19), for many genes, the RNA can be spliced in more than one way. This allows the production of different, related mRNAs and proteins from one gene.

Current data suggest that both the cutting and rejoining reactions that occur during splicing are catalyzed by the snRNA molecules in the spliceosome—meaning that the reactions are catalyzed by a ribozyme. Section 17.5 will demonstrate that ribozymes also play a key role in translation. As the RNA world hypothesis (Chapter 4) predicts, proteins are not the only important catalysts in cells.

What is the origin of introns? One hypothesis is that introns in eukaryotes arose from an ancient type of DNA sequence that is present in many bacteria and archaea. These ancient sequences are related to viruses (Chapter 36) and, like viruses, can infect cells and insert into their genomes. Remarkably, when this DNA sequence inserts into a gene and is transcribed, the RNA catalyzes its own splicing out of the primary transcript. This is possible in part because these virus-like elements have sequences similar to snRNAs.

The bacterium that was the source of mitochondria (see Chapter 30) likely carried some of these virus-like DNA sequences. When this bacterium was taken up by an ancestral eukaryote, the virus-like sequences are hypothesized to have spread rapidly. Later in evolution, the portion of the sequence that was a precursor to today's snRNA may have separated from the portion of the sequence that was spliced. This spliced sequence is hypothesized to be the ancestor of the modern eukaryotic intron.

## Adding Caps and Tails to Transcripts

For pre-mRNAs, intron splicing is accompanied by other important processing steps.

- As soon as the 5′ end of a eukaryotic pre-mRNA emerges from RNA polymerase, enzymes add a structure called the **5′ cap** (**FIGURE 17.7**). The cap consists of a modified guanine (7-methylguanylate) nucleotide with three phosphate groups.

- An enzyme cleaves the 3′ end of the pre-mRNA downstream of the poly(A) signal (introduced in Section 17.1). Another enzyme adds a long row of 100–250 adenine nucleotides that are not encoded on the DNA template strand. This string of adenines is known as the **poly(A) tail.**

With the addition of the cap and tail and completion of splicing, processing of the pre-mRNA is complete. The product is a mature mRNA.

Figure 17.7 also shows that in the mature RNA molecule, the coding sequence for the polypeptide is flanked by sequences that are not destined to be translated. These 5′ and 3′ untranslated regions (or UTRs) help stabilize the mature RNA and regulate its translation. The mRNAs in bacteria also possess 5′ and 3′ UTRs.

Not long after the caps and tails on eukaryotic mRNAs were discovered, evidence began to accumulate that they protect mRNAs from degradation by ribonucleases—enzymes that

check your understanding

**If you understand that . . .**

- Eukaryotic genes consist of exons, which are parts of the primary transcript that remain in mature RNA, and introns, which are regions of the primary transcript that are removed in forming mature RNA.
- Macromolecular machines, called spliceosomes, splice introns out of pre-mRNAs.
- Enzymes add a 5′ cap and a poly(A) tail to spliced transcripts, producing a mature mRNA that is ready to be translated.

✔ **You should be able to . . .**

1. Explain why ribonucleoprotein is an appropriate name for the subunits of the spliceosome.
2. Explain the function of the 5′ cap and the poly(A) tail.

*Answers are available in Appendix A.*

degrade RNA—and enhance the efficiency of translation. For example:

- Experimental mRNAs that have a cap and a tail last longer when they are introduced into cells than do experimental mRNAs that lack a cap or a tail.
- Experimental mRNAs with caps and tails produce more proteins than do experimental mRNAs without caps and tails.

Follow-up work has shown that the 5′ cap and the poly(A) tail are bound by proteins that prevent ribonucleases in the cytoplasm from recognizing and destroying the mRNA. The 5′ cap and the poly(A) tail also are important for initiating translation.

**RNA processing** is the general term for any of the modifications, such as splicing or poly(A) tail addition, needed to convert a primary transcript into a mature RNA. It is summarized in **TABLE 17.1** along with other important differences in how RNAs are produced in eukaryotes as compared with bacteria.

## 17.3 An Introduction to Translation

To synthesize a protein, the sequence of bases in a messenger RNA molecule is translated into a sequence of amino acids in a polypeptide. The genetic code specifies the correspondence between each triplet codon in mRNA and the amino acid it codes for (see Chapter 16). But how are the amino acids assembled into a polypeptide according to the information in messenger RNA?

**(a)** Bacterial ribosomes during translation

**(b)** In bacteria, transcription and translation are tightly coupled.

Studies of translation in cell-free systems proved extremely effective in answering this question. Once in vitro translation systems had been developed from human cells, *E. coli*, and a variety of other organisms, biologists could see that the sequence of events is similar in bacteria, archaea, and eukaryotes. As with similarities in transcription across the domains of life, the shared mechanisms of translation argue for a common ancestor of all cells living today.

### Ribosomes Are the Site of Protein Synthesis

The first question that biologists answered about translation concerned where it occurs. The answer grew from a simple observation: There is a strong correlation between the number of **ribosomes** in a given type of cell and the rate at which that cell synthesizes proteins. Based on this observation, investigators proposed that ribosomes are the site of protein synthesis.

To test this hypothesis, Roy Britten and collaborators did a pulse–chase experiment similar in design to experiments introduced earlier (Chapter 7). Recall that a pulse–chase experiment labels a population of molecules as they are being produced. The location of the tagged molecules is then followed over time.

In this case, the tagging was done by supplying a pulse of radioactive sulfur atoms that would be incorporated into the amino acids methionine and cysteine, followed by a chase of unlabeled sulfur atoms. If the ribosome hypothesis were correct, the radioactive signal should be associated with ribosomes for a short period of time—when the amino acids are being polymerized into proteins. Later, when translation was complete, all the radioactivity should be found in proteins that are not associated with ribosomes.

This is exactly what the researchers found. Based on these data, biologists concluded that proteins are synthesized at ribosomes and then released.

### Translation in Bacteria and Eukaryotes

About a decade after the ribosome hypothesis was confirmed, electron micrographs showed bacterial ribosomes in action (**FIGURE 17.8a**). The images showed that in bacteria, ribosomes

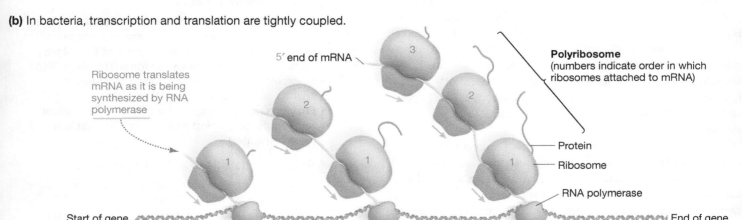

**FIGURE 17.8 Transcription and Translation Occur Simultaneously in Bacteria.** In bacteria, ribosomes attach to mRNA transcripts and begin translation while RNA polymerase is still transcribing the DNA template strand.

TABLE 17.1 **Transcription and RNA Processing in Bacteria and Eukaryotes**

| Point of Comparison | Bacteria | Eukaryotes |
|---|---|---|
| RNA polymerase(s) | One | Three; each produces a different class of RNA |
| Promoter structure | Typically contains a −35 box and a −10 box | More variable; often includes a TATA box about −30 from the transcription start site |
| Proteins involved in recognizing promoter | Sigma; different versions of sigma bind to different promoters | Many basal transcription factors |
| RNA processing | None | Extensive; several processing steps occur in the nucleus before RNA is exported to the cytoplasm: **(1)** Enzyme-catalyzed addition of 5′ cap on mRNAs, **(2)** Splicing (intron removal); by spliceosome to produce mRNA, **(3)** Enzyme-catalyzed addition of 3′ poly(A) tail on mRNAs |

attach to mRNAs and begin synthesizing proteins even before transcription is complete. In fact, multiple ribosomes attach to each mRNA, forming a **polyribosome** (**FIGURE 17.8b**). In this way, many copies of a protein can be produced from a single mRNA.

Transcription and translation can occur concurrently in bacteria because there is no nuclear envelope to separate the two processes.

The situation is different in eukaryotes. In these organisms, primary transcripts are processed in the nucleus to produce a mature mRNA, which is then exported to the cytoplasm (**FIGURE 17.9**). This means that in eukaryotes, transcription and translation are separated in time and space. Once mRNAs are outside the nucleus, ribosomes can attach to them and begin translation. As in bacteria, polyribosomes form.

## How Does an mRNA Triplet Specify an Amino Acid?

When an mRNA interacts with a ribosome, instructions encoded in nucleic acids are translated into a different chemical language—the amino acid sequences found in proteins. The discovery of the genetic code revealed that triplet codons in mRNA specify particular amino acids in a protein. How does this conversion occur?

One early hypothesis was that mRNA codons and amino acids interact directly. This hypothesis proposed that the bases in a particular codon were complementary in shape or charge to the side group of a particular amino acid (**FIGURE 17.10a**, see page 326). But Francis Crick pointed out that the idea didn't make chemical sense. For example, how could the nucleic acid bases interact with a hydrophobic amino acid side group, which does not form hydrogen bonds?

Crick proposed an alternative hypothesis. As **FIGURE 17.10b** shows, he suggested that some sort of adapter molecule holds amino acids in place while interacting directly and specifically with a codon in mRNA by hydrogen bonding. In essence, Crick predicted the existence of a chemical go-between that produced a physical connection between the two types of molecules. As it turns out, Crick was right.

**(a)** mRNAs are exported to the cytoplasm.

**(b)** Polypeptides grow from ribosomes translating mRNA.

**FIGURE 17.9 Transcription and Translation Are Separated in Space and Time in Eukaryotes.**

**(a) Hypothesis 1:** Amino acids interact directly with mRNA codons.

**(b) Hypothesis 2:** Adapter molecules hold amino acids and interact with mRNA codons.

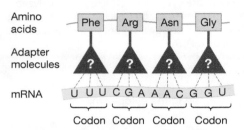

**FIGURE 17.10 How Do mRNA Codons Interact with Amino Acids?**

## 17.4 The Structure and Function of Transfer RNA

Crick's adapter molecule was discovered by accident. Biologists were trying to work out an in vitro protein-synthesis system and reasoned that ribosomes, mRNA, amino acids, ATP, and a molecule called guanosine triphosphate, or GTP, would be needed. (GTP is similar to ATP but contains guanine instead of adenine.)

These results were logical: Ribosomes provide the catalytic machinery, mRNAs contribute the message to be translated, amino acids are the building blocks of proteins, and ATP and GTP supply potential energy to drive the endergonic polymerization reactions responsible for forming proteins.

But, in addition, a cellular fraction that contained a previously unknown type of RNA turned out to be indispensable. If this type of RNA is missing, protein synthesis does not occur. What is this mysterious RNA, and why is it essential to translation?

The novel class of RNAs eventually became known as **transfer RNA (tRNA)**. The role of tRNA in translation was a mystery until some researchers happened to add a radioactive amino acid—leucine—to an in vitro protein-synthesis system. The treatment was actually done as a control for an unrelated experiment. To the researchers' amazement, some of the radioactive leucine attached to tRNA molecules.

What happens to the amino acids bound to tRNAs? To answer this question, Paul Zamecnik and colleagues tracked the fate of radioactive leucine molecules that were attached to tRNAs. They found that the amino acids are transferred from tRNAs to proteins.

The data supporting this conclusion are shown in the "Results" section of **FIGURE 17.11**. The graph shows that radioactive amino acids are lost from tRNAs and incorporated into polypeptides synthesized by ribosomes. To understand this conclusion:

**RESEARCH**

**QUESTION:** What happens to the amino acids attached to tRNAs?

**HYPOTHESIS:** Aminoacyl tRNAs transfer amino acids to growing polypeptides.

**NULL HYPOTHESIS:** Aminoacyl tRNAs do not transfer amino acids to growing polypeptides.

**EXPERIMENTAL SETUP:**

**PREDICTION:** Radioactive amino acids will be found in proteins.

**PREDICTION OF NULL HYPOTHESIS:** Radioactive amino acids will not be found in proteins.

**CONCLUSION:** Aminoacyl tRNAs transfer amino acids to growing polypeptides.

**FIGURE 17.11 Evidence that Amino Acids Are Transferred from tRNAs to Proteins.**

SOURCE: Hoagland, M. B., M. L. Stephenson, J. F. Scott, et al. 1958. A soluble ribonucleic acid intermediate in protein synthesis. *Journal of Biological Chemistry* 231: 241–257.

✔ **QUESTION** What would the graphed results look like if the null hypothesis were correct?

1. Put your finger on the point on the $x$-axis that indicates that one minute has passed since the start of the experiment.

2. Read up until you hit the green line and the gray line. The green line represents data from proteins; the gray line represents data from tRNAs.

**3.** Check the *y*-axis—which indicates the amount of radioactive leucine present—at each point.

**4.** It should be clear that early in the experiment, almost all the radioactive leucine is attached to tRNA, not protein.

Next, do the same four steps at the point on the *x*-axis labeled 10 minutes (since the start of the experiment). Your conclusion now should be that late in the experiment, almost all the radioactive leucine is attached to proteins, not tRNA.

These results inspired the use of the word *transfer* in tRNA's name, because amino acids are transferred from the RNA to a growing polypeptide. The experiment also confirmed that tRNAs act as the interpreter during translation: tRNAs are Crick's adapter molecules.

## What Do tRNAs Look Like?

Transfer RNAs serve as chemical go-betweens that allow amino acids to interact with an mRNA template. But precisely how does the connection occur?

This question was answered by research on tRNA's molecular structure. The initial studies established the sequence of nucleotides in various tRNAs, or what is termed their primary structure. Transfer RNA sequences are relatively short, ranging from 75 to 85 nucleotides in length.

When biologists studied the primary sequence closely, they noticed that certain parts of the molecules can form secondary structures. Specifically, some sequences of bases in the tRNA molecule can form hydrogen bonds with complementary base sequences elsewhere in the same molecule. As a result, portions of the molecule form stem-and-loop structures (introduced in Chapter 4). The stems are short stretches of double-stranded RNA; the loops are single stranded.

Two aspects of tRNA's secondary structure proved especially important. A CCA sequence at the 3′ end of each tRNA molecule offered a site for amino acid attachment, while a triplet on the loop at the other end of the structure could serve as an anticodon. An **anticodon** is a set of three ribonucleotides that forms base pairs with the mRNA codon.

Later, X-ray crystallography studies revealed the tertiary structure of tRNAs. Recall that the tertiary structure of a molecule is the three-dimensional arrangement of its atoms (Chapter 3). As **FIGURE 17.12** shows, tRNAs fold into an L-shaped molecule. The anticodon is at one end of the structure; the CCA sequence and attached amino acid are at the other end.

All the tRNAs in a cell have the same general structure, shaped like an upside-down L. They vary at the anticodon and attached amino acid. The tertiary structure of tRNAs is important because it maintains a precise physical distance between the anticodon and amino acid. As it turns out, this separation is important in positioning the amino acid and the anticodon within the ribosome.

✔ If you understand the structure of tRNAs, you should be able to (1) describe where on the L-shaped structure the amino acid attaches; and (2) explain the relationship between the anticodon of a tRNA and a codon in an mRNA.

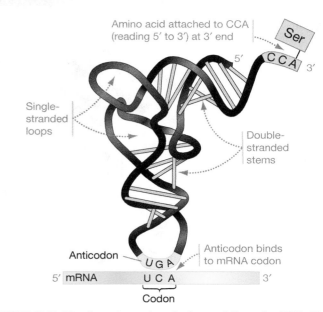

**FIGURE 17.12 The Structure of an Aminoacyl Transfer RNA.** The anticodon forms complementary base pairs with an mRNA codon.

## How Are Amino Acids Attached to tRNAs?

How are amino acids linked to tRNAs? Just as important, what allows the right amino acid for a particular tRNA to be attached?

- An input of energy, in the form of ATP, is required to attach an amino acid to a tRNA.

- Enzymes called **aminoacyl-tRNA synthetases** catalyze the addition of amino acids to tRNAs—what biologists call "charging" a tRNA.

- For each of the 20 major amino acids, there is a different aminoacyl-tRNA synthetase and one or more tRNAs.

Each aminoacyl-tRNA synthetase has a binding site for a particular amino acid and a particular tRNA. Subtle differences in tRNA shape and base sequence allow the enzymes to recognize the correct tRNA for the correct amino acid. The combination of a tRNA molecule covalently linked to an amino acid is called an **aminoacyl tRNA**. **FIGURE 17.13** (see page 328) shows an aminoacyl-tRNA synthetase bound to a tRNA that has just been charged with an amino acid. Note how tightly the two structures fit together—making it possible for the enzyme and its tRNA and amino acid substrates to interact in a precise way.

## How Many tRNAs Are There?

After characterizing all the different types of tRNAs, biologists encountered a paradox. According to the genetic code (Chapter 16), the 20 most common amino acids found in proteins are specified by 61 different mRNA codons. Instead of containing 61 different tRNAs with 61 different anticodons, though, most cells contain only about 40. How can all 61 codons be translated with only two-thirds that number of tRNAs?

**FIGURE 17.13 Aminoacyl-tRNA Synthetases Couple the Appropriate Amino Acid to the Appropriate tRNA.**

To resolve this paradox, Francis Crick proposed what is known as the **wobble hypothesis.** Recall that:

1. Many amino acids are specified by more than one codon.

2. Codons for the same amino acid tend to have the same nucleotides at the first and second positions but a different nucleotide at the third position.

For example, both of the codons CAA and CAG code for the amino acid glutamine. Surprisingly, experimental data have shown that a tRNA with an anticodon of GUU can base-pair with both CAA and CAG in mRNA. The GUU anticodon matches the first two bases (C and A) in both codons, but the U in the anticodon's third position forms a nonstandard base pair with a G in the CAG codon.

Crick proposed that inside the ribosome, certain bases in the third position of tRNA anticodons can bind to bases in the third position of a codon in a manner that does not match Watson–Crick base pairing. If so, this would allow a limited flexibility, or "wobble," in the base pairing.

According to the wobble hypothesis, particular nonstandard base pairs—such as G-U—are acceptable in the third position of a codon and do not change the amino acid that the codon specifies. In this way, wobble in the third position of a codon allows just 40 or so tRNAs to bind to all 61 mRNA codons.

## 17.5 The Structure and Function of Ribosomes

Recall that protein synthesis occurs when the sequence of bases in an mRNA is translated into a sequence of amino acids in a polypeptide. The translation of each mRNA codon begins when the anticodon of an aminoacyl tRNA binds to the codon. Translation of a codon is complete when a peptide bond forms between the tRNA's amino acid and the growing polypeptide chain.

Both of these events take place inside a ribosome. Biologists have known since the 1930s that ribosomes contain many proteins and **ribosomal RNAs (rRNAs).** Later work showed that ribosomes can be separated into two major substructures, called the large subunit and small subunit. Each ribosome subunit consists of a complex of RNA molecules and proteins. The small subunit holds the mRNA in place during translation; the large subunit is where peptide-bond formation takes place.

**FIGURE 17.14** shows two views of how the molecules required for translation fit together. Note that during protein synthesis, three distinct tRNAs are lined up inside the ribosome. All three are bound to their corresponding mRNA codons.

- The tRNA that is on the right in the figure, and colored red, carries an amino acid. This tRNA's position in the ribosome is called the A site—"A" for acceptor or aminoacyl.

- The tRNA that is in the middle (green) holds the growing polypeptide chain and occupies the P site, for peptidyl, inside the ribosome. (Think of "P" for peptide-bond formation.)

- The left-hand (blue) tRNA no longer has an amino acid attached and is about to leave the ribosome. It occupies the ribosome's E site—"E" for exit.

Because all tRNAs have similar secondary and tertiary structure, they all fit equally well in the A, P, and E sites.

The ribosome is a macromolecular machine that synthesizes proteins in a three-step sequence:

1. An aminoacyl tRNA diffuses into the A site; if its anticodon matches a codon in mRNA, it stays in the ribosome.

2. A peptide bond forms between the amino acid held by the aminoacyl tRNA in the A site and the growing polypeptide, which was held by a tRNA in the P site.

3. The ribosome moves down the mRNA by one codon, and all three tRNAs move one position within the ribosome. The tRNA in the E site exits; the tRNA in the P site moves to the E site; and the tRNA in the A site switches to the P site.

The protein that is being synthesized grows by one amino acid each time this three-step sequence repeats. The process occurs up to 20 times per second in bacterial ribosomes and about 2 times per second in eukaryotic ribosomes. Protein synthesis starts at the amino end (N-terminus) of a polypeptide and proceeds to the carboxy end (C-terminus; see Chapter 3).

This introduction to how tRNAs, mRNAs, and ribosomes interact during protein synthesis leaves several key questions unanswered. How do mRNAs and ribosomes get together to start the process? Once protein synthesis is under way, how is peptide-bond formation catalyzed inside the ribosome? And how does protein synthesis conclude when the ribosome reaches the end of the message? Let's consider each question in turn.

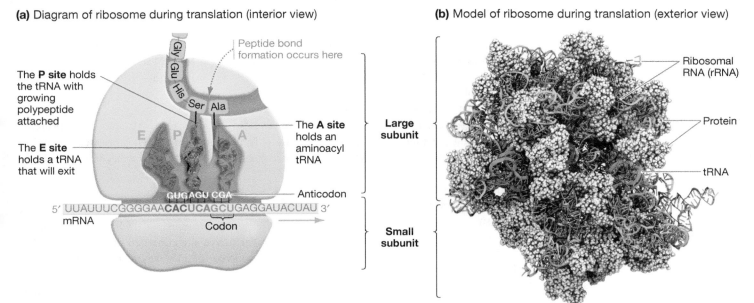

**(a)** Diagram of ribosome during translation (interior view)

Peptide bond formation occurs here

The **P site** holds the tRNA with growing polypeptide attached

The **E site** holds a tRNA that will exit

Gly Glu His Ser Ala

E P A

The **A site** holds an aminoacyl tRNA

Large subunit

GUGAGU CGA — Anticodon

5′ UUAUUUCGGGGAA**CACUCAGCUGAGGAUACUAU** 3′
mRNA

Codon

Small subunit

**(b)** Model of ribosome during translation (exterior view)

Ribosomal RNA (rRNA)

Protein

tRNA

**FIGURE 17.14 The Structure of the Ribosome.** Ribosomes have three distinct tRNA binding sites in their interior.

## Initiating Translation

To translate an mRNA properly, a ribosome must begin at a specific point in the message, translate the mRNA up to the message's termination codon, and then stop. Using the same terminology that they apply to transcription, biologists call these three phases of protein synthesis initiation, elongation, and termination, respectively.

One key to understanding translation initiation is to recall that a start codon (usually AUG) is found near the 5′ end of all mRNAs and that it codes for the amino acid methionine (Chapter 16).

**FIGURE 17.15** shows how translation gets under way in bacteria. The process begins when a section of rRNA in a small ribosomal subunit binds to a complementary sequence on an mRNA. The mRNA region is called the **ribosome binding site,** or **Shine–Dalgarno sequence,** after the biologists who discovered it. The site is about six nucleotides upstream from the start codon.

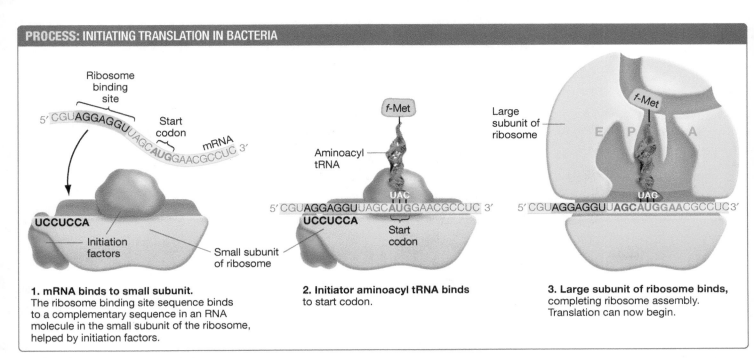

**PROCESS: INITIATING TRANSLATION IN BACTERIA**

Ribosome binding site

5′ CGU**AGGAGGU**UAGC**AUG**GAACGCCUC 3′

Start codon

mRNA

**UCCUCCA**

Initiation factors

Small subunit of ribosome

**1. mRNA binds to small subunit.**
The ribosome binding site sequence binds to a complementary sequence in an RNA molecule in the small subunit of the ribosome, helped by initiation factors.

f-Met

Aminoacyl tRNA

UAC

5′ CGU**AGGAGGU**UAGC**AUG**GAACGCCUC 3′

**UCCUCCA**

Start codon

**2. Initiator aminoacyl tRNA binds** to start codon.

Large subunit of ribosome

f-Met

E P A

UAC

5′ CGU**AGGAGGU**UAGC**AUG**GAACGCCUC 3′

**3. Large subunit of ribosome binds,** completing ribosome assembly. Translation can now begin.

**FIGURE 17.15 Initiation of Translation.**

The interactions between the small subunit, the message, and the tRNA are mediated by proteins called **initiation factors** (Figure 17.15, step 1). Initiation factors help in preparing the ribosome for translation, including binding the first aminoacyl tRNA to the ribosome. In bacteria this initiator tRNA bears a modified form of methionine called *N*-formylmethionine (abbreviated *f*-met) (Figure 17.15, step 2). In eukaryotes, this initiating tRNA carries a normal methionine. Initiation factors also prevent the small and large subunits of the ribosome from coming together until the initiator tRNA is in place at the AUG start codon, and they help bind the mRNA to the small ribosomal subunit.

Initiation is complete when the large subunit joins the complex (Figure 17.15, step 3). When the ribosome is completely assembled, the tRNA bearing *f*-met occupies the P site.

To summarize, translation initiation is a three-step process in bacteria: **(1)** The mRNA binds to a small ribosomal subunit, **(2)** the initiator aminoacyl tRNA bearing *f*-met binds to the start codon, and **(3)** the large ribosomal subunit binds, completing the complex.

In eukaryotes, the details of initiation are different, but they still involve recognition of a start codon, assembly of the ribosome, assistance from initiation factors, and the positioning of a methionine-carrying tRNA in the P site. The cap and poly(A) tail are also important in assembling the ribosome on the mRNA.

## Elongation: Extending the Polypeptide

At the start of elongation, the E and A sites in the ribosome are empty of tRNAs. As a result, an mRNA codon is exposed in the A site. As step 1 in **FIGURE 17.16** illustrates, elongation proceeds when an aminoacyl tRNA binds to the codon in the A site by complementary base pairing between the anticodon and codon.

When both the P site and A site are occupied by tRNAs, the amino acids on the tRNAs are in the ribosome's active site. This is where peptide-bond formation—the essence of protein synthesis—occurs.

Peptide-bond formation is one of the most important reactions that take place in cells because manufacturing proteins is among the most fundamental of all cell processes. Biologists wondered, is it the ribosome's proteins or RNAs that catalyze this reaction?

**Is the Ribosome an Enzyme or a Ribozyme?** Because ribosomes contain both protein and RNA, researchers had argued for decades over whether the active site consisted of protein or RNA. The debate was not resolved until the year 2000, when researchers completed three-dimensional models that were detailed enough to reveal the structure of the active site. These models confirmed that the active site consists entirely of ribosomal RNA. Based on these results, biologists are now convinced that protein synthesis is catalyzed by RNA. The ribosome is a ribozyme—not a protein-based enzyme.

The observation that protein synthesis is catalyzed by RNA is important because it supports the RNA-world hypothesis (Chapter 4). Recall that proponents of this hypothesis claim that life began with RNA molecules and that the presence of DNA and proteins in cells evolved later. If the RNA-world hypothesis is correct, then it would make sense that the production of proteins is catalyzed by RNA.

**PROCESS: ELONGATION OF POLYPEPTIDES DURING TRANSLATION**

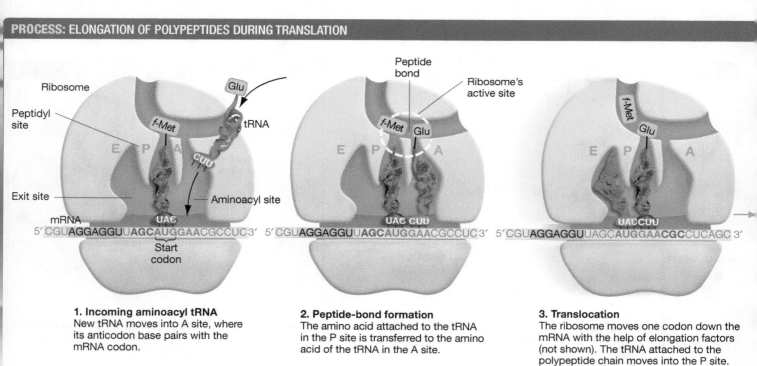

**1. Incoming aminoacyl tRNA**
New tRNA moves into A site, where its anticodon base pairs with the mRNA codon.

**2. Peptide-bond formation**
The amino acid attached to the tRNA in the P site is transferred to the amino acid of the tRNA in the A site.

**3. Translocation**
The ribosome moves one codon down the mRNA with the help of elongation factors (not shown). The tRNA attached to the polypeptide chain moves into the P site. The A site is empty.

**FIGURE 17.16 The Elongation Phase of Translation.**

**Moving Down the mRNA**   What happens after a peptide bond forms? Step 2 in Figure 17.16 shows that when peptide-bond formation is complete, the polypeptide chain is transferred from the tRNA in the P site to the amino acid held by the tRNA in the A site. Step 3 shows the process called **translocation,** which occurs when proteins called **elongation factors** help move the ribosome relative to the mRNA so that translation occurs in the 5′ → 3′ direction. Translocation is an energy-demanding event that requires GTP.

Translocation does several things: It moves the uncharged RNA into the E site; it moves the tRNA containing the growing polypeptide into the P site; and it opens the A site and exposes a new mRNA codon. The empty tRNA that finds itself in the E site is ejected into the cytosol.

The three steps in elongation—**(1)** arrival of aminoacyl tRNA, **(2)** peptide-bond formation, and **(3)** translocation—repeat down the length of the mRNA. Recent three-dimensional models of ribosomes in various stages of translation show that the machine is highly dynamic. The ribosome constantly changes shape as tRNAs come and go and catalysis and translocation occur. The ribosome is a complex and dynamic macromolecular machine.

## Terminating Translation

How does protein synthesis end? Recall that the genetic code includes three stop codons: UAA, UAG, and UGA (see Chapter 16). In most cells, no aminoacyl tRNA has an anticodon that binds to these sequences. When the translocating ribosome reaches one of the stop codons, a protein called a **release factor** recognizes the stop codon and fills the A site (**FIGURE 17.17**, see page 333).

Release factors fit tightly into the A site because they have the size and shape of a tRNA coming into the ribosome. However, release factors do not carry an amino acid. When a release factor occupies the A site, the protein's active site catalyzes the hydrolysis of the bond that links the tRNA in the P site to the polypeptide chain. This reaction frees the polypeptide.

The newly synthesized polypeptide and uncharged tRNAs are released from the ribosome, the ribosome separates from the mRNA, and the two ribosomal subunits dissociate. The subunits are ready to attach to the start codon of another message and start translation anew. Termination occurs in very similar ways in bacteria and eukaryotes.

## Post-Translational Modifications

Proteins are not fully formed and functional when termination occurs. From earlier chapters, it should be clear that most proteins go through an extensive series of processing steps, collectively called post-translational modification, before they are completely functional. These steps require a wide array of molecules and events and take place in many different locations throughout the cell.

**Folding**   Recall that a protein's function depends on its shape, and that a protein's shape depends on how it folds (see Chapter 3). Although folding can occur spontaneously, it is frequently speeded up by proteins called **molecular chaperones.**

Recent data have shown that in some bacteria, chaperone proteins bind to the ribosome near the "tunnel" where the growing polypeptide emerges from the ribosome. This finding suggests that folding occurs as the polypeptide emerges from the ribosome.

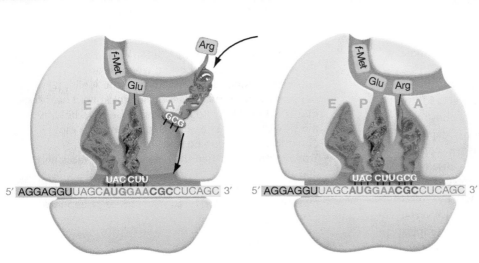

**4. Incoming aminoacyl tRNA**
New tRNA moves into A site, where its anticodon base pairs with the mRNA codon.

**5. Peptide-bond formation**
The polypeptide chain attached to the tRNA in the P site is transferred to the aminoacyl tRNA in the A site.

**6. Translocation**
The ribosome once again moves one codon down the mRNA. The tRNA attached to polypeptide chain moves into P site. Empty tRNA from P site moves to E site, where tRNA is ejected. The A site is empty again.

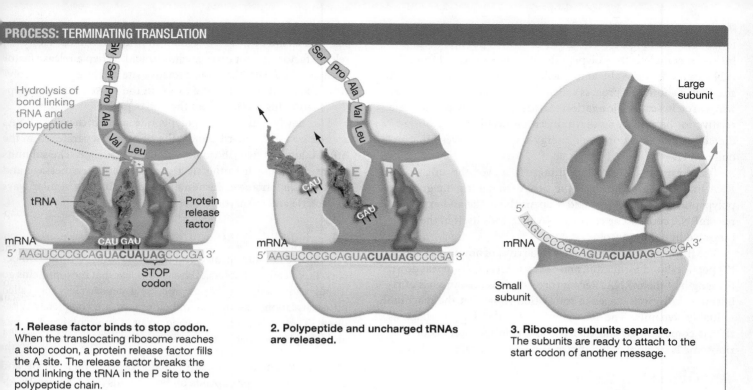

Hydrolysis of bond linking tRNA and polypeptide

tRNA

Protein release factor

mRNA

5′ AAGUCCCGCAGUA**CUAUAG**CCCGA 3′

STOP codon

**1. Release factor binds to stop codon.** When the translocating ribosome reaches a stop codon, a protein release factor fills the A site. The release factor breaks the bond linking the tRNA in the P site to the polypeptide chain.

mRNA

5′ AAGUCCCGCAGUA**CUAUAG**CCCGA 3′

**2. Polypeptide and uncharged tRNAs are released.**

Large subunit

5′

mRNA

Small subunit

**3. Ribosome subunits separate.** The subunits are ready to attach to the start codon of another message.

**FIGURE 17.17 Termination of Translation.**

**Chemical Modifications** An earlier chapter pointed out that many eukaryotic proteins are extensively modified after they are synthesized (see Chapter 7). For example, in the organelles called the rough endoplasmic reticulum and the Golgi apparatus, small chemical groups may be added to proteins—often sugar or lipid groups that are critical for normal functioning. In some cases, the proteins receive a sugar-based sorting signal that serves as an address label and ensures that the molecule will be carried to the correct location in the cell. (Other proteins have a sorting signal built into their primary structure.)

In addition, many completed proteins are altered by enzymes that add or remove a phosphate group. Phosphorylation (addition of phosphate) and dephosphorylation (removal of phosphate) of proteins were introduced in previous chapters (Chapters 9 and 11). Recall that because a phosphate group has two negative charges, adding or removing a phosphate group can cause major changes in the shape and chemical reactivity of proteins. These changes have a dramatic effect on the protein's activity—often switching it from an inactive state to an active state, or vice versa.

The take-home message is that gene expression is a complex, multistep process that begins with transcription but may not end with translation. Instead, even completed and folded proteins may be activated or deactivated by events such as phosphorylation. In general, how are genes turned on or off? How does a cell "decide" which of its many genes should be expressed at any one time? These questions are the focus of the next two chapters.

check your understanding

 C Y U

**If you understand that . . .**

- Translation begins when (1) the ribosome binding site on an mRNA binds to an rRNA sequence in the small ribosomal subunit, (2) the initiator aminoacyl tRNA binds to the start codon in the mRNA, and (3) the large subunit of the ribosome attaches to the small subunit to complete the ribosome.
- Translation elongation occurs when (1) an appropriate aminoacyl tRNA enters the A site, (2) a peptide bond forms between the amino acid held by that tRNA in the A site and the polypeptide held by the tRNA in the P site, and (3) the ribosome moves down the mRNA one codon.
- Translation ends when the ribosome reaches a stop codon.
- Completed proteins are modified by folding and, in many cases, addition of sugar, lipid, or phosphate groups.

✔ **You should be able to . . .**

Explain why the E, P, and A sites in the ribosome are appropriately named.

*Answers are available in Appendix A.*

## If you understand . . .

### 17.1   An Overview of Transcription

- RNA polymerase catalyzes the production of an RNA molecule whose base sequence is complementary to the base sequence of the DNA template strand.

- RNA polymerase binds DNA with the help of other proteins.

- RNA polymerase begins transcription by binding to promoter sequences in DNA.

- In bacteria, this binding occurs in conjunction with a protein called sigma. Sigma associates with RNA polymerase and then recognizes particular sequences within promoters that are centered 10 bases and 35 bases upstream from the start of the actual genetic message.

- Eukaryotic promoters vary more than bacterial promoters.

- In eukaryotes, transcription begins when a large array of proteins called basal transcription factors bind to a promoter. In response, RNA polymerase binds to the site.

- In both bacteria and eukaryotes, the RNA elongates in a $5' \rightarrow 3'$ direction.

- Transcription in bacteria ends when RNA polymerase encounters a stem-loop structure in the just transcribed RNA; in eukaryotes, transcription terminates after the RNA is cleaved downstream of the poly(A) sequence.

✓ You should be able to predict the consequences of a mutation in bacteria that inserts random nucleotides into the hairpin-coding region near the 3' end of a transcribed region.

### 17.2   RNA Processing in Eukaryotes

- In eukaryotes, the primary (initial) transcript must be processed to produce a mature RNA.

- In primary transcripts, stretches of RNA called introns are spliced out and regions called exons are joined together.

- Complex macromolecular machines called spliceosomes splice introns out of pre-mRNA.

- A "cap" is added to the 5' end of pre-mRNAs, and a poly(A) tail is added to their 3' end.

- The cap and tail serve as recognition signals for translation and protect the message from degradation by ribonucleases.

- RNA processing occurs in the nucleus.

✓ You should be able to predict whether the protein-coding portion of a gene for an identical protein will be of the same or different lengths in a bacterium and a eukaryote.

### 17.3   An Introduction to Translation

- Ribosomes translate mRNAs into proteins with the help of adaptor molecules called transfer RNAs.

- In bacteria, an RNA is often transcribed and translated at the same time because there is no nucleus.

- In eukaryotes, transcription and translation of an RNA cannot occur together, because transcription and RNA processing occur in the nucleus and translation occurs in the cytoplasm.

- Experiments with radioactively labeled amino acids showed that transfer RNAs (tRNAs) serve as the chemical bridge between the RNA message and the polypeptide product.

✓ You should be able to explain why it is correct to say that transfer RNAs work as molecular adaptors.

### 17.4   The Structure and Function of Transfer RNA

- Each transfer RNA carries an amino acid corresponding to the tRNA's three-base-long anticodon.

- tRNAs have an L-shaped, tertiary structure. One leg of the L contains the anticodon, which forms complementary base pairs with the mRNA codon. The other leg holds the amino acid appropriate for that codon.

- Enzymes called aminoacyl-tRNA synthetases link the correct amino acid to the correct tRNA.

- Imprecise pairing—or "wobble pairing"—is allowed in the third position of the codon and anticodon, so only about 40 different tRNAs are required to translate the 61 codons that code for amino acids.

✓ You should be able to predict what would occur if a mutation caused an aminoacyl-tRNA synthetase to recognize two different amino acids.

## 17.5 The Structure and Function of Ribosomes

- Ribosomes are large macromolecular machines made of many proteins and RNAs.

- In the ribosome, the tRNA anticodon binds to a three-base-long mRNA codon to bring the correct amino acid into the ribosome.

- Peptide-bond formation by the ribosome is catalyzed by a ribozyme (RNA), not an enzyme (protein).

- Protein synthesis occurs in three steps: **(1)** an incoming aminoacyl tRNA occupies the A site; **(2)** the growing polypeptide chain is transferred from a peptidyl tRNA in the ribosome's P site to the amino acid bound to the tRNA in the A site, and a peptide bond is formed; and **(3)** the ribosome is translocated to the next codon on the mRNA, accompanied by ejection of the uncharged RNA from the E site.

- Chaperone proteins help fold newly synthesized proteins into their three-dimensional conformation (tertiary structure).

- Most proteins need to be modified after translation (post-translational modification) to activate them or target them to specific locations.

✔ You should be able to create a concept map (see BioSkills 15 in Appendix B) that describes the relationships among the following concepts and structures: translation, initiation, elongation, termination, growing polypeptide in P site, start codon, ribosome subunits.

**(MB) MasteringBiology**

**1. MasteringBiology Assignments**

**Tutorials and Activities** Chromosomal Mutations; Following the Instructions in DNA; Point Mutations Protein Synthesis (1 of 3): Overview; Protein Synthesis (2 of 3): Transcription and RNA Processing; Protein Synthesis (3 of 3): Translation and Protein Targeting Pathways; RNA Processing; RNA Synthesis; Synthesizing Proteins; Transcription; Translation; Types of RNA

**Questions** Reading Quizzes, Blue-Thread Questions, Test Bank

**2. eText** Read your book online, search, take notes, highlight text, and more.

**3. The Study Area** Practice Test, Cumulative Test, BioFlix® 3-D Animations, Videos, Activities, Audio Glossary, Word Study Tools, Art

## You should be able to . . .

### ✔ TEST YOUR KNOWLEDGE
Answers are available in Appendix A

1. How did the A site of the ribosome get its name?
   a. It is where amino acids are joined to tRNAs, producing aminoacyl tRNAs.
   b. It is where the amino group on the growing polypeptide chain is available for peptide-bond formation.
   c. It is the site occupied by incoming aminoacyl tRNAs.
   d. It is surrounded by α-helices of ribosomal proteins.

2. Where is the start codon located?
   a. at the very start (5′ end) of the mRNA
   b. at the downstream end of the 3′ untranslated region (UTR)
   c. at the downstream end of the 5′ untranslated region (UTR)
   d. at the upstream end of the 3′ untranslated region (UTR)

3. What is the function of a molecular chaperone?

4. What does a bacterial RNA polymerase produce when it transcribes a protein-coding gene?

   a. rRNA
   b. tRNA
   c. mRNA
   d. pre-mRNA

5. Where is an amino acid attached to a tRNA?

6. Compared with mRNAs that have a cap and tail, what do researchers observe when eukaryotic mRNAs that lack a cap and poly(A) tail are translated within a cell?
   a. The primary transcript cannot be processed properly.
   b. Translation occurs inefficiently.
   c. Enzymes on the ribosome add back a cap and poly(A) tail.
   d. tRNAs become resistant to degradation (being broken down).

### ✔ TEST YOUR UNDERSTANDING
Answers are available in Appendix A

7. Explain the relationship between eukaryotic promoter sequences, basal transcription factors, and RNA polymerase. Explain the relationship between bacterial promoter sequences, sigma, and RNA polymerase.

8. According to the wobble rules, the correct amino acid can be added to a growing polypeptide chain even if the third base in the mRNA codon is not complementary to the corresponding base in the tRNA anticodon. How do the wobble rules relate to the redundancy of the genetic code?

9. RNases and proteases are enzymes that destroy RNAs and proteins, respectively. Which of the following enzymes when added to a spliceosome is predicted to prevent recognition of pre-mRNA regions critical for splicing?
   a. an RNase specific for tRNAs
   b. an RNase specific for snRNAs
   c. a protease specific for initiation factors
   d. a protease specific for a release factor

**10.** Describe the sequence of events that occurs during translation as a protein elongates by one amino acid and the ribosome moves down the mRNA. Your answer should specify what is happening in the ribosome's A site, P site, and E site.

**11.** QUANTITATIVE Controlling the rates of transcription and translation is important in bacteria to avoid collisions between ribosomes and RNA polymerases. Calculate the maximum rate of translation by a ribosome in a bacterial cell, provided in units of amino acids per second, so that the ribosome doesn't overtake an RNA polymerase that is transcribing mRNA at a rate of 60 nucleotides per second. How long would it take for this bacterial cell to translate an mRNA containing 1800 codons?

**12.** In an aminoacyl tRNA, why is the observed distance between the amino acid and the anticodon important?

**✓ TEST YOUR PROBLEM-SOLVING SKILLS**                    *Answers are available in Appendix A*

**13.** The 5′ cap and poly(A) tail in eukaryotic mRNAs protect the message from degradation by ribonucleases. But why do ribonucleases exist? What function would an enzyme that destroys messages serve? Answer this question using the example of an mRNA for a hormone that causes human heart rate to increase.

**14.** The nucleotide shown below is called cordycepin triphosphate.

If cordycepin triphosphate is added to a cell-free transcription reaction, the nucleotide is added onto the growing RNA chain but no more nucleotides can be added. The added cordycepin is always found at the 3′ end of an RNA, confirming that synthesis occurs in the 5′ → 3′ direction. Why does cordycepin end transcription?

**a.** It prevents the association of RNA polymerase and sigma.
**b.** It irreversibly binds to the active site of RNA polymerase.
**c.** It cannot be recognized by RNA polymerase.
**d.** It lacks a 3′ OH.

**15.** Certain portions of the rRNAs in the large subunit of the ribosome are very similar in all organisms. To make sense of this finding, Carl Woese suggests that the conserved sequences have an important functional role. His logic is that these conserved sequences evolved in a common ancestor of all modern cells and are so important to cell function that any changes in the sequences cause death. In addition to rRNAs, which specific portions of the ribosome would you expect to be identical or nearly identical in all organisms? Explain your logic.

**16.** Recent structural models show that a poison called α-amanitin inhibits transcription by binding to a site inside eukaryotic RNA polymerase II but not to the active site itself. Based on the model of RNA polymerase in Figure 17.2, predict a place or places where α-amanitin might bind to inhibit transcription.

# 19 Control of Gene Expression in Eukaryotes

**In this chapter you will learn that**

Eukaryotes control gene expression many different ways

beginning with

Gene regulation in eukaryotes (an overview)    19.1

then explore

| Regulation via chromatin remodeling 19.2 | Regulation during transcription initiation 19.3 | Regulation following transcription 19.4 |

compare

Regulation in prokaryotes 19.5

apply

Regulation defects and cancer 19.6

A model of eukaryotic DNA in the condensed state. The DNA (shown in red and pink) is wrapped around proteins (in green). The DNA has to be uncoiled before transcription can take place.

B acteria regulate gene expression to respond to changes in their environment. *Escherichia coli* thrive best if the genes that are required to import and cleave lactose are expressed only when the cells are relying on lactose as a source of energy (see Chapter 18).

Unicellular eukaryotes face similar challenges. Consider the yeast *Saccharomyces cerevisiae*, which is used extensively in the production of beer, wine, and bread. In nature this species lives on the skins of grapes and other fruits, where the sugars that the cells use as food vary in type and concentration as the fruit ripens, falls, and rots. For yeast cells to grow and reproduce efficiently, gene expression has to be modified in response to these changes.

The cells that make up multicellular eukaryotes face additional challenges. Consider your body, which contains trillions of cells, each with a specialized structure and function. You have heart

**BIG PICTURE**

This chapter is part of the Big Picture. See how on pages 366–367.

✔ When you see this checkmark, stop and test yourself. Answers are available in Appendix A.

muscle cells, lung cells, nerve cells, skin cells, and so on. Even though these cells are different, they contain the same genes. Your bone cells and blood cells aren't different because of a difference in their genes but because they *express* different genes. Your bone cells have blood-cell genes—they just don't transcribe them.

Why not? The answer is that your cells respond to their environment, just as bacteria and unicellular eukaryotes do. But there's a key difference. The cells in a multicellular eukaryote express different genes in response to changes in the *internal* environment—specifically, to signals from other cells. As a human being or an oak tree develops, cells that are located in different parts of the organism are exposed to different cell–cell signals. As a result, they express different genes. **Differential gene expression** is responsible for creating different cell types, arranging them into tissues, and coordinating their activity to form the multicellular society we call an individual.

How does all of this regulation and differentiation happen? Later chapters introduce the signals that trigger the formation of muscle, bone, leaf, and flower cells (see Unit 4). In contrast, this chapter focuses on what happens after a eukaryotic cell receives such a signal. Let's start with an overview of how gene expression can be controlled, and close with a look at how defects in the process can trigger cancer.

## 19.1 Gene Regulation in Eukaryotes— An Overview

Like bacteria, eukaryotes can control gene expression at the levels of transcription, translation, and post-translation. But as **FIGURE 19.1** shows, three additional levels of control occur in eukaryotes as genetic information flows from DNA to proteins.

The first additional level of control involves the DNA–protein complex at the top of the figure. In eukaryotes, DNA is wrapped around proteins to create a structure called **chromatin.** Eukaryotic genes have promoters, just as bacterial genes do; but before transcription can begin in eukaryotes, the stretch of DNA containing the promoter must be released from tight interactions with proteins, so that RNA polymerase can make contact with the promoter. To capture this idea, biologists say that **chromatin remodeling** must occur before transcription.

The second level of regulation that is unique to eukaryotes is **RNA processing**—the steps required to produce a mature, processed mRNA from a primary RNA transcript. Recall that introns have to be spliced out of primary transcripts (see Chapter 17). In many cases, carefully orchestrated alternative splicing occurs—meaning that different combinations of exons are included in the mRNA. If different cells use different splicing patterns, different gene products result.

Third, mRNA life span is regulated in eukaryotes: mRNAs that remain in the cell for a long time tend to be translated more than mRNAs that have a short life span.

Each of the six potential control points shown in Figure 19.1 is employed in eukaryotic cells. This chapter explores all six—chromatin

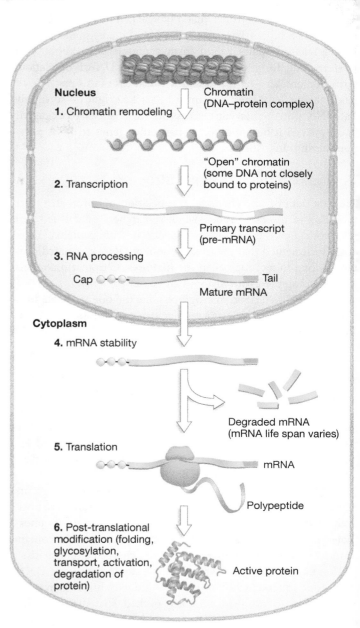

**FIGURE 19.1 In Eukaryotes, Gene Expression Can Be Controlled at Many Different Levels.**

remodeling, transcription, RNA processing, mRNA stability, translation, and post-translational modification of proteins.

To appreciate the breadth and complexity of gene regulation in eukaryotes, let's follow the series of events that occur as an embryonic cell responds to a developmental signal. Suppose a molecule arrives that specifies the production of a muscle-specific protein. What happens next?

## 19.2 Chromatin Remodeling

For a molecular signal to trigger the transcription of a particular gene, the chromatin around the target gene must be remodeled.

To appreciate why, consider that a typical cell in your body contains about 6 billion base pairs of DNA. Lined up end to end, these nucleotide pairs would form a double helix about 2 m (6.5 feet) long. But the nucleus that holds this DNA is only about ₅ μm in diameter—far less than the thickness of this page. To fit inside the nucleus, the DNA must be packed tightly—so tightly that RNA polymerase can't access it. How is DNA packaged? And how can it be unpacked at particular genes so RNA polymerase can transcribe it?

## What Is Chromatin's Basic Structure?

The first data on the chemical composition of chromatin were published in the early 1900s, when researchers established that eukaryotic DNA is intimately associated with proteins. Later work documented that the most abundant DNA-associated proteins belong to a group called the **histones.** Chromatin consists of DNA complexed with histones and other proteins.

In the 1970s electron micrographs like the one in **FIGURE 19.2a** revealed that chromatin has a regular structure. In some preparations for electron microscopy, chromatin looked like beads on a string. The "beads" came to be called **nucleosomes.**

More information emerged in 1984 when researchers determined the three-dimensional structure of eukaryotic chromatin by using X-ray crystallography (see **BioSkills 11** in Appendix B). The X-ray crystallographic data indicated that each nucleosome consists of DNA wrapped almost twice around a core of eight histone proteins. As **FIGURE 19.2b** indicates, a histone called H1 "seals" DNA to each nucleosome. Between each pair of nucleosomes there is a "linker" stretch of DNA.

The intimate association between DNA and histones occurs in part because DNA is negatively charged and histones are positively charged. DNA has a negative charge because of its phosphate groups; histones are positively charged because they contain many lysines and arginines, two positively charged amino acids.

There are additional layers of complexity in packaging DNA. H1 histones interact with one another and with histones in other nucleosomes to produce a tightly packed structure like that shown in Figure 19.2b. Based on its width, this structure is called the 30-nanometer fiber. (Recall that a nanometer is one-billionth of a meter and is abbreviated nm.)

Finally, the 30-nm fibers are attached at intervals along their length to proteins that form a scaffold or framework inside the nucleus. In this way, the entire chromosome is organized and held in place. When chromosomes condense before mitosis or meiosis, the scaffold proteins and 30-nm fibers are folded into still larger and more tightly packed structures.

A eukaryotic chromosome, then, is made up of chromatin that has several layers of organization: The DNA is wrapped around histones to form nucleosomes, nucleosomes are packed into 30-nm fibers, 30-nm fibers are attached to scaffold proteins, and the entire assembly can be folded into the highly condensed structure observed during cell division.

Although research has shown that bacterial DNA interacts with proteins that are organized similarly to nucleosomes,

**(a)** Nucleosomes in chromatin

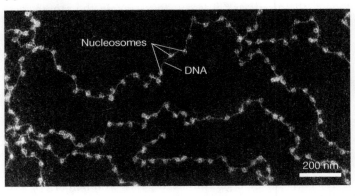

Nucleosomes

DNA

200 nm

**(b)** Nucleosome structure

Linker DNA

H1 protein attached to linker DNA and nucleosome

Nucleosome

Group of 8 histone proteins

**30-nm fiber**

30 nm

Protein scaffold

**Chromosome** in its condensed form (the form it's in during cell division)

**FIGURE 19.2 Chromatin Has Several Levels of Organization.**

nothing like the 30-nm fibers or higher-order arrangements has been observed in bacterial chromosomes.

The elaborate structure of eukaryotic chromatin does more than just package DNA so that it fits into the nucleus. Chromatin structure also has profound implications for the control of gene expression. To appreciate this point, consider the 30-nm fiber illustrated in Figure 19.2b. If this tightly packed stretch of DNA contains a promoter, how can RNA polymerase bind to it and initiate transcription?

## Evidence that Chromatin Structure Is Altered in Active Genes

Once the nucleosome-based structure of chromatin was established, biologists hypothesized that the close physical interaction between DNA and histones must be altered for RNA polymerase to make contact with DNA. More specifically, biologists hypothesized that a gene could not be transcribed until the condensed chromatin near its promoter was remodeled.

The central idea is that chromatin must be decondensed, to expose the promoter so RNA polymerase can bind to it. If so, then chromatin remodeling would represent the first step in the control of eukaryotic gene expression. Two types of studies have provided strong support for this hypothesis.

**DNA in Condensed Chromatin Is Protected from DNase** DNases are enzymes that cut DNA. Some DNases cleave DNA at random locations, and these cannot cut efficiently if DNA is tightly wrapped with proteins. As **FIGURE 19.3** shows, this type of DNase works effectively only if DNA is in a decondensed configuration.

Harold Weintraub and Mark Groudine used this observation to test the hypothesis that the DNA of actively transcribed genes is in an open configuration. In chicken blood cells, they compared chromatin structure in two genes: β-globin and ovalbumin. β-globin is a protein that is part of the hemoglobin found in red blood cells; ovalbumin is a protein found in egg white. In blood cells, the β-globin gene is transcribed at high levels, but the ovalbumin gene is not transcribed at all.

After treating blood cells with DNase and then analyzing the state of chromatin at the β-globin and ovalbumin genes, the researchers found that DNase cut the β-globin gene DNA much more readily than DNA of the ovalbumin gene. They interpreted this finding as evidence that in blood cells, chromatin of the actively transcribed β-globin gene was decondensed; and conversely, chromatin of the non-transcribed ovalbumin gene was condensed. Studies using DNase on different genes in different cell types yielded similar results.

**Histone Mutants** The second type of evidence in support of the chromatin-remodeling hypothesis comes from studies of mutant brewer's yeast cells that do not produce the usual complement of histones. In these mutant cells, many genes that are normally never transcribed are instead always transcribed at high levels.

To interpret this finding, biologists hypothesized that the lack of histone proteins prevented the assembly of normal chromatin. If the absence of normal histone–DNA interactions promotes transcription, then the presence of normal histone–DNA interactions must prevent it.

Taken together, the data suggest that in their normal, or default, state, eukaryotic genes are turned off. This is a new mechanism of negative control—different from repressor proteins (introduced in Chapter 18). When DNA is wrapped into a 30-nm fiber, the parking brake is on. If so, then gene expression depends on chromatin being opened up in the promoter region.

## How Is Chromatin Altered?

Research on chromatin remodeling has been proceeding at a furious pace, and biologists have succeeded in identifying some of the key players that work to change the state of chromatin condensation. These include enzymes that add methyl groups to DNA, enzymes that chemically modify histones, and macromolecular machines that actively reshape chromatin. Let's examine each of these in turn.

**DNA Methylation** A group of enzymes known as **DNA methyltransferases** add methyl groups ($-CH_3$) to cytosine residues in DNA. In mammals, the sequence recognized by these enzymes is a C next to a G in one strand of the DNA. This sequence is abbreviated CpG and is shown below in methylated form within a stretch of DNA.

$$5'-\text{ATAT}\boxed{\text{CG}}\text{TA}-3'$$
$$3'-\text{TATA}\boxed{\text{GC}}\text{AT}-5'$$

Why is **DNA methylation** important? Methylated CpG sequences are recognized by proteins that trigger chromatin condensation. Actively transcribed genes usually have low levels of methylated CpG near their promoters, and non-transcribed genes usually have high levels of methylated CpG.

**Histone Modification** DNA methylation is only one part of the chromatin alteration story. A large set of enzymes adds a variety of chemical groups to specific amino acids of histone proteins. These include phosphate groups, methyl groups, short polypeptide chains, and acetyl groups ($-COCH_3$). Addition of these groups to histones promotes condensed or decondensed chromatin depending on the specific set of modifications.

Condensed chromatin      Decondensed chromatin

Treatment with DNase I

Condensed chromatin      Degraded DNA

**FIGURE 19.3 DNase Assay for Chromatin Structure.** DNase is an enzyme that cuts DNA at random locations. It cannot cut condensed chromatin.

To account for these effects, researchers have proposed the existence of a **histone code.** The histone code hypothesis postulates that particular combinations of histone modifications set the state of chromatin condensation for a particular gene. In turn, this has an important role in regulating transcription. Let's take a closer look at one way histone modifications can control chromatin structure.

As shown in **FIGURE 19.4**, two different types of enzymes can add or remove acetyl groups from histones. **Histone acetyltransferases (HATs)** add acetyl groups to the positively charged lysine residues in histones, and **histone deacetylases (HDACs)** remove them. **Acetylation** of histones usually results in decondensed chromatin, a state associated with active transcription. How can acetylation of histones promote chromatin decondensation? When HATs add acetyl groups, the acetyl groups neutralize the positive charge on lysine residues and loosens the close association of nucleosomes with the negatively charged DNA. The addition of acetyl groups also creates a binding site for other proteins that help open the chromatin.

In contrast, when HDACs remove acetyl groups from histones, this process usually leads to condensed chromatin, a state associated with no transcription. HATs are an on switch for transcription, and HDACs are an off switch.

**Chromatin-Remodeling Complexes**   Other major players in chromatin alteration and gene regulation are enzymes that form macromolecular machines called **chromatin-remodeling complexes.** These machines harness the energy in ATP to reshape chromatin. Chromatin-remodeling complexes cause nucleosomes to slide along the DNA or, in some cases, knock the histones completely off the DNA to open up stretches of chromatin and allow gene transcription.

**FIGURE 19.4 Acetyl Groups Decondense Chromatin.** Histone acetyltransferases (HATs) cause chromatin to decondense; histone deacetylases (HDACs) cause it to condense.

✔**QUESTION** Are HAT and HDAC elements in positive control or negative control? Explain your reasoning.

DNA methylation, histone modifications, and chromatin-remodeling complexes work together to fine-tune chromatin condensation at specific genes. The take-home message from work on chromatin remodeling is simple: The condensation state of chromatin is critical in determining whether transcription occurs.

## Chromatin Modifications Can Be Inherited

The pattern of chromatin modifications varies from one cell type to another. For example, suppose within an individual you analyzed the same gene in a muscle cell and a brain cell. This and other genes would likely have a different pattern of DNA methylation and histone acetylation in the two cell types.

DNA methylation and histone modifications are an example of **epigenetic inheritance,** the collective term for patterns of inheritance that are due to something other than differences in DNA sequences. The *epi–* of epigenetics comes from the Greek word meaning "upon." It implies another level of inheritance that adds to standard DNA-based mechanisms to explain how different phenotypes are transmitted.

With epigenetic inheritance, if a cell received a "become muscle" signal early in development, it would modify its chromatin in distinctive ways and pass those modifications on to its descendants. Muscle cells are different from brain cells not because they contain different genes, but largely because they have inherited different patterns of DNA methylation and histone modifications during the course of their development.

But the story of epigenetic inheritance involves more than just differentiation of cell types during development. Evidence is emerging that epigenetic mechanisms can record early-life events and that this archive can be difficult to erase. This is the case when prenatal conditions alter the patterns of chromatin modification and the later-life phenotypes of a mother's offspring.

For example, biologists have long known that rats born to mothers fed low-protein diets during pregnancy and while nursing have a greatly increased risk of developing disorders similar to type 2 diabetes. Type 2 diabetes is a serious and increasingly common disease that alters the cellular uptake of glucose (Chapter 44). Both genetic factors and environmental factors, such as diet, play important roles in diabetes development.

One significant gene associated with diabetes is *Hnf4a*. *Hnf4a* codes for a regulator of genes involved in glucose uptake. Rats born to protein-deprived mothers develop symptoms of diabetes later in life, even when these rats are fed a normal, healthy diet from the time they are weaned. These diabetic rats also express the *Hnf4a* regulatory gene at lower levels than normal rats. Could epigenetic mechanisms be at work in silencing *Hnf4a* expression?

One team's approach to probing this question is shown in **FIGURE 19.5**. Using a treatment group and a control group, the researchers measured the types of histone modifications found at a key regulatory region of the *Hnf4a* gene. A regulatory region is a section of DNA that, like prokaryotic operators (Chapter 18), is involved in controlling the activity of a gene. The chromatin at this region has to be opened up for transcription to occur. Levels

## QUESTION: Does poor nutrition in a mother produce epigenetic effects in offspring?

**HYPOTHESIS:** Protein-deprived mothers will produce offspring with abnormal histone modifications.

**NULL HYPOTHESIS:** Protein-deprived mothers will produce offspring with normal histone modifications.

**EXPERIMENTAL SETUP:**

1. Provide rat mothers with a normal or a low-protein diet during pregnancy and while nursing.

2. After weaning, feed rat pups a normal diet and raise to old age.

3. Determine types of histone modifications for a regulatory gene involved in diabetes. (Also measure gene transcription.)

TRANSCRIPTION

*Hnf4a*

Modifications promoting: **condensed chromatin**

Modifications promoting: **decondensed chromatin**

**PREDICTION:** Offspring of mothers fed a low-protein diet will have abnormal histone modifications.

**PREDICTION OF NULL HYPOTHESIS:** Offspring of mothers fed a low-protein diet will have normal histone modifications.

**RESULTS:**

Relative enrichment levels — Modifications promoting **condensed chromatin** / Modifications promoting **decondensed chromatin** — Normal diet / Low protein

Relative gene expression levels — *Hnf4a* transcription — Normal diet / Low protein

**CONCLUSION:** A mother's diet influences chromatin modifications and gene expression patterns throughout her offspring's life.

**FIGURE 19.5 Events in Early Life Can Be Recorded through Epigenetic Mechanisms.**

SOURCE: Sandovici, I., N. H. Smith, and M. D. Nitert. 2011. Maternal diet and aging alter the epigenetic control of a promoter-enhancer interaction at the *Hnf4a* gene in rat pancreatic islets. *Proceedings of the National Academy of Sciences USA* 108: 5449–5454.

✔ **QUESTION** What could researchers do to prove that the histone modifications are causing reduced regulatory gene transcription?

---

of *Hnf4a* transcription in the control and treatment groups were also measured. What did the team learn?

As the graph on the left in the "Results" section of Figure 19.5 shows, they found that histone modifications that lead to condensed chromatin were *elevated* in rats born to malnourished mothers compared to control offspring. Conversely, histone modifications associated with decondensed chromatin were significantly *reduced* in the treatment group. The graph on the right confirms that transcription of *Hnf4a* was much lower in the treatment group than the control group. Together these results demonstrate a correlation between altered histone modifications and decreased levels of *Hnf4a* gene expression.

Remember that in this study, all rats were provided a healthy diet after weaning. This finding implies that a mother's nutritional status during pregnancy and nursing is responsible for the types of chromatin modifications seen in rats that develop diabetes.

Chromatin remodeling must occur before transcription. Now the question is, What happens once a section of chromatin is opened and DNA becomes accessible to RNA polymerase?

## check your understanding

### C Y U

**If you understand that . . .**

- Eukaryotic DNA is wrapped tightly around histones, forming nucleosomes, which are then coiled into structures called 30-nm chromatin fibers.
- Before transcription can begin, the DNA–protein complex of chromatin must be decondensed so that RNA polymerase can contact the promoter.
- Methylation of DNA and specific chemical modifications of histones play a key role in determining whether chromatin is opened and a gene is expressed.
- In many cases, the patterns of DNA methylation and histone modification in a cell are passed on to its daughter cells.

✔ **You should be able to . . .**

1. Predict how gene expression will be affected if a cell is grown with compounds that prevent DNA methylation.
2. Explain how certain patterns of histone acetylation or DNA methylation could influence whether a cell became a muscle cell or a brain cell.

*Answers are available in Appendix A.*

---

## 19.3 Initiating Transcription: Regulatory Sequences and Regulatory Proteins

As in bacteria, the **promoter** is a site in DNA where RNA polymerase binds to initiate transcription. Recent findings from genome sequencing projects (see Chapter 20) have shown that there is still much to be learned about eukaryotic promoters. What is known is that promoters in eukaryotes are more complex than bacterial promoters, often containing two or three conserved sequences that serve as binding sites for proteins needed to start transcription. The most intensively studied of these is a sequence known as the **TATA box.**

Once a promoter that contains a TATA box has been exposed by chromatin remodeling, the first step in initiating transcription is binding of the **TATA-binding protein (TBP).** Proteins related to TBP also work on promoters with other conserved sequences. But the binding of TBP or any of its relatives does not guarantee that a gene will be transcribed. In eukaryotes, a wide array of other DNA sequences and proteins work together to allow transcription.

## Promoter-Proximal Elements Are Regulatory Sequences Near the Promoter

The first **regulatory sequences** in eukaryotic DNA were discovered in the late 1970s, when Yasuji Oshima and co-workers set out to understand how yeast cells control the metabolism of the sugar galactose.

When galactose is absent, *S. cerevisiae* cells produce only tiny quantities of the enzymes required to metabolize it. But when galactose is present, transcription of the genes encoding these enzymes increases by a factor of 1000.

The team's first major result was the discovery of mutant cells that failed to produce any of the five enzymes required for galactose metabolism, even if galactose was present. To interpret this observation, they hypothesized that

1. the five genes are regulated together, even though they are not on the same chromosome;

2. normal cells have an activator protein that exerts positive control over the five genes;

3. the mutant cells have a mutation that completely disables the activator protein.

Other researchers were able to isolate the regulatory protein and confirm that it binds to a short stretch of DNA located just upstream from the promoter for all five genes required for galactose use.

In bacteria, genes that need to be regulated together are often clustered into a single operon and transcribed into a single mRNA. In contrast, eukaryotes use the strategy uncovered by Oshima's group for the galactose-metabolizing genes in yeast—co-regulated genes are not clustered together, but instead share a regulatory DNA sequence that binds the same regulatory protein.

Regulatory DNA sequences similar to those first discovered in yeast have now been found in a wide array of eukaryotic genes and species. Regulatory sequences like these that are located close to the promoter and bind regulatory proteins are termed **promoter-proximal elements.**

Unlike the promoter itself, promoter-proximal elements have sequences that are unique to specific sets of genes. In this way, they furnish a mechanism for eukaryotic cells to express certain genes but not others.

The discovery of promoter-proximal elements and a mechanism of positive control suggested a satisfying parallel between gene regulation in bacteria and in eukaryotes. This picture changed, however, when researchers discovered a new class of eukaryotic DNA regulatory sequences—sequences unlike anything in bacteria.

## Enhancers Are Regulatory Sequences Far from the Promoter

Susumu Tonegawa and colleagues made a startling discovery while exploring how human cells regulate gene expression. The gene studied by Tonegawa's group was broken into many introns and exons. Recall that introns are transcribed sequences that are spliced out of the primary transcript; exons are transcribed regions that are included in the mature RNA once splicing is complete (Chapter 17). The researchers discovered a regulatory sequence within one of the introns that was required for transcription of the gene.

This finding was remarkable for two reasons: **(1)** The regulatory sequence was thousands of bases away from the promoter, and **(2)** it was downstream of the promoter instead of upstream. Regulatory sequences that are far from the promoter and activate transcription are termed **enhancers.** Follow-up work has shown that enhancers occur in all eukaryotes and that they have several key characteristics:

- Enhancers can be more than 100,000 bases away from the promoter. They can be located in introns or in untranscribed sequences on either the 5′ or 3′ side of the gene (See **FIGURE 19.6**).

- Like promoter-proximal elements, many types of enhancers exist.

- Most genes have more than one enhancer.

- Enhancers usually have binding sites for more than one protein.

- Enhancers can work even if their normal 5′→3′ orientation is flipped, or if they are moved to a new location in the vicinity of the gene.

Enhancers are regulatory DNA sequences unique to eukaryotes. When regulatory proteins called **transcriptional activators** bind to enhancers, transcription begins. Thus, enhancers and activators are like a gas pedal—an element in positive control. Eukaryotes also possess regulatory sequences that are similar in structure and share key characteristics with enhancers but work to inhibit transcription. These DNA sequences are called **silencers.** When regulatory proteins called **repressors** bind to silencers, transcription is shut down. Silencers and repressors are like a brake—an element in negative control.

## The Role of Transcription Factors in Differential Gene Expression

Follow-up work supported the hypothesis that enhancers and silencers are binding sites for activators and repressors that regulate transcription. Collectively, these proteins are termed

Enhancer      Promoter ⌐ Start site      Enhancer      Enhancer

◄——┤ Upstream    Promoter-proximal element    Exon   Intron   Exon   Intron   Exon    Downstream ├——►

**FIGURE 19.6 Enhancers and Promoter-Proximal Elements Regulate the Expression of Eukaryotic Genes.** Promoter-proximal elements are near the promoter. Enhancers are located farther away, may be upstream or downstream of the promoter, and may even be within introns. Exons and introns are not drawn to scale. They are typically very large compared with regulatory sequences.

✔**EXERCISE** Compare and contrast the structure of this typical eukaryotic gene and the structure of a bacterial operon.

**regulatory transcription factors,** or often **transcription factors** for short. By analyzing mutant yeast, fruit flies, and roundworms that have defects in the expression of particular genes, biologists have identified a large number of transcription factors that bind to enhancers, silencers, and promoter-proximal elements.

These results support one of the most general statements researchers are able to make about gene regulation in eukaryotes: Different types of cells express different genes because they have different transcription factors. In multicellular species, the transcription factors, in turn, are produced in response to signals that arrive from other cells early in embryonic development.

For example, if a signal that says "become a muscle cell" reaches a cell in the early embryo, it triggers a signal transduction cascade (see Chapter 11) that leads to the production of transcription factors specific to muscle cells. Because different transcription factors bind to specific regulatory sequences, they turn on the production of muscle-specific proteins. But if no "become-a-muscle-cell" signal arrives, then no muscle-specific transcription factors are produced and no muscle-specific gene expression takes place.

Differential gene expression is a result of the production or activation of specific transcription factors. Eukaryotic genes are turned on when transcription factors bind to enhancers and promoter-proximal elements; the genes are turned off when transcription factors bind to silencers or when chromatin is condensed. Distinctive transcription factors are what make a muscle cell a muscle cell and a bone cell a bone cell.

## How Do Transcription Factors Recognize Specific DNA Sequences?

Each transcription factor must be able to recognize and bind to a specific DNA sequence. How can it do this?

Recall that DNA bases are partially exposed in the major and minor grooves of the DNA double helix (see Figure 4.7 for a review). The edges of an AT base pair and a GC base pair that project into the grooves of the DNA helix contain different sets of atoms and have different surface shapes (**FIGURE 19.7a**). These differences in composition and shape can be recognized by transcription factors.

**(a)** AT and CG base pairs present different shapes and chemical groups in the grooves of DNA.

**(b)** Transcription factors recognize a specific sequence of bases in target DNA.

**FIGURE 19.7 How Transcription Factors Bind to Regulatory Sequences. (a)** The edges of base pairs that project into the major and minor grooves of the double helix present a different structure and set of atoms. Atoms that can participate in hydrogen bonding with amino acids of transcription factors are indicated by arrows. The methyl group on thymine (T) is also important in recognition. **(b)** A transcription factor (green) involved in muscle-cell differentiation binding to a regulatory sequence in DNA. The bases recognized by the protein are highlighted in red.

Just as base pairs come together by complementary molecular interactions, so too can proteins and specific DNA sequences. An example is shown in **FIGURE 19.7b**. In this case, a transcription factor that is essential for the development of muscle cells inserts amino acid side chains into two major grooves of DNA. This particular transcription factor binds to a specific enhancer sequence because of complementary interactions between base pairs and its amino acids. Without such specific interactions between transcription factors and DNA, the development of muscle cells—or any other specialized cell type—would not be possible.

## A Model for Transcription Initiation

Although gene expression can be controlled at many levels, regulating the start of transcription is at center stage. For a process so important, many questions remain. What is clear is that transcription factors must interact with regulatory sequences to initiate transcription.

Besides the regulatory transcription factors you've learned about that bind to enhancers, silencers, and promoter-proximal elements, there is another type: **basal transcription factors.** These are proteins that interact with the promoter and are not restricted to particular genes or cell types. The term basal implies that these proteins are necessary for transcription to occur, but they do not provide much in the way of regulation. The promoter-recognized TATA-binding protein (TBP) that you learned about earlier is an example of a basal transcription factor that is common to many genes. ✔ If you understand this concept, you should be able to compare and contrast the regulatory and basal transcription factors found in muscle cells versus nerve cells.

In addition to transcription factors, a large complex of proteins called **Mediator** acts as a bridge between regulatory transcription factors, basal transcription factors, and RNA polymerase II.

**FIGURE 19.8** summarizes one model for how transcription is initiated in eukaryotes.

**Step 1** Transcriptional activators bind to DNA and recruit chromatin-remodeling complexes and histone acetyltransferases (HATs).

**Step 2** The chromatin-remodeling complexes and HATs open a swath of chromatin that includes the promoter, promoter-proximal elements, and enhancers.

**Step 3** Other transcriptional activators bind to the newly exposed enhancers and promoter-proximal elements; basal transcription factors bind to the promoter and recruit RNA polymerase II.

**Step 4** Mediator connects the transcriptional activators and basal transcription factors that are bound to DNA. This step is made possible through DNA looping. RNA polymerase II can now begin transcription.

✔ If you understand this model, you should be able to explain why DNA forms loops near the promoter in order for transcription to begin.

An important point in this model of transcription initiation the dual role of transcriptional activators. Activators work not only to stimulate transcription but also to bring chromatin-remodeling proteins to the right place at the right time. None of the proteins that remodel chromatin can recognize specific DNA sequences. It is the transcriptional activators that bind to regulatory sequences at particular genes to recruit the proteins needed to remodel chromatin.

The role of transcriptional activators in bringing in proteins that decondense chromatin leads to a chicken-and-egg paradox: How can an activator bind to DNA in the first place if chromatin is condensed? It turns out that except in its most highly condensed forms, chromatin is dynamic. DNA occasionally dissociates from nucleosomes, exposing regulatory sequences to activators that are present in a particular cell type.

Getting RNA polymerase to initiate transcription requires interactions between many proteins, including transcriptional activators that are bound to enhancers and promoter-proximal elements, Mediator, basal transcription factors, and RNA polymerase itself. The result is a large, macromolecular machine that is positioned at a gene's start site and capable of starting transcription.

Compared with what happens in bacteria, where just three to five proteins may interact at the promoter to initiate transcription, the process in eukaryotes is remarkably complicated.

check your understanding

**If you understand that . . .**

- Eukaryotic genes have regulatory sequences called promoter-proximal elements close to their promoters.
- Eukaryotic genes also have regulatory sequences called enhancers or silencers far from their promoters.
- Transcription initiation is a multistep process that begins when transcriptional activators bind to DNA and recruit proteins that open chromatin.
- Interactions between regulatory transcription factors, Mediator, and basal transcription factors position RNA polymerase II at the gene's start site.

✔ **You should be able to . . .**

1. Compare and contrast the nature of regulatory sequences and regulatory proteins in bacteria versus eukaryotes.

2. Explain why the presence of certain transcription factors could influence whether a cell becomes a muscle cell or a brain cell.

*Answers are available in Appendix A.*

## 19.4 Post-Transcriptional Control

Chromatin remodeling and transcription are just the opening to the story of gene regulation. Once a gene is transcribed, a series of events has to occur before a final product appears (see Figure 19.1). Each of these events offers an opportunity

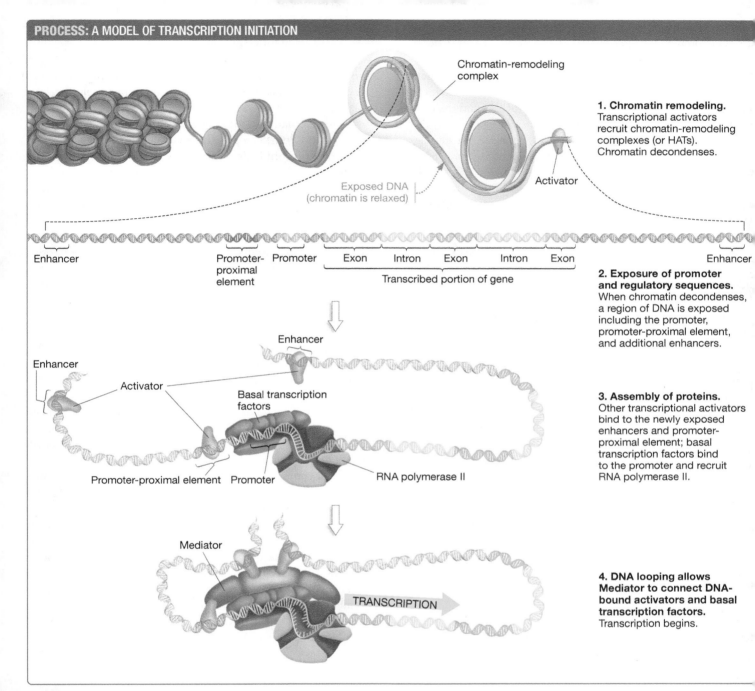

**FIGURE 19.8 Transcription Initiation in Eukaryotes.**

to regulate gene expression, and each is used in some cells at least some of the time. These control mechanisms include (1) splicing RNAs in various ways, (2) modifying the life span of mRNAs, (3) altering the rate at which translation is initiated, and (4) activating or inactivating proteins after translation has occurred. Let's consider each in turn.

## Alternative Splicing of mRNAs

Introns are spliced out in the nucleus as the primary RNA is transcribed. Recall that the mRNA that results from splicing consists of sequences encoded by exons, and that it is protected by a cap on the 5′ end and a long poly(A) tail on the 3′ end (see Chapter 17). You may also recall that splicing is accomplished by macromolecular machines called **spliceosomes,** and that many primary transcripts can be spliced in more than one way. This turns out to be a major way of regulating eukaryotic gene expression.

During splicing, gene expression is regulated when selected exons are removed from the primary transcript along with the introns. As a result, the same primary RNA transcript can yield more than one kind of mature, processed mRNA, consisting of different combinations of exons.

This is important. Since these mature mRNAs contain differences in their sequences, the polypeptides translated from them will likewise differ. Splicing the same primary RNA transcript in different ways to produce different mature mRNAs and thus different proteins is referred to as **alternative splicing.**

To see how alternative splicing works, consider the muscle-cell protein tropomyosin. The tropomyosin gene is expressed in both skeletal muscle cells and smooth muscle cells. These cells make up two distinct kinds of muscle tissue. Skeletal muscle is responsible for moving your bones; smooth muscle lines many parts of your gut and certain blood vessels.

As **FIGURE 19.9a** shows, the primary transcript from the tropomyosin gene contains 14 exons. In each type of muscle cell, a different subset of the 14 exons are spliced together to produce two different mRNAs (**FIGURE 19.9b**). As a result of alternative splicing, the tropomyosin proteins found in these two cell types are distinct. One reason skeletal muscle and smooth muscle are different is that they contain different types of tropomyosin.

Alternative splicing is controlled by proteins that bind to RNAs in the nucleus and interact with spliceosomes to influence which sequences are used for splicing. When cells that are destined to become skeletal muscle or smooth muscle are developing, they receive signals leading to the production of specific proteins that are active in the regulation of splicing. Instead of transcribing different tropomyosin genes, the cells transcribe a single gene and splice the same primary RNA transcript in different ways.

Before the importance of alternative splicing was widely appreciated, a gene was considered to be a nucleotide sequence that encodes one specific protein or RNA, along with its regulatory sequences. Based on this view, estimates for the number of genes in the human genome were typically in the range of 60,000 to 100,000. But once the complete human genome sequence became available, researchers realized that we may have as few as 20,000 sequences for primary mRNA transcripts.

Even though our genomes contain a relatively low number of genes, recent data indicate that over 90 percent of them undergo alternative splicing to produce multiple products. Thus, the number of different proteins that your cells can produce is far larger than the number of genes.

Given the extent of alternative splicing, the definition of protein-coding genes has been changed to the coding and regulatory sequences that direct the production of one *or more* related mRNAs and polypeptides.

Many alternatively spliced genes produce just a few different products, but some can produce a bewildering array of mRNAs. The current record is the *Dscam* gene of the fruit fly *Drosophila melanogaster*. The products of this gene help to guide growing nerve cells within the embryo. The primary transcript can be spliced into more than 38,000 distinct forms of mRNA, and the *Dscam* gene can produce thousands of different products.

Alternative splicing is a major mechanism in the control of gene expression in multicellular eukaryotes. ✔ If you understand alternative splicing, you should be able to explain why it does not occur in bacteria and describe where it occurs in Figure 19.1.

## mRNA Stability and RNA Interference

Once splicing is complete and processed mRNAs are exported to the cytoplasm, new regulatory mechanisms come into play. For example, it has long been known that the life span of an mRNA in a cell can vary. The mRNA for casein—the major protein in milk—is produced in the mammary gland tissue of female mammals. Normally, casein mRNA persists in cells for only about an hour, and little casein protein is produced. But when a female mouse is lactating, regulatory molecules help the mRNAs persist almost 30 times longer—leading to a huge increase in the production of casein. In this instance, shortening of the poly(A) tail decreases the life-span of the mRNA.

More recent discoveries in a variety of organisms, from worms to plants to people, have uncovered a widespread and important form of post-transcriptional gene regulation known as **RNA interference.** RNA interference occurs when a tiny, single-stranded RNA held by a protein complex binds to a complementary sequence in an mRNA. This event unleashes either the destruction of the mRNA or a block to the mRNA's translation. How does it work?

**(a)** Tropomyosin gene

Intron    Intron    Intron

Exon 1    Exon 2    Exon 3    Exon 4    5    6    7    8    9    10    11    12    13    14

**(b)** Alternative splicing produces more than one mature mRNA.

mRNA produced in skeletal muscle

1    3    4    5    6    7    8    9    10    11    12    13

mRNA produced in smooth muscle

1    2    4    5    6    7    8    9    10    13    14

Exons found only in **skeletal muscle** tropomyosin

Exons found only in **smooth muscle** tropomyosin

Exons found in **both** types of tropomyosin

**FIGURE 19.9 Alternative Splicing Produces More than One Mature mRNA from the Same Gene.**

**FIGURE 19.10** walks through the sequence of events.

**Step 1** RNA interference begins when RNA polymerase transcribes genes that code for RNAs that double back on themselves to form a hairpin. Hairpin formation occurs because pairs of bases within the RNA transcript are complementary.

**Step 2** Some of the RNA is trimmed by enzymes in the nucleus; then the double-stranded hairpin that remains is exported to the cytoplasm.

**Step 3** In the cytoplasm, another enzyme cuts out the hairpin loop to form double-stranded RNA molecules that are only about 22 nucleotides long.

**Step 4** One of the strands from this short RNA is taken up by a group of proteins called the *RNA-induced silencing complex*, or RISC. The RNA strand held by the RISC is a **microRNA (miRNA).**

**Step 5** Once it is part of a RISC, the miRNA binds to its complementary sequences in a target mRNA.

**Step 6** If the match between a miRNA and an mRNA is perfect, an enzyme in the RISC destroys the mRNA by cutting it in two. In effect, tight binding by a miRNA is a "kiss of death" for the mRNA. If the match isn't perfect, however, the mRNA is not destroyed. Instead, its translation is inhibited. Either way, miRNAs "interfere" with gene expression.

The first papers on RNA interference were published in the mid-1990s, and the first miRNAs were characterized in 2001. Since then, research on miRNAs and RNA interference has exploded. Current data suggest that a typical animal or plant species has at least 500 genes that code for miRNAs and that each miRNA regulates more than one mRNA. Because of this evidence, it is estimated that a large percentage of all animal and plant genes are controlled by these tiny molecules. miRNAs are critical for normal development, and mutations in miRNA genes are associated with many diseases. RNA interference is increasingly recognized as a key aspect of post-transcriptional control.

Researchers are currently testing whether certain miRNAs could be used to knock out specific genes associated with illness, or to destroy mRNAs produced by viruses during an infection. Research on RNA interference has quickly moved from an exciting new frontier in basic biology to possible applications in medicine.

✔ If you understand RNA interference, you should be able to describe where it occurs in Figure 19.1.

## How Is Translation Controlled?

RNA interference is not the only mechanism of gene control that acts on mRNAs and affects whether translation occurs. For example, cells may slow or stop translation in response to a sudden increase in temperature or infection by a virus. The slowdown occurs because regulatory proteins that are activated by the temperature spike or viral invasion add a phosphate group to a protein that is part of the ribosome.

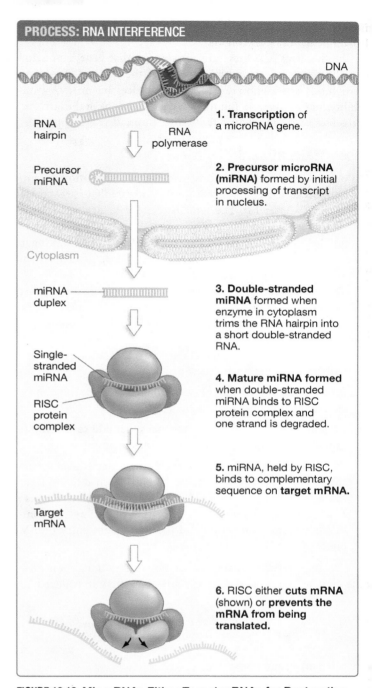

**PROCESS: RNA INTERFERENCE**

1. **Transcription** of a microRNA gene.

2. **Precursor microRNA (miRNA)** formed by initial processing of transcript in nucleus.

3. **Double-stranded miRNA** formed when enzyme in cytoplasm trims the RNA hairpin into a short double-stranded RNA.

4. **Mature miRNA formed** when double-stranded miRNA binds to RISC protein complex and one strand is degraded.

5. miRNA, held by RISC, binds to complementary sequence on **target mRNA.**

6. RISC either **cuts mRNA** (shown) or **prevents the mRNA from being translated.**

**FIGURE 19.10 MicroRNAs Either Target mRNAs for Destruction or Prevent Their Translation.** MicroRNAs are held by the RISC protein complex and bind to target mRNAs by complementary base pairing.

You might recall that phosphorylation frequently leads to changes in the shape and chemical reactivity of proteins. In the case of the phosphorylated ribosomal protein, the shape change slows or prevents translation.

For the cell, this dramatic change in gene expression can mean the difference between life and death. High temperatures disrupt protein folding, so shutting down translation prevents the production of improperly folded polypeptides. If the problem is an invading virus, the cell stops the infection because it avoids manufacturing viral proteins.

Mechanisms like these are a reminder that gene expression can be regulated at multiple points: at the level of chromatin structure, transcription initiation, RNA processing, mRNA availability, and translation. But that's not all. Let's look at the last level possible: altering protein activity, after translation is complete.

## Post-Translational Control

In bacteria, mechanisms of post-translational regulation are important because they allow cells to respond rapidly to new conditions (see Chapter 18). The same is true for eukaryotes. Instead of waiting for transcription, RNA processing, and translation to occur, the cell can keep an existing but inactive protein waiting in the wings and then quickly activate it in response to altered conditions. This is the essence of post-translational control.

There is a trade-off, however: Speed is gained at the expense of efficiency. Transcription, RNA processing, and translation use up energy and materials; it is wasteful to produce proteins that won't be used.

You have already encountered several important mechanisms of post-translational control over gene expression.

- Proteins are folded into their final, active conformation by chaperone proteins (see Chapters 3 and 17).

- Proteins may be modified by enzymes that add carbohydrate groups (see Chapter 7) or cleave off certain amino acids.

- Phosphorylation is an extremely common mechanism for activating or deactivating proteins. You just learned how a ribosomal protein is deactivated by adding a phosphate. You also might recall discussion of the activation of cyclin–Cdk complexes by phosphorylation and the subsequent entry into M phase of the cell cycle (see Chapter 12).

Yet another key mechanism of post-translational control—the targeted destruction of proteins—was first introduced by

describing the short life span of cyclin proteins. When a protein such as a cyclin needs to be destroyed, enzymes mark it by adding many copies of a small polypeptide called ubiquitin. Ubiquitin got its name because it is ubiquitous in cells. A macromolecular machine called the **proteasome** recognizes proteins that have a ubiquitin tag and cuts them into short segments.

As you can see, the regulation of gene expression in eukaryotes includes everything from opening chromatin in the nucleus to controlling the life span of proteins.

Do bacteria use the same range of regulatory mechanisms? Let's explore this question next.

## 19.5 How Does Gene Expression Compare in Bacteria and Eukaryotes?

Almost as soon as biologists knew that information in DNA is transcribed into RNA and then translated into proteins, they began asking questions about how that flow of information is regulated. **TABLE 19.1** summarizes what biologists have learned over the past half century about how bacterial and eukaryotic gene expression is controlled—organized by the six steps in gene expression introduced in Figure 19.1.

How does the regulation of gene expression differ in bacteria and eukaryotes? Biologists point to five fundamental differences in the control of gene expression in bacteria and eukaryotes:

1. *DNA Packaging* The chromatin of eukaryotic DNA must be decondensed for basal and regulatory transcription factors to gain access to genes and for RNA polymerase to initiate transcription. The tight packaging of eukaryotic DNA means that the default state of transcription in eukaryotes is "off." In contrast, the default state of transcription in bacteria, which lack histone proteins and have freely accessible promoters, is "on." Chromatin structure provides a mechanism of negative control that does not exist in bacteria.

2. *Complexity of transcription* Transcriptional control is much more complex in eukaryotes than in bacteria. The sheer number of eukaryotic proteins involved in regulating transcription dwarfs that in bacteria, as does the complexity of their interactions.

3. *Coordinated transcription* In bacteria, genes that take part in the same cellular response are often organized into operons and transcribed together from a single promoter. In contrast, operons are rare in eukaryotes. Instead, for coordinated gene expression, eukaryotes rely on the strategy used in bacterial regulons—physically scattered genes are expressed together when the same regulatory transcription factors trigger the transcription of genes with the same DNA regulatory sequences.

4. *Greater reliance on post-transcriptional control* Eukaryotes make greater use of post-transcriptional control, such as alternative splicing. Alternative splicing allows eukaryotes to regulate the production of many proteins from each gene.

| Level of Regulation | Bacteria | Eukaryotes |
|---|---|---|
| Chromatin remodeling | • Limited packaging of DNA<br>• Remodeling not a major issue in regulating gene expression. | • Extensive packaging of DNA<br>• Chromatin must be decondensed for transcription to begin. |
| Transcription | • Positive and negative control by regulatory proteins that act at sites close to the promoter<br>• Sigma interacts with promoter. | • Positive and negative control by regulatory proteins that act at sites close to *and* far from promoter<br>• Large set of basal transcription factors interact with promoter.<br>• Mediator required. |
| RNA processing | • Rare | • Extensive processing: alternative splicing of introns |
| mRNA stability | • Rarely used for control | • Commonly used: RNA interference limits life span or translation rate of many mRNAs. |
| Translation | • Regulatory proteins bind to mRNAs and ribosomes and affect translation rate. | • Regulatory proteins bind to mRNAs and ribosomes and affect translation rate. |
| Post-translational modification | • Folding by chaperone proteins<br>• Chemical modification (e.g., phosphorylation) changes protein activity. | • Folding by chaperone proteins<br>• Chemical modification (e.g., phosphorylation) changes protein activity.<br>• Ubiquitination targets proteins for destruction by proteasome. |

Alternative splicing, microRNAs, and regulation of mRNA stability are seldom seen in bacteria, but these constitute major elements of control in eukaryotes.

To date, biologists do not have a good explanation for why gene expression is so much more complex in eukaryotes than it is in bacteria. After decades of research, the debate continues.

For multicellular eukaryotes, one hypothesis is that the requirement for complex regulation of gene expression during development has driven the evolution of such complicated and multilayered means of controlling genes.

Normal regulation of gene expression results in the orderly development of an embryo and appropriate responses to environmental change in adults. What happens when gene expression goes awry? Unfortunately, one answer is uncontrolled cell growth and the set of diseases called cancer. Understanding how changes in gene expression can lead to cancer is one of today's great research frontiers.

# 19.6 Linking Cancer with Defects in Gene Regulation

All cancers involve uncontrolled cell division. What allows this unbridled increase in cell number? Each type of cancer is caused by a different set of mutations that lead to cancer when they affect one of two classes of genes: (1) genes that stop or slow the cell cycle, and (2) genes that trigger cell growth and division by initiating specific phases in the cell cycle. Many of the genes

that are mutated in cancer influence gene regulation. Let's take a closer look at how altered gene regulation can cause uncontrolled cell growth.

## The Genetic Basis of Uncontrolled Cell Growth

As you learned in the chapter on the cell cycle (Chapter 12), proteins that stop or slow the cell cycle when conditions are unfavorable for cell division are called tumor suppressors. Logically enough, the genes that code for these proteins are called **tumor suppressor** genes. If the function of a tumor suppressor gene is lost because of mutation, then a key brake on the cell cycle is eliminated.

Genes that stimulate cell division are called **proto-oncogenes** (literally, "first cancer genes"). In normal cells, the proteins produced from proto-oncogenes are active only when conditions are appropriate for growth. In cancerous cells, defects in the regulation of proto-oncogenes can cause these genes to stimulate growth at all times. (In the context of cancer, cell growth refers to an increase in cell numbers, not an increase in the size of individual cells.) In such cases, a mutation has converted the proto-oncogene into an **oncogene**—an allele that promotes cancer development.

For cancers to develop, many mutations are required within a single cell, and these alter both tumor suppressor genes and proto-oncogenes.

## The *p53* Tumor Suppressor: A Case Study

To gain a deeper understanding of how defects in gene expression can lead to cancer, consider research on the gene that is most often defective in human cancers. The gene is called *p53* because

**(a)** Normal cell

**(b)** *p53* mutant cell

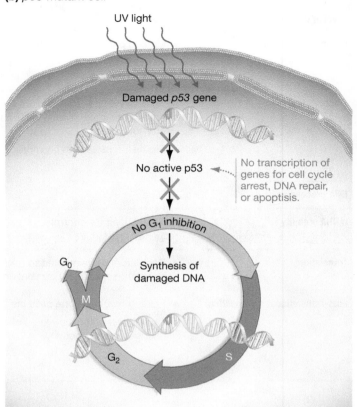

**FIGURE 19.11 Consequences of *p53* Mutation.**

he protein it codes for has a molecular weight of approximately 53 kilodaltons. Sequencing studies have revealed that mutant, nonfunctional forms of *p53* are found in over half of all human cancers. The *p53* gene codes for a regulatory transcription factor.

Researchers began to understand what *p53* does when they exposed normal, noncancerous human cells to UV radiation and noticed that levels of active *p53* protein increased markedly. Recall that UV radiation damages DNA (see Chapter 15). Follow-up studies confirmed that there is a close correlation between DNA damage and the amount of *p53* in a cell. In addition, analyses of the protein's primary structure suggested that it might contain a DNA-binding region similar to the one shown for the muscle-specific transcription factor in Figure 19.7.

These observations inspired the hypothesis that *p53* is a regulatory transcription factor that serves as a master brake on the cell cycle. In this model, shown in **FIGURE 19.11**, *p53* is activated by DNA damage. Activated *p53* binds to the enhancers of genes that arrest the cell cycle, repair DNA damage, and when all else fails, trigger apoptosis (cell death). Expression of these genes allows the cell to halt the cell cycle in order to repair its DNA, if this is possible, or commit suicide if the DNA damage is too severe. In mutant cells that lack a form of *p53* that can bind to enhancers, DNA damage cannot arrest the cell cycle, the cell cannot kill itself, and damaged DNA is replicated. This situation leads to mutations that can move the cell farther down the road to cancer. The *p53* protein is like a quality control officer. If it is missing, errors are made and things go downhill.

Here are some of the results that support this model of *p53* function:

- *p53* activates many different genes, including genes for cell cycle regulation, DNA repair, and apoptosis.

- X-ray crystallography studies show that *p53* binds directly to DNA regulatory sequences of the genes it controls.

- Virtually all the *p53* mutations associated with cancer are located in the protein's DNA-binding region and alter amino acids that interfere with *p53*'s ability to bind to regulatory DNA sequences.

The role of *p53* in preventing cancer is so important that biologists call this gene "the guardian of the genome." Today, biologists are searching for molecules that can restore *p53* activity to protect the genome and act against cancer.

---

## CHAPTER 19 REVIEW

For media, go to MasteringBiology

## If you understand . . .

### 19.1 Gene Regulation in Eukaryotes— An Overview

- Changes in gene expression allow eukaryotic cells to respond to changes in the environment and cause distinct cell types to develop.

- In a multicellular eukaryote, cells are different because they express different genes, not because they have different genes.

- Gene expression is regulated at six levels: Chromatin has to be remodeled, the transcription of specific genes may be initiated or repressed, mRNAs may be spliced in different ways to produce a different product, the life span of specific mRNAs may be extended or shortened, translation rate may be increased or decreased, and the life span or activity of particular proteins may be altered.

✔ You should be able to describe how the presence of the nuclear envelope, and the physical separation of transcription and translation, influences the levels of gene regulation observed in eukaryotes versus bacteria and archaea.

### 19.2 Chromatin Remodeling

- Eukaryotic DNA is packaged with proteins into chromatin that must be opened before transcription can occur.

- Eukaryotic DNA is wrapped around histone proteins to form bead-like nucleosomes that are then coiled into 30-nm fibers and higher-order chromatin structures.

- Transcription cannot be initiated until chromatin around regulatory regions is decondensed.

- The state of chromatin condensation depends on the methylation of cytosines in DNA, acetylation and other modifications of histones, and the action of molecular machines called chromatin-remodeling complexes.

- Patterns of DNA methylation and histone modifications can be passed from mother cells to daughter cells.

- Epigenetic inheritance is the inheritance of different phenotypes due to anything other than differences in alleles; transmitting patterns of chromatin condensation from mother to daughter cells or from parent to offspring is a mechanism of epigenetic inheritance.

✔ You should be able to explain why chromatin remodeling has to be the first step in gene activation.

### 19.3 Initiating Transcription: Regulatory Sequences and Regulatory Proteins

- In eukaryotes, transcription is triggered by regulatory proteins called transcription factors that bind to sequences both close to and far from the promoter.

- Regulatory transcription factors can be activators or repressors; these bind to regulatory sequences called (1) promoter-proximal sequences that are near promoters or (2) enhancers and silencers that are often located at a distance from gene promoters.

- Amino acids on regulatory transcription factors interact with the projections of base pairs in the grooves of the DNA helix to allow binding to specific regulatory sequences.

- The first regulatory transcription factors that bind to DNA recruit proteins that loosen the interaction between nucleosomes and DNA, making the promoter, promoter-proximal elements, and enhancers accessible to other transcription factors.

- Interactions between regulatory and basal transcription factors occur through a complex of proteins called Mediator and lead to the positioning of RNA polymerase at the promoter and the start of transcription.

✔ You should be able to draw a model of a eukaryotic gene undergoing transcription. Label enhancers, promoter-proximal elements, the promoter, activators, basal transcription factors, Mediator, and RNA polymerase.

## 19.4 Post-Transcriptional Control

- Once transcription is complete, gene expression is controlled by (1) alternative splicing, (2) RNA interference, and (3) activation or inactivation of protein products.

- Alternative splicing allows a single gene to produce more than one version of an mRNA and more than one kind of protein. It is regulated by proteins that interact with potential splice sites in the primary transcript to control which ones the spliceosome uses.

- RNA interference occurs when tiny strands of complementary RNA bind to mRNAs in association with the protein complex called RISC. This marks the mRNAs for destruction or prevents their translation. If the short RNA strands come from a transcribed cellular gene, they are known as microRNAs (miRNAs).

- Once translation occurs, proteins may be activated or inactivated by the addition or removal of chemical groups such as phosphates, or marked for destruction in the proteasome by adding polypeptides known as ubiquitin.

✓ You should be able to explain why humans can have so few genes.

## 19.5 How Does Gene Expression Compare in Bacteria and Eukaryotes?

- Examine Table 19.1 Regulating Gene Expression in Bacteria and Eukaryotes.

✓ You should be able to compare and contrast how bacteria and eukaryotes regulate the transcription of genes that need to be turned on together.

## 19.6 Linking Cancer with Defects in Gene Regulation

- If mutations alter regulatory proteins that promote or inhibit progression through the cell cycle, then uncontrolled cell growth and tumor formation may result.

✓ You should be able to explain why mutations of *p53* that prevent the protein from binding to DNA set the stage for cancer.

 **MasteringBiology**

**1. MasteringBiology Assignments**

**Tutorials and Activities** Control of Gene Expression; Control of Transcription; DNA Packing; Overview: Control of Gene Expression; Post-Transcriptional Control Mechanisms; Regulation of Gene Expression in Eukaryotes; Transcription Initiation in Eukaryotes

**Questions** Reading Quizzes, Blue-Thread Questions, Test Bank

**2. eText** Read your book online, search, take notes, highlight text, and more.

**3. The Study Area** Practice Test, Cumulative Test, BioFlix® 3-D Animations, Videos, Activities, Audio Glossary, Word Study Tools, Art

## You should be able to . . .

### ✓ TEST YOUR KNOWLEDGE
Answers are available in Appendix A

1. What is chromatin?
   a. the histone-containing protein core of the nucleosome
   b. the 30-nm fiber
   c. the complex of DNA and proteins found in eukaryotes
   d. the histone *and* non-histone proteins in eukaryotic nuclei

2. What is a tumor suppressor?

3. Which of the following statements about enhancers is correct?
   a. They contain a unique base sequence called a TATA box.
   b. They are located only in 5′-flanking regions.
   c. They are located only in introns.
   d. They are found in a variety of locations and are functional in any orientation.

4. In eukaryotes, what allows only certain genes to be expressed in certain types of cells?

5. What is alternative splicing?
   a. phosphorylation events that lead to different types of post-translational regulation
   b. mRNA processing events that lead to different combinations of exons being spliced together
   c. folding events that lead to proteins with alternative conformations
   d. action by regulatory proteins that leads to changes in the life span of an mRNA

6. What types of proteins bind to promoter-proximal elements?
   a. the basal transcription complex
   b. the basal transcription complex plus RNA polymerase
   c. basal transcription factors such as TBP
   d. regulatory transcription factors such as activators

7. Compare and contrast (a) enhancers and the *E. coli araC* binding site (see Chapter 18), (b) promoter-proximal elements and the operator of the *lac* operon, and (c) basal transcription factors and sigma.

8. Explain how alternative splicing could play a role in changing eukaryotic gene expression in response to changes in the environment.

9. Compare and contrast (a) enhancers and silencers; (b) promoter-proximal elements and enhancers; and (c) regulatory transcription factors and Mediator.

10. Predict how a drug that inhibits histone deacetylase will alter gene expression.

11. Relative to the genetic code, the histone code
    a. has more triplets.
    b. is much simpler to read because of complementary base pairing.
    c. does not depend on particular base sequences.
    d. requires methylated Cs rather than standard Cs in DNA.

12. Predict how a mutation that caused continuous production of active *p53* would affect the cell.

13. In the follow-up work to the experiment shown in Figure 19.5, the researchers used a technique that allowed them to see if two DNA sequences are in close physical proximity (association). They applied this method to examine how often an enhancer and the promoter of the *Hnf4a* regulatory gene were near each other. A logical prediction is that compared with rats born to mothers fed a healthy diet, the *Hnf4a* gene in rats born to mothers fed a protein poor diet would
    a. show no difference in how often the promoter and enhancer associated.
    b. never show any promoter–enhancer association.
    c. show a lower frequency of promoter–enhancer association.
    d. show a higher frequency of promoter–enhancer association.

14. **QUANTITATIVE** Imagine repeating the experiment on epigenetic inheritance that is shown in Figure 19.5. You measure the amount of radioactive uridine (U) incorporated into *Hnf4a* mRNA in counts per minute (cpm) to determine the level of *Hnf4a* gene transcription in rats born to mothers fed either a normal diet or a low protein diet. The results are 11,478 cpm for the normal diet and 7368 cpm for the low-protein diet conditions. You should prepare a graph similar to the one at the bottom of Figure 19.5 that shows the normalized results relative to the normal diet condition. Normalizing values means that value obtained from one condition is expressed as 1.0 (the norm; the normal diet in this case) and the values obtained from any other conditions (low-protein diet in this case) are expressed as decimal values relative to the norm.

15. After DNA damage, levels of activated p53 protein in the cytoplasm increase. Design an experiment to determine whether this increase is due to increased transcription of the *p53* gene or to activation of preexisting p53 proteins by a post-translational mechanism such as phosphorylation.

16. Researchers have discovered that if a single-stranded mRNA produced by a virus is used as a template to create a double-stranded RNA, that this double-stranded RNA often blocks infection by the virus. Propose an explanation for how infection can be blocked by this type of double-stranded RNA.

# THE BIG PICTURE

## BIG PICTURE

Copying, using, and transmitting genetic information is fundamental to life. Cells use the genetic information archived in their DNA to respond to changes in the environment and, in multicellular organisms, to develop into specific cell types.

Hereditary information is transmitted to offspring with random changes called mutations. Thus, genetic information is dynamic—both within generations and between generations.

Note that each box in the concept map indicates the chapter and section where you can go for review. Also, be sure to do the blue exercises in the Check Your Understanding box below.

## GENETIC INFORMATION

is archived in base sequences of

**DNA** 4.2

is packaged with proteins to form

Text section where you can find more information

consists of functional units called

**Genotype** 14.2 ◄ make up **Genes** 16.1

have different versions called

can be ▼

**EXPRESSED** 16.2
18.1-4
19.1-4

may regulate whether genes

if first TRANSCRIBED by ▼

**RNA polymerase** 17.1

to form ▼

**RNA** 4.3

may be processed by ▼

- Splicing
- Addition of 5′ cap
- Addition of poly(A) tail 17.2

may function directly in cell as

- tRNA (transfer RNA) 17.4
- rRNA (ribosomal RNA) 17.5

to form ▼

**mRNA (messenger RNA)** 16.2 17.2

is then TRANSLATED by ▼

**Ribosomes** 17.5 ◄ affect

to form ▼

**Proteins** 3.2 17.5

changed by ▼

- Folding 3.4
- Glycosylation 5.3
- Phosphorylation 8.2
- Degradation 19.4

**Phenotype** 14.1 ◄ produce

## check your understanding

### If you understand the big picture . . .
✔ You should be able to . . .

1. Draw stars next to the three elements of the central dogma of molecular biology.
2. Add arrows and labels indicating what reverse transcriptase does.
3. Draw an E in the corners of boxes that refer only to eukaryotes, not prokaryotes.
4. Fill in the blue ovals with appropriate linking verbs or phrases.

*Answers are available in Appendix A.*

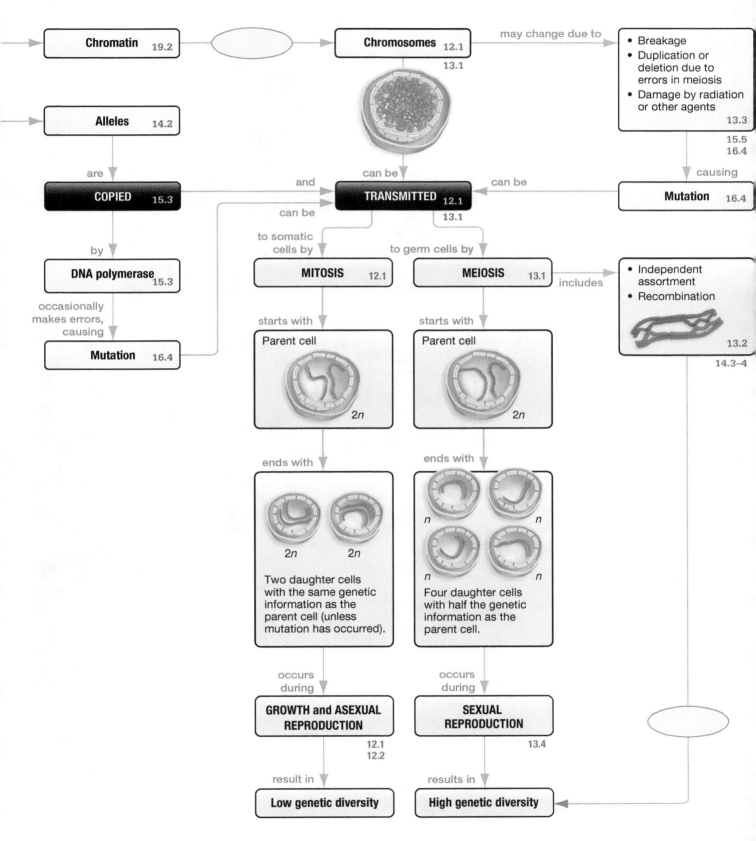

**Chromatin** 19.2

**Alleles** 14.2

**Chromosomes** 12.1
13.1

may change due to

- Breakage
- Duplication or deletion due to errors in meiosis
- Damage by radiation or other agents

13.3
15.5
16.4

causing

**Mutation** 16.4

are

**COPIED** 15.3

and

can be

**TRANSMITTED** 12.1
13.1

can be

by

**DNA polymerase** 15.3

can be

to somatic cells by

to germ cells by

occasionally makes errors, causing

**Mutation** 16.4

**MITOSIS** 12.1

**MEIOSIS** 13.1

includes

- Independent assortment
- Recombination

13.2
14.3–4

starts with

starts with

Parent cell

2n

Parent cell

2n

ends with

ends with

2n        2n

Two daughter cells with the same genetic information as the parent cell (unless mutation has occurred).

n        n

n        n

Four daughter cells with half the genetic information as the parent cell.

occurs during

occurs during

**GROWTH and ASEXUAL REPRODUCTION**

12.1
12.2

**SEXUAL REPRODUCTION**

13.4

result in

results in

**Low genetic diversity**

**High genetic diversity**

# 20 Analyzing and Engineering Genes

In this chapter you will learn that

**Biotechnology depends on methods to analyze and alter genomes**

by exploring

**Case studies of key genetic technologies**

applied to

Recombinant DNA technologies **20.1**

Finding genes by mapping **20.4**

Gene therapy **20.5**

Genome analysis

Medicine

Agriculture

The polymerase chain reaction **20.2**

Dideoxy DNA sequencing **20.3**

Transgenic crops **20.6**

The rice plants in these bottles have been genetically engineered—using techniques introduced in this chapter—to produce a molecule needed for a key vitamin.

The molecular revolution in biological science got its start when researchers confirmed that DNA is the hereditary material and succeeded in describing the molecule's secondary structure. But when biologists discovered how to remove DNA sequences from an organism, manipulate them, and insert them into different individuals, the molecular revolution really took off.

Efforts to manipulate DNA sequences in organisms are often referred to as genetic engineering. Genetic engineering became possible with the discovery of enzymes that cut DNA at specific sites and of other enzymes that paste DNA sequences together. These new molecular tools were extremely powerful. Biologists no longer had to rely solely on controlled breeding experiments to change the genetic characteristics of individuals. Instead, they could mix and match specific DNA sequences in

✔ When you see this checkmark, stop and test yourself. Answers are available in Appendix A.

the lab. Because successful efforts to manipulate genes usually result in novel combinations of DNA, techniques used to engineer genes are often referred to as **recombinant DNA technology.**

This chapter uses a series of case histories to introduce basic molecular biology techniques in the context of solving problems. It also considers the ethical and economic issues raised by efforts to manipulate genes. What are the potential perils and benefits of introducing recombinant genes into human beings, food plants, and other organisms? This question, one of the great ethical challenges of the twenty-first century, is a recurrent theme in the following pages.

## 20.1 Case 1–The Effort to Cure Pituitary Dwarfism: Basic Recombinant DNA Technologies

To understand the basic techniques and tools of genetic engineering, let's consider the role they played in developing a treatment for pituitary dwarfism in humans.

The pituitary gland is a structure at the base of the mammalian brain that produces several important biomolecules, including a protein that stimulates growth. This protein, which was found to be just 191 amino acids long, was named human growth hormone (HGH). In humans, the gene that codes for it is called *GH1*.

The discovery of growth hormone led researchers immediately to suspect that at least some forms of inherited dwarfism might be caused by a defect in the *GH1* gene. This hypothesis was confirmed by studies showing that people with certain types of dwarfism produce little growth hormone or none at all. These people have defective copies of *GH1* and exhibit pituitary dwarfism, type I (**FIGURE 20.1a**).

By studying the pedigrees of families in which dwarfism was common, several teams of researchers established that pituitary dwarfism, type I, is an autosomal recessive trait (see Chapter 14). In other words, affected individuals have two copies of the defective allele. Individuals who are affected by pituitary dwarfism have normal body proportions but grow more slowly than average people, reach puberty from two to 10 years later than average, and are short in stature as adults—typically no more than 120 cm (4 feet) tall (**FIGURE 20.1b**).

## Why Did Early Efforts to Treat the Disease Fail?

Once the molecular basis of pituitary dwarfism was understood, physicians began treating the disease with injections of naturally produced growth hormone. This approach was inspired by the spectacular success that had been achieved in treating type I diabetes mellitus. This form of diabetes is caused by a deficiency of the peptide hormone insulin, and clinicians had been able to alleviate the disease's symptoms by injecting patients with insulin from pigs.

Early trials showed that people with pituitary dwarfism could be treated successfully with growth hormone therapy, but only if the protein came from humans. Growth hormones isolated from pigs, cows, or other animals were ineffective. Until the 1980s, however, the only source of human growth hormone was pituitary glands from human cadavers. As a result, the drug was extremely scarce and expensive.

It turned out that meeting demand was the least of the problems with growth hormone therapy. To understand why, recall that infectious proteins called prions can cause degenerative brain disorders in mammals (see Chapter 3). When some of the children treated with human growth hormone developed a prion disease in their teens and twenties, physicians realized that the supply of growth hormone was contaminated with a prion protein from

**(a)** *GH1* codes for a pituitary growth hormone.

Normal *GH1* gene

Defective *GH1* gene

Normal amount of GH1 protein produced

Little or no GH1 protein produced in pituitary gland

**Pituitary dwarfism** (slower growth, shorter stature)

**(b)** Normal versus GH1-deficient

**FIGURE 20.1 Pituitary Dwarfism Is a Genetic Disease. (a)** If mutations in the human *GH1* sequence are severe enough to inactivate the gene, pituitary dwarfism may result. **(b)** William Harrison and Charles Stratton, in a photo taken about 1860. Harrison and Stratton were both celebrated comedians and performers. Stratton, whose stage name was Tom Thumb, enjoyed audiences in the White House with Abraham Lincoln and Buckingham Palace with Queen Victoria. Stratton had pituitary dwarfism; Harrison had normal height.

some of the cadavers supplying the hormone. In 1984, the use of growth hormone isolated from cadavers was banned.

## Steps in Engineering a Safe Supply of Growth Hormone

To replace natural sources of growth hormone, researchers turned to genetic engineering. Their plan was to insert fully functional copies of human *GH1* into the bacterium *Escherichia coli*, which they hoped would then produce huge quantities of recombinant progeny. If the plan worked, the recombinant cells would produce uncontaminated growth hormone in sufficient quantities to meet demand at an affordable price.

The plan required investigators to find *GH1*, obtain many copies of the gene, and insert them into *E. coli* cells. Their ability to do these things hinged on using basic tools of molecular biology.

**Using Reverse Transcriptase to Produce cDNAs** An enzyme called reverse transcriptase (Chapter 16) is responsible for an exception to the central dogma of molecular biology: It allows information to flow from RNA to DNA. More specifically, reverse transcriptase catalyzes the synthesis of DNA from an RNA template.

DNA that is produced from RNA is called **complementary DNA, or cDNA.** Although reverse transcriptase initially produces a single-stranded cDNA, it is also capable of synthesizing the complementary strand to yield a double-stranded DNA. In many cases, however, researchers add a chemically synthesized primer to single-stranded cDNAs and use DNA polymerase to synthesize the second strand (**FIGURE 20.2**).

Reverse transcriptase played a key role in the search for the growth hormone gene. Knowing that *GH1* is actively transcribed in the pituitary gland, researchers isolated mRNAs from pituitary-gland cells and used the enzyme to reverse-transcribe those mRNAs to cDNAs. These reaction products contained double-stranded cDNAs corresponding to each gene that is actively expressed in pituitary cells.

The next move? Isolating each of the cDNAs and making many identical copies of them.

**Using Plasmids in Cloning** Producing many copies of a gene is referred to as **DNA cloning.** If a researcher says that she has cloned a gene, it means that she has isolated it and then produced many identical copies.

In many cases, researchers can clone a gene by inserting it into a small, circular DNA molecule called a **plasmid.** You might recall that plasmids are common in bacterial cells (see Chapter 7). They are physically separate from the bacterial chromosome and are not required for normal growth and reproduction. Most replicate independently of the chromosome. Some plasmids carry genes for antibiotic resistance or other traits that increase the cell's ability to grow in a particular environment.

Researchers realized that if they could splice a loose piece of DNA into a plasmid and then insert the modified plasmid into a bacterial cell, the engineered plasmid would be replicated and passed on to daughter cells as the bacterium grew and divided. If this recombinant bacterium were then placed in a nutrient broth and allowed to grow and reproduce overnight, billions of copies of the original cell, each containing identical modified plasmid DNA, would result. When a plasmid is used in this way—to make copies of a foreign DNA sequence—it is called a **cloning vector,** or simply a **vector.**

Biologists harvest the recombinant genes by breaking the bacteria open, isolating all the DNA, and then separating the plasmids from the main chromosomes. But how do they insert a gene into a plasmid in the first place?

**Using Restriction Endonucleases and DNA Ligase to Cut and Paste DNA** To cut a gene out for later insertion into a cloning vector, researchers use enzymes called restriction endonucleases. A **restriction endonuclease** is a bacterial enzyme that cuts DNA molecules at specific base sequences. In bacterial cells, these enzymes cut up DNA from invading viruses and prevent a fatal infection.

**FIGURE 20.2 Reverse Transcriptase Catalyzes the Synthesis of DNA from RNA.** The single-stranded DNA produced by reverse transcriptase is complementary to the RNA template. The cDNA can be made double stranded by reverse transcriptase or DNA polymerase. DNA polymerase requires a primer.

More than 800 restriction endonucleases are known, and many of them cut DNA only at sequences that form palindromes. In English, a word or sentence is a palindrome if it reads the same way backward as it does forward. "Madam, I'm Adam" is an example. In biology, a stretch of double-stranded DNA forms a palindrome if the 5′→3′ sequence of one strand is identical to the 5′→3′ sequence on the antiparallel, complementary strand.

To insert the pituitary-gland cDNAs into plasmids, researchers performed the sequence of steps outlined in **FIGURE 20.3**.

**Step 1** The left side of the figure shows a plasmid containing a palindromic sequence, or recognition site, that is cut by a specific restriction endonuclease. As the right side of the figure shows, the researchers attached the same palindromic sequence to the ends of each cDNA in their sample.

**Step 2** They cut the recognition sites in each plasmid (left) and at the ends of each cDNA (right) with a restriction endonuclease called EcoRI. (The name comes from the fact that this

enzyme was the first (Roman numeral *I*) restriction endonuclease discovered in *E. coli* strain *R*Y13.)

**Step 3** Like most restriction endonucleases, EcoRI makes a staggered cut in the palindrome. The resulting DNA fragments are described as having **sticky ends,** because the single-stranded bases on one fragment are complementary to the single-stranded bases on the other fragment. As a result, the two ends can pair up and hydrogen-bond to each other: The complementary sequences in the sticky ends of the plasmid (in grey) will bind to the sticky ends in the cDNA (in red) by complementary base pairing.

**Step 4** Finally, researchers used **DNA ligase**—the enzyme that connects Okazaki fragments during DNA replication (see Chapter 15)—to seal the pieces of DNA together at the arrows marked in green.

The creation of sticky ends in DNA is important. If restriction sites in different DNA sequences are cut with the same restriction

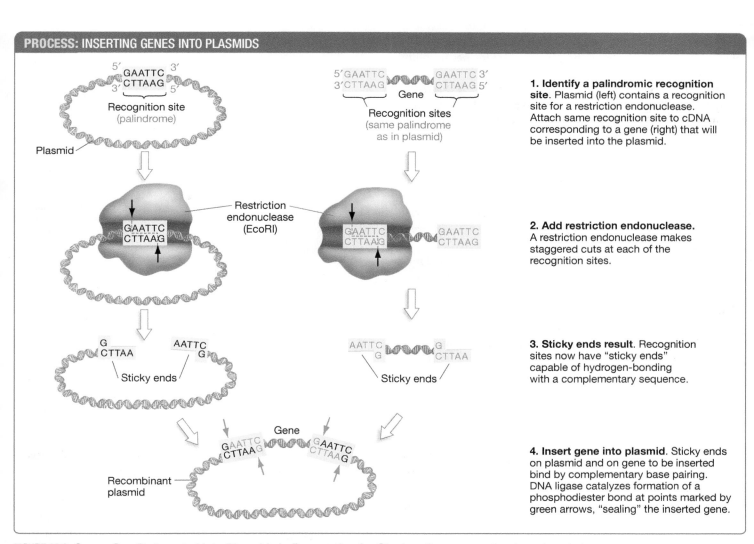

**PROCESS: INSERTING GENES INTO PLASMIDS**

**1. Identify a palindromic recognition site**. Plasmid (left) contains a recognition site for a restriction endonuclease. Attach same recognition site to cDNA corresponding to a gene (right) that will be inserted into the plasmid.

**2. Add restriction endonuclease.** A restriction endonuclease makes staggered cuts at each of the recognition sites.

**3. Sticky ends result**. Recognition sites now have "sticky ends" capable of hydrogen-bonding with a complementary sequence.

**4. Insert gene into plasmid**. Sticky ends on plasmid and on gene to be inserted bind by complementary base pairing. DNA ligase catalyzes formation of a phosphodiester bond at points marked by green arrows, "sealing" the inserted gene.

**FIGURE 20.3 Genes Can Be Inserted into Plasmids in Preparation for Cloning.** Once a gene has been inserted into a plasmid, the recombinant plasmid can be introduced into bacterial cells that grow and divide to produce many identical copies of the gene.

endonuclease, the presence of the same sticky ends in both samples of DNA promotes joining of the resulting fragments. This is the essence of recombinant DNA technology—the ability to create novel combinations of DNA sequences by cutting specific sequences and pasting them into new locations.

After performing this procedure, the researchers who were hunting for the growth hormone gene had a set of recombinant plasmids. Each contained a cDNA made from one of the many human pituitary-gland mRNAs. But the *GH1* gene was still not cloned.

### Transformation: Introducing Recombinant Plasmids into Bacterial Cells

If a recombinant plasmid can be inserted into a bacterial or yeast cell, the foreign DNA will be copied and transmitted to new cells as the host cell grows and divides. In short, it can be cloned. In this way, researchers can obtain millions or billions of copies of specific genes. How is the insertion brought about?

Cells that take up DNA from the environment and incorporate it into their genomes are said to undergo **transformation.** Most bacterial cells do not take up DNA on their own under laboratory conditions. So, to get plasmid DNA into *E. coli* and other common laboratory species, researchers use simple chemical treatments or an electrical shock to increase the permeability of the cell's plasma membrane.

Typically, just a single plasmid enters the cell during this treatment. The cells are then spread out on plates under conditions that allow only cells with plasmids to grow into colonies. Each colony contains millions of identical cells, each with many identical copies of the recombinant plasmid.

### Producing a cDNA Library

**FIGURE 20.4** summarizes the steps covered thus far in the hunt for the growth hormone gene. The result, shown in step 5, is a collection of transformed bacterial cells. Each of the cells contains a plasmid with one cDNA from a pituitary gland mRNA.

A collection of DNA sequences, each of which is inserted into a vector, is called a **DNA library.** If the sequences are cDNAs made from a particular cell type or tissue, the library is called a **cDNA library.** If the sequences are fragments of DNA from the genome of an individual, the library is called a **genomic library.**

DNA libraries are made up of cloned genes. Each gene can be produced in large quantity and isolated in pure form. ✔ If you understand this concept, you should be able to describe how you could make a genomic library starting with DNA from your own cells and using the restriction endonuclease EcoRI to cut the genome into fragments that can be inserted into a plasmid vector.

DNA libraries are important because they provide researchers a way to store DNA fragments from a particular cell type or genome in a form that is accessible for gene cloning. But like a college library, a DNA library isn't very useful unless there is a way to retrieve specific pieces of information. At your school's library, you use call numbers or computer searches to retrieve a particular book or article. How do you go about retrieving a particular gene from a DNA library? For example, how did researchers find

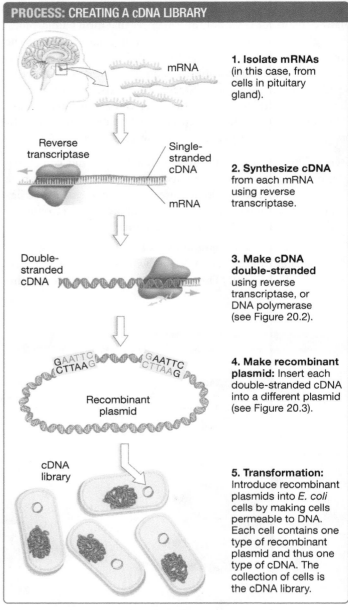

**PROCESS: CREATING a cDNA LIBRARY**

1. **Isolate mRNAs** (in this case, from cells in pituitary gland).

Reverse transcriptase
Single-stranded cDNA
mRNA

2. **Synthesize cDNA** from each mRNA using reverse transcriptase.

Double-stranded cDNA

3. **Make cDNA double-stranded** using reverse transcriptase, or DNA polymerase (see Figure 20.2).

GAATTC
CTTAAG
GAATTC
CTTAAG
Recombinant plasmid

4. **Make recombinant plasmid:** Insert each double-stranded cDNA into a different plasmid (see Figure 20.3).

cDNA library

5. **Transformation:** Introduce recombinant plasmids into *E. coli* cells by making cells permeable to DNA. Each cell contains one type of recombinant plasmid and thus one type of cDNA. The collection of cells is the cDNA library.

**FIGURE 20.4 Complementary DNA (cDNA) Libraries Represent a Collection of the mRNAs in a Cell.**

✔**QUESTION** Would each type of cDNA in the library be represented just once? Why or why not?

the growth hormone gene in the cDNA library of the human pituitary gland?

### Screening a DNA Library

Molecular biologists are often faced with the task of finding one specific gene in a large collection of DNA fragments. To do this requires a **probe**—a marked molecule that binds to the molecule the biologist is looking for.

A DNA probe is a single-stranded fragment that will bind to a particular single-stranded complementary sequence in a mixture of DNAs. By binding to the target sequence, the probe marks the fragment containing that sequence, distinguishing it from all the other DNA fragments in the sample. As **FIGURE 20.5** shows, a DNA probe must be labeled in some way so that it can be found after it has bound to the complementary sequence in the large sample of fragments.

✔ If you understand the concept of a DNA probe, you should be able to explain why the probe must be single stranded and labeled in order to work, and why it binds to just one specific fragment. You should also be able to indicate where a probe with the sequence AATCG (recall that sequences are always written $5' \rightarrow 3'$) will bind to a target DNA with the sequence TTTTACCCATTTACGATTGGCCT (again written $5' \rightarrow 3'$).

To find an appropriate probe for the human growth hormone gene, researchers began by using the genetic code to predict possible DNA sequences of *GH1*. They could do this because they knew the sequence of amino acids in the polypeptide, which they could use to infer the codons that coded for each amino acid. You made similar inferences in some of the exercises in earlier chapters. But recall that there is more than one codon for most amino acids (see Chapter 16). As a result, the researchers could not infer a unique sequence for the growth hormone gene. Instead, they deduced a set of possible sequences that could encode the *GH1* gene.

The next step was to chemically synthesize the set of short, single-stranded DNAs that were complementary to the possible *GH1* sequences. Because one of these sequences would bind to single-stranded fragments from the actual gene by complementary base pairing, it could act as a probe. In this case, the label the researchers attached to the probe was a radioactive atom.

**FIGURE 20.6** shows how researchers used this probe to find the plasmid in the cDNA library that contained *GH1*. (For more information on how to use probes, see **BioSkills 9** in Appendix B.) As predicted, the labeled probe bound to its complementary sequence in the cDNA library—identifying the recombinant cell that contained the human growth hormone cDNA.

**Mass-Producing Growth Hormone**  To accomplish their goal of producing large quantities of the human growth hormone, the investigators used recombinant DNA techniques to transfer the growth hormone cDNA to a new plasmid. The plasmid in question contained a promoter sequence recognized by *E. coli*'s RNA polymerase holoenzyme (see Chapter 17). The recombinant plasmids were then introduced into *E. coli* cells.

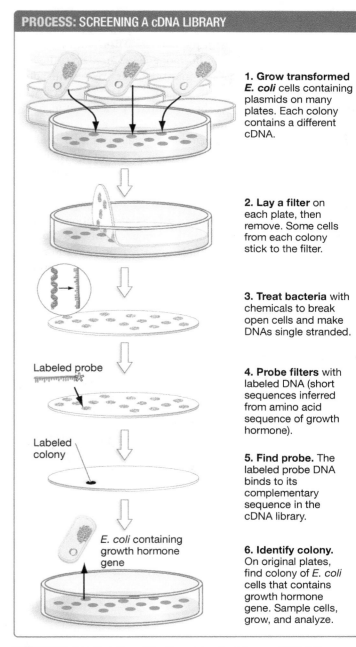

**PROCESS: SCREENING A cDNA LIBRARY**

**1. Grow transformed *E. coli* cells** containing plasmids on many plates. Each colony contains a different cDNA.

**2. Lay a filter** on each plate, then remove. Some cells from each colony stick to the filter.

**3. Treat bacteria** with chemicals to break open cells and make DNAs single stranded.

Labeled probe

**4. Probe filters** with labeled DNA (short sequences inferred from amino acid sequence of growth hormone).

Labeled colony

**5. Find probe.** The labeled probe DNA binds to its complementary sequence in the cDNA library.

*E. coli* containing growth hormone gene

**6. Identify colony.** On original plates, find colony of *E. coli* cells that contains growth hormone gene. Sample cells, grow, and analyze.

**FIGURE 20.6 Finding Specific Genes by Probing a cDNA Library.**

**PROCESS: USING A DNA PROBE**

Labeled probe

**1. Make probe.** Single-stranded DNA probe has a label that can be visualized.

**2. Expose probe** to collection of single-stranded DNA sequences.

**3. Find probe.** Probe binds to complementary sequences in target DNA—and only to that DNA. Target DNA is now labeled and can be isolated.

**FIGURE 20.5 DNA Probes Bind to and Identify Specific Target Sequences.**

The resulting transformed *E. coli* cells now contained a gene for human growth hormone attached to a promoter. These cells began to transcribe and translate the human growth hormone gene. Human growth hormone accumulated in the cells and was subsequently isolated and purified.

Today, bacterial cells containing the human growth hormone gene are grown in huge quantities. These cells have proved to be a safe and reliable source of the human growth hormone protein. The effort to cure pituitary dwarfism using recombinant DNA technology was a spectacular success—a triumph of applied biology, or **biotechnology.**

## Ethical Concerns over Recombinant Growth Hormone

As supplies of growth hormone increased, physicians used it in treating not only people with pituitary dwarfism but also short children who had no growth hormone deficiency. Even though the treatment requires several injections per week until adult height is reached, growth hormone therapy was popular because it often increased the height of these children by a few centimeters.

In essence, growth hormone was being used as a cosmetic—a way to improve appearance in cultures where height is deemed attractive. But if short people are discriminated against in a culture, is a medical treatment a better solution than education and changes in attitudes? And what if parents wanted a tall child to be even taller, to enhance her potential success as, say, a basketball player?

Currently, the U.S. Food and Drug Administration has approved the use of human growth hormone for only the shortest 1.2 percent of children. These individuals are projected to reach adult heights of less than 160 cm (5′3″) in males and 150 cm (4′11″) in women.

check your understanding

**If you understand that . . .**

- The essence of recombinant DNA technology is to cut DNA into fragments with a restriction endonuclease, paste specific sequences together using DNA ligase, and insert the resulting recombinant genes into a bacterial (or yeast) cell to express the genes.
- A DNA library consists of different sequences that have been inserted into plasmids or other vectors. A probe can be used to find specific sequences in the library.

✔ **You should be able to . . .**

1. Explain why restriction endonucleases like EcoRI create DNA fragments with sticky ends.
2. Explain why the word probe is appropriate to describe a labeled sequence that is used to find a particular gene in a DNA library.

*Answers are available in Appendix A.*

Growth hormone has also become a popular performance-enhancing drug for athletes, because it improves the maintenance of bone density and muscle mass. Part of its popularity stems from the fact that it is difficult to detect in current drug tests.

Should athletes be able to enhance their physical skills by taking hormones or other types of drugs? Is the drug safe at the dosages athletes are using? These questions are being debated by physicians, researchers, agencies that govern sports, and legislative bodies.

In the meantime, it is clear that while solving one important problem, recombinant DNA technology created others. One of this chapter's recurring themes is that genetic engineering has costs that must be carefully weighed against its benefits.

## 20.2 Case 2–Amplification of Fossil DNA: The Polymerase Chain Reaction

Inserting a gene into a bacterial plasmid is one method for cloning DNA. The polymerase chain reaction is another.

The **polymerase chain reaction (PCR)** is an in vitro DNA synthesis reaction that uses DNA polymerase to replicate a specific section of DNA over and over. It generates many identical copies of a particular region of DNA.

### Requirements of PCR

Although PCR is much faster and technologically easier than cloning genes into a DNA library, there is a catch: PCR is possible only when a researcher already has some information about DNA sequences near the gene in question. Sequence information is required because to do a polymerase chain reaction, you have to start by synthesizing short lengths of single-stranded DNA that match sequences on either side of the gene. These short segments act as primers for the DNA synthesis reaction.

As **FIGURE 20.7a** shows, the primer sequences must be complementary to bases on either side of the target gene—the DNA you want to copy. One primer is complementary to a sequence on one side of the target gene; the other primer is complementary to a sequence on the opposite strand of DNA, on the other side of the target gene. If the target DNA molecule is made single stranded, then the primers will bind, or anneal, to their complementary sequences, as shown in **FIGURE 20.7b**. You might recall that DNA polymerase cannot work without a primer. Once the primers are bound, DNA polymerase can extend each new strand of DNA in the 5′→3′ direction.

**FIGURE 20.8** shows the sequence of the polymerase chain reaction.

*Step 1* The researcher creates a reaction mix containing an abundant supply of the four deoxyribonucleoside triphosphates (dNTPs; see Chapter 15), a DNA sample that includes the gene of interest, many copies of the two primers, and a heat-resistant DNA polymerase called *Taq* polymerase.

**(a)** PCR primers must bind to sequences on either side of the target sequence, on opposite strands.

**(b)** When target DNA is made single stranded, primers bind and allow DNA polymerase to work.

**FIGURE 20.7 The Polymerase Chain Reaction Requires Appropriate Primers. (a)** To design an appropriate primer, the base sequence at the primer binding sites must be known. **(b)** The primers bind by complementary base pairing to single-stranded target DNA.

✔**EXERCISE** Indicate where DNA polymerase would begin to work on each strand; add an arrow indicating the direction of DNA synthesis.

***Step 2*** The reaction mix is heated to 95°C. At this temperature, the double-stranded template DNA denatures. This means that the two DNA strands separate, forming single-stranded templates.

***Step 3*** The mixture is allowed to cool to 50–60°C. In this temperature range, the primers bind, or anneal, to complementary portions of the single-stranded template DNA. This step is called primer annealing.

***Step 4*** The reaction mix is heated to 72°C. At this temperature, *Taq* polymerase efficiently synthesizes the complementary DNA strand from the dNTPs, starting at the primer. This step is called *extension*.

***Step 5*** Repeat steps 2 through 4.

***Step 6*** Continue repeating steps 2 through 4 until the necessary number of copies is obtained.

The temperature changes required in each step are controlled by automated PCR machines, and there is no need to add more components once the reaction starts.

*Taq* polymerase is a DNA polymerase found in the thermophilic ("heat-loving") bacterium *Thermus aquaticus*, which was discovered in a hot spring in Yellowstone National Park. Researchers use *Taq* polymerase because the PCR mixture has to be heated, and *Taq* polymerase is heat stable. Enzymes from most organisms are destroyed at high temperature, but *Taq* polymerase functions normally even when heated to 95°C.

The denaturation, primer annealing, and extension steps constitute a single PCR cycle. If one copy of the template sequence existed in the original sample, then two copies are present at the

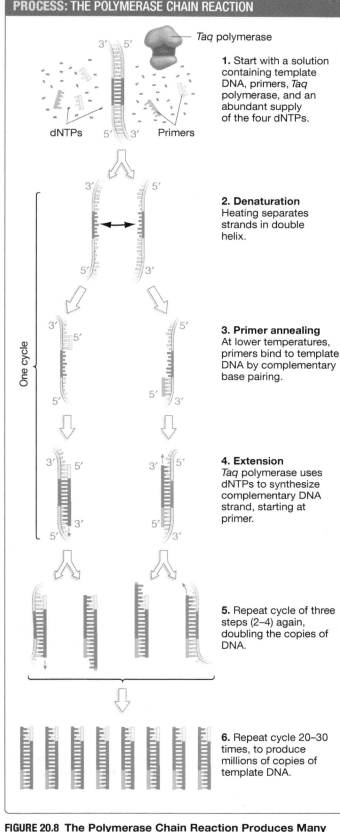

**FIGURE 20.8 The Polymerase Chain Reaction Produces Many Copies of a Specific Sequence.** Each PCR cycle (denaturation, primer annealing, and extension) results in a doubling of the number of target sequences.

end of the first cycle (see step 4 in Figure 20.8). These two copies then act as templates for the second cycle—another round of denaturation, primer annealing, and extension—after which four copies of the target gene are present (see step 5).

Each time the cycle repeats, the amount of template sequence in the reaction mixture doubles (step 6). Doubling occurs because each newly synthesized segment of DNA serves as a template in the subsequent cycle, along with the previously synthesized segments. Starting with a single copy, successive cycles result in the production of 2, 4, 8, 16, 32, 64, 128, 256 copies, and so on. A total of $n$ cycles can generate $2^n$ copies. In just 20 cycles, one sequence can be amplified to over a million copies.

## PCR in Action

To understand why PCR is so valuable, consider a study by biologist Svante Pääbo and colleagues, who wanted to analyze DNA recovered from the 30,000-year-old bones of a fossilized human of the species *Homo neanderthalensis*. Their goal was to determine the sequence of bases in the ancient DNA and compare it with DNA from modern humans (*Homo sapiens*).

If modern humans have sequences that are identical or almost identical to the sequences found in Neanderthals, it would suggest that some of us inherited DNA directly from a Neanderthal ancestor. That could happen only if *H. sapiens* and *H. neanderthalensis* interbred while they coexisted in Europe.

The Neanderthal bone was so old, however, that most of the DNA in it had degraded into tiny fragments. The biologists could recover only a minute amount of DNA that was still in even moderate-sized pieces. Fortunately, the Neanderthal DNA sample included a few fragments of the gene region that Pääbo's team wanted to study. The researchers were able to design primers that bracketed this region, based on the sequence of highly conserved sections of the same gene from *H. sapiens*.

Using PCR, the researchers produced millions of copies of the Neanderthal DNA fragment. After analyzing these sequences, the team found that they differ from the same gene segment found in modern humans. Subsequent work with DNA from 14 other Neanderthal fossils, from locations throughout Europe, gave the same result. These data support the hypothesis that Neanderthals never interbred with modern humans—even though the two species lived in the same areas of Europe at the same time.

But a nagging doubt remained—the conclusion was based on the analysis of a small region of the genome, the best that could be done at the time. Would the conclusion hold if more of the genome was analyzed?

To answer this question, Pääbo's team went on to use a form of DNA sequencing that has a DNA amplification step similar to PCR (see Section 20.3). They extracted DNA from fossilized bones and were able to sequence the entire genome of three Neanderthals. The researchers next compared the Neanderthal sequence with the genome sequences of people from different populations living today.

Their conclusion? For African populations there was no evidence of inbreeding with Neanderthals. The story is different,

however, for non-African populations. People from these groups have a small amount of DNA, roughly 1 percent to 4 percent of each person's genome, that is derived from Neanderthal ancestors. So, many people living today can claim just a touch of Neanderthal in their family tree.

PCR has opened new research possibilities in countless areas beyond ancient DNA. For example:

- Forensic scientists, who use biological analyses to help solve crimes, clone DNA from tiny drops of blood or hair. The copied DNA can then be analyzed to identify victims, implicate perpetrators, or exonerate the falsely accused.

- Genetic counselors, who advise couples on how likely their offspring are to suffer from inherited diseases, can use PCR to find out if an embryo conceived by the couple has alleles associated with deadly illness.

Because the complete genomes of a wide array of organisms have now been sequenced, researchers can easily find appropriate primer sequences to use in cloning almost any target gene by PCR. The polymerase chain reaction is now one of the most basic and widely used techniques in biology.

## check your understanding

**If you understand that . . .**

- PCR is a technique for amplifying a specific region of DNA into millions of copies, which can then be sequenced or used for other types of analyses.

✓ **You should be able to . . .**

1. Explain the purpose of the denaturation, annealing, and extension steps in a PCR cycle, and why "chain reaction" is an appropriate part of the term PCR.

2. Write down the sequence of a double-stranded DNA that is 50 base pairs long. Then design 21-base-pair-long primers that would allow you to amplify the segment by PCR.

*Answers are available in Appendix A.*

## 20.3 Case 3–Sanger's Breakthrough: Dideoxy DNA Sequencing

Once researchers have cloned a gene from a DNA library or by PCR, determining the gene's base sequence is usually one of the first things they want to do. Learning a gene's sequence is valuable for a variety of reasons. For example:

- Once a gene's sequence is known, the amino acid sequence of its product can be inferred from the genetic code. Knowing a protein's primary structure often provides clues to its function.

- Comparing sequences is fundamental to understanding why alleles vary in function—for example, why one allele causes disease and another doesn't.

- Researchers can infer evolutionary relationships by comparing the sequences of the same gene in different species (see Chapter 1). This information can be used to study an array of questions, ranging from how new traits evolve to where new diseases come from.

How do researchers sequence DNA? In 1977 Frederick Sanger published a technique called dideoxy sequencing that is still in use today.

## The Logic of Dideoxy Sequencing

As **FIGURE 20.9** shows, **dideoxy sequencing** is a clever variation on the basic in vitro DNA synthesis reaction. But saying "clever" is an understatement. Sanger had to link three important insights to make his sequencing strategy work.

**Dideoxynucleotides Terminate DNA Synthesis** Sanger's first insight was to use monomers for DNA synthesis called dideoxyribonucleoside triphosphates (ddNTPs) along with the normal deoxyribonucleoside triphosphates (dNTPs) (Chapter 15) in the reaction mix. The ddNTPs are identical to dNTPs except that they lack a hydroxyl group at their 3′ carbon. Four types of ddNTPs are used in dideoxy sequencing, each named according to whether it contains adenine (ddATP), thymine (ddTTP), cytosine (ddCTP), or guanine (ddGTP). The use of ddNTPs inspired the name dideoxy sequencing.

Sanger realized that if a ddNTP were added to a growing DNA strand, it would terminate synthesis. Why? After a ddNTP is added, no hydroxyl group is available on a 3′ carbon to link to the 5′ carbon on an incoming dNTP monomer. As a result, DNA polymerization stops once a ddNTP is added.

**Fragment Length Correlates with the Location of Each Base** Sanger linked the ability of ddNTPs to stop DNA synthesis to a second fundamental insight: Every time a ddNTP is added to a growing strand, the result is a fragment with a length corresponding to the position in the template of a base complementary to the ddNTP. To produce these fragments, biologists create a reaction mix containing (1) many copies of the template DNA with (2) a primer, (3) DNA polymerase, (4) a large supply of the four dNTPs, and (5) a small amount of the four ddNTPs (Figure 20.9, step 1). Each of the four ddNTPs carries a different fluorescent tag. (In the figure, ddGTP is purple, ddCTP is blue, ddATP is green, and ddTTP is orange.) Fluorescent molecules absorb light at one wavelength and reemit the light at a longer wavelength. As described in **BioSkills 10** (see Appendix B), fluorescent tags provide a very sensitive way of detecting molecules.

Under these conditions, many daughter strands of different lengths are synthesized. All fragments that are the same length end in the same kind of ddNTP.

Step 2 in Figure 20.9 shows why:

- DNA polymerase synthesizes a complementary strand from each template in the reaction mix.

- The synthesis of each one of these complementary strands starts at the same point—the primer.

**FIGURE 20.9 Dideoxy Sequencing Can Determine the Base Sequence of DNA.**

- Because there are many dNTPs and relatively few ddNTPs in the reaction mix, dNTPs are usually incorporated opposite each complementary base on the template strand as DNA polymerase works its way along the template strand. Incorporating a dNTP allows DNA synthesis to continue.

- Occasionally, one of the few ddNTPs is incorporated into the growing strand, opposite the corresponding base in the template. The complementary base in the template strand pairs randomly with either a ddNTP or a dNTP.

- The addition of the ddNTP stops further elongation.

- "Stops" of this kind happen for each base in the template strand. As a result, the overall reaction produces a collection of newly synthesized strands (fragments) whose various lengths correspond to the location of each base in the template strand (see step 3 in Figure 20.9). Each fragment will fluoresce in the color of its ddNTP.

### DNA Sequence Can Be Read from Fragments Lined Up by Size

Sanger's third insight? When the DNA fragments produced by the synthesis reactions are lined up by size, the dideoxy monomers on the successive fragments reveal the sequence of bases in the template DNA. To line up fragments in order of size, biologists separate them using gel electrophoresis (step 4 in Figure 20.9). As step 5 shows, a machine can read the pattern of fluorescence, indicating the sequence of bases in the newly synthesized strand.

Dideoxy sequencing ranks among the greatest of all technological advances in the history of biological science. Its impact is comparable to the development of light and electron microscopes, microelectrodes for recording membrane potentials, and recombinant gene technology.

### "Next Generation" Sequencing

Sequencing technology is advancing at a blindingly fast pace. Dideoxy sequencing is still performed, particularly when relatively long sequences need to be read with great accuracy. But new, "next generation" sequencing approaches now make it possible to sequence much faster and more cheaply.

Most of the newer methods are based on amplification steps related to PCR. These create many copies of each template DNA molecule and allow sequencing of minute quantities of DNA. Even more important, millions of different DNAs can be amplified and sequenced in a single run. Methods that allow simultaneous sequencing or analysis of huge numbers of different molecules are called massively parallel approaches. These sequencing technologies are opening research possibilities that were barely imaginable only a few years ago. Today, instead of sequencing individual genes, researchers often obtain the sequence of entire genomes. A case in point is the sequencing of the Neanderthal genome—this was made possible using a massively parallel approach.

The project to sequence the human genome for the first time took 10 years and cost $3 billion U.S. dollars. Now researchers could sequence your genome in a day for less than $5,000.

## 20.4 Case 4–The Huntington's Disease Story: Finding Genes by Mapping

Mendel had no idea what a "hereditary determinant" actually was. But now we know. Biology's molecular revolution has allowed researchers to find and characterize individual genes—to explore the connection between genotype and phenotype as explicitly and directly as possible. The question is, How do researchers find the genes associated with certain traits in the first place? How do you find the gene responsible for seed shape in peas, or white eyes in flies, or DNA polymerase III in *E. coli*?

One widely used approach is conceptually simple: You begin with a map of known sites in the genome and then look for an association between one of those known sites and the phenotype you're interested in. The gene that affects the phenotype is probably close to the known site.

In practice, the process is not so simple. As an example of how this type of gene hunt is done, let's consider one of the first successful searches ever conducted for a human gene—the gene associated with Huntington's disease.

### How Was the Huntington's Disease Gene Found?

Huntington's disease is a rare but devastating illness. Typically, affected individuals first show symptoms between the ages of 35 and 45. At onset, an individual appears to be clumsier than normal and tends to develop small tics and abnormal movements. As the disease progresses, uncontrollable movements become more pronounced. Eventually the affected individual twists and writhes involuntarily. Personality and intelligence are also compromised—to the extent that the early stage of this disease is sometimes misdiagnosed as the brain disorder schizophrenia. The illness may continue to progress for 10 to 20 years and is eventually fatal.

Because Huntington's disease runs in families, physicians suspected that it was a genetic disease. An analysis of pedigrees from families affected by Huntington's disease suggested that the trait was due to a single, autosomal dominant allele (see Chapter 14). To understand the molecular basis for the disease, researchers used many of the tools and techniques of genetic engineering that are shown in **TABLES 20.1** and **20.2** (see pages 380–381) as they set out to locate and identify the gene or genes involved. It took over 10 years of intensive effort to reach this goal.

The search for the Huntington's disease gene was led by Nancy Wexler, whose mother had died of the disease. If the trait was indeed due to an autosomal dominant allele, it meant that Wexler had a 50 percent chance of receiving the allele from her mother and would begin to show symptoms when she reached middle age.

### Using Genetic Markers

To locate the gene or genes associated with a particular phenotype, such as a disease, researchers traditionally start with a **genetic map,** also known as a **linkage map** (see Chapter 14). Recall that a genetic map shows the relative positions of genes on the same chromosome, determined by analyzing the frequency of recombination between pairs of genes. Biologists also use **physical maps** of the genome. A physical map shows the absolute position of a gene—in numbers of base pairs—along a chromosome. Genome sequencing (see Chapter 21) has produced physical maps for a wide array of species.

A genetic map is valuable in gene hunts because it contains **genetic markers**—easily identified genes or DNA sequences that have known locations. Each genetic marker provides a landmark—a position along a chromosome that is known relative to other markers. The key is to find where the unknown gene lies relative to the established genetic markers.

To understand how genetic markers can be used, let's use a hypothetical example. Suppose that you knew the position of a hair-color gene in humans relative to other genetic markers. Suppose too that various alleles of this gene contributed to the development of black hair, red hair, blond hair, and brown hair in the group of people you were studying. This variation in phenotype associated with the marker is crucial. To be useful in a gene hunt, a genetic marker has to be **polymorphic,** meaning that the phenotype associated with the marker varies. In our hypothetical example, hair color is a polymorphic genetic marker.

Now suppose that the genetic disease called cystic fibrosis is common among the individuals you were studying and that your goal is to find the gene associated with cystic fibrosis. Further, suppose that people who have cystic fibrosis almost always have black hair—even though they are just as likely as unaffected individuals to have any other inherited trait observed in the study population, such as the presence or absence of a widow's peak or detached earlobes.

If you observe that a certain form of a marker and a certain disease are almost always inherited together, this means that the marker gene and disease gene are physically close to each other on the same chromosome—they are closely linked. If they were not closely linked, then crossing over in between them would be common and they would *not* be inherited together. In this hypothetical study, you could infer that the gene for cystic fibrosis is very close to the hair-color gene. ✔ If you understand this concept, you should be able to explain why it's helpful to hunt for genes using a genetic map with many genetic markers rather than only a few.

Gene hunts in humans boil down to this: Researchers have to find a large number of people who are affected and unaffected. Then they must attempt to locate a genetic marker that almost always occurs in one form in the affected individuals but only rarely in unaffected people. If such a marker is found, the disease gene is almost guaranteed to be nearby.

The types of genetic markers used in gene mapping have changed over time. Today, researchers often have a large catalog of polymorphic genetic markers available, including the particularly abundant markers known as **single nucleotide polymorphisms** (**SNPs,** pronounced *snips*). A SNP is a site in DNA that varies between alleles at a single base pair. Below is an example of a SNP:

To date, roughly 10 million human SNPs have been identified.

In the late 1970s and early 1980s, when biologists were searching for the Huntington's disease gene, SNPs were unknown. The best genetic markers available were restriction sites—short stretches of DNA where restriction endonucleases cut the double helix. These sequences are also known as restriction endonuclease recognition sites.

The restriction sites that Wexler's team used were polymorphic: Some alleles had a sequence that allowed cuts to occur; but in other alleles, the DNA sequence at the same site varied slightly, and no cuts occurred. Thus, just as an individual might have an A instead of a C at a certain SNP, an individual might have a restriction site allele that allowed cutting or not. Wexler's team was looking for restriction site alleles that were almost always present in diseased individuals but not found any more often than predicted by chance in healthy individuals (**FIGURE 20.10**).

**FIGURE 20.10 Genetic Markers Can be Used to Locate Disease Alleles.** Because of genetic recombination, genetic markers that are far from the gene of interest are equally likely to be found in both affected and unaffected individuals—there will be no association between particular forms of the marker and either the normal or the disease-causing allele.

**Some Common Tools Used in Genetic Engineering**

| Tool | Description | How Used | Illustration |
|------|-------------|----------|--------------|
| Reverse transcriptase | Enzyme that catalyzes synthesis of a complementary DNA (cDNA) from an RNA template. | Many applications, including making cDNAs used in constructing a genetic library. | cDNA / RNA |
| Restriction endonucleases | Enzymes that cut DNA at a specific sequence—often a palindromic sequence that is six base pairs long. | Allows researchers to cut DNA at specific locations. Cuts in palindromic sites create "sticky ends." | GAATTC / CTTAAG |
| DNA ligase | An enzyme that catalyzes the formation of a phosphodiester bond between nucleotides on the same DNA strand. | Ligates (joins) sequences that were cut with a restriction endonuclease. Gives researchers the ability to splice fragments of DNA together. | GAATTC / CTTAAG |
| Plasmids | Small, extrachromosomal circles of DNA found in many bacteria and in some yeast. | After a target gene is inserted into a plasmid, the recombinant plasmid serves as a vector for transferring the gene into a bacterial or yeast cell, so the gene can be cloned. | GAATTC / CTTAAG  GAATTC / CTTAAG |
| *Taq* polymerase | DNA polymerase from the bacterium *Thermus aquaticus*. Catalyzes synthesis of DNA from a primed DNA template; remains stable at 95°C. | Responsible for the "primer extension" step in the polymerase chain reaction. Heat stability allows enzyme to be active even after the 95°C denaturation step of PCR. | |
| Single nucleotide polymorphisms (SNPs) | Sites in DNA where the identity of a single base pair varies between alleles. | An important type of polymorphic DNA sequence that is useful in creating the genetic maps required for gene hunts. | ... CTAAGAATAATTGATGCG ... / ... GATTCTTATTAACTACGC ... / ... CTAAGAACAATTGATGCG ... / ... GATTCTTGTTAACTACGC ... Base pairs vary |

**Linkage Study** Once a genetic map containing many genetic markers has been assembled, to find the gene in question, biologists need help from groups of people that include individuals affected by an inherited disease. Recall that the fundamental goal is to find a genetic marker that is almost always inherited along with the disease-causing allele. Biologists call this a linkage study. Gene hunts based on linkage studies are more likely to be successful if large groups are involved. Large sample sizes reduce the possibility that researchers will observe an association between one or more markers and the disease just by chance, rather than because they are closely linked.

Huntington's disease is rare, but Wexler's team was fortunate to find a large, extended family affected with the disease living along the shores of Lake Maracaibo, Venezuela. The researchers followed the inheritance of Huntington's disease and various polymorphic genetic markers within this extended family.

From historical records, the researchers deduced that the Huntington's disease allele was introduced to this family by an English sailor who visited the area in the early 1800s. At the time of the study, over 3000 of his descendants were living in the area. Hundreds of these people had been diagnosed with Huntington's disease. To help in the search for the gene, family members agreed to donate skin or blood samples for DNA analysis.

When Wexler's team looked for associations between the presence or absence of the disease phenotype and genetic markers observed in each family member, they found one marker that

| Technique | Description | How Used | Illustration |
|---|---|---|---|
| Recombinant DNA technology | Taking a copy of a gene from one individual and placing it in the genome of a different individual (usually of a different species). | Many applications, including DNA cloning, gene therapy (see Section 20.5), and biotechnology (see Sections 20.1 and 20.6). | Inserted gene |
| DNA libraries | A collection of all DNA sequences present in a particular source. The library consists of individual DNA fragments that are isolated and inserted into a plasmid or other vector, so they can be cloned. | cDNA libraries allow researchers to catalog the genes being expressed in a particular cell type and to work with coding sequences uninterrupted by introns. Genomic libraries allow researchers to archive all the DNA sequences present in a genome. Libraries can be screened to find a particular target gene. | Stored cDNA |
| Probing/screening a DNA library | Use of a labeled, known DNA fragment to hybridize (by complementary base pairing) with a collection of unlabeled, unknown fragments. | Allows a researcher to find a particular DNA sequence in a large collection of sequences. | Labeled probe |
| Polymerase chain reaction (PCR) | A DNA synthesis reaction that uses known primer sequences on either side of a target gene. Reaction is based on many cycles of DNA denaturation, primer annealing, and primer extension. | Produces many identical copies of a target sequence. A shortcut method for DNA cloning. | |
| Dideoxy sequencing | In vitro DNA synthesis reaction that includes dideoxyribo-nucleoside triphosphates (ddNTPs) as monomers. | Determining the base sequence of a gene or other section of DNA. | G C C T A A T G |
| Genetic mapping | Creation of a map showing the relative positions of genes or specific DNA sequences on chromosomes. Done by analyzing the frequency of recombination between sequences. | Many applications, including use of mapped genetic markers in genetic association studies to find unknown genes associated with diseases or other distinctive phenotypes. | Yellow body / White eyes / Ruby eyes — 1.4 / 6.1 |

turned out to be especially important. Four different restriction site alleles (*A, B, C,* and *D*) were present at this location in the genome. The key finding was that the *C* form of the marker was almost always found in diseased individuals. Almost certainly, the English sailor who introduced the Huntington's disease allele had the *C* form of the marker in his DNA. The marker and the Huntington's disease gene are so close together that recombination in between them has been extremely rare. No other genetic marker showed this tight association with Huntington's disease.

From the human genetic map that was available at the time, Wexler's team knew that the marker they had identified was on chromosome 4. Eventually the team succeeded in narrowing down the location of the marker, and thus the Huntington's

disease gene, to a region about 500,000 base pairs long. Because the haploid human genome contains over 3 billion base pairs, this was a huge step in focusing the search for the gene.

**Pinpointing the Defect** Once the general location of the Huntington's disease gene was known, biologists looked in that region for exons that encode an mRNA. Then they used dideoxy sequencing to determine the sequence of exons from diseased and normal individuals, compared the data, and pinpointed specific bases that differed between the two groups.

When this analysis was complete, the research team found that individuals with Huntington's disease have an unusually large number of CAG codons near the 5′ end of one gene. CAG odes for glutamine. Healthy individuals have 11–25 copies of the CAG codon at that location, while affected individuals have 42 or more copies.

When the Huntington's disease research team confirmed that the increased number of CAG codons was always observed in affected individuals, they concluded that the long search for the Huntington's disease gene was over. They named the newly discovered gene *IT15* and its protein product huntingtin. The huntingtin protein is involved in the development of nerve cells. Only later in life do the mutant forms of the protein cause disease.

## What Are the Benefits of Finding a Disease Gene?

How have efforts to find disease genes improved human health and welfare? Has the effort to locate the Huntington's disease gene helped researchers and physicians understand and treat the illness? Biomedical researchers point to three major benefits of disease-gene discovery.

**Improved Understanding of the Phenotype**  Once a disease gene is found and its sequence is known, researchers can usually figure out why its product causes disease. In the case of *IT15*, autopsies of Huntington's patients had shown that their brains decrease in size, and that the brain tissue contains clumps, or aggregates of the protein now called huntingtin.

Huntingtin aggregates are a direct consequence of the increased number of CAG repeats in the *IT15* gene. Long stretches of glutamine are known to promote protein aggregations. The leading hypothesis to explain Huntington's disease proposes that a gradual buildup of huntingtin aggregates triggers neurons to undergo apoptosis, or programmed cell death.

These results explained why Huntington's disease is pleiotropic (see Chapter 14). Patients suffer from abnormal movements and personality changes because neurons throughout the brain are killed. The results also help explain why the disease takes so long to appear, and why it is progressive: The defective huntingtin proteins take time to build up to harmful levels and then continue to increase over time. Finally, understanding the molecular mechanism responsible for the illness explained why the disease allele is dominant. One copy of the defective gene is enough to produce fatal concentrations of huntingtin aggregates.

**Therapy**  Once *IT15* was found, biologists began a search for new therapies for Huntington's disease by introducing the defective allele into mice, using the types of genetic engineering techniques discussed in Section 20.5. These mice with alleles that have been modified by genetic engineering are called **transgenic** (literally, "across-genes").

Transgenic mice that produce defective versions of the huntingtin protein develop a version of Huntington's disease, exhibiting tremors and abnormal movements, higher-than-normal levels of aggression toward litter and cage mates, and a loss of neurons in the brain. Laboratory animals with disease symptoms that parallel those of a human disease provide an **animal model** of the disease (see **BioSkills 13** in Appendix B).

Animal models are valuable in disease research because they can be used to test potential treatments. For example, research groups are using transgenic mice to test drugs that may prevent or reduce the aggregation of the huntingtin protein.

**Genetic Testing**  When the Huntington's gene was found and sequenced, biologists used the knowledge to develop a test for the presence of the defective allele. The test consists of obtaining a DNA sample from an individual and using the polymerase chain reaction to amplify the chromosome region that contains the CAG repeats responsible for the disease. If the number of CAG repeats is 35 or less, the individual is not considered at risk. Forty or more repeats results in a positive diagnosis for Huntington's.

Thanks to genetic maps based on SNPs, gene hunts are increasingly successful. Biologists have recently documented alleles associated with a predisposition to developing type I and type II diabetes, breast and ovarian cancer, obesity, coronary heart disease, bipolar disorder, Crohn's disease, and rheumatoid arthritis. Genetic testing for these alleles is now available for both prenatal and adult screens.

## Ethical Concerns over Genetic Testing

Knowing the genetic basis of human diseases offers hope, but it also raises difficult ethical issues.

Genetic testing, for example, can create serious moral and legal dilemmas as well as harrowing personal choices. Consider that some people maintain that it is morally wrong to terminate any pregnancy, even if the fetus is certain to be born with a debilitating or fatal genetic disease. Think too about Nancy Wexler's position soon after the discovery of *IT15*: Would you choose to be tested for the defective allele and risk finding out that you were almost certain to develop an incurable disease such as Huntington's?

There are other, equally serious, questions. Should people be tested for any disease that has no cure? Should it be legal for insurance companies to test clients? If so, can companies refuse to insure people at risk for diseases that require expensive treatments? What about employers?

These questions are being debated by political and religious leaders, health-care workers, philosophers, and the public at large. In many cases, we've yet to find answers.

check your understanding

**C**  
**Y**  
**U**

**If you understand that . . .**
- Genes for particular traits can be located if they are inherited together with a known genetic marker.

✔ **You should be able to . . .**
Describe how you would design a study aimed at identifying alleles associated with alcoholism.

*Answers are available in Appendix A.*

## Case 5–Severe Immune Disorders: The Potential of Gene Therapy

For physicians who treat inherited disorders such as Huntington's disease, sickle-cell anemia, and cystic fibrosis, the ultimate goal is to cure the disease. This may be done by replacing or augmenting defective copies of the gene with normal alleles. This approach to treatment is called **gene therapy.**

For gene therapy to succeed, two crucial requirements must be met. First, the sequence of the allele associated with the healthy phenotype must be known. Second, a method must be available for introducing this allele into affected individuals and having it be expressed in the correct tissues, in the correct amount, and at the correct time. If the defective allele is dominant, then the introduction step may be even more complicated: In at least some cases, the introduced allele must physically replace or block the expression of the undesirable dominant allele.

### How Can Genes Be Introduced into Human Cells?

Section 20.1 reviewed how recombinant DNA sequences are packaged into plasmids and taken up by *E. coli* cells. However, humans and other mammals lack plasmids. How can foreign genes be introduced into human cells?

Researchers have focused on packaging foreign genes into viruses for transport into human cells. These viruses have been engineered so they can deliver genes to cells but cannot replicate to produce new viruses. Viral infection begins when a virus particle attaches to a cell and delivers its genome into the cell (Chapter 36). For some viruses, the viral DNA becomes integrated into a host-cell chromosome. This trait makes it possible to use these viruses as vectors to carry engineered genes into the chromosomes of target cells. Potentially, the genes delivered by the virus could be expressed and produce a product capable of curing a genetic disease.

Vectors used today in gene therapy are often modified retroviruses. Retroviruses have genomes made of single-stranded RNA. When a **retrovirus** infects a human cell, a reverse transcriptase encoded by the virus catalyzes the production of a DNA copy of the virus's RNA genome. Other viral enzymes catalyze the insertion of the viral DNA into a host-cell chromosome. If an RNA version of a human gene can be packaged into a recombinant retrovirus, then the virus will insert a DNA copy of the human gene into a chromosome in a target cell (**FIGURE 20.11**).

Unfortunately, there are problems associated with using retroviruses as agents in gene therapy. For example, if the virus happens to insert the recombinant human gene in a position that disrupts the function of an important gene in the target cell, the consequences may be serious. Despite these risks, modified retroviruses are still among the best vectors currently available for human gene therapy.

### Using Gene Therapy to Treat X-Linked Immune Deficiency

In 2000, a research team reported the successful use of gene therapy to treat an illness called severe combined immunodeficiency (SCID). Children who are born with SCID lack a normal immune system and are unable to fight off infections.

The type of SCID the team treated is designated SCID-X1, because it is caused by mutations in a gene on the X chromosome.

**PROCESS: INTRODUCING A FOREIGN GENE INTO HUMAN CELLS**

**1. Retrovirus engineered** to contain recombinant RNA, which has both viral sequences and human sequences.

**2. Target cell infected.** RNA version of human gene enters host cell.

**3. DNA produced.** Viral enzymes make double-stranded DNA version of introduced gene.

**4. DNA inserted.** Human gene is inserted into host chromosome and transcribed.

**FIGURE 20.11 Modified Retroviruses Can Insert a Foreign Gene into a Host-Cell Chromosome.** (Many details have been omitted for conceptual clarity.)

✔**QUESTION** What happens if the recombinant DNA is inserted in the middle of a gene that is critical to normal cell function?

**FIGURE 20.12 A "Bubble Child."** Children with SCID cannot fight off bacterial or viral infections. As a result, such children must live in a sterile environment.

The gene codes for a receptor protein necessary for the development of immune system cells, called T cells, that develop in bone marrow (Chapter 51).

Traditionally, physicians have treated SCID-X1 by keeping the patient in a sterile environment, isolated from any direct human contact, until the person could receive a transplant of bone-marrow tissue from a close relative (**FIGURE 20.12**). In most cases, the T cells that the patient needs are produced by the transplanted bone-marrow cells and allow the individual to live normally. In some cases, though, no suitable donor is available. Could gene therapy cure this disease by furnishing functioning copies of the defective gene?

After extensive testing suggested that their treatment plan was safe and effective, the research team gained approval to treat 10 boys, each less than 1 year old, who had SCID-X1 but no suitable bone-marrow donor. The researchers removed bone marrow from each child, collected the stem cells that produce mature T cells, and infected those cells with an engineered retrovirus that delivered the normal receptor gene. Cells that began to produce normal receptor protein were then isolated and transferred back into the patients (**FIGURE 20.13**).

Within four months after reinsertion of the transformed marrow cells, nine of the boys had normal levels of functioning T cells. These patients were removed from germ-free isolation rooms and began residing at home, where they grew and developed normally.

Subsequently, however, four of the boys developed a cancer characterized by unchecked growth of T cells. Follow-up analyses of their bone-marrow cells showed that the normal receptor gene had been inserted either near a gene for a transcription factor that triggers T-cell growth, or near a gene for a cyclin that drives the cell cycle (see Chapter 12). The inserted receptor gene provided an enhancer that led to constitutive (constant) expression of the transcription factor or cyclin.

Three of the four boys responded to cancer chemotherapy and are healthy. The fourth did not respond to treatment and died of cancer.

The tenth boy to receive gene therapy never produced T cells. For unknown reasons, his recombinant stem cells failed to function normally when they were transplanted back into his bone marrow. Fortunately, physicians were later able to find a bone-marrow donor whose cells matched the boy's closely enough to make a successful transplant possible.

## Ethical Concerns over Gene Therapy

Throughout the history of medicine, efforts to test new drugs, vaccines, and surgical protocols have always carried a risk for the patients involved. Gene therapy experiments are no different. The researchers who run gene therapy trials must explain the risks clearly and make every effort to minimize them.

**PROCESS: ONE APPROACH TO GENE THERAPY**

SCID patient

1. **Stem cells** are isolated from the patient's bone marrow and grown in vitro.

2. **Engineered retroviruses** carry the normal allele into host cells.

3. **Cells that express normal alleles** are isolated and implanted into patient.

**FIGURE 20.13 Gene Therapy Can Cure a Genetic Disorder.** For gene therapy to work in the case of a loss-of-function allele, copies of a normal allele have to be introduced into a patient's cells and be expressed.

The initial report on the development of cancer in the boys who received gene therapy for SCID-X1 concluded with the following statement: "We have proposed . . . a halt to our trial until further evaluation of the causes of this adverse event and a careful reassessment of the risks and benefits of continuing our study of gene therapy."

When recombinant DNA technology first became possible, many researchers thought they would live to see most or all of the serious inherited diseases caused by single-gene mutations cured by gene therapy. After several decades of rare successes punctuated by tragic failures, that optimism was tempered. In the past few years, however, renewed hope has emerged for gene therapy. Improved vectors have been used successfully to treat two different forms of blindness, a brain disorder, and another type of SCID. Perhaps gene therapy is finally poised to deliver on some of its promises.

## 20.6 Case 6—The Development of Golden Rice: Biotechnology in Agriculture

Progress in transforming crop plants with recombinant genes has been breathtaking. In 2010, a total 10 percent of all farmland worldwide was planted with transgenic crops—and this number is predicted to show double-digit growth over the foreseeable future. In the same year, roughly 90 percent of soybeans, cotton, and corn grown in the United States were genetically engineered. You almost certainly have eaten food from a genetically modified plant sometime, if not today.

Transgenic crops have been engineered largely to meet three objectives:

1. *Reducing losses from herbivore damage*   For instance, researchers have transferred a gene from the bacterium *Bacillus thuringiensis* into corn; the presence of the "Bt toxin" encoded by this gene protects the plant from corn borers and other caterpillar pests.

2. *Reducing competition with weeds*   An example is the genetic engineering of soybeans for resistance to an herbicide—a molecule that kills plants—called glyphosate. Soybean fields with the engineered strain can be sprayed with glyphosate to kill weeds without harming the soybeans.

3. *Improving food quality*   An important example is engineering soybeans and canola to produce a higher percentage of unsaturated fatty acids relative to saturated fatty acids (Chapter 6). Reducing the amounts of saturated fatty acids helps prevent heart disease, so these crops produce healthier vegetable oils.

How is this work done?

### Rice as a Target Crop

Almost half the world's population depends on rice as its staple food. Unfortunately, rice is a poor source of some vitamins and essential nutrients—including vitamin A. Vitamin A deficiency causes blindness in 250,000 Southeast Asian children each year. It also increases susceptibility to diarrhea, respiratory infections, and childhood diseases such as measles.

Humans and other mammals synthesize vitamin A from a precursor molecule known as β-carotene (beta-carotene). β-carotene belongs to a family of orange, yellow, and red plant pigments called the carotenoids (Chapter 10).

Rice plants synthesize β-carotene in their chloroplasts but not in the carbohydrate-rich seed tissue called endosperm—the part of the rice seed that you eat. Could genetic engineering produce a strain of rice plants that synthesizes β-carotene in the endosperm?

### Synthesizing β-Carotene in Rice

To explore the possibility of genetically engineering rice, a research team searched for compounds in rice endosperm that could serve as precursors for the synthesis of β-carotene. They found that maturing rice endosperm contains a molecule that could be converted to β-carotene in three enzyme-catalyzed reactions. The researchers reasoned that if genes that encode these enzymes could be introduced into rice plants along with regulatory sequences that would trigger their synthesis in endosperm, it should be possible to create a transgenic strain of rice that would contain β-carotene.

Fortunately, genes that encode two of the required enzymes had already been isolated from daffodils, and the gene for the third enzyme had been purified from a bacterium. These genes had been cloned in bacteria. To each of the coding sequences, biologists added regulatory sequences from an endosperm-specific protein. This segment would promote transcription of the recombinant sequences in endosperm cells.

Next, the three sets of sequences had to be inserted into rice plants. How are foreign genes introduced into plants?

### The *Agrobacterium* Transformation System

*Agrobacterium tumefaciens* is a bacterium that infects plant tissues and triggers formation of tumorlike growths called galls. When researchers looked into how these infections occur, they found that a plasmid carried by the *Agrobacterium* cells, called a **Ti (tumor-inducing) plasmid,** plays a key role (**FIGURE 20.14**, see page 386).

Ti plasmids contain several sets of genes. One set encodes products that allow the bacterium to bind to the cell walls of a host. Another set, referred to as the virulence genes, encodes the proteins required to transfer part of the Ti DNA, called T-DNA (transferred DNA), into the plant cell. The T-DNA then travels to the nucleus and integrates into host-cell chromosomes (Figure 20.14, step 1). T-DNA genes are expressed and their products induce the infected cell to grow and divide. This results in the formation of a gall that houses a growing population of *Agrobacterium* cells (Figure 20.14, step 2).

Researchers soon realized that the Ti plasmid offers an efficient way to introduce recombinant genes into plant cells. Follow-up experiments confirmed that recombinant genes could be

Plant cells

*Agrobacterium* cell

— Main chromosome

— Ti (*tumor-inducing*) plasmid

T-DNA

Host-cell chromosomes

Nucleus

Gall

*Agrobacterium* cells

**1. Transfer of Ti genes.** A section of DNA from the Ti plasmid, called T-DNA, integrates into the chromosomes of plant cells infected by the bacterium.

**2. Transcription of Ti genes.** When transcribed, Ti genes induce the infected plant cell to begin growing and dividing. The resulting gall encloses an increasing number of *Agrobacterium* cells.

**FIGURE 20.14 *Agrobacterium* Infections Introduce Genes into a Plant Host-Cell Chromosome.** Ti plasmids of *Agrobacterium* cells induce gall formation—a tumorlike growth.

Tumor-inducing genes

T-DNA

**1.** Start with normal Ti plasmids.

T-DNA

**2.** Remove tumor-inducing genes.

Regulatory sequences

Genes for three enzymes

**3.** Add genes for enzymes required for β-carotene synthesis along with regulatory sequences that will activate gene expression in endosperm.

**(b)** Golden rice (right) is engineered to synthesize β-carotene.

Conventional rice

Golden rice

**FIGURE 20.15 Constructing a Ti Plasmid to Produce "Golden Rice."** Golden rice is a transgenic strain capable of synthesizing β-carotene in the endosperm of its seeds.

added to the T-DNA that integrates into the host chromosome, that the gall-inducing genes could be removed from the T-DNA, and that the resulting sequence is efficiently transferred and expressed in its new host plant.

## Using the Ti Plasmid to Produce Golden Rice

To generate a strain of rice that produces all three enzymes needed to synthesize β-carotene in endosperm, the researchers exposed embryos to *Agrobacterium* cells containing genetically modified Ti plasmids (**FIGURE 20.15**). When the transgenic rice plants grew and produced seeds, the researchers found that some rice grains contained so much β-carotene that they were yellow. The biologists called the engineered plants "golden rice."

Follow-up experiments used gene sequences from corn, rather than daffodil, to produce 23 times more β-carotene in rice than the original transformants contained.

Will golden rice help solve a serious public health problem? The answer is not clear. Many environmental groups are strongly opposed to golden rice and any other engineered crops. Regulatory agencies in an array of countries would need to approve the use of golden rice—but there is strong resistance in some nations—and seed would have to be made available to farmers at an affordable price. The barriers to answering the question of whether golden rice can solve health problems are more societal than scientific.

It's important to recognize that each solution offered by genetic engineering introduces new issues to resolve. Biology students and others who are well informed about the techniques and issues involved will be important participants in this debate.

## If you understand . . .

### 20.1 Basic Recombinant DNA Technologies

- In genetic engineering, DNA is added to a cell either to modify the cell's properties or to clone (obtain many identical copies of) the DNA.

- Restriction endonucleases cut DNA at specific locations. The resulting DNA fragments can be inserted into plasmids or other vectors with the help of DNA ligase.

- In many cases, the DNA fragments are inserted into vectors containing regulatory sequences that control expression of inserted genes.

✓ You should be able to explain why a plasmid is needed for gene cloning.

### 20.2 The Polymerase Chain Reaction

- The polymerase chain reaction (PCR) produces many identical copies of a gene without using cells for cloning.

- PCR depends on having primers that bracket a target stretch of DNA. These allow *Taq* polymerase, a heat-stable DNA polymerase, to amplify a single target DNA sequence to millions of identical copies.

✓ You should be able to list the advantages and disadvantages of cloning in cells versus using PCR to obtain many copies of genes.

### 20.3 Dideoxy DNA Sequencing

- Dideoxy sequencing determines the sequence of bases in DNA.

- Dideoxy sequencing is based on an in vitro DNA synthesis reaction in which dideoxyribonucleotides stop different DNA replication reactions at different bases in the sequence.

- The DNA fragments of different lengths that are generated by a dideoxy sequencing reaction are separated via gel electrophoresis to determine the sequence of bases.

✓ You should be able to explain how the newly synthesized DNA fragments—when they are lined up by size—can be used to determine the sequence of bases in the template DNA.

### 20.4 Finding Genes by Mapping

- Genetic maps are often used to find genes associated with phenotypes such as diseases.

- If individuals with a certain phenotype share a particular form of a polymorphic genetic marker (a mapped site with two or more forms in DNA that is unrelated to the phenotype), the gene responsible for the phenotype is likely to be near that marker.

- Once the general area of a gene is known, DNA in the region can be sequenced to determine exactly where the gene is located.

✓ You should be able to explain why genetic markers that are not polymorphic (come in only one form) are not useful in gene hunts.

### 20.5 The Potential of Gene Therapy

- Researchers are working to cure genetic diseases by gene therapy. This involves inserting normal copies of the defective gene into patients.

- In humans, genes used for gene therapy are often introduced using modified viruses.

- Gene therapy has faced many difficulties but recently has met with some notable successes.

✓ You should be able to describe what makes retroviruses well suited for gene therapy and what the concerns are about their use.

### 20.6 Biotechnology in Agriculture

- Many important crop plants are genetically engineered for traits that include pest and herbicide resistance, and improved food quality.

- Genes are often introduced into crops by infecting plant cells with bacteria that integrate their plasmid genes into the host-plant genome. By adding recombinant genes to these plasmids, researchers have been able to introduce genes that improve crops.

✓ You should be able to explain how genes are inserted into plants.

(MB) **MasteringBiology**

**1. MasteringBiology Assignments**

**Tutorials and Activities** Analyzing DNA Fragments Using Gel Electrophoresis; Cloning a Gene in Bacteria; Gel Electrophoresis of DNA; Making Decisions about DNA Technology: Golden Rice; Producing Human Growth Hormone; Restriction Enzymes; Restriction Enzymes, Recombinant DNA, and Gene Cloning; The Polymerase Chain Reaction

**Questions** Reading Quizzes, Blue-Thread Questions, Test Bank

**2. eText** Read your book online, search, take notes, highlight text, and more.

**3. The Study Area** Practice Test, Cumulative Test, BioFlix® 3-D Animations, Videos, Activities, Audio Glossary, Word Study Tools, Art

# You should be able to . . .

1. What do restriction endonucleases do?

2. What is a plasmid?
   a. an organelle found in many bacteria and certain eukaryotes
   b. a circular DNA molecule that often replicates independently of the main chromosome(s)
   c. a type of virus that has a DNA genome and that infects certain types of human cells, including lung and respiratory tract tissue
   d. a type of virus that has an RNA genome, codes for reverse transcriptase, and inserts a cDNA copy of its genome into host cells

3. When present in a DNA synthesis reaction mixture, a ddNTP molecule is added to the growing chain of DNA. No further nucleotides can be added afterward. Why?

4. Once the gene that causes Huntington's disease was found, researchers introduced the defective allele into mice to create an animal model of the disease. Why was this model valuable?
   a. It allowed the testing of potential drug therapies without endangering human patients.
   b. It allowed the study of how the gene is regulated.
   c. It allowed the production of large quantities of the huntingtin protein.
   d. It allowed the study of how the gene was transmitted from parents to offspring.

5. To begin the hunt for the human growth hormone gene, researchers created a cDNA library from cells in the pituitary gland. What did this library contain?
   a. only the sequence encoding growth hormone
   b. DNA versions of all the mRNAs in the pituitary-gland cells
   c. all the coding sequences in the human genome, but no introns
   d. all the coding sequences in the human genome, including introns

6. What does it mean to say that a genetic marker and a disease gene are closely linked?
   a. The marker lies within the coding region for the disease gene.
   b. The sequence of the marker and the sequence of the disease gene are extremely similar.
   c. The marker and the disease gene are on different chromosomes.
   d. The marker and the disease gene are in close physical proximity and tend to be inherited together.

7. Explain how restriction endonucleases and DNA ligase are used to insert foreign genes into plasmids and create recombinant DNA. Make a drawing that shows why sticky ends are sticky and that identifies the location where DNA ligase catalyzes a key reaction.

8. QUANTITATIVE  If a particular sequence of DNA were amplified using 25 PCR cycles, then the amount of this DNA would be predicted to increase by _____ -fold.

9. What is a cDNA library? Would you expect the cDNA library from a human muscle cell to be different from the cDNA library from a human nerve cell in the same individual? Explain why or why not.

10. What are genetic markers, and how are they used to create a genetic map?

11. Researchers added regulatory sequences from an endosperm-specific gene to the Ti plasmids used in creating golden rice. This was important to
    a. allow inserted genes to integrate into the plant genome.
    b. increase the endosperm growth rate.
    c. prevent the introduced plasmid from harming the endosperm.
    d. promote expression of introduced genes in the rice grain.

12. Compare and contrast PCR with the DNA synthesis that occurs in cells (see Chapter 15).

13. Suppose you had a large amount of sequence data, similar to the data that Nancy Wexler's team had in the region of the Huntington's disease gene, and that you knew that mRNAs of the species being studied typically contain protein-coding regions about 1500 bases long. How would you use the genetic code (see Chapter 16) and information on the structure of promoters (see Chapters 17 and 18) to find the precise location of one or more genes in your sequence?

14. Modifying germ-line or somatic cells for gene therapy involves the same ethical concerns. True or false?

15. Describe similarities between how researchers screen a DNA library and how they perform a genetic screen—for example, for mutant *E. coli* cells that cannot metabolize lactose (see Chapter 18).

16. A friend of yours is doing a series of PCRs and comes to you for advice. She purchased two sets of primers, hoping that one set would amplify the template sequence shown here. (The dashed lines in the template sequence stand for a long sequence of unspecified bases.) Neither of the primer pairs produced any product DNA, however.

|  | Primer a | | Primer b |
| --- | --- | --- | --- |
| **Primer Pair 1:** | 5' CAAGTCC 3' | & | 5' GCTGGAC 3' |
| **Primer Pair 2:** | 5' GGACTTG 3' | & | 5' GTCCAGC 3' |
| **Template:** | 5' ATTCGGACTTG---GTCCAGCTAGAGG 3' | | |
|  | 3' TAAGCCTGAAC---CAGGTCGATCTCC 5' | | |

   a. Explain why each primer pair didn't work. Indicate whether both primers are at fault, or just one of them.
   b. Your friend doesn't want to buy new primers. She asks you whether she can salvage this experiment. What do you tell your friend to do?

# 22 Principles of Development

**In this chapter you will learn that**

A common set of principles guides development

*first surveying* ↓

Developmental processes shared by all multicellular organisms **22.1**

*then asking* ↓

How do cells containing the same genes express different specialized subsets? **22.2**

*via* ↓

Chemical signals and regulatory genes **22.3**

*which, if mutated, can produce* →

Evolutionary change **22.4**

An embryonic fish, still attached to the nutrient-filled yolk in the egg. This chapter introduces the processes responsible for transforming a fertilized egg into an individual that has specialized cells, tissues, and organs.

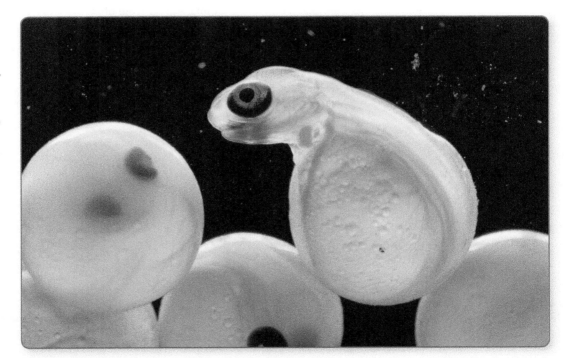

What is today's greatest challenge in biological science? Although there are many candidates, one of the most compelling is the question addressed in Unit 4: How does a multicellular individual develop from a single cell—a fertilized egg?

It's important to pause for a moment and think about the magnitude of this problem. Consider that once you were a single cell. If you could have watched your own development, you would have seen that single cell divide rapidly and form a ball of tiny, identical-looking cells. At that point, the fertilized egg had become an **embryo**—a young, developing organism. After continued cell division, large groups of cells suddenly began moving into the interior of the embryo. Cell division continued at a dizzying pace. After a week or two the embryo elongated, and a recognizable head and tail portion appeared. Tiny precursors of vertebrae became visible, along with rudimentary eyes. Eventually

✔ When you see this checkmark, stop and test yourself. Answers are available in Appendix A.

405

buds emerged and went on to form your limbs. As development continued, the embryo became you.

Biologists who have watched this process in humans or other organisms never cease to marvel at it. How does all the growth and formation of body parts happen?

To understand how researchers are answering this question, you'll need to draw on what you've already learned about cell–cell interactions, the regulation of gene expression, and a host of other topics described in previous units. Part of the excitement surrounding developmental biology is that it draws on insights from biochemistry, cell biology, genetics, and evolution. It is one of the most interdisciplinary fields in all of biology. Let's delve in.

## 22.1 Shared Developmental Processes

Over one hundred years of research has culminated in one of the great insights of contemporary biology: A few fundamental principles are common to all developmental processes in every multicellular organism. This discovery has brought a unified understanding to how the embryos of fruit flies, oak trees, and humans each grow and develop from a single cell into complex, multicellular individuals.

An individual develops as cells divide; signal to one another about where they are, what they are doing, and what type of cell they are becoming; begin to express certain genes rather than others; move or expand in specific directions; and, in the case of some cells, die (**TABLE 22.1**). Let's first consider these processes in turn, while keeping in mind that in the embryo they are interdependent and occur together. Then, let's go on to consider more specific questions about how cells interact and specialize.

### Cell Division

For an embryo to grow and develop, its cells have to proliferate—they must divide and make more cells. This statement is obvious, but less obvious and equally important is the following point: The location, timing, and extent of cell division have to be tightly controlled.

How is cell division controlled? You might recall that mitosis and cytokinesis are responsible for cell proliferation in eukaryotes (Chapter 12) and that cells initiate mitosis in response to a regulatory protein complex called M phase–promoting factor (MPF). You also may remember that each stage of the cell cycle has carefully regulated checkpoints, and that cells control their division in response to what biologists call "social controls"—meaning, signals from other cells.

SUMMARY TABLE 22.1   **Essential Developmental Processes**

| | | |
|---|---|---|
| Cell proliferation |  | Cells divide by mitosis and cytokinesis. The timing, location, and amount of cell division are regulated. |
| Cell–cell interactions |  | Signals that are produced by cells influence their neighbors to divide, die, move, or differentiate. |
| Cell differentiation |  | Undifferentiated cells specialize at specific times and places in a stepwise fashion. |
| Cell movement and expansion |  | Cells can move past one another within a block of animal cells, causing drastic shape changes in the embryo.<br><br>Cells can break away from a block of animal cells and migrate to new locations.<br><br>Plant cells can regulate the plane of cell division and expand in specific directions, causing dramatic changes in shape. |
| Programmed cell death |  | The timing, location, and amount of cell death are regulated. |

As development proceeds in both plants and animals, most cells stop dividing when they mature. But in later stages of development and in the adult, populations of undifferentiated cells keep proliferating throughout the individual's life. These are **stem cells.** Stem cells divide to produce a daughter cell that remains a stem cell and another daughter cell that ultimately differentiates into a specialized cell type. By producing one daughter that stays a stem cell, populations of stem cells are maintained.

- In plants, stem cells are located in **meristems.** Meristems are present in embryos and adults and produce the stems, roots, leaves, flowers, and other structures that develop throughout a plant's life (see Chapter 24).

- In animals, stem cells exist in specific locations in the body. In adults, stem cells proliferate to replace skin, blood, and gut cells that die; repair wounds; and create a constant supply of disease-fighting cells in the immune system.

## Cell–Cell Interactions

Cells interact constantly during development. They engage in "conversations" with their neighbors through a diverse set of chemical signals. This ongoing communication drives most of the cellular behaviors that are the foundation of development.

You might recall that when a signal arrives at the surface of a cell that possesses the appropriate receptor, the message is received and processed (Chapter 11). Signal molecules used in development may diffuse in the watery environment that surrounds cells, but they also can be present on the surface of other cells or bound to the extracellular matrix. These nondiffusible signals are detected by developing cells as they expand or move within the embryo.

In most cases in development, when a signal is bound by a receptor, it activates a signal transduction cascade that triggers the production of transcription factors (Chapter 19). As a result, patterns of gene expression change, and this alters the cell's activity. In response to a chemical signal, embryonic cells may divide, differentiate, move, expand, or die. In this way, the fate of a cell inside an embryo hinges on the signals it receives from other cells.

## Cell Differentiation

As development progresses, most cells undergo **differentiation**—the process of becoming a specialized type of cell. Differentiation is a progressive, step-by-step process. As cells differentiate, decisions are made at branch points to follow one developmental path or another. As a result, a fertilized egg may give rise to hundreds of distinctive cell types.

In the case of your own development, some of your embryonic cells differentiated to form muscle cells that contract and relax, while others became nerve cells that conduct electrical signals throughout the body. As an oak tree develops, some cells secrete thickened walls and transport water as part of a woody stem; other cells become flattened and secrete the waxy coating found on the surface of leaves.

Remarkably, sometimes the process of differentiation can be reversed. For example, some plant cells can "de-differentiate" after they have become specialized. When a branch of a western red cedar tree droops low enough to make contact with the soil, cells in the branch de-differentiate. These cells then re-differentiate to form root cells, resulting in the growth of a fully formed root where the branch came to rest on the ground.

For decades, biologists thought that animal cells could not de-differentiate. As you'll see in Section 22.2, however, the cloning of frogs and mammals reversed this view. In a spectacular recent study, scientists found that it is even possible to de-differentiate many adult human cells. Adding as few as three transcription factors to adult cells can cause them to de-differentiate into cells that resemble those of the early embryo. The hope is that these de-differentiated cells can be coaxed to re-differentiate in tissue culture to create any desired cell type that might be needed to replace cells damaged by disease. If this dream becomes reality, it will largely be through understanding cell differentiation during normal development.

## Cell Movement and Cell Expansion

Many animal cells have to move to new locations for normal development to occur. In plants, cells cannot move because of the cell wall. However, plants are masters at controlling both the direction of cell expansion—the growth of an individual cell—and the orientation of cell division to determine where cells are added.

Some of the most dramatic cell movements in animals occur early in development once rapid cell divisions have produced a mass of cells. During a sequence of events called **gastrulation,** cells in different parts of the mass rearrange themselves into three distinctive layers, which then give rise to the skin, gut, and other basic parts of the body (gastrulation is described in Chapter 23).

Later in development, some animal cells break away from their original sites and migrate to new locations in the embryo. There they give rise to germ cells (cells that produce sperm or eggs), pigment-containing cells, precursors of blood cells, or certain nerve cells. If these cell movements go awry, the embryo will be deformed or die.

Plant cells, in contrast, are encased in stiff cell walls and do not move. Instead, the direction of cell division and cell expansion is carefully regulated to form stems, leaves, roots, and all other parts of the plant. Differential cell expansion is a key part of plant development, just as regulated cell movement is a key part of animal development.

## Cell Death

Cell division is controlled by signals from other cells. But sometimes, signals trigger cell death. Cell death is a highly regulated aspect of plant and animal development. **Programmed cell death** occurs as certain tissues and organs take shape.

There are a few different forms of programmed cell death. In animals, the predominant one used in development is **apoptosis** (literally, "falling away"). Although biologists debate whether to call the form of programmed cell death that occurs plants apoptosis, an important role for cell death in plant development is undisputed.

Apoptosis plays fascinating roles. For example, the feet of a [ch]icken embryo initially develop with webs. Cells that are pres[en]t between the toes must die to form separate toes (**FIGURE 22.1a**). [Th]e same is true for you—without apoptosis, your hands and feet [wo]uld be webbed like a duck's feet. A duck has webbed feet because [cel]ls between the toes do not undergo apoptosis. Apoptosis doesn't [en]d with digits. Vertebrate nerve cells are overproduced in the em[br]yo. As a normal part of "wiring" an effective nervous system, at [lea]st half of embryonic nerve cells are destroyed by apoptosis.

The initial studies on apoptosis were done on the roundworm *[Ca]enorhabditis* (pronounced *see-no-rab-DIE-tiss*) *elegans*. This [sp]ecies is a popular model organism in developmental biology [be]cause the adult contains only about a thousand cells and be[ca]use the embryonic worm is transparent, so biologists can fol[lo]w individual cells throughout development. (For more on *C. [ele]gans*, see **BioSkills 13** in Appendix B.)

As a *C. elegans* worm matures, exactly 131 of its cells undergo apoptosis. To explore how this happens, Hillary Ellis and Robert Horvitz studied mutant embryos that do *not* exhibit the normal pattern of cell death and then used techniques (introduced in Chapter 20) to locate the mutated genes responsible for the defect. Their early work uncovered two genes required for apoptosis. The researchers proposed that the genes are part of a genetic program for apoptosis—in short, they are cell-death genes.

In follow-up work, researchers searched databases of DNA sequences and discovered that mice have similar genes. When a research team used genetic engineering techniques to produce mice in which both copies of one of their cell-death genes were knocked out, the embryos had severe malformation of the brain (**FIGURE 22.1b**). The defect occurred because nerve cells that normally die during development survived.

The same genes exist in humans and other mammals. Abnormal apoptosis—either too much or too little—occurs in certain diseases. For example, inappropriate activation of programmed cell death is proposed to be involved in some devastating neurodegenerative diseases such as ALS (Lou Gehrig's disease).

## 22.2 Genetic Equivalence and Differential Gene Expression in Development

The differentiation of a cell occurs through differential gene expression. The muscle cells in your body are different from your nerve cells because they express different genes and therefore produce different proteins. The water-transport cells in an oak tree are different from its leaf-surface cells for the same reason.

If you think about these statements, you'll realize that they have to be true. The only way that cells can have different structures and functions is if they contain different molecules. What is less obvious is whether cells express different genes because they contain different genes, or whether all the cells in a body contain the same genes but express only a specialized subset.

### Evidence that Differentiated Plant Cells Are Genetically Equivalent

If cells from the branch of a cedar tree can de-differentiate to form roots, the branch cells must contain the genes required by root cells. Gardeners and farmers have known for centuries that in many plant species, complete new plants can be produced from a small section of a root or shoot.

From observations like this, researchers strongly suspected that all plant cells contain the same genes—meaning that they show **genetic equivalence.** This notion of genetically equivalent cells was confirmed in the 1950s when biologists were able to grow entire tobacco plants or carrots from a single, differentiated cell taken from an adult. (For more information on how plant cells are grown in culture, see **BioSkills 12** in Appendix B.) These experiments confirmed that differentiated plant cells are genetically equivalent.

[Figure 22.1a] Chicken embryo with normal (left) and defective (right) [cel]l-death genes.

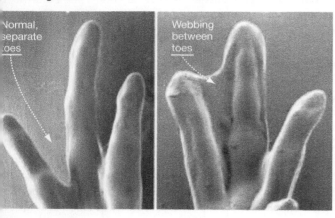

Normal, separate toes

Webbing between toes

[Figure 22.1b] Mouse embryo with normal (left) and defective (right) [cel]l-death genes.

Normal brain

Malformed brain

**[FIG]URE 22.1 Programmed Cell Death Is a Normal Part [of] Development.**

## Evidence that Differentiated Animal Cells Are Genetically Equivalent

The issue of genetic equivalence proved more difficult to resolve in animals than plants. Serious work began in the 1950s, but the question wasn't settled until the late 1990s.

Early experiments were based on transferring nuclei from differentiated frog cells into unfertilized egg cells whose nuclei had been removed. Some of these transplanted nuclei were able to direct the development of tadpoles. These results provided strong evidence that all cells in the same individual are genetically equivalent.

This conclusion was confirmed in a stunning way in 1997 when Ian Wilmut and colleagues reported their results of nuclear transfer experiments in sheep. As **FIGURE 22.2** shows, the researchers removed mammary-gland cells from a female, grew them in culture, and fused them with eggs whose nuclei had been removed. As the upper drawings show, the eggs came from a black-faced breed of sheep, while the donor nuclei came from a white-faced breed. After developing in culture, the embryos were implanted into surrogate mothers. In one of several hundred such transfer attempts, an apparently normal white-faced lamb named Dolly was born.

Genetic tests showed that Dolly was a **clone**—a genetically identical copy—of the white-faced donor of the mammary-gland cell. Dolly grew into a fertile adult. Soon after, other research groups reported similar results in mice and cows. More recently, a menagerie of animals, including horses, cows, monkeys, and dogs, have been cloned. The success rate of the procedure remains low, however, with the vast majority of nuclear transplants failing to produce healthy newborns.

Taken together, research on cloning plants and animals has shown that cellular differentiation typically does not involve changes in the genetic makeup of cells. Instead, it results from differential gene expression.

## How Does Differential Gene Expression Occur?

Eukaryotic cells control gene expression at several different levels: chromatin remodeling and modification, transcriptional regulation, alternative splicing of mRNAs, selective destruction of mRNAs, translation rate, and activation and deactivation of proteins after they are translated (see Chapter 19). All of these processes occur during development. Which is most important in differentiation?

The answer is transcriptional control. To understand why, ask yourself whether a muscle cell should produce mRNAs and proteins that are specifically required by nerve cells. The answer is no. If it did, it would also have to either produce microRNAs that disable nerve-cell mRNAs or expend the energy to translate the mRNAs into nerve-cell proteins that would then have to be maintained in an inactive state. It is more logical to expect that muscle cells transcribe genes required by muscle cells and not genes needed for specialized functions in other types of cells. This is exactly what researchers have found.

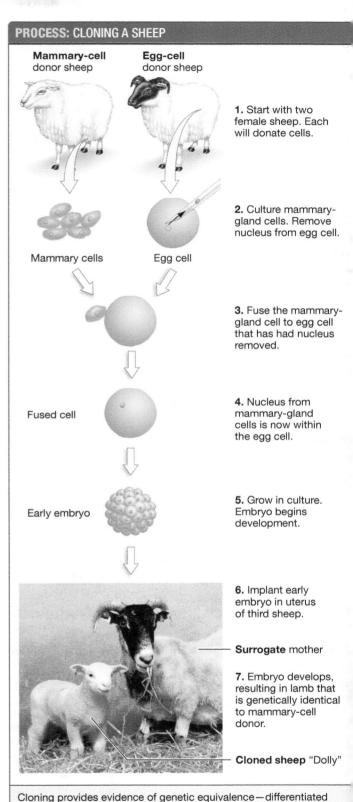

**PROCESS: CLONING A SHEEP**

**Mammary-cell** donor sheep

**Egg-cell** donor sheep

1. Start with two female sheep. Each will donate cells.

Mammary cells

Egg cell

2. Culture mammary-gland cells. Remove nucleus from egg cell.

3. Fuse the mammary-gland cell to egg cell that has had nucleus removed.

Fused cell

4. Nucleus from mammary-gland cells is now within the egg cell.

Early embryo

5. Grow in culture. Embryo begins development.

6. Implant early embryo in uterus of third sheep.

**Surrogate** mother

7. Embryo develops, resulting in lamb that is genetically identical to mammary-cell donor.

**Cloned sheep** "Dolly"

Cloning provides evidence of genetic equivalence—differentiated cells contain all the genes in the genome.

**FIGURE 22.2 Mammals Can Be Cloned.** The lamb that resulted from this experiment was genetically identical to the white-faced individual that donated the nucleus, not the black-faced egg donor or surrogate mother.

Transcription is the fundamental level of control during differentiation. In eukaryotes, transcription is controlled primarily by the presence of **regulatory transcription factors** that influence chromatin remodeling and bind to promoter-proximal elements, enhancers, silencers, and other regulatory sites in DNA.

This simple insight is extremely important. To understand differentiation, researchers have to understand how and why regulatory transcription factors vary among cells.

## check your understanding

### If you understand that . . .

- Differentiation occurs because embryonic cells express distinctive subsets of genes, not because they contain different genes.
- Differential gene expression is predominantly based on transcriptional control. Different types of cells have different combinations of transcription factors.

✔ **You should be able to . . .**

Explain the evidence for genetic equivalence in both plant and animal cells.

*Answers are available in Appendix A.*

## 22.3 Chemical Signals Trigger Differential Gene Expression

To understand development, you have to think like a cell. Suppose that you were one of the thousands of cells in a developing animal embryo. Your fate—whether you ended up as part of an arm or a kidney, or whether you differentiated into a nerve cell or a blood cell—would depend on your position in four dimensions—time during development and the three body axes illustrated in FIGURE 22.3.

1. One axis runs **anterior** (toward the head) to **posterior** (toward the tail).

2. One axis runs **dorsal** (toward the back) to **ventral** (toward the belly).

3. One axis runs left to right.

Chemical signals tell cells where they are in time and space. This information works through signal receptors and signal transduction cascades to activate transcription factors that turn specific genes on or off, resulting in differentiation. As development proceeds, the distinctive sets of genes that are activated at successive stages determine the fate of each cell.

Let's consider how chemical signals activate differential gene expression, beginning with one of the first developmental signals ever discovered. Although you'll be analyzing what happens as a fruit fly embryo develops, keep an important point in mind: Principles that were discovered in fruit flies are relevant to all multicellular organisms—from mustard plants to humans.

**(a)** The three body axes observed in humans and other animals...

**(b)** ...are initially established in embryos.

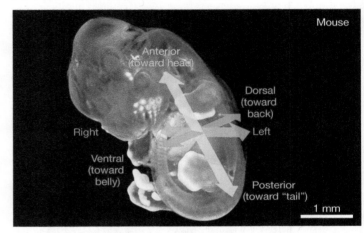

**FIGURE 22.3 Most Animals Have Three Major Body Axes.**

## Morphogens Set Up the Major Body Axes

Biologists use the term **pattern formation** to describe the events that determine the spatial organization of an embryo. If a molecule signals that a target cell is in the head or tail, or dorsal or ventral side of an embryo, then that molecule is involved in pattern formation.

Many molecules that work in pattern formation are present in a concentration gradient, with high concentrations near the source of the molecule and lower concentrations farther away. If cells detect the different concentrations to learn their position, then this molecule is a **morphogen.** Morphogens play central roles in setting up the body axes and at many later stages of development.

Complex patterns don't develop all at once. Instead, pattern formation is progressive. Morphogens set up the major elements of the body—the anterior–posterior, dorsal–ventral, and left–right axes. Genes activated by these morphogens generate signals of their own with more specific information about the location of cells. As development continues, the process repeats: New signals arrive and activate genes that specify finer and finer control over

**(a) A normal fruit fly embryo**

Anterior structures

Posterior structures

**(b) A mutant that does not express *bicoid***

Posterior structures

Posterior structures

**FIGURE 22.4 Pattern-Formation Mutants Have Misshapen Bodies.**

✓QUESTION Predict the phenotype of a mutant that expresses twice the normal levels of Bicoid instead of no Bicoid at all.

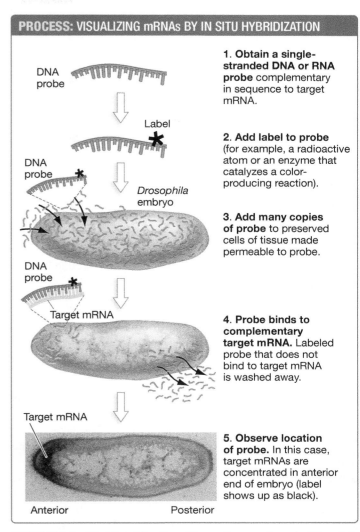

PROCESS: VISUALIZING mRNAs BY IN SITU HYBRIDIZATION

DNA probe

1. **Obtain a single-stranded DNA or RNA probe** complementary in sequence to target mRNA.

Label

2. **Add label to probe** (for example, a radioactive atom or an enzyme that catalyzes a color-producing reaction).

DNA probe

*Drosophila* embryo

3. **Add many copies of probe** to preserved cells of tissue made permeable to probe.

DNA probe

Target mRNA

4. **Probe binds to complementary target mRNA.** Labeled probe that does not bind to target mRNA is washed away.

Target mRNA

5. **Observe location of probe.** In this case, target mRNAs are concentrated in anterior end of embryo (label shows up as black).

Anterior          Posterior

**FIGURE 22.5 In Situ Hybridization Allows Researchers to Pinpoint the Location of Specific mRNAs.** The micrograph in the last step shows the location of the *bicoid* mRNA in a fruit fly embryo.

what a cell becomes. Development unfolds in a cascade of events unleashed by a few key signals.

**The Discovery of Bicoid**    Morphogens had long been proposed on theoretical grounds, but discovery of the first morphogen emerged from work on the fruit fly *Drosophila melanogaster*—a key model organism in genetics and development (see **BioSkills 13** in Appendix B).

Christiane Nüsslein-Volhard and Eric Wieschaus started this work in the 1970s, taking an approach based on genetics. They began by exposing adult flies to chemicals that cause mutations and examining their offspring for defects in development. One of the most dramatic mutations affected the anterior–posterior axis of the embryos. As **FIGURE 22.4** shows, the mutant embryos were missing all the structures normally found in the anterior end. Instead, the anterior end contained some structures normally found in the posterior.

The mutated gene responsible for this phenotype was dubbed *bicoid*, meaning two tailed. Based on its phenotype, Nüsslein-Volhard and Wieschaus suspected that the product of the normal *bicoid* gene must provide positional information. In other words, they hypothesized that the *bicoid* gene coded for a morphogen that tells cells where they are located along the anterior–posterior body axis.

**The Importance of Morphogen Concentration Gradients**    To test their hypothesis that *bicoid* encodes a morphogen, Nüsslein-Volhard and colleagues cloned and sequenced the *bicoid* gene (using techniques introduced in Chapter 20). They then used **in situ** (literally, "in place") **hybridization** to find where *bicoid* mRNAs are located. As **FIGURE 22.5** shows, in situ hybridization works by adding a label to single-stranded DNA or RNA molecules to create a probe that is complementary in sequence to the

mRNA of interest. In this case, the probe sequence was designed to bind to *bicoid* mRNA inside the embryo. As a result, the labeled probes marked the location of the *bicoid* mRNAs.

When Nüsslein-Volhard's group treated eggs and early embryos with labeled probes, they found the *bicoid* mRNA was tightly localized to the anterior end (see step 5 in Figure 22.5). In related studies they also made another surprising discovery: the *bicoid* gene is not expressed in the egg or embryo—it is only transcribed in special cells of the mother fruit fly that are near the egg. The *bicoid* mRNA is then deposited by these maternal cells into the developing egg at the anterior end. Follow-up work showed that when these mRNAs are translated, the protein product forms a steep concentration gradient: Bicoid protein is abundant in the anterior end but declines to progressively lower concentrations in the posterior end.

Later work showed that the Bicoid morphogen is a regulatory transcription factor (see Chapter 19). It binds to DNA and

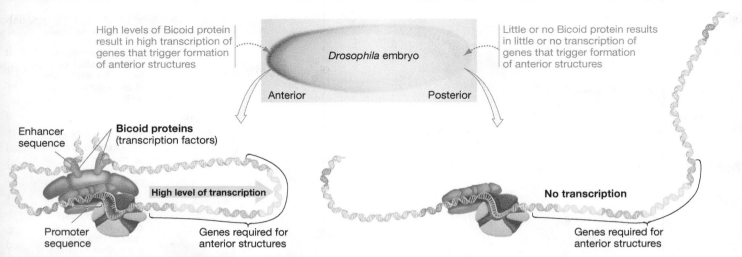

**FIGURE 22.6 Differential Gene Expression Occurs through the Presence or Absence of Regulatory Transcription Factors.** Bicoid protein is a regulatory transcription factor that triggers the formation of anterior structures. Because the concentration of Bicoid decreases toward the embryo's posterior, different genes are expressed in the anterior of the embryo than in the posterior.

✓**QUESTION** Predict the effect on development if some cytoplasm from the anterior of a normal early *Drosophila* embryo were added to the central region of a mutant embryo that lacked *bicoid* mRNA.

activates genes required for the formation of anterior structures. In effect, cells learn their position along the anterior-to-posterior axis through the concentration of Bicoid. High levels of Bicoid result in high levels of transcription of genes with Bicoid binding sites. In this way, high concentrations tell a cell that it's in the anterior, and lower concentrations tell the cell that it's more posterior (**FIGURE 22.6**). When Bicoid is lacking, cells throughout the embryo get a "you're in the posterior" message from a different morphogen that has its source in the posterior of the embryo— leading to the mutant phenotype you saw in Figure 22.4.

**Morphogens in Plant Development**   Plants also use morphogens to provide positional information. One important example is auxin, a small molecule that is used first in early development and then repeatedly and in different ways throughout the plant's life. In the embryo, auxin enters cells and triggers the production of transcription factors that affect differentiation.

Auxin is produced in the embryo's meristem cells that lie at the tip of what will become the stem. Auxin is actively transported toward the base of the embryo—what will become the root. In the process, an auxin concentration gradient forms. A high concentration of auxin signals, "You're near the top of the stem"; lower auxin concentrations that accumulate at the base of the embryo signal, "You're the root."

## Regulatory Genes Provide Increasingly Specific Positional Information

The initial work on *bicoid* illustrated the importance of morphogens as a general theme in development. A second fundamental developmental principle common to both plants and animals soon emerged: Differentiation is a progressive, step-by-step process.

**Dividing Up the Embryo**   Along with the "two-tailed monster" *bicoid* mutants, Nüsslein-Volhard and Wieschaus found an array of embryos that had defects in smaller regions of their body. Flies and many other animals are constructed from a set of **segments**—portions of the body that are repeated along its length. The mutants with altered segments had defective **segmentation genes.**

Researchers have now identified four classes of segmentation genes that act in a cascade:

1. First, maternally expressed genes deposit morphogen mRNAs in the egg. Morphogens, such as *bicoid*, control the formation of large groups of segments that span the anterior or the posterior halves of the embryo.

2. Gap genes are expressed second, in broad regions along the head-to-tail axis (**FIGURE 22.7a**). Gap genes control the formation of groups of segments that define large body regions.

3. Pair-rule genes are expressed next, in alternating bands along the embryo (**FIGURE 22.7b**). This pattern suggests that these genes control the formation of individual segments.

4. Segment polarity genes are expressed later, in a restricted band within every segment (**FIGURE 22.7c**). This pattern and order of expression imply that segment polarity genes create specific regions within each segment.

**Specifying Segment Identity**   Once segmentation gene products create segments along the anterior–posterior axis of a fly embryo, development continues with the activation of **Hox genes.** These genes are turned on by products of the segmentation genes. *Hox* genes have spectacular and far-reaching effects. While segmentation gene products establish each segment, *Hox* gene products specify each segment's identity by activating effector genes.

## (a) Gap genes

Early in development, gap genes define broad regions that often span several segments.

Anterior                    Posterior

## (b) Pair-rule genes

Later in development, pair-rule genes demarcate individual segments.

## (c) Segment polarity genes

Still later, segment polarity genes delineate regions within individual segments.

**FIGURE 22.7 Domains of Gene Expression Demarcate Body Regions in Fruit Flies.** The embryos in **(a)** and **(b)** were stained for two different segmentation gene products. The embryo in **(c)** was stained for one segmentation gene product.

Effector gene expression leads to the production of the specialized proteins and structures of differentiated cells.

The *Hox* genes were discovered when researchers found adult fruit flies with body parts in the wrong place. This bizarre outcome is called homeosis, and the types of mutations that cause it are termed **homeotic mutations.** For example, homeotic mutations in *Hox* genes can turn a segment in the middle part of the body into a segment just like the one that lies in front of it. Instead of bearing the pair of small balancing structures called halteres, the transformed segment now bears a pair of wings—as does the segment in front of it. The mutant has four wings instead of the normal two (**FIGURE 22.8**).

*Hox* genes code for transcription factors that trigger the development of the structures appropriate to each type of segment, such as antennae, wings, or legs. The *Hox* genes are distinguished by a sequence called the **homeobox** that encodes a DNA-binding domain.

To put all this information into perspective, it helps to realize that the genes involved in early development form a regulatory cascade (**FIGURE 22.9**; see page 414). Morphogens—produced by maternally expressed genes and deposited in the egg—trigger the production of other regulatory signals and transcription factors, which initiate the production of another set of signals and regulatory proteins, and so on down the chain. Ultimately, the genes needed to form antennae, wings, and legs are turned on in the right places and times within the developing embryo. Similar types of regulatory cascades exist in all animal and plant species.

The unfolding regulatory cascades provide progressively detailed information about where cells are located. This positional information, in turn, causes changes in cell proliferation, death, movement, interactions, and differentiation.

- Because chemical signals vary in identity and concentration along the three major body axes, cells in different locations receive unique positional information.

Normal fruit fly

Haltere

Antenna

Homeotic mutant

Wings in place of halteres

Homeotic mutant

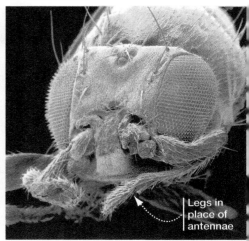

Legs in place of antennae

**FIGURE 22.8 Homeotic Mutants in *Drosophila* Have Structures in the Wrong Locations.** These colorized scanning electron micrographs show homeotic mutants in fruit flies. Wings are growing where small, stabilizing structures called halteres should be, or legs are growing where antennae should be.

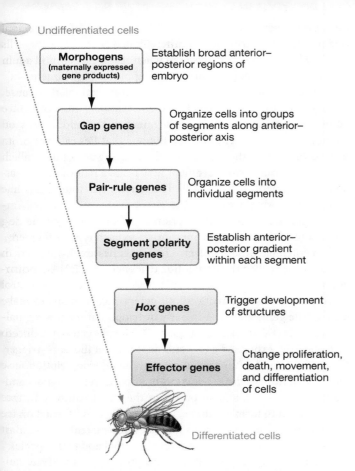

FIGURE 22.9 A Regulatory Gene Cascade in Fruit Flies. This cascade establishes the positions and identities of structures along the anterior-to-posterior axis. Morphogens—products of maternally expressed genes that are deposited in the egg—unleash the sequential expression of genes that work at each level of the cascade. Genes at one level of the cascade control the expression of genes at lower levels. The *Hox* genes are controlled by gap, pair-rule, and segment polarity genes. The effector genes are controlled by both segment polarity and *Hox* genes.

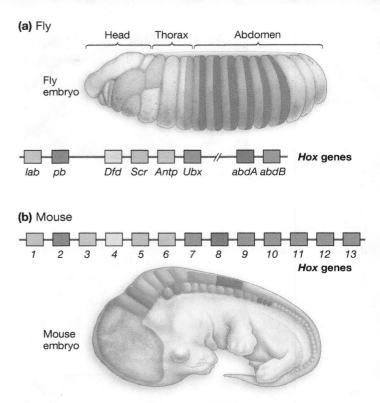

FIGURE 22.10 Organization and Expression of *Hox* Genes. The location of *Hox* genes on the chromosome correlates with their pattern of expression in the embryos of flies and mice. Matching colors of genes and regions in the embryo indicate where each gene is expressed at its highest levels. The genes represented by same-color boxes in the fly (a) and mouse (b) are considered homologous. For simplicity, three features are not shown in this figure: the fly genes are present in two separate groups that were created by a relatively recent chromosome breakage in the fly lineage, the mouse has three similar *Hox* gene clusters in addition to the one shown, and there is overlap in the regions in which *Hox* genes are expressed.

✓QUESTION What evidence would support the claim that these genes are homologous?

- Each level in a regulatory cascade provides more specific information about where a cell is located.

- As regulatory cascades are deployed over time, a cell's identity becomes more and more finely specified.

## Chemical Signals and Regulatory Genes Are Evolutionarily Conserved

Early genetic mapping studies revealed that the *Drosophila Hox* genes were present in clusters as shown in **FIGURE 22.10a**. Once methods to isolate and sequence DNA were available (see Chapter 20), researchers soon applied them to the *Hox* genes. The results of molecular studies were striking—the order of the *Hox* genes along the chromosome corresponds to the order of where the genes are expressed along the anterior-to-posterior axis.

### Conservation of *Hox* Gene Organization
With information about fruit fly *Hox* genes in hand, a few biologists thought it was worth looking for similar genes in other animals. This was a long shot, because it seemed unlikely that creatures as different as flies, sea urchins, mice, and humans would use the same genes to build such vastly different bodies. The gamble paid off. Virtually all animals were found to possess related sets of *Hox* genes. Incredibly, these *Hox* genes were organized in clusters in an order that aligned with the *Drosophila* genes. Even more amazing, the curious relationship first seen in *Drosophila* between *Hox* gene order along the chromosome and where a particular *Hox* gene is expressed was shared by all these animals.

A comparison of *Hox* genes in flies and mice (**FIGURE 22.10b**) reveals that there are more *Hox* genes in the mouse, but their chromosomal organization is similar. Notice how genes at the "left-hand" side of the cluster are expressed in the anterior end of both embryos, while genes at the opposite end of the cluster are expressed in posterior regions. The discovery that similar regulatory genes are used to build such a diverse array of animals ranks as one of the greatest surprises in modern biology.

**Conservation of *Hox* Gene Function**   Is there evidence that *Hox* genes in organisms other than *Drosophila* actually specify parts of the animal? Could it be that these genes are organized and expressed in similar ways but aren't used to specify pattern except in flies? Mutations discovered in many animals, including humans, have shown that when *Hox* genes are altered, defects in pattern formation result. Based on these data, biologists conclude that in flies, mice, humans, and most other animals, *Hox* genes play a key role in specifying which body structures to build.

This conclusion was supported in dramatic fashion when researchers in William McGinnis's lab introduced the *Hoxb6* gene from mice into fruit fly eggs. The *Hoxb6* gene in mice is similar in structure and sequence to the *Antp* gene of flies (Figure 22.10). Because it was introduced without its normal regulatory sequences, the *Hoxb6* gene was expressed throughout the treated fly embryos. The resulting larvae had defects identical to those observed in naturally occurring fly mutants in which the *Antp* gene is improperly expressed throughout the embryo. This is a stunning result: A mouse gene not only affected the development of a fly, but even mimicked the effect of the related fly gene.

To interpret these observations, biologists hypothesize that the genes in *Hox* complexes of animals are **homologous**—meaning that they are similar because they are descended from genes in a common ancestor. This hypothesis implies that the first *Hox* genes arose very early in animal evolution. For the past roughly 600 million years of animal evolution, *Hox* gene products have been helping to direct the development of animals.

The take-home message from these studies is that key molecular mechanisms of pattern formation have been highly conserved during animal evolution. The discovery of these shared mechanisms is one of the most significant results to have emerged from studies of animal development. Although animal bodies are spectacularly diverse in size and shape, the underlying mechanisms responsible for their development are similar.

## One Regulator Can Be Used Many Different Ways

Regulatory gene cascades and the evolutionary conservation of key developmental genes are general features of animal and plant development. But biologists have articulated another organizing principle as well: During development, the same regulatory genes, proteins, and chemical signals are used over and over in a variety of contexts.

The Wnt signal protein offers an impressive example of repeated uses of the same molecule to achieve different ends. *Drosophila* has a single *Wnt* gene known as *wingless*. From the name, you can guess that *wingless* is involved in wing development—flies that have a mutated *wingless* gene lack wings. The first role of *wingless*, however, is not in controlling wing formation, but in specifying boundaries between segments. The list doesn't stop here—it turns out that *wingless* is also a regulator of many other

developmental decisions. The *wingless* gene produces a signal protein that binds to specific receptors on different target cells and controls development of the leg, head, and digestive system as well as specifying particular nerve cells.

An analogy for this developmental principle of one signal, many messages is the signal called a pinch. When you were little, a pinch on the cheek from your grandmother indicated something very different from a pinch on the arm from an older sibling. It also means something different from a pinch you might receive now from someone you are romantically attracted to. In development, as in human communication, the context in which a signal is sent and received—its location, timing, and intensity—has a major effect on the signal's meaning and consequences.

In contrast to single genes such as *wingless* that are used in many different ways during the development of one organism, in many different organisms there are genes that control similar events in development. Animals and plants each have a conserved set of **tool-kit genes** that code for signals, signal-transduction pathways, and regulatory proteins that are used to direct related aspects of development in many different species.

*Hox* genes are an important example of tool-kit genes because they are present in a wide array of animals and are used to specify body structures. Similar tool-kit genes can, however, produce dramatically different structures such as the wing of a bat or the flipper of a whale if they are used at different times, in different places, and in different developmental contexts.

What determines the ways tool-kit genes are used? The answer lies largely in the regulatory sequences of DNA. Mutation of these sequences allows tool-kit genes to be used in new ways in different species. As you'll see in the next section, changes in regulatory sequence have profound effects on evolution.

## check your understanding

**If you understand that . . .**

- Chemical signals trigger the production of specific sets of transcription factors that change gene expression in signal-receiving cells.
- Different cells express different genes because they receive different sets of signals, and because they produce different sets of transcription factors in response to these signals.

✔ **You should be able to . . .**

1. Explain how a gradient of Bicoid protein delivers information about where cells are along the anterior–posterior axis of a fly embryo.
2. Describe how the cascade of transcription factors triggered by Bicoid leads to the gradual differentiation of segments along the anterior–posterior axis of a fly embryo.

*Answers are available in Appendix A.*

This chapter has shown that for an embryo to develop, cells have to proliferate, move or expand, differentiate, interact in specific ways, and sometimes die. Differentiation is caused by differential gene expression. It results from signals that tell cells where they are in time and space, triggering deployment of a complex cascade of transcription factors.

If any of these processes are disrupted, the embryo is likely to die. But if one of these processes is modified, the effect may be a structure with a different size, shape, or activity. As a result, the embryo will develop new features, and the adult will have a novel phenotype.

Once biologists began working out the regulatory signals and cascades introduced earlier in the chapter, they realized that the genetic changes altering these developmental processes must be the foundation of evolutionary change. The increase in body size that has occurred during human evolution, for example, must have resulted from mutations that altered the signals, regulatory sequences in DNA, or transcription factors that are involved in the amount and timing of cell proliferation throughout the body.

An emerging research field called evolutionary developmental biology, or **evo-devo,** focuses on understanding how changes in developmentally important genes have led to the evolution of new forms such as the flower, the leaf, and animal limbs. As an example of this exciting work, let's consider how snakes *lost* their limbs.

Although some snakes do not develop any sort of forelimb or hindlimb, boas and pythons have tiny pelvic (hip) bones and a rudimentary femur (thigh bone). The fossil record shows that the ancestor of all snakes had four functional legs. How did snakes lose their legs?

Researchers were able to answer this question because the signals and genes responsible for limb development are well understood. In chicken embryos, scientists had learned that *Hox* genes called *Hoxc6* and *Hoxc8* are expressed together in cells where ribs form, but *Hoxc6* is expressed alone in the region that gives rise to the forelimbs (**FIGURE 22.11a**).

Could modifications in where homologous *Hox* genes are expressed in snakes explain their limb loss? As **FIGURE 22.11b** shows, *Hoxc6* and *Hoxc8* are expressed together throughout the snake embryo—including in the region where forelimbs should form. These data suggest that a change in the regulation of where *Hoxc8* is expressed led to the evolutionary loss of the forelimb. Snakes make ribs instead of forelimbs.

It turns out that there's more than one way to lose a limb, even in the same animal. Hindlimb loss in snakes is due to defects in production of a signaling molecule encoded by the gene *sonic hedgehog*. This gene is homologous to a *Drosophila* segment polarity gene, *hedgehog,* which also produces a signal protein. Recent work has shown that defects in *sonic hedgehog* signaling affect animals other than snakes, as well—loss of *sonic hedgehog* signals in the pelvic region of whales led to the disappearance of their hindlimbs. Changes in the regulation of one widespread tool-kit gene—*sonic hedgehog*—have achieved extraordinary outcomes in animals as different as snakes and whales.

In limb loss, biologists can point to alterations in gene expression or in the production of specific signals that explain why an important evolutionary change occurred. Changes in the regulation of tool-kit genes led to developmental changes that build a snake or whale. These creatures have been legless ever since.

**(a)** Pattern of gene expression in tetrapods.

In the area where *Hoxc6* is expressed by itself, the forelimb forms

In the areas where *Hoxc6* and *Hoxc8* are expressed together, ribs form

Chick embryo

Forelimb

*Hoxc8*

*Hoxc6*

**(b)** Pattern of gene expression in snakes.

*Hoxc6* and *Hoxc8* are always expressed together, so no forelimbs form

Snake embryo

*Hoxc8*

*Hoxc6*

**FIGURE 22.11 Changes in Homeotic Gene Expression Led to Limb Loss in Snakes.** *Hoxc6* and *Hoxc8* code for transcription factors. If both transcription factors are present in a population of cells along the anterior–posterior axis of a tetrapod (a four-limbed vertebrate), genes that lead to the formation of vertebrae and ribs are activated. But if only *Hoxc6* is expressed, then genes that lead to the formation of forelimbs are activated.

## If you understand . . .

### 22.1 Shared Developmental Processes

- During development in all organisms, cells divide, interact, differentiate, move or expand in a directed manner, and sometimes die.
- Cells have to proliferate in a regulated manner to promote growth of the body.
- Chemical signals sent between cells provide a constant flow of information about where cells are in space and time.
- Cells undergo a step-by-step process of differentiation that leads to specialized cell types.
- Development requires the controlled movement and expansion of cells. In animals, many cells move in a coordinated way throughout development. Plant cells cannot move because of the cell wall, but plant cells precisely control the plane of cell cleavage and the direction of cell expansion to shape the embryo and the adult.
- Programmed cell death of some cells is an essential part of normal development.

✓ You should be able to predict how a mutation that disrupts control of the plane of cell cleavage would affect the development of an oak seedling.

### 22.2 Genetic Equivalence and Differential Gene Expression in Development

- Cells become specialized because they express different genes, not because they contain different genes.
- Cloning of plants and animals from differentiated adult cells indicates the genetic equivalence—that is, all cells of an individual contain the same genetic information.
- An implication of genetic equivalence is that cells are different because they express a common set of genes differently. Creating different cell types by expression of different genes from the same genome is differential gene expression.
- Stem cells in animals and plants do not fully differentiate, but proliferate throughout life to provide a source of cells that can specialize to replace damaged cells or promote growth.
- Transcriptional regulation through the production of different sets of transcription factors in different types of cells is the most important form of gene control during development.

✓ You should be able to explain why it's possible to propagate banana trees from cuttings. Your answer should cover how cells in a stem cutting can give rise to roots.

### 22.3 Chemical Signals Trigger Differential Gene Expression

- Cells "know" where they are in the body and how far along development has progressed because they receive a steady stream of signals. These signals are produced by other cells and diffuse or are transported throughout the body.

- Morphogens are signals present in a gradient. Cells can learn where they are along a body axis by "reading" the concentration of morphogen.
- Cells respond to chemical signals by activating signal transduction pathways that lead to expression of a distinctive set of proteins. These proteins are expressed because new groups of genes are transcribed in response to the signal.
- Cells gradually acquire positional information, first learning where they are in broad regions and later in smaller parts of each region.
- In some organisms, products of maternally expressed genes (morphogens) are deposited in the egg, and these activate the sequential expression of many other segmentation genes that are linked in regulatory cascades.
- Chemical signals are conserved across species.
- Each specific signaling pathway is used over and over in development in different contexts to achieved different outcomes.
- A set of conserved tool-kit genes is used to control core developmental processes in a wide array of species.

✓ You should be able to explain why a mutation in a *Drosophila* pair-rule gene affects the expression of segment polarity genes but has no effect on the expression of gap genes.

### 22.4 Changes in Developmental Gene Expression Underlie Evolutionary Change

- Mutations in genes responsible for development can lead to the evolution of new body sizes, shapes, and structures. These changes are important components of evolution.
- Mutations in regulatory sequences of DNA are especially important because they can change when, where, and to what levels key regulators are expressed.

✓ You should be able to use the information in Figure 22.11 to predict the effect on chick development of replacing the *Hoxc8* gene regulatory sequence with the regulatory sequences of *Hoxc6* gene.

### (MB) MasteringBiology

1. **MasteringBiology Assignments**

   **Tutorials and Activities** Early Pattern Formation in *Drosophila*; Pattern Formation; Role of *bicoid* Gene in *Drosophila* Development

   **Questions** Reading Quizzes, Blue-Thread Questions, Test Bank

2. **eText** Read your book online, search, take notes, highlight text, and more.

3. **The Study Area** Practice Test, Cumulative Test, BioFlix® 3-D Animations, Videos, Activities, Audio Glossary, Word Study Tools, Art

# You should be able to . . .

1. What is apoptosis?
   a. an experimental technique used to kill specific cells
   b. programmed cell death that is required for normal development
   c. a pathological condition observed only in damaged or diseased organisms
   d. a developmental mechanism unique to the roundworm *C. elegans*

2. In adult animals, _____ are a source of undifferentiated cells that can divide to produce cells that can specialize.

3. Why is in situ hybridization such a valuable tool for studying development?
   a. It can identify the location of specific mRNAs to provide information on where particular genes are being expressed.
   b. It allows researchers to understand how cell–cell signals and regulatory transcription factors interact.

   c. It provides information on gene evolution.
   d. It can locate promoters and enhancers of important developmental genes.

4. Embryonic cells can learn their position by "reading" the concentration of a morphogen.
   a. True
   b. False

5. What is a homeotic mutant?
   a. an individual with a structure located in the wrong place
   b. an individual with an abnormal head-to-tail axis
   c. an individual that is missing segments
   d. An individual with double the normal number of structures

6. A tool-kit gene is _____.

7. What does it mean to say that cell proliferation, death, movement, or expansion; differentiation; and interaction are shared developmental processes?

8. Explain the logic of cloning animals to test the hypothesis that all cells in the animal body are genetically equivalent.

9. How did researchers go about looking for genes that have important roles in establishing the anterior–posterior body axis and body segments in *Drosophila*?

10. Why is it significant that many of the genes involved in development encode regulatory transcription factors?

11. Explain the connection between the existence of regulatory cascades and the observation that differentiation is a step-by-step process.

12. Which of the following provides the strongest evidence for the conservation of tool-kit genes?
   a. Bicoid moved from one fly embryo into the posterior of another fly embryo causes the formation of two head regions.
   b. Mutation of an unrelated gene in another species of fly has a similar effect to mutation of *bicoid* in *Drosophila*.
   c. A mouse *Hox* gene can be used to take over the function of a mutated *Drosophila Hox* gene.
   d. Sheep can be cloned by fusing a differentiated adult cell with an enucleated egg.

13. Biologists found that the products of two different *Drosophila* genes are required to keep *bicoid* mRNA concentrated at the anterior end of the egg. In individuals with mutant forms of these proteins, *bicoid* mRNA spreads farther toward the posterior pole than it normally does. Predict what effect these mutations will have on segmentation of the larva.

14. In 1992 David Vaux and colleagues used genetic engineering technology to introduce a human gene for a protein that inhibits apoptosis into embryos of the roundworm *C. elegans*. When the team examined the embryos, they found that cells that normally undergo programmed cell death survived. What is the significance of this observation?

15. QUANTITATIVE Imagine a situation in which a morphogen has its source at the posterior end of a *Drosophila* embryo. Every 100 μm from the posterior pole, the morphogen concentration decreases by half. If a cell required 1/16th the amount of morphogen found at the posterior pole to form part of a leg, how far from the posterior pole would the leg form?
   a. 100 μm
   b. 160 μm
   c. 400 μm
   d. 1600 μm

16. Fruit flies have 6 legs; spiders have 8 legs; centipedes have many; earthworms have none. All these species are segmented and have *Hox* genes. Generate a hypothesis to explain how variation in leg number evolved in these species.

# 28 Phylogenies and the History of Life

**In this chapter you will learn that**

Vast amounts of change have occurred in the 3.6-billion-year history of life

by asking ↓

**How can we study the history of life?**

via ↓

| Phylogenetic trees | The fossil record |
|---|---|
| 28.1 | 28.2 |

by asking ↓

**How does the diversity of life undergo big changes?**

via ↓

| Adaptive radiation | Mass extinction |
|---|---|
| 28.3 | 28.4 |

A fossilized trilobite. The last trilobites disappeared during a mass extinction event analyzed in Section 28.4.

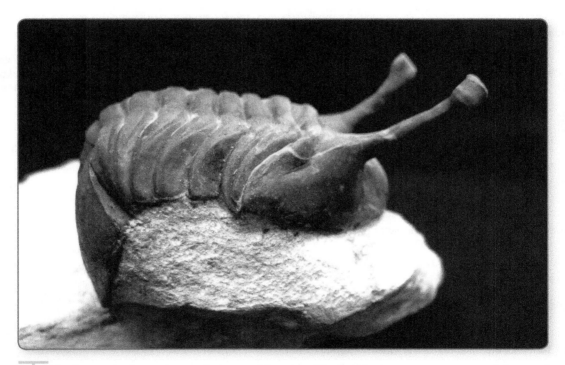

This chapter is about time and change. More specifically, it's about vast amounts of time and profound change in organisms. Both of these topics can be difficult for humans to grasp. Our lifetimes are measured in decades, and our knowledge of history is usually measured in centuries or millennia. But this chapter analyzes events that occurred over millions and even billions of years.

It takes practice to get comfortable analyzing the profound changes that occur in organisms over deep time. To help you get started, the chapter begins by introducing the two major analytical tools that biologists use to reconstruct the history of life: phylogenetic trees and the fossil record. The remaining two sections explore evolutionary episodes called adaptive radiations and mass extinctions, which can cause major changes to the tree of life. The Big Picture of Evolution on pages 526–527 shows how the tree of life relates to speciation (Chapter 27) and the four evolutionary processes (Chapters 25 and 26).

This chapter is part of the Big Picture. See how on pages 526–527.

✔ When you see this checkmark, stop and test yourself. Answers are available in Appendix A.

## 28.1 Tools for Studying History: Phylogenetic Trees

The evolutionary history of a group of organisms is called its **phylogeny**. A **phylogenetic tree** is a graphical summary of this history, showing the ancestor–descendant relationships among populations, species, or higher taxa, and clarifying who is related to whom. The **tree of life** is the most universal of all phylogenetic trees, depicting the evolutionary relationships among all living organisms on Earth (see Chapter 1). Phylogenetic trees have revolutionized the study of evolution and many related fields. For example:

Phylogenetic trees can be used in taxonomy to define species (Chapter 27).

Phylogenetic trees provide evidence for the endosymbiosis theory—that mitochondria and chloroplasts originated as free-living bacteria (Chapter 30).

Phylogenetic trees can be used to examine how the HIV virus jumped from other primates to humans (Chapter 36).

Phylogenetic trees can aid in identifying species that are a priority for conservation (Chapter 57).

Phylogenetic trees are extremely effective at summarizing data and testing hypotheses. However, they are unusual diagrams—it can take practice to interpret them correctly.

Take a moment to review the parts of a phylogenetic tree in **TABLE 28.1**. Notice that the tree in this table, like all the trees used in this text, is rooted, which means that the **branches** on the left are more ancient, or ancestral, while the ones on the right are most recent, or derived. Notice also that the **nodes** (forks) represent *hypothetical* common ancestors—the taxa themselves are always located on the branch **tips**, never within the tree. That is, none of the taxa are presumed to be ancestors of others, even if some of the taxa are extinct.

Let's practice reading phylogenetic trees by focusing on how biologists go about building them.

### How Do Biologists Estimate Phylogenies?

Like any other pattern or measurement in nature, from the average height of a person in a particular human population to the speed of a passing flock of geese, the historical relationships among species cannot be known with absolute certainty. In addition, humans have not been around to observe most evolutionary events directly. Thus, the relationships depicted in phylogenetic trees must be *estimated* from the best available data.

**Creating the Data Matrix** The first step in inferring evolutionary relationships is to decide which populations, species, or higher taxa to compare and which characteristics to use—usually morphological or genetic characteristics, or both. For example, to reconstruct relationships among fossil species of humans (there were many; see Chapter 35), scientists analyze aspects of tooth, jaw, and skull structure, since this is often the only

---

**SUMMARY TABLE 28.1** Anatomy of a Phylogenetic Tree

**Graphical Symbols and Definitions**

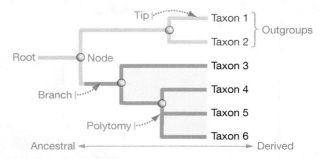

**Branch** Represents a population through time

**Node (fork)** A point within the tree where a branch splits into two or more branches

**Outgroup** A taxon that diverged prior to the taxa that are the focus of the study; helps to root the tree

**Root** The most ancestral branch in the tree

**Polytomy** A node that depicts an ancestral branch dividing into three or more (rather than two) descendant branches; usually indicates that insufficient data were available to resolve which taxa are more closely related

**Tip (terminal node)** Endpoint of a branch; represents a living or extinct group of genes, species, families, phyla, or other taxa

---

sort of evidence available. To reconstruct relationships among contemporary human populations, investigators usually compare the sequences of bases in a particular gene.

Consider the simple case of estimating a phylogenetic tree for four closely related species using a short DNA sequence as the character set, where a **character** is any genetic, morphological, physiological, or behavioral characteristic to be studied. The data matrix for this group is shown in **FIGURE 28.1a**. The sequence consists of six characters (nucleotides 1, 2, 3, 4, 5, and 6), each with four possible character states: A, T, C, and G.

Notice that a fifth species is included in the matrix as an **outgroup**—a species that is closely related to the group being studied, but not part of it. Outgroups are used to establish the polarity of each trait—that is, whether a character state is ancestral or derived. An **ancestral trait** is a characteristic that existed in an ancestor; a **derived trait** is one that is a modified form of the ancestral trait, found in a descendant. Derived traits originate via mutation, selection, and genetic drift (see Chapter 26).

It's important to recognize that ancestral and derived traits are relative. If you are comparing mammals with the fossil forms called mammal-like reptiles, then fur and lactation are derived traits. But if you are comparing whales and humans, then fur and lactation are ancestral traits. In the example in Figure 28.1a, the ancestral DNA sequence is estimated to be AAA GCT based on the outgroup; any nucleotides that differ from those in this sequence are considered derived. Since outgroup lineages can

**(a)** Data matrix

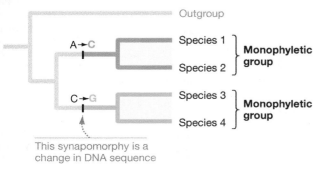

DNA nucleotide sequence

| 1 | 2 | 3 | 4 | 5 | 6 | |
|---|---|---|---|---|---|---|
| A | A | A | G | C | T | Outgroup |
| A | A | C | G | C | T | Species 1 |
| A | A | C | G | C | T | Species 2 |
| A | A | A | G | G | T | Species 3 |
| A | A | A | G | G | T | Species 4 |

**(b)** Phylogenetic tree inferred from the data

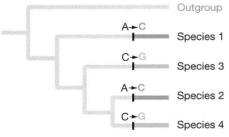

Outgroup

A→C

Species 1 ⎱ Monophyletic
Species 2 ⎰ group

C→G

Species 3 ⎱ Monophyletic
Species 4 ⎰ group

This synapomorphy is a change in DNA sequence

**(c)** One of many alternate trees

Outgroup

A→C — Species 1

C→G — Species 3

A→C — Species 2

C→G — Species 4

**FIGURE 28.1 Constructing a Phylogenetic Tree.** Cladistic analysis **(a)** begins with a data matrix and **(b)** builds trees based on the principle that closely related species are likely to share derived traits, called synapomorphies. **(c)** The tree that best fits the data must be selected from many alternate trees (only one shown here).

✔ **EXERCISE** Draw another alternate tree for the same data set.

evolve too, multiple outgroups are often used to estimate ancestral character states (for simplicity, only one is used here).

**Using the Data Matrix to Estimate a Tree** The most commonly used method of inferring phylogenetic trees, called cladistics, was introduced by German biologist Willi Hennig in the 1960s. The **cladistic approach** is based on the principle that relationships among species can be reconstructed by identifying shared derived characters—synapomorphies (introduced in Chapter 27).

A **synapomorphy** is a trait found in two or more taxa that is present in their most recent common ancestor but is missing in more distant ancestors. Synapomorphies allow biologists to recognize monophyletic groups—also called **clades** or **lineages.** A **monophyletic group** is an evolutionary unit that includes an ancestral population and all of its descendants, but no others.

**SUMMARY TABLE 28.2   Mapping Traits and Groups on Trees**

| Graphical Symbol | Definition |
|---|---|
| Synapomorphy ⸺ A | **Homology** Similarity in organisms due to common ancestry (trait **A** is homologous among the red branches)<br><br>**Monophyletic group** An evolutionary unit that includes an ancestral population and all of its descendants but no others (also called a lineage, or clade)<br><br>**Synapomorphy** A shared, *derived* trait (trait **A** occurs *only* in the red branches) |
| B ⸺ B | **Homoplasy** Similarity in organisms due to reasons other than common ancestry (trait **B** arose twice independently)<br><br>**Polyphyletic group** An unnatural group (shown in purple) that does not include the most recent common ancestor (see segmented animals in Chapter 33) |
| C ⸺ Loss of trait ⸺ −C | **Paraphyletic group** A group (shown in blue) that includes an ancestral population and some of its descendents, but not all (see dicots in Chapter 31, and fish and reptiles in Chapter 35) |

See **TABLE 28.2** for a comparison of monophyletic groups and two types of non-monophyletic groups.

In the case of the character set in Figure 28.1a, species 1 and 2 can be recognized as a monophyletic group based on their shared, derived trait, a C in the third position of the DNA sequence. Similarly, species 3 and 4 can be recognized as a different monophyletic group based on their shared, derived trait, a G in the fifth position of the sequence. This logic is summarized by the tree in **FIGURE 28.1b.**

In this example, it is relatively easy to infer a tree that represents the data set in a logical way. In common practice, there are several possible complications to resolve. For example:

● Traits can be similar in two species not because those traits were present in a common ancestor, but because similar traits evolved independently in two different lineages. For example, the A → C changes in DNA sequence at nucleotide 3 may have arisen separately in species 1 and 2 rather than once in their common ancestor (**FIGURE 28.1c**).

● Sometimes a reversal in a change occurs, such as an A → C transition in a nucleotide in one branch followed by a C → A change in the same nucleotide in a subsequent branch, thus creating the appearance that no change occurred.

- Sometimes the species forms a monophyletic group one way according to one trait in the matrix and a different way according to a different trait in the matrix (as would occur if species 1 and 3 had a unique base change at position 1).

- The example in Figure 28.1 shows a small number of species with a small number of traits. The larger the number of species and traits added to the matrix, the greater the number of possible trees and character combinations. There are 15 possible trees for a phylogeny of 4 taxa but over 100,000 trees for a phylogeny of 8 taxa.

How can researchers identify the tree with the best fit to the data? And how can they avoid an erroneous conclusion? Biologists often invoke the logical principle of **parsimony** to address these questions. Under parsimony, the most likely explanation or pattern is the one that implies the least amount of change.

To implement a parsimony analysis, biologists use computer programs that compare the branching patterns that are theoretically possible in a phylogenetic tree and count the number of changes in DNA sequences required to produce each pattern. For example, the tree in Figure 28.1b requires two changes in base sequence; the tree in Figure 28.1c requires four.

Since independent evolution of traits should be rare compared with similarity due to shared descent, the tree that implies the fewest overall evolutionary changes is hypothesized to be the one that most accurately reflects what really happened during evolution. If the branching pattern in Figure 28.1b is the most parsimonious of all possible trees, then biologists conclude that it is the most likely representation of actual phylogeny based on the data in hand.

There are methods other than parsimony to find the tree with the best fit to the data, each guided by different assumptions. However, all the methods are similar in serving as "filters" to identify optimal trees out of a pool of hundreds, thousands, or millions of possible trees. Some researchers use multiple methods to gain more confidence in their results.

It's important to recognize that the trees created using cladistic analysis (called cladograms) focus on branching *patterns*—the branch *lengths* themselves are arbitrary. Some analyses produce trees whose branch lengths represent genetic distance or time since divergence. You can identify these trees by the presence of scale bars (see **TABLE 28.3**). (If you feel that you need more practice interpreting phylogenetic trees, you can turn to **BioSkills 7** in Appendix B at any time.)

## How Can Biologists Distinguish Homology from Homoplasy?

The cladistic approach is a powerful method of estimating phylogenies because it is based on one of the central concepts in evolutionary biology—homology (see Table 28.2). **Homology** (literally, "same-source") occurs when traits are similar due to shared ancestry; in contrast, **homoplasy** ("same-form") occurs when traits are similar for reasons other than common ancestry.

**SUMMARY TABLE 28.3  Branch Lengths in Phylogenetic Trees**

| Graphical Symbol | Meaning of Branch Lengths |
|---|---|
| | Branch lengths are *arbitrary*. Emphasis is on the branching *pattern*, which estimates evolutionary relationships among populations. This is the type of tree used in this book. |
| 0.1 — Number of base substitutions per site | Horizontal branch lengths show the extent of *genetic difference* among populations. A scale bar is included. |
| 4  3  2  1  0 — Millions of years ago | Horizontal branch lengths show the extent of *evolutionary time* between nodes. A scale bar is included. |

A common cause of homoplasy is convergent evolution. **Convergent evolution** occurs when natural selection favors similar solutions to the problems posed by a similar way of making a living in different species. Since species have many characteristics, some may be homologous with characteristics in other species, while others may be convergent. Let's consider how to distinguish homology and homoplasy.

**Are *Hox* Genes in Fruit Flies and Humans Homologous or Convergent?**  Consider the *Hox* genes of insects and vertebrates (introduced in Chapter 22). Even though insects and vertebrates last shared a common ancestor some 600–700 million years ago, biologists argue that their *Hox* genes are derived from the same ancestral sequences—that is, they are homologous. Several lines of evidence support this hypothesis:

- Groups of *Hox* genes are organized on chromosomes in a similar way. **FIGURE 28.2** shows that *Hox* genes in both insects and vertebrates are found in gene clusters, and similar genes are often found in the same order on the chromosome. Genes with these characteristics are called gene families (Chapter 21). The organization of the gene families is nearly identical among insect and vertebrate species.

- All *Hox* genes share a 180-base-pair sequence called the homeobox. The portion of a protein encoded by the homeobox (introduced in Chapter 22) is almost identical in insects and vertebrates and has a similar function. It binds to DNA and regulates the expression of other genes.

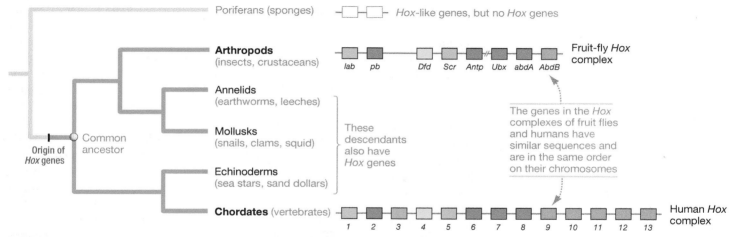

**FIGURE 28.2 Homology: Similarities Are Inherited from a Common Ancestor.** All animals except sponges have *Hox* complexes that are similar to those illustrated for fruit flies and humans. (Human *Hox* genes occur in four clusters but are summarized here in one for simplicity.)

- The products of the *Hox* genes have similar functions (see Chapter 22): identifying the locations of cells in embryos. They are also expressed in similar patterns in time and space.

Further, if traits found in distantly related lineages are similar due to common ancestry, then similar traits should be found in many intervening lineages on the tree of life—because all of the species in question inherited the trait from the same common ancestor. Indeed, all other lineages of animals that branched off between insects and mammals have similar *Hox* genes. Sponges serve as an outgroup to the clade since they appear to have split off before *Hox* genes arose.

The internal consistency of the genetic, developmental, and phylogenetic data provide strong evidence that *Hox* genes in fruit flies and humans are homologous.

**Are Streamlined Bodies in Dolphins and Ichthyosaurs Homologous or Convergent?** The extinct aquatic reptiles called ichthyosaurs were strikingly similar to modern dolphins (**FIGURE 28.3**). Both are large marine predators with streamlined bodies and large dorsal fins. Are these characteristics homologous in dolphins and ichthyosaurs?

Figure 28.3 shows a phylogenetic tree based on skeletal characters, such as the number and placement of openings in the skull (since ichthyosaurs are known only from their fossilized skeletons). This analysis shows that dolphins occur within the mammal clade, whereas ichthyosaurs are most closely related to lizards. Notice that the sister groups to dolphins and ichthyosaurs—that is, the most closely related branches on the tree—do not possess streamlined bodies, flippers, and fins.

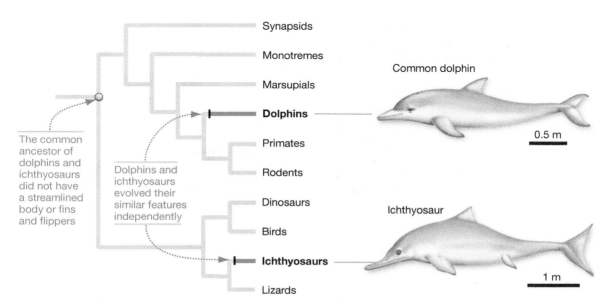

**FIGURE 28.3 Homoplasy: Traits Are Similar but Not Inherited from a Common Ancestor.** Dolphins and ichthyosaurs look similar but are not closely related.

Based on these data, it is logical to argue that the similarities between ichthyosaurs and dolphins result from convergent evolution. The convergent traits do not occur in the common ancestor of the similar species. Streamlined bodies, flippers, and dorsal fins are adaptations that help *any* aquatic species—whether it is a reptile or a mammal—chase down fish in open water.

## Whale Evolution: A Case Study

Let's apply what you've learned about phylogenetic trees and the concept of homology to an interesting evolutionary case study: the origin of a unique clade of mammals, the whales. Scientists since Darwin have puzzled over the rightful place of whales (including dolphins) on the tree of life. Data from the fossil record support the hypothesis that whales evolved from terrestrial mammals. More specifically, hippos, which are semiaquatic, appear to be the closest living relative of today's whales. How can phylogenetic trees be used to test this claim?

**Data Set 1: A Phylogeny Based on Morphological Traits**   Hippos, along with cows, deer, pigs, and camels, are artiodactyls. Members of this mammal group have hooves and an even number of toes. They also share another feature: the unusual pulley shape of an ankle bone called the astragalus. Along with having a unique foot morphology, the shape of the astragalus is a synapomorphy that identifies the artiodactyls as a monophyletic group. Members of the outgroup, perissodactyls (including horses and rhinos), do not possess a pulley-shaped astragalus.

These data support the tree shown in **FIGURE 28.4a**. Notice that whales do not have an astragalus (indeed, no ankles at all) and are shown as an outgroup to the artiodactyls on this tree based on other morphological characteristics. It is logical to map the gain of the pulley-shaped astragalus in the ancestral population, marked by a black bar in Figure 28.4a, because all descendants of that ancestor have the trait, but members of the outgroup do not.

**Data Set 2: A Phylogeny Based on DNA Sequence Data**   When researchers began comparing DNA sequences of artiodactyls and other species of mammals, however, the data showed that whales share many similarities with hippos. These results supported the tree shown in **FIGURE 28.4b**.

Here, it is still logical to map the evolution of the pulley-shaped astragalus at the same ancestor as in Figure 28.4a. But to recognize that the trait had to have been lost in an ancestor of today's whales—which do not have a pulley-shaped astragalus—the tree contains another black bar mapping the trait loss.

The tree supported by the DNA data conflicts with the tree supported by morphological data because it implies that the pulley-shaped astragalus evolved in artiodactyls and then was lost during whale evolution. These two changes (a gain *and* a loss of the astragalus) are less parsimonious than just one change (a gain only).

**Data Set 3: Transposable Elements**   The conflict between the two phylogenies was resolved when researchers analyzed the distribution of the parasitic DNA sequences called **SINEs (short interspersed nuclear elements),** which occasionally insert themselves into the genomes of mammals. (SINEs are transposable elements, similar to the LINEs introduced in Chapter 21.) SINEs provide convincing evidence of relationships because the chance of the same SINE inserting itself in exactly the same place in the genomes of two species is astronomically small.

As the data in **FIGURE 28.4c** show, whales and hippos share several types of SINEs (4, 5, 6, and 7) that are not found in other groups. Other SINEs are present in some artiodactyls but not in others. Camels have no SINEs at all.

To explain these data, biologists hypothesize that no SINEs were present in the population that is ancestral to all of the species in the study. Then, after the branching event that led to the split between the camels and all the other artiodactyls, different SINEs inserted themselves into the genomes of descendant populations.

If this hypothesis is correct, then the presence of a particular SINE represents a derived character. Because whales and hippos share four of these unique derived characters, it is logical to conclude that these animals are closely related.

✔ If you understand this concept, you should be able to explain why SINEs numbered 4–7 are synapomorphies that identify whales and hippos as a monophyletic group, and why the similarity in these SINEs is unlikely to represent homoplasy.

**Conclusion: Whales Are Closely Related to Hippos**   If a phylogenetic tree were estimated based on the SINE data, it would have the same branching pattern as the one shown in Figure 28.4b. (To convince yourself, try the exercise in the figure caption.) Thus, most biologists accept the phylogeny shown in Figure 28.4b as the most accurate estimate of whale evolutionary history. According to this phylogeny, whales are artiodactyls and share a relatively recent common ancestor with hippos. This observation inspired the hypothesis that both whales and dolphins are descended from a population of artiodactyls that spent most of their time feeding in shallow water, much as hippos do today.

In 2001, the discovery of fossil artiodactyls supported this hypothesis in spectacular fashion. These fossil species were clearly related to whales—they have an unusual ear bone found only in whales—and yet had a pulley-shaped astragalus.

The combination of DNA sequence data and data from the fossil record has clarified how a particularly interesting group of mammals evolved. What else do fossils have to say?

## check your understanding

**If you understand that . . .**

• Phylogenies can be estimated by finding synapomorphies that identify monophyletic groups.

✔ **You should be able to . . .**

Determine whether the following traits represent homology or homoplasy: hair in humans and whales; extensive hair loss in humans and whales; limbs in humans and whales; social behavior in humans and certain whales (e.g., dolphins).

*Answers are available in Appendix A.*

**(a) Data set 1 (morphological traits):**
Whales diverged before the origin of artiodactyls.

**(b) Data set 2 (DNA sequences):**
Whales and hippos share a common ancestor.

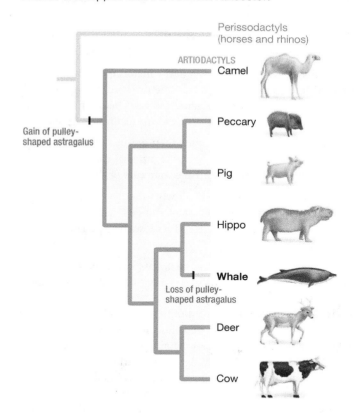

**(c) Data set 3 (presence and absence of SINEs):** Supports the close relationship between whales and hippos.

| Locus | 1 | 2 | 3 | 4 | 5 | 6 | 7 | 8 | 9 | 10 | 11 | 12 | 13 | 14 | 15 | 16 | 17 | 18 | 19 | 20 |
|-------|---|---|---|---|---|---|---|---|---|----|----|----|----|----|----|----|----|----|----|----|
| Cow | 0 | 0 | 0 | 0 | 0 | 0 | 0 | 1 | 1 | 1 | 1 | 1 | 1 | 1 | 1 | 1 | 1 | 1 | 0 | 0 |
| Deer | 0 | 0 | 0 | 0 | 0 | 0 | 0 | 1 | ? | 1 | 1 | 1 | 1 | 1 | 1 | ? | 1 | 1 | 0 | 0 |
| Whale | 1 | 1 | 1 | 1 | 1 | 1 | 1 | 0 | ? | 1 | 0 | 1 | 1 | 0 | 0 | 0 | ? | 1 | 0 | 0 |
| Hippo | 0 | ? | 0 | 1 | 1 | 1 | 1 | 0 | 1 | 1 | 0 | 1 | 1 | 0 | 0 | 0 | ? | 1 | 0 | 0 |
| Pig | 0 | 0 | 0 | ? | 0 | 0 | 0 | 0 | ? | 0 | 0 | 0 | ? | ? | 0 | 0 | 0 | 1 | 1 | 1 |
| Peccary | ? | ? | ? | ? | ? | ? | ? | ? | ? | ? | ? | ? | ? | ? | ? | ? | ? | ? | 1 | 1 |
| Camel | 0 | 0 | 0 | 0 | 0 | 0 | 0 | 0 | 0 | 0 | 0 | 0 | 0 | 0 | 0 | 0 | 0 | 0 | 0 | 0 |

1 = SINE present
0 = SINE absent
? = still undetermined

Whales and hippos share four *unique* SINEs (4, 5, 6, and 7)

**FIGURE 28.4  Where Do Whales Belong on the Tree of Life?**

DATA for (c): Nikaido, M., A. P. Rooney, and N. Okada. 1999. *Proceedings of the National Academy of Sciences, USA* 96: 10261–10266.

✔**EXERCISE**  Map the origin of the following groups of SINEs on the tree in part (b): Group (4, 5, 6, 7) identifies hippos and whales as part of a monophyletic group; (8, 11, 14, 15, 17) identifies deer and cows as part of a monophyletic group; (10, 12, 13) identifies hippos, whales, deer, and cows as part of a monophyletic group. What two species does SINEs group (19, 20) identify as part of a monophyletic group?

---

## 28.2  Tools for Studying History: The Fossil Record

Phylogenetic analyses are powerful ways to infer the order in which events occurred during evolution and to understand how particular groups of species are related. But only the fossil record provides *direct* evidence about what organisms that lived in the past looked like, where they lived, and when they existed.

A **fossil** is a piece of physical evidence from an organism that lived in the past. The **fossil record** is the total collection of fossils that have been found throughout the world. The fossil record is housed in thousands of private and public collections.

Let's review how fossils form, analyze the strengths and weaknesses of the fossil record, and then summarize major events that have taken place in life's approximately 3.5-billion-year history.

### How Do Fossils Form?

Most of the processes that form fossils begin when part or all of an organism is buried in ash, sand, mud, or some other type of sediment. For example, imagine that leaves, pollen, seeds, branches, or entire trees fall onto a muddy swamp, where they are buried by soil and debris before they decay. Once burial occurs, several things can happen.

- If decomposition does not occur, the organic remains can be preserved intact—like the fossil pollen in **FIGURE 28.5a**.

- If sediments accumulate on top of the material and become cemented into rocks such as mudstone or shale, the sediments' weight can compress the organic material below into a thin, carbonaceous film. This happened to the leaf in **FIGURE 28.5b**.

- If the remains decompose *after* they are buried—as did the branch in **FIGURE 28.5c**—the hole that remains can fill with dissolved minerals and create an accurate **cast** of the remains.

- If the remains rot extremely slowly, dissolved minerals can gradually infiltrate the interior of the cells and harden into stone, forming a permineralized fossil, such as petrified wood (**FIGURE 28.5d**).

After many centuries have passed, fossils can be exposed at the surface by erosion, a road cut, quarrying, or other processes. If researchers find a fossil, they can prepare it for study by painstakingly clearing away the surrounding rock.

If the species represented is new, researchers describe its morphology in a scientific publication, name the species, estimate the fossil's age based on dates assigned to nearby rock layers, and add the specimen to a collection so that it is available for study by other researchers. It is now part of the fossil record.

This scenario is based on conditions that are ideal for fossilization: The trees fell into an environment where decomposition was slow and burial was rapid. In most habitats the opposite situation occurs—decomposition is rapid and burial is slow. In reality, then, fossilization is an extremely rare event.

To appreciate this point, consider that there are 10 specimens of the first bird-like dinosaur to appear in the fossil record, *Archaeopteryx*. If you accept an estimate that crow-sized birds native to wetland habitats would have a population size of around 10,000 and a life span of 10 years, and if you accept the current estimate that the species existed for about 2 million years, then you can calculate that about 2 billion *Archaeopteryx* lived. But as far as researchers currently know, only 1 out of every 200,000,000 individuals were fossilized and discovered. For this species, the odds

of becoming part of the fossil record were almost 40 times worse than your odds are of winning the grand prize in a state lottery.

## Limitations of the Fossil Record

Before looking at how the fossil record is used to answer questions about the history of life, it is essential to review the nature of this archive and recognize several features.

**Habitat Bias** Because burial in sediments is so crucial to fossilization, there is a strong habitat bias in the database. Organisms that live in areas where sediments are actively being deposited—including beaches, mudflats, and swamps—are much more likely to form fossils than are organisms that live in other habitats.

Within these habitats, burrowing organisms such as clams are already underground—pre-buried—at death and are therefore much more likely to fossilize. Organisms that live aboveground in dry forests, grasslands, and deserts are much less likely to fossilize.

**Taxonomic and Tissue Bias** Slow decay is almost always essential to fossilization, so organisms with hard parts such as bones or shells are most likely to leave fossil evidence. This requirement introduces a strong taxonomic bias into the record. Clams, snails, and other organisms with hard parts have a much higher tendency to be preserved than do worms.

A similar bias exists for tissues within organisms. For instance, pollen grains are encased in a tough outer coat that resists decay, so they fossilize much more readily than do flowers. Shark teeth are abundant in the fossil record, but shark skeletal elements, which are made of cartilage, are almost nonexistent.

**Temporal Bias** Recent fossils are much more common than ancient fossils. This causes a temporal bias in the fossil record. The reason is straightforward—the older a fossil is, the longer it has been exposed to potentially destructive forces.

Older fossils usually occur in sedimentary rock layers deep below newer layers (see Chapter 25). These fossils are more vulnerable to crushing, heating, melting, and distortion by various chemical and physical processes. Older fossils are also more likely to be subducted further into the Earth's interior by the sliding and collision of Earth's tectonic plates. The fossils that survive these destructive forces will be discovered by scientists only if the

**(a)** Intact fossil (pollen)

**(b)** Compression fossil (leaf)

**(c)** Cast fossil (bark)

**(d)** Permineralized fossil (tree trunk)

10 μm

**FIGURE 28.5 Fossils Are Formed in Several Ways.** Different preservation processes give rise to different types of fossils.

deep layers of sedimentary rock they occupy are exposed to the surface by erosion (such as in the Grand Canyon) or by uplift.

**Abundance Bias**  The fossil record has an abundance bias; it is weighted toward common species. Organisms that are abundant, widespread, and/or present on Earth for long periods of time leave evidence much more often than do species that are rare, local, or ephemeral.

To summarize, the fossil database represents a highly nonrandom sample of the past. **Paleontologists**—scientists who study fossils—recognize that they are limited to asking questions about tiny and scattered segments on the tree of life. ✔ *If you understand the biases of the fossil record, you should be able to predict at least two ways that paleontologists could be misled by their observations of fossils.*

And yet, as this chapter shows, the fossil record is a scientific treasure trove. Analyzing fossils is the only way scientists have of examining the physical appearance of extinct forms and inferring how they lived. The fossil record is like an ancient library, filled with volumes that give us glimpses of what life was like millions of years before humans appeared.

## Life's Time Line

It is very difficult to date the origin of life precisely. Our best estimate is that the Earth started to form about 4.6 billion years ago, and that life began before 3.5 billion years ago—probably in the warm, hydrothermal vents at the bottom of the ocean (see Chapter 2). To organize the tremendous sweep of time between then and now, researchers divide Earth history into segments called eons, eras, and periods.

Originally, geologists used distinctive rock formations or fossilized organisms to identify the boundaries between named time intervals. Later, researchers were able to use radiometric dating to assign absolute dates—expressed as years before the present—to events in the fossil record. Radiometric dating is based on the well-studied decay rates of certain radioactive isotopes (see Chapter 25). By dating rocks near fossils, researchers can also assign an absolute age to many of the species in the fossil record.

To summarize the history of life, researchers create time lines that record key "evolutionary firsts"—the appearance of important new lineages or innovations. It's important to recognize, though, that the times assigned to these first appearances underestimate when lineages appeared and events occurred. The reason is simple: A particular species or lineage can exist for millions of years before leaving fossil evidence. The fossil record and efforts to date fossils are constantly improving, so time lines are always a work in progress.

**Precambrian**  The interval between the formation of Earth about 4.6 billion years ago and the appearance of most animal groups about 542 million years ago (abbreviated mya) is called the **Precambrian** (**FIGURE 28.6**); it is divided into the Hadean, Archaean, and Proterozoic eons.

**FIGURE 28.6 Major Events of the Precambrian.** Life, photosynthesis, and the oxygen atmosphere all originated in the Precambrian.

**Eons** — **First appearances**

Present

*Millions of years ago*

Phanerozoic Eon

See Figure 28.7

542 mya
— First **bilaterally symmetric** animals
— Present-day **oxygen** levels
— First **sponges**

Proterozoic Eon

— First **red algae**; first evidence of **sexual structures**

— First **photosynthetic eukaryotes**

— First **eukaryotic** fossils

— First rocks containing evidence of **oxygen** (in atmosphere and ocean)

Precambrian

2500
— First **cyanobacteria**

— First evidence of **oxygenic** photosynthesis

Archaean Eon

— First evidence of **photosynthetic cells**
— Origin of **life**

4000
— First **oceans**; heavy bombardment (collisions with large asteroids and other bodies) from space ends

Hadean Eon

— Liquid **water** on Earth

— **Earth** formation complete
— **Moon** forms
— Formation of **solar system**

4570

| Periods | Epoch | First appearances | Representative organisms |
|---------|-------|-------------------|--------------------------|

Present
2.6

23.0
mya

65.5

145.5

199.6

251

299

359.2

416

443.7

488

542

**Cenozoic Era**

Quaternary — Holocene / Pleistocene
Neogene — Pliocene / Miocene
Paleogene — Oligocene / Eocene / Paleocene

*Homo sapiens;* first chimpanzees
Earliest hominins
Oldest pollen from daisy-family plants
First apes
First fully aquatic whales
First horses; first primates; first rabbits/hares

**Mesozoic Era**

Cretaceous

First bee; first ant
First magnolia-family plants
First water lilies
First centric diatoms
First angiosperm (flowering plant)

Jurassic

First bird-like reptile
First placental mammals
First tyrannosaurid dinosaur

Triassic

First mammals
First dinosaurs
First nectar-drinking insects

**Paleozoic Era**

Permian

First vessels in plants
First basidiomycete fungi

Carboniferous — Pennsylvanian / Mississippian

Origin of amniotes

Devonian

First seed plants; first plants with leaves
First tetrapods (amphibians)
First winged insects
First tree-sized plants
First ferns, vascular plants, ascomycete fungi, lichens
First fish with jaws
First insects

Silurian

First bony fish

Ordovician

First mycorrhizal fungi (Glomales); first cartilaginous fish
First land plants
First bryozoans
(most recent origin of an animal phylum)

Cambrian

Arthropods diversify; first echinoderm
First arthropods, mollusks, vertebrates, other phyla

**Phanerozoic Eon**

Cretaceous extinction
Triassic extinction
Permian extinction
Devonian extinction
Ordovician extinction

**FIGURE 28.7 Major Events of the Phanerozoic Eon** (at left). The Phanerozoic began with the initial diversification of animals, continued with the evolution and early diversification of land plants and fungi, and includes the subsequent movement of animals to land. A total of five mass extinctions occurred during the eon.

Here are the important things to know about the Precambrian:

- Life was exclusively unicellular for most of Earth's history.
- Oxygen was virtually absent from the oceans and atmosphere for almost 2 billion years after the origin of life. Photosynthetic bacteria were responsible for the creation of the oxygen atmosphere (see Chapter 29).

**Phanerozoic Eon** The interval between 542 mya and the present is called the Phanerozoic eon and is divided into three eras (**FIGURE 28.7**). Each of these eras is further divided into intervals called periods, which are themselves divided into epochs.

1. The **Paleozoic** ("ancient life") **era** begins with the appearance of most major animal lineages and ends with the obliteration of almost all multicellular life-forms at the end of the Permian period. The Paleozoic includes the origin and initial diversification of the animals, land plants, and fungi, as well as the appearance of land animals.

2. The **Mesozoic** ("middle life") **era** begins with the end-Permian extinction events and ends with the extinction of the dinosaurs (except birds) and other groups at the boundary between the Cretaceous period and Paleogene period. In terrestrial environments of the Mesozoic, gymnosperms were the most dominant plants and dinosaurs were the most dominant vertebrates.

3. The **Cenozoic** ("recent life") **era** is divided into the Paleogene, Neogene, and Quaternary periods. On land, angiosperms were the most dominant plants and mammals were the largest vertebrates.

At the top of Figure 28.7 you can see that the periods of the Cenozoic are divided into epochs, and that we are presently in the Holocene epoch. However, many scientists have called for the delineation of a new epoch—the Anthropocene ("new human epoch")—to reflect the dramatic physical, chemical, and biological changes that humans are causing on Earth, especially since the industrial revolution. Much discussion will take place before any official change is made.

**Changes in the Oceans and Continents** The changes in environments and life-forms that are recorded in Figures 28.6 and 28.7 took place in the context of radical changes in climate and in the extent and location of Earth's oceans and continents. Earth's crust is broken into enormous plates that are in constant motion, driven by heat rising from the planet's core.

**FIGURE 28.8** summarizes the most recent data on how the positions of the continents and oceans have changed through time,

**FIGURE 28.8 Continental Positions during the Phanerozoic** (at right). Dramatic changes in the extent and position of the continents took place during the Phanerozoic. These changes affected the total amount of land area, the relative amounts of land in the tropics versus northern latitudes, and the nature of ocean currents.

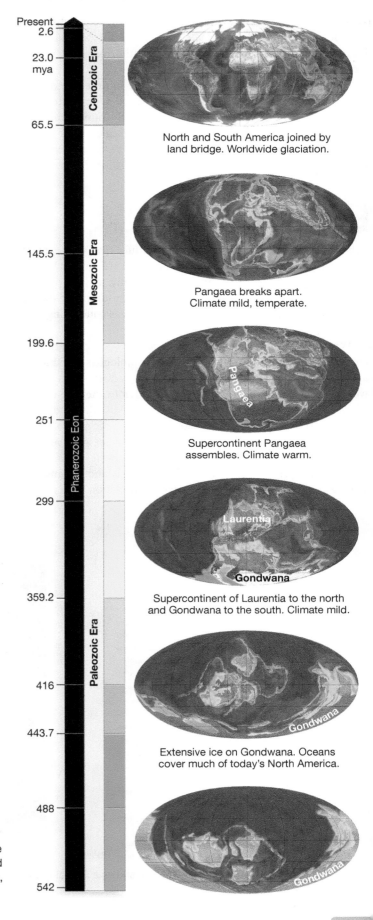

North and South America joined by land bridge. Worldwide glaciation.

Pangaea breaks apart. Climate mild, temperate.

Supercontinent Pangaea assembles. Climate warm.

Supercontinent of Laurentia to the north and Gondwana to the south. Climate mild.

Extensive ice on Gondwana. Oceans cover much of today's North America.

starting at the beginning of the Phanerozoic Eon. The figure also includes notes on the prevailing climate. Over the past 542 million years alone, terrestrial and marine landforms and climates have changed radically.

Taken together, the fundamental message in time-line data is a story of constant change. The changes are well documented, but the sweep of time involved is still difficult for the human mind to comprehend. If the history of the Earth were scaled to fit in one calendar year, our species, *Homo sapiens*, would not appear until one hour before the stroke of midnight on December 31st.

## 28.3 Adaptive Radiation

When biologists consider the history of life, two of the most compelling types of evolutionary events to study are (1) periods when species originate and diversify rapidly, and (2) periods when species go extinct rapidly. Let's focus on dramatic events that create biological diversity first; the chapter's concluding section analyzes how that diversity gets wiped out.

When a single lineage rapidly produces *many* descendant species with a wide range of adaptive forms, biologists say that an **adaptive radiation** has occurred. Adaptive radiations are noteworthy because they cause dramatic changes to the tree of life. They can be observed as a sudden appearance of related, diverse species in the fossil record and also by phylogenetic analysis.

**FIGURE 28.9** provides an example: the Hawaiian silverswords. The 30 species in this lineage evolved from a species of tarweed, native to California, that colonized the islands about 5 million years ago. This is an example of allopatric speciation by dispersal

(see Chapter 27). Compared to speciation rates in other groups, this rate is extremely rapid. Further, today's silverswords vary from mosslike mats to vines and rosettes. They live in habitats ranging from lush rain forests to austere lava flows.

The Hawaiian silverswords fulfill the three hallmarks of an adaptive radiation: (1) they are a monophyletic group, (2) they speciated rapidly, and (3) they diversified ecologically—meaning, in terms of the resources they use and the habitats they occupy.

Biologists use the term niche to describe the range of resources that a species can use and the range of conditions that it can tolerate (see Chapter 27). Silverswords occupy a wide array of niches.

### Why Do Adaptive Radiations Occur?

Adaptive radiations are a major pattern in the history of life. But why do some lineages diversify rapidly, while others do not?

Two general mechanisms can trigger adaptive radiations: new resources, and new ways to exploit resources. Let's consider each in turn.

**Ecological Opportunity** Ecological opportunity—meaning the availability of new or novel types of resources—has driven a wide array of adaptive radiations. For example, biologists explain the diversification of silverswords by hypothesizing that few other flowering plant species were present on the Hawaiian Islands 5 million years ago. With few competitors, the descendants of the colonizing tarweed were able to grow in a wide range of habitats. Over time—by the processes of mutation, genetic drift, and natural selection (discussed in Chapter 26)—some became specialized for growth in different niches.

**FIGURE 28.9 An Adaptive Radiation.** This tree shows a subset of the Hawaiian silverswords, illustrating the extent of morphological divergence.

**(a)** Short-legged lizard species spend most of their time on the twigs of trees and bushes.

*Anolis insolitus* (twig anole)

**(b)** Long-legged lizard species live on tree trunks and the ground.

*Anolis cybotes* (trunk/ground anole)

**FIGURE 28.10 Adaptive Radiations of *Anolis* Lizards. (a, b)** Species of *Anolis* lizards vary in leg length and tail length. **(c)** Evolutionary relationships among lizard species on the islands of Hispaniola and Jamaica. The initial colonist species was different on these islands, but in terms of how they look and where they live, a similar suite of four species evolved.

**(c)** The same adaptive radiation of *Anolis* has occurred on different islands, starting from different types of colonists.

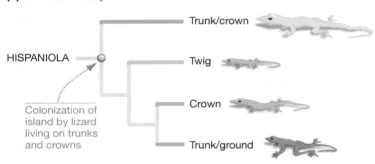

HISPANIOLA

Colonization of island by lizard living on trunks and crowns

- Trunk/crown
- Twig
- Crown
- Trunk/ground

JAMAICA

Colonization of island by lizard living on twigs

- Twig
- Trunk/ground
- Crown
- Trunk/crown

The same type of ecological opportunity was hypothesized to explain the adaptive radiation of *Anolis* lizards on islands in the Caribbean. The lineage includes 150 species. They thrive in a wide array of habitats and have diverse body sizes and shapes. And in most cases, a lizard's size and shape are correlated with the habitat it occupies. For example:

- Species that live on tree twigs have short legs and tails that allow them to move efficiently on narrow surfaces (**FIGURE 28.10a**).

- Species that spend most of their time clinging to broad tree trunks or running along the ground have long legs and tails, making them fast and agile on broad surfaces (**FIGURE 28.10b**).

Most islands in the Caribbean have a distinct suite of lizard species. And in most cases, each island has a species that lives only in the twigs, on the ground, or in other distinctive habitats. The classical explanation for this pattern was that a mini-radiation occurred on each island: An original colonizing group encountered no competitors, and diversified in a way that led to efficient use of the available resources by a group of descendant species.

To test this hypothesis rigorously, Jonathan Losos and his colleagues estimated the phylogeny of *Anolis* from DNA sequence data. The results supported a key claim of the ecological opportunity hypothesis: The lizards on each island were monophyletic.

The critical data, though, are shown in **FIGURE 28.10c**. These phylogenetic trees, for species found on two different islands, are typical. The key observation is that the original colonist on each island was specialized for a different niche. The initial species on Hispaniola lived on the trunks and crowns of trees, while the original colonist on Jamaica occupied twigs.

From different evolutionary starting points, then, an adaptive radiation filled the same niches on both islands. This is exactly what the ecological opportunity hypothesis predicts. In *Anolis* lizards in the Caribbean, a series of mini-radiations were triggered when colonists arrived on an island that had food, space, and other resources, but lacked competitors. ✔ If you understand this concept, you should be able to generate a hypothesis to explain why tarweeds in California and *Anolis* lizards on the mainland are not particularly species-rich or ecologically diverse.

**Morphological Innovation** The evolution of a key morphological trait—one that allowed descendants to live in new areas, exploit new sources of food, or move in new ways—triggered many of the important diversification events in the history of life. For example:

- *Flowers* are a unique reproductive structure that helped trigger the diversification of angiosperms (flowering plants). Because flowers are particularly efficient at attracting pollinators, the evolution of the flower made angiosperms more efficient in reproduction. Today angiosperms are far and away the most species-rich lineage of land plants. Over 250,000 species are known.

- *Feathers and wings* gave some dinosaurs the ability to fly. Feathers originally evolved for display or insulation; later they were used in gliding and in powered flight. Today the lineage called birds contains about 10,000 species, whose representatives live in virtually every habitat on the planet.

In each case, the evolution of new morphological features is hypothesized to have supported rapid speciation and ecological divergence.

# The Cambrian Explosion

Almost all life-forms were unicellular for almost 3 *billion* years after the origin of life. The exceptions were several lineages of small multicellular algae, which show up in the fossil record about 1 billion years ago. Then, the first animals—early sponges—appear, perhaps as early as 635 million years ago.

In a relatively short time, creatures with shells, exoskeletons, internal skeletons, legs, heads, tails, eyes, antennae, jaw-like mandibles, segmented bodies, muscles, and brains had evolved.

It was arguably the most spectacular period of evolutionary change in the history of life. Because much of it occurred during the Cambrian period, this adaptive radiation of animals is called the **Cambrian explosion.**

All organisms were small for 3 billion years; then life got big, in just 50 million years—1/60th of the total time life had existed. Before asking how this happened, let's explore the fossilized evidence for what happened.

**The Doushantuo, Ediacaran, and Early Cambrian Fossils** The Cambrian explosion is documented by three major fossil assemblages that record the state of animal life near the beginning of the Cambrian. As **FIGURE 28.11a** indicates, the species collected from each of these intervals are referred to respectively as the Doushantuo fossils (named after the Doushantuo formation in China), Ediacaran fossils (named after the Ediacara Hills, Australia), and Cambrian fossils (from the Burgess Shale in Canada, the Chengjiang region of China, and several other sites around the world).

Each fossil assemblage records a distinctive **fauna**—or collection of animal species:

* *Doushantuo microfossils* include tiny sponges and corals, less than 1 mm across. These creatures—the first animals on Earth—probably made their living by filtering organic debris from the water.

* *Ediacaran faunas* include sponges, jellyfish, and comb jellies as well as fossilized burrows, tracks, and other traces from unidentified animals. None of these organisms have shells, limbs, heads, or feeding appendages (**FIGURE 28.11b, bottom**). Ediacaran animals likely filtered or absorbed organic material as they burrowed in sediments, sat immobile on the seafloor, or floated in the water.

* *Cambrian faunas* are among the most sensational additions ever made to the fossil record. Sponges, jellyfish, and comb jellies are abundant in these rocks, but so are several worm-like creatures and arthropods (**FIGURE 28.11b, top**), in addition to mollusks, echinoderms, and virtually all the other major animal lineages (see Chapter 33). This list includes our own lineage—the chordates—represented by early vertebrate fossils with streamlined, fishlike bodies and a skull made of cartilage (**FIGURE 28.12**). A tremendous increase in the size and morphological complexity of animals occurred, accompanied by diversification in how they made a living. Species in these faunas swam, burrowed, walked, ran, slithered, clung, or floated; there were predators, scavengers, filter feeders, and grazers. The diversification filled many of the ecological niches found in marine habitats today.

**(a)** A time line of early animal evolution

**(b)** Early animals from two major macroscopic fossil assemblages

Cambrian fossils are diverse, large, and have hard parts.

Ediacaran fossils are soft-bodied.

**FIGURE 28.11 Fossils Document the Cambrian Explosion.** The origin of animals and their diversification during the Cambrian explosion is documented by three major fossil assemblages, two of them represented by macroscopic fossils.

**FIGURE 28.12 Life in the Cambrian.** This artist's interpretation of animal diversity during the Cambrian is based on fossils found in the Chengjiang formation of China. Chengjiang is famous for its unique fossils of fishlike early vertebrates.

**What Triggered the Cambrian Explosion?** The Doushantuo, Ediacaran, and Cambrian faunas document what happened during the Cambrian explosion. Now the question is: *How* did all this speciation, morphological change, and ecological diversification come about?

To answer this question, biologists point to an array of data sets and hypotheses:

- *Higher oxygen levels* By analyzing the composition of rocks formed during the Proterozoic, geologists have established

that oxygen levels gradually rose in the atmosphere and ocean. Increased oxygen levels make aerobic respiration more efficient (see Chapter 9); increased aerobic respiration is required to support larger bodies and more active movements. Some biologists suggest that oxygen levels reached a critical threshold at the start of the Cambrian explosion, making the evolution of big, mobile animals possible.

- *The evolution of predation* Before the Cambrian explosion, animals made their living by eating organic material that settled on the seafloor or filtering cells and debris from the water. But Cambrian fossils include shelled animals with holes in the shells—evidence that a predator drilled through and ate the animal inside. When predators evolved, they exerted selection pressure for shells, hard exoskeletons, rapid movement, and other adaptations for prey to defend themselves. This selection would drive morphological divergence.

- *New niches beget more new niches* The vast majority of Doushantuo and Ediacaran animals lived on the ocean floor—in what biologists call benthic habitats. Once animals could move off this substrate, they could exploit algae and other resources that were available above the ocean floor. The presence of animals at an array of depths created selection pressure for the evolution of species that could eat them. In this way, the ability to exploit new niches created new niches, driving speciation and ecological diversification.

- *New genes, new bodies* *Hox* genes play a key role in organizing the development of the body in diverse animals by signaling where cells are in the embryo (Chapter 22). **FIGURE 28.13** summarizes the *Hox* genes found in some major animal

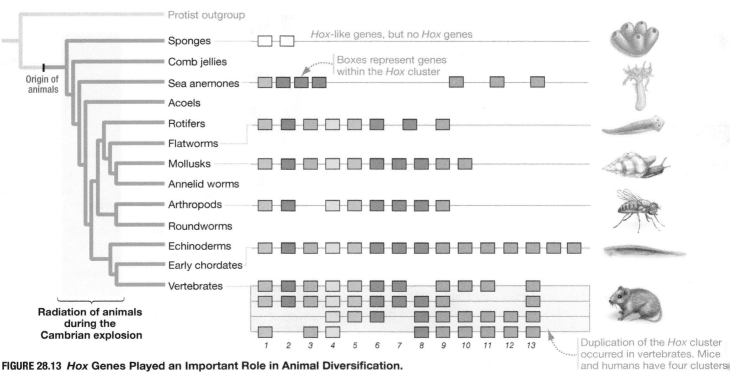

**FIGURE 28.13 *Hox* Genes Played an Important Role in Animal Diversification.**

groups. The key observation is that the earliest animals in the fossil record had few or no *Hox* genes; most groups that appeared later have more. The idea here is that gene duplication and diversification increased the number of *Hox* genes in animals and made it possible for larger, more complex bodies to evolve.

It's important to recognize that most or all of these hypotheses could be correct. They are not mutually exclusive. If increased oxygen levels made larger bodies and more rapid movement possible, then animals could move into new habitats off the seafloor and become large enough to eat smaller animals. Selection would favor individuals with mutations in *Hox* genes and other DNA sequences that make the development of a large, complex body possible.

About 100 million years after the Cambrian explosion, a similar adaptive radiation occurred after the first plants—the descendants of green algae—adapted to life on land. In the span of about 56 million years, an array of growth forms and most major lineages of plants appear in the fossil record. This "Devonian explosion" resulted from the morphological innovations that allowed green plants to thrive on land, coupled with the ecological opportunity provided by an environment awash in sunlight (Chapter 31).

Adaptive radiations occur when species originate and diversify rapidly. Now let's consider how dramatic events can *wipe out* diversity.

## check your understanding

**If you understand that . . .**

- Adaptive radiations are triggered by ecological opportunity and morphological innovation.

✔ **You should be able to . . .**

Explain the role of ecological opportunity and morphological innovation in the Cambrian explosion.

*Answers are available in Appendix A.*

## 28.4 Mass Extinction

A **mass extinction** refers to the rapid extinction of a large number of lineages scattered throughout the tree of life. More specifically, a mass extinction occurs when at least 60 percent of the species present are wiped out within 1 million years.

Mass extinction events are evolutionary hurricanes. They buffet the tree of life, snapping twigs and breaking branches. They are catastrophic episodes that wipe out huge numbers of species and lineages in a short time, giving the tree of life a drastic pruning. They are the polar opposite of adaptive radiation.

Before analyzing two of the best-studied mass extinctions in the fossil record, let's step back and ask how they differ from normal extinction events.

## How Do Mass Extinctions Differ from Background Extinctions?

**Background extinction** refers to the lower, average rate of extinction observed when a mass extinction is not occurring. Although there is no hard-and-fast rule for distinguishing between background and mass extinction rates, paleontologists traditionally recognize and study five historic mass extinction events. **FIGURE 28.14**, for example, plots the percentage of plant and animal lineages called families that died out during each stage in the geologic time scale since the Cambrian explosion. Five spikes in the graph—denoting a large number of extinctions within a short time—are drawn in red. These are referred to as "The Big Five."

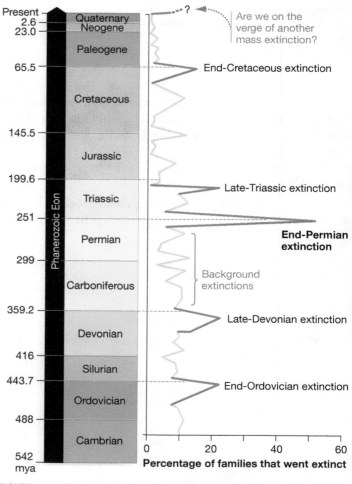

**FIGURE 28.14 The Big Five Mass Extinction Events.** This graph shows the percentage of lineages called families that went extinct over each interval in the fossil record since the Cambrian explosion. Over 50 percent of families and 90 percent of species went extinct during the end-Permian extinction.

DATA: Benton, M. J., 1995. *Science* 268: 52–58.

✔**QUANTITATIVE** Which extinction event ended the era of the dinosaurs 65 million years ago? About what percentage of families went extinct?

Biologists are interested in distinguishing between background and mass extinctions because these events have contrasting causes and effects.

- *Background extinctions* are thought to occur when normal environmental change, emerging disease, predation pressure, or competition with other species reduces certain populations to zero.

- *Mass extinctions* result from extraordinary, sudden, and temporary changes in the environment. During a mass extinction, species do not die out because individuals are poorly adapted to normal or gradually changing environmental conditions. Rather, species die out from exposure to exceptionally harsh, short-term conditions—such as huge volcanic eruptions or catastrophic sea-level changes.

To drive these points home, consider a mass extinction event that nearly uprooted the tree of life entirely. The end-Permian extinction, which occurred about 251 million years ago, came close to ending multicellular life on Earth.

## The End-Permian Extinction

The end-Permian has been called the Mother of Mass Extinctions. To appreciate the scale of the event, imagine that while walking along a seashore, you identified 100 different species of algae and animals living on the beach and in tide pools and the shallow water offshore. Now imagine that you snapped your fingers, and 90 of those species disappeared forever. Only 10 species are left. An area that was teeming with diverse forms of life would look barren.

This is what happened, all over the world, during the end-Permian extinction. The event was a catastrophe of almost unimaginable proportions. On a personal level, it would be like nine of your ten best friends dying.

Although biologists have long appreciated the scale of the end-Permian extinction, research on its causes is ongoing. Consider the following:

- Flood basalts are outpourings of molten rock that flow across Earth's surface. The largest flood basalts on Earth, called the Siberian traps, occurred during the end-Permian. They added enormous quantities of heat, $CO_2$, and sulfur dioxide to the atmosphere.

- High levels of atmospheric $CO_2$ trapped heat, causing intense global warming, the stratification of the oceans, and reaction of deep-ocean sulfur dioxide with water to form sulfuric acid, which is toxic to most organisms.

- Rocks that formed during the interval indicate that the oceans became completely or largely anoxic—meaning that they lacked oxygen. These conditions are fatal to organisms that rely on aerobic respiration.

- There is convincing evidence that sea level dropped dramatically during the extinction event, reducing the amount of habitat available for marine organisms.

- Terrestrial animals may have been restricted to small patches of low-elevation habitats, due to low oxygen concentrations and high $CO_2$ levels in the atmosphere.

In short, both marine and terrestrial environments deteriorated dramatically for organisms that depend on oxygen to live. A prominent researcher has captured this point by naming the suite of killing mechanisms the "world went to hell hypothesis."

What biologists don't understand is *why* the environment changed so radically, and so quickly. For example, no one has yet been able to establish a convincing connection between the eruption of the Siberian traps and the other, more global, environmental changes that occurred.

The cause of the end-Permian extinction may be the most important unsolved question in research on the history of life, aside from the origin of life itself (see Chapter 2). The cause of the dinosaur's demise, in contrast, is settled.

## What Killed the Dinosaurs?

The end-Cretaceous extinction of 65 million years ago is as satisfying a murder mystery as you could hope for, but the butler didn't do it. The **impact hypothesis** for the extinction of the dinosaurs, first put forth in the early 1970s by father-and-son team Luis and Walter Alvarez, proposed that an asteroid struck Earth and snuffed out an estimated 60–80 percent of the multicellular species alive.

**Evidence for the Impact Hypothesis** The impact hypothesis was intensely controversial at first. As researchers set out to test its predictions, however, support began to grow (**TABLE 28.4**):

- Worldwide, sedimentary rocks that formed at the Cretaceous–Paleogene (K–P) boundary were found to contain extremely high quantities of the element iridium. Iridium is vanishingly rare in Earth rocks, but it is an abundant component of asteroids and meteorites.

- Shocked quartz and microtektites are minerals that are found only at documented meteorite impact sites. In Haiti and an array of other locations, both shocked quartz and microtektites have been discovered in abundance in rock layers dated to 65 million years ago.

- A crater larger than New Jersey was found just off the northwest coast of Mexico's Yucatán peninsula. Microtektites are abundant in sediments from the crater's walls, and the crater dates to the K–P boundary.

Taken together, these data provided conclusive evidence in favor of the impact hypothesis. Researchers agree that the mystery is solved.

**Nature of the Impact** The shape of the Yucatán crater and the distribution of shocked quartz and microtektites dated to 65 mya indicates that the asteroid hit Earth at an angle and splashed material over much of southeastern North America. Based on

| Type of Evidence | Explanation |
|---|---|
|  | **Spike of iridium in 65-million-year-old rocks worldwide** Iridium is very rare on Earth but abundant in asteroids and meteors |
|  | **Spike of shocked quartz in 65-million-year-old rocks worldwide** Shocked quartz forms only under extremely high pressures created from events like impacts (not from volcanoes) |
|  | **Spike of micro-tektites in 65-million-year-old rocks in Gulf of Mexico** These glass droplets form only under extremely high temperatures and pressures as rock is splashed, molten, from an impact site |
|  | **Huge, 65-million-year-old crater discovered off coast of Mexico** The crater is 180 kilometers in diameter (absolutely massive), so an impact of this size would have far-reaching effects |

currently available data, astronomers and paleontologists estimate that the asteroid was about 10 km across.

To get a sense of the event's scale, consider that Mt. Everest is about 10 km above sea level and that planes cruise at an altitude of about 10 km. Imagine Earth being hit by a rock the size of Mt. Everest, or a rock that would fill the space between you and a jet in the sky.

According to both computer models and geologic data, the consequences of the K–P asteroid strike were nothing short of devastating.

- A tremendous fireball of hot gas would have spread from the impact site; large soot and ash deposits in sediments dated to 65 million years ago testify to catastrophic wildfires, worldwide.

- The largest tsunami in the last 3.5 billion years would have disrupted ocean sediments and circulation patterns.

- The impact site itself is underlain by a sulfate-containing rock called anhydrite. The $SO_4^{2-}$ released by the impact would have reacted with water in the atmosphere to form sulfuric acid, triggering extensive acid rain.

- Massive quantities of dust, ash, and soot would have blocked the Sun for long periods, leading to rapid global cooling and a crash in plant productivity.

**Selectivity of the Extinctions** The asteroid impact did not kill indiscriminately. Perhaps by chance, certain lineages escaped virtually unscathed while others vanished. Among vertebrates, for example, most dinosaurs (except birds), pterosaurs (flying reptiles), and all of the large-bodied marine reptiles (mosasaurs and plesiosaurs) expired; birds, mammals, crocodilians, amphibians, and turtles survived.

Why? Answering this question has sparked intense debate. For years the leading hypothesis was that the K–P extinction event was size selective. The logic here was that the extended darkness and cold would affect large organisms disproportionately, because they require more food than do small organisms. But extensive data on the survival and extinction of marine clams and snails have shown no hint of size selectivity, and small-bodied dinosaurs (except for birds) perished along with large-bodied forms.

One hypothesis currently being tested is that organisms that were capable of inactivity for long periods—by hibernating or resting as long-lived seeds or spores—were able to survive the catastrophe. Also, recent data show selectivity according to habitat; organisms in the open oceans suffered higher extinction rates than those in coastal waters. The reason for selectivity of the extinctions is still unsolved.

**Recovery from the Extinction** After the K–P extinction, fern fronds and fern spores dominate the plant fossil record from North America and Australia. These data suggest that extensive stands of ferns replaced diverse assemblages of cone-bearing and flowering plants after the impact. The fundamental message here is that terrestrial ecosystems around the world were radically simplified by the extinction event. In marine environments, some invertebrate groups do not exhibit typical levels of species diversity in the fossil record until 4–8 million years past the K–P boundary. Recovery was slow.

The organisms present in the Paleogene were markedly different from those of the preceding period. The lineage called

Mammalia had begun to diversify before the K–P extinction, during a period of rapid diversification of flowering plants. But early mammals were mostly rat-sized predators and scavengers in the heyday of the dinosaurs. It wasn't until after the dinosaurs became extinct that each of the major lineages of mammals diversified into the orders we recognize today—from bats to bears, and pigs to primates—and average body size increased exponentially. Why? A major branch on the tree of life had disappeared. With competitors removed from many ecological niches, mammals flourished.

The change in the terrestrial vertebrate fauna was not due to a competitive superiority conferred by adaptations such as fur and lactation. Rather, it was due to a chance event: a once-in-a-billion-years collision with a massive rock from outer space.

## The Sixth Mass Extinction?

Are mass extinctions events of the distant past? Not likely. Many scientists now propose that life on Earth is on the verge of the sixth mass extinction, precipitated by human impacts such as habitat loss, pollution, overfishing, invasive species, and climate change. Could human activities really cause such dire consequences as massive as those caused by an asteroid impact?

There is mounting evidence that the answer to this question is yes. The exponential increase of human populations, combined with our hunger for resources, has put the diversity of life as we know it at risk.

Unit 6 explores the diversity of life itself. Then Unit 9 examines how human actions are rapidly pruning branches from the tree of life during your lifetime.

---

## CHAPTER 28 REVIEW

For media, go to MasteringBiology

## If you understand . . .

### 28.1 Tools for Studying History: Phylogenetic Trees

- Phylogenetic trees show the evolutionary history of a group of organisms—who is most closely related to whom. They have revolutionized the study of evolution and many related fields.

- Phylogenetic trees are usually estimated by analyzing shared, derived characters (synapomorphies) that identify monophyletic groups.

- Researchers often use the principle of parsimony to decide which of the many possible trees is most likely to reflect actual evolutionary history. Parsimony assumes that the most likely explanation or pattern is the one that implies the least amount of change.

- Homology occurs when traits are shared due to common ancestry. Homoplasy occurs when traits are similar due to reasons other than common ancestry, such as convergent evolution.

✔ You should be able to explain why upright posture and bipedalism (walking on two legs) is a synapomorphy that defines a monophyletic group called hominins, which includes humans.

### 28.2 Tools for Studying History: The Fossil Record

- The fossil record is the only direct source of data about what extinct organisms looked like and where they lived.

- The fossil record is biased: Common, recent, and abundant species that burrow and that have hard parts are most likely to be present in the record.

- During the Precambrian, which started with the formation of the Earth 4.6 billion years ago and ended with the origin of most animals about 542 million years ago, life was almost exclusively unicellular.

- Oxygen was virtually absent from the oceans and atmosphere for almost 2 billion years after the origin of life. The oxygen atmosphere was generated by photosynthetic bacteria.

- During the Phanerozoic, which began about 542 million years ago and continues to the present, animals originated and diversified first in the ocean and then on land. Land plants and fungi also originated and diversified.

- If the history of the Earth were scaled to fit in one calendar year, our species, *Homo sapiens*, would not appear until one hour before the stroke of midnight on December 31st.

✔ You should be able to explain why some paleontologists use snail fossils rather than other types of fossils to estimate how biodiversity has changed over time.

### 28.3 Adaptive Radiation

- Adaptive radiations occur when a single lineage rapidly produces many descendant species with a wide range of adaptive forms.

- Adaptive radiations can be triggered by ecological opportunity, such as the availability of unoccupied niches on an island, or morphological innovations, such as flowers and wings.

- The Cambrian explosion was one of the most spectacular adaptive radiations of all time, producing virtually all of the major animal lineages existing today. During this event, the size and morphological complexity of animals increased tremendously, and animals diversified in how they made a living.

✔ You should be able to explain why the evolution of animals that could swim free of benthic habitats—such as fishlike early vertebrates—created an ecological opportunity.

## 28.4 Mass Extinction

- Mass extinctions are short-term environmental catastrophes that eliminate most of the species alive. Mass extinctions have altered the course of evolutionary history at least five times.

- Mass extinctions such as the end-Permian and end-Cretaceous prune the tree of life more or less randomly and have marked the end of several branches within prominent lineages and the subsequent rise of new branches.

- After the devastation of a mass extinction, the fossil record indicates that it can take 10–15 million years for ecosystems to recover their former levels of diversity.

- A mass extinction may presently be under way due to the drastic effects of humans on the Earth in recent history.

✓ You should be able to evaluate this statement: Environmental changes caused by humans are eliminating species that are poorly adapted to their natural environment.

## (MB) MasteringBiology

**1. MasteringBiology Assignments**

**Tutorials and Activities** Adaptive Radiation, Constructing Phylogenetic Trees, Fossil Record, History of Life, Overview of Macroevolution, Scrolling Geologic Record

**Questions** Reading Quizzes, Blue-Thread Questions, Test Bank

**2. eText** Read your book online, search, take notes, highlight text, and more.

**3. The Study Area** Practice Test, Cumulative Test, BioFlix® 3-D Animations, Videos, Activities, Audio Glossary, Word Study Tools, Art

# You should be able to . . .

## ✓ TEST YOUR KNOWLEDGE
*Answers are available in Appendix A*

1. Choose the best definition of a fossil.
   a. any trace of an organism that has been converted into rock
   b. a bone, tooth, shell, or other hard part of an organism that has been preserved
   c. any trace of an organism that lived in the past
   d. the process that leads to preservation of any body part from an organism that lived in the past

2. What is the difference between a branch and a node on a phylogenetic tree?
   a. A branch is a population through time; a node is where a population splits into two independent populations.
   b. A branch represents a common ancestor; a node is a species.
   c. A branch is a lineage; a node is any named taxonomic group.
   d. A branch is a population through time; a node is the common ancestor of all species or lineages present on a particular tree.

3. Which of the following best characterizes an adaptive radiation?
   a. Speciation occurs extremely rapidly, and descendant populations occupy a large geographic area.
   b. A single lineage diversifies rapidly, and descendant populations occupy many habitats and ecological roles.
   c. Natural selection is particularly intense, because disruptive selection occurs.
   d. Species recover after a mass extinction.

4. True or false? The dinosaurs (other than birds) went extinct during the asteroid impact at the K–P boundary because they were poorly adapted to their ecological niches.

5. Which of the following is an example of homoplasy?
   a. hair in humans and fur in mice
   b. astragalus ankle bones in hippos and deer
   c. *Hox* genes in humans and flies
   d. streamlined bodies in dolphins and ichthyosaurs

6. True or false? Monophyletic groups are identified by shared, derived traits.

## ✓ TEST YOUR UNDERSTANDING
*Answers are available in Appendix A*

7. The text claims that the fossil record is biased in several ways. What are these biases? If the database is biased, is it still an effective tool to use in studying the diversification of life? Why or why not?

8. The initial diversification of animals took place over some 50 million years, mostly during the Cambrian period. Propose an analogy from everyday life to illustrate the significance of this event.

9. Why is parsimony a useful tool for assessing which phylogenetic tree is most accurate? Why was parsimony misleading in the case of the astragalus during the evolution of artiodactyls?

10. Give an example of an adaptive radiation that occurred after a colonization event and another that occurred after a key innovation. In each case, provide a hypothesis to explain why the adaptive radiation occurred.

11. QUANTITATIVE The end-Permian extinction was devastating. If each student in your graduating class represented a different species during the Permian and there were 1880 students in your graduating class, about how many students would make it to graduation?

12. BioSkills 7 in Appendix B recommends a "one-snip test" to identify monophyletic groups—meaning that if you cut any branch on a tree, everything that "falls off" is a monophyletic group. Why is this valid?
   a. Monophyletic groups are nested on a tree—meaning that they are hierarchical.
   b. Monophyletic groups can also be called clades or lineages.
   c. Species are the smallest monophyletic groups on the tree of life.
   d. One snip gets an ancestor and all of its descendants.

**13.** Suppose that the dying wish of a famous eccentric was that his remains be fossilized. His family has come to you for expert advice. What method would you recommend as most likely to maximize the chances that his wish will be fulfilled?

   **a.** Place the corpse in an environment where decomposition is rapid (such as a forest).

   **b.** Place the corpse in an environment where decomposition is slow (such as a swamp or bog).

   **c.** Bury only the bones, since soft parts don't fossilize well.

   **d.** Place the corpse in an environment where plenty of oxygen is available.

**14.** Use the data matrix below to draft at least three alternate phylogenetic trees. Label the outgroup. Indicate which tree is most parsimonious, and explain why. How could you change your analysis to increase your confidence that the tree represents true evolutionary relationships?

**Presence or Absence of *Hox* Genes***

|              | *Hox1* | *Hox2* | *Hox3* | *Hox4* | *Hox12* |
|--------------|--------|--------|--------|--------|---------|
| Mouse        | 1      | 1      | 1      | 1      | 1       |
| Snail        | 1      | 1      | 1      | 1      | 0       |
| Fly          | 1      | 1      | 1      | 1      | 0       |
| Sea anemone  | 1      | 1      | 0      | 0      | 0       |
| Sponge       | 0      | 0      | 0      | 0      | 0       |

*1 = gene present; 0 = gene absent.

**15.** Some researchers contend that the end-Permian extinction event was caused by an impact with a large extraterrestrial object. Describe three forms of evidence that you would like to see before you accept this hypothesis.

**16.** One of the "triggers" proposed for the Cambrian explosion is a dramatic rise in oxygen concentrations that occurred in the oceans about 800 mya. (Review material in Chapter 9 on how oxygen compares with other atoms or compounds as an electron acceptor during cellular respiration; look near the end of Section 9.6, where aerobic and anaerobic respiration are compared.) Make a small concept map outlining the logic behind the "oxygen-trigger" hypothesis for the Cambrian explosion. (See **BioSkills 15** in Appendix B if you need help making concept maps.)

Geneticist and evolutionary biologist Theodosius Dobzhansky said that "Nothing in biology makes sense except in the light of evolution." Use this concept map to study how ideas introduced in Unit 5 fit together.

The key is to connect the four evolutionary processes that work at the level of populations— natural selection, genetic drift, mutation, and gene flow—to processes, events, and outcomes at higher levels of organization: speciation, adaptive radiation, mass extinction, and the tree of life.

It's all about changes in allele frequencies. Over time, small changes that occur between populations lead to large changes that distinguish major lineages on the tree of life.

Note that each box in the concept map indicates the chapter and section where you can go for review. Also, be sure to do the blue exercises in the Check Your Understanding box below.

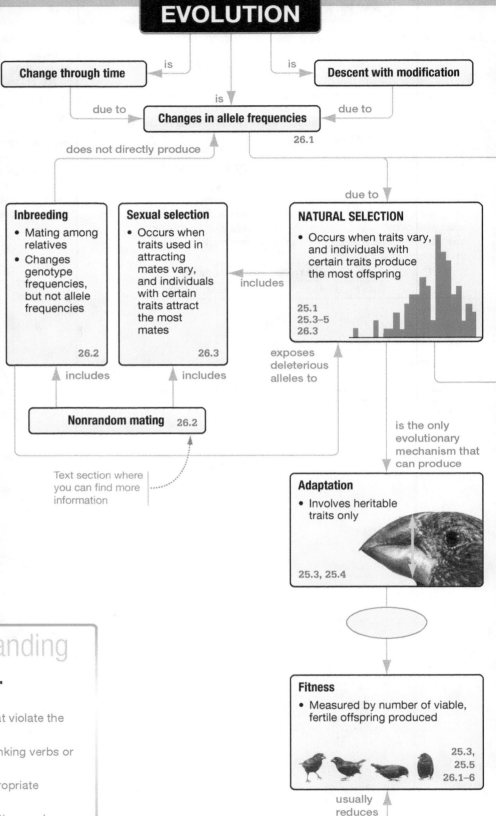

# EVOLUTION

Change through time  —is→  Changes in allele frequencies  ←is—  Descent with modification

due to →  Changes in allele frequencies  ← due to

**26.1**

does not directly produce

due to ↓

**Inbreeding**
- Mating among relatives
- Changes genotype frequencies, but not allele frequencies

**26.2**

**Sexual selection**
- Occurs when traits used in attracting mates vary, and individuals with certain traits attract the most mates

**26.3**

**NATURAL SELECTION**
- Occurs when traits vary, and individuals with certain traits produce the most offspring

25.1
25.3–5
26.3

includes

exposes deleterious alleles to

**Nonrandom mating**  **26.2**

includes

includes

Text section where you can find more information

is the only evolutionary mechanism that can produce

**Adaptation**
- Involves heritable traits only

25.3, 25.4

usually reduces

**Fitness**
- Measured by number of viable, fertile offspring produced

25.3,
25.5
26.1–6

## check your understanding

### If you understand the big picture . . .
✔ You should be able to . . .

1. Draw a circle around the processes that violate the Hardy–Weinberg principle.

2. Fill in the blue ovals with appropriate linking verbs or phrases.

3. Add a box for "Fossil record" with appropriate connections.

4. Draw arrows linking genetic drift, mutation, and gene flow to the appropriate box using the linking phrase "is random with respect to."

*Answers are available in Appendix A.*

due to ▼

**GENETIC DRIFT**
- Changes in allele frequencies due entirely to chance
- Especially important in small populations

26.4

due to ▼

**MUTATION**
- Random changes in DNA
- Creates new alleles
- Occurs in every individual in every generation, at low frequency

AT TAT TGT CTA GTA CCC CA

16.4, 26.6

due to ▼

**GENE FLOW**
- Occurs when individuals move between populations
- Homogenizes allele frequencies between populations

Gene flow

26.5

due to lack of ▲

produces divergence required for

produces divergence required for

provides raw material for

**Speciation**

Results from:
1. Genetic isolation, followed by
2. Genetic divergence

27.2–4

creates new branches on

form smallest possible tips on

**The Tree of Life**
- Describes the evolutionary relationships among all species

1.3, 28.1

"prune" ▲

forms new ▼

**Species**

Evolutionarily independent units in nature, identified by:
1. Reproductive isolation, and/or
2. Phylogenetic analysis, and/or
3. Morphological differences

27.1

**Mass extinctions**
- 60% of species are lost in less than 1 million years
- 5 events in the past 542 million years. A sixth mass extinction is now underway

28.4

may occur after ▲

with ▼

**Synapomorphies**
- Shared, derived traits that are unique to a single lineage
- Arise in a common ancestor

27.1
28.1

that may be

**Key innovations**
- Traits that allow species to exploit resources in a new way or use new habitats

28.4

may result in

**Adaptive radiations**
- Rapid and extensive speciation in a single lineage
- Dramatic divergence in morphology or behavior (species use a wide array of resources/habitats)

28.3

# 29 Bacteria and Archaea

In this chapter you will learn that

**Bacteria and archaea are the most abundant and diverse forms of life on Earth**

which are → **Prokaryotes**

in contrast to ↓

**Eukaryotes Ch. 30–36**

by asking ↓ **Why and how do biologists study these organisms? 29.1, 29.2**

by examining ↓ **Three themes in their diversification 29.3** → **Metabolism** / **Morphology** / **Ecological diversity**

then, looking closer at ↓

**Key lineages of bacteria and archaea 29.4**

Although this hot spring looks devoid of life, it is actually teeming with billions of bacterial and archaeal cells.

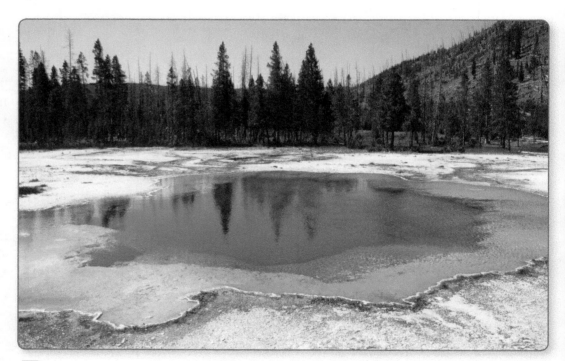

Bacteria and Archaea (usually pronounced *ar-KEE-ah*) form two of the three largest branches on the tree of life (**FIGURE 29.1**). The third major branch, or domain, consists of eukaryotes and is called the Eukarya. Virtually all members of the Bacteria and Archaea domains are unicellular, and all are prokaryotic—meaning that they lack a membrane-bound nucleus.

Although their relatively simple morphology makes bacteria and archaea appear similar to the untrained eye, in some ways they are strikingly different at the molecular level (**TABLE 29.1**). Organisms in the Bacteria and Archaea domains are distinguished by the types of molecules that make up their plasma membranes and cell walls:

- **Bacteria** have a unique compound called peptidoglycan in their cell walls (see Chapter 5).

✔ When you see this checkmark, stop and test yourself. Answers are available in Appendix A.

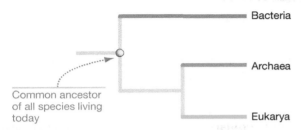

**FIGURE 29.1 Bacteria, Archaea, and Eukarya Are the Three Domains of Life.** Archaea are more closely related to eukaryotes than they are to bacteria.

✔**QUESTION** Was the common ancestor of all species living today prokaryotic or eukaryotic? Explain your reasoning.

- **Archaea** have unique phospholipids in their plasma membranes—the hydrocarbon tails of the phospholipids are made from isoprene (see Chapter 6).

If you were unicellular, bacteria and archaea would look as different to you as mammals and fish.

In addition, the machinery that bacteria and archaea use to process genetic information is strikingly different. More specifically, the DNA polymerases, RNA polymerases, transcription-initiation proteins, and ribosomes found in Archaea and Eukarya are distinct from those found in Bacteria and similar to each other. These differences have practical consequences: Antibiotics that poison bacterial ribosomes do not affect the ribosomes of archaea or eukaryotes. If all ribosomes were identical, these

antibiotics would kill you along with the bacterial species that was supposed to be targeted.

As an introductory biology student, you may know less about bacteria and archaea than about any other group on the tree of life. Before taking this course, it's likely that you'd never even heard of the Archaea. You might be surprised to find out that biologists suspect that the first eukaryotic cells may have formed as a result of a symbiotic event between these two groups of prokaryotes. Notice in Table 29.1 that cells in the domain Eukarya share some features with both Bacteria and Archaea. Studying these shared features has helped biologists understand the early evolution of life on Earth.

This chapter's goal is to convince you that even though bacteria and archaea are tiny, they have an enormous impact on you and the planet in general. By the time you finish reading the chapter, you should understand why a researcher summed up the bacteria and archaea by claiming, "They run this joint."

## 29.1 Why Do Biologists Study Bacteria and Archaea?

Biologists study bacteria and archaea for the same reasons they study any organisms. First, they are intrinsically fascinating. Discoveries such as finding bacterial cells living a kilometer underground or in 95°C hot springs keep biologists awake at night, staring at the ceiling. They can't wait to get into the lab in the morning and figure out how those cells stay alive.

SUMMARY TABLE 29.1 **Characteristics of Bacteria, Archaea, and Eukarya**

| | Bacteria | Archaea | Eukarya |
|---|---|---|---|
| **DNA enclosed by a nuclear envelope?** (see Chapter 7) | No | No | Yes |
| **Circular chromosome present?** | Yes (but linear in some species) | Yes | No (linear) |
| **Organelles enclosed by membranes present?** (see Chapter 7) | No | No | Yes |
| **Rotating flagella present?** (see Chapter 7) | Yes | Yes | No (flagella and cilia undulate) |
| **Multicellular species?** | No (with some exceptions) | No | Yes |
| **Plasma membrane lipids composed of glycerol bonded to unbranched fatty acids by ester linkages?** (see Chapter 6) | Yes | No (branched lipids bonded by ether linkages) | Yes |
| **Cell walls, when present, contain peptidoglycan?** (see Chapter 5) | Yes | No | No |
| **RNA polymerase composed of >10 subunits?** | No (only 5 subunits) | Yes | Yes |
| **Translation initiated with methionine?** (see Chapter 17) | No (initiated with N-formylmethionine; f-met) | Yes | Yes |

✔**EXERCISE** Using the data in this table, add labeled marks to Figure 29.1 indicating where the following traits evolved: peptidoglycan in cell wall, archaeal-type plasma membrane, archaeal- and eukaryotic-type translation initiation, and nuclear envelope.

Second, there are practical benefits to understanding the species that share the planet with us. Understanding bacteria and archaea is particularly important—in terms of both understanding life on Earth and improving human health and welfare.

## Biological Impact

The lineages in the domains Bacteria and Archaea are ancient, diverse, abundant, and ubiquitous. The oldest fossils of any type found to date are 3.5-billion-year-old carbon-rich deposits derived from bacteria. Because eukaryotes do not appear in the fossil record until 1.75 billion years ago, biologists infer that prokaryotes were the only form of life on Earth for at least 1.7 billion years.

Just how many bacteria and archaea are alive today? Although a mere 5000 species have been formally named and described to date, it is virtually certain that millions exist. Consider that over 1000 species of prokaryotes are living in your large intestine right now, and another 700 species are living in your mouth. Well-known microbiologist Norman Pace points out that there may be tens of millions of different insect species but notes, "If we squeeze out any one of these insects and examine its contents under the microscope, we find hundreds or thousands of distinct microbial species." Most of these **microbes** (microscopic organisms) are bacteria or archaea. Virtually all are unnamed and undescribed. If you want to discover and name new species, then study bacteria or archaea.

**Abundance** Besides recognizing how diverse bacteria and archaea are in terms of numbers of species, it's critical to appreciate their abundance.

The approximately $10^{13}$ (10 trillion) cells in your body are outnumbered ten to one by the bacterial and archaeal cells living on and in you. You are a walking, talking habitat—one that is teeming with bacteria and archaea.

A mere teaspoon of good-quality soil contains *billions* of microbial cells, most of which are bacteria and archaea.

In sheer numbers, species in a lineage of marine archaea may be the most successful organisms on Earth. Biologists routinely find these cells at concentrations of over 10,000 individuals per milliliter in most of the world's oceans. At these concentrations, one liter of seawater contains a population equivalent to that of the largest human cities. Yet this lineage was not described until the early 1990s.

Recent research has found enormous numbers of bacterial and especially archaeal cells in rocks and sediments as much as 1600 meters underneath the world's oceans. Although recently discovered, the bacteria and archaea living under the ocean may make up 10 percent of the world's total mass of living material.

Biologists estimate the total number of individual bacteria and archaea alive today at over $5 \times 10^{30}$. If they were lined up end to end, these cells would make a chain longer than the Milky Way galaxy. They contain 50 percent of all the carbon and 90 percent of all the nitrogen and phosphorus found in organisms.

In terms of the total volume of living material on our planet, bacteria and archaea are dominant life-forms.

**Habitat Diversity** Bacteria and archaea are found almost everywhere. They live in environments as unusual as oxygen-free mud, hot springs, and salt flats. In seawater they are found from the surface to depths of 10,000 meters (m), and at temperatures over 120°C (well above water's boiling point) near submarine volcanoes.

Although there are far more prokaryotes than eukaryotes, much more is known about eukaryotic diversity than about prokaryotic diversity. Researchers who study prokaryotic diversity are exploring one of the most wide-open frontiers in all of science. So little is known about the extent of these domains that recent collecting expeditions have turned up entirely new **phyla** (singular: **phylum**). These are names given to major lineages within each domain. To a biologist, this achievement is equivalent to the sudden discovery of a new group of eukaryotes as distinctive as flowering plants or animals with backbones.

The physical world has been explored and mapped, and many of the larger plants and animals are named. But in **microbiology**—the study of organisms that can be seen only with the aid of a microscope—this is an age of exploration and discovery.

## Some Microbes Thrive in Extreme Environments

Bacteria or archaea that live in high-salt, high-temperature, low-temperature, or high-pressure habitats are **extremophiles** ("extreme-lovers"). Studying them has been extraordinarily fruitful for understanding the tree of life, developing industrial applications, and exploring the structure and function of enzymes.

As an example of these habitats, consider hydrothermal vents at the bottom of the ocean, where water as hot as 300°C emerges and mixes with 4°C seawater. At locations like these, archaea are abundant forms of life.

Researchers recently discovered an archaeon that grows so close to these hydrothermal vents that its surroundings are at 121°C—a record for life at high temperature. This organism can live and grow in water that is heated past its boiling point (100°C) and at pressures that would instantly destroy a human. Since high temperature breaks non-covalent bonds holding macromolecules together, extreme heat usually denatures proteins, makes membranes leaky, and separates the strands of the DNA double helix. Biologists are intrigued by how these unusual archaeal cells can thrive under such extreme conditions.

Other discovered bacteria and archaea can grow

- at a pH less than 1.0;

- at temperatures of 0°C under Antarctic ice;

- in water that is virtually saturated with salt (**FIGURE 29.2**).

Extremophiles have become a hot area of research. The genomes of a wide array of extremophiles have been sequenced, and expeditions regularly seek to characterize new species. Why?

- *Origin of life* Based on models of conditions that prevailed early in Earth's history, it appears likely that the first forms of life lived at high temperature and pressure in environments

Archaeal cells tint these salt crystals different colors

Salt ponds where seawater is evaporating

**FIGURE 29.2 Some Archaeal Cells Live in High-Salt Habitats.** The evaporating water is colored red by these photosynthetic cells.

that lacked oxygen—conditions that humans would call extreme. Thus, understanding extremophiles may help explain how life on Earth began.

- *Extraterrestrial life?* In a similar vein, many astrobiologists ("space-biologists") use extremophiles as model organisms in the search for extraterrestrial life. The idea is that if bacteria and archaea can thrive in extreme habitats on Earth, cells might possibly be found in similar environments on other planets or moons of planets.

- *Commercial applications* Because enzymes that function at extreme temperatures and pressures are useful in many industrial processes, extremophiles are of commercial interest as well. Recall that *Taq* polymerase—a DNA polymerase that is stable up to 95°C—is used to run the polymerase chain reaction (PCR) in research and commercial settings (see Chapter 20). This enzyme was isolated from a bacterium called *Thermus aquaticus* ("hot water"), which was discovered in a hot spring in Yellowstone National Park.

Bacteria and archaea may be small, but they thrive in an amazing range of conditions.

## Medical Importance

The first paper documenting that an archaeon was associated with a human disease—a dental condition called periodontitis—was published in 2004. But biologists have been studying disease-causing bacteria for over a century.

Of the thousands of bacterial species living in and on your body, only a tiny fraction can disrupt normal body functions enough to cause illness. Bacteria that cause disease are said to be **pathogenic** (literally, "disease-producing"). Pathogenic bacteria have been responsible for some of the most devastating epidemics in human history.

**TABLE 29.2** lists some of the bacteria that cause illness in humans. Here are the important things to note:

- Pathogenic forms come from several different lineages in the domain Bacteria.

**TABLE 29.2 Some Bacteria That Cause Illness in Humans**

| Lineage | Species | Tissues Affected | Disease |
|---------|---------|------------------|---------|
| Firmicutes | *Clostridium tetani* | Wounds, nervous system | Tetanus |
| | *Staphylococcus aureus* | Skin, urogenital canal | Acne, boils, impetigo, toxic shock syndrome |
| | *Streptococcus pneumoniae* | Respiratory tract | Pneumonia |
| | *Streptococcus pyogenes* | Respiratory tract | Strep throat, scarlet fever |
| Spirochaetes | *Borrelia burgdorferi* | Skin and nerves | Lyme disease |
| | *Treponema pallidum* | Urogenital canal | Syphilis |
| Actinobacteria | *Mycobacterium tuberculosis* | Respiratory tract | Tuberculosis |
| | *Mycobacterium leprae* | Skin and nerves | Leprosy |
| | *Propionibacterium acnes* | Skin | Acne |
| Chlamydiales | *Chlamydia trachomatis* | Urogenital canal | Genital tract infection |
| ε-Proteobacteria | *Helicobacter pylori* | Stomach | Ulcer |
| β-Proteobacteria | *Neisseria gonorrhoeae* | Urogenital canal | Gonorrhea |
| γ-Proteobacteria | *Haemophilus influenzae* | Ear canal, nervous system | Ear infections, meningitis |
| | *Pseudomonas aeruginosa* | Urogenital canal, eyes, ear canal, lungs | Infections of eye, ear, urinary tract, lungs |
| | *Salmonella enterica* | Gastrointestinal tract | Food poisoning |
| | *Yersinia pestis* | Lymph and blood | Plague |

Pathogenic bacteria tend to affect tissues at the entry points to the body, such as wounds or pores in the skin, the respiratory and gastrointestinal tracts, and the urogenital canal.

**Koch's Postulates**    Robert Koch was the first person to establish a link between a particular species of bacterium and a specific disease. When Koch began his work on the nature of disease in the late 1800s, microscopists had confirmed the existence of the particle-like organisms people now call bacteria, and Louis Pasteur had shown that bacteria and other microorganisms are responsible for spoiling milk, wine, broth, and other foods. Koch hypothesized that bacteria might also be responsible for causing infectious diseases, which spread by being passed from an infected individual to an uninfected individual.

Koch set out to test this hypothesis by identifying the organism that causes anthrax. Anthrax is a disease of cattle and other grazing mammals that can result in fatal blood poisoning. The disease also occurs infrequently in humans and mice.

To establish a causative link between a specific microbe and a specific disease, Koch proposed that four criteria had to be met:

1. The microbe must be present in individuals suffering from the disease and absent from healthy individuals. By careful microscopy, Koch was able to show that the bacterium *Bacillus anthracis* was always present in the blood of cattle suffering from anthrax, but absent from healthy individuals.

2. The organism must be isolated and grown in a pure culture away from the host organism. Koch was able to grow pure colonies of *B. anthracis* in glass dishes on a nutrient medium, using gelatin as a substrate.

3. If organisms from the pure culture are injected into a healthy experimental animal, the disease symptoms should appear. Koch demonstrated this crucial causative link in mice injected with *B. anthracis*. The symptoms of anthrax infection appeared and then the infected mice died.

4. The organism should be isolated from the diseased experimental animal, again grown in pure culture, and demonstrated by its size, shape, and color to be the same as the original organism. Koch did this by purifying *B. anthracis* from the blood of diseased experimental mice.

These criteria, now called **Koch's postulates,** are still used to confirm a causative link between new diseases and a suspected infectious agent. Microbiologists now recognize that many bacteria cannot be grown in culture, so they use other means of detection for those organisms.

**The Germ Theory**    Koch's experimental results were the first test of the **germ theory of disease.**

- The pattern component of this theory is that certain diseases are infectious—meaning that they can be passed from person to person.

- The process responsible for this pattern is the transmission and growth of certain bacteria and viruses.

Viruses are acellular particles that parasitize cells (see Chapter 36).

The germ theory of disease laid the foundation for modern medicine. Initially its greatest impact was on sanitation—efforts to prevent transmission of pathogenic bacteria. During the American Civil War, for example, records indicate that more soldiers died of bacterial infections contracted from drinking water contaminated with human feces than from wounds in battle. Also during that conflict it was common for surgeons to sharpen their scalpels on their shoe leather, after walking in horse manure.

Fortunately, improvements in sanitation and nutrition have caused dramatic reductions in mortality rates due to infectious diseases in the industrialized countries.

**What Makes Some Bacterial Cells Pathogenic?**    Virulence, or the ability to cause disease, is a heritable trait that varies among individuals in a population. Most *Escherichia coli*, for example, are harmless inhabitants of the gastrointestinal tract of humans and other mammals. But some *E. coli* cells cause potentially fatal food poisoning.

What makes some cells of the same species pathogenic, while others are harmless? Biologists have answered this question for *E. coli* by sequencing the entire genome of a harmless lab strain and the pathogenic strain called O157:H7, which is harmful to humans. The genome of the pathogenic strain is slightly larger because it has acquired virulence genes, including one coding for a protein **toxin.** After entering a host cell, this toxin binds to ribosomes and inhibits protein synthesis, killing the host cells. Because of key differences between the ribosomes of bacteria and eukaryotic cells, only host-cell protein synthesis is blocked by the toxin. Cells lining the blood vessels near the host's intestinal epithelium are most affected by the toxin, and the resulting damage leads to bloody diarrhea and possible death. If sanitation is poor, the pathogenic bacteria are likely to infect many new hosts.

Similar types of studies are identifying the genes responsible for virulence in a wide array of pathogenic bacteria.

**The Past, Present, and Future of Antibiotics**    **Antibiotics** are molecules that kill bacteria or stop them from growing. They are produced naturally by a wide array of soil-dwelling bacteria and fungi. In these environments, antibiotics are hypothesized to help cells reduce competition for nutrients and other resources.

The discovery of antibiotics in 1928, their development over subsequent decades, and widespread use starting in the late 1940s gave physicians effective tools to combat many bacterial infections.

Unfortunately, extensive use of antibiotics in the late twentieth century in clinics and animal feed led to the evolution of drug-resistant strains of pathogenic bacteria (see Chapter 25). One study found that there are now soil-dwelling bacteria in natural environments that—far from being killed by antibiotics—actually use them as food.

Coping with antibiotic resistance in pathogenic bacteria has become a great challenge of modern medicine. Some researchers even claim that humans may be entering the "post-antibiotic era" in medicine.

New research indicates that bacteria have another advantage: They usually grow as **biofilms,** dense bacterial colonies enmeshed

Bacterial cells (round)    Polysaccharide biofilm

5 µm

**FIGURE 29.3 Biofilm Growing Inside a Catheter.** This micrograph shows *Staphylococcus aureus* cells growing inside a catheter—a tube inserted into a body so that fluids can be withdrawn or injected. Bacterial communities that secrete polysaccharides and adhere to surfaces are sometimes more resistant to antibiotics.

**FIGURE 29.4 Bacteria and Archaea Can Play a Role in Cleaning Up Pollution.** These clean-up workers are spraying nitrogenous nutrients to encourage bacterial and archaeal growth following the 1989 *Exxon Valdez* oil spill in Alaska.

in a polysaccharide-rich matrix that helps shield the bacteria from antibiotics. Antibiotic-resistant biofilms on medical devices such as catheters are a growing problem in hospitals (**FIGURE 29.3**).

## Role in Bioremediation

Bacteria are often in the news because of their dire medical effects. However, only a tiny proportion of bacteria and archaea actually cause disease in humans or other organisms. In the vast majority of cases, bacteria and archaea either have no direct impact on humans or are beneficial. For example, microbes play an important role in wastewater treatment efforts, and researchers are using bacteria and archaea to clean up sites polluted with organic solvents—an effort called **bioremediation.**

Throughout the industrialized world, some of the most serious pollutants in soils, rivers, and ponds consist of organic compounds that were originally used as solvents or fuels but leaked or were spilled into the environment. Most of these compounds are highly hydrophobic. Because they do not dissolve in water, they tend to accumulate in sediments. If the compounds are subsequently ingested by burrowing worms or clams or other organisms, they can be passed along to fish, insects, humans, birds, and other species.

At moderate to high concentrations, these pollutants are toxic to eukaryotes. Petroleum from oil spills and compounds that contain ring structures and chlorine atoms, such as the family of compounds called dioxins, are particularly notorious because of their toxicity to humans.

Fortunately, naturally existing populations of bacteria and archaea can grow in spills and degrade the toxins. This growth can be enhanced using two complementary bioremediation strategies:

1. *Fertilizing contaminated sites to encourage the growth of existing bacteria and archaea that degrade toxic compounds.* After several oil spills, researchers added nitrogen to affected sites as a fertilizer (**FIGURE 29.4**). Dramatic increases

occurred in the growth of bacteria and archaea that use hydrocarbons in cellular respiration, probably because the cells used the added nitrogen to synthesize enzymes and other key compounds. In at least some cases, the fertilized shorelines cleaned up much faster than unfertilized sites.

2. *"Seeding," or adding, specific species of bacteria and archaea to contaminated sites.* Seeding shows promise of alleviating pollution in some situations. For example, researchers have recently discovered bacteria that are able to render certain chlorinated, ring-containing compounds harmless. Instead of being poisoned by the pollutants, these bacteria use the chlorinated compounds as electron acceptors during cellular respiration. In at least some cases, the byproduct is dechlorinated and nontoxic to humans and other eukaryotes.

To follow up on these discoveries, researchers are now growing the bacteria in quantity, to test the hypothesis that seeding can speed the rate of decomposition in contaminated sediments. Initial reports suggest that seeding may help clean up at least some polluted sites.

## 29.2 How Do Biologists Study Bacteria and Archaea?

Biologists' understanding of the domains Bacteria and Archaea is advancing more rapidly right now than at any time during the past 100 years—and perhaps faster than our understanding of any other lineages on the tree of life.

As an introduction to the domains Bacteria and Archaea, let's examine a few of the techniques that biologists use to answer questions about them. Some of these research strategies have been used since bacteria were first discovered; some were invented less than 10 years ago.

## Using Enrichment Cultures

Which species of bacteria and archaea are present at a particular location, and what do they use as food? To answer questions like these, biologists rely heavily on their ability to culture organisms in the lab. Of the 5000 species of bacteria and archaea described to date, almost all were discovered when they were isolated from natural habitats and grown under controlled conditions in the laboratory.

One classical technique for isolating new types of bacteria and archaea is called **enrichment culture.** Enrichment cultures are based on establishing a specified set of growing conditions—temperature, lighting, substrate, types of available food, and so on. Cells that thrive under the specified conditions increase in numbers enough to be isolated and studied in detail.

To appreciate how this strategy works in practice, consider research on bacteria that live deep below Earth's surface. One study began with samples of rock and fluid from drilling operations in Virginia and Colorado. The samples came from sedimentary rocks at depths ranging from 860 to 2800 meters below the surface, where temperatures are between 42°C and 85°C. The questions posed in the study were simple: Is anything alive down there? If so, what do the organisms use to fuel cellular respiration?

The research team hypothesized that if organisms were living deep below the surface of the Earth, the cells might use hydrogen molecules ($H_2$) as an electron donor and the ferric ion ($Fe^{3+}$) as an electron acceptor (**FIGURE 29.5**). Recall that most eukaryotes use sugars as electron donors and use oxygen as an electron acceptor during cellular respiration (see Chapter 9). $Fe^{3+}$ is the oxidized form of iron, and it is abundant in the rocks the biologists collected from great depths. It exists at great depths below the surface in the form of ferric oxyhydroxide, $Fe(OH)_3$. The researchers predicted that if an organism in the samples reduced the ferric ions during cellular respiration, then a black, oxidized, and magnetic mineral called magnetite ($Fe_3O_4$) would start appearing in the cultures as a by-product of cellular respiration.

What did their enrichment cultures produce? In some cultures, a black compound began to appear within a week. A variety of tests confirmed that the black substance was indeed magnetite. As the "Results" section of Figure 29.5 shows, microscopy revealed the organisms themselves—previously undiscovered bacteria. Because they grow only when incubated at 45°C–75°C, these organisms are considered **thermophiles** ("heat-lovers"). The discovery was spectacular—it was one of the first studies demonstrating that Earth's crust is teeming with organisms to depths of over a mile below the surface. Enrichment culture continues to be a productive way to isolate and characterize new species of bacteria and archaea.

## Using Metagenomics

Researchers estimate that of all the bacteria and archaea living today, less than 1 percent have been grown in culture. To augment research based on enrichment cultures, researchers are

---

**RESEARCH**

**QUESTION:** Can bacteria live a mile below Earth's surface?

**HYPOTHESIS:** Bacteria are capable of cellular respiration deep below Earth's surface by using $H_2$ as an electron donor and $Fe^{3+}$ as an electron acceptor.

**NULL HYPOTHESIS:** Bacteria from this environment are not capable of using $H_2$ as an electron donor and $Fe^{3+}$ as an electron acceptor.

**EXPERIMENTAL SETUP:**

Heat

Rock and fluid samples

**1.** Prepare enrichment culture abundant in $H_2$ and $Fe^{3+}$; raise temperatures above 45°C.

**2.** Add rock and fluid samples extracted from drilling operations at depths of about 1000 m below Earth's surface.

**PREDICTION:** Black, magnetic grains of magnetite ($Fe_3O_4$) will accumulate because $Fe^{3+}$ is reduced by growing cells and shed as a waste product. Cells will be visible.

**PREDICTION OF NULL HYPOTHESIS:** No magnetite will appear. No cells will grow.

**RESULTS:** Cells are visible, and magnetite is detectable.

1 μm

**CONCLUSION:** At least one bacterial species that can live deep below Earth's surface grew in this enrichment culture. Different culture conditions might result in the enrichment of different species present in the same sample.

**FIGURE 29.5 Enrichment Cultures Isolate Large Populations of Cells That Grow under Specific Conditions.**

✓**QUESTION** Suppose no organisms had grown in this culture. Explain why the lack of growth would be either strong or weak evidence on the question of whether organisms live a mile below the Earth's surface.

SOURCE: Liu, S. V., J. Zhou, C. Zhang, et al. 1997. Thermophilic Fe(III)-reducing bacteria from the deep subsurface: the evolutionary implications. *Science* 277: 1106–1109.

## PROCESS: METAGENOMIC ANALYSIS

**1. Collect samples** from an environment containing organisms and extract DNA.

TCCCGAT...
CGGATAG...
GTTATTTA...
GCAAATA...
GTTCTCA...

**2. Generate small DNA fragments** and sequence as many as possible.

```
AACTCG
AACTCGTTT
AACTCGTTTAGATTC
AACTCGTTTAGATTCC
AACTCGTTTAGATTCCGTGAT
   TCGTTTAGATTCCGTGATAG
      TAGATTCCGTGATAG
         ATTCCGTGATAG
```

**3. Assemble overlapping DNA sequences** into longer regions that contain genes. Compare these sequences with those of known genes.

**FIGURE 29.6 Metagenomics Allows Researchers to Identify Species That Have Never Been Seen.** Metagenomic analysis is used to generate DNA sequences from an environmental sample. That information can then be used to identify novel species and investigate biological processes.

employing a technique called **metagenomics** or **environmental sequencing** (see Chapter 21). Metagenomics is employed in part to document the presence of bacteria and archaea in an environmental sample that cannot be grown in culture. It is based on extracting and sequencing much of the DNA from a sample and then identifying species and biochemical pathways by comparing the DNA sequences with those of known genes. **FIGURE 29.6** outlines the steps performed in a metagenomics study.

Metagenomic analysis allows biologists to rapidly identify and characterize organisms that have never been seen. The technique has revealed huge new branches on the tree of life and produced revolutionary data on the habitats where bacteria and archaea are found.

In one recent study biologists extracted DNA from 125 human fecal samples and generated over 500 billion base pairs of sequence, over 150 times more than the entire human genome. The results they obtained are fascinating:

- In total, the samples contained about 1000 different species of bacteria. Some species were found in most of the samples while others were found in only a few of the humans sampled;

- the vast majority of bacterial species identified were from three phyla: Bacteroidetes, Firmicutes, and Actinobacteria;

- the identified bacterial genes that were shared by all of the human subjects suggest that bacteria play important roles in human physiology, including digestion of complex carbohydrates and synthesis of essential amino acids and vitamins.

Results like these make it clear that humans harbor a diverse ecosystem of symbiotic bacteria. Some bacteria may make us sick, but we depend on many others to stay healthy.

In combination with **direct sequencing**—a technique based on isolating and sequencing a specific gene from organisms found in a particular habitat—metagenomics is revolutionizing biologists' understanding of bacterial and archaeal diversity.

## Evaluating Molecular Phylogenies

To put data from enrichment culture and metagenomic studies into context, biologists depend on the accurate placement of species on phylogenetic trees. Recall that phylogenetic trees illustrate the evolutionary relationships among species and lineages (see Chapter 1, Chapter 28, and **BioSkills 7** in Appendix B). They are a pictorial summary of which species are more closely or distantly related to others.

Some of the most useful phylogenetic trees for the Bacteria and the Archaea have been based on studies of the RNA molecules found in the small subunit of ribosomes, or what biologists call 16S and 18S RNA. (See Chapter 17 for more information on the structure and function of ribosomes.) In the late 1960s Carl Woese and colleagues began a massive effort to determine and compare the base sequences of 16S and 18S RNA molecules from a wide array of species. The result of their analysis was the **tree of life,** illustrated in Figure 29.1.

check your understanding

**If you understand that . . .**

- Enrichment cultures isolate cells that grow in response to specific conditions. They create an abundant sample of bacteria that thrive under particular conditions, allowing further study.
- Metagenomics is based on isolating DNA from samples taken directly from the environment, generating random DNA fragments for sequencing, and then analyzing the DNA sequences to identify the organisms and genes present.

✔ **You should be able to . . .**

1. Design an enrichment culture that would isolate species that could be used to clean up oil spills.
2. Outline a study designed to identify the bacterial and archaeal species present in a soil sample near the biology building on your campus.

*Answers are available in Appendix A.*

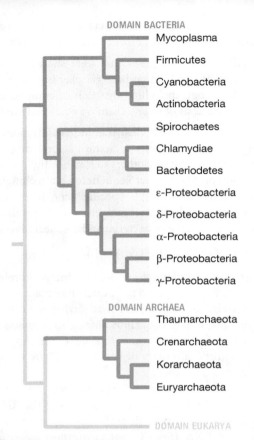

DOMAIN BACTERIA
- Mycoplasma
- Firmicutes
- Cyanobacteria
- Actinobacteria
- Spirochaetes
- Chlamydiae
- Bacteriodetes
- ε-Proteobacteria
- δ-Proteobacteria
- α-Proteobacteria
- β-Proteobacteria
- γ-Proteobacteria

DOMAIN ARCHAEA
- Thaumarchaeota
- Crenarchaeota
- Korarchaeota
- Euryarchaeota

DOMAIN EUKARYA

**FIGURE 29.7 Phylogeny of Some Major Lineages in Bacteria and Archaea.**

Woese's tree is now considered a classic result. Before its publication, biologists thought that the major division among organisms was between prokaryotes and eukaryotes. But based on data from ribosomal RNA molecules, the major divisions of life-forms are actually the Bacteria, Archaea, and Eukarya. Tracing the early evolutionary history of these domains is extremely difficult since the events distinguishing the lineages took place so long ago. In addition, lateral gene transfer (described in Chapter 21) has blurred the boundaries of the domains. However, recent studies suggest that Eukarya may have formed from a symbiosis between an archaeal cell and a bacterial cell. Traits of both lineages are found within Eukarya (see Chapter 30).

More recent analyses of morphological and molecular characteristics have succeeded in identifying a large series of monophyletic groups within the domains. Recall that a **monophyletic group** consists of an ancestral population and all of its descendants (see Chapter 28). Monophyletic groups can also be called clades or lineages.

The phylogenetic tree in **FIGURE 29.7** summarizes recent results but is still considered highly provisional. Work on molecular phylogenies continues at a brisk pace. Section 29.4 explores some of these lineages in detail, but for now let's turn to the question of how all this diversification took place.

## 29.3 What Themes Occur in the Diversification of Bacteria and Archaea?

At first, the diversity of bacteria and archaea can seem almost overwhelming. To make sense of the variation among lineages and species, biologists focus on two themes in diversification: morphology and metabolism. Regarding metabolism, the key question is which molecules are used as food. Bacteria and archaea are capable of living in a wide array of environments because they vary in cell structure and in how they make a living.

### Morphological Diversity

Because we humans are so large, it is hard for us to appreciate the morphological diversity that exists among bacteria and archaea. To us, they all look small and similar. But at the scale of a bacterium or archaean, different species are wildly diverse in morphology.

**Size, Shape, and Motility**  To appreciate how diverse these organisms are in terms of morphology, consider bacteria alone:

- *Size*  Bacterial cells range in size from the smallest of all free-living cells—bacteria called mycoplasmas with volumes as small as $0.15 \ \mu m^3$—to the largest bacterium known, *Thiomargarita namibiensis*, which has volumes as large as $200 \times 10^6 \ \mu m^3$. Over a billion *Mycoplasma* cells could fit inside an individual *T. namibiensis* (**FIGURE 29.8a**).

- *Shape*  Bacterial cells range in shape from filaments, spheres, rods, and chains to spirals (**FIGURE 29.8b**).

- *Motility*  Many bacterial cells are motile; their swimming movements are powered by rotating flagella. Depending on the direction of rotation, cells either swim ahead or tumble, which allows them to change direction. Gliding movement, which enables cells to creep along a surface, also occurs in several groups, though the molecular mechanism responsible for this form of motility is still unknown (**FIGURE 29.8c**).

**Cell-Wall Composition**  For single-celled organisms, the composition of the plasma membrane and cell wall are particularly important. The introduction to this chapter highlights the dramatic differences between the plasma membranes and cell walls of bacteria versus archaea.

Within bacteria having cell walls, biologists distinguish two general types of wall using a dyeing system called the **Gram stain**. As **FIGURE 29.9a** shows, Gram-positive cells look purple but Gram-negative cells look pink.

At the molecular level, most cells that are **Gram-positive** have a plasma membrane surrounded by a cell wall with extensive peptidoglycan (**FIGURE 29.9b**). You might recall that peptidoglycan is a complex substance composed of carbohydrate strands that are cross-linked by short chains of amino acids (see Chapter 5). Most cells that are **Gram-negative**, in contrast, have a plasma

**(a) Size varies.**

Most bacteria are about 1 μm in diameter, but some are much larger.

Smallest (*Mycoplasma mycoides*)

0.3 μm

Compare sizes

100 μm

Largest (*Thiomargarita namibiensis*)

**(b) Shape varies...**

... from rods to spheres to spirals. In some species, cells adhere to form chains.

Rods, chains of spheres (compost bacteria)

Spirals (*Campylobacter jejuni*)

**(c) Motility varies.**

Some bacteria are nonmotile, but swimming and gliding are common.

Swimming (*Pseudomonas aeruginosa*)

Gliding (*Oscillatoria limosa*)

**FIGURE 29.8 Morphological Diversity among Bacteria Is Extensive.** Some of the cells in these micrographs have been colorized to make them more visible.

membrane surrounded by a cell wall that has two components—a thin gelatinous layer containing peptidoglycan and an outer phospholipid bilayer (**FIGURE 29.9c**).

Analyzing cell cultures with the Gram stain can be an important preliminary step in treating bacterial infections. Because they contain so much peptidoglycan, Gram-positive cells may respond to treatment by penicillin-like drugs that disrupt peptidoglycan synthesis. Gram-negative cells, in contrast, are more

likely to be affected by erythromycin or other types of drugs that poison bacterial ribosomes.

To summarize, members of the Bacteria and the Archaea are remarkably diverse in their overall size, shape, and motility as well as in the composition of their cell walls and plasma membranes. But when asked to name the innovations that were most responsible for the diversification of these two domains, biologists do not point to their morphological diversity. Instead, they

**(a)** Gram-positive cells stain more than Gram-negative cells.

Gram-positive    Gram-negative

**(b)** Gram-positive cell wall

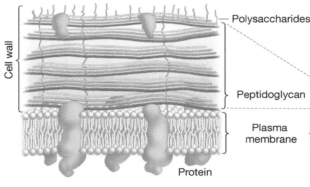

Cell wall

Polysaccharides

Peptidoglycan

Plasma membrane

Protein

**(c)** Gram-negative cell wall

Outer membrane

Cell wall

Protein

**FIGURE 29.9 Gram Staining Distinguishes Two Types of Cell Walls in Bacteria.** Cells with extensive peptidoglycan retain a large amount of stain and look purple; others retain little stain and look pink, as can be seen in part (a).

point to metabolic diversity—variation in the chemical reactions that go on inside these cells.

## Metabolic Diversity

The most important thing to remember about bacteria and archaea is how diverse they are in the types of compounds they can use as food. Bacteria and archaea are the masters of metabolism. Taken together, they can subsist on almost anything—from hydrogen molecules to crude oil. Bacteria and archaea look small and relatively simple to us in their morphology, but their biochemical capabilities are dazzling.

Just how varied are bacteria and archaea when it comes to making a living? To appreciate the answer, recall that all organisms have two fundamental nutritional needs—acquiring chemical energy in the form of adenosine triphosphate (ATP) and obtaining molecules with carbon–carbon bonds that can be used as building blocks for the synthesis of fatty acids, proteins, DNA, RNA, and other large, complex compounds required by the cell.

Bacteria and archaea produce ATP in three ways:

1. **Phototrophs** ("light-feeders") use light energy to excite electrons. ATP is produced by photophosphorylation (see Chapter 10).

2. **Chemoorganotrophs** oxidize organic molecules with high potential energy, such as sugars. ATP may be produced by cellular respiration—with sugars serving as electron donors—or via fermentation pathways (see Chapter 9).

3. **Chemolithotrophs** ("rock-feeders") oxidize inorganic molecules with high potential energy, such as ammonia ($NH_3$) or methane ($CH_4$). ATP is produced by cellular respiration, and inorganic compounds serve as the electron donor.

Bacteria and archaea fulfill their second nutritional need—obtaining building-block compounds with carbon–carbon bonds—in two ways:

1. By synthesizing their own compounds from simple starting materials such as $CO_2$ and $CH_4$. Organisms that manufacture their own building-block compounds are termed **autotrophs** ("self-feeders").

2. By absorbing ready-to-use organic compounds from their environment. Organisms that acquire building-block compounds from other organisms are called **heterotrophs** ("other-feeders").

Because there are three distinct ways of producing ATP and two general mechanisms for obtaining carbon, there are a total of six methods for producing ATP and obtaining carbon. The names that biologists use for organisms that employ these six "feeding strategies" are given in **TABLE 29.3**.

Of the six possible ways of producing ATP and obtaining carbon, just two are observed among eukaryotes. But bacteria and archaea do them all. In addition, certain species can switch among modes of living, depending on environmental conditions. In their metabolism, eukaryotes are simple compared with bacteria and archaea. ✔ If you understand the essence of metabolic diversity in bacteria and archaea, you should be able to match the six example species described in **TABLE 29.4** to the appropriate category in Table 29.3.

What makes this remarkable diversity possible? Bacteria and archaea have evolved dozens of variations on the basic processes of respiration and photosynthesis (see Chapters 9 and 10). They use compounds with high potential energy to produce ATP via cellular respiration (electron transport chains) or fermentation, they use light to produce high-energy electrons, and they reduce carbon from $CO_2$ or other sources to produce sugars or other building-block molecules with carbon–carbon bonds.

The story of bacteria and archaea can be boiled down to two sentences: The basic chemistry required for photosynthesis, cellular respiration, and fermentation originated in these lineages. Then the evolution of variations on each of these processes allowed prokaryotes to diversify into millions of species that occupy diverse habitats. Let's take a closer look.

**Producing ATP Through Cellular Respiration: Variation in Electron Donors and Acceptors** Millions of bacterial, archaeal, and eukaryotic species—including animals and some plants—are chemoorganotrophs. These organisms obtain the energy required to make ATP by breaking down organic compounds such as sugars, starch, or fatty acids.

**SUMMARY TABLE 29.3  Six General Methods for Obtaining Energy and Carbon–Carbon Bonds**

| | Source of C–C Bonds (for synthesis of complex organic compounds) | |
|---|---|---|
| | **Auto**trophs: self-synthesized from $CO_2$, $CH_4$, or other simple molecules | **Hetero**trophs: from molecules produced by other organisms |
| **Photo**trophs: from sunlight | photoautotrophs | photoheterotrophs |
| **Chemoorgano**trophs: from organic molecules | chemoorganoautotrophs | chemoorganoheterotrophs |
| **Chemolitho**trophs: from inorganic molecules | chemolitho[auto]trophs | chemolithotrophic heterotrophs |

Source of Energy (for synthesis of ATP)

**TABLE 29.4  Six Examples of Metabolic Diversity**

| Example | How ATP Is Produced | How Building-Block Molecules Are Synthesized |
|---|---|---|
| Cyanobacteria | via oxygenic photosynthesis | from $CO_2$ via the Calvin cycle |
| *Clostridium aceticum* | via fermentation of glucose | from $CO_2$ via reactions called the acetyl-CoA pathway |
| Ammonia-oxidizing archaea (e.g., *Nitrosopumilus* sp.) | via cellular respiration, using ammonia ($NH_3$) as an electron donor | from $CO_2$ via the Calvin cycle |
| Helicobacteria | via anoxygenic photosynthesis | absorb carbon-containing building-block molecules from the environment |
| *Escherichia coli* | via fermentation of organic compounds or cellular respiration, using organic compounds as electron donors | absorb carbon-containing building-block molecules from the environment |
| *Beggiatoa* | via cellular respiration, using hydrogen sulfide ($H_2S$) as an electron donor | absorb carbon-containing building-block molecules from the environment |

Cellular enzymes can strip electrons from organic molecules that have high potential energy and then transfer these high-energy electrons to the electron carriers NADH and $FADH_2$ (see Chapter 9). These compounds feed electrons to an electron transport chain (ETC), where electrons are stepped down from a high-energy state to a low-energy state (**FIGURE 29.10a**). In eukaryotic cells the ETC is located in the highly folded inner mitochondrial membrane. In bacteria and archaea, this membrane is the plasma membrane.

The energy that is released allows components of the ETC to generate a proton gradient across the plasma membrane (**FIGURE 29.10b**). The resulting flow of protons back through the enzyme ATP synthase results in the production of ATP, via the process called chemiosmosis.

The essence of this process, called **cellular respiration,** is that a molecule with high potential energy serves as an original electron donor and is oxidized, while a molecule with low potential energy serves as a final electron acceptor and becomes reduced. The potential energy difference between the electron donor and electron acceptor is eventually transformed into chemical energy in the form of ATP or is used for other processes (see Chapter 9).

**(a)** Model of Electron Transport Chain (ETC)

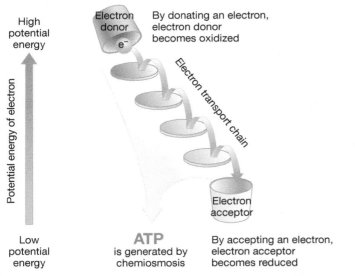

**(b)** ETC generates proton gradient across plasma membrane.

**FIGURE 29.10  Cellular Respiration Is Based on Electron Transport Chains.** Protons may diffuse away from the cell but a gradient will still form.

✔**EXERCISE** In part (a), add the chemical formula for a specific electron donor, electron acceptor, and reduced by-product for a species of bacteria or archaea. Then write in the electron donor, electron acceptor, and reduced by-product observed in humans.

Most eukaryotes carry out aerobic respiration:

- Organic compounds with high potential energy—often glucose—serve as the original electron donor. When cellular respiration is complete, glucose is completely oxidized to $CO_2$, which is given off as a by-product.

- Oxygen is the final electron acceptor, and water is also produced as a by-product.

Many bacteria and archaea also rely on these molecules.

It is common, however, to find bacteria and archaea that employ an electron donor other than sugars and an electron acceptor other than oxygen during cellular respiration. These species produce by-products other than carbon dioxide and water (TABLE 29.5):

- Molecules with high potential energy serve as electron donors. The substances used as electron donors range from hydrogen molecules ($H_2$) and hydrogen sulfide ($H_2S$) to ammonia ($NH_3$) and methane ($CH_4$).

- Compounds with relatively low potential energy—including sulfate ($SO_4^{2-}$), nitrate ($NO_3^-$), carbon dioxide ($CO_2$), or ferric ions ($Fe^{3+}$)—act as electron acceptors.

It is only a slight exaggeration to claim that researchers have found bacterial and archaeal species that can use almost any compound with relatively high potential energy as an electron donor and almost any compound with relatively low potential energy as an electron acceptor.

Because the electron donors and electron acceptors used by bacteria and archaea are so diverse, one of the first questions biologists ask about a species is whether it undergoes cellular respiration—and if so, how. The best way to answer this question is through the enrichment culture technique introduced in Section 29.2. Recall that in an enrichment culture, researchers supply specific electron donors and electron acceptors in the medium and try to isolate cells that can use those compounds to support growth.

The remarkable metabolic diversity of bacteria and archaea explains why they play such a key role in cleaning up some types of pollution. Species that use organic solvents or petroleum-based fuels as electron donors or electron acceptors may excrete waste products that are less toxic than the original compounds.

Producing ATP via Fermentation: Variation in Substrates One strategy for making ATP that does not involve electron transport chains is called **fermentation** (see Chapter 9). In fermentation, no outside electron acceptor is used.

Because fermentation is a much less efficient way to make ATP compared with cellular respiration, in many species it occurs as an alternative metabolic strategy when no electron acceptors are available to make cellular respiration possible. In other species, fermentation does not occur at all. But in many bacteria and archaea, fermentation is the only way that cells make ATP.

Although some eukaryotic organisms can ferment glucose to ethanol or lactic acid (see Chapter 9), some bacteria and archaea are capable of using other organic compounds as the starting point for fermentation. Bacteria and archaea that produce ATP via fermentation are still classified as organotrophs, but they are much more diverse in the substrates used. For example:

- The bacterium *Clostridium aceticum* can ferment ethanol, acetate, and fatty acids as well as glucose.

- Other species of *Clostridium* ferment complex carbohydrates (including cellulose or starch), proteins, purines, or amino acids. Species that ferment amino acids produce by-products with names such as cadaverine and putrescine. These molecules are responsible for the odor of rotting flesh.

- Other bacteria can ferment lactose, a prominent component of milk. In some species this fermentation has two end products: propionic acid and $CO_2$. Propionic acid is responsible for the taste of Swiss cheese; the $CO_2$ produced during fermentation creates the holes in cheese.

- Many bacterial species in the human digestive tract ferment complex carbohydrates in our diet. The human cells then absorb the by-products and extract even more energy from them using $O_2$ as the final electron acceptor.

The diversity of enzymatic pathways observed in bacterial and archaeal fermentations extends the metabolic repertoire of these organisms. The diversity of substrates that are fermented also

**TABLE 29.5 Some Electron Donors and Acceptors Used by Bacteria and Archaea**

| Electron Donor | By-Product from Electron Donor | Electron Acceptor | By-Product from Electron Acceptor | Category* |
|---|---|---|---|---|
| Sugars | $CO_2$ | $O_2$ | $H_2O$ | Organotrophs |
| $H_2$ or organic compounds | $H_2O$ or CO | $SO_4^{2-}$ | $H_2S$ or $S^{2-}$ | Sulfate reducers |
| $H_2$ | $H_2O$ | $CO_2$ | $CH_4$ | Methanogens |
| $CH_4$ | $CO_2$ | $O_2$ | $H_2O$ | Methanotrophs |
| $H_2S$ or $S^{2-}$ | $SO_4^{2-}$ | $O_2$ | $H_2O$ | Sulfur bacteria |
| Organic compounds | $CO_2$ | $Fe^{3+}$ | $Fe^{2+}$ | Iron reducers |
| $NH_3$ | $NO_2^-$ | $O_2$ | $H_2O$ | Ammonia oxidizers |
| Organic compounds | $CO_2$ | $NO_3^-$ | $N_2O$, NO, or $N_2$ | Nitrate reducers |

*The name biologists use to identify species that use a particular metabolic strategy.

supports the claim that as a group, bacteria and archaea can use virtually any molecule with relatively high potential energy as a source of high-energy electrons for producing ATP.

**Producing ATP via Photosynthesis: Variation in Electron Sources and Pigments** Instead of using molecules as a source of high-energy electrons, phototrophs pursue a radically different strategy: **photosynthesis.** Among bacteria and archaea, photosynthesis can happen in three different ways:

1. Light activates a pigment called bacteriorhodopsin, which uses the absorbed energy to transport protons across the plasma membrane and out of the cell. The resulting flow of protons back into the cell drives the synthesis of ATP via chemiosmosis (see Chapter 9).

2. A recently discovered bacterium that lives near hydrothermal vents on the ocean floor performs photosynthesis not by absorbing light, but by absorbing geothermal radiation.

3. Pigments that absorb light raise electrons to high-energy states. As these electrons are stepped down to lower energy states by electron transport chains, the energy released is used to generate ATP.

An important feature of this last mode of photosynthesis is that the process requires a source of electrons (see Chapter 10). Recall that in cyanobacteria and plants, the required electrons come from water. When these organisms "split" water molecules apart to obtain electrons, they generate oxygen as a by-product. Species that use water as a source of electrons for photosynthesis are said to complete **oxygenic** ("oxygen-producing") photosynthesis.

In contrast, many phototrophic bacteria use a molecule other than water as the source of electrons. In some cases, the electron donor is hydrogen sulfide ($H_2S$); a few species can use the ion known as ferrous iron ($Fe^{2+}$). Instead of producing oxygen as a by-product of photosynthesis, these cells produce elemental sulfur (S) or the ferric ion ($Fe^{3+}$). This type of photosynthesis is said to be **anoxygenic** ("no oxygen-producing").

The photosynthetic pigments found in plants are chlorophylls *a* and *b* (see Chapter 10). Cyanobacteria have these two pigments. But researchers have isolated seven additional chlorophylls from different lineages of bacterial phototrophs. Each lineage has one or more of these distinctive chlorophylls, and each type of chlorophyll absorbs light best at a different wavelength.
✔ If you understand that different photosynthetic bacteria contain different kinds of light-absorbing pigments, you should be able to explain how several different photosynthetic species can live in the same habitat without competing for light.

**Obtaining Building-Block Compounds: Variation in Pathways for Fixing Carbon** In addition to acquiring energy, organisms must obtain building-block molecules that contain carbon–carbon bonds. Organisms use two mechanisms to procure usable carbon—either making their own or getting it from other organisms (see Chapters 9 and 10). Autotrophs make their own building-block compounds; heterotrophs consume them.

In many autotrophs, including cyanobacteria and plants, the enzymes of the Calvin cycle transform carbon dioxide ($CO_2$) into organic molecules that can be used in synthesizing cell material. The carbon atom in $CO_2$ is reduced during the process and is said to be "fixed." Animals and fungi, in contrast, obtain carbon from living plants or animals, or by absorbing the organic compounds released as dead tissues decay.

Bacteria and archaea pursue these same two strategies. Some interesting twists occur among bacterial and archaeal autotrophs, however. Not all of them use the Calvin cycle to make building-block molecules, and not all start with $CO_2$ as a source of carbon atoms. For example, consider these biochemical pathways:

- Some proteobacteria are called **methanotrophs** ("methane-eaters") because they use methane ($CH_4$) as their carbon source. (They also use $CH_4$ as an electron donor in cellular respiration.) Methanotrophs process $CH_4$ into more complex organic compounds via one of two enzymatic pathways, depending on the species.

- Some bacteria can use carbon monoxide (CO) or methanol ($CH_3OH$) as a starting material.

These observations drive home an important message from this chapter: Compared with eukaryotes, the metabolic capabilities of bacteria and archaea are remarkably complex and diverse.

## Ecological Diversity and Global Impacts

The metabolic diversity observed among bacteria and archaea explains why these organisms can thrive in such a wide array of habitats.

- The array of electron donors, electron acceptors, and fermentation substrates exploited by bacteria and archaea allows the heterotrophic species to live just about anywhere.

- The evolution of three distinct types of photosynthesis—based on bacteriorhodopsin, geothermal energy, or pigments that donate high-energy electrons to ETCs—extends the types of habitats that can support phototrophs.

The complex chemistry that these cells carry out, combined with their numerical abundance, has made them potent forces for global change throughout Earth's history. Bacteria and archaea have altered the chemical composition of the oceans, atmosphere, and terrestrial environments for billions of years. They continue to do so today.

**The Oxygen Revolution** Today, oxygen represents almost 21 percent of the molecules in Earth's atmosphere. But researchers who study the composition of the atmosphere are virtually certain that no free molecular oxygen ($O_2$) existed for the first 2.3 billion years of Earth's existence. This conclusion is based on two observations:

1. There was no plausible source of oxygen at the time the planet formed.

2. Chemical analysis of the oldest Earth rocks suggests that they formed in the absence of atmospheric oxygen.

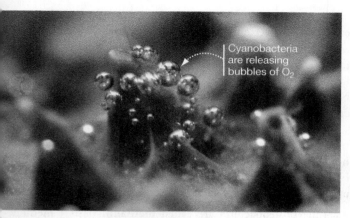

**FIGURE 29.11 Cyanobacteria Were the First Organisms to Perform Oxygenic Photosynthesis.**

**FIGURE 29.12 Cellular Respiration Can Produce More Energy When Oxygen Is the Final Electron Acceptor.** More potential energy in glucose can be released when oxygen is the final acceptor compared to other molecules or ions.

DATA: Wilson, D. F., M. Erecińska, and P. L. Dutton. 1974. *Annual Review of Biophysics and Bioengineering* 3: 203–230; Tables 1 and 3.

✔ **QUESTION** Which organisms grow faster—those using aerobic respiration or those using anaerobic respiration? Explain your reasoning.

Early in Earth's history, the atmosphere was dominated by nitrogen and carbon dioxide. Where did the oxygen we breathe come from? The answer is cyanobacteria.

**Cyanobacteria** is a lineage of photosynthetic bacteria. According to the fossil record, species of cyanobacteria first became numerous in the oceans about 2.7–2.5 billion years ago. Their appearance was momentous because cyanobacteria were the first organisms to perform oxygenic ("oxygen-producing") photosynthesis (**FIGURE 29.11**).

The fossil record and geologic record indicate that oxygen concentrations in the oceans and atmosphere began to increase 2.3–1 billion years ago. Once oxygen was common in the oceans, cells could begin to use it as the final electron acceptor during cellular respiration. **Aerobic** respiration was now a possibility. Before that, organisms had to use compounds other than oxygen as a final electron acceptor—only **anaerobic** respiration was possible. (Aerobic and anaerobic respiration are introduced in Chapter 9.)

The evolution of aerobic respiration was a crucial event in the history of life. Because oxygen is extremely electronegative, it is an efficient electron acceptor. Much more energy is released as electrons move through electron transport chains with oxygen as the ultimate acceptor than is released with other substances as the electron acceptor.

To drive this point home, study the graph in **FIGURE 29.12**. Notice that the vertical axis plots free energy changes; the graph shows the energy released when glucose is oxidized with iron, nitrate, or oxygen as the final electron acceptor. Once oxygen was available, then, cells could produce much more ATP for each electron donated by NADH or $FADH_2$. As a result, the rate of energy production rose dramatically.

To summarize, data indicate that cyanobacteria were responsible for a fundamental change in Earth's atmosphere—a high concentration of oxygen. Never before, or since, have organisms done so much to alter the nature of our planet.

**Nitrogen Fixation and the Nitrogen Cycle** In many environments, fertilizing forests or grasslands with nitrogen results in increased growth. Researchers infer from these results that plant growth is often limited by the availability of nitrogen.

Organisms must have nitrogen to synthesize proteins and nucleic acids. Although molecular nitrogen ($N_2$) is extremely abundant in the atmosphere, most organisms cannot use it because of the strong triple bond linking the nitrogen atoms. To incorporate nitrogen atoms into amino acids and nucleotides, all eukaryotes and many bacteria and archaea have to obtain N in a form such as ammonia ($NH_3$) or nitrate ($NO_3^-$).

Certain bacteria and archaea are the only species that are capable of converting molecular nitrogen to ammonia. The steps in the process, called **nitrogen fixation,** are highly endergonic reduction-oxidation (redox) reactions (see Chapter 9). The key enzyme that catalyzes the reaction—nitrogenase—is found only in selected bacterial and archaeal lineages. Many of these organisms are free living, but some form important relationships with plants:

- Some species of cyanobacteria live in association with a water fern that grows in rice paddies and helps fertilize the plants.

- In terrestrial environments, nitrogen-fixing bacteria live in close association with plants—often taking up residence in special root structures called nodules (see Chapter 39).

Why is nitrogenase not found in all organisms? The answer lies in an interesting property of the enzyme. When exposed to $O_2$, nitrogenase is irreversibly poisoned and is degraded. The only organisms with the nitrogenase gene are those that live in anaerobic habitats or are able to protect the enzyme from $O_2$.

Nitrogen fixation is only the beginning of the story, however. A quick glance back at Table 29.5 should convince you that bacteria and archaea use a wide array of nitrogen-containing

**FIGURE 29.13 Bacteria and Archaea Drive the Movement of Nitrogen Atoms through Ecosystems.** Nitrogen atoms cycle in different molecular forms.

✔**EXERCISE** Add arrows and labels to indicate that animals ingest amino groups from plants or other animals and release amino groups or ammonia.

compounds as electron donors and electron acceptors during cellular respiration.

To understand why this is important, consider that the nitrite ($NO_2^-$) produced by some bacteria as a by-product of respiration does not build up in the environment. Instead, other species of bacteria and archaea use it as an electron donor, and it is oxidized to molecular nitrate ($NO_3^-$). Nitrate, in turn, is reduced to molecular nitrogen ($N_2$) by yet another suite of bacterial and archaeal species. In this way, bacteria and archaea are responsible for driving the movement of nitrogen atoms through ecosystems around the globe in a process called the **nitrogen cycle** (**FIGURE 29.13**).

Similar types of interactions occur with molecules that contain phosphorus, sulfur, and carbon. In this way, bacteria and archaea play a key role in the cycling of nitrogen and other nutrients. ✔ If you understand the role of bacteria and archaea in the nitrogen cycle, you should be able to provide a plausible explanation of what the composition of the atmosphere and what the nitrogen cycle might be like if bacteria and archaea did not exist.

**Nitrate Pollution** Most crop plants—including corn, rice, and wheat—do not live in association with nitrogen-fixing bacteria. To increase yields of these crops, farmers use fertilizers that are high in nitrogen. In parts of the world, massive additions of nitrogen in the form of ammonia are causing serious pollution problems.

**FIGURE 29.14** shows why. When ammonia is added to a corn-field—in midwestern North America, for example—much of

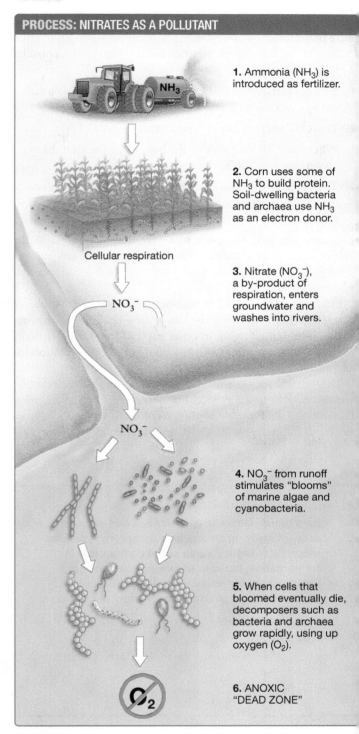

**FIGURE 29.14 Nitrates Act as a Pollutant in Aquatic Ecosystems.**

it never reaches the growing corn plants. Instead, bacteria and archaea in the soil use a significant fraction of the ammonia as food. Microbes that use ammonia as an electron donor to fuel cellular respiration release nitrite ($NO_2^-$) as a waste product. Other microbes use nitrite as an electron donor and release nitrate ($NO_3^-$). Nitrate molecules are extremely soluble in water and tend to be washed out of soils into groundwater or streams.

From there they eventually reach the ocean, where they can cause pollution.

To understand why nitrates can pollute the oceans, consider the Gulf of Mexico:

1. Nitrates carried by the Mississippi River are used as a nutrient by cyanobacteria and algae that live in the Gulf.

2. These cells explode in numbers in response.

3. When they die and sink to the bottom of the Gulf, bacteria and archaea and other decomposers use them as food.

4. The decomposers use so much oxygen as an electron acceptor in cellular respiration that oxygen levels in the sediments and even in Gulf waters decline.

Nitrate pollution has been so severe that large areas in the Gulf of Mexico are anoxic (lacking in oxygen). The oxygen-free "dead zone" in the Gulf of Mexico is devoid of fish, shrimp, and other organisms that require oxygen.

Lately, the dead zone has encompassed about 22,000 square kilometers ($km^2$)—roughly the size of New Jersey. Similar problem spots are cropping up in other parts of the world. Virtually every link in the chain of events leading to nitrate pollution involves bacteria and archaea.

The general message of this section is simple: Bacteria and Archaea may be small in size, but because of their abundance, ubiquity, and ability to do sophisticated chemistry, they have an enormous influence on the global environment.

## check your understanding

**If you understand that . . .**

• As a group, Bacteria and Archaea can use a wide array of electron donors and acceptors in cellular respiration and a diverse set of compounds in fermentation, perform anoxygenic as well as oxygenic photosynthesis, and fix carbon from several different sources via a variety of pathways.

✔ **You should be able to . . .**

Defend the claim that the metabolism of bacteria and archaea is much more sophisticated than that of eukaryotes.

*Answers are available in Appendix A.*

## 29.4 Key Lineages of Bacteria and Archaea

In the decades since the phylogenetic tree identifying the three domains of life was first published, dozens of studies have confirmed the result. It is now well established that all organisms alive today belong to one of the three domains, and that archaea and eukaryotes are more closely related to each other than either group is to bacteria.

Although the relationships among the major lineages within Bacteria and Archaea are still uncertain in some cases, many of the lineages themselves are well studied. Let's survey the attributes of species from selected major lineages within the Bacteria and Archaea, with an emphasis on themes explored earlier in the chapter: their morphological and metabolic diversity, their impacts on humans, and their importance to other species and to the environment.

### Bacteria

The name *bacteria* comes from the Greek root *bacter*, meaning "rod" or "staff." The name was inspired by the first bacteria to be seen under a microscope, which were rod shaped. But as the following descriptions indicate, bacterial cells come in a wide variety of shapes.

Biologists who study bacterial diversity currently recognize at least 21 lineages, or phyla, within the domain. Some of these lineages were recognized by distinctive morphological characteristics and others by phylogenetic analyses of gene sequence data. The lineages reviewed here are just a sampling of bacterial diversity.

- Bacteria > Firmicutes
- Bacteria > Cyanobacteria
- Bacteria > Actinobacteria
- Bacteria > Spirochaetes (Spirochetes)
- Bacteria > Chlamydiae
- Bacteria > Proteobacteria

### Archaea

The name *archaea* comes from the Greek root *archae*, for "ancient." The name was inspired by the hypothesis that this is a particularly ancient group, which turned out to be incorrect. Also incorrect was the initial hypothesis that archaeans are restricted to hot springs, salt ponds, and other extreme habitats. Archaea live in virtually every habitat known.

Recent phylogenies based on DNA sequence data indicate that the domain is composed of at least four major phyla, called the Thaumarchaeota, Crenarchaeota, Euryarchaeota, and Korarchaeota. The Korarchaeota are known only from direct sequencing studies. They have never been grown in culture, and almost nothing is known about them.

- Archaea > Thaumarchaeota
- Archaea > Crenarchaeota
- Archaea > Euryarchaeota

## Bacteria > Firmicutes

The Firmicutes have also been called "low-GC Gram positives" because their cell walls react positively to the Gram stain and because their DNA contains a relatively low percentage of guanine and cytosine (G and C). In some species, G and C represent less than 25 percent of the bases present. There are over 1100 species. ✓ You should be able to mark the origin of the Gram-positive cell wall on Figure 29.7.

**Morphological diversity** Most are rod shaped or spherical. Some of the spherical species form chains or tetrads (groups of four cells). A few form a durable resting stage called a spore. One subgroup synthesizes a cell wall made of cellulose.

**Metabolic diversity** Some species can fix nitrogen; some perform anoxygenic photosynthesis. Others make all of their ATP via various fermentation pathways; still others perform cellular respiration, using hydrogen gas ($H_2$) as an electron donor.

**Human and ecological impacts** Recent metagenomic studies have shown that members of this lineage are extremely common in the human gut. Species in this group also cause a variety of diseases, including anthrax, botulism, tetanus, walking pneumonia, boils, gangrene, and strep throat. *Bacillus thuringiensis* produces a toxin that is one of the most important insecticides currently used in farming. Species in the lactic acid bacteria group are used to ferment milk products into yogurt or cheese (**FIGURE 29.15**).

*Lactobacillus bulgaricus* (rods) and *Streptococcus thermophilus*

**FIGURE 29.15 Firmicutes in Yogurt.** (The cells in this scanning electron micrograph have been colorized.)

## Bacteria > Cyanobacteria

The cyanobacteria were formerly known as the "blue-green algae"—even though algae are eukaryotes. Only about 80 species of cyanobacteria have been described to date, but they are among the most abundant organisms on Earth. In terms of total mass, cyanobacteria dominate the surface waters in many marine and freshwater environments.

**Morphological diversity** Cyanobacteria may be found as independent cells, in chains that form filaments (**FIGURE 29.16**), or in the loose aggregations of individual cells called colonies. The shape of *Nostoc* colonies varies from flat sheets to ball-like clusters of cells.

**Metabolic diversity** All perform oxygenic photosynthesis; many can also fix nitrogen. Because cyanobacteria can synthesize virtually every molecule they need, they can be grown in culture media that contain only $CO_2$, $N_2$, $H_2O$, and a few mineral nutrients. Some species associate with fungi, forming lichens, while others form associations with protists, sponges, or plants. In each case the cyanobacterium provides some form of nutritional benefit to the host. ✓ You should be able to mark the origin of oxygenic photosynthesis on Figure 29.7.

**Human and ecological impacts** If cyanobacteria are present in high numbers, their waste products can make drinking water smell bad. Some species release molecules called microcystins that are toxic to plants and animals. Cyanobacteria were responsible for the origin of the oxygen atmosphere on Earth. Today they still produce much of the oxygen and nitrogen and many of the organic compounds that feed other organisms in freshwater and marine environments.

*Nostoc* species

**FIGURE 29.16 Cyanobacteria Contain Chlorophyll and Are Green.**

## Bacteria > Actinobacteria

Actinobacteria are sometimes called the "high-GC Gram positives" because (1) their cell-wall material appears purple when treated with the Gram stain—meaning that they have a peptidoglycan-rich cell wall and lack an outer membrane—and (2) their DNA contains a relatively high percentage of guanine and cytosine. In some species, G and C represent over 75 percent of the bases present. Over 1100 species have been described to date (**FIGURE 29.17**). ✔ You should be able to mark the origin of this high-GC genome on Figure 29.7.

**Morphological diversity** Cell shape varies from rods to filaments. Many of the soil-dwelling species are found as chains of cells that form extensive branching filaments called **mycelia.** Because of their morphology they were initially misclassified as fungi, and the incorrect name Actinomyces persists.

**Metabolic diversity** Many are heterotrophs that use an array of organic compounds as electron donors and oxygen as an electron acceptor. There are several parasitic species that get most of their nutrition from host organisms.

**Human and ecological impacts** Two serious human diseases, tuberculosis and leprosy, are caused by parasitic *Mycobacterium* species. Over 500 distinct antibiotics have been isolated from species in the genus *Streptomyces*; 60 of these—including streptomycin, neomycin, tetracycline, and erythromycin—are now actively prescribed to treat diseases in humans or domestic livestock. One actinobacterium species is critical to the manufacture of Swiss cheese. Species in the genus *Streptomyces* and *Arthrobacter* are abundant in soil and are vital as decomposers of dead plant and animal material. Some species live in association with plant roots and fix nitrogen; others can break down toxins such as herbicides, nicotine, and caffeine.

*Streptomyces griseus*

**FIGURE 29.17 A *Streptomyces* Species That Produces the Antibiotic Streptomycin.**

## Bacteria > Spirochaetes (Spirochetes)

Based on numbers of species, the spirochetes are one of the smaller bacterial phyla: Only 13 genera and a total of 62 species have been described to date.

**Morphological diversity** Spirochetes are distinguished by their unique corkscrew shape and flagella (**FIGURE 29.18**). Instead of extending into the water surrounding the cell, spirochete flagella are contained within a structure called the outer sheath, which surrounds the cell. When these flagella beat, the cell lashes back and forth and swims forward. ✔ You should be able to mark the origin of the spirochete flagellum on Figure 29.7.

**Metabolic diversity** Most spirochetes manufacture ATP via fermentation. The substrate used in fermentation varies among species and may consist of sugars, amino acids, starch, or the pectin found in plant cell walls. A spirochete that lives only in the hindgut of termites can fix nitrogen.

**Human and ecological impacts** The sexually transmitted disease syphilis is caused by a spirochete. Syphilis is thought to have been brought by European explorers to the Western hemisphere, where it was responsible for killing tens of millions of native people. Lyme disease, also caused by a spirochete, is transmitted to humans by deer ticks. Spirochetes are extremely common in freshwater and marine habitats; many live only under anaerobic conditions.

*Treponema pallidum*

**FIGURE 29.18 Spirochetes Are Corkscrew-Shaped Cells Inside an Outer Sheath.**

## Bacteria > Chlamydiae

In terms of numbers of species living today, Chlamydiae may be the smallest of all major bacterial lineages. Although the group is highly distinct phylogenetically, only 13 species are known. All are Gram-negative.

**Morphological diversity** Chlamydiae are spherical. They are tiny, even by bacterial standards.

**Metabolic diversity** All known species in this phylum live as parasites *inside* host cells and are termed **endosymbionts** ("inside-together-living"). Chlamydiae acquire almost all of their nutrition from their hosts. In **FIGURE 29.19**, the chlamydiae have been colored red; the animal cells that they live in are colored brown. ✔ You should be able to mark the origin of the endosymbiotic lifestyle in this lineage on Figure 29.7. (The endosymbiotic lifestyle has also arisen in other bacterial lineages, independently of Chlamydiae.)

**Human and ecological impacts** *Chlamydia trachomatis* infections are the most common cause of blindness in humans. When the same organism is transmitted from person to person via sexual intercourse, it can cause serious urogenital tract infections. If untreated in women, this disease can lead to ectopic pregnancy, premature births, and infertility. One species causes epidemics of a pneumonia-like disease in birds.

*Chlamydia trachomatis*

Vesicle containing many *Chlamydia* cells

Host cell

1 µm

**FIGURE 29.19 Chlamydiae Live Only Inside Animal Cells.**

## Bacteria > Proteobacteria

The approximately 1200 species of proteobacteria form five major subgroups, designated by the Greek letters α (alpha), β (beta), γ (gamma), δ (delta), and ε (epsilon). Because they are so diverse in their morphology and metabolism, the lineage is named after the Greek god Proteus, who could assume many shapes.

**Morphological diversity** Proteobacterial cells can be rods, spheres, or spirals. Some form stalks (**FIGURE 29.20a**). Some are motile. In one group, cells may move together to form colonies, which then transform into the specialized cell aggregate shown in **FIGURE 29.20b**. This structure is known as a **fruiting body.** At their tips, the fruiting bodies produce cells that are surrounded by a durable coating. These spores sit until conditions improve, and then they resume growth.

**Metabolic diversity** Proteobacteria make a living in virtually every way known to bacteria—except that none perform oxygenic photosynthesis. Various species may perform cellular respiration by using organic compounds, nitrite, methane, hydrogen gas, sulfur, or ammonia as electron donors and oxygen, sulfate, or sulfur as electron acceptors. Some perform anoxygenic photosynthesis.

**Human and ecological impacts** *Escherichia coli* may be the best studied of all organisms and is a key species in biotechnology (see Chapter 20, and **BioSkills 13** in Appendix B). Pathogenic proteobacteria cause Legionnaire's disease, cholera, food poisoning, plague, dysentery, gonorrhea, Rocky Mountain spotted fever, typhus, ulcers, and diarrhea. *Wolbachia* infections are common in insects and are often transmitted from mothers to offspring

**(a)** Stalked bacterium

*Caulobacter crescentus*

Stalk
1 µm

**(b)** Fruiting bodies

*Chondromyces crocatus*

Spores

50 µm

**FIGURE 29.20 Some Proteobacteria Grow on Stalks or Form Fruiting Bodies.** The stalked bacterium (a) has been colorized.

via eggs. Biologists use *Agrobacterium* cells to transfer new genes into crop plants. Certain acid-loving species of proteobacteria are used in the production of vinegars. Species in the genus *Rhizobium* (α-proteobacteria) live in association with plant roots and fix nitrogen. A group in the δ-proteobacteria, the bdellovibrios, are predators—they drill into other proteobacterial cells and digest them. Because some species use nitrogen-containing compounds as electron acceptors, proteobacteria are critical players in the cycling of nitrogen atoms through terrestrial and aquatic ecosystems.

## Archaea > Thaumarchaeota

The Thaumarchaeota were recently recognized as a monophyletic, ancient lineage of archaea. Members of this phylum are extremely abundant in oceans, estuaries, and terrestrial soils. Unlike the extremophiles, species in this lineage are considered mesophilic because they grow best at moderate temperatures.

**Morphological diversity** Only a few members of this group have been observed, and all consist of rod-shaped cells that are less than 1 micrometer (μm) in length, smaller than typical prokaryotes. One species, *Nitrosopumilus maritimus* (**FIGURE 29.21**), is so abundant it is estimated to constitute possibly 25 percent of the total prokaryotic cell biomass in open oceans.

**Metabolic diversity** Members of this phylum are called ammonia oxidizers because they use ammonia as a source of electrons and generate nitrite as a by-product. They use the energy from ammonia oxidation to fix $CO_2$.

**Human and ecological impacts** Because of their abundance, these organisms are thought to play a major role in Earth's nitrogen and carbon cycles (see Chapter 56). Their presence in deep ocean waters that lack reduced carbon and sunlight may help explain the productivity of these habitats. The species *Cenarchaeum symbiosum* lives as an endosymbiont inside a marine sponge.

*Nitrosopumilus maritimus*

0.1 μm

**FIGURE 29.21 This Species of Thaumarchaeota Has Rod-Shaped Cells and Is Extremely Abundant in the Open Ocean.**

✔**QUANTITATIVE** Use the scale bar in the figure to measure the length of a *N. maritimus* cell. If these cells were placed end to end, how many of them would fit along a meter stick?

## Archaea > Crenarchaeota

The Crenarchaeota got their name because they are considered similar to the oldest archaeans; the word root *cren–* refers to a source or fount. Biologists have named only 37 species so far, but they are virtually certain that thousands are yet to be discovered.

**Morphological diversity** Crenarchaeota cells can be shaped like filaments, rods, discs, or spheres. One species that lives in extremely hot habitats has a tough cell wall consisting solely of glycoprotein.

**Metabolic diversity** Depending on the species, cellular respiration can involve organic compounds, sulfur, hydrogen gas, or $Fe^{2+}$ ions as electron donors and oxygen, nitrate, sulfate, sulfur, carbon dioxide, or $Fe^{3+}$ ions as electron acceptors. Some species make ATP exclusively through fermentation pathways.

**Human and ecological impacts** Crenarchaeota have yet to be used in the manufacture of commercial products. In certain extremely hot, high-pressure, cold, or acidic environments, crenarchaeota may be the only life-form present (**FIGURE 29.22**). Acid-loving species thrive in habitats with pH 1–5; some species are found in ocean sediments at depths ranging from 2500 to 4000 m below the surface.

*Sulfolobus* species

0.5 μm

**FIGURE 29.22 Some Crenarchaeota Live in Sulfur-Rich Hot Springs.** The cells in the micrograph have been colorized to make them more visible.

The Euryarchaeota are aptly named, because the word root *eury–* means "broad." Members of this phylum live in every conceivable habitat. Some species are adapted to high-salt habitats with pH 11.5—almost as basic as household ammonia. Other species are adapted to acidic conditions with a pH as low as 0. Species in the genus *Methanopyrus* live near hot springs called black smokers that are 2000 m (over 1 mile) below sea level (**FIGURE 29.23**).

**Morphological diversity** Euryarchaeota cells can be spherical, filamentous, rod shaped, disc shaped, or spiral. Rod-shaped cells may be short or long or arranged in chains. Spherical cells can be found in ball-like aggregations. Some species have several flagella. Some species lack a cell wall; others have a cell wall composed entirely of glycoproteins.

**Metabolic diversity** The group includes a variety of methane-producing species. These **methanogens** can use up to 11 different organic compounds as electron acceptors during cellular respiration; all produce $CH_4$ as a by-product of respiration. In other species of Euryarchaeota, cellular respiration is based on hydrogen gas or $Fe^{2+}$ ions as electron donors and nitrate or sulfate as electron acceptors. Species that live in high-salt environments can use the molecule retinal—which is responsible for light reception in your eyes—to capture light energy and perform photosynthesis.

**Human and ecological impacts** Species in the genus *Ferroplasma* live in piles of waste rock near abandoned mines. As a by-product of metabolism, they produce acids that drain into streams and pollute them. Methanogens live in the soils of swamps and the guts of mammals (including yours). They are responsible for adding about 2 billion tons of methane to the atmosphere each year. A methanogen in this phylum was also recently implicated in gum disease.

*Methanopyrus kandleri*

1 μm

**FIGURE 29.23 Some Euryarchaeota Cells Live in the Chimneys of "Black Smokers" on the Seafloor.**

---

## CHAPTER 29 REVIEW

*For media, go to MasteringBiology*

## If you understand . . .

### 29.1 Why Do Biologists Study Bacteria and Archaea?

- Bacteria and archaea are the most abundant organisms on Earth and are found in every habitat that has been sampled.

- Bacteria and archaea are very small, prokaryotic cells, and most are unicellular.

- Bacteria and archaea can be distinguished by their different kinds of membrane lipids and cell walls as well as by their different transcription machinery.

- Bacteria play many beneficial roles in animal digestion, bioremediation, and the production of antibiotics.

- Bacteria cause some of the most dangerous human diseases, including plague, syphilis, botulism, cholera, and tuberculosis.

✔ You should be able to explain the difference between a bacterium, an archaeon, and a eukaryote.

### 29.2 How Do Biologists Study Bacteria and Archaea?

- Enrichment cultures are used to grow large numbers of bacterial or archaeal cells that thrive under specified conditions.

- Using metagenomic analysis, biologists can study bacteria and archaea that cannot be cultured by extracting DNA directly from an environment and then sequencing and characterizing DNA fragments. Information obtained is used to identify biochemical processes and novel organisms that are then placed on the tree of life.

✔ You should be able to explain how metagenomic analysis might be used to reveal whether bacteria carry out nitrogen fixation in the gut of an insect.

## 29.3 What Themes Occur in the Diversification of Bacteria and Archaea?

- Metabolic diversity and complexity are the hallmarks of the bacteria and archaea, just as morphological diversity and complexity are the hallmarks of the eukaryotes.

- Among bacteria and archaea, a wide array of inorganic or organic compounds with high potential energy may serve as electron donors in cellular respiration, and a wide variety of inorganic or organic molecules with low potential energy may serve as electron acceptors. Dozens of distinct organic compounds are fermented.

- Photosynthesis is widespread in bacteria. In cyanobacteria, water is used as a source of electrons and oxygen gas is generated as a by-product. But in other species, the electron excited by photon capture comes from a source other than water, and no oxygen is produced.

- To acquire building-block molecules containing carbon–carbon bonds, some bacteria and archaea species use the enzymes of the Calvin cycle to reduce $CO_2$. But several other biochemical pathways found in bacteria and archaea can also reduce simple organic compounds to sugars or carbohydrates.

- Because of their metabolic diversity, bacteria and archaea play a large role in carbon and nitrogen cycling and alter the global atmosphere, oceans, and terrestrial environments.

- Nitrogen-fixing species provide nitrogen in forms that can be used by many other species, including plants and animals.

✔ You should be able to explain why species that release $H_2S$ as a by-product and that use $H_2S$ as an electron donor often live side by side.

## 29.4 Key Lineages of Bacteria and Archaea

- Prokaryotes can be divided into two lineages, the Bacteria and the Archaea, based on a wide variety of morphological, biochemical, and molecular characters.

- Bacteria are divided into 21 major lineages including organisms that play major roles in ecosystems as primary producers, decomposers, and parasites.

- Archaea are divided into four major lineages and were thought to exist only in extreme environments; they are now recognized to be widespread.

MB° **MasteringBiology**

1. **MasteringBiology Assignments**

**Tutorials and Activities** Classification of Prokaryotes, Diversity in Bacteria, Tree of Life, Water Pollution from Nitrates

**Questions** Reading Quizzes, Blue-Thread Questions, Test Bank

2. **eText** Read your book online, search, take notes, highlight text, and more.

3. **The Study Area** Practice Test, Cumulative Test, BioFlix° 3-D Animations, Videos, Activities, Audio Glossary, Word Study Tools, Art

## You should be able to . . .

### ✔ TEST YOUR KNOWLEDGE
Answers are available in Appendix A

1. How do the molecules that function as electron donors and those that function as electron acceptors differ?
   a. Electron donors are almost always organic molecules; electron acceptors are always inorganic.
   b. Electron donors are almost always inorganic molecules; electron acceptors are always organic.
   c. Electron donors have relatively high potential energy; electron acceptors have relatively low potential energy.
   d. Electron donors have relatively low potential energy; electron acceptors have relatively high potential energy.

2. What do some photosynthetic bacteria use as a source of electrons instead of water?
   a. oxygen ($O_2$)
   b. hydrogen sulfide ($H_2S$)
   c. organic compounds (e.g., $CH_3COO^-$)
   d. nitrate ($NO_3^-$)

3. What is distinctive about the chlorophylls found in different photosynthetic bacteria?
   a. their membranes
   b. their role in acquiring energy
   c. their role in carbon fixation
   d. their absorption spectra

4. What are organisms called that use inorganic compounds as electron donors in cellular respiration?
   a. phototrophs
   b. heterotrophs
   c. organotrophs
   d. lithotrophs

5. True or False. Certain aerobic bacteria in the presence of oxygen can convert nitrogen gas to ammonia.

6. Unlike plant cell walls that contain cellulose, bacterial cell walls are composed of _____.

7. What has metagenomic analysis allowed researchers to do for the first time?
   a. sample organisms from an environment and grow them under defined conditions in the lab
   b. isolate organisms from an environment and sequence their entire genome
   c. study organisms that cannot be cultured (grown in the lab)
   d. identify important morphological differences among species

8. Biologists often use the term energy source as a synonym for "electron donor." Why?

9. The text claims that the tremendous ecological diversity of bacteria and archaea is possible because of their impressive metabolic diversity. Do you agree with this statement? Why or why not?

10. Would you predict that disease-causing bacteria, such as those listed in Table 29.2, obtain energy from light, organic molecules, or inorganic molecules? Explain your answer.

11. The text claims that the evolution of an oxygen atmosphere paved the way for increasingly efficient cellular respiration and higher growth rates in organisms. Explain.

12. From what we know about the evolutionary relationship between the three largest domains, as depicted in Figure 29.1, explain the statement, "Prokaryotes are a paraphyletic group."

13. When using Koch's postulates, which of the following is an essential requirement for the suspected pathogen?
    a. It is present in all organisms with the disease.
    b. It can be cultured on an agar plate.
    c. It is pathogenic on a wide variety of organisms.
    d. It can reproduce sexually within the host.

14. The researchers who observed that magnetite was produced by bacterial cultures from the deep subsurface carried out a follow-up experiment. These biologists treated some of the cultures with a drug that poisons the enzymes involved in electron transport chains. In cultures where the drug was present, no more magnetite was produced. Does this result support or undermine their hypothesis that the bacteria in the cultures perform cellular respiration? Explain your reasoning.

15. *Streptococcus mutans* obtains energy by oxidizing sucrose. This bacterium is abundant in the mouths of Western European and North American children and is a prominent cause of cavities. The organism is virtually absent in children from East Africa, where tooth decay is rare. Propose a hypothesis to explain this observation. Outline the design of a study that would test your hypothesis.

16. Suppose that you've been hired by a firm interested in using bacteria to clean up organic solvents found in toxic waste dumps. Your new employer is particularly interested in finding cells that are capable of breaking a molecule called benzene into less toxic compounds. Where would you go to look for bacteria that can metabolize benzene as an energy or carbon source? How would you design an enrichment culture capable of isolating benzene-metabolizing species?

# 30 Protists

**In this chapter you will learn that**

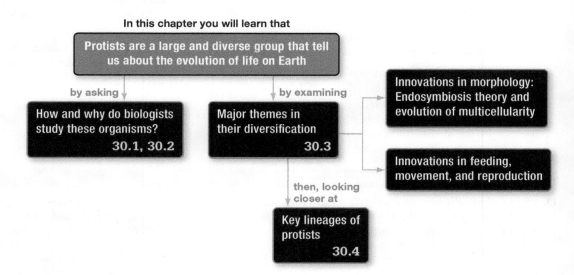

Protists are a large and diverse group that tell us about the evolution of life on Earth

by asking ↓

How and why do biologists study these organisms?
**30.1, 30.2**

by examining ↓

Major themes in their diversification
**30.3**

Innovations in morphology: Endosymbiosis theory and evolution of multicellularity

Innovations in feeding, movement, and reproduction

then, looking ↓ closer at

Key lineages of protists
**30.4**

The brown alga (giant kelp) shown here lives attached to rocks in ocean waters. This algae and other species featured in this chapter are particularly abundant in the world's oceans.

This chapter introduces the third domain on the tree of life: the **Eukarya.** Eukaryotes range from single-celled organisms that are the size of bacteria to sequoia trees and blue whales. The largest and most morphologically complex organisms on the tree of life—algae, plants, fungi, and animals—are eukaryotes.

Although eukaryotes are astonishingly diverse, they share fundamental features that distinguish them from bacteria and archaea:

• Compared to bacteria and archaea, most eukaryotic cells are large, have many more organelles, and have a much more extensive system of structural proteins called the cytoskeleton.

✔ When you see this checkmark, stop and test yourself. Answers are available in Appendix A.

- The nuclear envelope is a **synapomorphy** that defines the Eukarya. Recall that a synapomorphy is a shared, derived trait that distinguishes major monophyletic groups (see Chapter 28).

- Multicellularity is rare in bacteria and unknown in archaea, but has evolved multiple times in eukaryotes.

- Bacteria and archaea reproduce asexually by fission; many eukaryotes reproduce asexually via mitosis and cell division.

- Many eukaryotes undergo meiosis and reproduce sexually.

One of this chapter's fundamental goals is to explore how these morphological innovations—features like organelles and the nuclear envelope—evolved. Another goal is to analyze how morphological innovations allowed eukaryotes to pursue novel ways of performing basic life tasks such as feeding, moving, and reproducing.

In introducing the Eukarya, this chapter focuses on a diverse collection of lineages known as the protists. The term **protist** refers to all eukaryotes that are not land plants, fungi, or animals. Protist lineages are colored orange in **FIGURE 30.1**.

Protists do not make up a monophyletic group. Instead, they refer to a **paraphyletic group**—they represent some, but not all, of the descendants of a single common ancestor. No synapomorphies define the protists. Protists have no trait that is found only in protists and in no other organisms.

By definition, then, the protists are a diverse lot. The common feature among protists is that they tend to live in environments where they are surrounded by water most of the time (**FIGURE 30.2**). Most plants, fungi, and animals are terrestrial, but protists are found in wet soils and aquatic habitats or inside the bodies of other organisms—including, perhaps, you.

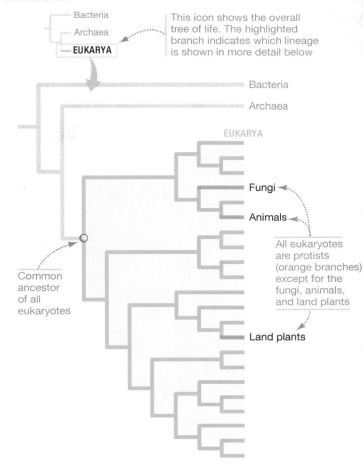

This icon shows the overall tree of life. The highlighted branch indicates which lineage is shown in more detail below

Common ancestor of all eukaryotes

All eukaryotes are protists (orange branches) except for the fungi, animals, and land plants

**FIGURE 30.1 Protists Are Paraphyletic.** The protists include some, but not all, descendants of a single common ancestor.

**Open ocean:** Surface waters teem with microscopic protists, such as these diatoms.

1 mm

**Shallow coastal waters:** Gigantic protists, such as these kelp, form underwater forests.

**Intertidal habitats:** Protists such as these sea palms are particularly abundant in tidal habitats.

**FIGURE 30.2 Protists Are Particularly Abundant in Aquatic Environments.**

# 30.1 Why Do Biologists Study Protists?

Biologists study protists for three reasons, in addition to their intrinsic interest: (1) they are important medically, (2) they are important ecologically, and (3) they are critical to understanding the evolution of plants, fungi, and animals. The rest of the chapter focuses on why protists are interesting in their own right and how they evolved. Let's first consider their impact on human health and the environment.

## Impacts on Human Health and Welfare

The most spectacular crop failure in history, the Irish potato famine, was caused by a protist. In 1845 most of the 3 million acres that had been planted to grow potatoes in Ireland became infested with *Phytophthora infestans*—a parasite that belongs to a group of protists called water molds. Potato tubers that were infected with *P. infestans* rotted in the fields or in storage.

As a result of crop failures in Ireland for two consecutive years, an estimated 1 million people out of a population of less than 9 million died of starvation or starvation-related illnesses. Several million others emigrated. Many people of Irish heritage living in North America, New Zealand, and Australia trace their ancestry to relatives who left Ireland to evade the famine. As devastating as the potato famine was, however, it does not begin to approach the misery caused by the protist *Plasmodium*.

**Malaria** Physicians and public health officials point to three major infectious diseases that are currently afflicting large numbers of people worldwide: tuberculosis, HIV, and malaria. Tuberculosis is caused by a bacterium (see Chapter 25); HIV is caused by a virus (see Chapter 36). Malaria is caused by a protist—specifically, by apicomplexan species in the eukaryotic lineage Alveolata.

**Malaria** ranks as one of the world's worst infectious diseases. In India alone, over 30 million people each year suffer from debilitating fevers caused by malaria. At least 300 million people worldwide are sickened by it each year, and nearly 1 million die from the disease annually. The toll is equivalent to eight 747s, loaded with passengers, crashing every day. Most of the dead are children of preschool age.

Five species of the protist *Plasmodium* are capable of parasitizing humans. Infections start when *Plasmodium* cells enter a person's bloodstream during a mosquito bite. As **FIGURE 30.3** shows, *Plasmodium* initially infects liver cells; later, some of the *Plasmodium* cells change into a distinctive cell type that infects the host's red blood cells. The *Plasmodium* cells multiply asexually inside the host cells, which are killed as parasite cells exit to infect additional liver cells or red blood cells. Large numbers of *Plasmodium* cells in a human host's blood increase the chance that a mosquito's blood meal will contain some of them.

After blood from an infected human is transferred to a mosquito during a bite, *Plasmodium* cells differentiate to form gametes. Inside the mosquito, gametes fuse to form a diploid zygote, which undergoes meiosis. Sexual reproduction in the mosquito is beneficial to the parasite because it generates genetic diversity to help evade the host's immune system. The haploid cells that result from meiosis can infect a human when the mosquito bites again.

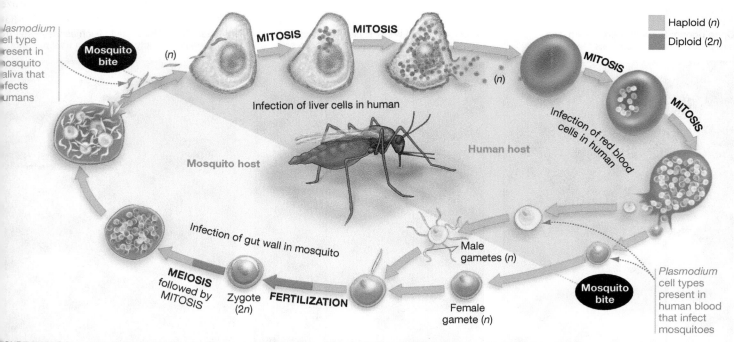

**FIGURE 30.3 *Plasmodium* Lives in Mosquitoes and in Humans, Where It Causes Malaria.** Over the course of its life cycle, *Plasmodium falciparum* alternates between a mosquito host where sexual reproduction takes place, and a human host where asexual reproduction takes place. In humans, it infects and kills liver cells and red blood cells, contributing to anemia and high fever. In mosquitoes, the protist lives in the gut and salivary glands.

**TABLE 30.1 Some Human Health Problems Caused by Protists**

| Species | Disease |
| --- | --- |
| Five species of *Plasmodium,* primarily *P. falciparum* and *P. vivax* | Malaria has the potential to affect 40 percent of the world's total population. |
| *Toxoplasma gondii* | Toxoplasmosis may cause eye and brain damage in infants and in AIDS patients. |
| Many species of dinoflagellates | Toxins released during harmful algal blooms accumulate in clams and mussels and poison people if eaten. |
| Many species of *Giardia* | Diarrhea due to giardiasis (beaver fever) can last for several weeks. |
| *Trichomonas vaginalis* | Trichomoniasis is a reproductive tract infection and one of the most common sexually transmitted diseases. About 2 million young women are infected in the United States each year; some of them become infertile. |
| Several species of *Leishmania* | Leishmaniasis can cause skin sores or affect internal organs—particularly the spleen and liver. |
| *Trypanosoma gambiense* and *T. rhodesiense* | Trypanosomiasis ("sleeping sickness") is a potentially fatal disease transmitted through bites from tsetse flies. Occurs in Africa. |
| *Trypanosoma cruzi* | Chagas disease affects 16–18 million people and causes 50,000 deaths annually, primarily in South and Central America. |
| *Entamoeba histolytica* | Amoebic dysentery results from severe infections. |
| *Phytophthora infestans* | An outbreak of this protist wiped out potato crops in Ireland in 1845–1847, causing famine. |

Although *Plasmodium* is arguably the best studied of all protists, researchers have still not been able to devise effective and sustainable measures to control it.

- *Plasmodium* has evolved resistance to some of the drugs used to control its growth in infected people.

- Efforts to develop a vaccine against *Plasmodium* have been fruitless to date, in part because the parasite evolves so quickly. Flu virus and HIV pose similar problems (see Chapter 51).

- Natural selection has favored mosquito strains that are resistant to the insecticides that have been sprayed in their breeding habitats in attempts to control malaria's spread.

Unfortunately, malaria is not the only important human disease caused by protists. **TABLE 30.1** lists some protists that cause human suffering and economic losses.

**Harmful Algal Blooms** When a unicellular species experiences rapid population growth and reaches high densities in an aquatic environment, it is said to "bloom." Unfortunately, a handful of the many protist species involved in blooms can be harmful.

Harmful algal blooms are usually due to photosynthetic protists called dinoflagellates. Certain dinoflagellates synthesize toxins to protect themselves from predation by small animals called copepods. Because these organisms sometimes have high concentrations of accessory pigments called xanthophylls, their blooms can sometimes discolor seawater (**FIGURE 30.4**).

Algal blooms can be harmful to people because clams and other shellfish filter photosynthetic protists out of the water as food. During a bloom, high levels of toxins can build up in the flesh of these shellfish. Typically, the shellfish themselves are not harmed. But if a person eats contaminated shellfish, several types of poisoning can result.

Paralytic shellfish poisoning, for example, occurs when people eat shellfish that have fed heavily on protists that synthesize poisons called saxitoxins. Saxitoxins block ion channels that have to open for electrical signals to travel through nerve cells

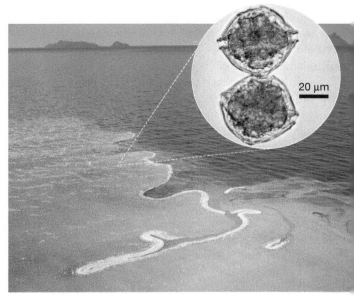

20 µm

**FIGURE 30.4 Harmful Algal Blooms Are Caused by Dinoflagellates.**

(see Chapter 46). In humans, high dosages of saxitoxins cause unpleasant symptoms such as prickling sensations in the mouth or even life-threatening symptoms such as muscle weakness and paralysis.

But like the bacteria and archaea, most species of protists are not harmful. Let's have a look at some protists that are essential to healthy ecosystems.

## Ecological Importance of Protists

As a whole, the protists represent just 10 percent of the total number of named eukaryote species. Although the number of named species of protists is relatively low, their abundance is extraordinarily high. The number of individual protists found in some habitats is astonishing.

- One milliliter of pond water can contain well over 500 single-celled protists that swim with the aid of flagella.
- Under certain conditions, dinoflagellates can reach concentrations of 60 thousand cells per milliliter of seawater.

Why is this important?

**Protists Play a Key Role in Aquatic Food Chains** Photosynthetic protists take in carbon dioxide from the atmosphere and reduce, or "fix," it to form sugars or other organic compounds with high potential energy (see Chapter 10). Photosynthesis transforms some of the energy in sunlight into chemical energy that organisms can use to grow and produce offspring.

Species that produce chemical energy in this way are called **primary producers.** Diatoms, in the Stramenopila lineage, are photosynthetic protists that rank among the leading primary producers in the oceans simply because they are so abundant. Primary production in the ocean represents almost half of the total carbon dioxide that is fixed on Earth.

Diatoms and other organisms that drift in the open oceans or lakes are called **plankton.** The sugars and other organic compounds produced by photosynthetic plankton are the basis of food chains in freshwater and marine environments.

A **food chain** describes nutritional relationships among organisms, and thus how chemical energy flows within ecosystems. In this case, photosynthetic protists and other primary producers are eaten by primary consumers, many of which are protists. Primary consumers are eaten by fish, shellfish, and other secondary consumers, which in turn are eaten by tertiary consumers—whales, squid, and large fish (such as tuna).

Many of the species at the base of food chains in aquatic environments are protists.

**Could Protists Help Limit Global Climate Change?** Carbon dioxide levels in the atmosphere are increasing rapidly because humans are burning fossil fuels and forests (see Chapter 56). Carbon dioxide traps heat that is radiating from Earth, so high $CO_2$ levels in the atmosphere contribute to the rise in temperatures associated with global climate change—an issue that many observers consider today's most pressing environmental problem.

The carbon atoms in carbon dioxide molecules move to organisms on land or in the oceans and then back to the atmosphere, in what researchers call the **global carbon cycle.** To restrict global climate change, researchers are trying to figure out ways to decrease carbon dioxide concentrations in the atmosphere and increase the amount of carbon stored in terrestrial and marine environments.

To understand how this might be done, consider the marine carbon cycle diagrammed in **FIGURE 30.5**. The cycle starts when $CO_2$ from the atmosphere dissolves in water and is taken up by primary producers—photosynthetic plankton called phytoplankton—and converted to organic matter. The plankton are eaten by primary consumers, die and are consumed by decomposers or scavengers, or die and sink to the bottom of the ocean. There they may enter one of two long-lived repositories:

1. **Sedimentary rocks** Several lineages of protists have shells made of calcium carbonate ($CaCO_3$). When these shells rain down from the ocean surface and settle in layers at the bottom, the deposits that result are compacted by the weight of the water and by sediments accumulating above them. Eventually the deposits turn into rock. The limestone used to build the pyramids of Egypt consists largely of protist shells.

2. **Petroleum** Although the process of petroleum (oil) formation is not well understood, it begins with accumulations of dead bacteria, archaea, and protists at the bottom of the ocean.

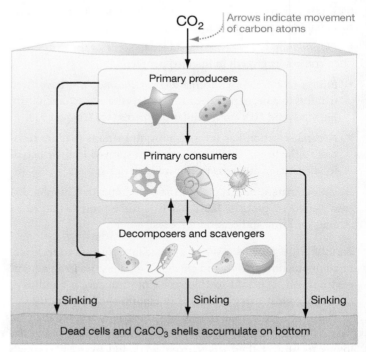

FIGURE 30.5 Protists Play a Key Role in the Marine Carbon Cycle. At the surface, carbon atoms tend to shuttle quickly among organisms. But if carbon atoms sink to the bottom of the ocean in the form of shells or dead cells, they may be locked up for long periods in carbon sinks. (The bottom of the ocean may be miles below the surface.)

Recent experiments have shown that the carbon cycle speeds up when habitats in the middle of the ocean are fertilized with iron. Iron is a critical component of the electron transport chains responsible for photosynthesis and respiration, but it is in particularly short supply in the open ocean. After iron is added to ocean waters, it is not uncommon to see populations of protists and other primary producers increase by a factor of 10.

Some researchers hypothesize that when these blooms occur, the amount of carbon that rains down into carbon sinks in the form of shells and dead cells may increase. If so, then fertilizing the ocean to promote blooms might be an effective way to reduce $CO_2$ concentrations in the atmosphere.

The effectiveness of iron fertilization is hotly debated, however. Fertilizing the ocean with iron might lead to large accumulations of dead organic matter and the formation of anaerobic dead zones (see Chapter 29). But if further research shows that iron fertilization is safe and effective, it could be added to the list of approaches to limit global climate change.

## check your understanding

### C Y U

**If you understand that . . .**

- Malaria is caused by a protist that lives in mosquitoes and in humans in different parts of its life cycle.
- Harmful algal blooms are caused by protists that produce a toxin as a defense against predation.
- Protists are key primary producers in aquatic environments. As a result, they play a key role in the global carbon cycle.

✔ **You should be able to . . .**

1. Explain why public health workers are promoting the use of insecticide-treated sleeping nets as a way of reducing malaria.

2. Make a flowchart showing the chain of events that would start with massive iron fertilization and end with large deposits of carbon-containing compounds on the ocean floor.

*Answers are available in Appendix A.*

## 30.2 How Do Biologists Study Protists?

Although biologists have made great strides in understanding pathogenic protists and the role that protists play in the global carbon cycle, they have found it extremely difficult to gain any sort of solid insight into how the group as a whole diversified over time. The problem is that the eukaryotic lineages split over a billion years ago and diverged so much that it is not easy to find any overall patterns in the evolution of the group.

Recently, researchers have made progress in understanding protist diversity by combining data on the morphology of key groups with phylogenetic analyses of DNA sequences. However, despite the progress, significant questions remain about how the Eukarya diversified. Let's analyze how this work is being done, beginning with classical results on the morphological traits that distinguish major eukaryote groups.

### Microscopy: Studying Cell Structure

Using light microscopy (see **BioSkills 11** in Appendix B), biologists were able to identify and name many of the protist species known today. For example, the early microscopist Anton van Leeuwenhoek identified the parasite *Giardia intestinalis* by examining samples of his own feces.

When transmission electron microscopes became available, a major breakthrough in understanding protist diversity occurred: Detailed studies revealed that protists could be grouped according to overall cell structure, according to organelles with distinctive features, or both.

For example, both light and electron microscopy confirmed that the species that caused the Irish potato famine has reproductive cells with an unusual type of **flagellum**. Flagella are organelles that project from the cell and whip back and forth to produce swimming movements (see Chapter 7). In reproductive cells of this species, one of the two flagella present has tiny, hollow, hairlike projections. Biologists noted that kelp and other species of brown algae also have cells with this type of flagellum.

To make sense of these results, researchers interpreted these types of distinctive morphological features as synapomorphies. Species that have a flagellum with hollow, hairlike projections became known as stramenopiles (literally, "straw-hairs"); the hairs typically have branches at the tip (**FIGURE 30.6**).

**FIGURE 30.6 Species in the Lineage Called Stramenopila Have a Distinctive Flagellum.** The unusual, hollow "hairs" that decorate the flagella of stramenopiles often have three branches at the tip.

| Lineage | Distinguishing Morphological Features (synapomorphies) |
|---|---|
| ■ Amoebozoa | Cells lack cell walls. When portions of the cell extend outward to move the cell, they form large lobes. |
| ■ Opisthokonta | Reproductive cells have a single flagellum at their base. The cristae inside mitochondria are flat, not tube-shaped as in other eukaryotes. (This lineage includes protists as well as the fungi and the animals. Fungi and animals are discussed separately (see Chapters 32 through 35). |
| ■ Excavata | Most cells have a pronounced "feeding groove" where prey or organic debris is ingested. Most species lack typical mitochondria, although genes derived from mitochondria are found in the nucleus. |
| ■ Plantae | Cells have chloroplasts with a double membrane. |
| ■ Rhizaria | Cells lack cell walls, although some produce an elaborate shell-like covering. When portions of the cell extend outward to move the cell, they are slender in shape. |
| ■ Alveolata | Cells have sac-like structures called alveoli that form a continuous layer just under the plasma membrane. Alveoli are thought to provide support. |
| ■ Stramenopila | If flagella are present, cells usually have two—one of which is covered with hairlike projections. |

In recognizing the Stramenopila lineage, investigators hypothesized that because an ancestor had evolved a distinctive flagellum, all or most of its descendants also had this trait. The qualifier *most* is important, because it is not unusual for certain subgroups within a lineage to lose particular traits over the course of evolution, much as humans are gradually losing fur and tailbones.

Eventually, seven major groups of eukaryotes came to be identified on the basis of diagnostic morphological characteristics. These groups and the synapomorphies that identify them are listed in **TABLE 30.2**. Notice that in almost every case, the synapomorphies that define eukaryotic lineages are changes in structures that protect or support the cell or that influence the organism's ability to move or feed. The plants, fungi, and animals represent subgroups within two of the seven major eukaryotic lineages (see Chapters 31 through 35).

## Evaluating Molecular Phylogenies

When researchers began using DNA sequence data to estimate the evolutionary relationships among eukaryotes, the analyses suggested that the seven groups identified on the basis of distinctive morphological characteristics were indeed monophyletic. This was important support for the hypothesis that the distinctive morphological features were shared, derived characters that existed in a common ancestor of each lineage.

The phylogenetic tree in **FIGURE 30.7** is the current best estimate of the eukaryotes' evolutionary history. As you read this tree, note that:

- The Amoebozoa and the Opisthokonta—which include fungi and animals—form a monophyletic group called the Unikonta.

- The other five major eukaryotic lineages form a monophyletic group called the Bikonta.

Understanding where the root or base of the tree of Eukarya lies has been more problematic. Finding it will help researchers understand what the common ancestor looked like and how eukaryotic lineages evolved over time. One hypothesis suggested that the first eukaryotic split was between unikonts and bikonts—meaning, between eukaryotes that have one flagellum and those with two flagella. This hypothesis is tentative and controversial, however, given the data analyzed to date. Researchers continue to work on the issue of placing the root of the Eukarya.

## Discovering New Lineages via Direct Sequencing

The effort to refine the phylogeny of the Eukarya is ongoing. But of all the research frontiers in eukaryotic diversity, the most exciting may be the one based on the technique called direct sequencing.

**Direct sequencing** is based on sampling soil or water, analyzing the DNA sequence of specific genes in the sample, and using the data to place the organisms in the sample on a phylogenetic tree. Direct sequencing and metagenomics have led to the discovery of previously unknown but major lineages of Archaea (see Chapter 29). To the amazement of biologists all over the world, the same thing happened when researchers used direct sequencing to survey eukaryotes.

The first direct sequencing studies that focused on eukaryotes were published in 2001. One study sampled organisms at depths from 250 to 3000 meters (m) below the surface in waters off Antarctica; another focused on cells at depths of 75 m in the Pacific Ocean, near the equator. Both studies detected a wide array of species that were new to science.

Investigators who examined the samples microscopically were astonished to find that many of the newly discovered eukaryotes were tiny—from 0.2 micrometers (μm) to 5 μm in diameter. Subsequent work has confirmed the existence of many,

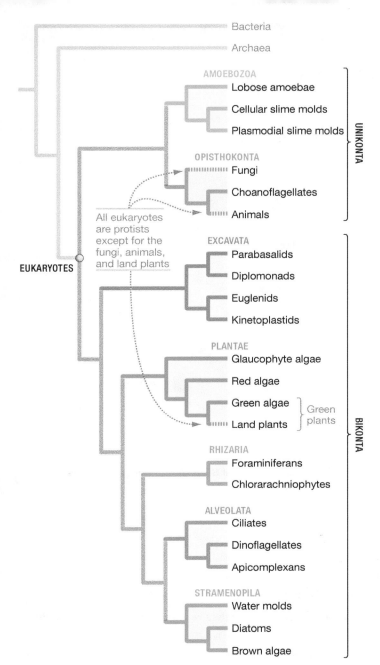

**FIGURE 30.7 Phylogenetic Analyses Have Identified Seven Major Lineages of Eukaryotes.** This tree shows selected subgroups from the seven major lineages discussed in this chapter. Kinetoplastids are not discussed in detail elsewhere in the chapter, but they include the pathogens *Trypanosoma* and *Leishmania* described in Table 30.1.

diverse species of protists that are less than 0.2 μm in diameter. These cells overlap in size with bacteria, which typically range from 0.5 μm to 2 μm in diameter.

Eukaryotic cells are much more variable in size than previously imagined. A whole new world of tiny protists has only recently been discovered.

## check your understanding

**If you understand that . . .**

- According to the most recent analyses, the domain Eukarya comprises seven major lineages. Members of each lineage have distinctive aspects of cell structure.
- Direct sequencing has allowed investigators to recognize large numbers of previously undescribed eukaryotes, some of which are extremely small.

✔ **You should be able to . . .**

1. Explain why opisthokonts, alveolates, and stramenopiles got their names. (The root *opistho* refers to the back of a cell; the root *kont* refers to a flagellum.)
2. Explain why direct sequencing studies allow researchers to characterize species that have never been seen before.

*Answers are available in Appendix A.*

## 30.3 What Themes Occur in the Diversification of Protists?

The protists range in size from bacteria-sized single cells to giant kelp. They live in habitats from the open oceans to the guts of termites. They are almost bewildering in their morphological and ecological diversity. Because they are a paraphyletic group, they do not share derived characteristics that set them apart from all other lineages on the tree of life.

One general theme that can help tie protists together is their amazing diversity. Once an important new innovation arose in protists, it triggered the evolution of species that live in a wide array of habitats and make a living in diverse ways.

### What Morphological Innovations Evolved in Protists?

Virtually all bacteria and all archaea are unicellular. Given the distribution of multicellularity in eukaryotes, it is logical to conclude that the first eukaryote was also a single-celled organism.

Further, all eukaryotes alive today have (1) either mitochondria or genes that are normally found in mitochondria, (2) a nucleus and endomembrane system, and (3) a cytoskeleton. Based on the distribution of cell walls in living eukaryotes, it is likely that the first eukaryotes lacked this feature.

Using these observations, biologists hypothesize that the earliest eukaryotes were probably single-celled organisms with mitochondria, a nucleus and endomembrane system, and a cytoskeleton, but no cell wall.

It is also likely that the first eukaryotic cells swam using a novel type of flagellum. Eukaryotic flagella are completely different structures from bacterial flagella and evolved independently.

The eukaryotic flagellum is made up of microtubules, and dynein is the major motor protein. An undulating motion occurs as dynein molecules walk down microtubules (see Chapter 7). The flagella of bacteria and archaea, in contrast, are composed primarily of a protein called flagellin. Instead of undulating, prokaryotic flagella rotate to produce movement.

✔ If you understand the synapomorphies that identify the eukaryotes as a monophyletic group, you should be able to map the origin of the nuclear envelope and the eukaryotic flagellum on Figure 30.7. Once you've done that, let's consider how several of these key new morphological features arose and influenced the subsequent diversification of protists, beginning with one of the traits that define the Eukarya.

**Endosymbiosis and the Origin of the Mitochondrion** Mitochondria are organelles that generate adenosine triphosphate (ATP) using pyruvate as an electron donor and oxygen as the ultimate electron acceptor (see Chapter 9).

In 1981 evolutionary biologist Lynn Margulis expanded on a radical hypothesis—first proposed in the nineteenth century—to explain the origin of mitochondria. The **endosymbiosis theory** proposes that mitochondria originated when a bacterial cell took up residence inside another cell about 2 billion years ago.

The theory's name was inspired by the Greek word roots *endo*, *sym*, and *bio* (literally, "inside-together-living"). **Symbiosis** is said to occur when individuals of two different species live in physical contact; **endosymbiosis** occurs when an organism of one species lives inside the cells of an organism of another species.

How and when this momentous event occurred is hotly debated. Some scientists think a primitive amoeba-like eukaryote engulfed a bacterium and simply failed to digest it in its lysosome, allowing it to take up residence. Evidence that was used to support this theory includes the similar feeding habits of today's amoeba, and the existence of some protist species that seem to lack mitochondria.

Recent evidence, however, indicates that all protists originally had mitochondria, and some lost them. A new idea gaining support is that the first eukaryote may have been formed as a result of an endosymbiosis between two prokaryotes—an archaeal host and a bacterium (**FIGURE 30.8**). After this chance union occurred, cells developed nuclei and became much larger. Both of these changes appear to have been triggered by the bacterial invader.

The relationship between the archaeal host and the engulfed bacterial cell was presumed to be stable because a mutual advantage existed between them: The host supplied the bacterium with protection and carbon compounds from its prey, while the bacterium produced much more ATP than the host cell could synthesize on its own.

When Margulis first began promoting the endosymbiosis theory, it met with a storm of criticism—largely because it seemed slightly preposterous. But gradually biologists began to examine it rigorously. For example, endosymbiotic relationships between protists and bacteria exist today. Among the α-proteobacteria alone (see Chapter 29), three major groups are found *only* inside eukaryotic cells. In many cases, the bacterial cells are transmitted to offspring in eggs or sperm and are required for survival.

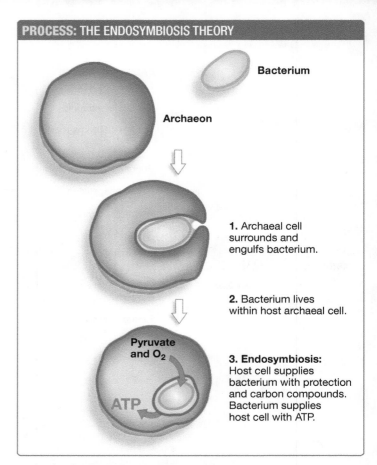

**PROCESS: THE ENDOSYMBIOSIS THEORY**

Bacterium

Archaeon

1. Archaeal cell surrounds and engulfs bacterium.

2. Bacterium lives within host archaeal cell.

Pyruvate and $O_2$

ATP

3. Endosymbiosis: Host cell supplies bacterium with protection and carbon compounds. Bacterium supplies host cell with ATP.

**FIGURE 30.8 Proposed Initial Steps in the Evolution of the Mitochondrion.**

✔QUESTION According to this hypothesis, how many membranes should surround a mitochondrion? Explain your logic.

Several observations about the structure of mitochondria are also consistent with the endosymbiosis theory:

- Mitochondria are about the size of an average α-proteobacterium.

- Mitochondria replicate by fission, as do bacterial cells. The duplication of mitochondria takes place independently of division by the host cell. When eukaryotic cells divide, each daughter cell receives some of the many mitochondria present.

- Mitochondria have their own ribosomes and manufacture some of their own proteins. Mitochondrial ribosomes closely resemble bacterial ribosomes in size and composition and are poisoned by antibiotics such as streptomycin that inhibit bacterial, but not eukaryotic, ribosomes.

- Mitochondria have double membranes, consistent with the engulfing mechanism of origin illustrated in Figure 30.8.

- Mitochondria have their own genomes, which are organized as circular molecules—much like a bacterial chromosome. Mitochondrial genes code for a few of the proteins needed to conduct electron transport and RNAs needed to translate the mitochondrial genome.

Although these data are impressive, they are only consistent with the endosymbiosis theory. Stated another way, they do not exclude other explanations. This is a general principle in science: Evidence is considered strong when it cannot be explained by reasonable alternative hypotheses. In this case, the key was to find data that tested predictions made by Margulis's idea against predictions made by an alternative theory: that mitochondria evolved within eukaryotic cells, separately from bacteria.

A breakthrough occurred when researchers realized that according to the "within-eukaryotes" theory, the genes found in mitochondria are derived from nuclear genes in ancestral eukaryotes. Margulis's theory, in contrast, proposed that the genes found in mitochondria were bacterial in origin.

These predictions were tested by studies on the phylogenetic relationships of mitochondrial genes. Specifically, researchers compared gene sequences isolated from eukaryotic mitochondrial DNA with sequences of similar genes isolated from eukaryotic nuclear DNA and with DNA from several species of bacteria. Exactly as the endosymbiosis theory predicted, mitochondrial gene sequences are much more closely related to the sequences from the α-proteobacteria than to sequences from the nuclear DNA of eukaryotes.

The result diagrammed in **FIGURE 30.9** was considered overwhelming evidence that the mitochondrial genome came from an α-proteobacterium rather than from a eukaryote. The endosymbiosis theory was the only reasonable explanation for the data.

The results were a stunning vindication of a theory that had once been intensely controversial. Mitochondria evolved via endosymbiosis between an α-proteobacterium and an archaeal host.

One intriguing feature of mitochondrial genomes is that they typically encode less than 50 genes, whereas the genomes of their bacterial cousins encode about 1500 genes. Most of the genes from the endosymbiotic bacterium moved into the nuclear genome in what was one of the most spectacular **lateral gene transfer** events in the history of life (see Chapter 21). Some unnecessary genes were lost, but many still encode proteins that are synthesized by cytosolic ribosomes and imported into mitochondria.

✔ If you understand the endosymbiosis theory and the evidence for it, you should be able to describe how the chloroplast—the organelle that is the site of photosynthesis in eukaryotes—could arise via endosymbiosis.

Now let's turn to another distinguishing feature of eukaryotic cells—the nucleus, with its unique double membrane called the nuclear envelope. The origin of the nuclear envelope is also a subject of debate.

**The Nuclear Envelope** The leading hypothesis to explain the origin of the nuclear envelope is based on infoldings of the plasma membrane. As the drawings in **FIGURE 30.10** show, a stepwise process could give rise to small infoldings that were elaborated

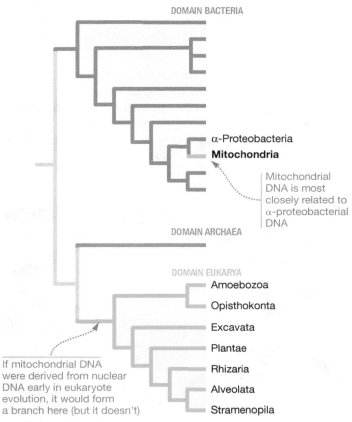

**FIGURE 30.9 Phylogenetic Data Support the Endosymbiosis Theory.**

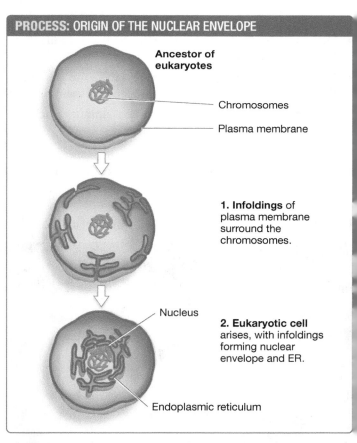

**FIGURE 30.10 A Hypothesis for the Origin of the Nuclear Envelope.** Infoldings of the plasma membrane, analogous to those shown here, have been observed in bacteria living today.

by mutation and natural selection over time, and the infolding could eventually become detached from the plasma membrane. Note that the infoldings would have given rise to the nuclear envelope and the endoplasmic reticulum (ER) together.

Two lines of evidence support this hypothesis: Infoldings of the plasma membrane occur in some bacteria living today, and the nuclear envelope and ER of today's eukaryotes are continuous (see Chapter 7). ✔ If you understand the infolding hypothesis, you should be able to explain why these observations support it.

According to current thinking, the evolution of the nuclear envelope was advantageous because it separated transcription and translation. Recall that RNA transcripts are processed inside the nucleus but translated outside the nucleus (see Chapter 17). In bacteria and archaea, transcription and translation occur together.

With a simple nuclear envelope in place, alternative splicing and other forms of RNA processing could occur—giving the early eukaryotes a novel way to control gene expression (see Chapter 19). The take-home message here is that an important morphological innovation gave the early eukaryotes a new way to manage and process genetic information.

Once a nucleus had evolved, it underwent diversification. In some cases, unique types of nuclei are associated with the founding of important lineages of protists.

- Ciliates (Alveolata) have a diploid micronucleus that is involved only in reproduction, and a polyploid macronucleus where transcription occurs.

- Diplomonads (Excavata) have two nuclei that look identical; it is not known how they interact.

- In foraminifera (Rhizaria), red algae (Plantae), and plasmodial slime molds (Amoebozoa), certain cells contain many nuclei.

- Dinoflagellates (Alveolata) have chromosomes that lack histones and attach to the nuclear envelope.

In each case, the distinctive structure of the nucleus is a synapomorphy that allows biologists to recognize these lineages as distinct monophyletic groups.

**Structures for Support and Protection** Many protists have cell walls outside their plasma membrane; others have hard external structures called a **shell;** others have rigid structures inside the plasma membrane. In many cases, these novel structures represent synapomorphies that identify monophyletic groups among protists. For example:

- Diatoms (Stramenopila) are surrounded by a glass-like, silicon-dioxide cell wall (**FIGURE 30.11a**). The cell wall is made up of two pieces that fit together in a box-and-lid arrangement, like the petri plates you may have seen in lab.

- Dinoflagellates (Alveolata) have a cell wall made up of cellulose plates (**FIGURE 30.11b**).

- Within the foraminiferans (Rhizaria), some subgroups secrete an intricate, chambered calcium carbonate shell (**FIGURE 30.11c**).

- Members of other foraminiferan subgroups, and some amoebae, cover themselves with tiny pebbles.

- The parabasalids (Excavata) have a unique internal support rod, consisting of cross-linked microtubules that run the length of the cell.

- The euglenids (Excavata) have a collection of protein strips located just under the plasma membrane. The strips are supported by microtubules and stiffen the cell.

- All alveolates (Alveolata) have distinctive sac-like structures called alveoli, located just under the plasma membrane, that help stiffen the cell.

In many cases, the diversification of protists has been associated with the evolution of innovative structures for support and protection.

**Multicellularity** One of the most significant changes in the history of life on Earth occurred when organisms containing more than one cell evolved. The mutations leading to **multicellularity** probably first caused cells to simply stick together after cell division. Selection pressures could then act on these larger, colonial organisms, allowing them to evolve and diversify.

**(a)** Diatom

**(b)** Dinoflagellate

**(c)** Foraminiferan

50 μm

10 μm

50 μm

Glassy cell wall made of silicon dioxide

Tough plates in cell wall made of cellulose

Chalky, chambered shell made of calcium carbonate

**FIGURE 30.11 Hard Outer Coverings in Protists Vary in Composition.**

Eventually cells became specialized for different functions. In the simplest multicellular species, certain cells are specialized for producing or obtaining food while other cells are specialized for reproduction. The key point about multicellularity is that not all cells express the same genes.

A few species of bacteria are capable of aggregating and forming structures called fruiting bodies (see Chapter 29). Because cells in the fruiting bodies of these bacteria differentiate into specialized stalk cells and spore-forming cells, they are considered multicellular. But the vast majority of multicellular species are members of the Eukarya.

Multicellularity arose independently in a wide array of eukaryotic lineages, including the green plants, fungi, animals, brown algae, slime molds, and red algae.

To summarize, an array of novel morphological traits played a key role as protists diversified: the mitochondrion, the nucleus and endomembrane system, structures for protection and support, and multicellularity. Evolutionary innovations allowed protists to build and manage the eukaryotic cell in new ways.

Once a new type of eukaryotic cell or multicellular individual existed, subsequent diversification was often triggered by novel ways of finding food, moving, or reproducing. Let's consider each of these life processes in turn.

## How Do Protists Obtain Food?

Bacteria and archaea can use a wide array of molecules as electron donors and electron acceptors during cellular respiration (see Chapter 29). Some get these molecules by absorbing them directly from the environment. Other bacteria don't absorb their nutrition—instead, they make their own food via photosynthesis. Many groups of protists are similar to bacteria in the way they find food: They perform photosynthesis or absorb their food directly from the environment.

But one of the most important stories in the diversification of protists was the evolution of a novel method for finding food.

Many protists ingest their food—they eat bacteria, archaea, or even other protists whole. This process is called **phagocytosis** (see Chapter 7). When phagocytosis occurs, an individual takes in packets of food much larger than individual molecules. Thus, protists feed by either (1) ingesting packets of food, (2) absorbing organic molecules directly from the environment, or (3) performing photosynthesis.

Some protists ingest food as well as performing photosynthesis—meaning that they use a combination of feeding strategies. It's also important to recognize that all three lifestyles—ingestive, absorptive, and photosynthetic—can occur within a single lineage.

To drive this last point home, consider the monophyletic group called the alveolates. This lineage has three major subgroups—dinoflagellates, apicomplexans, and ciliates. About half of the dinoflagellates are photosynthetic, but many others are parasitic and absorb nutrients from their hosts. Apicomplexans are parasitic. Ciliates include many species that ingest prey, but some ciliates live in the guts of cattle or the gills of fish. Other ciliate species make a living by holding algae or other types of photosynthetic endosymbionts inside their cells.

The punch line? Within each of the seven major lineages of eukaryotes, different methods for feeding helped trigger diversification.

**Ingestive Feeding** Ingestive lifestyles are based on eating live or dead organisms or on scavenging loose bits of organic debris. Protists such as the cellular slime mold *Dictyostelium discoideum* are large enough to engulf bacteria and archaea; many protists are large enough to surround and ingest other protists or even microscopic animals.

Feeding by phagocytosis is possible in protists that lack a cell wall. A flexible membrane and dynamic cytoskeleton give these species the ability to surround and "swallow" prey using long, fingerlike projections called **pseudopodia** ("false-feet") (**FIGURE 30.12a**). Phagocytosis was a prerequisite for the endosymbiosis event that led to chloroplasts.

**(a)** Pseudopodia engulf food.

**(b)** Ciliary currents sweep food into gullet.

**FIGURE 30.12 Ingestive Feeding.** Methods of prey capture vary among ingestive protists. **(a)** Some predators engulf prey with pseudopodia; **(b)** other predators sweep them into their gullets with water currents set up by the beating of cilia. Note that the cells in part (a) have been colorized.

Although many ingestive feeders actively hunt down prey and engulf them, others do not. Instead of taking themselves to food, these species attach themselves to a surface. Protists that feed in this way have cilia that surround the mouth and beat in a coordinated way. The motion creates water currents that sweep food particles into the cell (**FIGURE 30.12b**).

**Absorptive Feeding** Absorptive feeding occurs when nutrients are taken up directly from the environment, across the plasma membrane, usually through transport proteins. Absorptive feeding is common among protists.

Some protists that live by absorptive feeding are **decomposers,** meaning that they feed on dead organic matter, or **detritus.** But many of the protists that absorb their nutrition directly from the environment live inside other organisms. If an absorptive species damages its host, that species is called a **parasite.**

**Photosynthesis—Endosymbiosis and the Origin of Chloroplasts**
You might recall that photosystems I and II evolved in bacteria, and that both photosystems occur in cyanobacteria (see Chapter 10). None of the basic machinery required for photosynthesis evolved in eukaryotes. Instead, they "stole" it—via endosymbiosis.

The endosymbiosis theory contends that the eukaryotic chloroplast originated when a protist engulfed a cyanobacterium. Once inside the protist, the photosynthetic bacterium provided its eukaryotic host with oxygen and glucose in exchange for protection and access to light. If the endosymbiosis theory is correct, today's chloroplasts trace their ancestry to cyanobacteria.

All of the photosynthetic eukaryotes have both chloroplasts and mitochondria. The evidence for an endosymbiotic origin for the chloroplast is persuasive.

- Chloroplasts have the same list of bacteria-like characteristics presented earlier for mitochondria.

- Many examples of endosymbiotic cyanobacteria are living inside the cells of protists or animals today.

- Chloroplasts contain a circular DNA molecule containing genes that are extremely similar to cyanobacterial genes.

- The photosynthetic organelle of one group of protists, the glaucophyte algae, has an outer layer containing the same constituent (peptidoglycan) found in the cell walls of cyanobacteria.

Like mitochondria, the chloroplast genome is very small compared with genomes of living cyanobacteria; most of the original genes were either lost or transferred to the nucleus.

✔If you understand the evidence for the endosymbiotic origin of the chloroplast, you should be able to add a label indicating the location of chloroplast genes on the phylogenetic tree in Figure 30.7.

**Photosynthesis—Primary versus Secondary Endosymbiosis**
Which eukaryote originally obtained a photosynthetic organelle? Because all species in the Plantae have chloroplasts with two membranes, biologists infer that the original, or primary,

endosymbiosis occurred in these species' common ancestor. That species eventually gave rise to all subgroups in the Plantae lineage—the glaucophyte algae, red algae, and green plants (green algae and land plants).

But chloroplasts also occur in four of the other major lineages of protists—the Excavata, Rhizaria, Alveolata, and Stramenopila. In these species, the chloroplast is surrounded by more than two membranes—usually four.

To explain this observation, researchers hypothesize that the ancestors of these groups acquired their chloroplasts by ingesting photosynthetic protists that already had chloroplasts. This process, called secondary endosymbiosis, occurs when an organism engulfs a photosynthetic eukaryotic cell and retains its chloroplasts as intracellular symbionts. Secondary endosymbiosis is illustrated in **FIGURE 30.13**.

**FIGURE 30.14** shows where primary and secondary endosymbiosis occurred on the phylogenetic tree of eukaryotes. Once

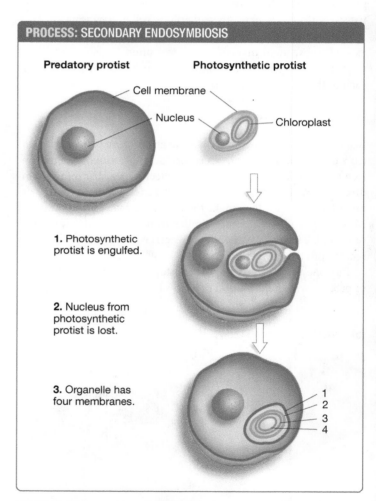

**FIGURE 30.13 Secondary Endosymbiosis Leads to Organelles with Four Membranes.** The chloroplasts found in some protists have four membranes and are hypothesized to be derived by secondary endosymbiosis. In species where chloroplasts have three membranes, biologists hypothesize that secondary endosymbiosis was followed by the loss of one membrane.

protists obtained the chloroplast, it was "swapped around" to new lineages via secondary endosymbiosis.

✔ If you understand endosymbiosis, you should be able to assess and explain why the primary and secondary endosymbiosis events introduced in this chapter represent the most massive lateral gene transfers in the history of life, in terms of the number of genes moved at once. (To review lateral gene transfer, see Chapter 21.)

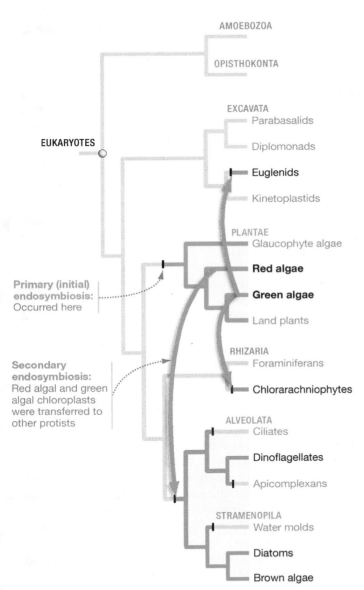

Primary (initial) endosymbiosis: Occurred here

Secondary endosymbiosis: Red algal and green algal chloroplasts were transferred to other protists

**FIGURE 30.14 Photosynthesis Arose in Protists by Primary Endosymbiosis and Then Spread among Lineages via Secondary Endosymbiosis.** Biochemical similarities link the chloroplasts found in alveolates and stramenopiles with red algae and the chloroplasts found in euglenids and chlorarachniophytes with green algae. Notice that among the alveolates and stramenopiles, only the dinoflagellates, diatoms, and brown algae have photosynthetic species. In ciliates, apicomplexans, and water molds, the chloroplast has been lost or has changed function.

## How Do Protists Move?

Many protists actively move to find food. Predators such as the slime mold *Dictyostelium discoideum* crawl over a substrate in search of prey. Most of the unicellular, photosynthetic species are capable of swimming to sunny locations, though others drift passively in water currents. How are these crawling and swimming movements possible?

**Amoeboid motion** is a sliding movement observed in some protists. In the classic mode illustrated in **FIGURE 30.15**, pseudopodia stream forward over a substrate, and the rest of the cytoplasm, organelles, and plasma membrane follow. The motion requires ATP and involves interactions between proteins called actin and myosin inside the cytoplasm. The mechanism is related to muscle movement in animals (see Chapter 48). But at the level of the whole cell, the precise sequence of events during amoeboid movement is still uncertain. The issue is attracting researchers' attention, because key immune system cells in humans use amoeboid motion as they hunt down and destroy disease-causing agents.

The other major mode of locomotion in protists involves flagella or cilia (**FIGURE 30.16**, see page 566). Recall that flagella and cilia both consist of nine sets of doublet (paired) microtubules arranged around two central, single microtubules (see Chapter 7). Flagella are long and are usually found alone or in pairs; cilia are short and usually occur in large numbers on any one cell.

Amoeboid motion via **pseudopodia**

*Chaos carolinensis*

0.2 mm

**FIGURE 30.15 Amoeboid Motion Is Possible in Species That Lack Cell Walls.** In amoeboid motion, long pseudopodia stream out from the cell. The rest of the cytoplasm, organelles, and external membrane follow.

**a) Swimming via flagella**

**b) Swimming via cilia**

**FIGURE 30.16 Many Protists Swim Using Flagella or Cilia.**
**(a)** Flagella are long and few in number. **(b)** Cilia are short and numerous. In many cases they are used in swimming.

Even closely related protists can use radically different forms of locomotion. For example, within the Alveolata, the ciliates swim by beating their cilia, the dinoflagellates swim by whipping their flagella, and mature apicomplexan cells move by amoeboid motion (though their gametes swim via flagella). It is also common to find protists that do not exhibit active movement, but instead float passively in water currents.

Movement is yet another example of the extensive diversification that occurred within each of the seven major monophyletic groups of eukaryotes.

## How Do Protists Reproduce?

Sexual reproduction originated in protists. Sexual reproduction can best be understood in contrast to asexual reproduction (see Chapter 13). The key issues are the type of nuclear division involved and the consequences for genetic diversity in the offspring produced.

Asexual reproduction is based on mitosis and cell division in eukaryotic organisms and on fission in bacteria and archaea. It results in daughter cells that are genetically identical to the parent.

Sexual reproduction is based on meiosis and fusion of gametes. It results in daughter cells that are genetically different from their parents and from each other.

Most protists undergo asexual reproduction routinely. But sexual reproduction occurs only intermittently in many protists—often at one particular time of year, or when individuals are stressed by overcrowding or scarce food supplies. The evolution of sexual reproduction ranks among the most significant evolutionary innovations observed in eukaryotes.

**Sexual versus Asexual Reproduction** The leading hypothesis to explain why meiosis evolved states that genetically variable offspring may be able to thrive if the environment changes. For example, offspring with genotypes different from those of their parents may be better able to withstand attacks by parasites that successfully attacked their parents (see Chapter 13). This is a key point because many types of parasites, including bacteria and viruses, have short generation times and evolve quickly.

Because the genotypes and phenotypes of parasites are constantly changing, natural selection favors host individuals with new genotypes. The idea is that novel genotypes in offspring generated by meiosis may contain combinations of alleles that allow hosts to withstand attack by new strains of parasites. In short, many biologists view sexual reproduction as an adaptation to fight disease.

✔ If you understand the changing-environment hypothesis for the evolution of sex, you should be able to evaluate and explain whether it is consistent with the observation that many protists undergo meiosis when food is scarce or the population density is high.

## Life Cycles—Haploid versus Diploid Dominated

A life cycle describes the sequence of events that occur as individuals grow, mature, and reproduce. The evolution of meiosis introduced a new event in the life cycle of protist species; what's more, it created a distinction between haploid and diploid phases in the life of an individual.

Recall that diploid individuals have two of each type of chromosome inside each cell (see Chapter 13). Haploid individuals have just one of each type of chromosome inside each cell. When meiosis occurs in diploid cells, it results in the production of haploid cells.

The life cycle of most bacteria and archaea is extremely simple: A cell divides, feeds, grows, and divides again. Bacteria and archaea are always haploid.

In contrast, virtually every aspect of a life cycle is variable among protists—whether meiosis occurs, whether asexual reproduction occurs, and whether the haploid or the diploid phase of the life cycle is the longer and more prominent phase.

**FIGURE 30.17** illustrates some of this variation. Figure 30.17a depicts the haploid-dominated life cycle observed in many unicellular protists. The specific example given here is the dinoflagellate *Gyrodinium uncatenum*.

To analyze a life cycle, start with **fertilization**—the fusion of two gametes to form a diploid zygote. Then trace what happens to the zygote. In this case, the diploid zygote undergoes meiosis. The haploid products of meiosis then grow into mature cells that eventually undergo asexual reproduction or produce gametes by mitosis and cell division.

Now contrast the dinoflagellate life cycle in Figure 30.17a with the diploid-dominated life cycle in Figure 30.17b. The specific organism shown here is the diatom *Thalassiosira punctigera*. Notice that after fertilization, the diploid zygote develops into a sexually mature, diploid adult cell that can reproduce asexually by dividing mitotically. Meiosis occurs in the adult and results in the formation of haploid gametes, which then fuse to form a diploid zygote. The important contrasts with the

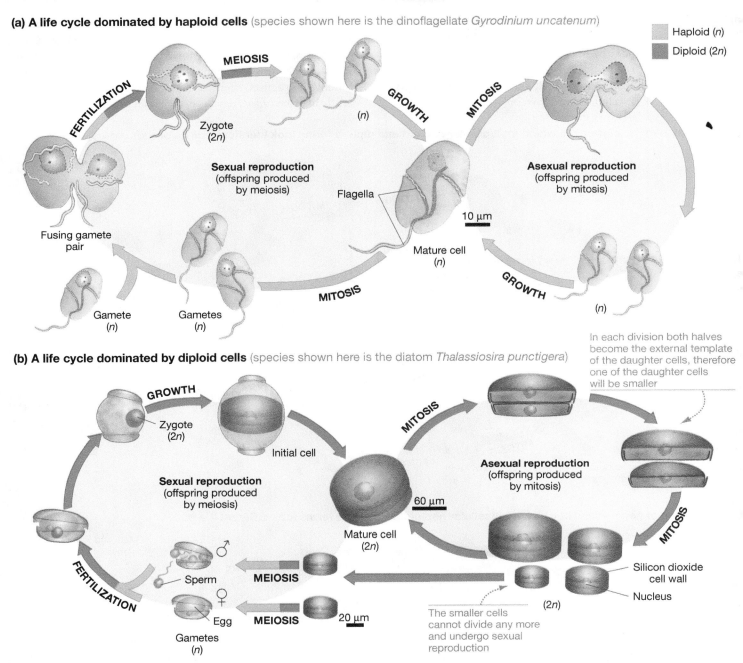

**(a) A life cycle dominated by haploid cells** (species shown here is the dinoflagellate *Gyrodinium uncatenum*)

Haploid (*n*)
Diploid (*2n*)

FERTILIZATION

MEIOSIS

GROWTH

MITOSIS

Zygote
(*2n*)

(*n*)

**Sexual reproduction**
(offspring produced
by meiosis)

**Asexual reproduction**
(offspring produced
by mitosis)

Flagella

10 µm

Fusing gamete
pair

Mature cell
(*n*)

Gamete
(*n*)

Gametes
(*n*)

MITOSIS

GROWTH

(*n*)

**(b) A life cycle dominated by diploid cells** (species shown here is the diatom *Thalassiosira punctigera*)

GROWTH

MITOSIS

In each division both halves
become the external template
of the daughter cells, therefore
one of the daughter cells
will be smaller

Zygote
(*2n*)

Initial cell

**Sexual reproduction**
(offspring produced
by meiosis)

**Asexual reproduction**
(offspring produced
by mitosis)

60 µm

MITOSIS

Mature cell
(*2n*)

Silicon dioxide
cell wall

Nucleus

FERTILIZATION

♂
Sperm

MEIOSIS

♀
Egg

MEIOSIS

20 µm

(*2n*)

The smaller cells
cannot divide any more
and undergo sexual
reproduction

Gametes
(*n*)

**FIGURE 30.17 Life Cycles Vary Widely among Unicellular Protists.** Many unicellular protists can reproduce by both sexual reproduction and asexual reproduction. The cell may be **(a)** haploid for most of its life or **(b)** diploid for most of its life.

haploid-dominated life cycle are that (**1**) meiosis occurs in the adult cell rather than in the zygote, and (**2**) gametes are the only haploid cells in the life cycle.

**Life Cycles—Alternation of Generations** In contrast to the relatively simple life cycles of single-celled protists shown in Figure 30.17, many multicellular protists have a multicellular haploid form in one phase of their life cycle alternating with a multicellular diploid form in another phase. This alternation of multicellular haploid and diploid forms is known as **alternation of generations.**

- The multicellular haploid form is called a **gametophyte,** because specialized cells in this individual produce gametes by mitosis and cell division.

- The multicellular diploid form is called a **sporophyte** because it has specialized cells that undergo meiosis to produce haploid cells called spores.

- A **spore** is a single haploid cell that divides mitotically to form a multicellular, haploid gametophyte. A gamete is also a single haploid cell, but its role is to fuse with another gamete to form a zygote.

When alternation of generations occurs, a diploid sporophyte undergoes meiosis and cell division to produce haploid spores. Each spore then divides by mitosis to form a haploid, multicellular gametophyte. The haploid gametes produced mitotically by gametophytes then fuse to form a diploid zygote, which grows into the diploid, multicellular sporophyte.

Gametophytes and sporophytes may be identical in appearance, as in the brown alga called *Ectocarpus siliculosus* (**FIGURE 30.18a**). In many cases, however, the gametophyte and sporophyte look different, as in the brown algae in the genus *Laminaria* (**FIGURE 30.18b**). Among the protists, alternation of generations evolved independently in brown algae, red algae, and other groups.

**(a) Alternation of generations in which multicellular haploid and diploid forms look identical** (*Ectocarpus siliculosus*)

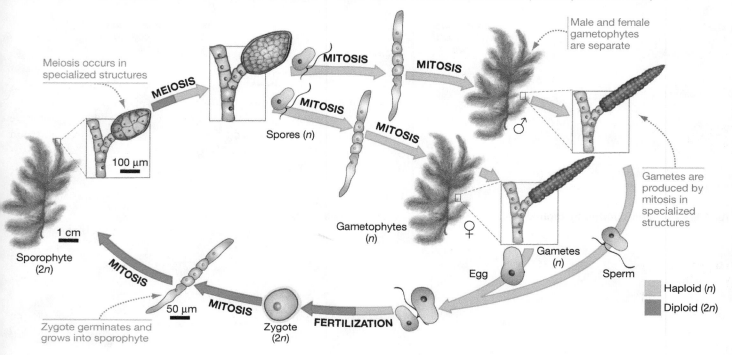

**(b) Alternation of generations in which multicellular haploid and diploid forms look different** (*Laminaria* sp.)

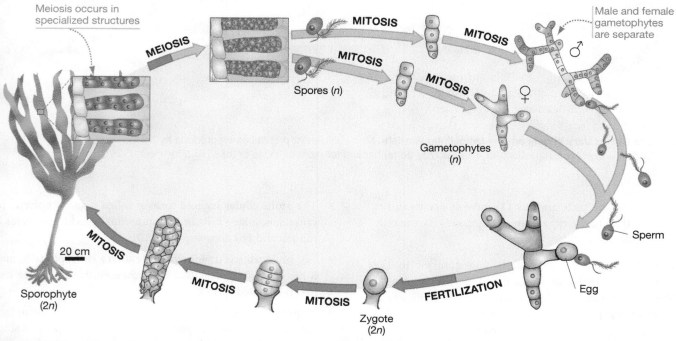

**FIGURE 30.18 Alternation of Generations Occurs in Many Multicellular Protists.** Compared here, two species of brown algae.

To understand alternation of generations, some students find it helpful to memorize this sentence: Sporophytes produce spores by meiosis; gametophytes produce gametes by mitosis.

✔ If you understand how life cycles vary among multicellular protists, you should be able to (1) define the terms alternation of generations, gametophyte, sporophyte, spore, zygote, and gamete; and (2) diagram a life cycle where alternation of generations occurs, without looking at Figure 30.18.

Why does so much variation occur in the types of life cycles observed among protists? The answer is not known. Variation in life cycles is a major theme in the diversification of protists and is discussed further in the chapter on green algae and land plants (see Chapter 31). Explaining why that variation exists remains a topic for future research.

## 30.4 Key Lineages of Protists

Each of the seven major Eukarya lineages has at least one distinctive morphological characteristic. But once an ancestor evolved a distinctive cell structure, its descendants diversified into a wide array of lifestyles. For example, parasitic species evolved independently in all seven major lineages. Photosynthetic species exist in most of the seven, and multicellularity evolved independently in at least four. Similar statements could be made about the evolution of life cycles and modes of locomotion.

In effect, each of the seven lineages represents a similar radiation of species into a wide array of lifestyles. Let's take a more detailed look at some representative taxa from six of the seven major lineages, starting with an overview of each one. The seventh major lineage—the opisthokonts—is featured in the chapters on fungi and the animals (see Chapters 32–35). The lineage called green plants is analyzed separately (see Chapter 31).

### Amoebozoa

Species in the Amoebozoa lack cell walls and take in food by engulfing it. They move via amoeboid motion and produce large, lobe-like pseudopodia. They are abundant in freshwater habitats and in wet soils; some are parasites of humans and other animals.

Major subgroups in the lineage are lobose amoebae, cellular slime molds, and plasmodial slime molds. The cellular slime mold *Dictyostelium discoideum* is described in detail in **BioSkills 13** in Appendix B. ✔ You should be able to mark the origin of this lineage's amoeboid form on Figure 30.7 and explain whether it evolved independently of the amoeboid form in Rhizaria.

● Amoebozoa > Plasmodial Slime Molds

### Excavata

The unicellular species that form the Excavata are named for the morphological feature that distinguishes them—an "excavated" feeding groove found on one side of the cell. Because some lack recognizable mitochondria, excavates were once thought to trace their ancestry to eukaryotes that existed before the origin of mitochondria. But researchers have found that excavates either have

(1) genes in their nuclear genomes that are of mitochondrial origin, or (2) unusual organelles that appear to be vestigial mitochondria. These observations support the hypothesis that the ancestors of excavates had mitochondria, but that these organelles were lost or reduced over time in this lineage. ✔ You should be able to mark the loss of the mitochondrion on Figure 30.7.

● Excavata > Parabasalids, Diplomonads, and Euglenids

### Plantae

Biologists are beginning to use the name **Plantae** to refer to the monophyletic group that includes glaucophyte algae, red algae, green algae, and land plants.

The glaucophyte algae are unicellular or colonial. They live as plankton or attached to substrates in freshwater environments—particularly in bogs or swamps. Some glaucophyte species have flagella or produce flagellated spores, but sexual reproduction has never been observed in the group. The chloroplasts of glaucophytes have a distinct bright blue-green color.

All subgroups within Plantae are descended from a common ancestor that engulfed a cyanobacterium, beginning the endosymbiosis that led to the evolution of the chloroplast—their distinguishing morphological feature. This initial endosymbiosis probably occurred in an ancestor of today's glaucophyte algae. To support this hypothesis, biologists point to several important similarities between cyanobacterial cells and the chloroplasts that are found in the glaucophytes.

- Both have cell walls that contain peptidoglycan and that can be disrupted by the antibacterial compounds lysozyme and penicillin.

- The glaucophyte chloroplast also has a membrane outside its wall that is similar to the membrane found in Gram-negative bacteria (see Chapter 29).

Consistent with these observations, phylogenetic analyses of DNA sequence data place the glaucophytes as the sister group to all other members of the Plantae. ✔ You should be able to mark the origin of the plant chloroplast on Figure 30.7.

Green algae and land plants are described later (see Chapter 31); here we consider just the red algae in detail.

● Plantae > Red Algae

### Rhizaria

The rhizarians are single-celled amoebae that lack cell walls, though some species produce elaborate shell-like coverings. They move by amoeboid motion and produce long, slender pseudopodia. Over 11 major subgroups in this lineage have been identified and named, including the planktonic organisms called actinopods—which synthesize glassy, silicon-rich skeletons—and the chlorarachniophytes, which obtained a chloroplast via secondary endosymbiosis and are photosynthetic. The best-studied and most abundant group is the foraminiferans. ✔ You should be able to mark the origin of the rhizarian amoeboid form on Figure 30.7.

● Rhizaria > Foraminiferans

## Alveolata

Alveolates are distinguished by small sacs, called alveoli, that are located just under their plasma membranes. Although all members of this lineage are unicellular, the ciliates, the dinoflagellates, and the apicomplexans are remarkably diverse in morphology and lifestyle. ✔ **You should be able to mark the origin of alveoli on Figure 30.7.**

● Alveolata > Ciliates, Dinoflagellates, and Apicomplexans

## Stramenopila (Heterokonta)

Stramenopiles are sometimes called heterokonts, which translates as "different hairs." At some stage of their life cycle, all stramenopiles have flagella that are covered with distinctive hollow "hairs." The structure of these flagella is unique to the stramenopiles (Figure 30.6). ✔ **You should be able to mark the origin of the "hairy" flagellum on Figure 30.7.** The lineage includes a large number of unicellular forms, although the brown algae are multicellular and include the world's tallest marine organisms, the kelp.

● Stramenopila > Water Molds, Diatoms, and Brown Algae

## Amoebozoa > Plasmodial Slime Molds

The plasmodial slime molds got their name because individuals form a large, weblike structure that consists of a single cell containing thousands of diploid nuclei (**FIGURE 30.19**). Like water molds, the plasmodial slime molds were once considered fungi on the basis of their general morphological similarity (see Chapter 32).

**Morphology** The huge "supercell" form, with many nuclei in a single cell, occurs in few protists other than plasmodial slime molds. ✔ **You should be able to mark the origin of the supercell on Figure 30.7.**

**Feeding and locomotion** Plasmodial slime molds feed on microorganisms associated with decaying vegetation and move by amoeboid motion or cytoplasmic streaming.

**Reproduction** Some evidence suggests that when food becomes scarce, part of the amoeba forms a stalk topped by a ball-like structure in which nuclei undergo meiosis and form spores. The spores are then dispersed to new habitats by the wind or small animals. After spores germinate to form amoebae, two amoebae fuse to form a diploid cell that begins to feed and eventually grows into a supercell.

**Human and ecological impacts** Like cellular slime molds, plasmodial slime molds influence nutrient cycling by feeding on microorganisms. Some species are important model organisms for the study of cell biology and the origin of multicellularity.

*Physarum polycephalum*

Single cell with many nuclei

5 mm

**FIGURE 30.19 Plasmodial Slime Molds Are Important Decomposers in Forests.**

The lineage Excavata includes free-living and symbiotic species, and some that are parasites. All are single-celled, and many lack functional mitochondria.

All of the 300 known species of parabasalids live inside animals; some live only in the guts of termites, where they aid in the digestion of cellulose. The relationship between termites and parabasalids is considered mutualistic, because both parties benefit from the symbiosis.

About 100 species of diplomonads have been named. Many live in the guts of animal species without causing harm to their host; other species live in stagnant-water habitats.

There are about 1000 known species of euglenids. Although most live in freshwater, a few are found in marine habitats.

**Morphology** Parabasalid cells have a distinctive rod of cross-linked microtubules that runs the length of the cell. The rod is attached to the basal bodies where a cluster of flagella arise (**FIGURE 30.20**). Diplomonad cells have two nuclei, which resemble eyes when viewed under the microscope (**FIGURE 30.21**). Each nucleus is associated with four flagella, for a total of eight flagella per cell. Euglenid cells have a unique system of interlocking proteins just inside the plasma membrane that stiffen and support the cell. Some euglenid cells have a light-sensitive "eyespot" and use flagella to swim toward light (**FIGURE 30.22**).

**Feeding and locomotion** Some euglenids have chloroplasts and perform photosynthesis, and some diplomonads are parasitic, but most other members of the Excavata feed by engulfing bacteria, archaea, and organic matter. Most swim using their flagella. ✔ You should be able to explain how the observation of ingestive feeding in euglenids relates to the hypothesis that this lineage gained chloroplasts via secondary endosymbiosis.

*Giardia intestinalis*

FIGURE 30.21 *Giardia* **Causes Intestinal Infections in Humans.**

**Reproduction** Nearly all members of the Excavata are known to reproduce only asexually. Sexual reproduction has been observed in just a few species of parabasalids.

**Human and ecological impacts** Infections of *Trichomonas*, a parabasalid, can sometimes cause reproductive tract problems in humans. However, members of this genus may also live in the gut or mouth of humans without causing harm. The diplomonad *Giardia intestinalis* is a common intestinal parasite in humans and causes giardiasis, or beaver fever. Euglenids are important components of freshwater plankton and food chains.

*Trichomonas vaginalis*

FIGURE 30.20 *Trichomonas* **Causes the Sexually Transmitted Disease Trichomoniasis.** The cell in this micrograph has been colorized.

*Euglena velata*

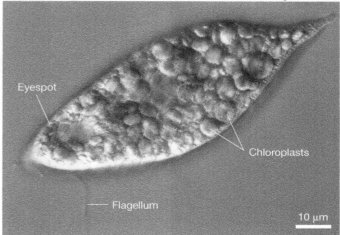

FIGURE 30.22 **Euglenids Are Common in Ponds and Lakes.**

## Plantae > Red Algae

The 6000 species of red algae live primarily in marine habitats. One species lives over 200 m below the surface; another is the only eukaryote capable of living in acidic hot springs. Although their color varies, many species are red because their chloroplasts contain large amounts of the accessory pigment phycoerythrin, which absorbs strongly in the blue and green portions of the visible spectrum. Because blue light penetrates water better than other wavelengths, red algae are able to live at considerable depth in the oceans. ✔ You should be able to mark the origin of high phycoerythrin concentrations on Figure 30.7.

**Morphology** Red algae cells have walls that are composed of cellulose and other polymers. A few species are unicellular, but most are multicellular. Many of the multicellular species are filamentous; others grow as thin, hard crusts on rocks or coral. Some species have erect, leaf-like structures called thalli (**FIGURE 30.23**).

**Feeding and locomotion** The vast majority of red algae are photosynthetic, though a few parasitic species have been identified. Red algae are the only type of algae that lack flagella.

**Reproduction** Asexual reproduction occurs through production of spores by mitosis. Alternation of generations is common, but the types of life cycles observed in red algae are extremely variable.

**Human and ecological impacts** On coral reefs, some red algae become encrusted with calcium carbonate. These species contribute to reef building and help stabilize the entire reef structure. Cultivation of *Porphyra* (or nori) for sushi and other foods is a billion-dollar-per-year industry in East Asia. Microbiological agar is also derived from the cell walls of various species of red algae.

*Mesophyllum lichenoides*

1 cm

**FIGURE 30.23 Red Algae Adopt an Array of Growth Forms.**

## Rhizaria > Foraminiferans

Foraminiferans, or forams, got their name from the Latin *foramen*, meaning "hole." Forams produce shells that have holes (see **FIGURE 30.24**) through which pseudopodia emerge. ✔ You should be able to mark the origin of the foram shell on Figure 30.7. Fossil shells of foraminifera are abundant in marine sediments—a continuous record of fossilized forams dates back 530 million years. A foram species was recently found living in sediments at a depth of 11,000 m below sea level. They are abundant in marine plankton as well as bottom habitats.

**Morphology** Foraminiferan cells generally have multiple nuclei. The shells of forams are usually made of organic material stiffened with calcium carbonate ($CaCO_3$), and most species have several chambers. One species known from fossils was 12 cm long, but most species are much smaller. The size and shape of the shell are traits that distinguish foram species from each other.

**Feeding and locomotion** Like other rhizarians, forams feed by extending their pseudopodia and using them to capture and engulf bacterial and archaeal cells or bits of organic debris, which are digested in food vacuoles. Some species have symbiotic algae that perform photosynthesis and contribute sugars to their host. Forams do not move actively but simply float in the water.

**Reproduction** Members of the foraminifera reproduce asexually by mitosis. When meiosis occurs, the resulting gametes are released into the open water, where pairs fuse to form new diploid individuals.

**Human and ecological impacts** The shells of dead forams commonly form extensive sediment deposits when they settle out of the water, producing layers that eventually solidify into chalk, limestone, or marble. Geologists use the presence of certain foram species to date rocks—particularly during petroleum exploration.

*Globigerinoides ruber*

0.1 mm

**FIGURE 30.24 Forams Are Shelled Amoebae.**

Members of the lineage Alveolata comprise three subgroups of single-celled species that are diverse in morphology and nutrition. All alveolates contain flattened, membrane-bound vesicles called alveoli that support the plasma membrane.

Ciliates are named for the cilia that cover them. Some 12,000 species are known from freshwater, marine, and wet soil environments. Most of the 4000 known species of dinoflagellates are marine or freshwater plankton. All of the 5000 known species of apicomplexans are parasitic.

**Morphology** Ciliate cells have two distinctive nuclei: a polyploid macronucleus that is actively transcribed and a diploid micronucleus that is involved only in gene exchange between individuals (both are stained dark red in **FIGURE 30.25**). ✔ You should be able to mark the origin of the macronucleus/micronucleus structure on Figure 30.7.

Each dinoflagellate species has a distinct shape, in some species maintained by cellulose plates. Apicomplexan cells lack cilia or flagella.

**Feeding and locomotion** Ciliates may be filter feeders, predators, or parasites. They use cilia to swim and have a mouth area where food is ingested. About half of the dinoflagellates are photosynthetic. They are distinguished by the arrangement of their two flagella, which allows them to swim in a spinning motion: One flagellum projects out from the cell while the other runs around the cell. Some dinoflagellate species are capable of **bioluminescence,** meaning they emit light via an enzyme-catalyzed reaction (**FIGURE 30.26**). Being parasitic, all apicomplexans absorb nutrition directly from their host. Some species can move by amoeboid motion.

**Reproduction** Ciliates undergo an unusual type of gene exchange called conjugation, in which micronuclei are passed between individuals. Both asexual and sexual reproduction occur in dinoflagellates. In some apicomplexan species, the life cycle involves two distinct hosts, and cells must be transmitted from one host to the next.

**Human and ecological impacts** Ciliates are abundant marine plankton and are also common in the digestive tracts of mammalian grazers, where they feed on plant matter and help the host animal digest it. Photosynthetic dinoflagellates are important primary producers in marine ecosystems. A few species are responsible for harmful algal blooms (see Figure 30.4). Apicomplexan species in the genus *Plasmodium* cause malaria. *Toxoplasma* is an important pathogen in people infected with HIV (**FIGURE 30.27**).

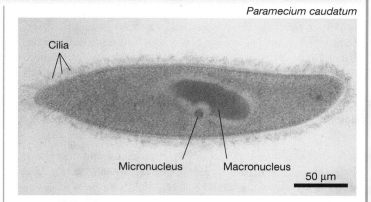

*Paramecium caudatum*

Cilia

Micronucleus     Macronucleus

50 µm

**FIGURE 30.25  Ciliates Are Abundant in Freshwater Plankton.**

*Noctiluca scintillans*

Light produced by cells

0.5 mm

**FIGURE 30.26  Some Dinoflagellate Species Are Bioluminescent.**

*Toxoplasma gondii*

Remnants of dead host cell

Toxoplasma cells

5 µm

**FIGURE 30.27** *Toxoplasma* **Causes Infections in AIDS Patients.**

The stramenopiles are a large and morphologically diverse group of eukaryotes. They include parasitic, saprophytic, and photosynthetic species, and they range in size from tiny, single-celled members to some of the largest multicellular organisms in the oceans.

Several morphological features are shared among the subgroups of stramenopiles, including flagella that are covered with tiny, hollow projections (see Figure 30.6). Photosynthetic diatoms and brown algae contain chloroplasts that originated from a secondary endosymbiosis involving a red alga (see Figure 30.13).

**Morphology** Some water molds are unicellular and some form long, branching filaments called **hyphae** (**FIGURE 30.28**). Most diatoms are unicellular (**FIGURE 30.29**), often in a box-and-lid arrangement (see Figure 30.11a). All species of brown algae are multicellular; the body typically consists of leaflike blades, a stalk known as a stipe, and a rootlike holdfast (**FIGURE 30.30**). ✔ You should be able to mark the origin of brown algal multicellularity on Figure 30.7.

**Feeding and locomotion** Most species of water molds feed on decaying organic material; a few are parasitic. Mature individuals are **sessile**—that is, permanently fixed to a substrate. Both diatoms and brown algae are photosynthetic, but diatoms are planktonic whereas brown algae are sessile.

**Reproduction** Many species of stramenopiles exhibit diploid-dominant life cycles. Several produce spores via asexual or sexual reproduction. Water mold spores form in special structures, like those shown in Figure 30.28. Most species of brown algae exhibit alternation of generations.

**Human and ecological impacts** Water molds are extremely important decomposers in freshwater ecosystems. Parasitic forms that affect humans indirectly include the organism that caused the Irish potato famine. Other water mold species are responsible for epidemic diseases of trees, including the diebacks currently occurring in oaks.

Diatoms are considered the most important primary producer in fresh and salt water. Their glassy cell walls settle into massive accumulations that are mined and sold as diatomaceous earth, which is used in filtering applications and as an ingredient in polishes, paint, cosmetics, and other products.

In many coastal areas with cool water, brown algae form kelp forests that are important habitats for a wide variety of animals.

*Phytophthora infestans*

Structures that produce spores

Potato leaf

50 μm

**FIGURE 30.28 *Phytophthora Infestans* Infects Potatoes.** This is a colorized scanning electron micrograph.

*Isthmia nervosa*

Glassy cell wall

100 μm

**FIGURE 30.29 Diatoms Have Glass-Like Cell Walls.**

*Durvillaea potatorum*

Blade

Stipe

Holdfast

**FIGURE 30.30 Many Brown Algae Have a Holdfast, Stalk (Stipe), and Leaflike Blades.**

## If you understand . . .

### 30.1 Why Do Biologists Study Protists?

- Protists include all eukaryotes except the land plants, fungi, and animals.

- Protists are often tremendously abundant in marine and freshwater plankton and other habitats. Protists provide food for many organisms in aquatic ecosystems and fix so much carbon that they have a large impact on the global carbon budget.

- Parasitic protists cause several important diseases in humans, including malaria.

- Toxin-producing protists that grow to high densities can result in a harmful algal bloom.

✔ You should be able to explain what is "primary" about primary production by photosynthetic protists.

### 30.2 How Do Biologists Study Protists?

- Microscopic investigation of protists led to the understanding that many are single celled. Unlike bacteria, they contain mitochondria, a nucleus and endomembrane system, and a cytoskeleton.

- Direct sequencing has revealed important new groups of protists.

- Phylogenies based on molecular data confirmed that there are seven major lineages of protists and that the group is paraphyletic.

✔ You should be able to describe the major differences between eukaryotic cells and prokaryotic cells.

### 30.3 What Themes Occur in the Diversification of Protists?

- The first eukaryote probably resulted from an ancient endosymbiosis that occurred when a prokaryotic host cell (likely an archaeal cell) engulfed an α-proteobacterium. This bacterium evolved into today's mitochondria.

- The nuclear envelope probably evolved to spatially separate the processes of transcription and translation.

- Multicellularity evolved in several different protist groups independently.

- Protists vary widely in the way they obtain food. They exhibit predatory, parasitic, or photosynthetic lifestyles, which evolved in many groups independently.

- The evolution of ingestive feeding was important for two reasons: **(1)** It allowed eukaryotes to obtain resources in a new way—by eating bacteria, archaea, and other eukaryotes; and **(2)** it made endosymbiosis and the evolution of mitochondria and chloroplasts possible.

- The chloroplast's size and its circular chromosome, ribosomes, and double membrane are consistent with the hypothesis that this organelle originated as an endosymbiotic cyanobacterium.

- After primary endosymbiosis occurred, chloroplasts were "passed around" to new lineages of protists via secondary endosymbiosis.

- Protists vary widely in the way they reproduce. They undergo cell division based on mitosis and reproduce asexually. Many protists also undergo meiosis and sexual reproduction at some phase in their life cycle.

- Alternation of generations is common in multicellular protist species—meaning the same species has separate haploid and diploid forms. When alternation of generations occurs, haploid gametophytes produce gametes by mitosis; diploid sporophytes produce spores by meiosis.

✔ You should be able to explain the original source of (1) the two membranes in a plant chloroplast and (2) the four membranes in the chloroplast-derived organelle of *Plasmodium*.

### 30.4 Key Lineages of Protists

- Protists are a highly diverse group of eukaryotic species organized into seven lineages.

- Protist lineages are defined by DNA sequence evidence and morphological traits such as the presence of chloroplasts or unique flagella.

- A wide range of traits including parasitism, autotrophy, and multicellularity evolved independently in several different lineages of protists.

(MB) **MasteringBiology**

1. **MasteringBiology Assignments**

   **Tutorials and Activities** Alternation of Generations in a Protist; Life Cycles of Protists; Tentative Phylogeny of Eukaryotes

   **Questions** Reading Quizzes, Blue-Thread Questions, Test Bank

2. **eText** Read your book online, search, take notes, highlight text, and more.

3. **The Study Area** Practice Test, Cumulative Test, BioFlix® 3-D Animations, Videos, Activities, Audio Glossary, Word Study Tools, Art

# You should be able to . . .

1. Why are protists considered paraphyletic?
   a. They include many extinct forms, including lineages that no longer have any living representatives.
   b. They include some but not all descendants of their most recent common ancestor.
   c. They represent all of the descendants of a single common ancestor.
   d. Not all protists have all of the synapomorphies that define the Eukarya, such as a nucleus.

2. What material is *not* used by protists to manufacture hard outer coverings?
   a. cellulose
   b. lignin
   c. glass-like compounds that contain silicon
   d. mineral-like compounds such as calcium carbonate ($CaCO_3$)

3. What does amoeboid motion result from?
   a. interactions among actin, myosin, and ATP
   b. coordinated beats of cilia
   c. the whiplike action of flagella
   d. action by the mitotic spindle, similar to what happens during mitosis and meiosis

4. According to the endosymbiosis theory, what type of organism is the original ancestor of the chloroplast?
   a. a photosynthetic archaean
   b. a cyanobacterium
   c. an algal-like, primitive photosynthetic eukaryote
   d. a modified mitochondrion

5. True or False: All protists are unicellular.

6. The most important primary producers in marine ecosystems are _____.

7. Which of the following is true of the parasite that causes malaria in humans?
   a. It undergoes meiosis immediately following zygote formation.
   b. It is a complex prokaryote.
   c. It makes gametes by meiosis.
   d. It has a diploid-dominant life cycle.

8. Explain the logic behind the claim that the nuclear envelope is a synapomorphy that defines eukaryotes as a monophyletic group.

9. Consider the endosymbiosis theory for the origin of the mitochondrion. What did each partner provide the other, and what did each receive in return?

10. Why was finding a close relationship between mitochondrial DNA and bacterial DNA considered particularly strong evidence in favor of the endosymbiosis theory?

11. The text claims that the evolutionary history of protists can be understood as a series of morphological innovations that established seven distinct lineages, each of which subsequently diversified based on innovative ways of feeding, moving, and reproducing. Explain how the Alveolata support this claim.

12. Multicellularity is defined in part by the presence of distinctive cell types. At the cellular level, what does this criterion imply?
    a. Individual cells must be extremely large.
    b. The organism must be able to reproduce sexually.
    c. Cells must be able to move.
    d. Different cell types express different genes.

13. Consider the following:
    - *Plasmodium* has an unusual organelle called an apicoplast. Recent research has shown that apicoplasts are derived from chloroplasts via secondary endosymbiosis and have a large number of genes related to chloroplast DNA.
    - Glyphosate is one of the most widely used herbicides. It works by poisoning an enzyme located in chloroplasts.
    - Biologists are testing the hypothesis that glyphosate could be used as an antimalarial drug in humans.
    How are these observations connected?

14. Suppose a friend says that we don't need to worry about the rising temperatures associated with global climate change. Her claim is that increased temperatures will make planktonic algae grow faster and that carbon dioxide ($CO_2$) will be removed from the atmosphere faster. According to her, this carbon will be buried at the bottom of the ocean in calcium carbonate shells. As a result, the amount of carbon dioxide in the atmosphere will decrease and global warming will decline. Comment.

15. Biologists are beginning to draw a distinction between "species trees" and "gene trees." A species tree is a phylogeny that describes the actual evolutionary history of a lineage. A gene tree, in contrast, describes the evolutionary history of one particular gene, such as a gene required for the synthesis of chlorophyll *a*. In some cases, species trees and gene trees don't agree with each other. For example, the species tree for green algae indicates that their closest relatives are protists and plants. But the gene tree based on chlorophyll *a* from green algae suggests that this gene's closest relative is a bacterium, not a protist. What's going on? Why do these types of conflicts exist?

# 33 An Introduction to Animals

**In this chapter you will learn that**

**Most animal phyla originated suddenly in the Cambrian period and then diversified**

by asking → **What is an animal?** 33.1

by asking → **What key innovations occurred during animal evolution?** 33.2

by asking → **What are the themes of animal diversification?** 33.3

looking closer at →

**Non-bilaterian animals** 33.4 — then — **Protostome animals** Ch. 34 — and — **Deuterostome animals** Ch. 35

Jellyfish such as this hydromedusa are among the most ancient of all animals—they appear in the fossil record over 560 million years ago.

Y ou're an animal, and you have plenty of company—animals are an extraordinarily diverse and species-rich lineage on the tree of life.

The radiation of animals began around 550 million years ago during an event called the **Cambrian explosion** (see Chapter 28). After a slow start, diverse animals suddenly appeared in the fossil record with shells, exoskeletons, internal skeletons, legs, heads, tails, eyes, antennae, jaw-like mandibles, segmented bodies, muscles, and brains. The Cambrian explosion was arguably the most spectacular period of evolutionary change in the history of life.

Today, estimates suggest that there are between 8 million and 50 million animal species alive on our planet, some strikingly similar to their Cambrian ancestors, others quite different. These species range in size and complexity from tiny sponges, which attach to a substrate and contain just a few

✔ When you see this checkmark, stop and test yourself. Answers are available in Appendix A.

cell types, to blue whales, which migrate thousands of kilometers each year in search of food and contain trillions of cells, dozens of distinct tissues, an elaborate skeleton, and highly sophisticated sensory and nervous systems.

Only about 1.4 million animal species have been described and given scientific names to date. As scientists race to discover and describe more animal species, the impact of humans on the planet—ranging from habitat loss to pollution, overharvesting, spread of invasive species, and climate change—is causing the modern rate of animal extinction to accelerate. Some species may go extinct before they are ever described (see Chapter 57).

To analyze the almost overwhelming number and diversity of species in the animal lineage, this chapter presents a broad over-view of how these species diversified, along with more detailed information on the characteristics of the lineages that appear first in the fossil record. (See Chapters 34 and 35 to focus on the most species-rich groups.) Let's start by considering what characteristics define animals.

## 33.1 What Is an Animal?

The ancestors to animals were single-celled protists (Chapter 30). **FIGURE 33.1** reviews how animals fit in the tree of life. Animals occur in a clade, or lineage, called Opisthokonta, along with fungi and the single-celled protists called choanoflagellates. Although scientists cannot be sure exactly what the protist ancestor to all animals looked like, it was likely very similar to today's choanoflagellates.

What characteristics define the animal lineage? Although you may be able to recognize most animals as animals when you see them, some animals look more like plants, fungi, or even protists.

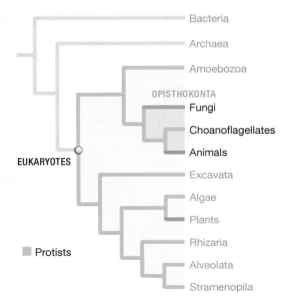

**FIGURE 33.1 Choanoflagellates are the Closest Living Relatives to Animals.**

**Animals** are eukaryotes that share key traits:

- *All animals are multicellular*, with cells that lack cell walls but have an extensive **extracellular matrix** (ECM; see Chapter 11). The ECM includes proteins specialized for cell–cell adhesion and communication.
- *All animals are heterotrophs*, meaning that they obtain the car-bon compounds they need from other organisms. Most ingest ("eat") their food, rather than absorbing it across their exte-rior body surfaces.
- *All animals move* under their own power at some point in their life cycle.
- *All animals other than sponges have* (1) *neurons* (nerve cells) that transmit electrical signals to other cells; and (2) *muscle cells* that can change the shape of the body by contracting.

Multicellular fungi and animals are similar in that they are both multicellular heterotrophs that digest (break down) and ab-sorb nutrients. However, animals are the only multicellular het-erotrophs on the tree of life that usually ingest their food first, before they digest it. As a result, digestion in animals typically occurs within the space, or lumen, of the digestive tract rather than in the open exterior, as occurs with fungi.

In most animals, neurons connect to each other, forming a nervous system, and some neurons connect to muscle cells—which may contract in response to electrical signals from neu-rons. Muscles and neurons are adaptations that allow a large, multicellular body to move efficiently.

What is produced by the combination of multicellularity, het-erotrophy, and efficient movement? Eating machines—animals are the largest predators, herbivores, and detritivores on Earth. They are key consumers in virtually every ecosystem, from the deep oceans and tropical forests to alpine ice fields.

Biologists currently recognize 30–35 **phyla,** or major lineages, of animals—the exact number is constantly being debated and revised as additional information comes to light. **TABLE 33.1** (see page 638) lists 29 phyla that are included in most published anal-yses. How can we make sense of all this diversity? Let's first take a closer look at the key events that occurred during the origin of major animal lineages. Then let's examine the key themes of diversification that occurred *within* lineages.

## 33.2 What Key Innovations Occurred during the Evolution of Animals?

Biologists who study the evolution of animals consider three types of data:

1. *Fossils* are important because they provide the only direct evidence of what ancient animals looked like, when they ex-isted, and where they lived. However, the fossil record does not represent all animals equally. Fossils are more likely to occur for animals that were abundant, had hard parts, lived in areas where sedimentation was occurring, and/or lived re-cently (Chapter 28).

## TABLE 33.1 An Overview of Major Animal Phyla

| Group and Phylum | Common Name or Example Taxa | Number of Described Species |
|---|---|---|
| **Non-bilaterian Groups** | | |
| Porifera | Sponges | 8500 |
| Placozoa | Placozoans | 1 |
| Ctenophora | Comb jellies | 190 |
| Cnidaria | Jellyfish, corals, anemones, hydroids, sea fans | 11,500 |
| Acoela | Acoelomate worms | 350 |
| **Protostomes (lacks typical protostome development)** | | |
| Chaetognatha | Arrow worms | 120 |
| **Protostomes: Lophotrochozoa** | | |
| Rotifera | Rotifers | 2100 |
| Platyhelminthes | Flatworms | 20,000 |
| Nemertea | Ribbon worms | 1200 |
| Gastrotricha | Gastrotrichs | 400 |
| Acanthocephala | Acanthocephalans | 1150 |
| Entoprocta | Entoprocts, kamptozoans | 170 |
| Gnathostomulida | Gnathostomulids | 100 |
| Annelida | Segmented worms | 16,800 |
| Mollusca | Mollusks (clams, snails, octopuses) | 85,000 |
| Phoronida | Horseshoe worms | 10 |
| Bryozoa | Bryozoa, ectoprocts, moss animals | 5700 |
| Brachiopoda | Brachiopods (lamp shells) | 550 |
| **Protostomes: Ecdysozoa** | | |
| Nematoda | Roundworms | 25,000 |
| Kinorhyncha | Kinorhynchs | 130 |
| Nematomorpha | Hair worms | 330 |
| Priapula | Priapulans | 16 |
| Onychophora | Velvet worms | 165 |
| Tardigrada | Water bears | 1045 |
| Arthropoda | Arthropods (spiders, insects, crustaceans) | 1,160,000 |
| **Deuterostomes** | | |
| Echinodermata | Echinoderms (sea stars, sea urchins, sea cucumbers) | 7000 |
| Xenoturbellida | Xenoturbillidans | 2 |
| Hemichordata | Acorn worms | 108 |
| Chordata | Chordates: tunicates, lancelets, sharks, bony fish, amphibians, reptiles (including birds), mammals | 65,000 |

2. *Comparative morphology* provides information about which embryonic, larval, or adult morphological characteristics are common among groups of animals and which are unique to individual lineages (synapomorphies). These data can be used to define the fundamental architecture, or **body plan,** of each animal lineage. In a phylogenetic context, these data can be used to infer which characteristics arose first during the evolution of animals, and which animal groups are more closely related.

3. *Comparative genomics* provides information about the relative similarity of genes or whole genomes of diverse organisms (see Chapter 21). This relatively new source of data is providing dramatic insights into phylogenetic relationships and evolutionary history.

Sometimes these various sources of data on animal evolution suggest the same sequence of evolutionary events. Sometimes they don't. Consider one of the most influential papers on the phylogeny of animals, published in 1997. Using sequences from a gene that codes for RNA in the small subunit of the ribosome, Anna Marie Aguinaldo and colleagues estimated the phylogeny of species from 14 animal phyla. The results were revolutionary, suggesting a different pattern of relationships among animal lineages than had been accepted for years based on morphological data.

The phylogenetic tree in **FIGURE 33.2** is an updated version of the 1997 result, based on further studies of many gene and protein sequences. Some important morphological innovations are mapped onto the tree. Let's explore them by starting at the root of the tree and working toward the branch tips. (See **BioSkills 7** in Appendix B to review how to interpret phylogenetic trees.)

## Origin of Multicellularity

Put your finger on the root of the animal tree in Figure 33.2, where the single-celled choanoflagellates outgroup meets the most basal animal branches. What happened at that node?

The first important insight is that animals are a monophyletic group, meaning that all animals share a common ancestor. Data from fossils, comparative morphology, and comparative genomics agree on a single origin of animals.

The second point to note is that sponges (phylum Porifera) include the two most basal, or ancient, lineages of animals. That is, multicellularity appears to have originated in a sponge-like animal. This hypothesis is well supported by diverse evidence. Let's take a closer look.

**Fossil Evidence**   Sponges are the earliest animals to appear in the fossil record, more than 600 million years ago. The early presence of multicellular sponges and absence of fossils of other multicellular organisms are consistent with the basal position of sponges on the phylogeny.

**Morphological Evidence**   Sponges share several key characteristics with the choanoflagellate outgroup:

- Both choanoflagellates and sponges are **sessile,** meaning that adults live permanently attached to a substrate.

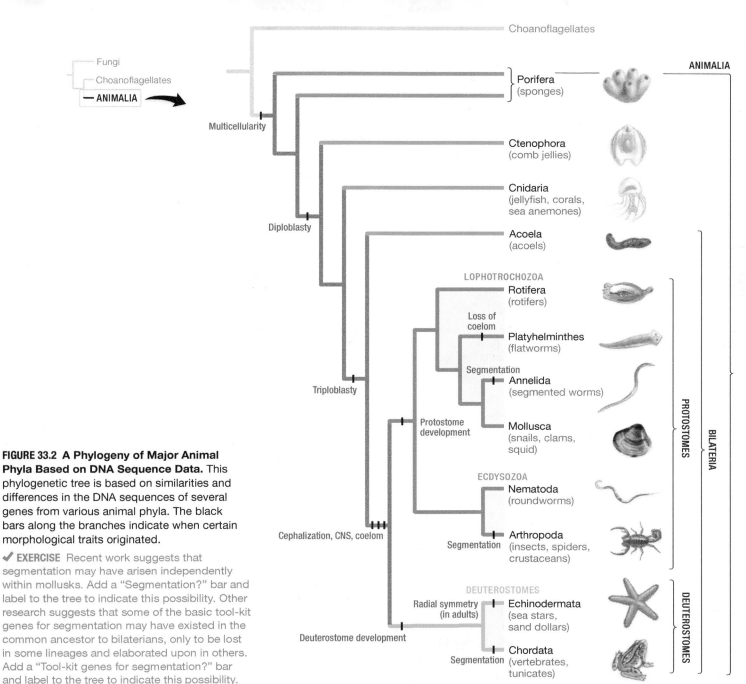

**FIGURE 33.2 A Phylogeny of Major Animal Phyla Based on DNA Sequence Data.** This phylogenetic tree is based on similarities and differences in the DNA sequences of several genes from various animal phyla. The black bars along the branches indicate when certain morphological traits originated.

✔ **EXERCISE** Recent work suggests that segmentation may have arisen independently within mollusks. Add a "Segmentation?" bar and label to the tree to indicate this possibility. Other research suggests that some of the basic tool-kit genes for segmentation may have existed in the common ancestor to bilaterians, only to be lost in some lineages and elaborated upon in others. Add a "Tool-kit genes for segmentation?" bar and label to the tree to indicate this possibility.

- Both feed in a similar way, using cells with nearly identical morphology. As **FIGURE 33.3** (see page 640) shows, the beating of flagella creates water currents that bring organic debris toward the feeding cells of choanoflagellates and sponges. Sponge feeding cells are called **choanocytes.** Within these choanocytes, food particles are trapped and ingested.

As you can see in the figure, choanoflagellates sometimes form **colonies**—groups of individuals that are attached to each other. Some biologists once considered sponges to be colonies of single-celled protists due to the ability of sponge cells to re-aggregate after being dissociated. But sponges contain many specialized cell types that are dependent on each other, some of which occur in organized layers surrounded by extracellular matrix (ECM). Recent research has shown that some sponges have true **epithelium**—a layer of tightly joined cells that covers the interior and/or exterior surface of the animal. Epithelium is essential to animal form and function (Chapter 42).

Sponges are diverse in size, shape, and composition, distinguished in part by the type of **spicules** they produce—stiff spikes of silica or calcium carbonate ($CaCO_3$) that, along with collagen fibers, provide structural support to the ECM. Despite this morphological diversity, many biologists have described sponges as a

**(a)** Choanoflagellates are sessile protists; some are colonial.

**(b)** Sponges are multicellular, sessile animals.

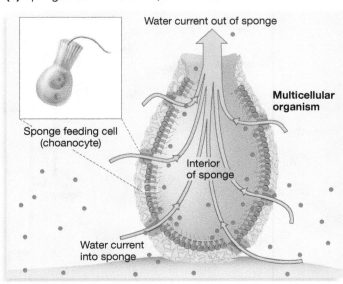

**FIGURE 33.3 Choanoflagellates and Sponge Feeding Cells Are Almost Identical in Structure and Function.** **(a)** Choanoflagellates are suspension feeders. **(b)** A cross section of a simple sponge as it suspension feeds. The beating of flagella produces a water current that brings food into the body of the sponge, where it can be ingested by feeding cells.

monophyletic group based on their unique body plan—systems of tubes and pores that create channels for water currents. Other biologists reject the monophyly of sponges. The recent availability of gene sequence data for diverse sponges has helped to advance the debate, but there is still no consensus.

**Molecular Evidence**   Comparative genomic studies support the hypothesis that sponges are the most basal group of animals, but some reject the hypothesis that the phylum Porifera is monophyletic. According to these studies, sponges are paraphyletic—containing some, but not all, descendants of a common ancestor (see Table 28.2). This concept is indicated on Figure 33.2 by two blue lines, instead of one, representing the sponges.

The paraphyly of sponges is important to the study of animal origins because it provides extra support for the hypothesis that the common ancestor of all animals was sponge-like. If sponges were a monophyletic group, it would be more plausible that their distinguishing characteristics could have evolved later rather than in the common ancestor to all animals (the same way that the most recent common ancestor of humans and chimpanzees was not necessarily chimp-like).

What were the other qualities of the animal ancestor? Comparative genomic studies suggest something surprising. Despite the relative morphological simplicity of sponges, they possess a remarkably complex developmental **tool kit** of genes (Chapter 22). This tool kit contains the genes necessary for all the basic molecular processes required by animals:

- Specialization of cell types
- Regulation of cell cycling and growth
- Adhesion among cells, and between cells and extracellular matrix
- Recognition of self and nonself, thus innate immunity
- Developmental signaling and gene regulation
- Programmed cell death

Thus, a series of important genetic innovations appears to have occurred at the very root of the animal tree along with multicellularity. Subsequent duplication and diversification of these genes contributed to the diversification of animal lineages. ✔If you understand this, you should be able to explain why cancer, which typically involves the mutation of genes in the basic animal genetic tool kit, is thought to be as ancient as multicellularity itself.

## Origin of Embryonic Tissue Layers

Sponges possess the basic genetic tool kit for cell–cell adhesion and cell–ECM adhesion, and some sponges even have rudimentary epithelium. However, sponges do not have complex **tissues,** groups of similar cells that are organized into tightly integrated structural and functional units. Animals other than sponges are typically divided into two major groups based on the number of embryonic tissue layers they have. Animals whose embryos have two types of tissue are called **diploblasts** (literally, "two-buds"); animals whose embryos have three types of tissue are called **triploblasts** ("three-buds").

The embryonic tissues are organized in layers, called **germ layers** (Chapter 23). In diploblasts these germ layers are called **ectoderm** and **endoderm** (**FIGURE 33.4**). The Greek roots *ecto* and

**FIGURE 33.4 Diploblastic Animals Have Bodies Built from Ectoderm and Endoderm.** This is a cross section through the tube-shaped portion of a hydra's body (phylum Cnidaria). The cells have been stained to make them more visible.

*endo* refer to outer and inner, respectively; the root *derm* means "skin." (See **BioSkills 2** in Appendix B to review common Latin and Greek roots.) In most cases the outer and inner "skins" of diploblast embryos are connected by a gelatinous material that may contain some cells. In triploblasts, however, there is a germ layer called **mesoderm** between the ectoderm and endoderm. (The Greek root *meso* refers to "middle.")

The embryonic tissues found in animals develop into distinct adult tissues, organs, and organ systems. In triploblasts:

- *Ectoderm* gives rise to skin and the nervous system.

- *Endoderm* gives rise to the lining of the digestive tract.

- *Mesoderm* gives rise to the circulatory system, muscle, and internal structures such as bone and most organs.

In general, then, ectoderm produces the covering of the animal and endoderm generates the digestive tract. Mesoderm gives rise to the tissues in between. The same pattern holds in diploblasts, except that (1) muscle is simpler in organization and is derived from ectoderm, and (2) reproductive tissues are derived from endoderm.

Look again at the animal phylogeny in Figure 33.2. Traditionally, two groups of animals have been recognized as diploblasts: the Ctenophora (pronounced *ten-AH-for-ah*), or comb jellies, and the Cnidaria (pronounced *ni-DARE-ee-uh*), which include the jellyfish, corals, sea pens, hydra, and anemones. Recent data suggest that some cnidarians have true mesoderm and are triploblasts, complicating the question of exactly when the triploblast body plan evolved. However, the take-home message for the animal phylogeny is still the same—the relatively simple diploblast body plan of ctenophores and cnidarians appears to have originated from ancestral animals later than the sponge lineages but before the other major groups of animals, which are all triploblasts.

The evolution of mesoderm was important because it gave rise to the first complex muscle tissue used in movement. Sponges lack muscle and are generally sessile, or nonmoving, as adults. Ctenophores have muscle cells that can change the body's shape, but both larvae and adults swim using cilia. Adult cnidarians have muscle cells that can extend and retract the body, such as in sea anemones, and can enable swimming by jet propulsion in jellyfish; but these movements are relatively simple compared to the complex movements performed by many triploblasts.

## Origin of Bilateral Symmetry, Cephalization, and the Nervous System

Body symmetry is a key morphological aspect of an animal's body plan. A body is said to be symmetrical if it can be divided by a plane such that the resulting pieces are nearly identical.

Ctenophores, many cnidarians, and some sponges have **radial symmetry** ("spoke symmetry")—meaning that they have at least two planes of symmetry. For example, almost any plane sectioned through the center of the hydra in **FIGURE 33.5a** produces two identical halves. Radial symmetry evolved independently in the phylum Echinodermata (pronounced *ee-KINE-oh-der-ma-ta*)—a group including species such as sea stars, sea urchins, feather stars, and brittle stars.

Organisms with **bilateral symmetry** ("two-sided symmetry") in contrast, have one plane of symmetry and tend to have a long, narrow body. The annelid worm in **FIGURE 33.5b**, for example, has only one plane of symmetry—running lengthwise down its middle.

Based on the topology of branches on the animal phylogeny in Figure 33.2, radial symmetry appears to have arisen earlier in the evolution of animals than bilateral symmetry. Bilateral symmetry occurs in all triploblastic lineages. Where on the tree did bilateral symmetry originate? The answer is more complex than it would seem at first glance. Let's explore why.

**(a)** Radial symmetry    **(b)** Bilateral symmetry

**FIGURE 33.5 Body Symmetry.** These colorized SEMs of **(a)** hydra (looking down on oral surface; phylum Cnidaria) and **(b)** a polychaete worm (phylum Annelida) illustrate the difference between radial and bilateral symmetry.

Bilateral symmetry

**FIGURE 33.6 Morphological Evidence for Bilateral Symmetry in a Sea Anemone.** Some corals and sea anemones have long been known to have bilateral symmetry despite the outward appearance of radial symmetry. *Nematostella* is a small sea anemone that burrows in soft marine sediments.

**Homology or Convergent Evolution?** Nearly all cnidarians appear radially symmetric at first glance, but a closer inspection of their internal morphology reveals bilateral symmetry in some species, especially in sea anemones (**FIGURE 33.6**). Recall that homology is defined as similarity in traits due to inheritance from a common ancestor (Chapter 25). Is the bilateral symmetry in sea anemones homologous to bilateral symmetry in triploblastic animals, or is it an example of convergent evolution?

Developmental biologists John Finnerty, Mark Martindale, and colleagues used developmental regulatory genes as a tool to address this evolutionary question. In triploblastic, bilaterally symmetric animals, called **bilaterians** for short, bilateral symmetry is achieved by the combination of anterior–posterior ("head–tail") axis formation and dorsal–ventral ("back–belly") axis formation. *Hox* genes are important in the development of the anterior–posterior axis (see Chapter 22), and *decapentaplegic* (*dpp*) genes are important in the development of the dorsal–ventral axis.

Finnerty and Martindale predicted that if bilateral symmetry in the sea anemone *Nematostella vectensis* (an increasingly important model organism in biology) is homologous to bilateral symmetry in bilaterians, the pattern of *Hox* and *dpp* gene expression in the sea anemone would be similar to that found in bilaterians. If convergent evolution had occurred, either *Hox* and *dpp* genes would not be expressed in *Nematostella* or their expression patterns would be unrelated to those in bilaterians.

**FIGURE 33.7** shows Finnerty and Martindale's results. During *Nematostella* development, *Hox* genes are expressed along the anterior–posterior axis and *dpp* is expressed asymmetrically about the dorsal–ventral axis, a pattern of gene expression that is parallel to that observed in bilaterians. This evidence supports the hypothesis that bilateral symmetry in this sea anemone is homologous to bilateral symmetry in triploblastic animals—meaning that parts of the genetic tool kit that determine bilateral symmetry arose before the evolutionary split of the cnidarian and bilaterian lineages.

## RESEARCH

**QUESTION:** Is bilateral symmetry in sea anemones homologous to bilateral symmetry in bilaterians?

**HYPOTHESIS:** Bilateral symmetry is homologous in sea anemones and bilaterians.

**NULL HYPOTHESIS:** Bilateral symmetry arose independently in sea anemones and bilaterians.

**EXPERIMENTAL SETUP:**

1. Stain gene products (proteins) of *Hox* gene in developing *Nematostella* embryos and larvae to reveal location of expression.

Future mouth ★        Larva + *Hox* stain

2. Repeat for other *Hox* and *dpp* gene products.

**PREDICTION:** The pattern of expression of *Hox* and *dpp* genes in *Nematostella* will be similar to that found in bilaterians.

**PREDICTION OF NULL HYPOTHESIS:** The pattern of expression of *Hox* and *dpp* genes in *Nematostella* will be unrelated to that found in bilaterians.

**RESULTS:** Schematic summary of gene expression patterns (longitudinal section):

*Hox* genes are expressed sequentially along the anterior–posterior axis—*as in bilaterians*

*dpp* genes are expressed asymmetrically along the dorsal–ventral axis—*as in bilaterians*

**CONCLUSION:** Bilateral symmetry is homologous in *Nematostella* and bilaterians.

**FIGURE 33.7 Genetic Evidence that Bilateral Symmetry Originated in a Common Ancestor of Cnidaria and Bilateria.**

SOURCE: Finnerty, J. R., K. Pang, P. Burton, et al. 2004. Origins of bilateral symmetry: *Hox* and *dpp* expression in a sea anemone. *Science* 304: 1335–1337.

✔ **QUESTION** What results would have supported the null hypothesis?

However, *Hox* and *dpp* gene expression in *Nematostella* is not identical to that in bilaterians—and the bilateral symmetry in *Nematostella* is not as extensive as in bilaterians. The take-home message is that the entire genetic tool kit for bilateral symmetry did not evolve all at once in the early Cambrian before the diversification of bilaterians. Some components of the tool kit evolved earlier—in the ancestor to cnidarians and bilaterians—and others evolved later, after the split of these two lineages.

### Origin of the Nervous System

Over 99 percent of modern animals are bilaterally symmetric. Is this body plan a "key innovation" that led to the diversification of the bilaterians during the Cambrian explosion? One hypothesis is that the evolution of the nervous system and the evolution of the head are tightly linked to bilateral symmetry and that together, these characteristics contributed to the radiation of bilaterians.

How are symmetry and nervous systems related? The function of neurons and nervous systems is to transmit and process information in the form of electrical signals (see Chapter 46).

- Sponges generally lack both nerve cells and symmetry.

- Ctenophores and cnidarians have nerve cells that are organized into a diffuse arrangement called a **nerve net** (**FIGURE 33.8a**). These generally radially symmetric animals either float in water or live attached to a substrate. Radially symmetric organisms are more likely to encounter prey and other aspects of the environment in any direction. As a result, a diffuse nerve net can receive and send signals efficiently.

- All other animals have a **central nervous system,** or CNS. In a CNS, some neurons are clustered into one or more large tracts or cords that project throughout the body; others are clustered into masses called **ganglia** (**FIGURE 33.8b**). Most of the bilaterally symmetric animals living today move through their environment. Bilaterally symmetric organisms tend to encounter prey and other aspects of the environment at the leading end. As a result, it is advantageous to the animal to have many neurons concentrated at that end, with nerve tracts that carry information down the length of the body.

It is intuitive that the evolution of the CNS would coincide with **cephalization:** the evolution of a head, or anterior region, where structures for feeding, sensing the environment, and processing information are concentrated. The large mass of neurons that is located in the head, and that is responsible for processing information to and from the body, is called the cerebral ganglion or **brain.**

To explain the pervasiveness of bilateral symmetry, biologists point out that locating and capturing food is particularly efficient when movement is directed by a distinctive head region and powered by the rest of the body. In combination with the origin of mesoderm, a bilaterally symmetric body plan enabled rapid, directed movement and hunting. Lineages with a triploblastic, bilaterally symmetric, cephalized body had the potential to diversify into an array of formidable eating and moving machines.

Notice in Figure 33.2 that the acoels (phylum Acoela), tiny worms that tend to live among sand grains, are bilaterally symmetric and triploblastic but have a nerve net rather than a CNS—and no head region. Although the position of the aceol branch on the tree is hotly debated, its current position supports the hypothesis that the CNS and cephalization were key to the subsequent radiation of bilaterians.

Acoel worms are named for their lack of a coelom. What is a coelom? What role did it play in the diversification of bilaterians?

### Origin of the Coelom

What would you expect an animal body to look like that is triploblastic (formed from ectoderm, mesoderm, and endoderm), bilaterally symmetric, elongated, and cephalized? The basic bilaterian body shape is a *tube within a tube*. The inner tube is the individual's gut with a mouth at one end and an anus at the other, and the outer tube forms the nervous system and skin (**FIGURE 33.9**). The mesoderm in between forms muscles and organs.

---

**(a) Nerve net:** diffuse neurons in hydra

**(b) Central nervous system:** clustered neurons in earthworm

Ganglia

**FIGURE 33.8 Associations between Body Symmetry and the Nervous System. (a)** Radially symmetric animals, like this hydra, have a nerve net. **(b)** Bilaterally symmetric animals, like this earthworm, have a central nervous system.

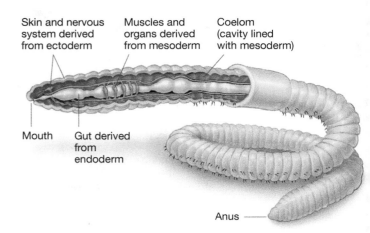

Skin and nervous system derived from ectoderm

Muscles and organs derived from mesoderm

Coelom (cavity lined with mesoderm)

Mouth

Gut derived from endoderm

Anus

**FIGURE 33.9 The Tube-within-a-Tube Body Plan Is Common in Animals.**

The "tube-within-a-tube" body plan can pose a potential biomechanical and physiological challenge if the inner tube is attached to the outer tube via the mesoderm. One bypass to this physical constraint is a fluid-filled cavity between the inner and outer tubes, called a **coelom** (pronounced *SEE-lum*), as shown in the earthworm in Figure 33.9. The coelom provides a space for the circulation of oxygen and nutrients. It also enables the internal organs to move independently of each other.

Phylogenetic evidence suggests that the coelom arose in the common ancestor of protostomes and deuterostomes (Figure 33.2). The bilaterians that possess a coelom that is completely lined in mesoderm are known as true **coelomates** (**FIGURE 33.10a**). The bilaterians that subsequently lost their coelom, such as the flatworms, are called **acoelomates** ("no-cavity-form"; see **FIGURE 33.10b**). The bilaterians that retained a coelom but lost the mesodermal lining in parts of their coelom, such as nematodes (roundworms), are known as **pseudocoelomates** ("false-cavity-form"; **FIGURE 33.10c**).

The coelom was a critically important innovation during animal evolution, in part because an enclosed, fluid-filled chamber can act as an efficient **hydrostatic skeleton.** Soft-bodied animals with hydrostatic skeletons can move effectively even if they do not have fins or limbs.

**(a) Coelomates** have an enclosed body cavity completely lined with mesoderm.

Coelom

Skin (from ectoderm)

Muscles, organs (from mesoderm)

Gut (from endoderm)

**(b) Acoelomates** have no enclosed body cavity.

No coelom

Skin (from ectoderm)

Muscles, organs (from mesoderm)

Gut (from endoderm)

**(c) Pseudocoelomates** have an enclosed body cavity partially lined with mesoderm.

Pseudocoelom

Skin (from ectoderm)

Muscles, organs (from mesoderm)

Gut (from endoderm)

**FIGURE 33.10 Animals May or May Not Have a Body Cavity.**

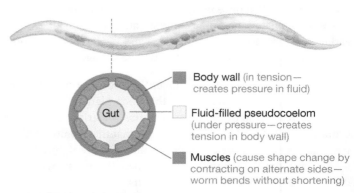

Body wall (in tension—creates pressure in fluid)

Fluid-filled pseudocoelom (under pressure—creates tension in body wall)

Muscles (cause shape change by contracting on alternate sides—worm bends without shortening)

**FIGURE 33.11 Hydrostatic Skeletons Allow Limbless Animals to Move.**

For example, movement in nematodes is possible because the fluid inside the pseudocoelom stretches the body wall—much like water stretches the wall of a water balloon—putting the wall under tension (**FIGURE 33.11**). In turn, this tension exerts pressure on the fluid inside the coelom. When certain muscles in the body wall contract against the pressurized fluid, the force is transmitted through the fluid, changing the body's shape.

Coordinated contractions and relaxations of different muscles in the body wall enable various shape changes and forms of locomotion (see Chapter 48). The evolution of the coelom improved the ability of bilaterians to move in search of food.

## Origin of Protostomes and Deuterostomes

Turn back to Figure 33.2 and put your finger on the node at the origin of the Bilateria, the monophyletic lineage of bilaterians. Now move your finger one node to the right, past the divergence of the Acoels. The common ancestor that existed at this node during the Cambrian was a bilaterally symmetric triploblast with a CNS, cephalization, and a coelom. This ancestor gave rise to a remarkable radiation of diverse animal lineages, only some of which are included in the tree.

What major groups occur within the Bilaterian coelomates? Despite the staggering diversity of adult animals, common themes during embryonic development have enabled biologists to recognize two major subgroups:

1. **protostomes,** in which the mouth develops before the anus, and blocks of mesoderm hollow out to form the coelom; and

2. **deuterostomes,** in which the anus develops before the mouth, and pockets of mesoderm pinch off to form the coelom.

Translated literally, protostome means "first-mouth" and deuterostome means "second-mouth."

To understand the contrasts in how protostome and deuterostome embryos develop, recall that the three embryonic germ layers form during a process called gastrulation (Chapter 23), which begins when cells move from the outside into the center of the embryo. These cell movements create a pore that opens to the outside (**FIGURE 33.12a**). In protostomes, this pore becomes the mouth. The other end of the gut, the anus, forms later. In

## (a) Gastrulation (formation of gut and embryonic germ layers)

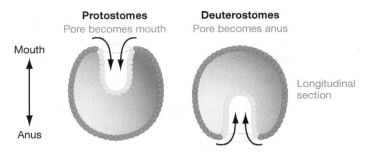

**Protostomes**
Pore becomes mouth

**Deuterostomes**
Pore becomes anus

Mouth

Anus

Longitudinal section

## (b) Formation of coelom (body cavity lined with mesoderm)

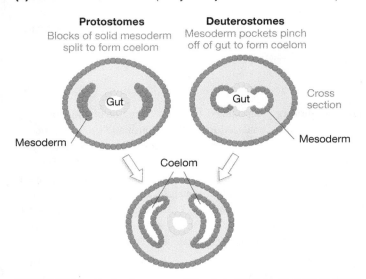

**Protostomes**
Blocks of solid mesoderm split to form coelom

**Deuterostomes**
Mesoderm pockets pinch off of gut to form coelom

Gut

Gut

Cross section

Mesoderm

Mesoderm

Coelom

**FIGURE 33.12 In Protostomes and Deuterostomes, Events in Early Development Differ.** The differences between protostomes and deuterostomes show that there is more than one way to build a bilaterally symmetric, coelomate body plan.

deuterostomes, however, this initial pore becomes the anus; the mouth forms later.

The other developmental difference between the groups arises as gastrulation proceeds and the coelom begins to form. Protostome embryos have two blocks of mesoderm beside the gut. As the left side of **FIGURE 33.12b** indicates, their coelom begins to form when cavities open within each of the two blocks of mesoderm. In contrast, deuterostome embryos have layers of mesodermal cells located on either side of the gut. As the right side of Figure 33.12b shows, their coelom begins to form when these layers bulge out and pinch off to create fluid-filled pockets lined with mesoderm.

In essence, the protostome and deuterostome patterns of development represent two distinct ways of achieving the same end—the construction of a bilaterally symmetric body that contains a cavity lined with mesoderm. The functional or adaptive significance of the differences—if any—is not known.

Two major groups occur within the protostomes: (1) the Lophotrochozoa (pronounced *low-foe-tro-ko-ZOH-ah*) includes the mollusks, annelids, flatworms, and rotifers; and (2) the

Ecdysozoa (pronounced *eck-die-so-ZOH-ah*) includes the arthropods and the nematodes. **Lophotrochozoans** grow continuously when conditions are good. **Ecdysozoans** grow by shedding their external skeletons or outer coverings and expanding their bodies.

Species in the phylum Platyhelminthes (flatworms) are protostomes but lack a coelom—meaning that the coelom was lost during flatworm evolution. The coelom has also been reduced in an array of lineages including arthropods—which have limbs and thus rely less on hydrostatic skeletons for movement.

The vast majority of animal species are protostomes (see Chapter 34). However, the largest animals and most voracious predators tend to be deuterostomes (see Chapter 35).

## Origin of Segmentation

**Segmentation** is defined by the presence of repeated body structures. A segmented backbone is one of the defining characteristics of **vertebrates,** a monophyletic lineage within the Chordata that includes fish, reptiles (including birds), amphibians, and mammals. Of the animals that are not vertebrates, called **invertebrates** (a paraphyletic group), segmentation occurs in annelids (earthworms and other segmented worms) and arthropods (insects, spiders, and crustaceans)—both very prolific and diverse lineages. Recent evidence suggests that segmentation also occurs to some extent in mollusks (snails, clams, squid).

Before molecular data were available, biologists grouped segmented animals like annelids and arthropods together in the same clade. Then Aguinaldo's landmark 1997 revision of animal relationships overturned this view, suggesting that segmentation arose independently in these groups (see Figure 33.2).

Is segmentation in different phyla an example of convergent evolution? Applying the same logic that Finnerty and Martindale used in their study of bilateral symmetry in sea anemones, several researchers are investigating whether the genes that regulate segmentation in different phyla are homologous. For example, one recent study found that one of the same gene regulatory pathways that regulate segmentation in arthropods, called the hedgehog pathway, is also important in regulating the segmentation in annelid worms.

The conclusion so far is that some of the tool-kit genes for segmentation may have arisen early in animal evolution, meaning that they are homologous in different phyla. However, these genes would subsequently have been lost in some lineages and co-opted in different ways and elaborated upon in others, contributing to the diversity of bilaterian body plans we see today. Research continues to test this hypothesis.

Why have organisms with segmented bodies been so successful in terms of diversity? One leading hypothesis is that segmentation enables specialization. Small changes in the expression of certain tool-kit genes along the length of a body can result in novel numbers, shapes, and sizes of body segments and appendages. *Hox* genes are a good example (see Chapters 22 and 34). Natural selection can then favor variations that have adaptive specializations for life in certain aquatic or terrestrial environments—leading to diversification.

In summing up this tour of the animal phylogeny, it's important to note that although biologists are increasingly confident that most or all of these inferences about animal relationships are correct, the phylogeny of animals is still a work in progress. As more taxa are sampled, larger numbers of characters are analyzed, and methods of phylogenetic analysis are refined, the resolution of the tree of life will continue to improve. Stay tuned.

## check your understanding

**If you understand that . . .**

- The origin of body plans in the major lineages of animals was marked by changes in four fundamental features: the number of embryonic tissues present; the evolution of nervous systems and a bilaterally symmetric, cephalized body; the evolution of a body cavity; and protostome versus deuterostome patterns of development.

✓ **You should be able to . . .**

1. Describe whether your body has a tube-within-a-tube design. Justify your answer.
2. Explain why cephalization was important.

*Answers are available in Appendix A.*

## 33.3 What Themes Occur in the Diversification of Animals?

One of the great unresolved mysteries in the study of animal diversity is this: Why did almost all of the phylum-level body plans evolve all at once during the Cambrian, rather than more gradually over time? Animals diversified tremendously *within* phyla after the Cambrian, but no major new lineages arose during the last 500 million years.

One mechanistic hypothesis is that gene regulatory networks are responsible for limiting the origin of new body plans. These networks determine patterns of animal development and thus lay down the body plan. The scientists studying these networks have observed that once the networks are established, they are very resistant to change—that is, changes tend to be fatal. However, a multitude of "switches" and "plug-ins" can be added to networks, providing a mechanism for diversification within lineages after the body plans are established.

As research continues on the origin of body plans, biologists' understanding of the subsequent diversification within lineages is also steadily improving. Several variables have been hypothesized to play a role in animal diversification (Chapter 28):

- *Higher oxygen levels* An increase in oxygen levels may have made the evolution of big, mobile animals possible due to the efficiency of aerobic respiration.
- *The evolution of predation* The earliest animals were sessile and ate organic material. When predators evolved, they exerted

selection pressure on other animals for shells, skeletons, rapid movement, and other adaptations for escaping capture.

- *New niches beget more new niches* As animals diversified, they themselves created new niches that could support yet more ecological diversification.
- *New genes, new bodies* As the animal genetic tool kit evolved—such as the duplication and diversification of *Hox* genes—the potential for morphological diversity increased.

It is likely that a combination of all of these variables was important to the diversification of animals. The result? Animals with the same body plan diversified in their strategies for finding food, ingesting food, and reproducing in different ecological niches. Conversely, animals with different body plans have independently evolved similar strategies for feeding and reproducing when they occupy similar ecological niches. What are the major themes of diversification?

### Sensory Organs

The evolution of a cephalized body was a major breakthrough in the evolution of animals. Along with a mouth and brain, a concentration of sensory organs in the head region—where the animal initially encounters the environment—is a key aspect of cephalization.

Certain senses are almost universal in animals (see Chapter 47). The common senses include sight, hearing, taste/smell, and touch (see examples in **TABLE 33.2**). At least some ability to sense temperature is also common. But as animals diversified, a wide array of specialized sensory abilities also evolved. For example:

- *Magnetic field* Many birds, sea turtles, sea slugs, and other animals can detect Earth's magnetic field and use it as an aid in navigation.
- *Electric field* Some aquatic predators, such as sharks, are so sensitive to electric fields that they can detect electrical activity in the muscles of passing prey.
- *Barometric pressure* Some birds can sense changes in air pressure, which may aid them in avoiding storms.

Variation in sensory abilities is important: It allows different species of animals to collect information about a wide array of environments, including the presence of food, predators, and mates.

### Feeding

To organize the diversity of ways that animals find food, biologists distinguish *what* individuals eat from *how* they eat. Animals within a lineage often pursue different food sources and feeding strategies when they occupy different niches. For example, sea cucumbers and sea stars both have the same echinoderm body plan, but they have different food sources and feeding strategies—the sea cucumber mops up detritus from the seafloor, and the sea star pries open clams and mussels and devours them.

Conversely, animals from *different* lineages often pursue the *same* food sources and feeding strategies when they occupy similar niches. For example, burrowing sea cucumbers and some burrowing polychaete worms (phylum Annelida and

## SUMMARY TABLE 33.2 Diversification of Sensory Organs

| Sense | Example |
|---|---|
| **Sight**<br>*Stimulus:* light<br><br>Flies use their compound eyes to find food and mates, and to escape predators |  |
| **Hearing**<br>*Stimulus:* sound<br><br>Bats use their sense of hearing to find prey and to avoid obstacles in the dark |  |
| **Taste/smell**<br>*Stimulus:* molecules<br><br>Some male moths have elaborate antennae to detect pheromones in the air |  |
| **Touch**<br>*Stimulus:* contact, pressure<br><br>Sea anemones detect and capture prey using their sense of touch |  |

| Other senses | Examples |
|---|---|
| *Stimulus:* temperature (thermal energy) | Pit vipers |
| *Stimulus:* magnetic field | Sea turtles |
| *Stimulus:* electric field | Sharks |
| *Stimulus:* barometric pressure | Birds |
| *Stimulus:* gravity | Squid |

Echinodermata, respectively) have different body plans but use a similar strategy of consuming detritus on the seafloor.

**What Animals Eat: Diversification of Ecological Roles** Animals can be classified as **(1) detritivores** that feed on dead organic matter, **(2) herbivores** that feed on plants or algae, or **(3) carnivores** that feed on animals (see **TABLE 33.3**). **Omnivores** eat both plants and animals. These ecological roles have important implications for whole ecosystems because animal feeding moves both energy and nutrients through food webs (Chapter 56).

Another way to categorize the diverse ecological impacts of animal consumption is to consider the impacts on the organisms that animals consume. **Predators** kill and consume all or most of their prey. Predators are usually larger than their prey and kill them quickly using an array of mouthparts and hunting strategies.

## SUMMARY TABLE 33.3 Diversification of Ecological Roles

| Ecological Role | Example |
|---|---|
| **Detritivores**<br>Feed on dead organic matter<br><br>Millipedes feed on decaying leaves |  |
| **Herbivores**<br>Feed on plants or algae<br><br>Pandas eat vast amounts of bamboo |  |
| **Carnivores**<br>Feed on animals<br><br>Owls sit and wait for prey | |
| **Omnivores**<br>Feed on both plants and animals | *Example:* Humans |

Herbivores usually consume plant tissue without killing the whole organism. However, seed predators are an exception because seeds contain an entire—although embryonic—plant.

Like herbivores, **parasites** often harvest nutrients from certain parts of their hosts, but parasites are usually much smaller than their victims. **Endoparasites** live inside their hosts and usually have simple, wormlike bodies. Tapeworms, of the phylum Platyhelminthes (flatworms), are endoparasites with no digestive system. Instead of a mouth, they have hooks or other structures on their head that attach to their host's intestinal wall. Instead of digesting food themselves, they absorb nutrients directly from their surroundings. **Ectoparasites** live on the outside of their hosts. Ectoparasites usually have limbs or mouthparts that allow them to grasp the host, and mouthparts that allow them to pierce their host's skin and suck the nutrient-rich fluids inside. Aphids and ticks are ectoparasites.

Whether animals consume their victims completely or partially, these consumers can drastically affect the fitness of the consumed organisms. Thus, animals are an important agent of natural selection—influencing the evolution of the species they eat (see Chapter 55).

**How Animals Feed: Four General Strategies** Animal mouthparts vary, and the structure of an animal's mouthparts correlates closely with its method of feeding. Keep this in mind as you review the four general tactics that animals use to obtain food, summarized in **TABLE 33.4**.

**Suspension feeders,** also known as **filter feeders,** employ a wide array of structures to trap suspended particles—usually detritus or plankton, small organisms that drift in the currents. Sponges, like the individual illustrated in Figure 33.3, are suspension feeders. So are clams and mussels, which pump water through their bodies and trap suspended food on their feathery gills—structures that also function in gas exchange. Baleen whales suspension feed by gulping water, squeezing it out between the horny baleen plates that line their mouths, and trapping shrimp-like organisms called krill inside. Barnacles capture particles with their feathery, jointed legs.

Because particles float in water much more readily than in air, suspension feeding is particularly common in aquatic environments. Many suspension feeders are sessile.

Many **deposit feeders** digest organic matter in the sediments; their food consists of sand- or mud-dwelling bacteria, archaea, protists, and fungi, along with detritus that settles on the surface of the sediments. Earthworms, for example, are annelids that swallow soil as well as leaves and other detritus on the surface of the soil.

The seafloor is also rich in organic matter, which rains down from the surface and collects in food-rich deposits. These deposits are exploited by a wide array of segmented worms (annelids) as well as sea cucumbers.

Unlike suspension feeders, which are diverse in size and shape and use various trapping or filtering systems, deposit feeders tend to be similar in appearance. They usually have simple mouthparts, and their body shape is wormlike. Like suspension feeders, however, deposit feeders occur in a wide variety of lineages.

SUMMARY TABLE 33.4　Diversification of Feeding Strategies

| Strategy | Example |
|---|---|
| **Suspension feeders** (filter feeders)<br><br>Capture food by filtering out or concentrating particles floating in water or drifting through the air<br><br>Barnacles use specialized legs to capture plankton |  |
| **Deposit feeders**<br><br>Ingest organic material that has been deposited within a substrate or on its surface<br><br>Sea cucumbers use feeding tentacles to mop up detritus from the seafloor |  |
| **Fluid feeders**<br><br>Suck or mop up liquids like nectar, plant sap, blood, or fruit juice<br><br>Butterflies and moths drink nectar through their extensible, hollow proboscis |  |
| **Mass feeders**<br><br>Take chunks of food into their mouths<br><br>Lions bite chunks of meat off of prey carcasses |  |

**Fluid feeders** range from butterflies and moths that feed on nectar with a straw-like proboscis to vampire bats that feed on blood. Fluid feeders are found in a wide array of lineages and often have mouthparts that allow them to pierce seeds, stems, skin, or other structures in order to withdraw the fluids inside.

**Mass feeders** ingest chunks of food. The structure of their mouthparts correlates with the type of food pieces that they harvest and ingest. Lions, for example, have razor-like teeth for tearing tough flesh into pieces small enough to be swallowed. Snails use a rasp-like structure called a radula to scrape bits of plant tissue or animal flesh into their mouths.

## Movement

Animal locomotion provides an array of important functions: finding food, finding mates, escaping from predators, and dispersing to new habitats. Animals move in highly variable ways; they burrow, slither, swim, fly, crawl, walk, or run—mostly powered by muscle (Chapter 48).

Limbs are a prominent feature of species in many phyla. They develop as outpockets of the body wall and tend to be perpendicular to the anterior–posterior and dorsal–ventral body axes. Limbs can take a variety of forms, from the lobe-like limbs of onychophorans (velvet worms) to the jointed limbs of arthropods and vertebrates to the more flexible tube feet of echinoderms and tentacles of mollusks (**TABLE 33.5**).

Traditionally, biologists have hypothesized that the major types of jointed and unjointed animal limbs were not homologous—that is, not descended from a common ancestor. Because the structure of animal appendages is so diverse, it was logical to maintain that at least some appendages evolved independently of each other. As a result, biologists predicted that completely different genes are responsible for each major type of appendage.

Recent results have challenged this view, however. The experiments in question involve a gene called *Distal-less*, or *Dll*, that was originally discovered in fruit flies. (*Distal* means "away from the body.") The *Dll* protein product seems to deliver a simple message as a fruit fly embryo develops: "Grow appendage out this way."

Biologists in Sean Carroll's lab set out to test the hypothesis that *Dll* might be involved in the initial phase of limb or appendage formation in other animals. The team used a fluorescent marker that sticks to the *Dll* gene product to locate tissues where the gene is expressed. When they introduced the fluorescent marker into embryos from annelids, arthropods, echinoderms, and other phyla, they found that it bound to *Dll* in all of them. More important, the highest concentrations of *Dll* gene products were found in cells that form appendages—even in phyla with wormlike bodies that have extremely simple appendages (**FIGURE 33.13**; see page 650). Other experiments have shown that *Dll* is also involved in limb formation in vertebrates.

Based on these findings, biologists are concluding that all animal appendages have some degree of genetic homology and that they are all derived from appendages that were present in a common ancestor. The idea is that simple appendages evolved early in the history of the Bilateria and that, subsequently, evolution by natural selection produced the diversity of limbs observed today.

---

**SUMMARY TABLE 33.5  Diversification of Limbs**

| Type of Limb | Example |
| --- | --- |
| **Lobe-like limbs** <br><br> Onychophorans (velvet worms) use lobe-like limbs to crawl |  |
| **Jointed limbs** <br><br> The jointed limbs of arthropods (such as this crab) and vertebrates are used for many modes of feeding and locomotion |  |
| **Parapodia** <br><br> Polychaete worms use bristled parapodia to crawl and swim |  |
| **Tube feet** <br><br> Echinoderms like this sea star use tube feet to crawl |  |
| **Tentacles** <br><br> Octopuses use muscular tentacles to crawl and grab prey |  |

| Arthropod | Onychophoran | Annelid |
|-----------|--------------|---------|

Developing legs

Developing segments

**FIGURE 33.13 Genetic Evidence that All Animal Appendages Are Homologous.** In diverse organisms, *Dll* gene products (stained green and dark brown) are localized in areas of the embryos where appendages are forming. These data suggest that the appendages are related by common ancestry.

## Reproduction

An animal may be efficient at moving and eating, but if it does not reproduce, the alleles responsible for its effective locomotion and feeding will not increase in frequency in the population. Evolution by natural selection occurs when individuals with certain alleles produce more surviving offspring than other individuals do (Chapter 25). Organisms live to reproduce.

Given the array of habitats and lifestyles of animals, it's not surprising that they vary tremendously in how they reproduce **(TABLE 33.6)**. A few examples here will help illustrate the diversity of animal reproduction (see Chapter 50 for details).

**Asexual or Sexual Reproduction?** In the phylum Rotifera, an entire lineage called the bdelloids (pronounced *DELL-oyds*) reproduces only asexually, through mitosis, by producing diploid eggs that can mature into adults without being fertilized (a process called parthenogenesis). Even certain fish, lizard, and snail species have never been observed to undergo sexual reproduction.

However, sexual reproduction via meiosis and fusion of gametes is much more common than asexual reproduction in animals; and some animals, like coral polyps, can reproduce either way depending on environmental circumstances. Asexual reproduction tends to be more efficient than sexual reproduction, but sexual reproduction leads to greater genetic diversity, which can be favored by natural selection in variable or unfavorable environments (Chapter 13).

**Where Does Fertilization Occur?** When sexual reproduction does occur, fertilization may be internal, usually within the body of the female, or external, in the environment.

When internal fertilization takes place, a male typically inserts a sperm-transfer organ into the body of a female. In some animal species, males produce sperm in packets, which females then pick up and insert into their own bodies. But in seahorses, females insert eggs into the male's body, where they are fertilized. (The male is pregnant for a time and then gives birth to live young.)

**SUMMARY TABLE 33.6** Diversification of Reproduction

| Reproductive Strategy | Example |
|-----------------------|---------|
| **Asexual reproduction** | |

Polyps within a coral colony are genetically identical clones. They are produced by fission (splitting) or budding

**Sexual reproduction**
External fertilization

Sea cucumbers reproduce sexually by releasing eggs and sperm into the open water, where fertilization occurs

Internal fertilization

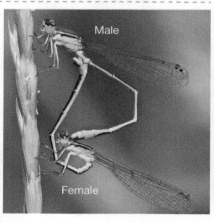

Male

Female

When damselflies copulate, the male holds the female behind her head with claspers and the female retrieves sperm from the male's sperm-transfer organ with the tip of her abdomen

| Modes of embryonic development following internal fertilization | Examples |
|-----------------------------------------------------------------|----------|
| **Viviparous** species nourish embryos internally and give birth to live young | Most mammals |
| **Oviparous** species deposit fertilized eggs; embryos are nourished by yolk | Most insects, birds |
| **Ovoviviparous** species retain eggs internally and then give birth to live young | Guppies, garter snakes |

External fertilization is extremely common in aquatic species. Females lay eggs onto a substrate or release them into open water. Males shed sperm, which swim, on or near the eggs or into open water.

**Where do Embryos Develop?**   Following internal fertilization, eggs and embryos may be retained in the female's body during development, or fertilized eggs may be laid outside of the body to develop independently of the mother:

- **Viviparous** ("live-bearing") species such as humans and most other mammals nourish embryos inside the body and give birth to live young.

- **Oviparous** ("egg-bearing") species such as chickens and crickets deposit fertilized eggs. The embryos within are nourished by yolk.

- **Ovoviviparous** ("egg-live-bearing") species such as guppies and garter snakes retain eggs inside their body during early development, but the growing embryos are nourished by yolk inside the egg and not by nutrients transferred directly from the mother, as in viviparous species. Ovoviviparous females then give birth to well-developed young.

Most mammals and a few species of sea stars, velvet worms, fish (including sharks), amphibians, and lizards are viviparous; some snails, insects, reptiles, and fishes are ovoviviparous. But the vast majority of animals are oviparous.

## Life Cycles

Reproduction is just one component of the diverse life cycles of animals. The vast majority of sexually reproducing animals have diploid-dominant life cycles because the haploid stages—the gametes—are relatively short lived and single celled. But even this general pattern has interesting exceptions, such as haploid males in honeybee colonies. How else do animal life cycles vary?

Perhaps the most spectacular innovation in animal life cycles involves the phenomenon known as **metamorphosis** ("change-form")—a drastic change from one developmental stage to another. The young of some animals, such as zebras, look similar to adults when they are born. Their development is said to be *direct*. However, other animals, such as sea urchins, undergo a dramatic transformation—a metamorphosis—during their life cycle and are said to undergo *indirect* development (**FIGURE 33.14**).

During indirect development, embryogenesis produces **larvae** (singular: **larva**) that look radically different from adults, live in different habitats, and eat different foods. In the case of the sea urchin in Figure 33.14, the larva is bilaterally symmetric and planktonic, and it suspension feeds on single-celled algae; but the adult is radially symmetric and sessile, and it scrapes macroalgae off of rocks.

Through the process of metamorphosis, larvae transform into **juveniles;** they look like adults and live in the same habitats and eat the same foods as adults, but they are still sexually immature. It is only after a period of growth and maturation that juveniles become **adults,** the reproductive stage in the life cycle.

Metamorphosis is extremely common in marine animals as well as in insects (insect metamorphosis is described in Chapter 34)

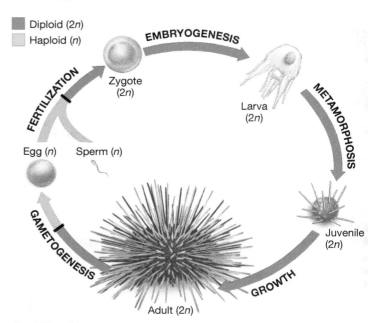

**FIGURE 33.14 Many Animal Life Cycles Include Metamorphosis.** Most sea urchins have a planktonic, feeding larva that is very different from the sessile adult. Drawings are not to scale.

✓ **EXERCISE** A few sea urchins produce especially large, yolk-rich eggs that develop directly into juveniles and adults, bypassing the feeding larval stage. Circle the part of the life cycle that would be different in this case, and pose a hypothesis to explain why or under what conditions this difference might be adaptive.

and many amphibians. Why would natural selection favor such an indirect path to adulthood? One hypothesis emphasizes dispersal. In marine species that have limited or no movement as adults—such as sponges, corals, sea anemones, clams, and sea urchins—larvae function as a dispersal stage. They are a little like the seeds of many land plants—a life stage that allows individuals to move to new habitats.

Another hypothesis for the occurrence of metamorphosis emphasizes feeding efficiency. Because larvae and adults feed on different foods in different ways, they do not compete with each other and can specialize to take advantage of available food sources. For example, the caterpillar larvae of butterflies can feast on nutritious leaves to acquire the energy needed for growth, while adult butterflies feast on flower nectar to acquire energy needed for finding mates.

The diversification of life cycles occurred not only among species in diverse lineages but also within species—such as in organisms that can opt between asexual and sexual reproduction or direct and indirect development, depending on environmental circumstances. The diversification of life cycles, as well as that of sensory structures, ecological roles, feeding strategies, limbs, and reproductive strategies, represent the consequences of evolutionary processes played out in ecological contexts over millions of years.

Let's now examine how the general themes of diversification apply to individual phyla, starting with the most ancient lineages first and then moving on to the extremely diverse protostomes (Chapter 34) and deuterostomes (Chapter 35).

**If you understand that . . .**

- Most of the animal body plans originated during the Cambrian and subsequently diversified.
- Themes of diversification include evolution of different sensory organs, ecological roles, feeding strategies, type of limbs, type of reproduction, and life cycles.

✔ **You should be able to . . .**

1. Explain how the mouthparts of deposit feeders and mass feeders are expected to differ.

2. Suggest why external fertilization is particularly common in aquatic environments, and internal fertilization is particularly common in terrestrial environments.

*Answers are available in Appendix A.*

# 33.4 Key Lineages of Animals: Non-Bilaterian Groups

The fossil record indicates that the phyla Porifera (sponges), Ctenophora (comb jellies), and Cnidaria (jellyfish and others) are the most ancient of all major animal lineages. The phylogeny of animals presented in this chapter is consistent with the fossil record—the first sponges, ctenophores, and cnidarians appear at the base of the tree (Figure 33.2). As you consider each group in more detail, try to pick out which characteristics are unique to the group, and which are common to organisms living in similar environments.

- Porifera (Sponges)
- Ctenophora (Comb Jellies)
- Cnidaria (Jellyfish, Corals, Anemones, Hydroids)

## Porifera (Sponges)

About 8500 species of sponges have been described to date. Although a few freshwater species are known, most are marine. All sponges are **benthic,** meaning that they live at the bottom of aquatic environments. Sponges are particularly common in rocky, shallow-water habitats of the world's oceans. One sponge species native to the Caribbean can grow to heights of 2 meters (m).

Sponges have commercial and medical value to humans. The dried bodies of certain sponge species are able to hold large amounts of water and thus are prized for use in bathing and washing. In addition, researchers are increasingly interested in the array of toxins that sponges produce to defend themselves against predators and bacterial parasites—possibly for use in cancer chemotherapy.

**Feeding** Most sponges are suspension feeders. Their cells beat in a coordinated way to produce a water current that flows through small pores in the outer body wall, into chambers inside the body, and out through a single larger opening (**FIGURE 33.15**). As water passes by feeding cells, organic debris and bacteria, archaea, and small protists are filtered out of the current and then digested. Some deep-sea sponges are predators, however—they capture small crustaceans on hooks that project from the body.

**Movement** Most adult sponges are sessile, though a few species are reported to move at rates of up to 4 millimeters (mm) per day. Most species produce larvae that swim with the aid of cilia, so they are capable of dispersal. Recent research has confirmed that at least one species can contract its body to expel waste products.

**Reproduction** Asexual reproduction occurs in a variety of ways, depending on the species. Some sponge cells are totipotent, meaning that when a fragment breaks off, small groups of adult cells have the capacity to develop into complete new adult organisms. Although individuals of most species produce both eggs and sperm, self-fertilization is rare because individuals release their male and female gametes at different times.

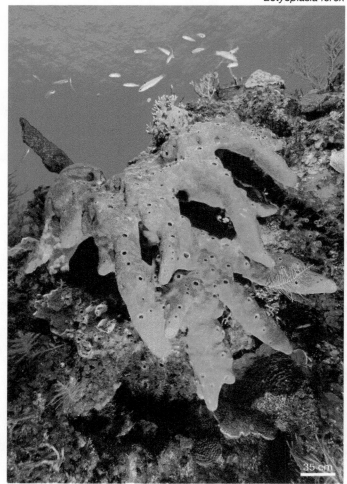
*Ectyoplasia ferox*

**FIGURE 33.15 Sponges Are Sessile Suspension Feeders.**

## Ctenophora (Comb Jellies)

Ctenophores are transparent, ciliated, gelatinous diploblasts that live in marine habitats (**FIGURE 33.16**). Although a few species live on the ocean floor, most are planktonic. Only about 190 species have been described to date, but some are abundant enough to represent a significant fraction of the total planktonic biomass. Accidental introductions of the ctenophore *Mnemiopsis leidyi*, which preys on fish larvae, have devastated fish production in the Black Sea and Caspian Sea. If you have gone swimming in an ocean or bay, you may have bumped up against ctenophores without realizing it since they can be abundant yet nearly invisible in the water. (Don't worry, they are harmless.) Some comb jellies can also be seen at night when they emit pulses of faint phosphorescent light.

**Feeding** Ctenophores are predators, but lack the stinging cells that are characteristic of Cnidarians. Feeding occurs in several ways, depending on the species. Some comb jellies have long tentacles covered with cells that release an adhesive when they contact prey. These tentacles are periodically wiped across the ctenophore's mouth so that captured prey can be ingested. In other species, prey can stick to mucus on the body and be swept toward the mouth by cilia. Still other species ingest large prey whole.

**Movement** Adults move via the beating of cilia, which occur in comblike plates. The plates form rows that run the length of the body. Ctenophores are the largest adult animals known to use cilia for locomotion. ✔You should be able to indicate the origin of adult swimming via rows of coordinated cilia on Figure 33.2.

**Reproduction** Most species have both male and female organs and routinely self-fertilize, though fertilization is external. Larvae are free swimming.

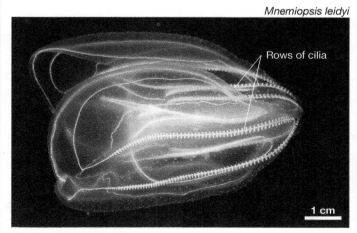

*Mnemiopsis leidyi*

Rows of cilia

1 cm

**FIGURE 33.16 Ctenophores Are Planktonic Predators.**

## Cnidaria (Jellyfish, Corals, Anemones, Hydroids)

Although a few species of Cnidaria inhabit freshwater, the vast majority of the 11,500 species are marine. They are found in all of the world's oceans, occupying habitats from the surface to the substrate, and are important predators. The phylum comprises four main lineages, as shown in **FIGURE 33.17**.

Many cnidarians are radially symmetric diploblasts consisting of ectoderm and endoderm layers that sandwich gelatinous material known as **mesoglea,** which contains a few scattered ectodermal cells. Recent research indicates that at least some jellyfish are triploblastic and have bilaterally symmetric larvae or are bilaterally symmetric as adults. Cnidarians have a gastrovascular cavity instead of a flow-through gut—meaning there is only one opening to the environment for both ingestion and elimination of wastes (see Chapter 44).

Jellyfish have a life cycle that includes both a sessile **polyp** form that reproduces asexually and a free-floating **medusa** that reproduces sexually, as shown in the case of a hydrozoan in **FIGURE 33.18** (see page 654). Anemones and coral, however, exist only as polyps—never as medusae. Reef-building corals secrete outer skeletons of calcium carbonate that create the physical structure of a coral reef—one of the world's most productive habitats (see Chapter 56).

**Feeding** A key synapomorphy of the cnidarians is a specialized cell called a **cnidocyte,** which is used in prey capture. When cnidocytes sense a fish or other type of prey, the cells forcibly eject a barbed, spear-like structure, which may contain toxins. The barbs hold the prey, and the toxins subdue it until it can be brought

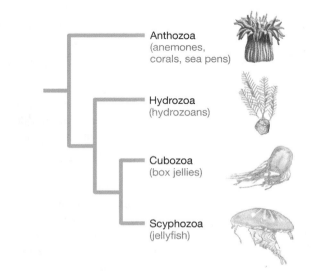

Anthozoa
(anemones, corals, sea pens)

Hydrozoa
(hydrozoans)

Cubozoa
(box jellies)

Scyphozoa
(jellyfish)

**FIGURE 33.17 There are Four Main Lineages within the Cnidaria.**

*(Continued on next page)*

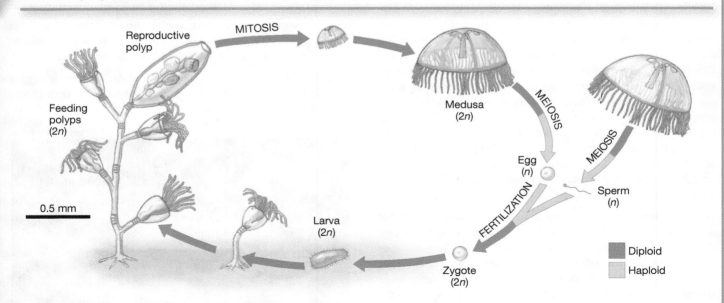

**FIGURE 33.18 Cnidarian Life Cycles May Include a Polyp and Medusa Form.** This is an example of a hydrozoan called *Obelia*. Colonies are often found attached to seaweed, shells, or rocks and contain hundreds of polyps.

to the mouth and ingested. Cnidocytes are commonly located near the mouths of cnidarians or on elongated structures called tentacles. In a very small number of species, cnidarian toxins can be deadly to humans as well as to prey organisms; in Australia, twice as many people die each year from stings by box jellyfish as from shark attacks (**FIGURE 33.19**). ✔You should be able to indicate the origin of cnidocytes on Figure 33.2.

Besides capturing prey actively, most species of coral, some jellyfish, and many anemones host photosynthetic dinoflagellates. The relationship is mutually beneficial, because the protists supply the cnidarian host with food in exchange for protection.

**Movement** Both polyps and medusae are capable of movement. In polyps, the gut cavity acts as a hydrostatic skeleton that works with the aid of muscle-like cells to contract or extend the body. Many polyps can also creep along a substrate, using muscle-like cells at their bases. Medusae can contract the muscle-like cells in the rims of their bell-shaped body rhythmically, enabling paddling motions as well as jet propulsion—the forcible flow of water in the opposite direction of movement. Cnidarian larvae swim by means of cilia.

**Reproduction** Polyps may produce new individuals asexually by (**1**) budding, in which a new organism grows out from the body wall of an existing individual; (**2**) fission, in which an existing adult splits lengthwise to form two individuals; or (**3**) fragmentation, in which parts of an adult regenerate missing pieces to form a complete individual. During sexual reproduction, gametes are usually released from the mouth of a polyp or medusa, and fertilization takes place in the open water. Eggs hatch into larvae that become part of the plankton before settling and developing into polyps.

*Chironex fleckeri*

**FIGURE 33.19 Some Jellyfish Have Long Tentacles, Packed with Cnidocytes That Sting Prey.**

## If you understand . . .

### 33.1  What Is an Animal?

- Animals are multicellular, heterotrophic eukaryotes that lack cell walls and ingest their prey.

- All animals move under their own power at some point in their life cycle. All animals other than sponges have specialized nerve and muscle cells that enable complex movements.

- Animals are eating machines, the largest consumers on Earth.

- Animals comprise 30–35 phyla and may number 8 million or more species.

✔ You should be able to predict how the total amount of plant material in a forest would change if all animals were excluded for one year.

### 33.2  What Key Events Occurred during the Evolution of Animals?

- Animals are a monophyletic group that originated from a protist ancestor that was probably similar to choanoflagellates.

- The basic genetic tool kit for multicellular animals originated at the very root of the animal lineage.

- Sponges lack highly organized, complex tissues other than rudimentary epithelium.

- Most ctenophores and cnidarians have radial symmetry, two embryonic germ layers, and neurons organized into a nerve net. However, some of the regulatory genes responsible for bilateral symmetry arose before the split of cnidarians and bilaterians.

- Most animal species are bilaterians. They have bilateral symmetry, three embryonic tissues, and a coelom—features that gave rise to a tube-within-a-tube body plan.

- Most bilaterians also have a centralized nervous system and cephalized bodies—meaning that a distinctive head region contains the mouth, brain, and sensory organs.

- The bilaterian tube-within-a-tube design is built in one of two fundamental ways—via the protostome or deuterostome patterns of embryonic development.

- Segmentation is a key innovation in annelids, arthropods, and vertebrates.

✔ You should be able to draw a bilaterian that lacks limbs, and label the gut, outer body wall, muscle layers, head region, mouth, anus, brain, and major nerve tracts.

### 33.3  What Themes Occur in the Diversification of Animals?

- Sensory abilities and sensory structures vary among species and correlate with their habitats and feeding methods.

- Animals fill three different ecological roles depending on their source of food: they are detritivores, herbivores, or carnivores—or omnivores, a combination.

- Animals capture food in four ways: Suspension or filter feeders filter organic material or small organisms from water; deposit feeders swallow sediments; fluid feeders lap or suck up liquids; mass feeders harvest chunks of tissue.

- Although the types of appendages used in animal locomotion range from simple lobe-like limbs to complex jointed legs, the genes that indicate where appendages develop may be homologous.

- Asexual reproduction occurs in many species, but sexual reproduction is predominant. Fertilization may be external or internal, and embryos may complete development inside or outside the mother.

- Development may be direct or indirect. During indirect development, a dramatic morphological transformation takes place from one life stage to another, called metamorphosis.

✔ You should be able to select a phylum and give examples of how the themes of diversification apply within that phylum.

### 33.4  Key Lineages of Animals: Non-Bilaterian Groups

- Sponges are diverse, benthic suspension feeders.

- Ctenophores are planktonic predators, the largest animals to use cilia for locomotion.

- Cnidarians are diverse and abundant in habitats around the world. The cnidocyte, or stinging cell, is a synapomorphy for this group.

✔ You should be able to recognize sponges, ctenophores, or cnidarians based on their morphology.

### MasteringBiology

1. **MasteringBiology Assignments**

   **Tutorials and Activities** Animal Phylogenetic Tree; Animal Body Plans; Architecture of Animals

   **Questions** Reading Quizzes, Blue-Thread Questions, Test Bank

2. **eText** Read your book online, search, take notes, highlight text, and more.

3. **The Study Area** Practice Test, Cumulative Test, BioFlix® 3-D Animations, Videos, Activities, Audio Glossary, Word Study Tools, Art

# You should be able to . . .

1. What synapomorphy (shared, derived trait) distinguishes animals as a monophyletic group, distinct from choanoflagellates?
   a. multicellularity
   b. coloniality
   c. heterotrophy
   d. no cell walls

2. True or false? All coelomates are triploblasts.

3. In _____, the mouth develops before the anus; but in _____, the anus develops before the mouth.

4. Why do some researchers maintain that the limbs of all animals are homologous?
   a. Homologous genes, such as *Dll*, are involved in their development.
   b. Their structure—particularly the number and arrangement of elements inside the limb—is the same.
   c. They all function in the same way—in locomotion.
   d. Animal appendages are too complex to have evolved more than once.

5. In a tube-within-a-tube body plan, what is the interior tube?
   a. ectoderm
   b. mesoderm
   c. the coelom
   d. endoderm

6. Which of the following characteristics does not apply to cnidarians?
   a. usually diploblastic
   b. possess a gastrovascular cavity with one opening
   c. undergo metamorphosis
   d. have a central nervous system

7. Explain the difference between a diploblast and a triploblast. How was the evolution of mesoderm associated with the evolution of a coelom?

8. Why is it ecologically significant that animals are heterotrophic *and* multicellular?

9. QUANTITATIVE To estimate the relative abundance of the major phyla, calculate how many named species of arthropods, mollusks, and nematode worms exist per named species of chordate (see Table 33.1). Do you think these calculations are likely to be underestimates, or overestimates? Why?

10. Explain how an animal mother nourishes an embryo in oviparous species versus viviparous species.

11. Specific genes are known to play an important role in the segmentation of arthropods. What approach could you use to test the hypothesis that segmentation in vertebrates (phylum Chordata) is homologous to segmentation in arthropods (phylum Arthropoda)?

12. Which of the following is an example of homology (similarity due to common ancestry)?
    a. suspension feeding in sponges and clams
    b. ectoparasite lifestyle in aphids and ticks
    c. cnidocytes (stinging cells) in jellyfish and sea anemones
    d. metamorphosis in sea urchins and insects

13. Suppose that a gene originally identified in nematodes (roundworms) is found to be homologous with a gene that can cause developmental abnormalities in humans. Would it be possible to study this same gene in fruit flies? Explain.

14. Some sea anemones can produce large colonies by reproducing asexually, but they can also produce planktonic larvae by reproducing sexually. Predict the circumstances under which each mode of reproduction would be favored.

15. Radial symmetry evolved in echinoderms (sea stars and sea urchins) from bilaterally symmetric ancestors. Predict whether the echinoderm nervous system is centralized or diffuse. Explain your logic.

16. You have a unique opportunity to explore a pristine coral reef in the South Pacific. You come across a small organism that you do not recognize and that is not in your field guide. Which of the following suites of characteristics would be most helpful in identifying the organism's phylum?
    a. sessile, green, 2 cm tall, abundant
    b. radial symmetry, suspension feeder
    c. nonsegmented, sessile, changes shape
    d. radial symmetry, sessile, two tissue layers

# 34 Protostome Animals

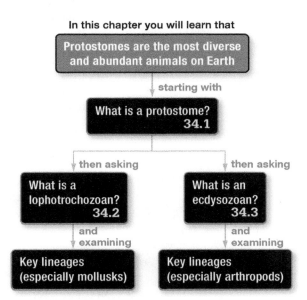

**In this chapter you will learn that**

**Protostomes are the most diverse and abundant animals on Earth**

*starting with*

**What is a protostome?**
**34.1**

*then asking*

**What is a lophotrochozoan?**
**34.2**

*and examining*

**Key lineages (especially mollusks)**

*then asking*

**What is an ecdysozoan?**
**34.3**

*and examining*

**Key lineages (especially arthropods)**

In numbers of individuals and species richness, protostomes are the most abundant and diverse of all animals—and the insects are by far the most abundant and diverse of the protostomes. The insects shown here come from all over the world.

Protostome animals are spectacularly diverse and abundant. To put this in perspective, consider that of the more than 30 animal phyla known to exist, at least 22 are protostomes. Table 33.1 summarized the major protostome phyla. You will likely recognize many of the more familiar ones:

- *Arthropoda*, including the insects, crustaceans (shrimp, lobsters, crabs), chelicerates (spiders and mites), and myriapods (millipedes, centipedes)

- *Mollusca*, including the snails, clams, octopuses, and squid

- *Annelida*, including the segmented worms such as the earthworms, polychaete worms, and leeches

✔ When you see this checkmark, stop and test yourself. Answers are available in Appendix A.

657

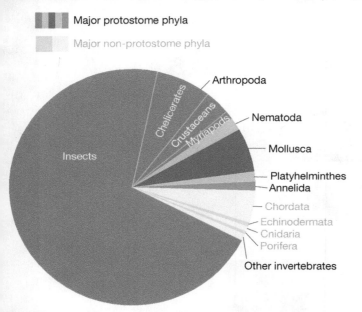

Arthropoda

Chelicerates

Crustaceans

Myriapods

Nematoda

Insects

Mollusca

Platyhelminthes

Annelida

Chordata

Echinodermata

Cnidaria

Porifera

Other invertebrates

**FIGURE 34.1 The Relative Diversity of Animal Lineages.** Most animals are protostomes. About 70 percent of all known species of animals on Earth are insects, most of them beetles. (Humans and other vertebrates are deuterostomes, in the phylum Chordata.)

DATA: Chapman, A. D. 2009. *Numbers of Living Species in Australia and the World,* 2nd ed. Canberra: Australian Biological Resources Study.

Some protostome phyla have only a few named species, such as the phylum Priapula, which contains 16 named species. On the other end of the spectrum, over 85,000 mollusks have been named thus far, and about 1.2 million arthropod species, of which about a million are insects. Scientists estimate that the actual number of arthropod species may be over 10 million.

The pie chart in **FIGURE 34.1** shows the relative numbers of named species in various animal phyla. Notice that the wedges representing non-protostome phyla, labeled Chordata, Cnidaria, Echinodermata, and Porifera, are small. Almost all animal species are protostomes.

Certain protostomes are not only diverse (in numbers of species), but also extremely abundant (in numbers of individuals). A typical acre of pasture in England is home to almost 18 *million* individual beetles and up to 9 *billion* roundworms. The world population of ants is estimated to be 1 million billion (1,000,000,000,000,000) individuals.

Given the diversity and abundance of protostomes, you should not be surprised that they fill very important ecological roles. As a group, protostomes live in virtually every aquatic and terrestrial habitat in the world and can be detritivores, herbivores, or carnivores. If one of biology's most fundamental goals is to understand the diversity of life on Earth, then protostomes—particularly the mollusks and arthropods—demand our attention.

The ecological importance of protostomes extends to the health and welfare of humans in profound and diverse ways. For example:

- Protostomes, especially shellfish (clams, oysters, scallops, crabs, shrimp, lobsters), are a major direct source of food for humans, which makes them economically important.

- Humans also rely on protostomes indirectly for their ecosystem services. For example, many farmers rely on protostomes like earthworms to prepare the soil, and on bees and other insects to pollinate their crops.

- Some insects have a massive negative impact on food production by damaging crops, while other insects protect crops from pests.

- Some protostomes produce valuable materials such as silk and pearls.

- Many protostomes play an important role in causing or transmitting human diseases, and are common parasites.

- The protostomes include two of the most important model organisms in all of biological science: the fruit fly *Drosophila melanogaster* and the roundworm *Caenorhabditis elegans* (see **BioSkills 13** in Appendix B).

Let's take a closer look at what defines the protostomes and then explore the diversity within the major phyla.

## 34.1 What Is a Protostome?

There are two major groups of bilaterally symmetric, triploblastic animals: the protostomes and deuterostomes (Chapter 33). The **protostomes** are distinguished from the deuterostomes by two developmental characteristics:

1. During gastrulation, the initial pore that forms in the embryo becomes the mouth—protostome translates to "first-mouth." (In deuterostomes the pore develops into the anus, and the mouth develops later.)

2. If a **coelom** (a body cavity) forms later in development, it forms from cavities that arise within blocks of mesodermal cells (rather than as mesoderm pockets pinching off the gut, as in deuterostomes).

Phylogenetic studies have long supported the hypothesis that protostomes are a monophyletic group, meaning the protostome developmental sequence arose just once. But biologists have found it difficult to sort out the relationships among protostome lineages. During the 500 million years of evolution that followed the diversification of protostomes during the Cambrian explosion, some morphological characteristics evolved independently in different lineages, resulting in convergent evolution. Other characteristics thought to be synapomorphies—shared, derived traits within a lineage—were lost in some groups. As a result, morphological data have led to many alternative hypotheses about phylogenetic relationships.

Recent analyses of DNA sequence data have rejected many previous hypotheses of relationships based on morphological data. As the phylogenetic tree in **FIGURE 34.2** shows, the recent data support two major subgroups within the protostomes. The Lophotrochozoa (pronounced *low-foe-tro-ko-ZOH-ah*) include mollusks and annelid worms. The Ecdysozoa (pronounced *eck-die-so-ZOH-ah*) include the arthropods.

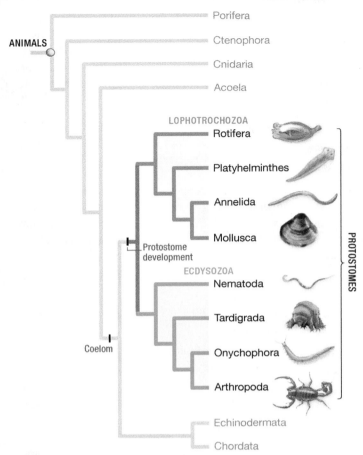

FIGURE 34.2 Protostomes Are a Monophyletic Group Comprising Two Major Lineages. There are 22 phyla of protostomes, but the eight major phyla shown account for about 99.5 percent of the known species.

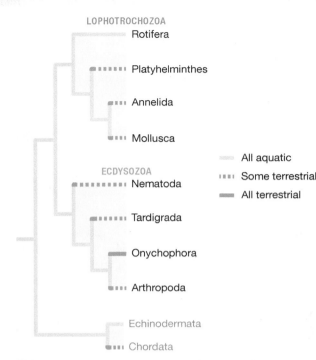

FIGURE 34.3 The Water-to-Land Transition Occurred Several Times in the Protostomes. The transition occurred only once in the deuterostomes, in phylum Chordata.

✔ QUESTION According to this tree, terrestrial living arose seven different times independently in protostomes. Why would you not instead conclude that terrestrial living was ancestral and the aquatic lifestyle arose seven times independently?

Before considering each of these groups in more detail, let's examine the key themes in the evolutionary diversification of the protostomes. Recall that all animal lineages evolved diverse ways of sensing the environment, feeding, moving, reproducing, and developing (see Chapter 33). In addition, diversification in protostomes was triggered by the transition from aquatic to terrestrial habitats, and the modular design of many protostome body plans.

## The Water-to-Land Transition

Fossils from the Burgess Shale in Canada, Chengjiang in China, and other sites show that protostome lineages originated in marine environments—that is, in the ocean. Today, protostomes are the most abundant animals in the world's oceans as well as in virtually every freshwater and terrestrial habitat. Like land plants and fungi, protostomes made the transition from aquatic to terrestrial environments.

To help put this achievement in perspective, note that green plants made the move from freshwater to land just once (Chapter 31). It is not yet clear whether fungi moved from aquatic habitats to land once or several times (Chapter 32). Only one lineage among deuterostomes moved onto land (Chapter 35).

But protostomes made a water-to-land transition multiple times as they diversified (**FIGURE 34.3**).

Water-to-land transitions are important because they open up entirely new habitats and new types of resources to exploit. Based on this reasoning, biologists propose that the ability to live in terrestrial environments was a key event in the diversification of several protostome phyla.

Several adaptations were required for protostomes to thrive on land, such as the ability to:

1. exchange gases,

2. avoid drying out, and

3. hold up their bodies under their own weight.

Recall that an **adaptation** is a trait that increases the fitness (reproductive success) of individuals in a particular environment.

Land animals exchange gases with the atmosphere readily as long as they have a large, moist surface area that is exposed to the air (Chapter 45). The bigger challenge is to prevent the gas-exchange surface and other parts of the body from drying out. How do terrestrial protostomes solve this problem?

• Roundworms, earthworms, and other terrestrial protostomes live in humid soils or other moist environments and exchange gases across their body surface. They have a high surface-area-to-volume ratio, which increases the efficiency of gas exchange.

Some terrestrial arthropods and mollusks have gills or other respiratory structures located *inside* the body, minimizing water loss, such as tracheae in insects (Chapter 43).

Insects evolved a waxy layer to minimize water loss from the body surface, with openings to respiratory passages that can be closed if the environment dries.

Insect eggs have a thick membrane that keeps moisture in, and the eggs of slugs and snails have a thin calcium carbonate shell that helps retain water. Desiccation-resistant eggs evolved repeatedly in populations that made the transition to life on land.

Unlike land plants and fungi, many land animals can also move to moister habitats if the area they are in gets too dry.

What are some of the mechanical constraints of living on land? Think for a moment of the weightless feeling you experience in a swimming pool. The upward buoyant force provided by the water counteracts the downward pull on your body mass that is exerted by gravity. Without this buoyant force, animals on land require greater structural support to hold their bodies up and to move. Further, as an animal doubles in length (assuming no change in shape), its weight increases by a factor of 8—so larger organisms feel the effect of gravity more than smaller organisms (Chapter 48). This mechanical constraint has limited the size of many protostomes, including insects, on land.

## Modular Body Plans

Morphological and physiological diversification has a genetic basis. Until recent decades, biologists assumed that very different genetic instructions were required to create very different organisms. This reasoning seems logical but turns out to be false. Consider that:

Multicellular animals have a common tool kit of genes that establish the animal body plan during development. *Hox* genes have been featured in several chapters because they are an important part of this tool kit (see Chapters 22 and 33).

The genetic tool kit can direct the development of dramatically different types and numbers of structures when the genes are expressed at different times and places during development.

The upshot is that the diversification of animal body plans can occur not just by the generation of new genes over time, but also—and especially—by the changing of the expression pattern of existing genes, in particular regulatory genes. Sean Carroll and colleagues demonstrated this principle clearly when they showed that the *Distal-less* gene is essential to the formation of different types of limbs in diverse lineages, ranging from annelids and arthropods to chordates (see Chapter 33).

When comparing diverse organisms within a lineage, genetically based *modularity* in body plans is evident, meaning that a small set of elements can be reused and rearranged to produce a large variety of outcomes. For example, the change in expression patterns of regulatory genes can account for both the dramatic

increase in the number of vertebrae (back bones) in snakes as well as the loss of limbs in this group (Chapter 22). Thus, a change in expression of preexisting genes generated a dramatically different body plan from that of a shorter, limbed ancestor. Keep the concept of modularity in mind as you read on about the diversity of protostomes.

## 34.2 What Is a Lophotrochozoan?

The 13 phyla of protostome subgroup Lophotrochozoa include the mollusks, annelids, and flatworms (phylum Platyhelminthes; pronounced *plah-tee-hell-MIN-theez*). Lophotrochozoans are named for two of the three unique morphological traits that define the lineage:

1. a feeding structure called a *lophophore*, which is found in three phyla;

2. a type of larva called a *trochophore*, which is common to many of the phyla; and

3. a spiral pattern of cleavage in embryos.

As **FIGURE 34.4a** shows, a **lophophore** (literally, "tuft-bearer") is a specialized structure that rings the mouth and functions in suspension feeding. Lophophores are found in bryozoans (moss animals), brachiopods (lamp shells), and phoronids (horseshoe worms), together called the lophophorates.

Trochophores are a type of larvae common to marine mollusks, marine annelids, and several other phyla in the Lophotrochozoa. As **FIGURE 34.4b** shows, a **trochophore** (literally, "wheel-bearer") larva has a ring of cilia around its middle. These cilia allow swimming and, in some species, sweep food particles into the mouth.

Trochophore larvae, like other larvae, occur in animals that undergo indirect development—where larvae often look radically different from adults, live in different habitats, and eat different foods (Chapter 33). The process of metamorphosis from larvae to adults in marine species is hypothesized to be an adaptation that allows larvae of sessile or slow-moving adults to disperse to new habitats by floating or swimming in the plankton.

Larvae are not unique to lophotrochozoans—even the earliest known animals, the sponges, had larvae. However, recent analyses suggest that the trochophore larva originated early in the evolution of lophotrochozoans and then evolved into different larval types later in some groups.

Recent phylogenetic analyses of lophotrochozoans have inspired the hypothesis that the spiral pattern of cleavage in embryos is a synapomorphy for this monophyletic group. When cells divide at oblique angles to each other during early embryogenesis, a spiraling pattern of cells results in the blastula (**FIGURE 34.5**). This is in contrast to other patterns of cleavage, such as radial cleavage, where cells divide at right angles to each other. Although spiral cleavage has been highly conserved in some lophotrochozoan phyla, it has been modified or lost in others. ✔ You should be able to indicate the origin of spiral cleavage on Figure 34.2.

**(a) Lophophores** function in suspension feeding in adults.

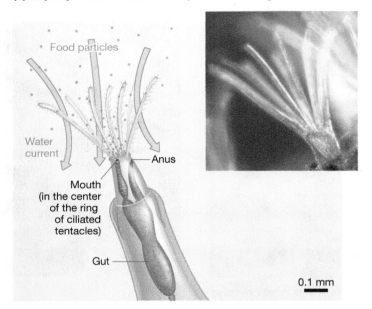

**(b) Trochophore** larvae swim and may feed.

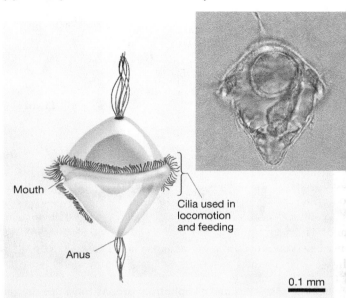

**FIGURE 34.4 Lophotrochozoans Have Distinctive Traits. (a)** Three phyla of lophotrochozoans, including the bryozoan shown here, have the feeding structure called a lophophore. **(b)** Many phyla of lophotrochozoans have the type of larva called a trochophore.

The implications of spiral cleavage to adult diversity are becoming evident as modern molecular techniques are applied to studies of comparative embryology. For example, spiral cleavage is clockwise in some snails but counterclockwise in others, resulting in adults with right-handed and left-handed whorls, respectively. It turns out that the cleavage pattern determines the downstream expression of *Nodal* and *Pitx*—tool-kit genes that establish the asymmetry of snails. *Nodal* and *Pitx* are also important in the left-right asymmetries of vertebrates, illustrating how homologous tool-kit genes can have similar but different effects in different lineages.

**(a)** Spiral cleavage is unique to lophotrochozoans.

**(b)** Radial cleavage, for comparison

**FIGURE 34.5 Spiral Cleavage is a Synapomorphy for the Lophotrochozoans.** This pattern of early cell divisions, here contrasted with radial cleavage, has been modified or lost in some lineages. (Some of the cells are stained to help compare the patterns.)

In sum, if you were to observe a lophophore, a trochophore larva, or spiral cleavage in an unfamiliar animal, you could be confident that the animal belongs to the Lophotrochozoa. However, all lophotrochozoans do not possess all three of these characteristics.

Let's briefly consider the diversity of wormlike lophotrochozoans and then look at the most diverse and abundant phylum, the mollusks.

## Wormlike Lophotrochozoans

Most protostome phyla include species that have long, thin, tubelike bodies that lack limbs. That is, they are **worms** with a basic tube-within-a-tube design (Chapter 33). The outside tube is the skin, which is derived from ectoderm; the inside tube is the gut, which is derived from endoderm. Muscles and organs derived from mesoderm are located between the two tubes.

Since the coelom evolved in the common ancestor of protostomes and deuterostomes (see Figure 34.2), many lophotrochozoans have a well-developed coelom—not only allowing space for fluids to circulate among organs but also serving as part of a hydrostatic skeleton for movement. The hydrostatic skeleton enables worms to crawl, burrow, and even swim. Specific movements depend on factors such as the organization of muscles within the body, whether the worms are segmented or unsegmented, and the presence or absence of bristles or other structures on the body surface.

As with spiral cleavage and the trochophore larva, however, the coelom was reduced or lost in several lineages. For example, the flatworms—which are mostly small and thin or parasitic—lack a coelom entirely.

**(a)** Mouthparts for suspension feeding

**(b)** Mouthparts for deposit feeding

**(c)** Mouthparts for mass feeding

Feathery mouthparts capture plankton

Long, sticky tentacles reach across substrate and deliver organic particles to mouth (worm body remains hidden)

Eversible proboscis with sharp fangs impales prey

**FIGURE 34.6 Many Wormlike Lophotrochozoans Have Specialized Mouthparts.** These three examples are polychaete worms, phylum Annelida.

✔**EXERCISE** It is common to find diverse worms in the same habitat. Suggest a hypothesis to explain why this is possible.

Wormlike lophotrochozoans include suspension, deposit, liquid, and mass feeders (see Chapter 33). Exploiting a diversity of foods is possible in part because worms have such a wide variety of mouthparts for capturing and processing food.

The lophophore feeding structure that is used by lophophorates, such as phoronid worms, is an example of one type of specialized mouthpart (see Figure 34.4a). Let's consider several other examples from the phylum Annelida, the segmented worms.

Segmented worms are a diverse group, especially the marine polychaetes (**FIGURE 34.6**). For example, they may live in tubes and extend their feathery tentacles into the water to suspension feed, burrow in the sediments and reach out with their spaghetti-like tentacles to deposit feed, or spear prey with sharp fangs on the tip of a tubular, extensible feeding appendage called a **proboscis.**

While the diversity of wormlike lophotrochozoans is impressive, you can see from the pie wedges in Figure 34.1 that they do not quite compare to the mollusks in terms of diversity.

## What Is a Mollusk?

Mollusks exhibit the lophotrochozoan mode of growth and development. But unlike the lophotrochozoans as a whole, the mollusks can be identified by distinctive characteristics. Mollusks have a specialized body plan based on three major components (**FIGURE 34.7**):

1. the **foot,** a large muscle located at the base of the animal and usually used in movement;

2. the **visceral mass,** the region containing most of the main internal organs and the external gill; and

3. the **mantle,** an outgrowth of the body wall that covers the visceral mass, forming an enclosure called the mantle cavity. In many species, the mantle secretes a hard calcium carbonate shell.

✔You should be able to indicate the origin of the molluscan body plan on Figure 34.2.

Once the molluscan body plan evolved, subsequent diversification was largely driven by adaptations that allowed the mollusks to move, feed, or reproduce in novel ways. The result was a dramatic radiation of mollusks into several lineages, including **bivalves** (clams and mussels), **gastropods** (slugs and snails), **chitons** (mollusks with dorsal shells made of plates), and **cephalopods** (squid and octopuses).

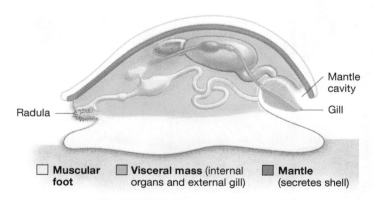

Radula

Mantle cavity

Gill

☐ **Muscular foot**   ☐ **Visceral mass** (internal organs and external gill)   ■ **Mantle** (secretes shell)

**FIGURE 34.7 Mollusks Have a Specialized Body Plan.** This diagram of a generalized mollusk shows that the mollusk body plan is based on a foot, a visceral mass, and a mantle. Gills are located inside a cavity created by the mantle.

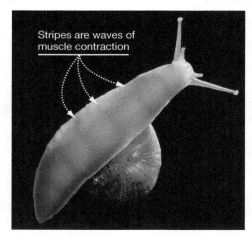

Stripes are waves of muscle contraction

**FIGURE 34.8 How Snails Walk on One Foot.** Waves of muscle contractions, moving forward or backward along the length of the foot, allow mollusks like this snail to creep along a substrate.

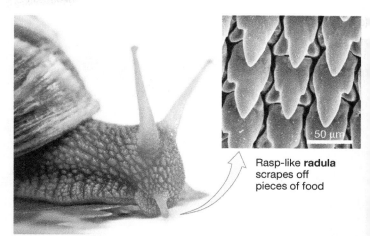

50 μm

Rasp-like **radula** scrapes off pieces of food

**FIGURE 34.9 The Radula Is Unique to Mollusks.** The size and shape of the radular teeth is highly correlated with the type of food eaten by the species.

**The Foot Is a Muscular Hydrostat** Snails and chitons have a large, muscular foot at the base of the body that—like your tongue—works as a type of hydrostatic skeleton called a muscular hydrostat. How can an animal move with just one foot? Waves of muscle contractions sweep backward or forward along the length of the foot, allowing individuals to crawl along a surface (**FIGURE 34.8**). Biologists in the field of biomechanics have measured the mechanical properties of snail mucus. They observed that it has the remarkable ability to increase traction for the parts of the foot that are not moving, while lubricating motion for the parts that are advancing.

In bivalves such as clams, the foot is modified as a digging appendage. The foot of cephalopods like squid and octopus is modified to form tentacles for crawling and grasping.

**The Visceral Mass Separates Internal Organs from the Hydrostatic Skeleton** The visceral mass is the space in all mollusks where organs and surrounding fluids are located. This might not seem like much of an innovation, but compare this body plan to that of worms, where the hydrostatic skeleton and internal organs are inseparable. The separation of the foot and visceral mass in mollusks may have enabled diversification of both.

The coelom itself is highly reduced in most mollusks, functioning mostly in reproduction and excretion of wastes. The organs occupy a different type of body cavity called a **hemocoel** ("blood-hollow"; pronounced *HEE-mah-seal*), where body fluids bathe the organs directly in an open circulatory system (see Chapter 45). A hemocoel is different from a coelom because it is not lined in mesoderm.

At the anterior end of the visceral mass, the mouth has a unique molluscan feeding structure called a **radula**, which functions like a rasp or file. The mollusk moves the radula back and forth over the food source, causing the many sharp plates to scrape material so that it can be ingested (**FIGURE 34.9**). Since it is highly unlikely that such a unique structure would evolve more than once, the radula probably evolved early in molluscan

evolution. It was later lost in the bivalves, which acquire food by suspension feeding.

**The Mantle Secretes a Shell** In many species the mantle secretes a shell made of calcium carbonate. Some mollusk species have a shell consisting of one, two, or eight parts, or valves; others have no shell at all. The ability to secrete a protective shell may have been an important adaptation during the Cambrian and beyond as the number of predators increased. Note, however, that shells made of calcium carbonate are heavy. Thus, there is a trade-off between protection and mobility. As you might predict, mollusks with thick shells are constrained to aquatic habitats where buoyant forces help support the load. The largest and most agile of all aquatic mollusks, cephalopods such as squid and octopus, have highly reduced shells or none at all. Terrestrial mollusks have thin shells or none at all.

The mantle was also modified in many ways to serve diverse functions other than secreting shells. For example, cephalopods have a mantle lined with muscle. When the cavity surrounded by the mantle fills with water and the mantle muscles contract, a stream of water is forced out of a tube called a **siphon.** The force of the water propels the squid in a form of locomotion called jet propulsion (**FIGURE 34.10**, see page 664). The mantle of bivalves such as clams is modified to form two siphons to control incurrent and excurrent water flow over their gills.

**Modular Mollusks** How did the novel body plan and lifestyle of mollusks such as squid evolve? Mark Martindale and his colleagues tried to address this question by looking at the role of *Hox* genes in the organization of the squid body plan. They found that:

- Squid have nine *Hox* genes that are homologous to those found in other bilaterians (recall that *Hox* genes are important in establishing the anterior–posterior axis of animals).

- Although *Hox* genes are usually organized in a collinear fashion (see Chapter 22), they were co-opted in a new pattern in

Cavity enclosed by
mantle fills with water

Water is forced out through
siphon; animal moves

**FIGURE 34.10 Jet Propulsion in Mollusks.** In jet propulsion, muscular contractions of the mantle force the water out through a movable siphon.

✔ **EXERCISE** Circle the part of the squid that is homologous to the snail foot.

squid, suggesting a mechanism by which a change in the regulation of tool-kit genes could result in novel body structures, such as the modification of the molluscan foot into a crown of muscular tentacles.

The take-home message is that mollusks have a modular design. That is, while all mollusks have a foot, visceral mass, and mantle, the sizes, shapes, and functions of these structures have diversified in ways that enable drastically different methods of feeding, moving, and reproducing.

Let's take a closer look at some of the diversity within the main lophotrochozoan phyla.

## Key Lineages: Lophotrochozoans

The phyla within Lophotrochozoa are united by shared mechanisms of early development and growth, but they are highly diverse in terms of their resulting morphology. You might not even recognize some of them as having a bilaterally symmetrical body plan.

Let's take a closer look at five key lophotrochozoan phyla: **(1)** Bryozoa, **(2)** Rotifera, **(3)** Platyhelminthes, **(4)** Annelida, and **(5)** Mollusca. Because the Mollusca is so species rich and diverse, the detailed descriptions in this section consider the four most familiar lineages of mollusks separately:

● Lophotrochozoans > Bryozoa (Bryozoans)

● Lophotrochozoans > Rotifera (Rotifers)

● Lophotrochozoans > Platyhelminthes (Flatworms)

● Lophotrochozoans > Annelida (Segmented Worms)

● Lophotrochozoans > Mollusca > Bivalvia (Clams, Mussels, Scallops, Oysters)

● Lophotrochozoans > Mollusca > Gastropoda (Snails, Slugs, Nudibranchs)

● Lophotrochozoans > Mollusca > Polyplacophora (Chitons)

● Lophotrochozoans > Mollusca > Cephalopoda (Nautilus, Cuttlefish, Squid, Octopuses)

## Lophotrochozoans > Bryozoa (Bryozoans)

Bryozoans, sometimes also called ectoprocts or moss animals, are tiny lophophorate animals that live in colonies that look more like a sponge or coral than a bilaterian (**FIGURE 34.11**). The oldest bryozoan fossils date back to the late Cambrian, giving this group the distinction of being the most recent animal phylum to appear in the fossil record. Today, bryozoans live mostly in marine environments, especially in the tropics, but also in some freshwater environments. So far, 5700 species have been described. The colonies range in size, from millimeters to meters, and in shape, from fans to encrusting sheets.

**Feeding** Bryozoan individuals, or zooids, suspension feed on plankton using a lophophore (see Figure 34.4).

**Movement** Most bryozoans are sessile. Only the (non-trochophore) larvae are capable of dispersing to new habitats.

**Reproduction** Bryozoans can increase the size of their colony by asexual reproduction, by budding. They can also reproduce sexually—zooids are hermaphrodites, some having both male and female reproductive organs at the same time, other serving first as males then as females.

*Triphyllozoan* species

1 cm

**FIGURE 34.11 A Bryozoan Colony.** You can see what an individual animal looks like in Figure 34.4.

## Lophotrochozoans > Rotifera (Rotifers)

The 2100 **rotifer** species that have been identified thus far live in damp soils as well as marine and freshwater environments. They are important components of the plankton in freshwater and in brackish (slightly salty) waters. Rotifers have a coelom, and most are less than 1 millimeter (mm) long. Although rotifers do not have a lophophore or a trochophore larval stage, their mode of growth and DNA sequences identify them as a member of the lophotrochozoan lineage.

**Feeding** Rotifers have a cluster of cilia called a **corona** at their anterior end (**FIGURE 34.12**). In many species, the beating of the cilia in the corona makes suspension feeding possible by creating a current that sweeps microscopic food particles into the mouth. The corona is a synapomorphy of this group. ✔ You should be able to indicate the origin of the corona on Figure 34.2.

**Movement** Although a few species of rotifers are sessile, most swim via the beating of cilia in the corona.

**Reproduction** Most reproduction is sexual, but females of some rotifer species can reproduce asexually by a process called **parthenogenesis**—the female produces unfertilized eggs by mitosis; the eggs then hatch into new, asexually produced individuals. In a group of rotifers called the bdelloids, only females have been found and all reproduction appears to be by parthenogenesis. Whether reproduction is sexual or asexual, rotifer development is direct, meaning that fertilized eggs hatch and grow into adults without going through metamorphosis.

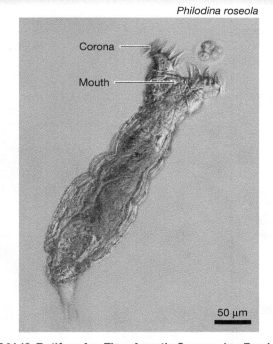

*Philodina roseola*

Corona

Mouth

50 μm

**FIGURE 34.12 Rotifers Are Tiny, Aquatic Suspension Feeders.**

The flatworms are a large and diverse phylum. More than 20,000 species have been described in four major lineages:

- *Turbellaria* are free-living flatworms. Although a few turbellarian species are terrestrial, most live on the substrates of freshwater or marine environments. Some marine flatworms are brightly colored and several centimeters long (**FIGURE 34.13a**). However, the freshwater planarians common to biology labs, such as *Dugesia*, are drab and only a few millimeters long.

- *Cestoda* are endoparasitic tapeworms that parasitize fish, mammals, or other vertebrates (**FIGURE 34.13b**).

- *Trematoda* are endoparasitic or ectoparasitic flukes that parasitize vertebrates, arthropods, annelids, and mollusks (**FIGURE 34.13c**). In humans, a fluke is responsible for schistosomiasis—a serious public health issue in many tropical and subtropical nations.

- *Monogenea* are ectoparasites that parasitize fish.

**Flatworms** are named for the broad, flattened shape of their bodies. (The Greek roots *platy* and *helminth* mean "flat-worm.") Species in the Platyhelminthes are unsegmented and lack a coelom. They also lack structures that are specialized for gas exchange. Further, they do not have blood vessels for circulating oxygen and nutrients to their cells. Based on these observations, biologists interpret the flattened bodies of these animals as an adaptation that gives flatworms an extremely high surface-area-to-volume ratio. This flat body plan allows nutrients and gases to diffuse efficiently to all of the cells inside the animal. The downside is that the body surface has to be moist for gas exchange to take place. Flatworms are restricted to aquatic and moist terrestrial environments. ✔ You should be able to indicate the origin of the flattened, acoelomate body plan on Figure 34.2.

**Feeding** The Platyhelminthes lack a lophophore and have a digestive tract that is "blind"—meaning it has only one opening for ingestion of food and elimination of wastes.

- Most turbellarians are hunters that prey on protists or small animals; others scavenge dead animals.

- Tapeworms are strictly parasitic and feed on nutrients provided by hosts. They do not have a mouth or a digestive tract, and they obtain nutrients by diffusion across their body wall.

- Flukes are parasites and feed by gulping host tissues and fluids through a mouth.

**Movement** In general, flatworms do not move much. Some turbellarians can swim by undulating their bodies, and most can creep along substrates with the aid of cilia on their ventral surface. Adult cestodes have hooked attachment structures at their anterior end that permanently attach them to the interior of their host.

**Reproduction** Turbellarians can reproduce asexually by splitting themselves in half. If they are fragmented as a result of a predator attack, the body parts can regenerate into new individuals. Most turbellarians contain both male and female organs and reproduce sexually by aligning with another individual and engaging in mutual and simultaneous fertilization.

In flukes and tapeworms, individuals reproduce sexually and either cross-fertilize or self-fertilize. The reproductive systems and life cycles of flukes and tapeworms are extremely complex, however. In many cases the life cycle involves two or even three distinct host species; sexual reproduction occurs in the **definitive host,** and asexual reproduction occurs in one or more **intermediate hosts.** For example, humans are the definitive host of the blood fluke *Schistosoma mansoni*, and snails are the intermediate host.

**(a) Turbellarians** are free living.

*Pseudoceros ferrugineus*

**(b) Cestodes** are endoparasitic.

*Taenia* species

**(c) Trematodes** are endoparasitic.

*Dicrocoelium dendriticum*

**FIGURE 34.13 Flatworms Have Simple, Flattened Bodies.**

Most **annelids** have a segmented body and a coelom. ✓You should be able to indicate the origin of annelid segmentation on Figure 34.2. The 16,800 described species were traditionally divided into groups called Polychaeta (*pol-ee-KEE-ta*) and Clitellata. Recent analyses have supported Clitellata as a monophyletic group, composed of Hirudinea (leeches), and Oligochaeta (*oh-LIG-oh-keet-a*; earthworms and other oligochaetes). However, the Polychaeta are paraphyletic—that is, including some but not all members of a clade (**FIGURE 34.14**). Further, unsegmented worms called Sipunculida and Echiura, which were traditionally thought to be independent phyla, are actually groups within Annelida—they lost their segmentation.

The common ancestor of the annelids had a key synapomorphy in addition to segmentation: numerous, bristle-like extensions called **chaetae** that extend from appendages called **parapodia.** As the name suggests, polychaetes ("many-bristles"; **FIGURE 34.15a**) have more chaetae than oligochaetes ("few-bristles"; **FIGURE 34.15b**). However, highly mobile polychaetes have larger parapodia and more chaetae than more sedentary polychaetes, which have reduced parapodia and chaetae adapted for burrowing in sediments or living in tubes.

**Feeding** The polychaete lineages have a wide variety of methods for feeding, including suspension feeding, deposit feeding, and mass feeding (Figure 34.6). Virtually all oligochaetes, in contrast, make their living by deposit feeding in soils. The tunnels that they make are critically important in aerating soil, and their feces contribute large amounts of organic matter. About half of the leeches are ectoparasites that attach themselves to fish or other hosts and suck blood and other body fluids (**FIGURE 34.15c**). The nonparasitic leech species are predators or scavengers.

**Movement** Polychaetes and oligochaetes crawl or burrow with the aid of their hydrostatic skeletons; the parapodia of polychaetes also act as paddles or tiny feet that aid in movement. Many polychaetes and leeches are good swimmers.

**Reproduction** Asexual reproduction occurs in some polychaetes and oligochaetes by transverse fission or fragmentation—meaning

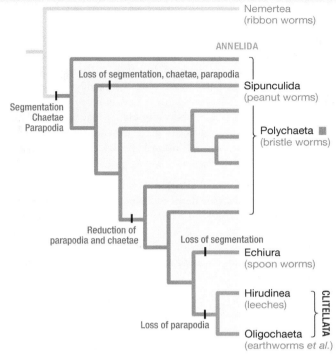

**FIGURE 34.14 Phylogeny of Major Groups of Annelids.**

that body parts can regenerate a complete individual. Sexual reproduction in polychaetes may begin with internal or external fertilization, depending on the species. Most of the polychaete lineages have separate sexes and usually release their eggs directly into the water. Some species produce eggs that hatch into trochophore larvae, then go on to develop into other larval forms. In oligochaetes and leeches, individuals produce both sperm and eggs and engage in mutual, internal cross-fertilization. Eggs are enclosed in a mucus-rich, cocoon-like structure; after fertilization, offspring develop directly into miniature versions of their parents.

**(a) Polychaetes** have many bristle-like chaetae.

*Hermodice carunculata*

Chaetae

1 cm

**(b) Oligochaetes** have few or no chaetae.

*Chaetogaster* species

100 μm

**(c)** Some **leeches** are ectoparasites.

*Haemadipsa* species

1 cm

**FIGURE 34.15 Annelids Are Segmented Worms.**

## Lophotrochozoans > Mollusca > Bivalvia (Clams, Mussels, Scallops, Oysters)

The bivalves are so named because they have a shell with two separate parts, or valves, made of calcium carbonate. The protective shell is hinged, and closes with the aid of muscles attached to the two valves (**FIGURE 34.16**). Because most bivalves live on or under the ocean floor and because they are covered by a hard shell, their bodies are often buried in sediment after death. Bivalves thus fossilize readily and have the most extensive fossil record of any animal, plant, or fungal group.

The smallest bivalves are freshwater clams that are less than 2 mm long; the largest bivalves are giant marine clams that may weigh more than 200 kilograms (kg). All bivalves can sense gravity, touch, and certain chemicals; scallops even have eyes.

**Feeding** Most bivalves are suspension feeders that take in any type of small animal or protist, or detritus. Suspension feeding is based on a flow of water across gas-exchange structures called **gills** located within the mantle cavity. A single oyster can filter the organic matter from as much as 60 gallons of seawater each day. Bivalves are the only major group of mollusks that lack the feeding structure called a radula.

**Movement** Clams burrow into sediments with the aid of their muscular foot but are otherwise sedentary. Scallops are able to swim along the surface of soft substrates by clapping their shells together and forcing water out, a form of jet propulsion. Mussels and oysters are sessile, attached to rocks or other solid surfaces.

*Chlamys pallium*

1 cm

**FIGURE 34.16 Bivalves Have Shells with Two Parts.**

**Reproduction** Most bivalves reproduce sexually. Eggs and sperm are shed into the water, and fertilized eggs develop into trochophore larvae. Trochophores then metamorphose into a distinct type of larva called a **veliger,** which continues to feed and swim before settling to the substrate and metamorphosing into an adult form that secretes a shell.

## Lophotrochozoans > Mollusca > Gastropoda (Snails, Slugs, Nudibranchs)

The gastropods ("belly-feet") are named for the large, muscular foot on their ventral side. Marine and terrestrial snails have shells (**FIGURE 34.17**), into which they can retract when they are attacked or when their tissues begin to dry out. Land slugs and nudibranchs (pronounced *NEW-da-branks*; also called sea slugs) lost their shells independently; these gastropods often contain toxins or foul-tasting chemicals to protect them from being eaten. About 70,000 species of gastropods are known, ranging in size from microscopic to almost a meter long. They are the only group of mollusks that made the water-to-land transition.

**Feeding** The gastropod radula is diverse, varying in size and shape among species (see Figure 34.9). Although most gastropods are herbivores or detritivores, specialized types of teeth allow some gastropods to act as predators. Species called drills, for example, use their radula to bore a hole in the shells of other mollusks.

**Movement** Waves of contractions along the length of the foot allow gastropods to move by creeping (see Figure 34.8). Sea butterflies are gastropods with a reduced or absent shell but a large, winglike foot that flaps and powers swimming movements.

**Reproduction** Most reproduction is sexual, but females of some gastropod species can reproduce asexually by producing eggs parthenogenetically. Sexual reproduction in some gastropods begins with internal fertilization. Most marine gastropods produce a veliger larva that may disperse up to several hundred kilometers from the parent. But in some marine species and all terrestrial forms, larvae are not free living. Instead, offspring remain in an egg case while passing through several larval stages and then hatch as miniature versions of the adults.

*Maxacteon flammea*

5 mm

**FIGURE 34.17 Gastropods Have a One-Part Shell or Lack Shells.**

## Lophotrochozoans > Mollusca > Polyplacophora (Chitons)

The name *Polyplacophora* ("many-plate-bearing") is apt because chitons (pronounced *KITE-uns*) have eight calcium carbonate plates, or valves, along their dorsal surface (**FIGURE 34.18**). The plates form a protective shell. The approximately 1000 species of chitons are exclusively marine, and are found worldwide; the largest reaches 33 centimeters (cm). They are usually found on rocky surfaces in the intertidal zone, where rocks are periodically exposed to air at low tides.

**Feeding** Chitons have a radula that they use to scrape algae and other organic matter off rocks.

**Movement** Chitons move by creeping on their broad, muscular foot—as gastropods do.

**Reproduction** In most chiton species, the sexes are separate and fertilization is external. In some species, however, sperm that are shed into the water enter the female's mantle cavity and fertilize eggs there. Depending on the species, eggs may be enclosed in a membrane and released, or they may be retained until hatching and early development are complete. Most species have trochophore larvae.

*Tonicella lineata*

1 cm

**FIGURE 34.18 Chitons Have Eight Shell Plates.**

## Lophotrochozoans > Mollusca > Cephalopoda (Nautilus, Cuttlefish, Squid, Octopuses)

The cephalopods ("head-feet") have a well-developed "head" that actually consists of the visceral mass, and a foot that is modified to form **tentacles:** long, thin, muscular extensions that aid in movement and prey capture (**FIGURE 34.19**). Except for the nautilus with its chambered shell, the cephalopod species living today have either highly reduced shells or none at all. Most have large brains and image-forming eyes with sophisticated lenses. They also include the largest of all invertebrates living today, the giant squid, which can be more than 10 m long, including the tentacles. The skin of cephalopods contains sophisticated chromatophore ("color-bearing") cells that enable the rapid color changes used for camouflage and communication.

**Feeding** Cephalopods are highly intelligent predators that hunt by sight and use their tentacles to capture prey—usually fish or crustaceans. They have a radula as well as a structure called a **beak,** which can exert powerful biting forces. Some cuttlefish and octopuses also inject poisons into their prey to subdue them.

**Movement** Cephalopods can swim by moving their fins to "fly" through the water, or by jet propulsion using the mantle cavity and siphon (see Figure 34.10). Squid are built for speed and hunt small fish by chasing them down. Octopuses, in contrast, crawl along the substrate using their tentacles. They chase down crabs or other crustaceans, or they pry mussels or clams from the substrate and then use their beaks to crush the exoskeletons of their prey. Most cephalopods are able to escape their own predators by releasing a jet of "ink" that disorients their predators while they slip away.

**Reproduction** Cephalopods have separate sexes, and some species have elaborate courtship rituals that involve color changes and interaction of tentacles. When a male is accepted by a female, he deposits sperm that are encased in a structure called a **spermatophore.** The spermatophore is transferred to the female, and fertilization is internal. Females lay eggs. When they hatch, juveniles develop directly into adults—that is, there is no larval stage.

*Octopus bimaculatus*

10 cm

**FIGURE 34.19 Cephalopods Have Highly Modified Bodies.**

## 34.3 What Is an Ecdysozoan?

Lophotrochozoans grow continuously and incrementally (**FIGURE 34.20a**)—the ancestral manner of growth for animals. In contrast, the Ecdysozoa are defined by a clear synapomorphy: All ecdysozoans grow intermittently by **molting**—that is, by shedding an exoskeleton or external covering.

The Greek root *ecdysis*, which means "to slip out or escape," is appropriate because during a molt, an individual sheds its outer layer, or **cuticle**—called an **exoskeleton** if it is hard—and slips out of it (**FIGURE 34.20b**). Once the old covering is gone, the body is pumped up with fluid to cause it to expand, and a larger cuticle or exoskeleton forms. As ecdysozoans grow and mature, they undergo a succession of molts, sometimes undergoing dramatic morphological transformations along the way.

A stiff body covering is advantageous because it provides an effective structure for muscle attachment and affords protection. However, the trade-off is that during molting, the soft bodies of ecdysozoans are exposed and vulnerable to predators. When a crab or other crustacean has shed an old exoskeleton, its new exoskeleton takes several hours to harden. During this interval, molting individuals hide and do not feed or move about. Experiments have shown that it is much easier for predators to attack and subdue individuals that are not protected by an exoskeleton during the intermolt period.

A hormone called ecdysone is important in regulating the molting cycle (Chapter 49). Is ecdysone a key innovation for the ecdysozoans? No—studies show that this steroid hormone serves a variety of functions in many other animals. Thus, it appears that ecdysone was co-opted in the ecdysozoans to serve a novel function.

The most prominent of the seven ecdysozoan phyla are the roundworms (Nematoda) and arthropods (Arthropoda). Here, let's consider the implications of having an exoskeleton for the most diverse phylum of animals on Earth, the arthropods.

## What Is an Arthropod?

In terms of duration in the fossil record, species diversity, and abundance of individuals, arthropods are the most important phylum within the Ecdysozoa. Arthropods appear in the fossil record over 520 million years ago and have long been the most abundant animals observed in both marine and terrestrial environments. Well over a million living species have been described, and biologists estimate that millions or perhaps even tens of millions of arthropod species have yet to be discovered. In terms of species diversity, arthropods are easily the most successful lineage of eukaryotes.

**The Arthropod Body Plan** In addition to their bilateral symmetry and other protostome characteristics, **arthropods** (literally "joint-foot") are defined by three key features:

1. a *segmented body*, which is organized into prominent regions, or **tagmata,** such as the head, thorax, and abdomen in the grasshopper (**FIGURE 34.21**);

2. an *exoskeleton* made primarily of the polysaccharide chitin (see Chapter 5), strengthened by calcium carbonate ($CaCO_3$) in crustaceans; and

3. *jointed appendages,* which enable the rigid bodies to move.

Instead of being based on muscle contraction within a hydrostatic skeleton, most arthropod locomotion is based on muscles

**(a)** Lophotrochozoans grow incrementally.

**(b)** Ecdysozoans grow by molting.

Growth bands

**FIGURE 34.20 Lophotrochozoans and Ecdysozoans Differ in Their Mechanism of Growth. (a)** Lophotrochozoans do not molt. The growth bands on this clam show periods of slow and rapid incremental growth. **(b)** Ecdysozoans such as this cicada must crawl out of their old exoskeletons and grow new, larger ones.

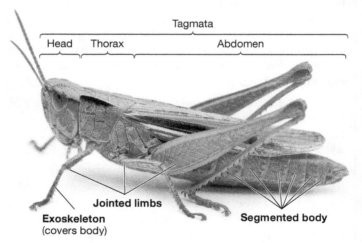

Tagmata

Head | Thorax | Abdomen

Jointed limbs

Exoskeleton (covers body)

Segmented body

**FIGURE 34.21 Arthropods Have a Specialized Body Plan.** Arthropods have segmented bodies and jointed limbs, which enable these animals to move despite their hard outer covering, the exoskeleton. Different arthropods have a different number of tagmata, or body regions; insects have three.

that apply force against rigid levers—the exoskeleton—to move legs or wings at the joints. This skeletal architecture enables very rapid and precise movements (Chapter 48).

Arthropods have a highly reduced coelom but, like mollusks, possess an extensive body cavity called a hemocoel. The hemocoel enables movements via a hydrostatic skeleton in caterpillars and other types of arthropod larvae.

The jointed appendages of arthropods are organized in pairs along the segmented body. They have an array of functions: exchanging gases, sensing the environment, feeding, and locomotion via swimming, walking, running, jumping, or flying (Chapter 33). Arthropod appendages provide the ability to sense stimuli and make sophisticated movements in response. ✔ You should be able to indicate the origin of jointed appendages on Figure 34.2.

**Why Has the Arthropod Body Plan Been So Successful?** You have already learned that mollusk bodies are modular in evolutionary terms. The modularity of arthropod segments, however, takes the prize for evolutionary potential.

Studies on the role of tool-kit genes—such as the *Hox* genes—during development of different arthropods have contributed enormously to our understanding of the process of arthropod diversification. These studies show that small changes in the timing and location of expression of certain tool-kit genes along the length of an arthropod can result in novel shapes and sizes of body segments and appendages.

To understand the evolutionary potential of modularity, consider a hypothetical ancestral arthropod with many uniform body segments, each with a pair of uniform appendages. The redundancy of this body plan can provide a fertile starting place for diversification because some of the segments can continue to function the old way, say for crawling, while other segments can become co-opted for new functions. For example, the appendages at the head end could become specialized as antennae or claws without compromising the ability of the animal to crawl.

Thus, genetic opportunity in the form of variation in the expression of tool-kit genes can combine with ecological opportunity by the process of natural selection to result in the diversification of arthropod body segments and appendages. **FIGURE 34.22** shows an example of how diverse, functionally specialized appendages can result in an animal with a "serialized" body plan, a reflection of its modular structure. The crayfish limbs are said to have serial homology.

**Origin of the Wing** The process of co-opting old parts for new functions is key to the origin of one of the most remarkable adaptations in the history of life—the insect wing. There are more species of animals on the planet today with insect wings than without. According to data in the fossil record, insects were also the first animals on Earth that had wings and could fly. How did wings evolve?

Some biologists have proposed that wings arose as outgrowths from the thorax, independent from the legs. Others have argued that wings arose from gill-like projections on the branched legs of a wingless ancestor, essentially co-opting the gill-like structures

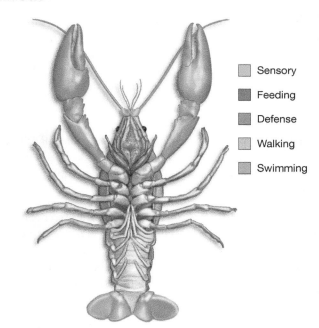

**FIGURE 34.22 Arthropods Have a Modular Body Plan.** This ventral view of a crayfish illustrates how arthropod segments and appendages can be specialized for different functions.

(**FIGURE 34.23**). Insects have unbranched appendages, but arthropods such as crustaceans have branched appendages.

Michalis Averof and Stephen Cohen attempted to settle the wing debate using developmental genetics. They probed the developing limbs of brine shrimp (a member of an ancient lineage of crustaceans) for the presence of tool-kit genes *nubbin* and *apterous*. These genes are known to be important in wing development in insects. The results were striking. *Nubbin* and *apterous* are expressed in the gill-like lobe of the crustacean limb, but nowhere else. These results provide strong support for the origin of insect wings from the gill-like branches of ancestral crustacean limbs.

**(a)** Independent origin hypothesis

**(b)** Gill co-option hypothesis

**FIGURE 34.23 Alternative Hypotheses for the Origin of Wings in Insects.**

Co-opting one structure to form another may sometimes require thousands or millions of years of evolution within a lineage. It is all the more remarkable, then, that dramatic shape changes can also occur during the lifetime of a single individual. Natural selection operates at all developmental stages in a life cycle.

## Arthropod Metamorphosis

Many arthropods undergo a morphological transformation from a larva to a very different adult form. Others do not. Let's use insects as a case study to consider the adaptive implications of metamorphosis in arthropods.

**Two Types of Insect Metamorphosis** In insects, the presence or absence of a larval stage defines two distinct types of metamorphosis.

In **hemimetabolous** ("half-change") **metamorphosis**—also called **incomplete metamorphosis**—juveniles called nymphs look like miniature versions of the adult. The aphid nymphs in **FIGURE 34.24a**, for example, shed their external skeletons several times and grow—gradually changing from wingless, sexually immature nymphs to sexually mature adults, some of which can fly. But throughout their life, aphids live in the same habitats and feed on the same food source in the same way: They suck sap.

In **holometabolous** ("whole change") **metamorphosis**—also called **complete metamorphosis**—there is a distinct larval stage. As an example, consider the life cycle of the mosquito, illustrated in **FIGURE 34.24b**:

1. Newly hatched mosquitoes live in quiet bodies of freshwater, where they suspension feed on bacteria, algae, and detritus.

2. When a larva has grown sufficiently, the individual stops feeding and moving and secretes a protective case. The individual is now known as a **pupa** (plural: pupae). During pupation, the pupa's body is completely remodeled into a new, adult form.

3. The adult mosquito flies and feeds—females take blood meals from mammals and males drink nectar from flowers.

**What Is the Adaptive Significance of Metamorphosis?** In insects, holometabolous metamorphosis is 10 times more common than hemimetabolous metamorphosis. How can this be explained?

Since most adult insects are mobile, using a larval stage for dispersal does not seem to be a sufficient explanation. The leading hypothesis is based on efficiency in feeding. Because juveniles and adults from holometabolous species feed on different materials in different ways and sometimes even in different habitats, they do not compete with each other.

An alternative hypothesis is based on the advantages of functional specialization. In many moths and butterflies, larvae are specialized for feeding, whereas adults are specialized for mating and feed rarely, if ever. Larvae are largely sessile, whereas adults are highly mobile. If specialization leads to higher efficiency in feeding and reproduction and thus higher fitness, then holometabolous metamorphosis would be advantageous. These hypotheses are not mutually exclusive, however—meaning that both could be correct, depending on the species being considered.

Let's explore the diversity of feeding, moving, and reproducing habits of ecdysozoans in more depth by examining the key lineages separately.

## Key Lineages: Ecdysozoans

Seven phyla are currently recognized in the Ecdysozoa (see Table 33.1). Second in diversity to Arthropoda, the phylum Nematoda, or roundworms, is especially noteworthy due to its large number of described species and the mind-boggling abundance of individuals. Of the smaller phyla, Onychophora (*on-ee-KOFF-er-uh*) and Tardigrada are of special interest due to their close relationship to arthropods. They are similar to arthropods

**(a)** Aphid:
Hemimetabolous metamorphosis
(Incomplete metamorphosis)

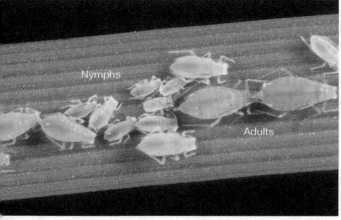

Nymphs look like miniature versions of adults and eat the same foods.

**(b)** Mosquito:
Holometabolous metamorphosis
(Complete metamorphosis)

Larvae look substantially different from adults and eat different foods.

**FIGURE 34.24 Insect Metamorphosis Can Be Incomplete or Complete.**

**(a)** Onychophorans are called velvet worms.

*Peripatus* species

0.5 cm

**(b)** Tardigrades are called water bears.

*Echiniscus* species

0.1 mm

**FIGURE 34.25 Onychophorans and Tardigrades Have Lobe-Shaped Limbs with Claws.** The scanning electron micrograph in part (b) has been colorized.

in having a segmented body and limbs. Unlike arthropods, they do not have an exoskeleton and their limbs are not jointed.

The onychophorans, or velvet worms, are small, caterpillar-like organisms that live in moist leaf litter and prey on small invertebrates. Onychophorans have lobe-shaped appendages and segmented bodies with a hemocoel (**FIGURE 34.25a**).

The tardigrades, or water bears, are microscopic animals that live in diverse marine, freshwater, and terrestrial environments, such as in the film of water that covers plants in moist habitats. Tardigrades have a reduced coelom but a prominent hemocoel, and they walk on their clawed, lobe-shaped legs (**FIGURE 34.25b**). Most feed by sucking fluids from plants or animals; others are detritivores, feeding on dead organic matter.

Although the phylogeny of arthropods is still being worked out, most data agree that the phylum as a whole is monophyletic. However, the relationships of lineages within the phylum are currently undergoing a major revision. Insects and myriapods have long been considered sister groups within the arthropods, due in part to their unbranched appendages. However, recent molecular phylogenetic studies—as well as comparisons of new morphological data, developmental data, and evidence in the fossil record—provide strong support for the placement of the insect clade *within* the crustacean lineage, making the crustaceans paraphyletic. It appears that crustaceans successfully invaded land as insects.

In the following exploration of ecdysozoan diversity, insects are described in a separate box, following tradition. However, the revised relationship between insects and crustaceans is then illustrated in the Crustacea box:

- Ecdysozoans > Nematoda (Roundworms)
- Ecdysozoans > Arthropoda > Myriapoda (Millipedes, Centipedes)
- Ecdysozoans > Arthropoda > Insecta (Insects)
- Ecdysozoans > Arthropoda > Crustacea (Shrimp, Lobsters, Crabs, Barnacles, Isopods, Copepods)
- Ecdysozoans > Arthropoda > Chelicerata (Sea Spiders, Horseshoe Crabs, Daddy Longlegs, Mites, Ticks, Scorpions, Spiders)

Species in the phylum Nematoda are commonly called **round-worms** or **nematodes.** Roundworms are unsegmented worms with a pseudocoelom, a tube-within-a-tube body plan, no appendages, and a thick, elastic cuticle that must be molted during growth. Although some nematodes can grow to lengths of several meters, most species are tiny—much less than 1 mm long. They lack specialized systems for exchanging gases and for circulating nutrients. Instead, gas exchange occurs across the body wall, and once ingested, nutrients move by simple diffusion from the gut to other parts of the body.

The nematode *Caenorhabditis elegans* is one of the most thoroughly studied model organisms in biology (see **BioSkills 13** in Appendix B). Species that parasitize humans have also been studied intensively. Pinworms, for example, infect about 40 million people in the United States alone, and *Onchocerca volvulus* causes an eye disease that infects around 20 million people in Africa and Latin America. Advanced infections by the roundworm *Wuchereria bancrofti* result in the blockage of lymphatic vessels, causing fluid accumulation and massive swelling—the condition known as elephantiasis. The potentially fatal disease trichinosis is caused by species in the genus *Trichinella*. The parasites are passed from infected animals to humans by ingesting raw or undercooked meat. An array of symptoms results, including discomfort caused by *Trichinella* larvae encasing themselves in cysts within muscle or other types of tissue (**FIGURE 34.26a**).

A recent phylogenetic analysis of the nematodes has produced an interesting insight: Convergent morphological evolution appears to be extensive. Animal parasitism and plant parasitism both arose several times in different lineages of nematodes. Thus, some nematodes that look very similar and fill a very similar ecological role may be distantly related.

Parasites represent a relatively small fraction of the nematode species that have been described to date, however. The free-living nematodes are important ecologically because they are found in virtually every habitat known (**FIGURE 34.26b**).

While around 25,000 species of roundworms have been named, the actual total may be over a million. Nematodes are also fabulously abundant. Biologists have found 90,000 roundworms in a single rotting apple and have estimated that rich farm soils contain up to 9 billion roundworms per acre. Although they are not the most species-rich animal group, they are among the most abundant. The simple nematode body plan has been extraordinarily successful.

**Feeding** Roundworms feed on a wide variety of materials, including bacteria, fungi, plant roots, small protists or animals, or detritus. In most cases, the structure of their mouthparts is specialized in a way that increases the efficiency of feeding on a particular type of organism or material.

**Movement** Roundworms move with the aid of their hydrostatic skeleton. They have no muscles that can change the diameter of the body—their body musculature consists solely of longitudinal muscles that bend the stiff body laterally. ✔ You should be able to indicate the loss of circumferential muscles on Figure 34.2. Most roundworms live in soil or inside a host, so when contractions of their longitudinal muscles cause them to undulate, the movements are resisted by a stiff substrate. As a result, the worm pushes off the substrate, and the body advances.

**Reproduction** Sexes are separate in most nematode species (but not in *C. elegans*, which is mostly hermaphroditic). Sexual reproduction begins with internal fertilization and culminates in egg laying and the direct development of offspring. Individuals go through a series of four molts over the course of their lifetime.

**(a)** Parasitic larvae encysted in muscle tissue

*Trichinella spiralis*

100 μm

**(b)** Most nematodes are free living.

*Caenorhabditis elegans*

0.1 mm

**FIGURE 34.26 Some Nematodes Are Parasites, but Most Are Free Living.**

The **myriapods** have relatively simple bodies, with a head region and a long trunk featuring a series of segments, each bearing one or two pairs of legs (**FIGURE 34.27**). If eyes are present, they consist of a few to many simple structures clustered on the sides of the head. The 16,000 species that have been described to date inhabit terrestrial environments all over the world.

Feeding Millipedes and centipedes have mouthparts that can bite and chew. These organisms live in rotting logs and other types of dead plant material that litters the ground in forests and grasslands. Millipedes are detritivores. Centipedes, in contrast, use a pair of poison-containing fangs just behind the mouth to hunt an array of insects. Large centipedes, with lengths up to 30 cm, can inject enough poison to debilitate a human.

Movement Myriapods walk or run on their many legs; a few species burrow. Some millipedes have over 190 trunk sections, each with two pairs of legs, for a total of over 750 legs. Centipedes usually have fewer than 30 segments, with one pair of legs per segment.

Reproduction Myriapod sexes are separate, and fertilization is internal. Males deposit sperm in packets that are picked up by the female or transferred to her by the male. After females lay eggs in the environment, the eggs hatch into juveniles that develop into adults via a series of molts.

*Scolopendra* species

**FIGURE 34.27 Myriapods Have One or Two Pairs of Legs on Each Body Segment.**

About one million species of insects have been named thus far, but it is certain that many more exist. In terms of species diversity and numbers of individuals, insects dominate terrestrial environments. In addition, the larvae of some species are common in freshwater streams, ponds, and lakes. **TABLE 34.1** (see page 676) describes seven of the most prominent orders of insects. The fruit fly *Drosophila melanogaster,* in the order Diptera, is one of the most thoroughly studied model organisms in biology (see **BioSkills 13** in Appendix B).

**Insects** are distinguished by having three tagmata—the head, **thorax,** and **abdomen** (see Figure 34.21). Three pairs of walking legs are mounted on the lateral surface of the thorax. Most species have one or two pairs of wings, mounted on the dorsal (back) side of the thorax. Typically the head contains four mouthpart structures, a pair of slender **antennae** that are used to touch and smell, and a pair of compound eyes. A **compound eye** contains many lenses, each associated with a light-sensing, columnar structure (see Chapter 47). (Human and cephalopod eyes are **simple eyes,** meaning they have just one lens.)

Feeding Most insect species have four mouthpart structures (labrum, paired mandibles, paired maxillae, and labium), which have diversified in structure and function in response to natural selection. As a result, insects are able to feed in every conceivable manner and on almost every type of food source available on land. In species with complete (holometabolous) metamorphosis, larvae have wormlike bodies; most tunnel their way through food sources, though some feed by biting leaves. Adults, however, are predators or parasites on plant or animal tissues. Thus, diversification in food sources occurs even within species. Because so many insects make their living by feeding on plant tissues or fluids, the diversification of insects was closely correlated with the diversification of land plants.

Movement Insects use their legs to walk, run, jump, or swim, or they use their wings to fly. When insects walk or run, the sequence of movements usually results in three of their six legs maintaining contact with the ground at all times.

Reproduction Insect sexes are separate, and sexual reproduction is the norm. Mating usually takes place through direct copulation; the male inserts a sperm-transfer organ into the female. Most females lay eggs, but in a few species eggs are retained until hatching. Many species are also capable of reproducing asexually through parthenogenesis, the production of unfertilized eggs via mitosis. Complete metamorphosis is far more common than incomplete metamorphosis.

TABLE 34.1   **Prominent Orders of Insects**

| Order | Description |
|---|---|
|  **Coleoptera** ("sheath-winged")<br>Beetles<br>360,000 known species | **Key traits:** Hardened forewings, called elytra, protect the membranous hindwings that power flight and act as stabilizers.<br>**Feeding:** Adults are important predators and scavengers. Larvae are called grubs and often have chewing mouthparts.<br>**Life Cycle:** All have complete metamorphosis.<br>**Notes:** The most species-rich lineage on the tree of life—about 25 percent of all described species are beetles. |
|  **Lepidoptera** ("scale-winged")<br>Butterflies, moths<br>180,000 known species | **Key traits:** Wings are covered with tiny, often colorful scales. The forewings and hindwings often hook together and move as a unit.<br>**Feeding:** Larvae usually have chewing mouthparts and either bore through food material or bite leaves; adults often feed on nectar.<br>**Life Cycle:** All have complete metamorphosis.<br>**Notes:** Some species migrate long distances. |
|  **Diptera** ("two-winged")<br>Flies (including mosquitoes, gnats, midges)<br>150,000 known species | **Key traits:** Reduced hindwings, called halteres, act as stabilizers during flight.<br>**Feeding:** Adults are usually liquid feeders; many larvae are maggots, which may be parasitic or feed on rotting material.<br>**Life Cycle:** All have complete metamorphosis.<br>**Notes:** The first flies in fossil record appear 240 million years ago. |
|  **Hymenoptera** ("membrane-winged")<br>Ants, bees, wasps<br>115,000 known species | **Key traits:** Membranous forewings and hindwings lock together.<br>**Feeding:** Most ants feed on plant material; most bees feed on nectar; wasps are predatory and often have parasitic larvae.<br>**Life Cycle:** All have complete metamorphosis. Males are haploid (they hatch from unfertilized eggs) and females are diploid (they hatch from fertilized eggs). Larvae are cared for by adults.<br>**Notes:** Most species live in colonies, and many are eusocial. |
|  **Hemiptera** ("half-winged")<br>Bugs (including leaf hoppers, aphids, cicadas, scale insects)<br>85,000 known species | **Key traits:** Some have a thickened forewing with a membranous tip. Mouthparts are modified for piercing and sucking.<br>**Feeding:** Most suck plant juices, but some are predatory.<br>**Life Cycle:** All have incomplete metamorphosis.<br>**Notes:** Called "half-winged" because the forewings of some bugs are hardened near the bases but membranous near the tips. |
|  **Orthoptera** ("straight-winged")<br>Grasshoppers, crickets<br>25,000 known species | **Key traits:** Large, muscular hind legs enable jumping.<br>**Feeding:** Most have chewing mouthparts and are leaf eaters.<br>**Life Cycle:** All have incomplete metamorphosis.<br>**Notes:** In many species, males give distinctive songs to attract mates. They produce sound by rubbing their wings against their legs or against each other, a process called stridulation. |
|  **Odonata** ("toothed")<br>Dragonflies, damselflies<br>6,500 known species | **Key traits:** Four membranous wings and long, slender abdomens.<br>**Feeding:** Larvae and adults are predatory, often on flies. The "odon" refers to strong, toothlike structures on their mandibles.<br>**Life Cycle:** All have complete metamorphosis: Nymphs are aquatic, adults are terrestrial.<br>**Notes:** They hunt by sight and have reduced antennae (used for touch and smell) but enormous eyes with up to 28,000 lenses. |

The 47,000 species of **crustaceans** that have been identified to date live primarily in marine and freshwater environments; they are the most diverse arthropods of the sea. A few species of crab and some isopods (known as sowbugs and pillbugs) are terrestrial, however, and recent phylogenetic evidence suggests that the insects represent a highly successful branch of terrestrial crustaceans (**FIGURE 34.28**). (For the purpose of describing diversity here, insects are covered separately on the previous page.)

Crustaceans—especially the planktonic copepods—are common in surface waters around the world, where they are important consumers. Crustaceans are also important grazers and predators in shallow-water benthic environments.

The segmented body of most crustaceans is divided into two distinct regions, or tagmata: (1) the cephalothorax, which combines the head and thorax, and (2) the abdomen. Many crustaceans have a **carapace**—a platelike section of their exoskeleton that covers and protects the cephalothorax (**FIGURE 34.29**). They are the only type of arthropod with two pairs of antennae, and have sophisticated, compound eyes—usually mounted on stalks. Crustacean appendages are usually branched (insect appendages are unbranched). Other than trilobites—a major arthropod lineage that did not survive the end-Permian mass extinction, 250 million years ago (Chapter 28)—crustaceans were the first arthropods to appear in the fossil record. The tiny ostracods (seed shrimp) have a particularly rich fossil record dating back to the Cambrian.

**Feeding** Most crustaceans have 4–6 pairs of mouthparts that are derived from jointed appendages, and as a group they use every type of feeding strategy known. Barnacles and many shrimp are suspension feeders that use feathery structures located on head or body appendages to capture prey. Crabs and lobsters are active hunters, herbivores, and scavengers. Typically they have a pair of mouthparts called **mandibles** that bite or chew. Individuals capture and hold their food source with claws or other feeding appendages and then use their mandibles to shred the food into small bits that can be ingested.

**Movement** Crustaceans typically have many pairs of limbs with diverse forms and functions, including claws, paddle-shaped forms used in swimming, feathery structures used in capturing food that is suspended in water, and slender legs that make sophisticated walking or running movements possible (see Figure 34.22). Barnacles are one of the few types of sessile crustaceans. Adult barnacles cement their heads to a hard substrate, secrete a protective shell of calcium carbonate, and use their feathery legs to capture food particles and transfer them to the mouth.

**Reproduction** Most individual crustaceans are either male or female, and sexual reproduction is the norm. Fertilization is usually internal, and eggs are typically retained by the female until they hatch. Most crustaceans pass through several distinct larval stages; many species include a larval stage called a **nauplius,** which is usually planktonic. A nauplius has a single eye and appendages that develop into the two pairs of antennae, the mouthparts, and walking/swimming legs of the adult.

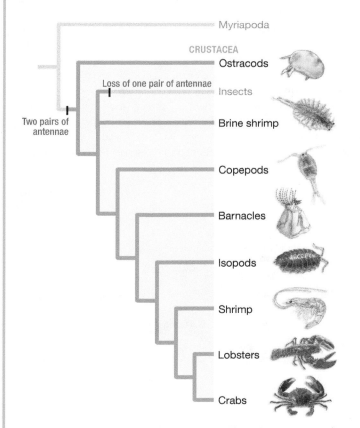

**FIGURE 34.28 Phylogeny of the Major Groups of Crustaceans.** This phylogeny illustrates the current hypothesis that insects are a terrestrial clade within the crustaceans, overturning traditional classification (which is nonetheless still in widespread use due to its long history).

*Cherax quadricarinatus*

**FIGURE 34.29 Crustaceans Have Two Tagmata: A Cephalothorax and an Abdomen.** The carapace protects the cephalothorax (literally "head-chest").

The most prominent lineage within the Chelicerata is the Arachnida, including spiders, scorpions, ticks, mites and daddy longlegs (**FIGURE 34.30**). Most of the 100,000 species of chelicerates are terrestrial, but the horseshoe crabs and sea spiders are marine.

The chelicerate body consists of 2 tagmata, the cephalothorax (prosoma) and abdomen (opisthosoma), and 6 pairs of appendages (**FIGURE 34.31**). The cephalothorax lacks antennae for sensing touch or odor but usually contains eyes. The group is named for a pair of appendages called **chelicerae,** found near the mouth. Depending on the species, the chelicerae are used in feeding, defense, copulation, movement, or sensory reception. In addition to 4 pairs of legs and 1 pair of chelicerae, chelicerates also have a pair of pedipalps, which can be used for diverse functions.

**Feeding**  Spiders, scorpions, and daddy longlegs capture insects or other prey. Although some of these species are active hunters that rove around in search of prey, most spiders are sit-and-wait predators that either pounce on prey that wander near, or that create sticky webs to capture prey. In this case, the spider senses the vibrations of the struggling prey on the web, pounces on it, and administers a toxic bite. Regardless of the mode of capture, spiders generally consume their meals in soup form—they secrete digestive enzymes into the prey to enable digestion to begin externally, then drink up the nutritious liquid. Often all that remains of the prey is an empty exoskeleton.

Mites and ticks are ectoparasitic and use their piercing mouthparts to feed on host animals or, in the case of dust mites, on their hosts' dead skin. Horseshoe crabs eat a variety of animals as well as algae and detritus. Most scorpions feed on insects; the largest scorpion species occasionally eat snakes and lizards. Although the venom of scorpion stings is an effective defense against predators, it is primarily used to kill or paralyze prey.

**Movement**  Like other arthropods, chelicerates move with the aid of muscles attached to an exoskeleton. They walk or crawl on their four pairs of jointed walking legs; some species are also capable of jumping. Horseshoe crabs and some other marine forms can swim slowly. Newly hatched spiders spin long, silken threads that serve as balloons and that can carry them on the wind more than 400 kilometers from the point of hatching.

**Reproduction**  Sexual reproduction is the rule in chelicerates, and fertilization is internal in most groups. Courtship displays are extensive in many chelicerates and may include both visual displays and the release of chemical odorants. In spiders, males may present a dead insect as a gift that the female eats as the pair mates; in some species, the male himself is eaten as sperm is being transferred—the longer the meal lasts, the more successful the sperm transfer. Males use pedipalps to transfer sperm to females. These organs fit into the female reproductive tract in a "lock-and-key" fashion. Differences in the size and shape of male genitalia are often the only way to identify closely related species of spider.

Development in chelicerates is direct, meaning that larval forms and metamorphosis do not occur. In scorpions, females retain fertilized eggs. After the eggs hatch, the young climb on the mother's back. They remain there until they are old enough to hunt for themselves.

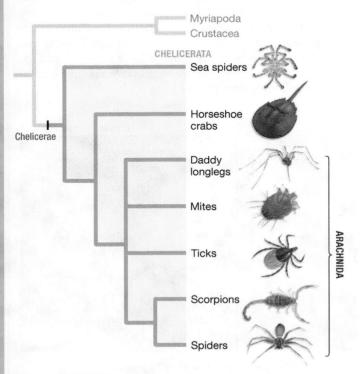

**FIGURE 34.30 Phylogeny of the Major Groups of Chelicerates.**

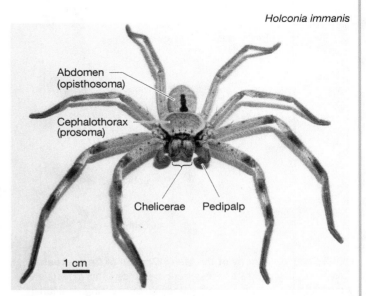

*Holconia immanis*

**FIGURE 34.31 Chelicerates Have Chelicerae and Two Tagmata.**

## If you understand . . .

### 34.1 What Is a Protostome?

- Molecular evidence supports the hypothesis that protostomes are a monophyletic group divided into two major subgroups: the Lophotrochozoa and the Ecdysozoa.

- All protostomes are bilaterally symmetric and triploblastic, but the coelom has been reduced or lost in several phyla.

- Protostomes diversified in their methods of sensing their environments, feeding, moving, reproducing, and developing.

- The transition to living on land occurred several times independently during the evolution of protostomes, opening new habitats and driving diversification. The transition was facilitated by watertight shells and exoskeletons, the evolution of specialized structures to minimize water loss and manage gas exchange, and the ability to move to moist locations.

- Many protostome body plans are highly modular due to the underlying expression patterns of developmental tool-kit genes.

✔ You should be able to explain how both ecological opportunity and genetic opportunity were important in the diversification of protostomes.

### 34.2 What Is a Lophotrochozoan?

- Lophotrochozoans grow incrementally. Some phyla have characteristic feeding structures called lophophores, and many have a distinctive type of larvae called trochophores. Spiral cleavage is a synapomorphy for the group but was modified or lost in some phyla.

- Mollusks, annelids, and flatworms are the most diverse phyla within the Lophotrochozoa. All three phyla made the water-to-land transition.

- The mollusk body plan includes a muscular foot, a visceral mass, and a mantle. These components diversified in many ways, enabling mollusks to occupy most aquatic, and some terrestrial, habitats.

✔ You should be able to explain why the absence of a trait known to be found in a clade, such as a trochophore larva, spiral cleavage, or a coelom, does not necessarily exclude a species from that clade.

### 34.3 What Is an Ecdysozoan?

- Species in the Ecdysozoa grow by molting—meaning that they shed their old external covering and grow a new, larger one.

- Arthropods and nematodes are the most diverse phyla within the Ecdysozoa. A majority of animals on Earth are arthropods.

- The arthropod body plan is segmented and protected by an exoskeleton made primarily of chitin. Appendages are jointed. The diversification of arthropod body plans is based on variation in the number and functional specialization of segments.

- Complete (holometabolous) metamorphosis enables larvae and adults to specialize, creating opportunities for diversification.

- Crustaceans are the most diverse group of arthropods in the sea, and insects are the most diverse group on land. (Recent data suggest that insects are a terrestrial subgroup of Crustacea.)

✔ You should be able to compare modularity in arthropod body plans with modularity in vertebrates.

 **MasteringBiology**

1. **MasteringBiology Assignments**

   **Tutorials and Activities** Characteristics of Invertebrates; Ecdysozoans; Protostome Diversity

   **Questions** Reading Quizzes, Blue-Thread Questions, Test Bank

2. **eText** Read your book online, search, take notes, highlight text, and more.

3. **The Study Area** Practice Test, Cumulative Test, BioFlix® 3-D Animations, Videos, Activities, Audio Glossary, Word Study Tools, Art

## You should be able to . . .

### ✔ TEST YOUR KNOWLEDGE
*Answers are available in Appendix A*

1. **True or false?** The transition from water to land reduced protostome diversity.

2. What is a lophophore?
   a. a specialized filter-feeding structure
   b. the single opening in species with a blind gut
   c. a distinctive type of larva with a band of cilia
   d. a synapomorphy that defines lophotrochozoans

3. What is the function of the arthropod exoskeleton?
   a. Because hard parts fossilize more readily than do soft tissues, the presence of an exoskeleton has given arthropods a good fossil record.
   b. It has no well-established function. (Trilobites had an exoskeleton, and they went extinct.)
   c. It provides protection and functions in locomotion.
   d. It makes growth by molting possible.

**4.** Why is it logical that Platyhelminthes have flattened bodies?

  **a.** They have simple bodies and evolved early in the diversification of protostomes.

  **b.** They lack a coelom, so their body cannot form a rounded tube-within-a-tube design.

  **c.** A flat body provides a large surface area for gas exchange, which compensates for their lack of gas-exchange organs.

  **d.** They are sit-and-wait predators that hide from passing prey by flattening themselves against the substrate.

**5.** One trait that is shared by the Lophotrochozoa and Ecdysozoa is_____.

**6.** Which protostome phylum is distinguished by having body segments organized into tagmata?

  **a.** Mollusca

  **b.** Arthropoda

  **c.** Annelida

  **d.** Nematoda

---

## ✔ TEST YOUR UNDERSTANDING
Answers are available in Appendix A

**7.** QUANTITATIVE Put the following phyla in order from least diverse (in terms of number of named species) to most diverse: Annelida, Mollusca, Arthropoda, Rotifera.

  **a.** Annelida, Rotifera, Mollusca, Arthropoda

  **b.** Mollusca, Rotifera, Annelida, Arthropoda

  **c.** Rotifera, Annelida, Arthropoda, Mollusca

  **d.** Rotifera, Annelida, Mollusca, Arthropoda

**8.** Predict why annelids and arthropods were thought to be closely related, before the phylogenetic analyses in the late 1990s.

**9.** Pose a hypothesis to explain why a larval stage is adaptive in clams. How could you test your hypothesis?

**10.** Use your understanding of protostome evolution to predict two adaptations for terrestrial living that occurred in land plants.

**11.** Pose a hypothesis to explain why the evolution of the wing was such an important event in the evolution of insects.

**12.** Propose a scenario wherein hemimetabolous metamorphosis would be adaptive.

---

## ✔ TEST YOUR PROBLEM-SOLVING SKILLS
Answers are available in Appendix A

**13.** Recall that the phylum Platyhelminthes includes three major groups: the free-living turbellarians, the parasitic cestodes, and the parasitic trematodes. Because the parasitic forms are so simple morphologically, researchers suggest that they are derived from more complex, free-living forms. Draw a phylogeny of Platyhelminthes that would support the hypotheses that ancestral flatworms were morphologically complex, free-living organisms and that parasitism is a derived condition.

**14.** Brachiopoda is a phylum within the Lophotrochozoa. Even though they are not closely related to mollusks, brachiopods look and act like bivalve mollusks (clams or mussels). Specifically, brachiopods suspension feed, live inside calcium carbonate shells with two valves that hinge together in some species, and attach to rocks or other hard surfaces on the ocean floor. How is it possible for brachiopods and bivalves to be so similar if they did not share a recent common ancestor?

**15.** The Mollusca includes a group of about 370 wormlike species called the Aplacophora. Although aplacophorans do not have a shell, their cuticle secretes calcium carbonate scales or spines. They lack a well-developed foot, and some species have a simple radula. They are mostly carnivores and detritivores in the deep sea. The reduced forms of several molluscan synapomorphies suggest that they are ancestral to other mollusks—that is, the earliest group to branch off in the molluscan phylogeny. Evaluate this hypothesis. How could you test it?

**16.** Examine the figure below summarizing the expression of *Ubx-AbdA Hox* genes (colored red) in different body segments during early development in four crustaceans. The blue appendages represent a novel type of feeding appendage called a maxilliped. Which statement best summarizes the data?

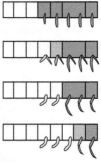

  **a.** Maxillipeds were lost in segments where *Ubx-AbdA* genes were expressed.

  **b.** Maxillipeds arose in segments where *Ubx-AbdA* genes were no longer expressed.

  **c.** Maxillipeds arose in segments where *Ubx-AbdA* genes were expressed.

  **d.** The presence of maxillipeds does not correlate with the pattern of *Ubx-AbdA* gene expression.

# 35 Deuterostome Animals

**In this chapter you will learn that**

Deuterostomes include the largest and most complex animals on Earth

*by asking* → What is an echinoderm? **35.1**

*by asking* → What is a chordate? **35.2**

*then asking* → What is a vertebrate? **35.3**

*then examining* → The primates and hominins **35.4**

In most habitats the "top predators"—animals that prey on other animals and aren't preyed upon themselves—are deuterostomes.

The **deuterostomes** include the largest-bodied and some of the most morphologically complex of all animals. They range from the sea stars that cling to dock pilings to the fish that dart in and out of coral reefs to the wildebeests that migrate across the Serengeti Plains of East Africa.

The deuterostomes were initially grouped together because they all undergo early embryonic development in a similar way. When a humpback whale, sea urchin, or human is just beginning to grow, the gut starts developing from posterior to anterior—the anus forms first and the mouth second. A coelom, if present, develops from outpocketings of mesoderm (see Chapter 33).

✔ When you see this checkmark, stop and test yourself. Answers are available in Appendix A.

More recently, phylogenies based on molecular evidence have confirmed the monophyly of the deuterostomes. Today, most biologists recognize four deuterostome phyla: the Echinodermata, Hemichordata, Xenoturbellida, and Chordata (**FIGURE 35.1**):

- The echinoderms include the sea stars and sea urchins.

- The hemichordates, or "acorn worms," burrow in marine sands or muds and make their living by deposit feeding or suspension feeding.

- A lone genus with two wormlike species, called *Xenoturbella*, was recognized as a distinct phylum in 2006. The phylogenetic placement of these small, ciliated animals has been debated by scientists for years.

- The chordates include the **vertebrates**, or animals with backbones. The vertebrates, in turn, comprise the hagfish, lampreys, sharks and rays, bony fishes, amphibians, mammals, and reptiles (including birds).

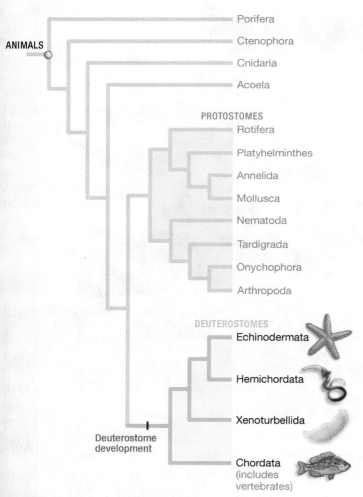

**FIGURE 35.1 There Are Four Phyla of Deuterostomes.** Vertebrates are in the phylum Chordata.

✔ **QUESTION** Are invertebrates monophyletic or paraphyletic? (Hint: See Table 28.2 if you need help.)

Animals that are not vertebrates are collectively known as **invertebrates.** Over 95 percent of the known animal species are invertebrates—but the vertebrates dominate the deuterostomes.

Although deuterostomes share important features of embryonic development, their adult body plans and their feeding methods, modes of locomotion, and reproductive strategies are highly diverse. This chapter explores deuterostome diversity by introducing the echinoderms and chordates and then taking a more in-depth look at the vertebrates and our own closest ancestors: the hominins.

## 35.1 What Is an Echinoderm?

The echinoderms (literally, "spiny-skins") were named for the spines or spikes observed in many species. Echinodermata is a large and diverse phylum but is exclusively marine.

In numbers of species and range of habitats occupied, echinoderms are the second-most successful lineage of deuterostomes—next to the vertebrates. To date, biologists have cataloged about 7000 species of echinoderms.

Echinoderms are also abundant. In some deepwater environments, species in this phylum represent 95 percent of the total mass of organisms.

How are these animals put together?

### The Echinoderm Body Plan

All deuterostomes are considered bilaterians, because they evolved from an ancestor that was bilaterally symmetric (see Chapter 33). Echinoderm larvae are also bilaterally symmetric (**FIGURE 35.2a**). But a remarkable event occurred early in the evolution of **echinoderms:** the origin of five-sided radial symmetry, called pentaradial symmetry, in adults (**FIGURE 35.2b**).

Radially symmetric animals do not have heads (Chapter 33). As a result, they tend to interact with the environment in all directions at once instead of facing the environment in one direction. Adult echinoderms that are capable of movement tend to move equally well in all directions.

A second noteworthy feature of the echinoderm body is its **endoskeleton:** a hard structure, located just inside a thin layer of epidermal tissue, which provides protection and support (shown without skin in Figure 35.2b). As an individual is developing, cells secrete plates of calcium carbonate inside the skin. Depending on the species, the plates may remain independent and result in a flexible structure or fuse into a rigid case. If the plates do not fuse, they are connected by an unusual tissue that can be reversibly stiff or flexible—depending on conditions.

Another remarkable event in echinoderm evolution was the origin of a unique morphological feature: a series of branching, fluid-filled tubes and chambers called the **water vascular system.** In some groups, one of the tubes is open to the exterior where it meets the body wall, so seawater can flow into and out

**(a)** Echinoderm larvae are bilaterally symmetric.

**(b)** Adult echinoderms are radially symmetric.

**FIGURE 35.2 Body Symmetry Differs in Adult and Larval Echinoderms. (a)** Bilaterally symmetric sea urchin larva. **(b)** Radially symmetric adult endoskeleton.

of the system. Inside, fluids move via the beating of cilia that line the interior of the tubes and chambers.

**FIGURE 35.3a** highlights a particularly important part of the water vascular system called tube feet. **Tube feet** are elongated, fluid-filled appendages, each consisting of a balloon-like *ampulla* on the inside of the body and a tube-like *podium* (literally, "foot"; plural *podia*) projecting on the outside (**FIGURE 35.3b**). The water vascular system forms a specialized hydrostatic skeleton that operates the tube feet. As tube feet extend and contract in a coordinated way along the base of an echinoderm, they alternately grab and release the substrate or food source, enabling movement and feeding. Tube feet can also aid in respiration by increasing the surface area of soft tissue exposed to the aquatic environment.

Radial symmetry in adults, an endoskeleton of calcium carbonate, and the water vascular system are all synapomorphies—traits that identify echinoderms as a monophyletic group. (Turn to Chapter 28 and **BioSkills 7** in Appendix B to review how to read phylogenetic trees.)

## How Do Echinoderms Feed?

Depending on the lineage and species in question, echinoderms make their living by mass feeding on algae or other animals, suspension feeding, or deposit feeding. In most cases, an echinoderm's tube feet play a key role in obtaining food.

Many sea stars, for example, prey on bivalves. Clams and mussels respond to sea star attacks by contracting muscles that close the two halves of their shell tight. But by clamping onto each half of the shell with their tube feet, making their endoskeleton rigid, and pulling, sea stars are often able to pry the shell apart a few millimeters (**FIGURE 35.4a**, see page 684). Once a gap exists, the sea star extrudes its stomach from its body and forces the stomach through the opening in the bivalve's shell. Upon contacting the visceral mass of the bivalve, the stomach of the sea star secretes digestive enzymes. It then begins to absorb the small molecules released by enzyme action. Eventually, only the shell of the prey remains.

Tube feet are also used in suspension feeding (**FIGURE 35.4b**). In most cases, tube feet are extended out into the water. When food particles contact them, the tube feet flick the food down to cilia, which sweep the particles toward the animal's mouth.

**(a)** Echinoderms have a water vascular system.

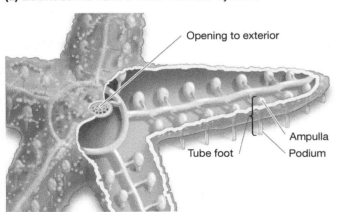

Opening to exterior

Tube foot

Ampulla

Podium

**(b)** Tube feet project from the underside of the body.

Tube feet

**FIGURE 35.3 Echinoderms Have a Water Vascular System. (a)** The water vascular system is a series of tubes and chambers that radiates throughout the body, forming a sophisticated hydrostatic skeleton. **(b)** Tube feet aid in movement because they extend from the body and can grab and release the substrate.

**(a)** Tube feet enable sea stars to get a grip on their prey.

**(b)** Tube feet enable feather stars to suspension feed.

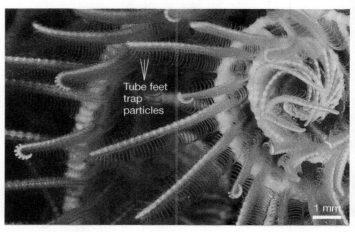

Tube feet
trap
particles

1 mm

**FIGURE 35.4 Echinoderms Use Their Tube Feet in Feeding.**

In deposit feeders, tube feet secrete mucus that is used to sop up food material on the substrate. The tube feet then roll the food-laden mucus into a ball and move it to the mouth.

## Key Lineages: The Echinoderms

The echinoderms living today make up five major lineages: (1) feather stars and sea lilies, (2) sea stars, (3) brittle stars and basket stars, (4) sea urchins and sand dollars, and (5) sea cucumbers (**FIGURE 35.5**). ✔ You should be able to indicate the origin of pentaradial symmetry in adults, the water vascular system, and the echinoderm endoskeleton on Figure 35.5.

Most feather stars and sea lilies are sessile suspension feeders.

Brittle stars and basket stars have five or more long arms that radiate out from a small central disk. They use these arms to suspension feed, deposit feed, or capture small prey animals.

- Sea cucumbers are sausage-shaped animals that suspension feed or deposit feed with the aid of modified tube feet called tentacles that are arranged in a whorl around their mouths.

Sea stars and the sea urchins and sand dollars are described in detail in the two boxes that follow.

- Echinodermata > Asteroidea (Sea Stars)
- Echinodermata > Echinoidea (Sea Urchins and Sand Dollars)

Protostomes

ECHINODERMATA

ECHINODERMATA
Deuterostomes

Crinoidea
(Feather stars, sea lilies)

Asteroidea
(Sea stars)

Ophiuroidea
(Brittle stars, basket stars)

Echinoidea
(Sea urchins, sand dollars)

Holothuroidea
(Sea cucumbers)

Hemichordata

Xenoturbellida

Chordata

**FIGURE 35.5 There Are Five Major Lineages of Echinoderms.**

## Echinodermata > Asteroidea (Sea Stars)

The 1900 known species of sea stars have bodies with five or more long arms—in some species, up to 40—radiating from a central region that contains the mouth, stomach, and anus (**FIGURE 35.6**). The sea star's arms are not set off from the central region by clear, joint-like articulations, in contrast to their sister group, the brittle stars. ✔ You should be able to indicate the origin of arms, and the origin of arms that are continuous with the central region, as in sea stars, on Figure 35.5. When fully grown, sea stars can range in size from less than 1 cm in diameter to 1 m across. They live on hard or soft substrates along the coasts of all the world's oceans. Although the spines that are characteristic of some echinoderms are reduced to knobs on the surface of most sea stars, the crown-of-thorns star and a few other species have prominent, upright, movable spines.

**Feeding** Sea stars are predators or scavengers. Some species pull bivalves apart with their tube feet and feed by everting their stomach into the prey's visceral mass. In some cases, sea star predation on bivalves opens up habitat for other organisms in the community—increasing biodiversity (see Chapter 55). Sponges, barnacles, and snails are also common prey. The crown-of-thorns sea star specializes in feeding on corals and is native to the Indian Ocean and western Pacific Ocean. Its population has skyrocketed recently—possibly because people are harvesting the sea star's major predator, a large snail called the triton, for its shell. Large crown-of-thorns star populations have led to the destruction of large areas of coral reef.

**Movement** Sea stars crawl with the aid of their tube feet.

**Reproduction** Sexual reproduction predominates in sea stars, and sexes are separate. At least one sea star arm in each individual is filled with reproductive organs that produce massive amounts of gametes—millions of eggs per female in some species. Some species care for their offspring by holding fertilized eggs on their body until the eggs hatch. Larvae are long-lived and may spend weeks or months in the plankton, possibly dispersing thousands of kilometers. Most sea stars are capable of regenerating arms that are lost in predator attacks or storms. Some species can reproduce asexually by dividing the body in two; each of the two individuals then regenerates the missing half.

*Crossaster papposus*

5 cm

**FIGURE 35.6 Sea Stars May Have Many Arms.**

## Echinodermata > Echinoidea (Sea Urchins and Sand Dollars)

About 1000 species of echinoids are living today; most are sea urchins or sand dollars. Sea urchins have globe-shaped bodies and long spines and crawl along substrates. Sand dollars are flattened and disk-shaped, have short spines, and burrow in soft sediments. ✔ You should be able to indicate the origin of globular or disk-shaped bodies on Figure 35.5.

**Feeding** Most types of sea urchins are herbivores. In some areas of the world, urchins are extremely important grazers on kelp and other types of algae. In cases when humans have removed predators such as sea otters, and urchin populations have grown in response, the urchins' grazing can destroy kelp forests. The urchins chew away a structure called a holdfast, which anchors kelp to the substrate; the kelp then float away and die. Most echinoids have a unique, jaw-like feeding structure in their mouths, called an Aristotle's lantern, that is made up of five calcium carbonate teeth attached to muscles (**FIGURE 35.7a**, see page 686). In many species, this apparatus can extend and retract as the animal feeds, allowing it to reach more food material. Sand dollars, in contrast, are suspension feeders. The beating of cilia on their spines creates tiny water currents that bring organic material toward the body. The food particles are then trapped in mucus and transported in long strings to the mouth. In this way, sand dollars harvest nutritious detritus found in sand or in other soft substrates (**FIGURE 35.7b**).

**Movement** Using their spines, sea urchins crawl and sand dollars burrow. Some species also use their tube feet to aid movement, or just to hold on to the substrate to prevent being washed away by waves and currents.

**Reproduction** Sexual reproduction predominates in sea urchins and sand dollars (see Figure 33.14). Fertilization is external, and sexes are separate. As in sea stars, larvae are long-lived and may disperse long distances. The larvae of some species undergo asexual reproduction by dividing in two or budding off new individuals, before they undergo metamorphosis.

*(Continued on next page)*

**(a)** Sea urchins graze with their teeth.

*Lytechinus variegatus*

Teeth at center of underside

5 mm

**(b)** Sand dollars suspension feed.

*Echinarachnius parma*

1 cm

**FIGURE 35.7 Sea Urchins and Sand Dollars Have Different Feeding Strategies.**

# 35.2  What Is a Chordate?

You are a chordate, yet chordates are so diverse that you would probably find it difficult to identify familiar features in some of your fellow chordates—such as the sea squirts, whose small, sessile, globular bodies hardly resemble animals at all. Which characteristics are shared within this phylum?

All **chordates** are defined by the presence of four morphological features at some stage in their life cycles:

1. openings into the throat called **pharyngeal gill slits;**

2. a **dorsal hollow nerve cord,** which runs the length of the body, composed of projections from neurons;

3. a stiff and supportive but flexible rod called a **notochord,** which runs the length of the body; and

4. a muscular, post-anal tail—meaning a tail that contains muscle and extends past the anus.

Electrical signals carried by the dorsal hollow nerve cord coordinate muscle movement, and the notochord stiffens the muscular tail. Together, these traits create a "torpedo"—a long, streamlined animal that can swim rapidly. Fossil evidence suggests that chordates diversified early during the Cambrian radiation of animals, about 550 million years ago.

## Three Chordate "Subphyla"

The phylum Chordata is made up of three major lineages: the (1) cephalochordates, (2) urochordates, and (3) vertebrates. Let's examine the four chordate morphological features in each group.

**The Cephalochordates**  **Cephalochordates** are also called lancelets or amphioxus; they are small, mobile, torpedo-shaped animals with a "fish-like" appearance, and they make their living by suspension feeding (**FIGURE 35.8a**). Adult cephalochordates live in ocean-bottom habitats, where they burrow in sand and suspension feed with the aid of their pharyngeal gill slits.

The dorsal hollow nerve cord in cephalochordates runs parallel to a notochord. Because the notochord stiffens the cephalochordates' bodies, muscle contractions on either side result in fishlike movement when the animals swim during dispersal or mating.

**The Urochordates**  **Urochordates** are also called tunicates or sea squirts. As **FIGURE 35.8b** shows, pharyngeal gill slits are present in both larvae and adults; these structures function in both feeding and gas exchange.

The dorsal hollow nerve cord, notochord, and tail are present in larvae and in the sexually mature forms of species that move as adults. As in cephalochordates, these features combine to enable swimming movements. As larvae swim or float in the upper water layers of the ocean, they drift to new habitats where food might be more abundant. As a result, larvae function as a dispersal stage in the life cycle.

**The Vertebrates**  Vertebrates (**FIGURE 35.8c**) include the hagfish, lampreys, sharks and rays, several lineages of bony fishes, amphibians, mammals, and reptiles (including birds). In vertebrates, the dorsal hollow nerve cord is the familiar spinal cord—a bundle of nerve cells that runs from the brain to the posterior of the body. Electrical signals from the spinal cord control movements and the function of organs (see Chapter 46).

Structures called pharyngeal pouches are homologous to pharyngeal gill slits and are present in all vertebrate embryos.

## Key Lineages: The Invertebrate Chordates

There are about 24 species of lancelets, 3000 species of tunicates, and over 62,000 vertebrates. Because they are so species rich and diverse, vertebrate chordates rate their own section in this chapter (Section 35.3). Here let's focus on the tunicates and lancelets. These lineages are sometimes referred to as the invertebrate chordates—meaning, members of the Chordata that lack vertebrae. They are of great interest to evolutionary biologists, who study the morphology, development, and genetics of these animals to better understand the evolutionary history of our own subphylum, the vertebrates.

- Chordata > Cephalochordata (Lancelets)
- Chordata > Urochordata (Tunicates)

Legend:
- Pharyngeal gill slits
- Dorsal hollow nerve cord
- Notochord
- Muscular, post-anal tail

**(a) Cephalochordates**

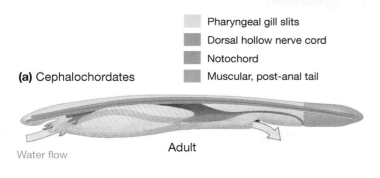

Water flow — Adult

**(b) Urochordates**

Larva — Water flow — Adult

**(c) Vertebrates**

Embryo — Cross section of embryo

Pharyngeal pouches become gill slits in aquatic vertebrates

**FIGURE 35.8 Four Features Distinguish the Three Lineages of Chordates.**

In aquatic species, the creases between pouches open into gill slits and develop into part of the main gas-exchange organ—the **gills.** In terrestrial species, however, gill slits do not develop after the pharyngeal pouches form. In these species, the pharyngeal pouches are a vestigial trait (see Chapter 25).

A notochord develops in all vertebrate embryos. It no longer functions in body support and movement, however, for these roles are filled by the vertebral column. Instead, the notochord helps organize the body plan early in development. The notochord secretes proteins that help induce the formation of somites—segmented blocks of tissue that form along the length of the body (Chapter 23). Although the notochord itself disappears, cells in the somites later differentiate into the vertebrae, ribs, and skeletal muscles of the back, body wall, and limbs. In this way, the notochord is instrumental in the development of the trait that gave vertebrates their name.

### Chordata > Cephalochordata (Lancelets)

About two dozen species of cephalochordates have been described to date, all of them found in marine sands. Lancelets—also called amphioxus—have several characteristics that are intermediate between invertebrates and vertebrates. Chief among these is a notochord that is retained in adults, where it functions as an endoskeleton.

**Feeding** Adult cephalochordates feed by burrowing in sediment until only their heads are sticking out into the water (**FIGURE 35.9**). They take water in through their mouths and trap food particles with the aid of mucus on their pharyngeal gill slits.

**Movement** Adults have large blocks of muscle arranged in a series along the length of the notochord. Lancelets are efficient swimmers because the flexible, rod-like notochord stiffens the body, making it wriggle when the blocks of muscle contract.

**Reproduction** Asexual reproduction is unknown, and individuals are either male or female. Gametes are released into the environment, and fertilization is external.

*Branchiostoma lanceolatum*

1 cm

**FIGURE 35.9 Lancelets Look Like Fish but Are Not Vertebrates.**

The urochordates are also called tunicates; they comprise two major sub-lineages: the sea squirts (or ascidians) and salps. All of the species described to date live in the ocean. Sea squirts live on the ocean floor (**FIGURE 35.10a**); salps live in open water (**FIGURE 35.10b**). The synapomorphies that define the urochordates include an external coat of polysaccharide, called a tunic, that covers and supports the body; a U-shaped gut; and two body openings, called siphons.

**Feeding** Adult urochordates use their pharyngeal gill slits to suspension feed. A mucus sheet on the inside of the pharynx traps particles present in the water that enters one siphon, passes through the slits, and leaves through the other siphon.

**Movement** Larvae swim with the aid of the notochord, which functions as a simple endoskeleton. Larvae are a dispersal stage and do not feed. Adult sea squirts are sessile while salps drift in currents.

**Reproduction** In most species, individuals produce both sperm and eggs. In some species, both sperm and eggs are shed into the water and fertilization is external; in other species, sperm are released into the water but eggs are retained, so that fertilization and early development are internal. Asexual reproduction by budding is also common in some groups, forming large sessile colonies in some sea squirts, and long chains in salps.

**(a) Sea squirt**

*Rhopalaea crassa*

1 cm

**(b) Salp**

*Salpa thompsoni*

1 cm

**FIGURE 35.10 Sea Squirts and Salps Live in Different Habitats.**

## 35.3 What Is a Vertebrate?

The vertebrates are a monophyletic group distinguished by two synapomorphies:

- a column of cartilaginous or bony structures called **vertebrae,** which form along the dorsal side of the body; and

- a **cranium,** a bony, cartilaginous, or fibrous case that encloses the brain. (A skull consists of the cranium in jawless vertebrates, and the cranium and mandible—or jaw—in jawed vertebrates.)

The vertebral column is important because it protects the spinal cord. The cranium is important because it protects the brain along with sensory organs such as eyes. Together, the vertebrae and cranium protect the central nervous system (CNS) and key sensory structures (see Chapter 33).

The vertebrate brain develops as an outgrowth of the most anterior end of the dorsal hollow nerve cord, and it is important to the vertebrate lifestyle. Vertebrates are active predators and herbivores that must sense stimuli in their environments and make rapid, directed movements in response. More complex brains enable more complex interactions with the environment.

In early vertebrates, the brain was divided into three regions with important sensory functions:

1. The **forebrain** housed the sense of smell;

2. the **midbrain** was associated with vision; and

3. the **hindbrain** was responsible for balance and, in some species, hearing.

All vertebrates living today have retained these three regions, but the structures and functions of the regions have evolved over time. For example, in the jawed vertebrates, or **gnathostomes** (pronounced *NATH-oh-stomes*), the hindbrain consists of enlarged regions called the **cerebellum** and **medulla oblongata.** Part of the forebrain also became elaborated into a large structure called the **cerebrum,** especially in birds and mammals. (The structure and functions of the vertebrate brain are analyzed in detail in Chapter 46.) The evolution of a large, three-part brain, protected by a hard cranium, was a key innovation in vertebrate evolution.

# An Overview of Vertebrate Evolution

Vertebrates have been the focus of intense research for well over 300 years, in part because they are large and conspicuous and in part because they include humans. All this effort has paid off in an increasingly thorough understanding of how the vertebrates diversified. Let's consider what the data from the fossil record have to say about key events in vertebrate evolution and then examine the current best estimate of the phylogenetic relationships among vertebrates.

**The Vertebrate Fossil Record**  Vertebrate fossils are present in the Chengjiang formation of China, dated to the Cambrian explosion. The detailed vertebrate fossils show that the earliest members of this lineage lived in the ocean about 540 million years ago; they had streamlined, fishlike bodies and a cranium made of cartilage (see an artist's interpretation of an early vertebrate species called *Haikouichthys* in Figure 28.12). **Cartilage** is a strong but flexible tissue—found in your ear and the tip of your nose—that consists of scattered cells in a gel-like matrix of polysaccharides and protein fibers (Chapter 42).

A cartilaginous endoskeleton is a basic vertebrate feature; only in the bony fishes and their descendants, the **tetrapods** (literally, "four-footed"), does the skeleton become composed of bone in the adult. **Bone** is a tissue consisting of cells and blood vessels encased in a matrix made primarily of calcium phosphate, along with a small amount of protein fibers. In species with bony skeletons, growing bones are cartilaginous first and become bony only later in their development.

Following the appearance of vertebrates, the fossil record documents a series of key innovations that occurred as this lineage diversified (**FIGURE 35.11**):

- *Bony exoskeleton*  Fossil vertebrates from the early part of the Ordovician period, about 480 million years ago, are the first fossils to have bone. When bone first evolved, it did not occur in the endoskeleton ("inside-skeleton"). Instead, bone was deposited in scalelike plates that formed an **exoskeleton** ("outside-skeleton") (compare with arthropod exoskeletons in Chapter 34). Most of your skull is made up of this type of dermal ("skin") bone—making your skull similar to the "head shields" in Ordovician fishes. Based on the fossils' overall morphology, biologists infer that these animals swam with the aid of a notochord and that they breathed and fed by gulping water and filtering it through their pharyngeal gill slits. Presumably, the bony plates helped provide protection from predators.

- *Jaws*  The first fishes with jaws show up early in the Silurian, about 440 million years ago. The evolution of jaws was significant because it improved the ability of fish to use suction feeding to capture prey, and also to bite, meaning that vertebrates were no longer limited to suspension feeding or deposit feeding. Instead, they could make a living as herbivores or predators. Soon after, jawbones with teeth appear in the fossil record. With jaws and teeth, vertebrates became armed and dangerous. The fossil record shows that a spectacular

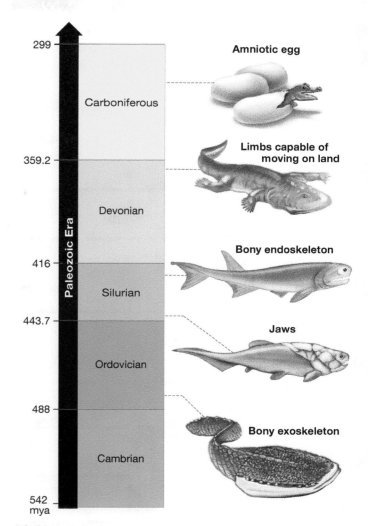

**FIGURE 35.11 Timeline of the Early Vertebrate Fossil Record.**

radiation of jawed fishes followed, filling marine and freshwater habitats.

- *Bony endoskeleton*  In some lineages of fishes from late in the Silurian period, the cartilaginous endoskeleton began to be stiffened by the deposition of bone. Unlike the dermal bone that had evolved earlier, the bony endoskeleton functioned to support movement—rapid swimming.

- *Limbs capable of moving on land*  The next great event in the evolution of vertebrates was the transition to living on land. The first animals that had limbs and were capable of moving on land are dated to about 365 million years ago, late in the Devonian. These were the first of the tetrapods—animals with four limbs.

- *Amniotic egg*  About 20 million years after the appearance of tetrapods in the fossil record, the first amniotes are present. The Amniota is a lineage of vertebrates that includes all tetrapods other than amphibians. The **amniotes** are named for a signature synapomorphy and adaptation: the amniotic egg. An **amniotic egg** is an egg that has membranes

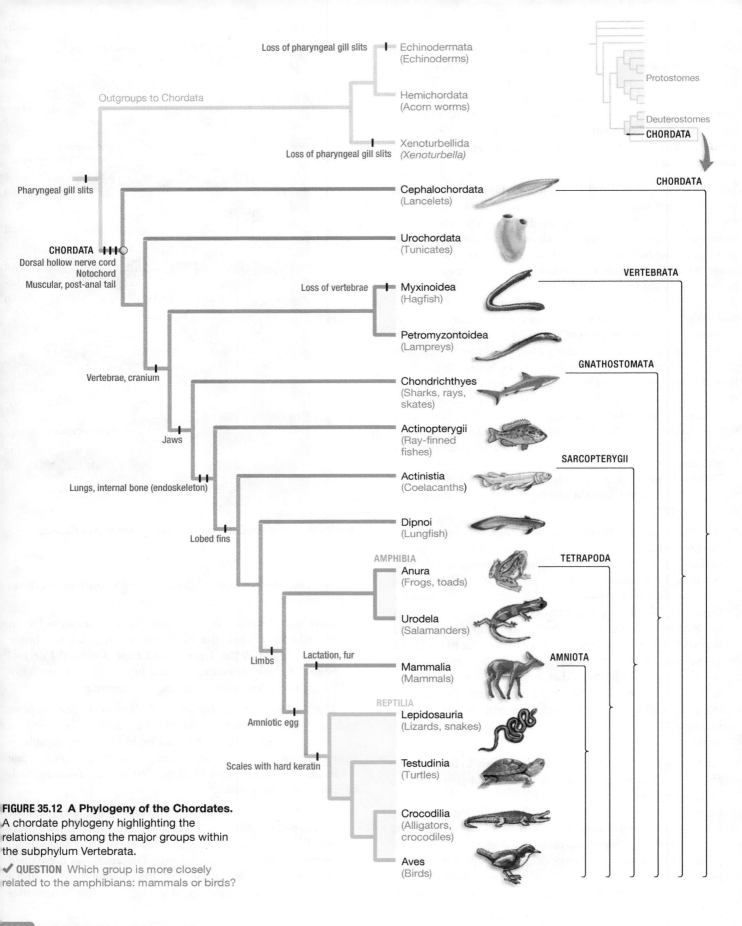

**FIGURE 35.12 A Phylogeny of the Chordates.**
A chordate phylogeny highlighting the relationships among the major groups within the subphylum Vertebrata.

✔ **QUESTION** Which group is more closely related to the amphibians: mammals or birds?

surrounding a food supply, a water supply, and a waste repository. These membranes provided support and extra surface area for gas exchange, allowing amniotes to produce larger, better-developed young.

To summarize, the fossil record indicates that vertebrates evolved through a series of major steps, beginning about 540 million years ago with vertebrates whose endoskeleton consisted of a notochord. The earliest vertebrates gave rise to fishes with bony exoskeletons. These fishes gave rise to the jawed vertebrates, including the cartilaginous fishes (sharks and rays) and several lineages of fishes with bony endoskeletons. After the tetrapods emerged and amphibians resembling salamanders began to live on land, the evolution of the amniotic egg paved the way for the diversification of amniotes—specifically, reptiles and the animals that gave rise to mammals. Do phylogenetic trees estimated from analyses of DNA sequence data agree or conflict with these conclusions?

**Evaluating Molecular Phylogenies**  **FIGURE 35.12** provides a phylogenetic tree that summarizes the relationships among living chordates, especially vertebrates, based on DNA and other molecular sequence data. The labeled bars on the tree indicate where major morphological innovations occurred as lineages diversified. Although the phylogeny of deuterostomes continues to be a topic of intense research, researchers are increasingly confident that the relationships described in Figure 35.12 are accurate. There are a few important take-home messages from the tree:

- *Outgroup to vertebrates*  According to the most recent molecular data, the urochordates are the closest living relatives of the vertebrates.

- *Living outgroup to gnathostomes*  The phylogenetic relationships among hagfish, lampreys, and the gnathostomes have been hotly debated. Two hundred years ago, hagfish and lampreys were grouped together as the class Cyclostomata ("round-mouthed"), based on their unique mouthparts. Then, starting in the 1970s, morphologists began to take a closer look and placed hagfish and lampreys in two independent lineages with lampreys as the sister group to gnathostomes. But molecular phylogenies have not supported this view, instead leaning toward the Cyclostomata grouping. So which is correct? Analysis of a new source of data—evolutionarily conserved microRNAs (Chapter 19)—has decided in favor of the Cyclostomata hypothesis. This result is important because it emphasizes that the ancestor to gnathostomes was probably not lamprey-like. Rather, some vertebrate characteristics appear to have been *lost* in the hagfish/lamprey lineages, especially in hagfish.

- *Fossil outgroup to gnathostomes*  The diverse lineages of extinct armored fishes are not included in the tree of living vertebrates. If pictured, they would occur as outgroups to the gnathostomes—more closely related to jawed vertebrates than are hagfish and lampreys.

- *"Fish"*  No monophyletic group includes all of the living fishlike lineages. Instead, "fishy" organisms are a series of

independent monophyletic groups (the living ones are indicated by blue branches in Figure 35.12). Taken together, they form what biologists call a **grade**—a sequence of lineages that are paraphyletic (that include some, but not all, of the descendants of a common ancestor). ✔ If you understand the difference between a paraphyletic and monophyletic group, you should be able to draw what Figure 35.12 would look like if there actually were a monophyletic group called "The Fishes." (See Table 28.2 if you need help.)

- *Mammals*  Mammals and reptiles are sister groups and thus are more closely related to each other than either is to the amphibians.

- *Birds*  Birds occur within the monophyletic group called reptiles. That is, birds *are* reptiles.

To understand what happened during the diversification of vertebrates, let's explore some of the major morphological innovations involved in feeding, movement, and reproduction in more detail. (For an overview of these themes, see Chapter 33.)

## Key Innovations in Vertebrates

Among vertebrates, the most species-rich and ecologically diverse lineages are the ray-finned fishes and the tetrapods. Ray-finned fishes occupy habitats ranging from deepwater environments, which are perpetually dark, to shallow ponds that dry up each year. Tetrapods include the large herbivores and predators in terrestrial environments all over the world. About the same number of species of ray-finned fishes and tetrapods are living today (**FIGURE 35.13**).

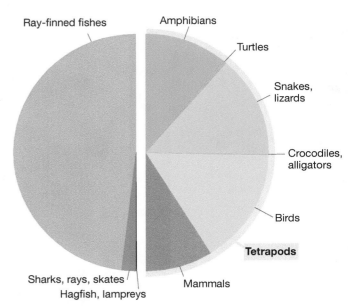

**FIGURE 35.13 Relative Species Abundance among Vertebrates.** Of the 63,000 species of described vertebrates, about half are ray-finned fishes and about half are tetrapods.

DATA: American Museum of Natural History; birdlife.org; fishbase.org; IUCN red list 2010; Reptile-database.org.

**The Vertebrate Jaw** The most ancient vertebrates in the fossil record had relatively simple mouthparts that lacked jaws. Until jaws evolved, vertebrates were not able to harvest food by biting.

The leading hypothesis for the origin of the jaw proposes that natural selection acted on developmental regulatory genes that determine the morphology of **gill arches,** which are curved regions of tissue between the gills. The jawless vertebrates have bars of cartilage that stiffen these gill arches. The gill-arch hypothesis proposes that mutation and natural selection increased the size of the most anterior arch and modified its orientation slightly, producing the first working jaw (**FIGURE 35.14**). Four lines of evidence support this hypothesis:

1. Both gill arches and jaws consist of flattened bars of bony or cartilaginous tissue that hinge and bend forward.

2. During development, the same population of cells gives rise to the muscles that move jaws and the muscles that move gill arches.

3. Unlike most other parts of the vertebrate skeleton, both jaws and gill arches are derived from specialized cells in the embryo called neural crest cells.

4. The expression patterns of key developmental regulatory genes, including *Hox* and *Dlx*, are similar in jaws and gill arches.

**(a)** Jawless vertebrate

Gill arches

Mouth

**(b)** Intermediate form (basal gnathostomes)

Gill arches

Jaw

**(c)** Fossil shark

Gill arches

Jaw

**FIGURE 35.14 The Gill-Arch Hypothesis for the Evolution of the Jaw. (a)** Gill arches support the gills in jawless vertebrates. **(b)** This intermediate form has yet to be found in the fossil record. **(c)** Fossil sharks that appeared later had more elaborate jaws.

Once jaws originated, changes in size and shape enabled a rapid diversification of feeding strategies from suction feeding to biting. Other modifications to the jaw also occurred:

- In most ray-finned fishes, the jaw is protrusible—meaning it can be extended to nip or bite at food.

- Several species-rich lineages of ray-finned fishes have a second specialized jaw called a **pharyngeal** ("throat") **jaw,** consisting of modified gill arches. It is located in the back of the throat and makes food processing particularly efficient. (For more on the structure and function of pharyngeal jaws, see Chapter 44.)

To summarize, the radiation of ray-finned fishes was triggered largely by the evolution and diversification of the jaw, by modifications that made it possible to protrude the jaw, and by the origin of the pharyngeal jaw. The story of tetrapods is different, however. Although jaw structure varies somewhat among tetrapod groups, the adaptation that triggered their initial diversification involved the ability to move and get to food, not to bite it and process it.

**The Tetrapod Limb** To understand how tetrapods made the water-to-land transition, consider the morphology and behavior of their closest living relatives, the lungfish (**FIGURE 35.15**). Most living species of lungfishes inhabit shallow, oxygen-poor water. To supplement the oxygen taken in by their gills, they have lungs and breathe air. (Note that although lungs originated before the divergence of ray-finned fishes and the Sarcopterygii, they serve primarily as a swim bladder to maintain buoyancy in ray-finned fishes.) Some lungfishes also have fleshy fins supported by bones and are capable of walking short distances along watery mudflats or the bottoms of ponds. In addition, some species can survive extended droughts by burrowing in mud.

Lungfish have a series of adaptations that allow them to survive on land for short periods. Could a lungfish-like organism have evolved into the first land-dwelling vertebrate with limbs?

Fossils provide strong links between the limbs of the ancestors of today's lungfish and the earliest land-dwelling vertebrates. **FIGURE 35.16** shows a phylogeny of the species involved. Note that during the Devonian, the fossil record documents a series of species that indicate a gradual transition from a lobe-like fin to a limb that could support walking on land. The fossil record

Fleshy fins

**FIGURE 35.15 Lungfish Have Limb-like Fins.** Some lungfishes can walk or crawl short distances on their fleshy fins.

is actually more complete than shown here—the figure is just a sample of the tetrapod and tetrapod-like species known from this interval.

The color coding in Figure 35.16 emphasizes that each fin or limb has a single bony element that is proximal (closest to the body; in blue) and then two bones that are distal (farther from the body) and arranged side by side (these are shown in red), followed by a series of distal elements (in orange). Because the structures are similar, and because no other animal groups have limb bones in this arrangement, the evidence for homology is strong.

The hypothesis that tetrapod limbs evolved from fish fins has also been supported by molecular genetic evidence. Recent work has shown that several regulatory proteins involved in the development of cartilaginous fish fins and ray-finned fish fins and the upper parts of mammal limbs are homologous. For example, the proteins produced by several different *Hox* genes are found at the same times during development and in the same locations in fins and limbs.

These data suggest that these appendages are patterned by the same genes. As a result, the data support the hypothesis that tetrapod limbs evolved from fins. Once the tetrapod limb evolved, natural selection elaborated it into diverse structures that are used for running, gliding, crawling, burrowing, swimming, and flying.

Once tetrapods made the water-to-land transition, they had to survive a number of new terrestrial challenges other than locomotion, such as keeping their eggs from drying out.

**The Amniotic Egg** Amphibians (frogs and toads, salamanders, and limbless species called caecilians) keep their eggs from drying out by laying their jelly-coated eggs in water. In contrast, reptiles (including birds) and the egg-laying mammals produce an amniotic egg, which has a protective covering that reduces the rate of drying significantly. Species that produce amniotic eggs lay them outside of water.

Amphibian eggs are surrounded by a single membrane, whereas amniotic eggs have four. As **FIGURE 35.17** shows, the outermost membrane of an amniotic egg encloses a supply of water in a protein-rich solution called **albumen.** Albumen cushions the developing embryo and provides nutrients. The three inner membranes surround the embryo itself, the yolk provided by the mother, and the waste from the embryo. The additional membranes are thought to be advantageous because they:

1. provide mechanical support—an important consideration outside of a buoyant aquatic environment; and

2. increase the surface area available for exchange of gases and other materials. Efficient diffusion of molecules is important because it allows females to lay larger eggs that hatch into larger, more independent young.

In addition, amniotic eggs are surrounded by a shell. This layer is leathery in lizards and snakes. It is stiffened by some calcium carbonate deposits in turtles and crocodiles, and by extensive

**FIGURE 35.16 Evidence for a Fin-to-Limb Transition.** The fossil record documents a series of species that indicate a gradual transition from a lobe-like fin to a limb that could support walking on land.

✓ **QUESTION** This phylogeny was estimated from traits other than the morphology of the limb. Why is this important in addressing how limbs evolved?

*Eusthenopteron* (~385 mya)

Lobe-like fin

*Panderichthys* (~380 mya)

*Tiktaalik* (~375 mya)

*Acanthostega* (~365 mya)

*Tulerpeton* (~362 mya)

Limb that can support walking on land

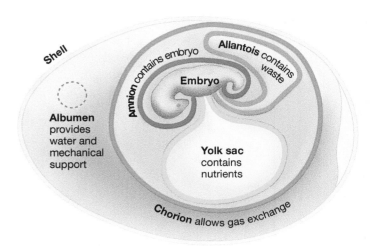

**FIGURE 35.17 An Amniotic Egg.** Amniotic eggs have four membrane-bound sacs.

Shell

Amnion contains embryo

Allantois contains waste

Embryo

Albumen provides water and mechanical support

Yolk sac contains nutrients

Chorion allows gas exchange

calcium carbonate deposits in birds. Lizards, snakes, turtles, and crocodiles often bury their eggs in moist soils, but bird eggs are more watertight and are laid in nests that are exposed to air.

During the evolution of mammals, however, a second major innovation in reproduction occurred—one that eliminated the need for any type of egg laying.

**The Placenta**   Egg-laying animals are said to be **oviparous,** while species that give birth are termed **viviparous** (Chapter 33). In many viviparous animals, females produce an egg that contains a nutrient-rich yolk. Instead of laying the egg, however, the mother retains it inside her body. In these **ovoviviparous** species, the developing offspring depends on the resources in the egg yolk.

In caecilians, some lizards, and most mammals, however, the eggs that females produce have little yolk. After fertilization occurs and the egg is retained, a combination of maternal and embryonic tissues produces a placenta within the uterus or oviduct. The embryo's contributions are the allantois and chorion—membranes that are involved in gas exchange in an amniotic egg. In the placenta, tissues derived from the allantois and chorion are also involved in the diffusion of gases, nutrients, and wastes.

The **placenta** is an organ that is rich in blood vessels and that facilitates a flow of oxygen and nutrients from the mother to the developing offspring, as well as the removal of nitrogenous wastes and carbon dioxide from the offspring (**FIGURE 35.18**). After a development period called **gestation,** the embryo emerges from the mother's body.

Why did viviparity and the placenta evolve? The leading hypotheses are that retaining the embryo inside the body has several advantages:

1. Offspring develop at a more constant, favorable temperature.

2. Offspring are protected.

3. Offspring are portable—mothers are not tied to a nest.

In effect, a placenta and viviparity are mechanisms for increasing the level of **parental care:** behavior by a parent that improves the ability of its offspring to survive. What other types of parental care evolved in vertebrates?

**Parental Care**   In species that provide extensive parental care—even if only in the form of exceptionally large amounts of yolk in eggs—mothers participate in a fitness trade-off (see Chapter 25). They can produce fewer offspring, but the offspring that they do produce have a higher probability of survival.

In animals, mechanisms of parental care include incubating eggs to keep them warm during early development, keeping young warm and dry, supplying young with food, and protecting them from danger. In some insect and frog species, mothers carry eggs or newly hatched young on their bodies. In fishes, parents commonly guard eggs during development and fan them with oxygen-rich water.

Mammals and birds provide particularly extensive parental care. In both groups, the mother (and often the father, in birds) continues to feed and care for individuals after birth or hatching—sometimes for many years. Female mammals also **lactate**—meaning that they produce milk and use it to feed their offspring after birth (**FIGURE 35.19**).

Among large animals, the evolution of extensive parental care is hypothesized to be a major reason for the evolutionary success of mammals and birds. In both lineages, mothers produce relatively small numbers of large, high-quality offspring.

**Wings and Flight**   Following the transition from water to land, the origin of the amniotic egg, and the elaboration of parental care, amniotes made another big transition—into the air. Wings and flight evolved independently in three lineages of tetrapod amniotes: the extinct flying reptiles called pterosaurs (pronounced *TARE-oh-sors*), the bats, and the birds.

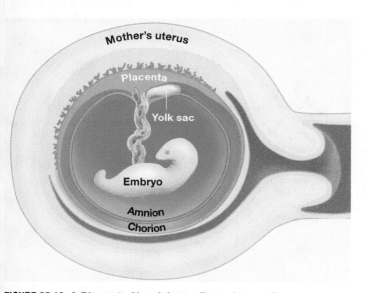

**FIGURE 35.18  A Placenta Nourishes a Fetus Internally.**

✓ **QUESTION** Compare the relative size of the yolk sac here with that in the amniotic egg (Figure 35.17).

**FIGURE 35.19  Parental Care Is Extensive in Mammals.** Female mammals, such as this timber wolf, produce highly nutritious milk to nourish their young.

How did flight evolve? The best data sets on this question involve feathered flight in birds. Since the early 2000s, paleontologists have discovered a spectacular series of feathered dinosaur fossils. The newly discovered species and exceptionally well-preserved feather specimens address key questions about the evolution of birds, feathers, and flight:

- **Did birds evolve from dinosaurs?** On the basis of skeletal characteristics, all of these recently discovered fossil species clearly show that birds are part of the monophyletic group called dinosaurs. That is—birds *are* dinosaurs.

- **How did feathers evolve?** The early fossils support a model of feathers evolving in a series of steps, beginning with simple projections from the skin (popularly called "dinofuzz") and culminating in the complex, branched structures familiar today. Although diverse, feathers observed in many non-avian dinosaurs were not strong enough to support gliding or flight. They may have been used for insulation and/or mating displays—recent analysis of pigments in fossil feathers have shown striking color patterns in some dinosaurs (**FIGURE 35.20**).

- **Did birds begin flying from the ground up or from the trees down?** More specifically, did flight evolve with running species that began to jump and glide or make short flights, with the aid of feathers to provide lift? Or did flight evolve from tree-dwelling species that used feathers to glide from tree to tree, much as flying squirrels do today? This question is still unresolved. The observation that many early feathered dinosaurs had "flight" feathers on their legs adds an intriguing piece to the puzzle (see Figure 35.20).

Once dinosaurs evolved feathers and took to the air, the fossil record shows that a series of adaptations made powered, flapping flight increasingly efficient (**FIGURE 35.21**).

- Most dinosaurs have a flat sternum ("breastbone"), but the bird sternum has a projection called the keel, which provides a large surface area to which flight muscles attach.

Elongated "keel" on sternum for attachment of flight muscles

Hollow bones strengthened by "struts"

Produce heat in their tissues (endothermic)

**FIGURE 35.21 In Addition to Feathers, Birds Have Several Features That Enable Flight.**

- Birds are extraordinarily light for their size, primarily because they have a drastically reduced number of bones and because their larger bones are thin walled and hollow—though strengthened by bony "struts."

- Birds are capable of sustained activity year-round because they are **endotherms** ("inside-heated")—they maintain a high body temperature by producing heat in their tissues.

From dinosaurs that jumped or glided from tree to tree, birds have evolved into extraordinary flying machines.

To summarize, the evolution of the jaw gave tetrapods the potential to capture and process a wide array of foods. With limbs, they could move efficiently on land in search of food. The amniotic egg and placenta further enabled vertebrates to diversify into terrestrial niches, and parental care increased the survivorship of their offspring. Finally, some tetrapods were able to defy the pull of gravity, expanding their realm into the air.

**FIGURE 35.20 Feathers Evolved in Dinosaurs.** This artist's depiction of what *Anchiornis huxleyi,* a feathered dinosaur, might have looked like in life incorporates recent data on fossil feather colors. The colors may have been important in mating displays. Unlike modern birds, many feathered dinosaurs had large feathers on their legs.

## check your understanding

**If you understand that . . .**

- Vertebrates have a distinctive body plan: bilateral symmetry with vertebrae that protect a spinal cord and a cranium that protects the brain.
- An array of key innovations occurred during the evolution of vertebrates: jaws, the tetrapod limb, the amniotic egg, the placenta, extensive parental care, and flight.

✔ **You should be able to . . .**

1. Explain the adaptive significance of each key innovation.
2. Compare adaptations in protostomes (Chapter 34) and deuterostomes for living on land.

*Answers are available in Appendix A.*

# Key Lineages: The Vertebrate Chordates

The fossil record provides an increasingly clear picture of early vertebrate evolution; intensive and continuing research has explored the origins of key vertebrate innovations such as the jaw, the tetrapod limb, and the amniotic egg. Now that you've been introduced to key vertebrate features, let's take a closer look at the key lineages.

**"Fish"** As discussed earlier, fish are a paraphyletic group consisting of diverse lineages, many of which are extinct. Four of the boxes that follow feature the six major lineages of fishes that are living today:

- Myxinoidea (Hagfish) and Petromyzontoidea (Lampreys)
- Chondrichthyes (Sharks, Rays, Skates)
- Actinopterygii (Ray-Finned Fishes)
- Actinistia (Coelacanths) and Dipnoi (Lungfish)

**Amphibia** Unlike fish, the **amphibians** form a monophyletic group, the Amphibia. Most amphibians lay their eggs in water and undergo metamorphosis from an aquatic larva to a terrestrial or semiterrestrial adult. The three lineages of amphibians are discussed together in one box:

- Amphibia (Frogs and Toads, Salamanders, Caecilians)

**Mammalia** **Mammals** are a monophyletic group, today comprising three major lineages:

- Mammalia > Monotremata (Platypuses, Echidnas)
- Mammalia > Marsupiala (Marsupials)
- Mammalia > Eutheria (Placental Mammals)

The relationships among these groups are shown in **FIGURE 35.22**. Monotremes lay eggs; marsupials have a poorly developed placenta

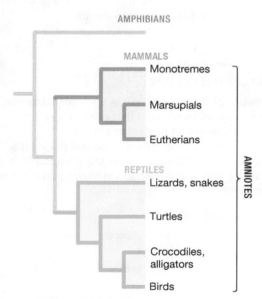

**FIGURE 35.22 Mammals and Reptiles Are Monophyletic Groups.**

but well-developed pouch for rearing offspring; eutherians have a well-developed placenta and extended pregnancy.

Mammals are endotherms that maintain high body temperatures by oxidizing large amounts of food and generating large amounts of heat. Instead of insulating themselves with feathers, though, mammals retain heat because the body surface is covered with layers of hair or fur. Endothermy evolved independently in mammals and birds. In both groups, endothermy is thought to be an adaptation that enables individuals to maintain high levels of activity—particularly at night or during cold weather.

In addition to being endothermic and having fur, mammals have **mammary glands**—unique structures that make lactation possible. The evolution of mammary glands gave mammals the ability to provide their young with particularly extensive parental care. Mammals are also the only vertebrates with cheek muscles and lips—traits that make suckling milk possible—and the only vertebrates that have a lower jaw formed from a single bone. ✔ You should be able to mark the origin of mammary glands and fur on Figure 35.22.

Mammals evolved when dinosaurs and other reptiles were the dominant large herbivores and predators in terrestrial and aquatic environments. The earliest mammals in the fossil record appear about 195 million years ago; most were small animals that were probably active only at night. Many of the 5500 species of mammals living today have good nocturnal vision and a strong sense of smell, as their ancestors presumably did.

The adaptive radiation that gave rise to today's diversity of mammalian orders did not take place until after the dinosaurs went extinct. Long after the dinosaurs were gone, the mammals diversified into lineages that included large herbivores and large predators—ecological roles that had once been filled by dinosaurs and the ocean-dwelling, extinct reptiles called ichthyosaurs and plesiosaurs.

**Reptilia** The **reptiles** are a monophyletic group and represent the second major living lineage of amniotes besides mammals (Figure 35.22). One major diagnostic feature distinguishing the reptilian and mammalian lineages is the number and placement of openings in the side of the skull. These skull openings are important: Jaw muscles required for biting and chewing pass through them and attach to bones on the upper part of the skull.

Reptiles have several adaptations for life on land. Their skin is made watertight by a layer of scales made of the protein keratin. Reptiles breathe air through well-developed lungs and lay shelled, amniotic eggs. In snakes and lizards, the egg has a leathery shell; in other reptiles, the shell includes some calcium carbonate.

In many reptiles, the sex of an individual is determined by the environment it experiences during early development. In certain species, for example, high temperatures produce mostly males while low temperatures produce mostly females.

The reptiles include the dinosaurs, ichthyosaurs, plesiosaurs, pterosaurs (flying reptiles), and other extinct lineages that flourished from about 250 million years ago until the mass extinction at the end of the Cretaceous period, 65 million years ago. Today the Reptilia are represented by four major lineages:

- Reptilia > Lepidosauria (Lizards, Snakes)
- Reptilia > Testudinia (Turtles)
- Reptilia > Crocodilia (Crocodiles, Alligators)
- Reptilia > Aves (Birds)

Except for birds, almost all of the reptiles living today are **ectotherms** ("outside-heated")—meaning that individuals do not use internally generated heat to regulate their body temperature. It would be a mistake, however, to conclude that reptiles other than birds do not regulate their body temperature closely. Reptiles bask in sunlight, seek shade, and perform other behaviors to keep their body temperature at an appropriate level.

## Chordata > Vertebrata > Myxinoidea (Hagfish) and Petromyzontoidea (Lampreys)

Hagfish and lampreys are the only living jawless vertebrates, comprising about 120 species. Their relationship to jawed vertebrates has been hotly debated; however, the most recent microRNA evidence suggests that the two groups are more closely related to each other than either is to the jawed vertebrates. These data indicated that hagfish and lampreys, collectively the cyclostomes ("round mouths"), may have *lost* many vertebrate characters over time.

Hagfish and lampreys have long, slender bodies and are aquatic (**FIGURE 35.23**). Hagfish are strictly marine; lampreys include both marine and freshwater forms. Most species are less than a meter long when fully grown. Adult hagfish lack any sort of vertebral column, but adult lampreys have small pieces of cartilage along the length of their dorsal hollow nerve cord. Both hagfish and lampreys have brains protected by a cranium, as do all vertebrates.

**Feeding** Hagfish are scavengers and predators. They deposit feed on the carcasses of dead fish and whales, and some are thought to burrow through ooze at the bottom of the ocean, feeding on polychaete worms and other buried prey. Lampreys, in contrast, are ectoparasites. They attach to fish or other hosts by suction and then use spines in their mouth and tongue to rasp a hole in the side of their victim. Once the wound is open, they suck blood and other body fluids.

**Movement** Hagfish and lampreys have a well-developed notochord and swim by making undulating movements. Hagfish are particularly flexible, sometimes forming "knots" with their bodies to rid themselves of the copious slime they create as a defense mechanism when disturbed. Lampreys can move themselves upstream, against the flow of water, by attaching their suckers to rocks and looping the rest of their body forward, like an inchworm. Both groups have tail fins, and lamprey have a dorsal (back) fin; but neither group has the paired lateral (side) appendages found in other vertebrates.

**Reproduction** Virtually nothing is known about hagfish mating or embryonic development. Some lampreys live in freshwater; others are **anadromous**—meaning they spend their adult life in the ocean but swim up streams to breed. Fertilization is external, and adults die after breeding once. Lamprey eggs hatch into larvae that look and act like lancelets (cephalochordates). The larvae burrow into sediments and suspension feed for several years before metamorphosing into free-swimming adults.

**(a)** Hagfish

*Eptatretus stoutii*

*Petromyzon marinus*

**(b)** Lamprey

**FIGURE 35.23 Hagfish and Lampreys Are Jawless Vertebrates.**

This lineage is distinguished by a specialized type of reinforced cartilaginous skeleton (*chondrus* is the Greek word for cartilage). Along with jawed vertebrates, or gnathostomes, sharks, rays, and skates also have jaws. They, like the other fish-like gnathostomes, also have paired lateral fins. Paired fins were an important evolutionary innovation because they stabilize the body during rapid swimming—keeping it from pitching up or down, yawing to one side or the other, or rolling. ✔ You should be able to indicate the origin of paired fins and the chondrichthyan form of cartilage on Figure 35.12.

Most of the 1200 species of sharks, rays, and skates are marine, though a few species live in freshwater. Sharks have streamlined, torpedo-shaped bodies and an asymmetrical tail—the dorsal portion is longer than the ventral portion (**FIGURE 35.24a**). In contrast, the dorsal–ventral plane of the body in rays and skates is strongly flattened (**FIGURE 35.24b**).

**Feeding** A few species of sharks and rays suspension feed on plankton, but most species in this lineage are predators. Skates and rays hunt along the ocean floor for snails, clams, and other benthic animals; electric rays capture their prey by stunning them with electric discharges of up to 200 volts. Most sharks, in contrast, are active hunters that chase down prey in open water and bite them. The larger species of sharks feed on large fish or marine mammals. In many marine ecosystems, sharks are referred to as the "top predator" because they are at the top of the food chain—nothing eats them. Yet the largest of all sharks, the whale shark, is a suspension feeder. Whale sharks filter plankton out of water as it passes over their gills.

**Movement** Rays and skates swim by flapping their greatly enlarged pectoral fins. Sharks swim by undulating their bodies from side to side and beating their large tails.

**Reproduction** Sharks use internal fertilization, and fertilized eggs may be shed into the water or retained until the young are hatched and well developed. In some viviparous species, embryos are attached to the mother by specialized tissues in a placenta, where the exchange of gases, nutrients, and wastes takes place. (A placenta evolved in certain shark lineages independently of its evolution elsewhere on the tree of life.) Skates are oviparous, but rays are viviparous.

**(a)** Sharks are torpedo shaped.

*Prionace glauca*

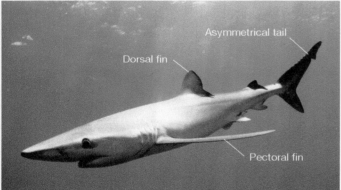

**(b)** Skates and rays are flat.

*Dasyatis americana*

**FIGURE 35.24 Sharks and Rays Have Cartilaginous Skeletons.**

Actinopterygii (pronounced *ack-tin-op-teh-RIJ-ee-i*) means "ray-finned." These **ray-finned fishes** have fins that are supported by long, bony rods arranged in a ray pattern, in addition to a skeleton made of bone (**FIGURE 35.25**). Their bodies are covered with interlocking scales that provide a stiff but flexible covering, and many have a gas-filled **swim bladder** that evolved from the lungs found in the earliest lineages of fish. The evolution of the swim bladder was an important innovation because it allowed ray-finned fishes to avoid sinking. Most tissues are heavier than water, so the bodies of aquatic organisms tend to sink. Sharks and rays, for example, have to swim to avoid sinking. But in ray-finned fishes, gas is added to the bladder when a fish swims down; gas is removed when the fish swims up. In this way, ray-finned fishes maintain neutral buoyancy in water of various depths and thus various pressures. ✔ You should be able to indicate the origin of rayed fins and the swim bladder on Figure 35.12.

The actinopterygians are the most successful vertebrate lineage based on number of species, duration in the fossil record, and extent of habitats occupied. About 30,500 species of ray-finned fishes are known, including the smallest known vertebrate—a species whose adult females average less than 8 mm in length.

*(Continued on next page)*

*Holocentrus rufus*

Bony rods in fin

**FIGURE 35.25  In Ray-Finned Fishes, Fins Are Supported by Long, Bony Rods.**

The most important major lineage of ray-finned fishes is the Teleostei. About 96 percent of all living fish species, including familiar groups like the tuna, trout, cod, and goldfish, are teleosts. The teleosts underwent an adaptive radiation about the same time that mammals did.

**Feeding**  Teleosts can suck food toward their mouths, grasp it with their protrusible jaws, and then process it with teeth on their jaws and with pharyngeal jaws in their throat. The size and shape of the mouth, the jaw teeth, and the pharyngeal jaw teeth all correlate with the type of food consumed. For example, most predatory teleosts have long, spear-shaped jaws armed with spiky teeth, as well as bladelike teeth on their pharyngeal jaws. Besides being major predators, ray-finned fishes are the most important large herbivores in both marine and freshwater environments.

**Movement**  Like other fish, ray-finned fishes swim by alternately contracting muscles on the left and right sides of their bodies from head to tail, resulting in rapid, side-to-side undulations. Their bodies are streamlined to reduce drag in water. Teleosts have a flexible, symmetrical tail, which reduces the need to use their pectoral (side) fins as steering and stabilizing devices during rapid swimming.

**Reproduction**  Most ray-finned fish species rely on external fertilization and are oviparous; some species have internal fertilization with external development; still others have internal fertilization and are viviparous. Although it is common for fish eggs to be released in the water and left to develop on their own, parental care occurs in some species. Parents may carry fertilized eggs on their fins, in their mouth, or in specialized pouches to guard them until the eggs hatch. In other cases the eggs are laid into a nest that is actively guarded and cared for. In freshwater teleosts, offspring develop directly; but marine species have larvae that undergo metamorphosis into a very different juvenile form, which then grows into an adult.

Chordata > Vertebrata > **Actinistia** (Coelacanths) and **Dipnoi** (Lungfish)

Although coelacanths (pronounced *SEEL-uh-kanths*) and lungfish represent independent lineages, they are sometimes grouped together and called **lobe-finned fishes.** Lobe-finned fishes are common and diverse in the fossil record in the Devonian period, about 400 million years ago, but only eight species are living today. They are important, however, because they represent a crucial evolutionary link between the fishes and the tetrapods. Early fishes in the fossil record have fins supported by stiff structures that extend from a base of bone. In ray-finned fishes, the bony elements are reduced. But in lobefins the bony elements extend down the fin, and they branch—similar to the bony elements in the limbs of tetrapods (**FIGURE 35.26**). ✔ You should be able to indicate the origin of extensive fin bones on Figure 35.12.

Coelacanths are marine and occupy habitats 150–700 m below the surface. In contrast, lungfish live in shallow, freshwater ponds and rivers (see Figure 35.15). As their name implies, lungfish have lungs and breathe air when oxygen levels in their habitats drop. Some species burrow in mud and enter a quiescent, sleeplike state when their habitat dries up during each year's dry season.

**Feeding**  Coelacanths prey on fish. Lungfish are omnivorous ("all-eating"), meaning that they eat algae and plant material as well as animals.

**Movement**  Coelacanths and lungfish swim by undulating their bodies; some lungfish can also use their fins to walk along pond bottoms.

**Reproduction**  Sexual reproduction is the rule; fertilization is internal in coelacanths and external in lungfish. Coelacanths are ovoviviparous; lungfish lay eggs. Lungfish eggs hatch into larvae that resemble juvenile salamanders.

*Latimeria menadoensis*

Fleshy lobes supported by bones

**FIGURE 35.26  Coelacanths Are Lobe-Finned Fishes.**

## Chordata > Vertebrata > Amphibia (Frogs and Toads, Salamanders, Caecilians)

Amphibians are found throughout the world and occupy ponds, lakes, or moist terrestrial environments. Translated literally, their name means "both-sides-living." The name is appropriate because adults of most amphibians feed on land but lay their eggs in water (**FIGURE 35.27**). In many amphibians, gas exchange occurs exclusively or in part across their moist, mucus-covered skin. ✔ You should be able to indicate the origin of "skin-breathing" on Figure 35.12. The 6800 named species of amphibians living today form three distinct clades: (**1**) frogs and toads, (**2**) salamanders, and (**3**) caecilians (pronounced *suh-SILL-ee-uns*). Caecilians lack limbs, and so resemble worms or snakes. They burrow underground in wet tropical regions.

**Feeding** Adult amphibians are carnivores. Most frogs and toads are sit-and-wait predators that use their long, extensible tongues to capture passing prey. Salamanders also have an extensible tongue, which some species use in feeding. Terrestrial caecilians prey on earthworms and other soil-dwelling animals; aquatic forms eat vertebrates and small fish.

**Movement** Most amphibians have four well-developed limbs. In water, frogs and toads move by kicking their hind legs to swim; on land, they kick their hind legs out to jump or hop. Salamanders walk on land; in water they undulate their bodies to swim. Caecilians lack limbs; terrestrial forms burrow in moist soils.

**Reproduction** Reproduction is sexual, breeding occurs in water, and larvae undergo a dramatic metamorphosis into land-dwelling adults. For example, the fishlike tadpoles of frogs and toads develop limbs, and their gills are replaced with lungs. Frogs have external fertilization, but salamanders and caecilians have internal fertilization. Frogs and most salamanders are oviparous, but many caecilians are viviparous.

*Rana temporaria*

Eggs

**FIGURE 35.27 Amphibians Are the Most Ancient Tetrapods.**

## Chordata > Vertebrata > Mammalia > Monotremata (Platypuses, Echidnas)

The **monotremes** are the most basal lineage of mammals living today and are found in nature only in Australia. Monotremes lay eggs and have metabolic rates that are lower than those of other mammals. Five species exist: one species of platypus (**FIGURE 35.28a**) and four species of echidnas (**FIGURE 35.28b**).

**Feeding** Monotremes have a leathery beak or bill. The platypus feeds on insect larvae, mollusks, and other small animals in streams. Echidnas feed on ants, termites, and earthworms.

**Movement** Platypuses swim with the aid of their webbed feet and walk when on land. Echidnas walk on their four legs.

**Reproduction** Platypuses lay their eggs in a burrow, while echidnas keep their eggs in a pouch on their belly. Young monotremes hatch quickly, and the mother must continue keeping them warm and dry for another four months. Like other mammals, monotremes produce milk and nurse their young. They lack well-defined nipples, however, and instead secrete milk from glands in the skin.

**(a)** Platypus

*Ornithorhynchus anatinus*

**(b)** Echidna

*Tachyglossus aculeatus*

**FIGURE 35.28 Platypuses and Echidnas Lay Eggs.**

## Chordata > Vertebrata > Mammalia > Marsupiala (Marsupials)

The 350 known species of **marsupials** live in the Australian region and the Americas and include the familiar opossums (**FIGURE 35.29**), kangaroos, wallabies, and koala.

**Feeding** Marsupials are herbivores, omnivores, or carnivores. In many cases, convergent evolution has resulted in marsupials that are similar to placental species in morphology and way of life. For example, a recently extinct marsupial called the Tasmanian wolf was a long-legged hunter similar to the wolves of North America and northern Eurasia. A species of marsupial native to Australia specializes in eating ants and looks and acts much like the South American anteater, which is not a marsupial.

**Movement** Marsupials move by crawling, gliding, walking, running, or hopping.

**Reproduction** Although females have a placenta that nourishes embryos during development, the young are born after a short embryonic period and are poorly developed. They crawl from the opening of the female's reproductive tract to her nipples, located within a pouch, where they suck milk. They stay attached to their mother until they grow large enough to move independently. ✔ You should be able to indicate the origin of the placenta and viviparity—traits that are also found in eutherian mammals—on Figure 35.22.

*Didelphis virginiana*

**FIGURE 35.29 Marsupials Give Birth after a Short Embryonic Period.** Opossums are the only marsupials living in North America.

## Chordata > Vertebrata > Mammalia > Eutheria (Placental Mammals)

The 5100 described species of **placental mammals,** or **eutherians,** are distributed worldwide. They are far and away the most species-rich and morphologically diverse group of mammals.

Biologists group placental mammals into 29 lineages called orders. The six most species-rich orders are the rodents (rats, mice, squirrels; 2255 species), bats (1150 species), insectivores (hedgehogs, moles, shrews; 450 species), artiodactyls (pigs, hippos, whales, deer, sheep, cattle, horses; 329 species), carnivores (dogs, bears, cats, weasels, seals; 285 species), and primates (lemurs, monkeys, apes, humans; 414 species).

**Feeding** The size and structure of the teeth correlate closely with the diet of placental mammals. Herbivores have large, flat teeth for crushing leaves and other coarse plant material; predators have sharp teeth that are efficient at biting and tearing flesh. The structure of the digestive tract also correlates with the placental mammals' diet. In some plant eaters, for example, the stomach hosts unicellular organisms that digest cellulose and other complex polysaccharides.

**Movement** In placental mammals, the structure of the limb correlates closely with the type of movement performed. Eutherians fly, glide, run, walk, swim, burrow, or swing from trees. Hindlimbs are reduced or lost in aquatic groups such as whales and dolphins, which swim by undulating their bodies.

**Reproduction** Eutherians have internal fertilization and are viviparous. An extensive placenta develops from a combination of maternal and fetal tissues; and at birth, young are much better developed than in marsupials—some are able to walk or run minutes after emerging from the mother. ✔ You should be able to indicate the origin of delayed birth (extended development before birth) on Figure 35.22. All eutherians feed their offspring milk until the young have grown large enough to process solid food. A prolonged period of parental care, extending beyond the nursing stage, is common as offspring learn how to escape predators and find food on their own. Some eutherians are highly social (**FIGURE 35.30**).

*Suricata suricatta*

**FIGURE 35.30 Eutherians Are Familiar and Diverse.**

Most lizards and snakes are small reptiles with elongated bodies and scaly skin. As these animals grow, they can shed the keratinized surface layer of their skin—all in one piece in snakes, and in flakes in lizards. ✔ You should be able to indicate the origin of scaly skin on Figure 35.22. Most lizards have well-developed jointed legs, but snakes are limbless (**FIGURE 35.31**). The hypothesis that snakes evolved from limbed ancestors is supported by the presence of vestigial hip and leg bones in boas and pythons. About 8900 species of lizards and snakes are alive now.

**Feeding** Small lizards prey on insects. Although most of the larger lizard species are herbivores, the spectacular 3-meter-long monitor lizard from the island of Komodo is a predator that can eat deer. Snakes are carnivores; some subdue their prey by injecting poison through modified teeth called fangs. Snakes prey primarily on small mammals, amphibians, and invertebrates, which they swallow whole—usually headfirst.

**Movement** Lizards crawl, climb, or run on their four limbs. Some lizards, such as the water dragons, use their powerful tails for swimming. Snakes and lizards that are limbless burrow through soil, crawl over the ground, or climb trees by undulating their bodies. One genus of snakes in Asia has several adaptations that enable them to glide down from treetops.

*Morelia viridis*

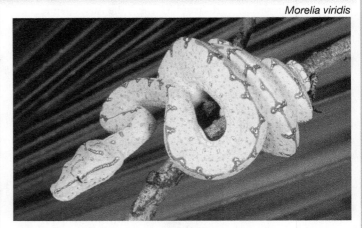

**FIGURE 35.31 Snakes Are Limbless Predators.**

**Reproduction** Although most lizards and snakes lay eggs, many are ovoviviparous; viviparity has also evolved numerous times in lizards. Most species reproduce sexually, but asexual reproduction, via the production of eggs by mitosis (parthenogenesis), is known to occur in six groups of lizards (including the Komodo dragon) and one snake lineage.

The 320 known species of turtles inhabit freshwater, marine, and terrestrial environments throughout the world. The testudines are distinguished by a shell composed of bony plates that fuse to the vertebrae and ribs (**FIGURE 35.32**). The shell functions in protection from predators—when threatened, most turtles can withdraw their head and legs into it. ✔ You should be able to indicate the origin of the turtle shell on Figure 35.22. The turtles' skulls are highly modified versions of the skulls of other reptiles. Turtles lack teeth, but their jawbone and lower skull form a bony beak. They range in size from the 2-m-long, 900-kg leatherback sea turtle to the 8-cm-long, 140-g speckled padloper tortoise. Tortoises are known for their longevity—some individuals are known to have lived well over 150 years.

**Feeding** Turtles are either carnivorous—feeding on whatever animals they can capture and swallow—or herbivorous. They may also scavenge dead material. Most marine turtles are carnivorous. Leatherback turtles, for example, feed primarily on jellyfish, and they are only mildly affected by the jellyfish's stinging cnidocytes (see Chapter 33). In contrast, species in the lineage of terrestrial turtles called the tortoises are plant eaters.

*Testudo hermanni*

**FIGURE 35.32 Turtles Have a Shell Consisting of Bony Plates.**

**Movement** Turtles swim, walk, or burrow. Some fully aquatic species have feet that are modified to function as flippers.

**Reproduction** All turtles are oviparous. Other than digging a nest prior to depositing eggs, parental care is lacking. Some aquatic species navigate long distances to their natal beaches with pinpoint accuracy, to lay eggs.

## Chordata > Vertebrata > Reptilia > Crocodilia (Crocodiles, Alligators)

About 24 living species of crocodiles and alligators are known. Most are tropical and live in freshwater or marine environments. They have eyes located on the top of their heads, nostrils located at the top of their long snouts, and other adaptations that allow them to sit semi-submerged in water for long periods of time, breathing air and visually monitoring activity around them (**FIGURE 35.33**).

**Feeding** Crocodilians are predators. Like other toothed vertebrates, except mammals, their jaws are filled with conical teeth that are continually replaced as they fall out during feeding. Their usual method of killing small prey is by biting through the body wall. Large prey are usually subdued by drowning. Crocodilians eat amphibians, turtles, fish, birds, and mammals; one of the common hunting strategies of crocodiles is to leap out of the water to snatch unwary prey that have come to drink.

**Movement** Crocodiles and alligators walk on land. In water they swim with the aid of their large, muscular tails.

**Reproduction** Although crocodilians are oviparous, parental care is extensive. Eggs are laid in earth-covered nests or mounds of vegetation that are guarded by the parents. When young inside the eggs begin to vocalize, parents dig them out and often carry the newly hatched young inside their mouths to nearby water.

*Alligator mississippiensis*

**FIGURE 35.33 Alligators Are Adapted for Aquatic Life.**

Crocodilian young can hunt when newly hatched but stay near their mother for up to three years. ✔ You should be able to indicate the origin of extensive parental care in crocodilians—which also occurs in birds (and other dinosaurs)—on Figure 35.22.

## Chordata > Vertebrata > Reptilia > Aves (Birds)

The fossil record provides conclusive evidence that birds descended from a lineage of dinosaurs that had **feathers.** Feathers provide insulation, are used for display, and furnish the lift, power, and steering required for flight (**FIGURE 35.34**). Birds have many other adaptations that make flight possible, including large breast muscles used to flap the wings. Bird bodies are lightweight because they have a reduced number of bones and organs and because their hollow bones are filled with air sacs linked to the lungs. Instead of teeth, birds have a horny beak. They are endotherms, meaning that they have a high metabolic rate and use the heat produced, along with the insulation provided by feathers, to maintain a constant body temperature. The 10,000 bird species alive today occupy virtually every habitat, including the open ocean. ✔ You should be able to indicate the origin of feathers, endothermy, and flight on Figure 35.22.

**Feeding** Plant-eating birds usually feed on nectar or seeds. Some birds are omnivores, although many are predators that capture insects, small mammals, fish, other birds, lizards, mollusks, or crustaceans. The shape of a bird's beak correlates with its diet.

**Movement** Almost all bird species can fly, although flightlessness has evolved repeatedly in certain groups. The size and shape of birds' wings correlate closely with the type of flying they do. Birds that glide or hover have long, thin wings; species that specialize in explosive takeoffs and short flights have short, stocky wings. Many seabirds are efficient swimmers, using their webbed feet to paddle or flapping their wings to "fly" underwater. Some ground-dwelling birds such as ostrich can run long distances at high speed.

**Reproduction** Birds are oviparous but provide extensive parental care. In most species, one or both parents build a nest and incubate the eggs. After the eggs hatch, parents feed offspring until they are large enough to fly and find food on their own.

*Eudocimus albus*

**FIGURE 35.34 Birds Are Descendants of Feathered Dinosaurs.**

**The Primates and Hominins**

Although humans occupy a tiny twig within the mammal branch on the tree of life, there has been a tremendous amount of research on human origins. This section introduces the lineage of mammals called the Primates, the fossil record of human ancestors, and data on the relationships among human populations living today.

## The Primates

The lineage known as Primates consists of two main groups: prosimians and anthropoids.

- The **prosimians** ("before-monkeys") typically consist of the lemurs, found in Madagascar, and the lorises, pottos, and tarsiers of Africa and south Asia. However, recent phylogenetic analyses indicate that tarsiers are more closely related to the anthropoids than to the other prosimians, making the prosimians a paraphyletic group (**FIGURE 35.35a**). Most prosimians living today are relatively small in size, reside in trees, and are active at night.

**(a) Prosimians**

*Lemur catta*

**(b) Anthropoids**

*Gorilla gorilla*

**FIGURE 35.35 There Are Two Main Lineages of Primates.**

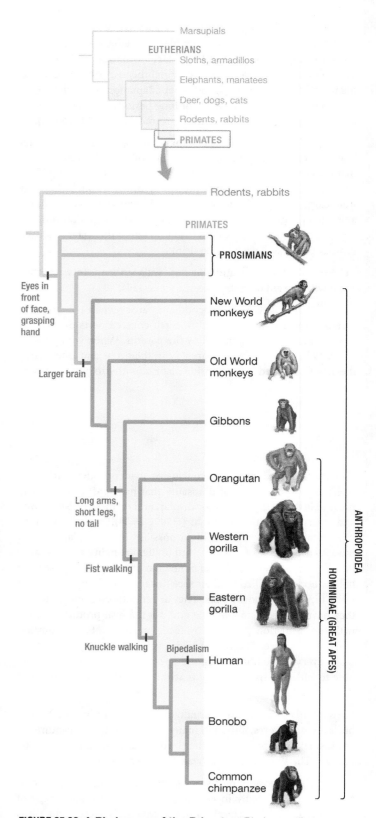

**FIGURE 35.36 A Phylogeny of the Primates.** Phylogenetic tree estimated from extensive DNA sequence data. According to the fossil record, humans and chimps shared a common ancestor 6 to 7 million years ago.

- The Anthropoidea or **anthropoids** ("human-like") include the New World monkeys found in Central and South America, the Old World monkeys that live in Africa and tropical regions of Asia, the gibbons of the Asian tropics, and the Hominidae, or **great apes**—orangutans, gorillas, chimpanzees, and humans (**FIGURE 35.35b**).

The phylogenetic tree in **FIGURE 35.36** shows the evolutionary relationships among these groups.

**What Makes a Primate a Primate?** **Primates** tend to have hands and feet that are efficient at grasping, flattened nails instead of claws on the fingers and toes, brains that are large relative to overall body size, color vision, complex social behavior, and extensive parental care of offspring.

Along with other mammal groups that live in trees or make their living by hunting, primates have eyes located on the front of the face. Eyes that look forward provide better depth perception than do eyes on the sides of the face. The hypothesis here is that good depth perception is important in species that run or swing through trees and/or attack prey.

**What Makes a Great Ape a Great Ape?** The great apes are also called **hominids**. Compared with most types of primate, the hominids are relatively large bodied and have long arms, short legs, and no tail.

Although all of the great ape species except for the orangutans live primarily on the ground, they have distinct ways of walking.

- When orangutans come to the ground, they occasionally walk with their knuckles pressed to the ground. More commonly though, they fist walk—that is, they walk with the backs of their hands pressed to the ground.

- Gorillas and chimps only knuckle walk. They also occasionally rise up on two legs—usually in the context of displaying aggression.

- Humans are the only living great ape that is fully **bipedal** ("two-footed")—meaning they walk upright on two legs. Fossil footprints in Tanzania provide direct evidence that bipedalism occurred at least 3.6 million years ago.

Bipedalism is the synapomorphy that defines the hominins. The **hominins** are a monophyletic group comprising *Homo sapiens* and more than twenty extinct, bipedal relatives.

## Fossil Humans

From extensive comparisons of DNA sequence data, it is clear that humans are most closely related to the common chimpanzees and bonobos, and that our next nearest living relatives are the gorillas. According to the fossil record, the common ancestor of chimps and humans lived in Africa 6 to 7 million years ago.

The fossil record of hominins, though not nearly as complete as investigators would like, is rapidly improving. More than 20 species have been named to date, and new fossils that inform the debate over the ancestry of humans are discovered every year.

Although naming the hominin species and interpreting their characteristics remain intensely controversial, most researchers agree that the hominins can be organized into four major groups that appeared after the recently characterized *Ardipithecus ramidus*—the oldest hominin known to date. **TABLE 35.1** summarizes key data for

TABLE 35.1 **Characteristics of Selected Hominins**

| Genus | Species | Location of Fossils | Estimated Average Braincase Volume (cm³) | Estimated Average Body Size (kg) | Associated with Stone Tools? |
|---|---|---|---|---|---|
| *Ardipithecus* | *A. ramidus* | Africa | 325 | 40 | no |
| *Australopithecus* | *A. afarensis* | Africa | 460 | 38 | no |
| | *A. africanus* | Africa | 465 | 34 | no |
| *Paranthropus* | *P. boisei* | Africa | 480 | 41 | no? |
| Early *Homo* | *H. habilis* | Africa | 610 | 33 | **yes** |
| | *H. ergaster* | Africa | 760 | 64 | **yes** |
| | *H. erectus* | Africa, Asia | 1000 | 58 | **yes** |
| Recent *Homo* | *H. heidelbergensis* | Africa, Europe | 1200 | 71 | **yes** |
| | *H. neanderthalensis* | Middle East, Europe, Asia | 1430 | 72 | **yes** |
| | *H. floresiensis* | Flores (Indonesia) | 380 | 28 | **yes** |
| | *H. sapiens* | Middle East, Europe, Asia | 1480 | 64 | **yes** |

Robson, S. L., and B. Wood. 2008. Hominin life history: Reconstruction and evolution. *Journal of Anatomy* 212: 394–425.

✔ **QUANTITATIVE** How much smaller is the average body size of *H. floresiensis* compared to the average *H. sapiens*? Express your answer as a percentage. How much smaller is the braincase volume of *H. floresiensis* compared to *H. sapiens*? What do these numbers suggest?

## (a) Gracile australopithecines (*Australopithecus africanus*)

Vertical posture

## (b) Robust australopithecines (*Paranthropus robustus*)

Sagittal crest

Massive cheek teeth

Massive cheekbones

## (c) Early *Homo* (*Homo habilis*)

Flatter face

Larger braincase

## (d) Recent *Homo* (*Homo sapiens*)

Flattest face

Largest braincase

**FIGURE 35.37 A Timeline of Hominin Evolution.** The colored bars indicate the first appearance and last appearance in the fossil record of each species. (Not all named species are shown.)

DATA: Lieberman, D.E. 2009. *Nature* 459: 41–42.

✔ **QUANTITATIVE** Of the species of hominin shown, how many existed 1.8 million years ago (mya) and 100,000 years ago?

**FIGURE 35.38 African Hominins Comprise Four Major Groups.** The color key links these fossils with Figure 35.37 and Table 35.1.

✔ **QUESTION** The skulls are arranged as they appear in the fossil record, from most ancient (a) to most recent (d). How did the forehead and brow ridge of hominins change through time?

selected species within the four groups. **FIGURE 35.37** provides the time range of each of these species in the fossil record.

**Gracile Australopithecines** The small hominins called gracile australopithecines are referred to as *gracile*, or "slender," because they had a slight build. Adult males were about 1.5 meters tall, and their estimated weight was about 36 kg.

The gracile australopithecines are placed in the genus *Australopithecus* ("southern ape"). The name was inspired by the earliest specimens, which came from South Africa. The most recent *Australopithecus* to be named, *A. sediba* in 2010, is also from South Africa.

Several lines of evidence support the hypothesis that the gracile australopithecines were bipedal. The shape of the australopithecine knee and hip are consistent with bipedal locomotion, and the hole in the back of their skulls where the spinal cord connects to the brain is oriented downward (**FIGURE 35.38a**), just as it is in our species, *Homo sapiens*. In chimps, gorillas, and other vertebrates that walk on four feet, this hole is oriented backward.

**Robust Australopithecines** The robust australopithecines are grouped in the genus *Paranthropus* ("beside-human"). The name *Paranthropus* was inspired by the hypothesis that the three known species are a monophyletic group that was a side branch during human evolution—an independent lineage that went extinct.

Like the gracile australopithecines, these robust australopithecines were bipedal. They were much stockier than the gracile forms, however—about the same height but an estimated 8–10 kilograms (20 pounds) heavier on average. In addition, their skulls were much broader and more robust.

All three *Paranthropus* species had massive cheek teeth and jaws, very large cheekbones, and a sagittal crest—a flange of bone at the top of the skull (**FIGURE 35.38b**). Because muscles that work the jaw attach to the sagittal crest and cheekbones, researchers conclude that these organisms had tremendous biting power—inspiring the nickname "nutcracker man" for one species. Recent analysis of tooth enamel revealed that the biting power of *Paranthropus* was probably used to crush large quantities of tough grasses.

**Early *Homo***  Species in the genus *Homo* are called **humans.** As **FIGURE 35.38c** shows, species in this genus have flatter and narrower faces, smaller jaws and teeth, and larger braincases than the earlier hominins do. (The **braincase** is the portion of the skull that encloses the brain.)

The appearance of early members of the genus *Homo* in the fossil record coincides closely with the appearance of tools made of worked stone—most of which are interpreted as handheld choppers or knives. Although the fossil record does not exclude the possibility that *Paranthropus* made tools, many researchers favor the hypothesis that extensive toolmaking was a diagnostic trait of early *Homo*.

**Recent *Homo***  The recent species of *Homo* date from 1.2 million years ago to the present. As **FIGURE 35.38d** shows, these species have even flatter faces, smaller teeth, and larger braincases than the early *Homo* species do. The 30,000-year-old fossil in the figure, for example, is from a population of *Homo sapiens* (our species) called the **Cro-Magnons.**

The Cro-Magnons were accomplished painters and sculptors who buried their dead in carefully prepared graves. There is also evidence that another species, the **Neanderthal** people (*Homo neanderthalensis*) made art and buried their dead in a ceremonial fashion.

Perhaps the most striking recent *Homo*, though, is *H. floresiensis*. This new species was discovered in 2003 on the island of Flores in Indonesia—also home to a species of dwarfed elephants. *H. floresiensis* consisted of individuals that had braincases smaller than those of gracile australopithecines and that were about a meter tall, inspiring the nickname Hobbit. While some researchers propose that the fossils represent a population of *H. sapiens* stunted by disease, most support full species status. Fossil finds suggest that *H. floresiensis* inhabited Flores from about 100,000 to as recently as 12,000 years ago.

**What Can Be Deduced from the Hominin Fossil Record?**  Although researchers do not have a solid understanding of the phylogenetic relationships among the hominin species, several points are clear from the available fossil data.

1. The shared, derived character that defines the hominins is bipedalism.

2. Several species from the lineage were present simultaneously during most of hominin evolution.

3. Compared with the gracile and robust australopithecines and the other great apes, species in the genus *Homo* have extremely large brains relative to their overall body size.

Why did humans evolve such gigantic brains? The leading hypothesis on this question is that early *Homo* began using symbolic spoken language and tools. The logic here is that increased language use and toolmaking triggered natural selection for the capacity to reason and communicate, which required a larger brain.

To summarize, *Homo sapiens* is the sole survivor of an adaptive radiation of hominins that began in Africa 6–7 million years ago. Why all but one species went extinct is still a mystery, though climate change and competition for food and space may have played a part.

## The Out-of-Africa Hypothesis

If hominins originated in Africa and then spread around the world, where did *H. sapiens* originate?

The leading hypothesis for the evolution of *H. sapiens* is called the **out-of-Africa hypothesis.** It contends that *H. sapiens* evolved its distinctive traits in Africa and then dispersed throughout the world. Further, it claims that *H. sapiens* evolved independently of the earlier European and Asian species of *Homo*—meaning there was no interbreeding between *H. sapiens* and Neanderthals, *H. erectus*, or *H. floresiensis*. Do the data support this hypothesis?

**Fossil Evidence**  The first *H. sapiens* fossils appear in East African rocks that date to about 195,000 years ago. For some 130,000 years thereafter, the fossil record indicates that our species occupied Africa while *H. neanderthalensis* resided in Europe and the Middle East. Some evidence suggests that *H. erectus* may still have been present in Asia at that time.

In rocks dated between 60,000 and 30,000 years ago, however, *H. sapiens* fossils are found throughout Europe, Asia, Africa, and Australia. *H. erectus* had disappeared by this time, and *H. neanderthalensis* went extinct after coexisting with *H. sapiens* in Europe for thousands of years.

Taken together, the fossil evidence provides strong support for the African origin of *H. sapiens* and subsequent migration, but it cannot resolve the question of whether *H. sapiens* ever interbred with Neanderthals during their coexistence.

**Molecular Evidence**  Some researchers have taken a molecular approach to understanding the history of our species, providing several major insights.

For example, Luigi Cavali-Sforza and others have created phylogenetic trees based on genetic comparisons of diverse human populations living today. These data agree with the pattern in the fossil record. As **FIGURE 35.39** (see page 708) shows, the first lineages to branch off led to descendant populations that live in Africa today. Later branches gave rise to lineages in central Asia, Europe, East Asia, Polynesia, and the Americas. Based on this observation, it is logical to infer that the ancestral population of modern humans lived in Africa.

Did *H. sapiens* leave Africa in one wave? Sequence data from modern Aboriginal Australians support the hypothesis that

Common ancestor
of all humans
alive today

HUMANS

Africa

North Africa

Europe, Russia

Central Asia,
South Asia

Northeast, East, and
Southeast Asia (Siberia,
Mongolia, China, Japan,
Cambodia, et al.)

Native North America
Native South America

New Guinea,
Pacific Islands

Most-
ancestral
lineages
from Africa;
highest genetic
diversity

Most-recent
lineages; lowest
genetic diversity

**FIGURE 35.39 Phylogeny of Human Populations Living Today.**
The phylogeny was estimated from DNA sequence data. As
predicted by the out-of-Africa hypothesis, the lineages with the
highest genetic diversity and deepest history occur in Africa.

the human migration out of Africa occurred in more than one wave—the first wave moved east and south to Australia, and the second wave moved to Europe and the rest of mainland Asia. While the exact migration routes of *H. sapiens* are hotly debated, **FIGURE 35.40** provides a general summary.

What about the question of interbreeding? There are now two lines of evidence that *H. sapiens* interbred with other species as they migrated out of Africa. First, Svante Pääbo and his colleagues compared gene sequences of extinct Neanderthals and diverse modern humans. They made the remarkable observation that 1 to 4 percent of the genome of indigenous Europeans and Asians—but not Africans—is derived from Neanderthals. These data suggest that *H. sapiens* and Neanderthals interbred in the Middle East after *H. sapiens* left Africa, but before migrating through Europe and Asia.

Second, sequence data from modern Asians and Aboriginal Australians suggest that modern humans interbred with a recently discovered descendant population of *H. erectus*, called the Denisovans, in Asia during their first migration out of Africa. As a result, Aboriginal Australians and their island neighbors—descendants of the first migration—inherited about 5 percent of their nuclear DNA from Denisovans.

In summary, the Neanderthal and Denisovan data reject the strict interpretation of the out-of-Africa hypothesis since a small amount of gene flow occurred between *H. sapiens* and Neanderthals as well as between *H. sapiens* and the Denisovans. However, other fossil and molecular evidence supports the general concept of the out-of-Africa hypothesis. That is, the overall data support an out-of-Africa hypothesis with "leakage."

The study of human evolution is an exciting and dynamic field. And humans continue to evolve.

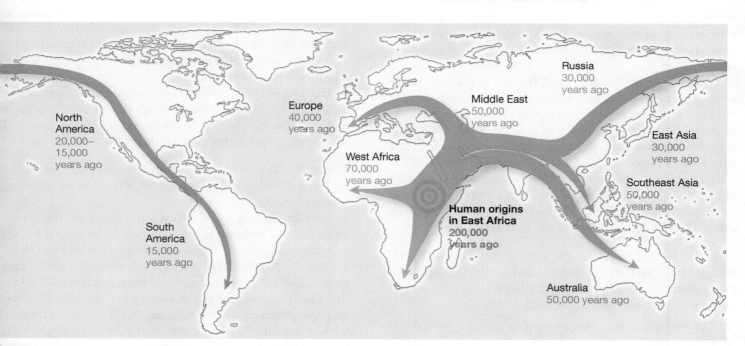

**FIGURE 35.40** *Homo sapiens* **Originated in Africa and Spread throughout the World.** The migration out of Africa probably occurred in two waves—first east and south to Australia, and later to Europe and the rest of Asia and the Americas.

## If you understand . . .

### 35.1 What Is an Echinoderm?

- Echinoderms are among the most important predators and herbivores in marine environments. They include the sea stars, sea urchins, sea cucumbers, and feather stars.

- Echinoderm larvae are bilaterally symmetric but most undergo a metamorphosis into radially symmetric adults.

- Echinoderms have a calcium carbonate endoskeleton.

- The echinoderm water vascular system is composed of fluid-filled tubes and chambers called tube feet. Tube feet may be used for movement, feeding, or respiration.

✔ You should be able to predict what happens when (1) sea stars that prey on mussels and clams are excluded from experimental plots, and (2) sea urchins that graze on kelp are excluded from experimental plots.

### 35.2 What Is a Chordate?

- Chordates are distinguished by the presence of pharyngeal gill slits, a dorsal hollow nerve cord, a notochord, and a muscular tail that extends past the anus.

- Chordates include cephalochordates, urochordates, and vertebrates.

✔ You should be able to make a simple cartoon of a generic chordate showing its defining features.

### 35.3 What Is a Vertebrate?

- Vertebrates are distinguished by the presence of a cranium and vertebrae. In some groups of vertebrates, the body plan features an extensive endoskeleton composed of bone.

- The origin of jaws in ray-finned fishes enabled these fishes and their descendants to bite food and process it with teeth.

- The origin of limbs in tetrapods enabled walking and running on land, and flying. Tetrapods include the amphibians, mammals, and reptiles (which include birds).

- The evolution of the amniotic egg allowed tetrapods to lay large eggs on land.

- Parental care was an important adaptation in some groups of ray-finned fishes and tetrapods—particularly mammals.

- Vertebrates are the most important large-bodied predators and herbivores in both marine and terrestrial environments.

✔ You should be able to explain why the tetrapod limb could have evolved in an animal that was aquatic.

### 35.4 The Primates and Hominins

- Humans are a tiny twig on the tree of life. Chimpanzees and humans diverged from a common ancestor that lived in Africa 6–7 million years ago.

- The fossil record of the past 4.5 million years contains many distinct species of hominins. *Homo sapiens* is the sole surviving representative of an adaptive radiation.

- For most of human evolution, several species were present in Africa or Europe at the same time. Some lineages went extinct without leaving descendant populations.

- The phylogeny of living humans, based on comparisons of DNA sequences, agrees with evidence in the fossil record that *H. sapiens* originated in Africa and later spread throughout Asia, Europe, and the Americas.

✔ You should be able to describe evidence supporting the hypothesis that *Homo sapiens* originated in Africa.

### MB MasteringBiology

1. **MasteringBiology Assignments**

   **Tutorials and Activities** Allometric Growth; Characteristics of Chordates; Chordates; Deuterostome Diversity; Human Evolution; Primate Diversity

   **Questions** Reading Quizzes, Blue-Thread Questions, Test Bank

2. **eText** Read your book online, search, take notes, highlight text, and more.

3. **The Study Area** Practice Test, Cumulative Test, BioFlix® 3-D Animations, Videos, Activities, Audio Glossary, Word Study Tools, Art

# You should be able to . . .

1. True or false? Both echinoderms and vertebrates have endoskeletons.

2. What trait(s) define(s) the vertebrates?
   a. vertebrae and a cranium
   b. jaws and a spinal cord
   c. endoskeleton constructed of bone
   d. endoskeleton constructed of reinforced cartilage

3. Why are the pharyngeal jaws of many ray-finned fishes important?
   a. They allow the main jaw to be protrusible (extendable).
   b. They make it possible for individuals to suck food toward their mouths.
   c. They give rise to teeth that are found on the main jawbones.
   d. They help process food.

4. The two major lineages that make up the living Amniota are reptiles and _____.

5. In chordates, what is the relationship between the dorsal hollow nerve cord and the spinal cord?
   a. The dorsal hollow nerve cord is found only in embryos; the spinal cord is found in adults.
   b. The dorsal hollow nerve cord stiffens the body and functions in movement; the spinal cord relays electrical signals.
   c. The dorsal hollow nerve cord is found in early fossils of chordates; living species have a spinal cord.
   d. The spinal cord is a type of dorsal hollow nerve cord.

6. Most species of hominins are known only from Africa. Which species have been found in other parts of the world as well?
   a. early *Homo*—*H. habilis* and *H. ergaster*
   b. *H. erectus*, *H. neanderthalensis*, and *H. floresiensis*
   c. gracile australopithecines
   d. robust australopithecines

7. Mammals and birds are both endothermic. Which statement is true?
   a. They both inherited this trait from a common ancestor.
   b. Birds are more closely related to mammals than to reptiles.
   c. Endothermy arose independently in these two lineages.
   d. All reptiles are ectothermic.

8. Explain why each of the four key synapomorphies that distinguish chordates is important in feeding or movement. Why is it possible to say that a certain animal is an "invertebrate chordate"?

9. The cells that make up jaws and gill arches are derived from the same population of embryonic cells. Why does this observation support the hypothesis that jaws evolved from gill arches in fish?

10. Explain how the evolution of the placenta and lactation in mammals improved the probability that mammalian offspring would survive, compared to offspring of species without parental care.

11. The text claims that *Homo sapiens* is the sole survivor of an adaptive radiation that took place over the past 6–7 million years. Do you agree with this statement? Why or why not?

12. Describe a phylogeny of modern humans that would reject the out-of-Africa hypothesis.

13. There is some evidence that pharyngeal gill slits occur in certain species of echinoderms that appear early in the fossil record. If confirmed, what do these data suggest?
    a. Echinoderms are chordates.
    b. Pharyngeal gill slits were present in the earliest echinoderms and lost later.
    c. Some lineages of echinoderms are more closely related to chordates than others.
    d. Pharyngeal gill slits should not be used as a trait in phylogenetic analysis.

14. Animals in the species *Xenoturbella* have extremely simple, wormlike bodies. For example, they have a blind gut (only one opening) and no brain. Propose a hypothesis to explain how this simple body plan evolved in this lineage.

15. In arthropods such as crustaceans and insects, changes in the expression patterns of tool-kit genes enabled a dramatic diversification of their segmented appendages and bodies. Design an experiment to test whether this concept applies to vertebrates.

16. QUANTITATIVE Genetic diversity in living human populations is highest in Africa and decreases as a function of distance from Africa. Draw a graph to show this result. Add a label where you would expect to find a data point for the Yanomamö tribe of South America. Why is it important to use indigenous people for this study?

# 42 Animal Form and Function

**In this chapter you will learn that**

Animal structure is fundamentally related to function

*starting with*

Adaptations and fitness trade-offs **42.1**

*then asking*

| How does function correlate with structure? **42.2** | Why is body size important? **42.3** | How do animals regulate their internal environment (homeostasis)? **42.4** |

*exploring*

Tissues, organs, and organ systems

*looking closer at*

Heat exchange and thermoregulation **42.5**

Oryx are adapted to desert life. They have an exceptional ability to withstand heat and can acquire most of their water from the food they eat.

## BIG PICTURE

This chapter is part of the Big Picture. See how on pages 840–841.

The Sahara and Arabian deserts are extreme environments. In some parts of the Sahara, several years can pass between rainfalls. In a single day, temperatures in these deserts can fluctuate between −0.5°C and 37.5°C; midday temperatures in summer can exceed 50°C. Yet few places in the Sahara or Arabian deserts are devoid of life. Even large animals, such as the oryx, thrive in both regions.

How do animals native to these areas cope? Small animals avoid the midday heat by retreating to a cool burrow deep underground or the shade of a small shrub. Large mammals have a harder time hiding from sunlight but possess traits that allow them to keep cool and conserve water.

The Arabian oryx, for example, seldom drinks. It gets 86 percent of the water it needs from the vegetation it eats and the other 14 percent from water synthesized as a by-product of cellular

✔ When you see this checkmark, stop and test yourself. Answers are available in Appendix A.

respiration—what biologists call **metabolic water.** To conserve what water they have, Arabian oryx produce extremely concentrated urine and exceptionally dry fecal pellets.

In addition, oryx do not sweat to cool off. Instead, their body temperature rises from a normal 37°C to just over 40°C as temperatures increase during the day. The excess body heat is released during the cool desert nights, when their body temperature returns to normal.

In contrast to oryx, humans may die of dehydration when denied water for just three days. And for a human, having a body temperature of 40°C is a life-threatening situation—equivalent to running a fever of 104°F. How do oryx do it? What aspects of their anatomy and physiology allow them to thrive in such an extreme environment?

**Anatomy** is the study of an organism's physical structure. **Physiology** is the study of how the physical structures in an organism function. The anatomy and physiology of an oryx are clearly different from those of a human—or those of a shark, frog, bird, fruit fly, or crab, for that matter. This chapter is an introduction to the study of anatomy and physiology in animals. You can review the importance of animal form and function in the Big Picture on pages 840–841.

# 42.1 Form, Function, and Adaptation

Biologists who study animal anatomy and physiology are studying **adaptations**—heritable traits that allow individuals to survive and reproduce in a certain environment better than individuals that lack those traits (see Chapter 25).

Recall that adaptation results from evolution by natural selection. Natural selection, in turn, occurs whenever individuals with certain alleles leave more offspring that survive to reproductive age than do individuals with different alleles. Because of this difference in reproductive success, the frequency of the selected alleles increases from one generation to the next.

Oryx with alleles that allow them to extract more water from their feces survive better and produce more offspring than do oryx with alleles that allow water to be lost in feces. The ability to produce extremely dry fecal pellets is an adaptation that helps oryx thrive in water-short environments.

## The Role of Fitness Trade-Offs

Adaptations increase fitness—the ability to produce viable offspring. But no adaptation is "perfect." Instead, adaptations are limited by which alleles are present in a population and by the nature of the traits that already exist—because all adaptations derive from preexisting traits.

The human spine, for example, is a highly modified form of the vertebral column in ancestors that walked on all fours (see Chapter 35). The modifications in the human spine can be considered adaptations to support our upright posture, but they are far from perfect—most adults experience back pain at some point during their lives. The evolution of the human spine has

been constrained by the nature of the ancestral trait and by a lack of alleles that would improve its structure and function.

The most important constraint on adaptation, though, may be **trade-offs**—inescapable compromises between traits. For example, it takes a lot of energy to produce offspring through the process of reproduction and also to mount an immune response during an infection. Animals sometimes do not have enough energy to satisfy both needs. In these cases, a trade-off emerges: The animal may devote more energy to reproduction at the expense of strong immune function, or vice versa, or both traits might be negatively affected.

How do biologists study trade-offs in animal physiology? Let's consider experimental work on trade-offs in crickets. During mating, a male cricket deposits a **spermatophore** on the female's genital opening (**FIGURE 42.1a**). This spermatophore consists of a packet of sperm surrounded by a large, gelatinous mass. After mating, the female begins to eat the gelatinous mass (**FIGURE 42.1b**). The sperm packet remains behind and the sperm slowly begin to enter her reproductive tract.

The longer it takes for the female to eat the mass, the more sperm are transferred to her, increasing the number of eggs fertilized by the male. It might seem advantageous for the male to make as large a spermatophore as possible. However, there is a

**(a)** Decorated crickets mating

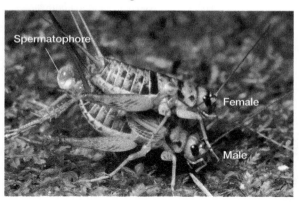

**(b)** The female eats the gelatinous mass.

**FIGURE 42.1 Mating in Crickets Involves Transfer of a Spermatophore from the Male to the Female.**

**QUESTION:** Is there a trade-off between reproductive and immune function in male crickets?

**HYPOTHESIS:** Male crickets need to make an energy trade-off between reproductive function and immune function.

**NULL HYPOTHESIS:** No energy trade-off between reproductive function and immune function is required.

**EXPERIMENTAL SETUP:**

1. Remove spermatophores from male crickets:

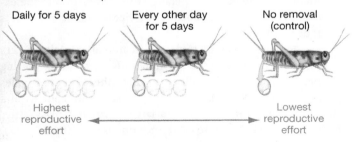

Daily for 5 days     Every other day for 5 days     No removal (control)

Highest reproductive effort ⟷ Lowest reproductive effort

**2.** Draw hemolymph samples from the three sets of crickets.

**3.** Add bacteria to samples; measure lysis of bacteria.

Spectrophotometer

**EXPERIMENTAL SETUP:**

1. Inject male crickets:

With lipopolysaccharide (LPS) to simulate bacterial infection     With placebo (control)

2. Remove spermatophores and measure size of gelatinous mass.

Gelatinous mass — Sperm packet

**PREDICTION:** Hemolymph from males forced to produce more spermatophores will exhibit lower lytic activity than controls.

**PREDICTION OF NULL HYPOTHESIS:** There will be no difference in lytic activity between treated males and control males.

**PREDICTION:** Spermatophores from LPS-injected males will have smaller gelatinous masses than those from control males.

**PREDICTION OF NULL HYPOTHESIS:** There will be no difference in gelatinous mass size between treated and control males.

**RESULTS:**

Treated males had lower lytic activity than controls

**RESULTS:**

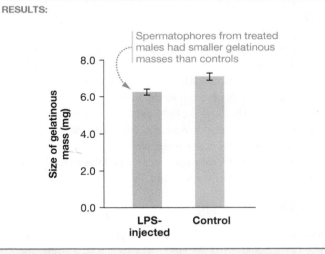

Spermatophores from treated males had smaller gelatinous masses than controls

**CONCLUSION:** Male crickets must make an energy trade-off to support increased reproductive effort.

**FIGURE 42.2 Trade-offs Between Reproduction and Immune Function in Male Crickets.** This study showed that males with experimentally increased investment in reproduction had a lower ability to kill bacteria than control males, and that males with experimentally stimulated immune function had lower reproductive function than control males.

SOURCE: Kerr, A. M., S. N. Gershman, and S. K. Sakaluk. 2010. Experimentally induced spermatophore production and immune responses reveal a trade-off in crickets. *Behavioral Ecology* 21: 647–654.

✔**QUESTION** If the null hypothesis were supported by the results, what would each graph look like?

cost involved. Spermatophores weigh up to 6 percent of a male cricket's body mass, and it takes males more than three hours to make a new one. During the time males spend making new spermatophores, they lose other mating opportunities.

Losing out on new mates while making spermatophores may not be the only cost a male cricket accrues. When an insect is infected with a pathogen such as a bacterium, it mounts an immune response. Activation of the insect defense system is energetically expensive. Is there a trade-off in male crickets between producing spermatophores and mounting an immune response?

To answer this question, biologists carried out an experiment using a powerful method—a reciprocal design. They altered the energetic investment crickets made into each of the systems in question—reproduction and immune function—and observed the effect on the other system (**FIGURE 42.2**).

First, the biologists removed spermatophores from male crickets, causing them to make new ones, daily or every other day. The biologists then took a sample of the crickets' hemolymph, or blood, and added bacteria to find out whether the hemolymph was able to destroy the pathogen. As bacteria are lysed, or ruptured, the opaque hemolymph becomes clear. Lytic activity was measured using a spectrophotometer to calculate the change in the opacity, or optical density, of the hemolymph over time.

Compared to control crickets, which did not have their spermatophores removed, the experimental crickets had lower lytic activity (fewer bacteria destroyed). Even more striking, the crickets that had to make new spermatophores daily had lower lytic activity than those that had to make new spermatophores only every other day. This suggested that increased investment into making spermatophores was traded off against investment into immune function.

Next, the biologists injected crickets with a component of the cell walls of bacteria called lipopolysaccharide (LPS), which caused the crickets to mount an immune response. What was the effect on spermatophore size? The result was dramatic. Male crickets injected with LPS produced smaller spermatophores than control crickets. When the researchers looked more closely, they realized the size of the sperm packet remained largely unchanged, but the size of the gelatinous mass decreased in injected crickets. This suggests that mounting an immune response may reduce male crickets' reproductive success. How? By causing males to make smaller gelatinous masses, which decreases the time females spend eating them, reducing sperm transfer.

Taken together, these two sets of experiments provide very strong evidence that there is a trade-off between reproductive and immune function in crickets.

Trade-offs, such as the compromise between energetic investment and the competing demands of reproductive and immune function, are common in nature. Desert animals that sweat to cool off are threatened with dehydration. An eagle's beak is superbly adapted for tearing meat but not for weaving nesting materials together. In studying animal anatomy and physiology, biologists study compromise and constraint as well as adaptation.

## Adaptation and Acclimatization

In biology, adaptation refers to a genetic change in a population in response to natural selection exerted by the environment. Short-term, reversible responses to environmental fluctuations are referred to as **acclimatization.** Acclimatization is a phenotypic change in an individual in response to short-term changes in the natural environment. Acclimation is similar to acclimatization, but acclimation refers to changes that occur in organisms in a laboratory setting.

If you moved to Tibet, your body would acclimatize to high elevation by making more of the oxygen-carrying pigment hemoglobin and more hemoglobin-carrying red blood cells. But populations that have lived in Tibet for many generations are adapted to this environment through genetic changes. Among native Tibetans, for example, an allele that increases the ability of hemoglobin to hold oxygen has increased to high frequency. In populations of Tibetans that do not live at high elevations, this allele is rare or nonexistent.

The ability to acclimatize is itself an adaptation. Light-skinned humans, for example, vary in the ability to tan in response to sunlight. Some individuals tan easily—they have alleles that allow them to acclimatize efficiently to environments with intense sunlight—while others do not. In this and many other cases, the ability to acclimatize is a genetically variable trait that can respond to natural selection.

## 42.2 Tissues, Organs, and Systems: How Does Structure Correlate with Function?

If a structure found in an animal is adaptive—meaning that it helps the individual survive and produce viable offspring—it is common to observe that the structure's size, shape, or composition correlates closely with its function.

For example, recall that biologists have documented extensive changes in beak size and shape in medium ground finches from the Galápagos Islands (see Chapter 25). Such changes are due to natural selection. Individuals with deep beaks are better able to crack the large fruits that predominate during drought years, while individuals with small beaks are better able to harvest the small seeds that predominate during wet years.

As **FIGURE 42.3** (see page 846) shows, a strong correlation between diet and beak structure is also found *among* species of Galápagos finch. Species with large, cone-shaped beaks eat large seeds; species with small, cone-shaped beaks eat small seeds. Species with long, tweezer-like beaks pick insects off tree trunks or other surfaces.

The mechanism responsible for these structure–function correlations is straightforward: If a mutant allele alters the size or shape of a structure in a way that makes it function more efficiently, individuals who have that allele will produce more offspring than will other individuals. As a result, the allele will increase in frequency in the population over time.

| Species of Galápagos finch | | Food source |
|---|---|---|
| *Geospiza fuliginosa* |  | Small seeds |
| *Geospiza fortis* | | Medium seeds |
| *Geospiza magnirostris* | | Large seeds |
| *Certhidea olivacea* | | Insects, nectar |

**FIGURE 42.3 In Animal Anatomy and Physiology, Form Often Correlates with Function.**

## Structure–Function Relationships at the Molecular and Cellular Levels

Correlations between form and function start at the molecular level. For example, earlier chapters emphasized that the shape of proteins correlates with their role as enzymes, structural components of the cell, or transporters. The membrane proteins called channels form pores that allow specific ions or molecules to pass in or out of cells (see Chapter 6). The ends and interior of a channel are hydrophilic, which allows the protein to interact with the surrounding solution or the interior of the cell, while the perimeter is hydrophobic—allowing the protein to interact with the lipid bilayer. The protein's structure fits its function.

Similar correlations between structure and function occur at the level of the cell. In fact, it is possible to predict a cell's specialized function by examining its internal structure. Cells that manufacture and secrete hormones or digestive enzymes are packed with rough endoplasmic reticulum (ER) and Golgi apparatuses; cells that store energy are dominated by large fat droplets; cells that ingest and destroy invading bacteria have many lysosomes.

The overall shape of a cell can also correlate with its function. For example, cells that are responsible for transporting materials into or out of the body often have extremely large areas of plasma membrane. As a result, they have room to accommodate the thousands of membrane channels, transporters, and pumps required for extensive transport.

## Tissues Are Groups of Cells That Function as a Unit

Animals are **multicellular,** meaning that their bodies contain distinct types of cells that are specialized for different functions. Frequently, animal cells that are similar in structure and function are physically attached to each other and form a tissue. A **tissue** is a group of cells that function as a unit.

**SUMMARY TABLE 42.1  Connective Tissues**

| Type | Example |
|---|---|
| **Loose** *soft* extracellular matrix; provides padding | 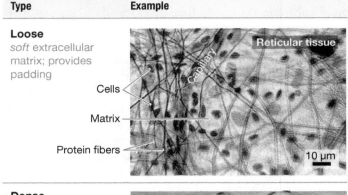 Reticular tissue — Cells, Matrix, Protein fibers, Capillary, 10 µm |
| **Dense** *fibrous* extracellular matrix; provides connections |  Tendon — Collagen fibers, Tendon cell nuclei, 10 µm |
| **Supporting** *firm* extracellular matrix; functions in structural support and protection |  Bone — Bone cells, Matrix, 50 µm |
| |  Cartilage — Cartilage cells, Matrix, 50 µm |
| **Fluid** *liquid* extracellular matrix; functions in transport |  Blood — Red blood cell, White blood cell, Plasma, 5 µm |

The embryonic tissues called ectoderm, mesoderm, and endoderm are found in most animals (see Chapter 23 and Chapter 33). As an individual develops, the embryonic tissues give rise to four adult tissue types: (**1**) connective tissue, (**2**) nervous tissue, (**3**) muscle tissue, and (**4**) epithelial tissue. In each case, the structure of the tissue correlates closely with its function. Let's consider each type in turn.

**Connective Tissue**   **Connective tissue** consists of cells that are loosely arranged in a liquid, jellylike, or solid matrix. The matrix comprises extracellular fibers and other materials, and it is secreted by the connective tissue cells themselves (**TABLE 42.1**). Each type of connective tissue secretes a distinct type of extracellular matrix. The nature of the matrix determines the nature of the connective tissue.

- **Loose connective tissue** contains an array of fibrous proteins in a soft matrix; it serves as a packing material between organs or padding under the skin. Reticular connective tissue—in lymphoid organs such as the spleen and bone marrow—and adipose tissue, or fat tissue, are loose connective tissues made up of cells suspended in a matrix of fibers and fluid.

- **Dense connective tissue** is found in the tendons and ligaments that connect muscles, bones, and organs. As Table 42.1 shows, the matrix in tendons and ligaments is dominated by tough collagen fibers (introduced in Chapter 11).

- **Supporting connective tissue** has a firm extracellular matrix. **Bone** and **cartilage** are connective tissues that provide structural support for the vertebrate body as well as protective enclosures for the brain and other components of the nervous system.

- **Fluid connective tissue** consists of cells surrounded by a liquid extracellular matrix. **Blood,** which transports materials throughout the vertebrate body, contains a variety of cell types and has a specialized extracellular matrix called plasma (see Chapter 45).

**Nervous Tissue**   **Nervous tissue** consists of nerve cells, which are also called **neurons,** and several types of supporting cells. Neurons transmit electrical signals, which are produced by changes in the permeability of the cell's plasma membrane to ions (see Chapter 46). Supporting cells have many functions, including regulating ion concentrations in the space surrounding neurons, supplying neurons with nutrients, or serving as scaffolding or support for neurons.

Although they vary widely in shape, all neurons have projections that contact other cells. As **FIGURE 42.4** shows, most neurons have two distinct types of projections from the cell body, where the nucleus is located: (**1**) highly branched, relatively short processes called **dendrites,** and (**2**) a relatively long structure called an **axon.** Dendrites contact other cells and transmit electrical signals from them to the cell body; the axon carries electrical signals from the cell body to other cells.

**Muscle Tissue**   **Muscle tissue** was a key innovation in the evolution of animals—like nervous tissue, it appears in no other

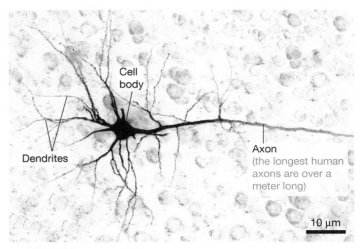

**FIGURE 42.4 Neurons Transmit Electrical Signals.** In a neuron, information is transmitted from dendrites to the cell body to the axon.

✔**QUESTION** Based on the structure of a neuron, does it provide signals to specific cells and tissues, or does it broadcast signals widely throughout the body?

lineage on the tree of life (see Chapter 33). Some of the functions of muscle include movement of the body, pumping of the heart, and mixing of food in the gastrointestinal tract. There are three types of muscle tissue (**FIGURE 42.5**); you, along with other vertebrates, have all three.

1. **Skeletal muscle** attaches to the bones of the skeleton and exerts a force on them when it contracts. Skeletal muscle is responsible for most body movements. In addition, it encircles the openings of the digestive and urinary tracts and controls swallowing, defecation, and urination.

**Long cells,** voluntary movement    **Branched cells,** involuntary movement    **Tapered cells,** involuntary movement

**FIGURE 42.5 Muscle Tissues Comprise Cells That Contract.** The three types of muscle tissue have distinctive structures and functions.

Faces outer environment

**Apical side of epithelium**

Epithelium

Basal lamina connects epithelium to other tissues

**Basolateral side of epithelium**

10 μm

**FIGURE 42.6 Epithelial Cells Provide Protection and Regulate which Materials Pass across Body Surfaces.**

2. **Cardiac muscle** makes up the walls of the heart and is responsible for pumping blood throughout the body.

3. **Smooth muscle** cells, which are tapered at each end, form a muscle tissue that lines the walls of the digestive tract and the blood vessels.

Muscle tissue and movement are explored in detail in Chapter 48.

**Epithelial Tissues**    **Epithelial tissues** are also called **epithelia** (singular: **epithelium**). Epithelium covers the outside of the body, lines the surfaces of organs, and forms glands. An **organ** is a structure that serves a specialized function and consists of several tissues; a **gland** is an organ that secretes specific molecules or solutions such as hormones or digestive enzymes.

Epithelia form the interface between the interior of an organ or body and the exterior. In addition to providing protection, epithelial tissues are gatekeepers. Water, nutrients, and other substances are transported, often selectively, across epithelia.

Because the primary function of epithelium is to act as a barrier and protective layer, it's not surprising to observe that epithelial cells typically form layers of closely packed cells (**FIGURE 42.6**).

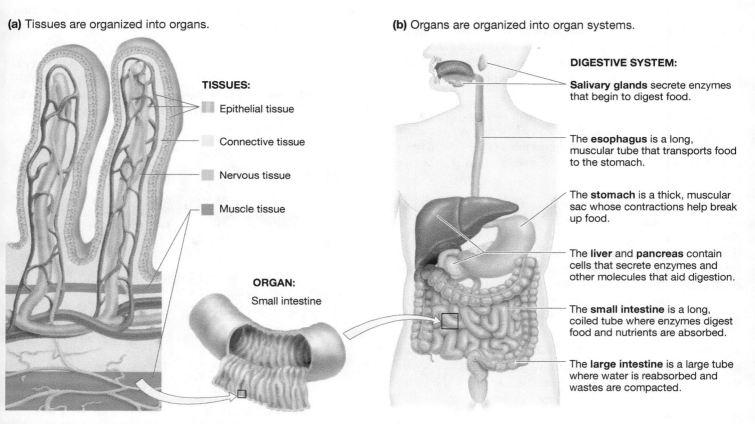

**(a)** Tissues are organized into organs.

**TISSUES:**

Epithelial tissue

Connective tissue

Nervous tissue

Muscle tissue

**ORGAN:**
Small intestine

**(b)** Organs are organized into organ systems.

**DIGESTIVE SYSTEM:**

**Salivary glands** secrete enzymes that begin to digest food.

The **esophagus** is a long, muscular tube that transports food to the stomach.

The **stomach** is a thick, muscular sac whose contractions help break up food.

The **liver** and **pancreas** contain cells that secrete enzymes and other molecules that aid digestion.

The **small intestine** is a long, coiled tube where enzymes digest food and nutrients are absorbed.

The **large intestine** is a large tube where water is reabsorbed and wastes are compacted.

**FIGURE 42.7 Organs Are Composed of Tissues; Organ Systems Are Made Up of Organs. (a)** The human small intestine is an organ composed of all four major tissue types. **(b)** The human digestive system is essentially one long tube divided into chambers where food is processed and nutrients are absorbed. The salivary glands, liver, and pancreas are organs that secrete specific enzymes or compounds into the tube.

In many cases, adjacent epithelial cells are joined by structures that hold them tightly together, such as tight junctions and desmosomes (introduced in Chapter 11).

Epithelial tissue has polarity, or sidedness. An epithelium has an **apical** side, which faces away from other tissues and toward the environment, and a **basolateral** side, which faces the interior of the animal and connects to connective tissues. This connection is made by a layer of fibers called the **basal lamina.**

The apical and basolateral sides of an epithelium have distinct structures and functions. Epithelial cells, for example, line the surface of your trachea, or windpipe. The apical side of these cells secretes mucus and is covered with cilia that help sweep away dust, bacteria, and viruses. The basolateral side lacks these features but is cemented to the basal lamina.

Epithelial cells have short life spans. The cells that line your esophagus—the tube connecting your mouth and stomach—live for 2 to 3 days, while the cells that line your large intestine live for a maximum of 6 days. Muscle cells and neurons, in contrast, normally live as long as the individual animal does. Epithelial cells are short lived because they are exposed to harsh environments, where they are likely to be killed or scraped away.

The tissue as a whole does not wear away, however, because it includes cells that actively undergo mitosis and cytokinesis—producing new epithelial cells to replace those lost on the side that faces the environment.

## Organs and Organ Systems

Cells with similar functions are organized into tissues, and tissues are organized into specialized structures called organs. Recall that an organ is a structure that serves a specialized function and consists of several types of tissues. The small intestine, for example, consists of muscle, nervous, connective, and epithelial tissues (**FIGURE 42.7a**).

An **organ system** consists of groups of tissues and organs that work together to perform one or more functions. Using the digestive system as an example, **FIGURE 42.7b** illustrates how the structure of organs correlates with their function and how the components of an organ system work together in an integrated fashion.

Because an animal's body contains molecules, cells, tissues, organs, and organ systems, biologists who study animal anatomy and physiology must work at various levels of organization to understand how that body operates.

**FIGURE 42.8** illustrates these levels of organization, using the human nervous system as an example. Because the structure and function of each component in the body are integrated with those of other components, and because each level of organization is integrated with other levels of organization, the organism as a whole is greater than the sum of its parts. In other words, an organism is more than just a collection of individual systems, and each system is more than just a collection of individual cells or tissues or even organs.

**Atomic and molecular levels:**
Membrane protein in neurons regulates flow of ions.

**Cellular level:**
Electrical signal travels down length of neuron.

**Tissue level:**
Electrical signals travel from cell to cell in nervous tissue.

**Organ level:**
Nervous tissue and connective tissue in brain aid in sight, smell, memory, and thought.

**Organ system level:**
Brain and nerves send signals throughout the body to control breathing, digestion, movement, and other functions.

**Organism level:**
Nervous system coordinates the functions of other systems to support life.

**FIGURE 42.8 Biologists Study Anatomy and Physiology at Many Levels.** The levels of organization within an organism are not independent of each other. Instead, they are tightly integrated.

In effect, each subsequent chapter in this unit focuses on a different organ system found in animals, beginning with the excretory system and ending with the immune system. Each of these systems can be interpreted as a suite of adaptations and trade-offs. Each system accomplishes a specific task required for survival and reproduction, and each works in conjunction with other systems.

Before delving into the various systems, however, it's essential to examine general phenomena that affect all systems in animals. Let's start by looking at how body size affects animal physiology.

## check your understanding

**If you understand that . . .**

- Biologists study structure and function at the molecular, cellular, tissue, organ, and organ system levels.
- Events at each level of organization in an individual interact to form an integrated whole that responds to the environment in appropriate ways.

✔ **You should be able to . . .**

Describe and compare the structure and function of the four major types of animal tissues.

*Answers are available in Appendix A.*

## 42.3 How Does Body Size Affect Animal Physiology?

Animals are living machines, made up of molecules, cells, tissues, organs, and organ systems that have changed over time in response to natural selection.

The laws of physics affect the anatomy and physiology of a living machine. The force of gravity, for example, limits how large an animal can be and still move efficiently. Or consider the forces exerted by the medium in which animals live. Because water is much denser than air, it is harder for animals to move through water. As a result, fish and aquatic mammals have much more streamlined bodies than terrestrial animals do.

Physical laws clearly affect body size. Just as clearly, body size has pervasive effects on how animals function. Large animals need more food than small animals do. Large animals also produce more waste, take longer to mature, reproduce more slowly, and tend to live longer. Conversely, small animals are more susceptible to damage from cold and dehydration than large animals are, because they lose heat and water faster. Juveniles and adults of the same species face different challenges simply because their body sizes are different.

Why is body size such an important factor in how animals work? How do biologists study the consequences of size? Let's consider each question in turn.

## Surface Area/Volume Relationships: Theory

From microscopic roundworms to gigantic blue whales, animals span an incredible range of body masses—a total of 12 orders of magnitude. Many of the challenges posed by increasing size are based on this fundamental relationship between surface area and volume.

You learned previously that the relationship between the surface area and volume of the roots and shoots of plants affects water and light absorption by the plant (see Chapter 37). Similarly, surface area is important in animals because oxygen and nutrients such as glucose must diffuse into the animal's body, and waste products such as urea and carbon dioxide must diffuse out. The rate at which these and other molecules and ions diffuse depends in part on the amount of surface area available for diffusion. In contrast, the rate at which nutrients are used and heat and waste products are produced depends on the volume of the animal.

The contrast between processes that depend on surface area and those that depend on volume is important for a simple reason. As an animal gets larger, its volume increases much faster than its surface area does.

Reviewing a little basic geometry will convince you why this is so. As **FIGURE 42.9a** shows:

- The surface area of a cube increases as a function of its linear dimension *squared*. Because a cube has six sides, the surface area of a cube of length $l$ is $6l^2$ (six times the area of any one side).

- The volume of the same structure increases as a function of its linear dimension *cubed*. Hence, the volume (or mass) of a cube of length $l$ is $l^3$.

Area has two dimensions; volume has three. In general:

$$\text{Surface area} \propto (\text{length})^2$$
$$\text{Volume (or mass)} \propto (\text{length})^3$$
$$\text{Surface area} \propto (\text{volume})^{2/3}$$

(The symbol $\propto$ means "is proportional to.")

**FIGURE 42.9b** graphs the consequences of these relationships. The $x$-axis plots the length of a side in a cube; the $y$-axis plots the cube's volume (orange line) or surface area (yellow line). As a cube gets bigger, its surface area increases much more slowly than does its volume (or mass).

The same general relationship holds for cells, tissues, organs, and organ systems. Larger cells, for example, have lower surface area/volume ratios than smaller cells. Quantities that are based on volume, such as body mass, increase disproportionately fast with increases in linear dimensions.

✔ If you understand the relationship between surface area and volume, you should be able to predict which of the following has the higher surface area/volume ratio: a newborn or an adult human.

How does the relationship between surface area and volume affect animal form and function?

**(a) What are the surface area and volume of each cube?**

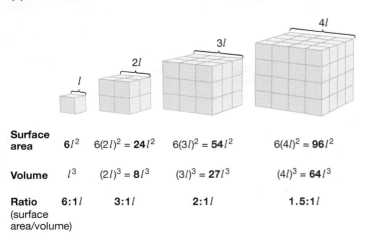

| Surface area | $6l^2$ | $6(2l)^2 = 24l^2$ | $6(3l)^2 = 54l^2$ | $6(4l)^2 = 96l^2$ |
|---|---|---|---|---|
| Volume | $l^3$ | $(2l)^3 = 8l^3$ | $(3l)^3 = 27l^3$ | $(4l)^3 = 64l^3$ |
| Ratio (surface area/volume) | $6{:}1l$ | $3{:}1l$ | $2{:}1l$ | $1.5{:}1l$ |

**(b) Surface area and volume of a cube versus length of a side**

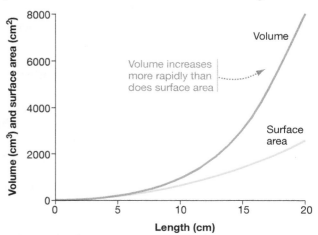

**FIGURE 42.9 Surface Area and Volume Change as a Function of Overall Size. (a)** The surface area of an object increases as the square of the length (*l*). The volume increases as the cube of the length. **(b)** Volume increases much more rapidly than does surface area as linear dimensions increase.

## Surface Area/Volume Relationships: Data

As an example of how surface area/volume relationships affect an animal's physiology, consider the metabolic rate of mammals. **Metabolic rate** is the overall rate of energy consumption by an individual. Because consumption and production of energy in mammals depend largely on aerobic respiration, metabolic rate is often measured in terms of oxygen consumption, and it is typically reported in units of milliliters of $O_2$ consumed per hour.

Because it is so much larger, an elephant consumes a great deal more oxygen per hour than a mouse does. But what is going on at the levels of cells and tissues in these animals?

**Comparing Mice and Elephants** To compare metabolic rates in different species, biologists divide metabolic rate by overall mass and report a mass-specific metabolic rate in units of milliliters of oxygen per gram per hour (mL $O_2$/g/hr). This mass-specific metabolic rate gives the rate of oxygen consumption per gram of tissue.

Because an individual's metabolic rate varies dramatically with its activity, the accepted convention is to report the **basal metabolic rate (BMR)**—the rate at which an animal consumes oxygen while at rest, with an empty stomach, under normal temperature and moisture conditions.

**FIGURE 42.10** plots per-gram or "mass-specific" BMR as a function of average body mass. Notice that the x-axis on the graph is logarithmic, to make it easier to compare very small species with very large ones. For help with logarithms, see **BioSkills 6** in Appendix B.

The graph's take-home message? On a per-gram basis, small animals have higher BMRs than do large animals. An elephant has more mass than a mouse, but a gram of elephant tissue consumes much less energy than a gram of mouse tissue does.

The leading hypothesis to explain this pattern is based on surface area/volume ratios. Many aspects of metabolism—including oxygen consumption, food digestion, delivery of nutrients to tissues, and removal of wastes and excess heat—depend on exchange across surfaces. As an organism's size increases, its mass-specific metabolic rate must decrease. Otherwise the surface area available for exchange of materials would fail to keep up with the metabolic demands generated by the organism's enzymes.

**Changes during Development** A king salmon weighs a few milligrams or less at hatching but grows into an adult weighing 50 kg or more—a millionfold increase in body mass. To explore the consequences of this change, biologists have studied how gas

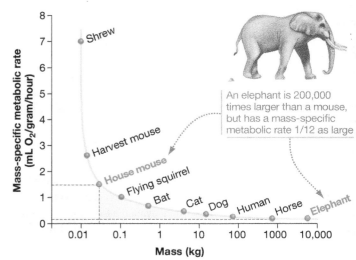

**FIGURE 42.10 Small Animals Have Higher Relative Metabolic Rates than Large Animals Do.** Overall body mass, plotted on a logarithmic scale, versus metabolic rate per gram of tissue.

✔**QUESTION** Which mammal has to eat more to support each gram of its tissue: a puppy or an adult dog?

exchange—uptake of oxygen and removal of carbon dioxide—occurs in newly hatched Atlantic salmon.

Like most fish species, young salmon have rudimentary gills but also exchange gases across their skin. In aquatic animals, **gills** are organs that allow the exchange of gases and dissolved substances between the animals' blood and the surrounding water.

To document the amount of gas exchange that occurs in the gills versus the skin, researchers inserted the heads of individual larval and juvenile salmon through a pinhole in a soft rubber membrane and then recorded the rate of oxygen uptake on either side of the membrane. As the "Experimental Setup" section of **FIGURE 42.11** indicates, the gills were responsible for oxygen uptake on one side of the membrane; skin was responsible for oxygen uptake on the other side of the membrane.

The graph in the figure's "Results" section plots the percentage of total oxygen uptake that took place across the skin (green line) versus gills (purple line), as a function of body mass. Each data point represents the recordings from an individual fish.

Note that newly hatched larvae take up most of the oxygen they need by diffusion across the body surface. As an individual grows, however, its skin surface area decreases in relation to its volume. To avoid suffocation, individuals switch from skin-breathing to gill-breathing at a body mass of about 0.1 grams. What makes gills so effective in oxygen uptake?

## Adaptations That Increase Surface Area

If the function of a cell or tissue depends on diffusion, it usually has a shape that increases its surface area relative to its volume. Flattening, folding, and branching are effective ways for structures to have a high surface area/volume ratio:

- *Flattening* Fish have **gill lamellae** (**FIGURE 42.12a**)—thin sheets of epithelial cells that provide the gill with an extremely high surface area relative to its volume. Because the surface available is so large, gases are able to diffuse across the gills rapidly enough to keep up with the growth in the volume of a developing fish.

- *Folding* In portions of the digestive tract where nutrients are transported into the body, the surface of the structure is folded. Extending from these folds are narrow projections called **villi** (**FIGURE 42.12b**). Together, the folds and villi make an extensive surface area available. Folded surfaces are common in diffusion-dependent organs.

- *Branching* The highly branched network shown in **FIGURE 42.12c** is a system of small, thin-walled blood vessels called **capillaries.** Capillaries have a high surface area available for gases, nutrients, and waste products to diffuse into and out of blood; branching increases the surface available in each square centimeter of tissue. In general, highly branched structures increase the surface area available for diffusion.

The amount of surface area created by flattening, folding, and branching can be impressive. The highly branched capillaries in a human have a total surface area of up to 1000 m²; extensive folding gives a total surface area of about 140 m² in your lungs and

**QUESTION:** Newly hatched salmon can breathe through their skin and through their gills. Which predominates?

**HYPOTHESIS:** The relative amount of gas exchange across gills and skin changes as a salmon grows.

**NULL HYPOTHESIS:** The relative amount of gas exchange across gills and skin does not change as a salmon grows.

**EXPERIMENTAL SETUP:**

One electrode measures oxygen uptake through skin

One electrode measures oxygen uptake through gills

Water flow

Water flow

Head of young salmon is inserted through a small hole in rubber membrane

**PREDICTION:** Juveniles will exchange a higher percentage of gas across gills and a lower percentage of gas across skin than larvae.

**PREDICTION OF NULL HYPOTHESIS:** Juveniles and larvae will exchange the same percentage of gas across gills and skin.

**RESULTS:**

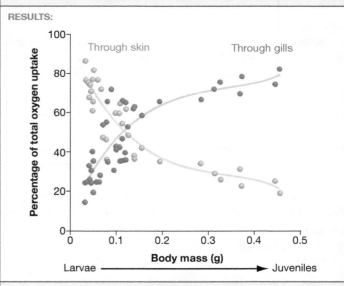

Through skin    Through gills

Larvae ——————————→ Juveniles

**CONCLUSION:** Breathing changes from skin to gills as larvae grow. Interpretation: Gills provide larger surface area relative to increasing volume of body.

**FIGURE 42.11 How Do Young Salmon Breathe?**

SOURCE: Wells, P. R., and A. W. Pinder. 1996. The respiratory development of Atlantic salmon. *Journal of Experimental Biology* 199: 2737–2744.

✓**QUESTION** Suppose the experimenters had measured oxygen uptake on either side of the apparatus in the absence of a fish. What would the results be?

**(a) Flattening:** fish gill lamellae

Lamellae

10 µm

**(b) Folding:** intestinal folds and villi

Villi

100 µm

**(c) Branching:** capillaries

25 µm

**FIGURE 42.12 Certain Structures Have High Surface Area/Volume Ratios.** The micrograph in part (c) has been colorized to highlight capillaries, colored pink.

250 m² in your small intestine. For comparison, a doubles tennis court has a surface area of 261 m².

Surface area/volume relationships have a pervasive influence on the structure and function of animals. They will be an issue in almost every chapter in this unit.

check your understanding

**If you understand that . . .**

- An animal's overall size is important in part because body mass is affected by an array of physical forces.
- The amount of heat and waste that an animal produces and the amount of food and oxygen that it requires are proportional to its mass or volume.
- The amount of surface area available relative to that mass or volume is critical, because heat exchange and other important processes take place across surfaces.

✔ **You should be able to . . .**

1. Explain why large animals have a relatively low surface area/volume ratio.
2. Explain why a squirrel needs to eat more energy per unit body mass than a bear.

*Answers are available in Appendix A.*

# 42.4 Homeostasis

Adaptation and surface area/volume ratios are important themes in the analysis of animal form and function. So is homeostasis.

**Homeostasis** (literally, "alike-standing") is defined as stability in the chemical and physical conditions within an animal's cells, tissues, and organs. Although conditions may vary as an animal's environment changes, internal chemical and physical states are usually kept within a tolerable range.

## Homeostasis: General Principles

Many of the structures and processes observed in animals can be interpreted as mechanisms for maintaining homeostasis with respect to some quantity, such as pH, temperature, or calcium ion concentration. Let's review some important general ideas about homeostasis and then analyze how homeostasis can be maintained in the face of environmental fluctuations.

**Two Approaches to Achieving Homeostasis**  Constancy of physiological state can be achieved by two processes: (1) conformation or (2) regulation.

1. **Conformation**  The body temperature of Antarctic rock cod closely matches that of the surrounding seawater, which is typically −1.9°C (seawater is still liquid at this temperature because of the high concentration of solutes). The rock cod does not actively regulate its body temperature to match that of seawater. Instead, its body temperature remains constant because it conforms to the temperature of its constant surroundings. If rock cod were placed into a different environment, for example warmer water, they would not maintain a constant body temperature of −1.9°C. Because these animals are adapted to such constant environmental conditions, their physiological systems cannot function properly outside of these conditions.

2. **Regulation**  Regulatory homeostasis is based on mechanisms that adjust the internal state to keep it within limits that can be tolerated, no matter what the external conditions. For example, a dog maintains a body temperature of about 38°C whether it's cold or hot outside. If the dog's body temperature rises, it might pant to cool off and maintain homeostasis. If body temperature falls, the dog might shiver to bring its temperature back up to the target value. There

are, however, limits to regulatory homeostasis. If the external temperature gets too cold or hot, animals cannot maintain homeostasis and will die.

**The Role of Epithelium** Because epithelium is the interface between the internal and external environments, it plays a key role in achieving homeostasis. Epithelium is responsible for forming an internal environment that can be dramatically different from the external environment such that physical and chemical conditions inside an animal can be maintained at relatively constant levels.

As subsequent chapters will show, many epithelial cells are studded with membrane proteins that regulate the transport of ions, water, nutrients, and wastes. No molecule can enter or leave the body without crossing an epithelium. Homeostasis is possible because epithelia control this exchange.

**Why Is Homeostasis Important?** Much of the answer to this question is based on enzyme function. Recall that enzymes are proteins that catalyze chemical reactions within cells (see Chapter 4). Temperature, pH, and other physical and chemical conditions have a dramatic effect on the structure and function of enzymes. Most enzymes function best under a fairly narrow range of conditions.

Other processes depend on homeostasis, too. Temperature changes affect membrane permeability and how quickly solutes diffuse. To take an extreme case, the expansion of water as it freezes can rip cells apart if tissues are allowed to drop much below 0°C. Conversely, extremely high temperatures can denature proteins—meaning that they lose their tertiary structure and cease to function.

When homeostasis occurs, conditions inside the body allow molecules, cells, tissues, organs, and organ systems to function at an optimal level. However, occasional departures from homeostasis can represent important adaptations. For example, a fever is a response to an infection by a pathogen. This increase in body temperature can help fight off the pathogen.

## The Role of Regulation and Feedback

To achieve homeostasis, most animals have regulatory systems that monitor internal conditions such as temperature, blood pressure, blood pH, and blood glucose. If one of these variables changes, a homeostatic system acts quickly to modify it. Like the thermostat in a home heating system, each of these systems has a **set point**—a normal or target range of values for the controlled variable.

Animals have a set point for blood pH, blood oxygen and nutrient concentrations, and other parameters. In most mammals, the set point for body temperature is somewhere between 35°C and 39°C. How does an individual maintain its tissues at the set point despite changes in activity and the environment?

A homeostatic system consists of three general components: a sensor, an integrator, and an effector. **FIGURE 42.13** shows how these components interact:

1. A **sensor** is a structure that senses some aspect of the external or internal environment.

**FIGURE 42.13 Animals Achieve Homeostasis through Negative Feedback.** Many animals use homeostatic systems similar to this one to maintain a preferred range of hydration, blood pH, blood pressure, calcium ion concentration, body temperature, and so on.

2. An **integrator** evaluates the incoming sensory information and "decides" whether a response is necessary to achieve homeostasis. (The word decides is in quotation marks because the decision is not a conscious one.)

3. An **effector** is any structure that helps restore the desired internal condition.

Without these three elements, homeostatic control systems can't maintain a desired set point; homeostasis is impossible.

Homeostatic systems are based on negative feedback. When **negative feedback** occurs, effectors reduce or oppose the change in internal conditions. For example, a rise in blood pH triggers effectors that act to reduce that rise. Blood pH returns to the set point in response to this negative feedback.

Homeostatic systems are a key aspect of one of the five attributes of life (see Chapter 1): acquiring information from the environment and responding to it. Subsequent chapters in this unit explore how animals use sensor–integrator–effector systems to achieve homeostasis with respect to the solute concentrations of their cells and tissues, their oxygen supply, and nutrient availability. In this chapter, let's focus on how different animals achieve homeostasis with respect to body temperature.

## 42.5 How Do Animals Regulate Body Temperature?

All animals exchange heat with their environment. Heat flows "downhill," from regions of higher temperature to regions of lower temperature. If an individual is warmer than its surroundings, it will lose heat; if it is cooler than its environment, it will gain heat.

How does heat exchange occur?

## Mechanisms of Heat Exchange

As **FIGURE 42.14** shows, animals exchange heat with the environment in four ways: conduction, convection, radiation, and evaporation.

1. **Conduction** is the direct transfer of heat between two physical bodies that are in contact with each other. For instance, when a turtle sits on a warm rock, heat is transferred from the rock to its body. The rate at which conduction occurs depends on the surface area of transfer, the steepness of the temperature difference between the two bodies, and how well each body conducts heat.

2. **Convection** is a special case of conduction. During conduction, heat is transferred between two solids; but during convection, heat is exchanged between a solid and a moving liquid or gas. For example, the heat loss that occurs when wind blows on your skin is due to convection. As the speed of the air or water flow increases, so does the rate of heat transfer.

3. **Radiation** is the transfer of heat between two bodies that are not in direct physical contact. All objects, including animals, radiate energy as a function of their temperature. The Sun radiates heat; so does your body, but to a much lesser degree.

4. **Evaporation** is the phase change that occurs when liquid water becomes a gas. Conduction, convection, and radiation can cause heat gain or loss, but evaporation leads only to heat loss. The turtle in the photograph is losing heat as water evaporates off its shell and skin. Because of the extensive hydrogen bonding in liquid water, a large amount of energy is needed

to heat water and produce evaporation (see Chapter 2). If you get overheated on a summer day, splashing water on your skin and sweating will allow you to use evaporative heat loss to cool your body. Conversely, getting wet on a cold day can be deadly. The water on your skin absorbs so much heat from your body that your temperature may drop dangerously.

Heat exchange is critical in animal physiology because individuals that get too hot or too cold may die. Overheating can cause enzymes and other proteins to denature and cease functioning. It may also lead to excessive water loss and dehydration. A sharp drop in body temperature, in contrast, can slow enzyme function and energy production. In humans, both heat stroke and hypothermia ("under-heating") are life-threatening conditions.

Although most organisms conform to the environmental temperature, some animals can regulate body temperature to keep it in an optimal range. Let's take a closer look.

## Variation in Thermoregulation

The ability of animals to **thermoregulate,** or control body temperature, varies widely. Two ways to organize this variation are by examining (1) how animals obtain heat, and (2) whether body temperature is held constant.

An **endotherm** ("inner-heat") produces adequate heat to warm its own tissues, while an **ectotherm** ("outer-heat") relies principally on heat gained from the environment. Endotherms and ectotherms represent two extremes along a continuum of heat sources. Many animals fall somewhere in between.

There are also two extremes on a continuum describing whether animals hold their body temperature constant: **Homeotherms** ("alike-heat") keep their body temperature constant, while **heterotherms** ("different-heat") allow their body temperature to rise or fall depending on environmental conditions.

Humans, along with most birds and most other mammals, are strictly endothermic homeotherms. These species produce their own heat and maintain a constant body temperature. In contrast, most freshwater and terrestrial invertebrates, fishes, amphibians, and reptiles are ectothermic heterotherms whose body temperatures change throughout the day and seasonally. But many animal species lie somewhere between these extremes:

- Some desert-adapted mammals, such as the oryx featured in the introduction to this chapter, allow their body temperature to rise during the hotter part of the day—meaning they are somewhat heterothermic.

- Small mammals that inhabit cold climates lose heat rapidly because their surface area is large relative to their volume. To survive when temperatures are cold, species such as dormice reduce their metabolic rate and allow their body temperature to drop, a form of heterothermy. This condition is called **torpor.** In animals in which torpor persists for weeks or months, it is called **hibernation.**

- Naked mole rats are mammals, but lack insulation because they have no fur. They live in underground tunnels and allow their body temperature to rise and fall with burrow

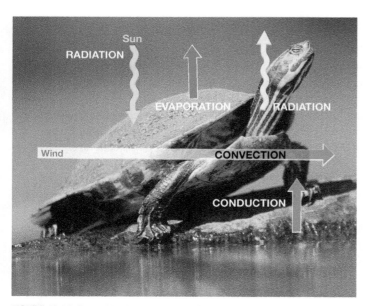

**FIGURE 42.14 Four Methods of Heat Exchange.** The arrows indicate the direction of heat exchange.

**(a)** A hornet preys on a honeybee.

**(b)** A swarm of bees surrounds a hornet ...

**(c)** ... forming a hot defensive ball.

1 mm

**FIGURE 42.15 Honeybees Use Heat to Kill Predators.**

temperatures. They are heterothermic and intermediate between ectotherms and endotherms.

- Japanese honeybees exhibit heterothermy when defending their hives from predatory hornets. The honeybees swarm an invading hornet and contract their flight muscles repeatedly to collectively produce heat endothermically (**FIGURE 42.15**). The temperature within the swarm rises to 47°C (117°F), killing the hornet but not the honeybees, which can tolerate temperatures up to 50°C (122°F).

Even in a homeothermic endotherm such as a mammal or bird, body temperature can vary widely in different body regions. When a Canada goose is standing on ice, its feet may be at a temperature of just 9°C, even though its body core is at 35°C. Similar variations exist in tuna and mackerel. These fish are ectotherms but generate heat to warm certain sections of their bodies, such as their eyes or swimming muscles.

## Endothermy and Ectothermy: A Closer Look

Endotherms can warm themselves because their basal metabolic rates are extremely high—the heat given off by the high rate of chemical reactions is enough to warm the body. Mammals and birds retain this heat because they have elaborate insulating structures such as feathers or fur.

Ectotherms can also generate heat as a by-product of metabolism. The amount of heat they generate is small compared with the amount generated by endotherms, however, because ectotherms have relatively low metabolic rates. The most important sources of heat gain in ectotherms are radiation and conduction: Ectotherms bask in sunlight or lie on warm rocks or soil.

Endothermy and ectothermy are best understood as contrasting adaptive strategies. Because endotherms maintain a high body temperature at all times, they can be active in winter and at night. Their high metabolic rates also allow them to sustain high levels of aerobic activities, such as running or flying.

These abilities come at a cost, however: To fuel their high metabolic rates, endotherms have to obtain large quantities of energy-rich food. The energy used to produce heat is then unavailable for other energy-demanding processes, such as reproduction and growth.

In contrast, ectotherms are able to thrive with much lower intakes of food. And because they are not oxidizing food to provide heat, they can use a greater proportion of their total energy intake to support reproduction.

What's the downside of ectothermy? Chemical reaction rates are temperature dependent, so muscle activity and digestion slow dramatically as the body temperature of an ectotherm drops. As a result, ectotherms are more vulnerable to predation in cold weather and in general are less successful than endotherms at inhabiting cold environments or remaining active in cool nighttime temperatures.

In short, each suite of adaptations has advantages and disadvantages. Like all adaptations, endothermy and ectothermy involve trade-offs.

## Temperature Homeostasis in Endotherms

Thermoregulation is an important aspect of homeostasis in many animals. **FIGURE 42.16** illustrates how the sensor–integrator–effector components of mammals function in thermoregulation.

Temperature receptors located throughout the body constantly monitor information about body temperature. For example, temperature receptors in the skin sense cooling or heating, and they respond by altering the pattern of electrical signals that they send to adjacent neurons. Receptors in the brain region called the **hypothalamus** respond in a similar fashion to changes in blood temperature.

The electrical signals that originate with temperature receptors are transmitted to an integrator, also located in the hypothalamus. Current evidence indicates that separate centers in the hypothalamus of the brain sense and integrate increases and decreases in body temperature.

If a mammal is cold, cells in the hypothalamus send signals to effectors that return body temperature to the set point. Signals from the hypothalamus might induce shivering to generate

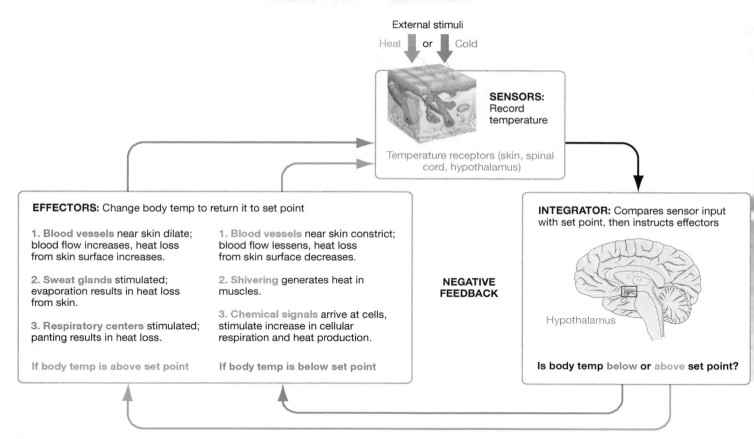

**FIGURE 42.16 Mammals Regulate Temperature through Negative Feedback.** In mammals, a set point for temperature is maintained by a complex negative feedback system that includes integrators in the anterior and posterior hypothalamus and sensors located throughout the body. The set point varies among species, from 30°C in monotremes to over 39°C in rabbits.

warmth, and fluffing of fur or feathers to improve insulation and retain heat. Signals from the same or nearby cells can also result in the release of blood-borne chemical signals that increase the rate at which cellular respiration takes place throughout the body—generating more body heat.

But if the same individual is too hot, an integrator in the hypothalamus sends signals that initiate sweating or panting—responses that cool the body. Other signals can induce behavioral changes that slow heat production, such as seeking shade or a cool burrow and then resting. Within cells, temperature spikes that are dramatic enough to denature proteins may activate **heat-shock proteins** (introduced in Chapter 3). Heat-shock proteins speed the refolding of proteins—a key step in the recovery process.

In response to either cooling or heating, behavioral and physiological responses move the body temperature back toward the set point via negative feedback. Figure 42.16 makes several points about the effectors that maintain homeostasis:

- It is common to observe redundancy in feedback systems—there are usually several ways to change a parameter.

- Feedback systems usually work in "antagonistic pairs": One set of responses increases a parameter while a corresponding set of responses decreases it.

- Input from sensors and integrators is constant, so feedback systems are constantly making fine adjustments relative to the set point.

## Countercurrent Heat Exchangers

Homeothermic endotherms such as birds and mammals have sophisticated systems for thermoregulation. One of their most impressive adaptations allows them to minimize heat loss from limbs. Heat loss is a particularly important problem for mammals that live in aquatic environments. If you've ever gone swimming in cold water, you can appreciate the problem faced by seals, otters, and whales. Water is such an effective conductor of heat that aquatic organisms lose metabolic heat rapidly. To conserve heat, otters have dense, water-repellent fur that maintains a layer of trapped air next to the skin. Seals and whales are insulated by thick layers of fatty blubber. In addition, some marine mammals have specially arranged blood vessels that minimize heat loss.

**An Example: Gray Whale Tongues** Gray whales have a feature that minimizes heat loss from their tongue, which is exposed to cold water during feeding. The tongue contains bundles of arteries and veins. Each bundle contains an artery that carries warm, oxygenated blood from the body core. The artery is encircled by

**(a)** Tongue of gray whale

Cross section of blood vessels of tongue

Arteries are surrounded by veins in each bundle

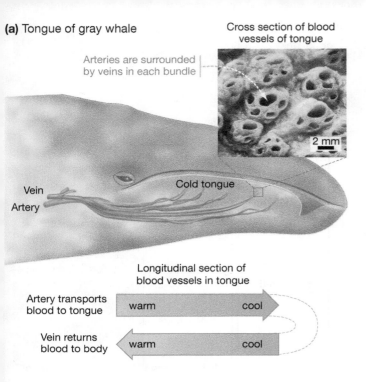

2 mm

Cold tongue

Vein
Artery

Longitudinal section of blood vessels in tongue

Artery transports blood to tongue

warm ────────── cool

Vein returns blood to body

warm ────────── cool

**(b)** Contrasting countercurrent with "concurrent" heat exchange

**Countercurrent flow:**
small gradients are maintained

**"Concurrent" flow:**
large gradients disappear quickly

33° 32° 31° 30° 29° 28°      33° 31° 30° 30° 30° 30°

heat

32° 31° 30° 29° 28° 27°      27° 29° 30° 30° 30° 30°

**FIGURE 42.17 Countercurrent Exchangers Conserve Heat.**
**(a)** Bundles of arteries and veins in whale tongues form heat exchangers that minimize heat loss from the tongue to the cold ocean water during feeding. **(b)** Countercurrent arrangements are much more efficient than "concurrent" arrangements. The data given here are hypothetical.

smaller veins, which transport cool blood from the tongue surface back toward the body core (**FIGURE 42.17a**).

The key is that the two types of blood vessel are arranged in an antiparallel fashion. Vessels with warm blood traveling out to the tongue are in close contact with vessels containing cool blood traveling back to the body.

This type of arrangement, with fluids flowing through adjacent pipes in opposite directions, is called a **countercurrent exchanger.** The "exchanger" part of the name is apt because in a case like the whale's tongue, heat is exchanged between the warm blood in the artery and the cool blood in the veins.

To see how the countercurrent exchange system works, study the longitudinal section in **FIGURE 42.17b**. Note that the fluid that enters the countercurrent heat exchanger is initially warm but steadily transfers heat to the adjacent, cooler fluid flowing in the opposite direction. There is a warmer-to-cooler gradient between the two currents at every point along the length of the countercurrent exchanger.

If the two solutions ran in the same direction, as in the right side of Figure 42.17b, the gradient between the two solutions would disappear quickly as the source current cooled and the recipient current heated. Countercurrent exchangers, including heat exchangers, are efficient because they maintain a gradient between the two fluids along their entire length.

**A Multiplier Effect** A second key point about countercurrent heat exchangers concerns the temperature differential between the solutions. Although the differential is small at any point along the pipes, there is a large temperature differential from one end of each pipe to the other.

In effect, small differences in heat along the length of the exchanger sum up to create a large overall temperature gradient from beginning to end. The longer the system, the greater the overall differential will be. To highlight this property, the systems are sometimes called countercurrent multipliers.

Similar heat-conserving arrangements of arteries and veins are found in the flippers of whales and dolphins, and in the legs of many mammals and birds that live in cold terrestrial environments.

Countercurrent exchangers are just one of many sophisticated adaptations you'll encounter in this unit—structures and systems that allow animals to thrive in a wide array of environments.

check your understanding

**If you understand that . . .**

- Two major aspects of temperature regulation vary among animal species: the amount of heat generated by the animal's own tissues and the degree to which body temperature varies over time.
- Negative feedback allows endothermic homeotherms to maintain homeostasis with respect to body temperature.
- Countercurrent heat exchangers are efficient adaptations for minimizing heat loss from extremities.

✔ **You should be able to . . .**

1. Discuss the advantages and disadvantages of endothermy and ectothermy.
2. Predict how the temperature of a whale's tongue would change if it employed concurrent rather than countercurrent flow of blood in its arteries and veins. Explain.

*Answers are available in Appendix A.*

## If you understand . . .

### 42.1 Form, Function, and Adaptation

- Animal structures and their functions represent adaptations, which are heritable traits that improve survival and reproduction in a certain environment.
- Adaptations involve trade-offs, or inescapable compromises between traits.
- Acclimatization is a reversible response to the environment that improves physiological function in that environment.

✓ You should be able to provide examples of an adaptation and acclimatization of a mammal to a cold environment.

### 42.2 Tissues, Organs, and Systems: How Does Structure Correlate with Function?

- Cells with a common function are grouped together into four general types of tissue: connective tissue, nervous tissue, muscle tissue, and epithelial tissue.
- Epithelium forms the interface between the animal's external and internal environments.
- Organs are structures that are composed of two or more tissues that together perform specific tasks.
- Organ systems comprise organs that work together in an integrated fashion to perform one or more functions.

✓ You should be able to predict the effect of a drug that loosens the tight junctions between epithelial cells.

### 42.3 How Does Body Size Affect Animal Physiology?

- Large animals have smaller surface area/volume ratios than small animals. As animals grow, the volume increases more rapidly than the surface area.
- Large animals have low mass-specific metabolic rates, because they have a relatively small surface area for exchanging the oxygen and nutrients required to support metabolism, the wastes produced by metabolism, and heat.
- The relatively high surface area of small animals means that they lose heat extremely rapidly.

✓ You should be able to explain why it would be impossible for a gorilla the size of King Kong to have fur. (In answering this question, explain how the surface area/volume ratio of a normal-sized gorilla would compare to Kong's; then relate this to the role of surface area and volume in heat generation and transfer and the function of fur.)

### 42.4 Homeostasis

- Homeostasis refers to relatively constant physical and chemical conditions inside the body.
- Homeostasis can be achieved by conformation to a constant environment or by regulation in a fluctuating environment.
- Animals have a set point, or target value, for blood pH, tissue oxygen concentration, nutrient concentrations, temperature, and other parameters.
- When a condition in the body is not at its set point, negative feedback occurs. Responses to negative feedback return conditions to the set point and result in homeostasis.

✓ You should be able to explain how, due to acclimatization as well as adaptation, the homeostatic system for maintaining body temperature in a species of mammal might change as global temperatures rise.

### 42.5 How Do Animals Regulate Body Temperature?

- Animals vary from endothermic to ectothermic and from homeothermic to heterothermic.
- Most mammals have a set point for body temperature. If an individual overheats, it will pant or sweat and seek a cool environment; if an individual is cold, it will shiver, bask in sunlight, or fluff its fur.
- Countercurrent heat exchangers work by placing warm and cool fluids next to each other and running in opposite directions.

✓ The dinosaur *Apatosaurus* is one of the largest terrestrial animals that has ever lived—over 20 m in length and weighing over 20 metric tons. Do you believe that *Apatosaurus* was homeothermic or heterothermic? Explain.

### MB MasteringBiology

1. **MasteringBiology Assignments**

   **Tutorials and Activities** Connective Tissue; Epithelial Tissue; Homeostasis; Muscle Tissue; Nervous Tissue; Overview of Animal Tissues; Surface Area/Volume Relationships; Thermoregulation

   **Questions** Reading Quizzes, Blue-Thread Questions, Test Bank

2. **eText** Read your book online, search, take notes, highlight text, and more.

3. **The Study Area** Practice Test, Cumulative Test, BioFlix® 3-D Animations, Videos, Activities, Audio Glossary, Word Study Tools, Art

# You should be able to . . .

1. True or False: The increase in red blood cell count in tourists visiting Tibet is an example of acclimatization.

2. _____ tissues form the interface between the inside of an animal's body and the environment.

3. As an animal gets larger, which of the following occurs?
   a. Its surface area grows more rapidly than its volume.
   b. Its volume grows more rapidly than its surface area.
   c. Its volume and surface area increase in perfect proportion to each other.
   d. Its volume increases, but its total surface area decreases.

4. Which of the following best describes the set point in a homeostatic system?
   a. the cells that collect and transmit information about the state of the system
   b. the cells that receive information about the state of the system and that direct changes to the system
   c. the various components that produce appropriate changes in the system
   d. the target or "normal" value of the parameter in question

5. What does it mean to say that an animal is a heterothermic endotherm?
   a. Its body temperature varies, but most of its heat is produced by its own tissues.
   b. Its body temperature varies because it gains most of its heat from sources outside its body.
   c. Its body temperature does not vary, because most of its heat is produced by its own tissues.
   d. Its body temperature does not vary, even though it gains most of its heat from sources outside its body.

6. Which of the following is an advantage that ectotherms have over endotherms of the same size?
   a. They require much less food.
   b. They are less vulnerable to predation events during cold weather.
   c. They can remain active in cold weather or at nighttime—when temperatures cool.
   d. They have higher metabolic rates and grow much more quickly.

7. Why is epithelium a particularly important tissue in achieving homeostasis with respect to temperature?

8. The metabolic rate of a frog in summer (at 35°C) is about eight times higher than in winter (at 5°C). Compare and contrast the individual's ability to move, exchange gases, and digest food at the two temperatures. During which season will the frog require more food energy, and why?

9. Consider the following:
   - absorptive sections of digestive tract
   - capillaries
   - beaks of Galápagos finches
   - fish gills

   In each case, how does the structure relate to the function?

10. Why is the surface area/volume ratio different in a small sphere versus a large sphere? If materials diffuse into and out of each sphere, in which of the two will diffusion occur more efficiently relative to the volume? Explain your answer.

11. QUANTITATIVE Consider three cubes with lengths of 1 cm, 5 cm, and 10 cm. Calculate the surface area and the volume of each cube, and plot them on a graph with length on the x-axis and surface area and volume on the y-axis. Explain how the graph shows the relationship between size and surface area/volume ratio.

12. Which of the following is an example of negative feedback? Explain why each is or is not negative feedback.
    a. Uterine contractions during childbirth stimulate release of a hormone that stimulates more uterine contractions.
    b. A viral infection stimulates the hypothalamus to increase the set point for body temperature.
    c. High blood sugar concentrations stimulate the release of the hormone insulin, which stimulates the sugars to move from the blood into cells.
    d. The body temperature of the Arabian oryx rises during the hottest parts of the day.

13. When food is scarce, bigger *Geospiza fortis* (medium ground finches) win contests over seeds. Biologists have documented that there is strong natural selection in favor of large body size under these conditions, and that the finch population evolves in response. If so, why aren't *G. fortis* a lot bigger than they are?

14. What data would you need to collect in order to document that adaptation is occurring in a particular population of lizards, as the warming associated with global climate change intensifies?

15. An engineer has to design a system for dissipating heat from a new type of car engine that runs particularly hot. Recall that heat is gained and lost as a function of surface area. Suggest ideas to consider that are inspired by biological structures with exceptionally high surface area/volume ratios.

16. Suppose a friend of yours is trying to decide whether to buy a pet turtle or a pet mouse. In making the decision, all he cares about is how much it will cost to feed the animal. Your friend says he can't decide because the two animals weigh the same and their food costs the same per pound. As a biologist, what's your advice?
    a. Buy the turtle, because it is an ectotherm and will therefore consume less food than the mouse.
    b. Buy the turtle, because it is an endotherm and will therefore consume less food than the mouse.
    c. Buy the mouse, because it is an ectotherm and will therefore consume less food than the turtle.
    d. Buy the mouse, because it is an endotherm and will therefore consume less food than the turtle.

# 43 Water and Electrolyte Balance in Animals

**In this chapter you will learn that**

> Different habitats pose different challenges with regard to maintaining water and electrolyte balance

*asking* ↓

How do animals control the concentration of water and salt in their bodies? **43.1**

*by reviewing* ↓

Diffusion  Osmosis  Transport across membranes

*looking closer at* ↓

Marine fishes **43.2**

*comparing to* ↓

Freshwater fishes **43.3**

*comparing to* ↓

Terrestrial insects **43.4**

*and to* ↓

Terrestrial vertebrates— the mammalian kidney **43.5**

Terrestrial animals lose water every time they breathe, defecate, and urinate. For many animals, drinking is an important way to gain water and achieve homeostasis. This chapter explores how terrestrial and aquatic animals maintain water balance.

This chapter is part of the Big Picture. See how on pages 840–841.

The chemical reactions that make life possible occur in an aqueous solution. If the balance of water and dissolved substances in the solution is disturbed, those chemical reactions—and life itself—may stop. Humans can stay alive for weeks without eating but can survive just three days without drinking water. If hurricanes introduce enough freshwater to the ocean shore to disrupt normal salt concentrations, marine animals die. Maintaining water balance is a matter of life or death.

An animal achieves water balance when its intake of water equals its loss of water. Water balance is an important element in homeostasis—the ability to keep cells and tissues in constant and favorable conditions.

✔ When you see this checkmark, stop and test yourself. Answers are available in Appendix A.

Water balance is intimately associated with sustaining a balanced concentration of electrolytes throughout the body. An **electrolyte** is a compound that dissociates into ions when dissolved in water. Electrolytes got their name because they conduct electrical current.

In many animals, the most abundant electrolytes are sodium ($Na^+$), chloride ($Cl^-$), potassium ($K^+$), and calcium ($Ca^{2+}$). Cells require precise concentrations of these ions to function normally. In humans, electrolyte imbalances can lead to muscle spasms, confusion, irregular heart rhythms, fatigue, paralysis, or even death.

Water and electrolyte balance is also associated with excretion. Animals produce urine to excrete wastes. Urine contains water, so excretion of urine inevitably leads to water loss. The amount of water lost in the urine of an animal depends both on its hydration state and on the type of wastes it produces.

This chapter is focused on a single question: How do animals maintain water and electrolyte balance in marine, freshwater, and terrestrial environments? Answering it will introduce you to some of the most complex and important homeostatic systems known. You can review the importance of maintaining water and electrolyte balance in the Big Picture of Plant and Animal Form and Function, on pages 840–841.

## 43.1 Osmoregulation and Excretion

In organisms, electrolytes and water move by two processes—diffusion and osmosis (introduced in Chapter 6).

**Diffusion** is the net movement of substances from regions of higher concentration to regions of lower concentration.

**Osmosis** is a special case of diffusion. It is the net movement of water from regions of higher water concentration to regions of lower water concentration, across a selectively permeable membrane.

A membrane that exhibits **selective permeability,** such as a phospholipid bilayer, is a membrane that some solutes can cross more easily than other solutes can. When either diffusion or osmosis occurs, net movement of ions and molecules occurs along their **concentration gradient.**

**FIGURE 43.1a** illustrates how dissolved substances, or **solutes,** move down their concentration gradients via diffusion across a selectively permeable membrane. When the solutes are randomly distributed throughout the solutions on both sides of the membrane, equilibrium is established. Molecules continue to move back and forth across the membrane at equilibrium, but at equal rates.

As **FIGURE 43.1b** shows, water can also move down its concentration gradient (see Chapter 6). The concentration of dissolved substances in a solution, measured in osmoles[1] per liter, is the solution's **osmolarity.** Because solutes interact with water molecules, an increase in solute concentration reduces the amount of water available for osmosis, effectively lowering water concentration. If dissolved substances are separated by a selectively permeable membrane and the solutes cannot cross that membrane, water moves from areas of lower osmolarity—that is, where solute concentrations are lower and water concentration is higher—to areas of higher osmolarity—where solute concentrations are higher and water concentration is lower.

Now let's examine how osmosis and diffusion affect water and ion balance living in different environments.

### What Is Osmotic Stress?

Osmotic stress occurs when the concentration of dissolved substances in a cell or tissue is abnormal. It means that water and solute concentrations are different from their set point.

Many organisms respond to osmotic stress by osmoregulating, just as they respond to heat or cold stress by thermoregulating (see Chapter 42). **Osmoregulation** is the process by which living organisms control the concentration of water and electrolytes in their bodies.

Not all animals encounter osmotic stress. For many marine invertebrates such as sponges, jellyfish, and flatworms, achieving homeostasis with respect to water and electrolyte balance is straightforward. Seawater is a fairly constant ionic and osmotic environment, and it nearly matches the normal electrolyte concentrations found within these animals. These species are **osmoconformers.**

Seawater is **isosmotic** with respect to tissue in these species. Stated another way, solute concentrations inside and outside these animals are equal. Because the tissues of osmoconforming marine invertebrates are isosmotic to seawater, diffusion and osmosis don't alter water and electrolyte balance and induce osmotic stress.

### Osmotic Stress in Seawater, in Freshwater, and on Land

In contrast to most marine invertebrates, marine bony fishes are **osmoregulators.** These fishes actively regulate osmolarity inside their bodies to achieve homeostasis.

By osmoregulating, marine bony fishes keep the osmolarity of their tissues lower than seawater. The difference in osmolarity is most important in the gills, which are organs involved in gas exchange. For gas exchange to occur with the environment, the epithelial cells on the surfaces of the gills must be in direct contact with seawater. But because there is a large difference in the concentration of solutes between the inside of each cell and the seawater outside, water tends to flow by osmosis out of the gill epithelium (**FIGURE 43.2**).

Seawater is **hyperosmotic** in comparison to the tissues of marine fishes—the solution inside the body contains fewer solutes than does the solution outside. If the water that marine fishes lose across their gills is not replaced, the cells will shrivel and die. These species face a trade-off between gas exchange and water and electrolyte balance.

Marine fishes replace the lost water by drinking large quantities of seawater. Drinking brings in excess electrolytes, however.

[1] The unit osmole is similar to a mole except that it takes into account molecules that dissociate in solution. For example, because NaCl dissociates into $Na^+$ and $Cl^-$ in solution, adding 1 mole of NaCl is equivalent to adding 2 osmoles.

## (a) PROCESS: DIFFUSION

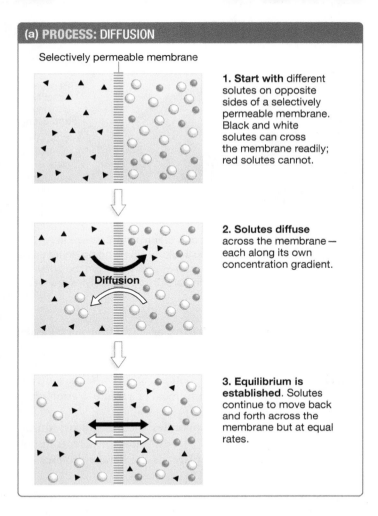

Selectively permeable membrane

**1. Start with** different solutes on opposite sides of a selectively permeable membrane. Black and white solutes can cross the membrane readily; red solutes cannot.

**2. Solutes diffuse** across the membrane — each along its own concentration gradient.

**Diffusion**

**3. Equilibrium is established.** Solutes continue to move back and forth across the membrane but at equal rates.

## (b) PROCESS: OSMOSIS

Selectively permeable membrane

Low osmolarity | High osmolarity

**1. Start with** more solute on one side of a selectively permeable membrane than the other. In this case, the solute cannot cross the membrane.

**2. Water diffuses** across the membrane — from the region of lower osmolarity (lower solute concentration) to the region of higher osmolarity (higher solute concentration).

**Osmosis**

**FIGURE 43.1 Solutes Move Down a Concentration Gradient via Diffusion; Water Moves Down a Concentration Gradient via Osmosis. (a)** Diffusion occurs any time a solute is at higher concentration in one location than another. **(b)** Osmosis is a special case of diffusion involving the movement of water across a selectively permeable membrane.

✔ **QUESTION** Why doesn't the presence of red molecules on the right side of part (a) affect the movement of the black and white molecules?

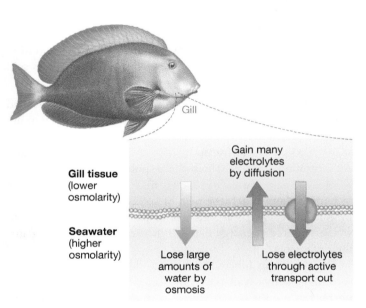

Gill

**Gill tissue** (lower osmolarity)

**Seawater** (higher osmolarity)

Gain many electrolytes by diffusion

Lose large amounts of water by osmosis

Lose electrolytes through active transport out

**FIGURE 43.2 Marine Fishes Lose Water by Osmosis and Gain Electrolytes by Diffusion.**

Electrolyte balance is thrown even further out of whack because ions and other solutes diffuse into the gill epithelium, following a concentration gradient from seawater to tissues.

To rid themselves of these excess electrolytes, marine fishes have to actively pump ions out of their bodies and back into seawater, using membrane proteins found in the gill epithelium.

Freshwater fishes osmoregulate in an environment dramatically different from the ocean. Marine fishes are under osmotic stress because they lose water and gain solutes; freshwater fishes are under osmotic stress because they gain water and lose solutes.

Why? In the gills of freshwater fishes, epithelial cells contain more solutes than the solution outside. The freshwater is **hyposmotic** relative to the fishes' tissues. As a result, the fishes gain water via osmosis across the gill epithelium (**FIGURE 43.3**, see page 864), which puts the body under osmotic stress. Just as in marine fishes, there is a trade-off between gas exchange and osmoregulation.

If a freshwater fish does not get rid of incoming water, its cells will burst and the individual will die. To achieve homeostasis and survive, freshwater fishes excrete large amounts of water in their urine and do not drink.

In addition to gaining water, freshwater fishes undergo osmotic stress because ions and other solutes tend to diffuse out of the gill epithelium into the environment, along a concentration

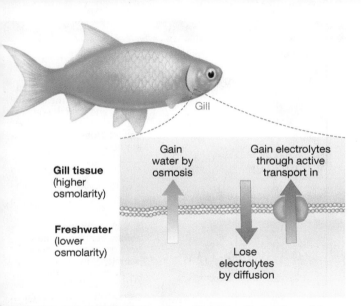

**Gill tissue** (higher osmolarity)

Gain water by osmosis

Gain electrolytes through active transport in

Lose electrolytes by diffusion

**Freshwater** (lower osmolarity)

**FIGURE 43.3 Freshwater Fishes Gain Water by Osmosis and Lose Electrolytes by Diffusion.**

gradient. Freshwater animals must replace electrolytes that are lost by obtaining them in food or by actively transporting them from the surrounding water—usually across the gills.

What about land animals? In terms of water balance, terrestrial environments are similar to the ocean. Land animals constantly lose water to the environment, just like many marine animals do. In this case, however, the process involved is not osmosis but evaporation (see Chapter 42).

The epithelial cells that line a turtle's lung and a fruit fly's gas exchange structures have a moist surface, in order to protect the integrity of their plasma membranes and to facilitate diffusion of gases across respiratory epithelia. Because the atmosphere is almost always drier than the wet gas exchange surface, terrestrial animals lose water by evaporation. Once again, there is a trade-off between breathing and balance of water and electrolytes.

Water balance is further complicated because animals lose water in the form of urine, and some terrestrial species lose additional water when they sweat or pant to lower their body temperature (**FIGURE 43.4**). The lost water has to be replaced by drinking, ingesting water in food, or gaining metabolic water—the $H_2O$ produced during cellular respiration (see Chapter 9). The relative importance of each of these methods of replacing water depends on the animal. For example, desert animals like the Arabian oryx (see Chapter 42) do not have access to drinking water throughout much of the year, so they rely more on ingested and metabolic water.

## How Do Electrolytes and Water Move across Cell Membranes?

What molecular mechanisms allow animals to cope with the diverse challenges they face in maintaining water and electrolyte balance? You might recall from earlier chapters that solutes

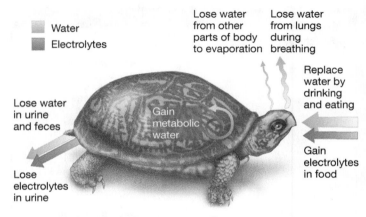

Water

Electrolytes

Lose water from other parts of body to evaporation

Lose water from lungs during breathing

Gain metabolic water

Replace water by drinking and eating

Lose water in urine and feces

Gain electrolytes in food

Lose electrolytes in urine

**FIGURE 43.4 Maintaining Water and Electrolyte Balance in Terrestrial Environments Is Particularly Challenging.** In terrestrial environments, animals lose water by evaporation from the body surface and as water vapor during breathing. Electrolytes are lost primarily in the urine and feces.

move across membranes by passive or active transport. **Passive transport** is driven by diffusion along an electrochemical gradient and does not require an expenditure of energy in the form of ATP. **Active transport,** in contrast, occurs when a source of energy like ATP powers the movement of a solute to establish an electrochemical gradient.

Because ions and large molecules such as glucose do not cross phospholipid bilayers readily, most passive transport and all active transport take place via membrane proteins (see Chapter 6).

- In many cases, passive transport occurs through **channels**— proteins that form a pore, or opening, that selectively admits specific ions or molecules (**FIGURE 43.5a**).

- Passive transport also occurs via **carrier proteins,** which are transmembrane proteins that bind a specific ion or molecule and transport it across the membrane by undergoing a conformational change.

- When solutes move from an area of high to low concentration via channels or carrier proteins, **facilitated diffusion** is said to occur.

Active transport is based on membrane proteins called pumps, which change conformation when they bind ATP or are phosphorylated (**FIGURE 43.5b**). This energy-demanding change in shape allows them to transport ions or molecules against their concentration gradient. The **sodium–potassium pump,** or $Na^+/K^+$-ATPase (introduced in Chapter 6), is a very important type of pump in animals. Movement of sodium and potassium ions by $Na^+/K^+$-ATPase is an example of **primary active transport,** where a source of energy like ATP is used to move ions against their gradients.

Once a pump has established an electrochemical gradient, **secondary active transport** can occur. Specifically, a **cotransporter** can use the energy stored in an electrochemical gradient across a cell membrane to transport a different solute *against* its

**(a)** Passive transport is based on diffusion down a gradient.

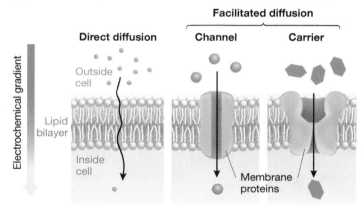

**Facilitated diffusion**

**Direct diffusion** | **Channel** | **Carrier**

Electrochemical gradient

Outside cell

Lipid bilayer

Inside cell

Membrane proteins

**(b)** Active transport requires an energy source to move molecules against a gradient.

**Secondary active transport**
(cotransport; driven by energy from gradient)

**Primary active transport**
(driven by energy from ATP)

**Pump** | **Symporter** | **Antiporter**

Electrochemical gradient

ATP ADP + $P_i$

**FIGURE 43.5 Mechanisms of Passive and Active Transport.**
**(a)** In passive transport, solutes diffuse along their electrochemical gradient either directly or through a membrane protein.
**(b)** In primary active transport, a pump uses ATP to move solutes against their electrochemical gradients. In secondary active transport (cotransport), energy stored in an electrochemical gradient for one molecule is used to move another molecule against its gradient.

electrochemical gradient. A cotransporter that moves solutes in the same direction is called a **symporter;** a cotransporter that moves solutes in opposite directions is called an **antiporter.**

How does water move? To date, there are no known mechanisms for actively transporting water across plasma membranes. Instead, cells use pumps to transport ions and set up an osmotic gradient; water then follows by osmosis—often through the specialized membrane channels called **aquaporins** (see Chapter 6). In essence, cells move water by moving solutes.

The body excretes excess solutes, along with waste products, using a urinary system. Because solutes and wastes often must be dissolved in water to be excreted, water balance is fundamentally related to excretion.

## Types of Nitrogenous Wastes: Impact on Water Balance

Animal cells contain amino acids and nucleic acids that are used to synthesize proteins, RNA, and DNA. Excess amino acids and nucleic acids can be broken down in catabolic reactions that result in the production of **ammonia** ($NH_3$). Ammonia is toxic to cells, because at high concentrations it raises the pH of intracellular and extracellular fluids enough to poison enzymes.

Because ammonia must be dissolved in water, excretion of ammonia inevitably leads to water loss. However, the amount of water lost during excretion depends on the method of ammonia excretion.

**Forms of Nitrogenous Waste Vary among Species**  How do animals get rid of ammonia safely and efficiently? Different species solve the problem in different ways (see **TABLE 43.1**, page 866).

- In freshwater fishes, ammonia is diluted to low concentration and excreted in watery urine.

- In freshwater and marine fishes, ammonia diffuses across the gills into the surrounding water along a concentration gradient.

- In mammals (including humans) and adult amphibians, enzyme-catalyzed reactions convert ammonia to a much less toxic compound called **urea,** which is excreted in urine.

- In terrestrial arthropods, birds, and other reptiles, reactions convert ammonia to **uric acid,** the white, paste-like substance that you have probably seen in bird feces.

Uric acid is a particularly interesting form of nitrogenous waste. Compared with urea and ammonia, uric acid is extremely insoluble in water—which explains why it is so difficult to wash bird droppings off a car. As a result, birds, snakes, lizards, and terrestrial arthropods can get rid of excess nitrogen while losing little water.

**Why Do Nitrogenous Wastes Vary among Species?**  The type of nitrogenous waste produced by an animal correlates with its lineage—its evolutionary history. For example, mammals excrete urea while reptiles (including birds) and insects excrete uric acid (Table 43.1).

Evolutionary history is not the entire story, however. Waste production is also related to the habitat that a species occupies, and thus the amount of osmotic stress it endures.

- Terrestrial birds conserve water by excreting about 90 percent of their nitrogenous waste as uric acid and only 3–4 percent as ammonia, but aquatic birds such as ducks excrete just 50 percent of their excess nitrogen as uric acid and 30 percent as ammonia.

- Tadpoles are aquatic and excrete ammonia, but many adult frogs and toads are terrestrial and excrete urea.

- Production of urea and uric acid is particularly common in animals—such as reptiles—that live in dry habitats.

| Attribute | Ammonia | Urea | Uric Acid |
|---|---|---|---|
| Solubility in water (moles/liter) | high | medium | very low |
| Water loss (amount required for excretion of waste) | high | medium | very low |
| Energy cost (amount of ATP required) | low | high | high |
| Toxicity | high | medium | low |
| Groups where it is the primary waste | bony fishes, aquatic invertebrates | mammals, amphibians, cartilaginous fishes | birds and other reptiles, most terrestrial insects and spiders (arthropods) |
| Method of synthesis | product of breakdown of amino acids and nucleic acids | synthesized in liver, starting with amino groups from amino acids | synthesis starts with amino acids and nucleic acids |
| Method of excretion | in urine, and diffuses across gills | in urine (mammals); diffuses across gills (sharks) | with feces |

To make sense of these observations, biologists point out that there is a fitness trade-off between the energetic cost of excreting each type of waste and the benefit of conserving water. Ammonia excretion requires a large water loss but little energy expenditure, because the molecule isn't processed by enzymes. Uric acid excretion, in contrast, requires almost no loss of water but a sophisticated series of enzyme-catalyzed, energy-demanding reactions. Different trade-offs are favored in different environments.

Now that you have a basic understanding of the osmoregulatory and excretory challenges facing animals, let's take a closer look at how marine, freshwater, and terrestrial animals maintain water and electrolyte homeostasis.

## 43.2 Water and Electrolyte Balance in Marine Fishes

Marine fishes experience severe osmotic stress because they live in water with a very high osmolarity. Since their divergence over 400 million years ago, marine bony and cartilaginous fishes have evolved distinct strategies for dealing with osmotic stress.

### Osmoconformation versus Osmoregulation in Marine Fishes

Marine bony fishes are osmoregulators. Recall that they maintain a lower blood osmolarity than seawater by drinking to replace water lost via osmosis, and by actively transporting electrolytes out of the body. This process comes with a significant energetic cost.

Cartilaginous fishes, such as sharks, have a different strategy. They are **osmoconformers**—their blood osmolarity nearly matches that of the sea water. However, the composition of their blood is quite different from seawater. Sharks have low

concentrations of ions in their blood, but they maintain relatively high blood concentrations of urea. This increases their blood osmolarity so that it is isosmotic with seawater. The result? Sharks lose less water by osmosis.

If sharks avoid water loss to the surrounding seawater by osmoconforming, then why don't all marine fishes osmoconform? The answer lies in a biological trade-off (see Chapter 42). Sharks must expend energy to make proteins that protect their cells from the toxic effects of high concentrations of urea. Osmoregulation and osmoconformation are two strategies for living in the ocean, and each has its own costs and benefits.

Even though they are osmoconformers, sharks still maintain relatively low concentrations of salt (NaCl) in their blood. Sharks need to excrete salt because sodium and chloride ions diffuse into their gill cells from seawater, down the concentration gradients for the ions. Research on the molecular mechanism of salt excretion in sharks revealed two key points:

1. The mechanism is general. The salt-excreting system discovered in sharks is found in a wide array of species, including *Homo sapiens*. It is functioning in your kidneys, right now.

2. The mechanism represents a critically important concept in physiology. Plant and animal cells use active transport to set up a strong electrochemical gradient for one ion—typically $Na^+$ in animals and $H^+$ in plants. The sodium or proton gradient is then used to transport a wide array of other substances, without further expenditure of energy.

This is fundamental stuff. Let's dig in.

### How Do Sharks Excrete Salt?

Research on salt excretion in sharks focused on an organ called the **rectal gland,** which secretes a concentrated salt solution. To determine how this gland works, researchers studied it in vitro—meaning outside the shark's body, in a controlled laboratory environment. The basic approach was to dissect rectal glands, immerse them in a solution with a defined composition and osmolarity, and analyze the fluid that the rectal gland produced in response.

Early experiments showed that normal salt excretion occurred only if the solution in the rectal gland contained ATP. This result supported the hypothesis that salt excretion involves active transport. Ions can be concentrated only if they are actively transported against a concentration gradient. The question was, How does concentration occur?

**The Role of Na+/K+-ATPase** An energy-demanding mechanism for salt excretion implies that a protein in the plasma membrane of epithelial cells is actively pumping $Na^+$, $Cl^-$, or both. The best-characterized candidate was the Na+/K+-ATPase.

To test the hypothesis that the sodium–potassium pump is involved in salt excretion by sharks, biologists used a plant defense compound called **ouabain** (pronounced *WAA-bane*). This molecule is toxic to animals because it binds to Na+/K+-ATPase and prevents it from functioning.

Just as predicted, rectal glands that are treated with ouabain stop producing a concentrated salt solution. This was strong evidence that Na+/K+-ATPase is essential for salt excretion.

**A Molecular Model for Salt Excretion** Subsequent work has shown that salt excretion in sharks is a multistep process, summarized in **FIGURE 43.6**.

1. Na+/K+-ATPase pumps sodium ions out of epithelial cells across the basolateral surface, into the extracellular fluid. The pump creates an electrochemical gradient favoring the diffusion of $Na^+$ into the cell. This "master gradient" allows the cell to transport other ions without an additional expenditure of energy.

2. $Na^+$, $Cl^-$, and $K^+$ all enter the cell by secondary active transport through a cotransporter, powered by the $Na^+$ master gradient. Note that this master gradient causes $Na^+$ to diffuse into the cell *along* its electrochemical gradient, allowing $Cl^-$ and $K^+$ to move into the cell *against* their electrochemical gradients. Movement of $Cl^-$ and $K^+$ is possible only because these ions move through a cotransporter with $Na^+$.

3. As $Cl^-$ builds up inside the cell, $Cl^-$ diffuses down its concentration gradient into the lumen of the gland through a chloride channel located in the apical membrane.

4. Following their electrochemical gradient, $Na^+$ ions diffuse into the lumen of the gland through spaces between the cells.

In many animals, epithelial cells that transport sodium and chloride ions contain the same combination of membrane proteins found in the shark rectal gland. These species include

- marine birds and reptiles that drink seawater and excrete NaCl via salt glands in their nostrils;
- marine fishes that excrete salt from their gills (see Figure 43.2);
- mammals that transport salt in their kidneys.

Research on the shark rectal gland also produced an unforeseen benefit for biomedical research. Several years after the shark chloride channel was characterized, investigators identified a human protein called cystic fibrosis transmembrane regulator

**PROCESS: MODEL OF SALT EXCRETION IN SHARK RECTAL GLAND**

Lumen side (interior of gland empties into environment)

Apical membrane

Epithelial cells of rectal gland

Basolateral membrane

Extracellular fluid, near blood vessels

$2K^+$

ATP / ADP

Na+/K+-ATPase

$3Na^+$

$Na^+$ $2Cl^-$ $K^+$

Na+/Cl-/K+ cotransporter

$Cl^-$

Chloride channel

$K^+$

Potassium channel

$Na^+$

1. **Na+/K+-ATPase pumps** $Na^+$ out of cell and $K^+$ into cell, creating an electrochemical gradient favoring diffusion of $Na^+$ into cell and $K^+$ out.

2. **Na+/Cl-/K+ cotransporter**, powered by the gradient favoring $Na^+$ diffusion, brings these three ions from the extracellular fluid into epithelial cells across their basolateral surfaces.

3. **$Cl^-$ diffuses into lumen** along its electrochemical gradient. **$K^+$ diffuses out** through channels in basolateral membrane.

4. **$Na^+$ diffuses into lumen** along its electrochemical gradient.

**FIGURE 43.6 The Shark Rectal Gland Rids the Body of Excess Salt.**

✔**QUESTION** Which of these membrane proteins are involved in (1) primary active transport, (2) secondary active transport, or (3) passive transport?

CFTR). Cystic fibrosis is the most common genetic disease in populations of northern European extraction (see Chapter 6). Although the disease was known to be associated with defects in the CFTR protein, no one knew what the molecule did.

When investigators realized that the amino acid sequence of CFTR is 80 percent identical to that of the shark chloride channel, it was their first hint that CFTR is involved in Cl⁻ transport. Subsequent studies supported the hypothesis that cystic fibrosis results from a defect in a chloride channel. With this result, studies on water and electrolyte balance in sharks shed light on an important human disease.

# 43.3 Water and Electrolyte Balance in Freshwater Fishes

Research on the shark rectal gland and the gills of marine bony fishes has uncovered the molecular mechanisms of salt balance in marine fishes. How do freshwater fishes achieve homeostasis with respect to electrolytes?

## How Do Freshwater Fishes Osmoregulate?

Recall from Figure 43.3 that freshwater fishes have to cope with an osmotic stress that is opposite the challenge facing marine fishes. Freshwater fishes lose electrolytes across their gill epithelium by diffusion across a concentration gradient. To maintain homeostasis, they have to actively transport ions back into the body across the gill epithelium. How do they do this?

**Salmon and Sea Bass as Model Systems** To understand how freshwater fishes gain electrolytes, researchers have focused on sea bass and several species of salmon. Over the course of a lifetime, individuals of these species move between seawater and freshwater. Thus, they move between environments that present dramatically different osmotic stressors.

In marine fishes, specialized cells in the gill epithelium called chloride cells move salt using the combination of membrane proteins illustrated in Figure 43.6. When sea bass and salmon are in seawater, these cells are abundant and active. What happens to these cells when individuals move into freshwater? Do the changes that occur provide any insight into how these species acclimatize to the new environment and avoid dying of osmotic stress?

**A Freshwater Chloride Cell?** Although research is continuing at a brisk pace, recent results support the hypothesis that there is a freshwater version of the classical chloride cell: one that moves ions in the opposite direction of the seawater version. Instead of excreting salt, these cells import it.

Three lines of evidence have accumulated to date:

1. **Osmoregulatory cells may be in different locations.** Young salmon taken from freshwater versus seawater have chloride cells in different locations on the gills. Adult salmon from freshwater versus seawater show the same pattern, and similar changes have been observed in other fish species that switch between freshwater and seawater habitats. The pattern suggests that when the nature of osmotic stress changes, the nature of the gill epithelium changes. Specifically, active pumping of ions takes place in a different population of cells in seawater versus freshwater.

2. **Different forms of Na⁺/K⁺-ATPase may be activated.** The salmon genome contains genes for several different forms of the Na⁺/K⁺-ATPase. There is now strong evidence that different forms are activated when individuals are in seawater versus freshwater.

3. **The orientation of key transport proteins "flips."** In sea bass, researchers have been able to stain epithelial cells to determine the location of the cotransporter illustrated in Figure 43.6—the one that brings Na⁺, Cl⁻, and K⁺ into the cell. When individuals are in seawater, the protein is located in the basolateral side of chloride cells. But when individuals are in freshwater, the protein is located in the apical side (**FIGURE 43.7**).

Taken together, the data suggest that freshwater fishes have a freshwater version of the chloride cell, with different forms of Na⁺/K⁺-ATPase and transporters that result in the import rather than export of ions. Identifying the mechanisms of electrolyte uptake in freshwater fishes is an important challenge for researchers who want to know how aquatic organisms cope with osmotic stress.

**FIGURE 43.7 In the Epithelial Cells of Bass Gills, the Location of a Key Ion Cotransporter Can "Flip."** Changes in the position of the Na⁺/Cl⁻/K⁺ cotransporter help sea bass deal with osmotic stress in both seawater and freshwater environments. (Other membrane channels and pumps are present but not shown here.)

**If you understand that . . .**

- Marine fishes lose water by osmosis. To replace it, they have to drink seawater.
- Marine fishes have to rid themselves of salt. They gain salt when they drink seawater or when sodium and chloride ions diffuse into their cells along a concentration gradient.
- Freshwater fishes gain water by osmosis. They have to rid themselves of excess water by urinating.
- Freshwater fishes lose electrolytes to the surrounding water by diffusion. They gain electrolytes in their food and by active transport from the surrounding water.

**✔ You should be able to . . .**

Predict what happens to the osmolarity of a freshwater fish's tissues when epithelial cells in its gills are treated with ouabain—a molecule that poisons $Na^+/K^+$-ATPase.

*Answers are available in Appendix A.*

## 43.4 Water and Electrolyte Balance in Terrestrial Insects

By studying extreme situations or unusual organisms, biologists can often gain insight into how organisms cope with more moderate environments. In studies on the molecular mechanisms of water and electrolyte balance in terrestrial insects, the most valuable model organisms have been the desert locust and a common household pest called the flour beetle. (You may have seen the larvae of flour beetles, called mealworms, in bags of flour that were not shut tightly enough to keep adults from entering and breeding.)

Desert locusts and flour beetles live in environments where osmotic stress is severe. These insects rarely, if ever, drink—simply because little or no water is available in the habitats they occupy.

How do they maintain water and electrolyte balance? The answer has two parts: They minimize water loss from their body surface, and they carefully regulate the amount of water and electrolytes that they excrete in their urine and feces. Let's look at each issue in turn.

### How Do Insects Minimize Water Loss from the Body Surface?

Terrestrial animals breathe by exposing an extremely thin layer of epithelium to the atmosphere (see Chapter 45). Oxygen diffuses into this epithelium, and carbon dioxide diffuses out. But water constantly leaks across the thin respiratory surface and is lost to the atmosphere via evaporation.

Evaporation from the body surface itself is another threat—a particular challenge to insects, because they are small. Small organisms have a high surface area/volume ratio (see Chapter 42). Insects have a relatively large surface area from which to lose water but a small volume in which to retain it.

How do desert locusts, flour beetles, and other insects minimize water loss during gas exchange? In these species, gas exchange occurs across the membranes of epithelial cells that line the **tracheae,** an extensive system of tubes. The insect tracheal system connects with the atmosphere at openings called **spiracles** (FIGURE 43.8a). Muscles just inside each spiracle open or close the pore, much as guard cells open or close the pores in plant leaves and stems.

When investigators manipulated insects called *Rhodnius* so that their spiracles stayed open and placed the animals in a dry environment, the insects died within three days. These data support the hypothesis that the ability to close spiracles is an important adaptation for minimizing water loss during respiration. If an insect is under osmotic stress, it may be able to close its spiracles and wait until conditions improve before resuming activity.

**FIGURE 43.8b** shows how insects minimize evaporation from the surface of their bodies. This diagram is a cross-sectional view of the exoskeleton of an insect, which consists of a tough,

**(a)** Spiracles can be closed to minimize water loss from tracheae.

**(b)** Except at spiracles, the insect body is covered with wax.

**FIGURE 43.8 In Desert Locusts, Adaptations Limit Water Loss during Respiration and from the Body Surface.**

✔**QUESTION** In desert grasshoppers, spiracles are located in a row along the underside of the abdomen. Why would this location help minimize water loss?

nitrogen-containing polysaccharide called chitin and layers of protein, with a layer of wax on the outside. This combination of chitin, protein, and wax is known as the **cuticle.**

Recall that waxes, a type of lipid, are highly hydrophobic and thus highly impermeable to water (see Chapter 6). Researchers who removed the wax from insect exoskeletons have confirmed that the rate of water loss from the body surface increases sharply. Based on this observation, the wax layer is interpreted as an adaptation that minimizes evaporative water loss.

For insects, minimizing water loss is only half the battle in avoiding osmotic stress. To maintain homeostasis, insects must also carefully regulate the composition of a blood-like fluid called **hemolymph.** Hemolymph is pumped by the heart and transports electrolytes, nutrients, and waste products.

To maintain water and electrolyte balance, insects rely on excretory organs called **Malpighian tubules,** and on their hindgut—the posterior portion of their digestive tract (**FIGURE 43.9a**).

**Filtrate Forms in the Malpighian Tubules** As Figure 43.9a shows, Malpighian tubules have a large surface area, are in direct contact with the hemolymph, and empty into the hindgut. The Malpighian tubules are responsible for forming a **filtrate** from the hemolymph. This "pre-urine" then passes into the hindgut, where it is processed and modified before excretion.

To explore how the Malpighian tubules work, biologists collected filtrate from the lumen of Malpighian tubules in mealworms and compared its composition with that of hemolymph from the same individuals. The two solutions were roughly isosmotic, but not identical.

How do they differ? Compared to hemolymph, the solution inside the tubules has a lower concentration of $Na^+$ and a higher concentration of $K^+$. This observation suggests that the epithelial cells in the Malpighian tubules are relatively impermeable to sodium ions but contain a pump that actively transports potassium ions into the tubules.

To test this hypothesis, researchers dissected the tubules, rinsed them, and bathed their interior and exterior in a solution containing a known concentration of potassium ions. When they measured the concentration of electrolytes on either side of the membrane over time, they found that $K^+$ accumulated in the tubule lumen, against its concentration gradient.

This result supported the hypothesis that cells in the membranes of Malpighian tubules contain pumps that actively transport potassium ions into the lumen of the organ. Subsequent work has shown that a high concentration of potassium ions brings water into the tubules by osmosis. Other electrolytes and nitrogenous wastes then diffuse into the filtrate along their concentration gradients.

**The Hindgut: Selective Reabsorption of Electrolytes and Water** The filtrate that accumulates inside the Malpighian tubules flows into the hindgut, where it joins material emerging from the digestive tract. If an insect is osmotically stressed due to a shortage of electrolytes and water, electrolytes and water from the filtrate are reabsorbed in the hindgut and returned to the hemolymph,

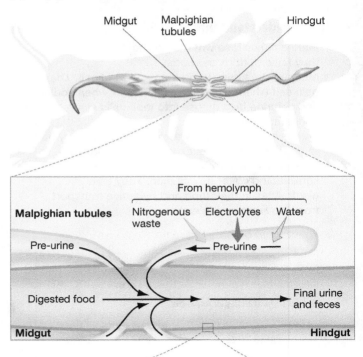

**(a)** Malpighian tubules produce an isosmotic pre-urine.

**(b)** Under osmotic stress, the hindgut reabsorbs electrolytes and water to form a hyperosmotic urine.

**FIGURE 43.9 In Insects, Urine Forms in the Malpighian Tubules and Hindgut. (a)** The isosmotic filtrate that forms in the Malpighian tubules empties into the hindgut. **(b)** In the hindgut, the primary driving forces for reabsorption of electrolytes and water are $H^+$ pumps in the apical membrane and $Na^+/K^+$-ATPases in the basolateral membrane.

while the uric acid remains in the hindgut. Reabsorption results in formation of hyperosmotic final urine, conservation of water, and efficient elimination of nitrogenous wastes.

In desert locusts, flour beetles, and other species in extremely dry environments, 80 to 95 percent of the water in the filtrate is reabsorbed and kept inside the body. The ability to recover this water allows these insects to live in dry habitats such as deserts and flour bins. How does reabsorption happen?

The mechanism involves a series of specific membrane pumps and channels, not unlike the system found in the chloride cells of fishes. To study it, researchers positioned the hindgut epithelium from a desert locust as a sheet dividing two solutions. They manipulated electrolyte concentrations on either side of the hindgut wall and measured changes in the solutions over time.

For example, when investigators removed $K^+$ and $Na^+$ from the solution on the lumen side of the organ, water reabsorption stopped. These data established that the hindgut's ability to recover water from urine depends on ion movement: The epithelial cells in the hindgut transport ions out of the filtrate and into the hemolymph. Water follows by osmosis, forming concentrated urine.

How do the ions move? By poisoning the experimental membranes with ouabain, biologists confirmed that $Na^+/K^+$-ATPase is involved in moving ions out of the lumen and into the hemolymph. Ouabain-treated membranes continued to transport $Cl^-$, however. Years of experiments on the locust hindgut resulted in the model in **FIGURE 43.9b**:

- $H^+$ is pumped into the hindgut lumen, creating an electrical gradient that favors movement of $K^+$ into the cells through potassium channels. Water follows via osmosis.

- $H^+$ diffuses along its gradient from the lumen into the cell through a $H^+/Cl^-$ cotransporter, bringing $Cl^-$ into the cell against its gradient.

- In the basolateral membrane, $Na^+/K^+$-ATPase sets up electrochemical and osmotic gradients that favor diffusion of $Na^+$ from the hindgut lumen into the epithelial cell, and diffusion of $Cl^-$ and $K^+$ from the epithelial cell into the hemolymph. Water moves into the hemolymph by osmosis.

**Regulating Water and Electrolyte Balance: An Overview**   Several general principles that have emerged from studies of insect excretion turn out to be relevant to vertebrate systems as well:

- Water moves only by osmosis—it is not pumped directly. Water moves between cells or body compartments via osmotic gradients that are set up by the active transport of ions.

- The formation of the filtrate is not particularly selective. Most of the molecules present in the hemolymph are also present in the Malpighian tubules.

- In contrast to filtrate formation, reabsorption is highly selective. The protein pumps and channels involved in reabsorption are highly specific for certain ions and molecules. Waste products do not pass through the hindgut membrane. Instead, they remain in the hindgut and are eliminated along with the feces. Only valuable ions and molecules are reabsorbed.

- In contrast to filtrate formation, reabsorption is tightly regulated. The membrane pumps and channels involved in reabsorption are activated and deactivated in response to osmotic stress. If an insect is dehydrated, virtually all of the water in the filtrate is reabsorbed. But if it has plenty to drink, reabsorption

does not occur and the urine is watery and hyposmotic to the individual's hemolymph. The system is dynamic and allows precise control over water and electrolyte balance.

Given the success of insects in terms of the numbers of species and individuals and the array of habitats they occupy, it is clear that their systems for maintaining water and electrolyte balance are remarkably effective.

## check your understanding

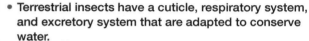

**If you understand that . . .**

- Terrestrial insects are prone to dehydration, primarily via evaporation from their respiratory surfaces.
- Terrestrial insects have a cuticle, respiratory system, and excretory system that are adapted to conserve water.
- In terrestrial insects, urine production begins with formation of a filtrate that is isosmotic with hemolymph, followed by selective and tightly regulated reabsorption of ions, nutrients, and water.

✔ **You should be able to . . .**

Explain how the following traits are involved in water retention:

1. Excretion of ammonia in the form of uric acid.
2. Selective reabsorption of electrolytes in the hindgut.

*Answers are available in Appendix A.*

## 43.5 Water and Electrolyte Balance in Terrestrial Vertebrates

With respect to water loss, terrestrial vertebrates face the same hazards that terrestrial insects do. Crocodiles, turtles, lizards, frogs, birds, and mammals lose water from their body surfaces, from the surface of their lungs every time they breathe, and in their urine. Electrolytes are also lost in urine and, in some species, in sweat. To replace the water they lose, most terrestrial vertebrates drink. They also ingest electrolytes in food.

In land-dwelling vertebrates, osmoregulation occurs primarily through events that take place in the key organ of the urinary system, the **kidney.** The kidney is responsible for water and electrolyte balance, as well as the excretion of nitrogenous wastes. In terms of function, it is analogous to the Malpighian tubules and hindgut of insects. Let's take a closer look at the kidney in mammals.

### The Structure of the Mammalian Kidney

Mammalian kidneys occur in pairs and tend to be bean shaped. A large blood vessel called the renal artery brings blood that contains nitrogenous wastes into the organ; the renal vein is a large blood vessel that carries "clean" blood away.

**(a)** Urinary system      **(b)** Kidney

**FIGURE 43.10 Anatomy of the Human Urinary System and Kidney.**
**(a)** In mammals, kidneys are paired and are located near the spinal column. **(b)** The kidney has an outer region called the cortex and an inner area called the medulla.

The urine that forms in the kidney is transported via a long tube called the **ureter** to a storage organ, the **bladder.** From the bladder, urine is transported to the body surface through the **urethra** and then excreted. In most vertebrates, the kidneys are located near the dorsal (back) side of the body. **FIGURE 43.10a** summarizes the parts of the urinary system.

Most of the kidney's mass is made up of small structures called nephrons. The **nephron** is the basic functional unit of the kidney. The work involved in maintaining water and electrolyte balance occurs in the nephron.

Most of the approximately 1 million nephrons in a human kidney are located in the outer region of the organ, or **cortex** (**FIGURE 43.10b**). But some nephrons extend from the cortex into the kidney's inner region, or **medulla.**

## The Function of the Mammalian Kidney: An Overview

The nephron shares important functional characteristics with the insect excretory system:

- Water cannot be transported actively—it moves only by osmosis.

- To move water, cells in the kidney set up strong osmotic gradients.

- By regulating these gradients and specific channel proteins, kidney cells exert precise control over loss or retention of water and electrolytes.

**(a)** The structure of the nephron and collecting duct      **(b)** Blood vessels serve each nephron.

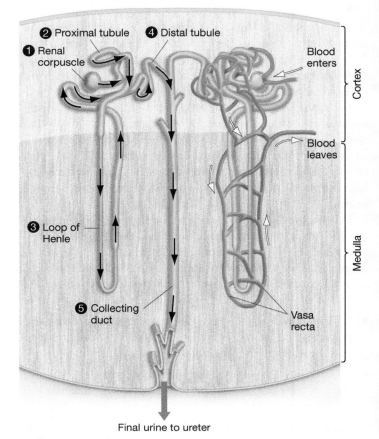

Final urine to ureter

**FIGURE 43.11 A Nephron Has Four Major Parts, Empties into a Collecting Duct, and Is Served by Blood Vessels.** Urine formation begins in the renal corpuscle and ends in the collecting duct.

**FIGURE 43.11a** provides a detailed view of the nephron. Note that it has four major regions and is closely associated with a tube called the collecting duct. **FIGURE 43.11b** illustrates a second key point about the anatomy of the nephron: It is served by blood vessels that wrap around each of its four regions.

The four major nephron regions and the collecting duct each have a distinct function:

1. The *renal corpuscle* filters blood, forming a filtrate or "pre-urine" consisting of ions, nutrients, wastes, and water.

2. The *proximal tubule* has epithelial cells that reabsorb nutrients, valuable ions, and water from the filtrate into the bloodstream.

3. The *loop of Henle* establishes a strong osmotic gradient in the interstitial fluid surrounding the loop, with osmolarity increasing as the loop descends.

4. The *distal tubule* reabsorbs ions and water in a regulated manner—one that helps maintain water and electrolyte balance according to the body's needs.

5. The *collecting duct* may reabsorb more water to maintain homeostasis. In addition, urea leaves the base of the collecting

duct and contributes to the osmotic gradient in the interstitial fluid set up by the loop of Henle.

The blood vessels associated with the nephron play a key role as well: They bring "dirty" blood into the nephron and then take away the molecules and ions that are reabsorbed from the initial filtrate.

Now let's delve into the details. The sections that follow trace the flow of material through each component of the nephron and out of the collecting duct.

## Filtration: The Renal Corpuscle

In terrestrial vertebrates, urine formation begins in the **renal corpuscle** (literally, "kidney-little-body"). Notice in Figure 43.11a that the nephron consists of a tube that is closed at one end and open at the other. The closed end is the beginning of the nephron; the open end is the terminus of the collecting duct.

As **FIGURE 43.12a** shows, the closed end of the nephron forms a capsule that encloses a cluster of tiny blood vessels, or capillaries. These vessels bring blood to the nephron from the renal artery. Collectively, the cluster of capillaries is called the **glomerulus** ("ball of yarn"). The region of the nephron that surrounds the glomerulus is named **Bowman's capsule.** Together, the glomerulus and Bowman's capsule make up the renal corpuscle.

**FIGURE 43.12b** illustrates a key feature of the glomerular capillaries: They have large pores, or openings. In addition, they are surrounded by unusual cells whose membranes fold into a series of slits and ridges.

The structure of the renal corpuscle allows it to function as a **filtration** device. Water and small solutes from the blood pass through the pores and slits into the Bowman's capsule. Filtration is based on size: Proteins, cells, and other large components of blood do not fit through the pores and do not enter the nephron. They remain in the blood instead.

Stated another way, urine formation starts with a size-selective filtration step—with blood pressure supplying the force required to perform filtration. In vertebrates, blood is under higher pressure than the surrounding tissues because it is pumped by the heart through a closed system of vessels. This pressure is enough to force water and small solutes through the pores in the glomerulus, so the renal corpuscle strains large volumes of fluid without expending energy in the form of ATP.

✔ If you understand this concept, you should be able to describe the contents of blood on one side of the filter (glomerulus) and the contents of the filtrate on the other side.

It is critical to note two additional facts about the filtration step in urine formation:

1. The renal corpuscles of a human kidney are capable of producing about 180 liters of filtrate per day. This is an impressive volume—think of 180 one-liter bottles of soft drink arranged on a supermarket shelf.

2. About 99 percent of the filtrate is reabsorbed—only a tiny fraction of the original volume is actually excreted as urine.

Filtering large volumes from the blood allows wastes to be removed effectively; pairing this process with selective

**(a)** Anatomy of the renal corpuscle

Blood leaves glomerulus.

Bowman's capsule

Glomerulus

Pre-urine leaves Bowman's capsule.

Blood enters glomerulus.

**(b)** Filtration

Pores in glomerulus

Large molecules and cells remain in bloodstream.

Filtration slits in cells that wrap around vessel

Fluid and small solutes are pushed through the pores and the filtration slits into Bowman's capsule.

Direction of blood movement

**FIGURE 43.12 Urine Formation Begins When Blood Is Filtered in the Renal Corpuscle. (a)** The renal corpuscle consists of Bowman's capsule and the glomerulus. **(b)** The capillaries in the glomerulus have pores and are surrounded by cells that have filtration slits. Blood pressure forces water and small molecules out of the capillaries, through the slits, and into Bowman's capsule.

reabsorption allows waste excretion to occur with a minimum of water and nutrient loss.

## Reabsorption: The Proximal Tubule

Where does filtrate reabsorption begin? Filtrate leaves Bowman's capsule and enters a convoluted structure called the **proximal tubule.** The filtrate inside this tubule contains water and small solutes such as urea, glucose, amino acids, vitamins, and electrolytes. Some of these molecules are waste products; others are valuable nutrients.

**Active Transport Occurs in Epithelial Cells** The epithelial cells of the proximal tubule have a prominent series of small projections, called **microvilli** ("little shaggy hairs"), facing the lumen. The microvilli greatly expand the surface area of this epithelium.

**(a)** Microvilli expand surface area of lumen of proximal tubule.

**(b)** Model of selective reabsorption in proximal tubules

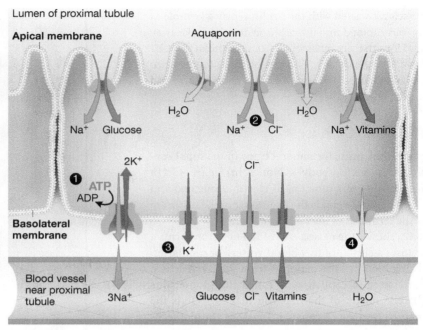

**IGURE 43.13 Water, Electrolytes, and Nutrients Are Reabsorbed in the Proximal Tubule.**

A large surface area provides space for membrane proteins that ct as pumps, channels, and cotransporters (**FIGURE 43.13a**).

Epithelial cells in the proximal tubule are also packed with mitochondria, which suggests that ATP-demanding active transport is occurring. Based on these observations, biologists hypothesized that the proximal tubule functions in the active transport of selected molecules out of the filtrate.

By injecting solutions of known composition into isolated rabbit and rat proximal tubules in the presence or absence of ATP, researchers confirmed that selected electrolytes and nutrients are ctively reabsorbed from the filtrate that enters the tubules.

When solutes move from the proximal tubule into epithelial ells, and then into the bloodstream, water follows along the osmotic gradient. In this way, valuable solutes and water are reabsorbed and returned to the bloodstream.

### on and Water Movement Is Driven by a "Master Gradient"

**IGURE 43.13b** summarizes the current model of the molecular mechanisms involved in selective reabsorption in the proximal tubule:

1. $Na^+/K^+$-ATPase in the basolateral membranes removes $Na^+$ from the interior of the cell. The active transport of sodium ions out of the cell creates a gradient favoring the entry of $Na^+$ from the lumen.

2. In the apical membrane adjacent to the lumen, $Na^+$-dependent cotransporters use this gradient to remove valuable ions and nutrients selectively from the filtrate. The movement of $Na^+$ into the cell, *along* its concentration gradient, provides the means for moving other solutes *against* a concentration gradient.

3. The solutes that move into the cell diffuse across the basolateral membrane into the interstitial fluid and then nearby blood vessels.

4. Water follows the movement of ions from the proximal tubule into the cell and then out of the cell and into blood vessels. Recall that water moves by osmosis across the membranes of these epithelial cells through membrane proteins called aquaporins.

Almost all of the nutrients, along with about two-thirds of the NaCl and water that is originally filtered by the renal corpuscle, are reabsorbed in the proximal tubule. The osmolarity of the tubular fluid is unchanged despite this huge change in volume, however, because water reabsorption is proportional to solute reabsorption.

In effect, then, the cells that line the proximal tubule act as a recycling center. The filtration step in the renal corpuscle is based on size; the reabsorption step in the proximal tubule selectively retrieves small substances that are valuable. The pumps and cotransporters in the proximal tubule reabsorb nutrients, electrolytes, and water but leave wastes. As the filtrate flows into the loop of Henle, it has a relatively high concentration of waste molecules and a relatively low concentration of nutrients.

### Creating an Osmotic Gradient: The Loop of Henle

In mammals, the fluid that emerges from the proximal tubule enters the **loop of Henle**—named for Jacob Henle, who described it in the early 1860s. In most nephrons, the loop is short and barely enters the medulla. But in about 20 percent of the nephrons present in a human kidney, the loop is long and plunges from the cortex of the kidney deep into the medulla.

In 1942 Werner Kuhn offered a hypothesis, inspired by countercurrent heat exchangers, to explain what the loop of Henle does. Recall that a countercurrent heat exchanger is a system in which two adjacent fluids flow through pipes in opposite directions (see Chapter 42). Kuhn proposed that the loop of Henle is a countercurrent exchanger and multiplier. It doesn't exchange heat, however. Instead, it sets up an osmotic gradient.

Specifically, Kuhn proposed that the osmolarity of the filtrate in the loop of Henle is low in the cortex and high in the medulla. Further, Kuhn maintained that the osmolarity in the interstitial fluid surrounding the loop mirrors the gradient inside the loop. This is a key point.

## Testing Kuhn's Hypothesis

A series of papers published during the 1950s and early 1960s supplied important experimental support for the countercurrent exchange model. **FIGURE 43.14** reproduces two particularly important data sets, obtained by comparing the osmolarity of kidney tissue slices. In both graphs, the x-axis shows the location in the kidney, from cortex to medulla. The y-axis indicates osmolarity, measured either as the percentage of the maximum observed or as solute concentration.

- Figure 43.14a shows data on the osmolarity of fluid inside the loop of Henle. The vertical lines represent the range of values observed at a particular location. As predicted by Kuhn's model, a strong gradient in osmolarity exists from the cortex to the medulla.

- Figure 43.14b shows that the concentrations of $Na^+$, $Cl^-$, and urea also increase sharply from the cortex to the medulla in the interstitial fluid outside the loop of Henle.

These results suggested that the solutes responsible for the gradient outside the loop are $Na^+$, $Cl^-$, and urea. The change in concentration of urea turned out to be particularly important.

## How Is the Osmotic Gradient Established?

The loop of Henle has three distinct regions: the descending limb, the thin ascending limb, and the thick ascending limb (**FIGURE 43.15a**, see page 876). The thin and thick ascending limbs differ in the thickness of their walls. Do the three regions also differ in their permeability to water and solutes?

It took over 15 years of experiments performed in laboratories around the world to formulate a definitive answer to that question. Researchers punctured the loop of Henle of rodents with a micropipette, analyzed the composition of the fluid inside, and compared it with the nephron's final product—urine.

In the ascending limb of the loop of Henle, $Na^+$ and $Cl^-$ constituted at least 60 percent of the solutes; urea constituted about 10 percent. But in the distal tubule, urea was the major solute. These data suggested that $Na^+$ and $Cl^-$, but not urea, were being removed somewhere in the ascending limb. How?

$Na^+$ and $Cl^-$ were also present at high concentrations in the tissue surrounding the thick ascending limb, so researchers hypothesized that sodium might be actively pumped out of this portion of the nephron. The hypothesis was that the active transport of $Na^+$ out of the filtrate in the thick ascending limb would create an electrical gradient that would also favor the loss of $Cl^-$.

**(a)** Fluid inside the loop of Henle

**(b)** Interstitial fluid outside the loop of Henle

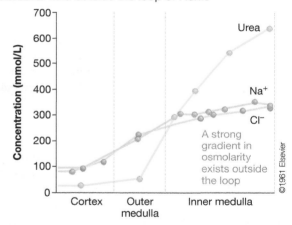

**FIGURE 43.14 Data Confirm the Existence of a Strong Osmotic Gradient Both Inside and Outside the Loop of Henle.** As the nephron plunges into the inner medulla, the concentration of dissolved solutes increases both inside **(a)** and outside **(b)** the loop of Henle.

DATA: K. J. Ullrich, K. Kramer, and J.W. Boyer. 1961. *Progress in Cardiovascular Diseases* 3: 395–431.

Follow-up experiments using ouabain and other poisons supported the hypothesis that sodium ions are actively transported out of the solution inside the thick ascending limb, and chloride ions follow along an electrochemical gradient. The epithelial cells responsible for salt excretion are configured almost exactly like the epithelium of the shark rectal gland (see Figure 43.6).

What is happening in the descending limb and the thin ascending limb of the loop of Henle? By injecting solutions of known concentration into the nephrons of rabbits, biologists documented that the descending limb is highly permeable to water but almost completely impermeable to solutes. The thin ascending limb of the loop, in contrast, is highly permeable to $Na^+$

**(a)** Three regions in the loop of Henle

**(b)** Water and ion movement differ in the three regions.

③ Thick ascending limb

① Descending limb

② Thin ascending limb

Osmolarity of fluid inside loop of Henle (milliosmol/L)

① Passive transport

③ Active transport

② Passive transport

Descending limb is highly permeable to water but impermeable to solutes

Ascending limb is nearly impermeable to water but highly permeable to Na⁺ and Cl⁻

**FIGURE 43.15 The Loop of Henle Maintains an Osmotic Gradient because Water Leaves the Descending Limb and Salt Leaves the Ascending Limb.** The values inside the loop in part (b) represent the osmolarity of the filtrate.

and Cl⁻, moderately permeable to urea, and almost completely impermeable to water.

**A Comprehensive View of the Loop of Henle** All of the observations just summarized came together in 1972 when two papers, published independently, proposed the same comprehensive model for how the loop of Henle works. To understand this model, follow the events in **FIGURE 43.15b**:

1. As fluid flows down the descending limb, the fluid inside the loop loses water to the interstitial fluid surrounding the nephron. This movement of water is passive—it does not require an expenditure of ATP. The water follows an osmotic gradient created by the ascending limb. At the bottom of the loop—in the inner medulla—the fluids inside and outside the nephron have high osmolarity. The filtrate does not continue to lose water, though, because the membrane in the ascending limb is nearly impermeable to water.

2. The fluid inside the nephron loses Na⁺ and Cl⁻ in the thin ascending limb. The ions move passively, along their concentration gradients.

3. Toward the cortex, the osmolarity of the surrounding interstitial fluid is low. Additional Na⁺ and Cl⁻ ions are actively transported out of the nephron in the thick ascending limb.

The countercurrent flow of fluid, combined with changes in permeability to water and in the types of channels and pumps that are active in the epithelium of the nephron, creates a self-reinforcing system. The presence of an osmotic gradient stimulates water and ion flows that in turn maintain an osmotic gradient.

Here's how it works: Movement of NaCl from the ascending limb into surrounding tissue increases the osmolarity of the fluid outside the descending limb, which results in a flow of water out of the water-permeable walls of the descending limb, via osmosis. This loss of water in the descending limb increases the osmolarity

in the fluid entering the ascending limb. The high concentration of salt in the fluid at the base of the ascending limb triggers a passive flow of ions out—reinforcing the osmotic gradient.

✔ If you understand this concept, you should be able to predict what happens to the osmotic gradient when the drug furosemide inhibits membrane proteins that pump sodium and chloride ions out of the thick ascending limb. Specifically, how does this drug affect (1) water reabsorption in the descending limb, (2) the osmolarity of the filtrate in the bottom of the loop of Henle, and (3) reabsorption of salt in the thin ascending limb?

**The Vasa Recta Removes Water and Solutes That Leave the Loop of Henle** What happens to the water and salt that move out of the loop from the filtrate into the interstitial fluid? They quickly diffuse into the **vasa recta,** a network of blood vessels that runs along the loop and eventually joins up with small veins in the kidney. As a result, the water and electrolytes that are reabsorbed are returned to the bloodstream instead of being excreted in urine (**FIGURE 43.16**).

The removal of water that leaves the descending limb is particularly important. If it were not drawn off into the bloodstream, it would dilute the concentrated fluid outside the loop of Henle and quickly destroy the osmotic gradient.

**The Collecting Duct Leaks Urea** Urea is the solute that is most responsible for the steep osmotic gradient in the space surrounding the nephron. Urea is at high concentration in the interstitial fluid in the inner medulla and low concentration in the outer medulla. This gradient exists because the innermost section of the collecting duct is permeable to urea.

Although the system created by the nephron, vasa recta, and collecting duct may seem complex, its outcome is simple: the creation and maintenance of a strong osmotic gradient with the minimum possible expenditure of energy.

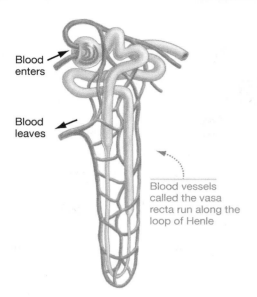

**FIGURE 43.16 Blood Supply to the Loop of Henle.** Water and solutes reabsorbed from the loop of Henle move into blood vessels (vasa recta).

Blood enters

Blood leaves

Blood vessels called the vasa recta run along the loop of Henle

## Regulating Water and Electrolyte Balance: The Distal Tubule and Collecting Duct

The first three steps in urine formation—filtration, reabsorption, and establishment of an osmotic gradient—result in a fluid that is slightly hyposmotic to blood. Once the filtrate has passed through the loop of Henle, the major solutes that it contains are urea and other wastes along with a low concentration of ions.

The filtrate that enters the distal tubule is always dilute. In contrast, the urine that leaves the collecting duct is dilute when the individual is well hydrated but concentrated when the individual is dehydrated. How is this possible?

**Urine Formation Is under Hormonal Control** The answer is based on two observations about the **distal tubule** and **collecting duct:** Their activity is **(1)** highly regulated, and **(2)** altered in response to osmotic stress. The amount of Na⁺, Cl⁻, and water that is reabsorbed in the distal tubule and in the collecting duct varies with the animal's hydration.

Changes in the distal tubule and collecting duct are controlled by **hormones**—signaling molecules (introduced in Chapter 11 and explored further in Chapter 49). Specifically:

- If Na⁺ levels in the blood are low, the adrenal glands release the hormone **aldosterone,** which leads to activation of sodium–potassium pumps and reabsorption of Na⁺ in the distal tubule. Water follows by osmosis. Aldosterone saves sodium and water.

- If an individual is dehydrated, the brain releases **antidiuretic hormone (ADH).** (The term diuresis refers to increased urine production, so antidiuresis means inhibition of urine production.) ADH is also referred to as vasopressin or arginine vasopressin. ADH saves water.

**How Does ADH Work?** Epithelial cells of the collecting duct are joined by tight junctions (see Chapter 11), making them impermeable to water and solutes. ADH has two important effects on the permeability of epithelial cells in the collecting duct:

1. ADH triggers the insertion of aquaporins into the apical membrane. As a result, cells become much more permeable to water and large amounts of water are reabsorbed.

2. ADH increases permeability to urea, which is reabsorbed into the surrounding fluid. This helps create a concentration gradient favoring water reabsorption from the filtrate.

As **FIGURE 43.17a** shows, water leaves the collecting duct passively—following the concentration gradient maintained by

**(a) ADH present:** Collecting duct is highly permeable to water.

**(b) No ADH present:** Collecting duct is not permeable to water.

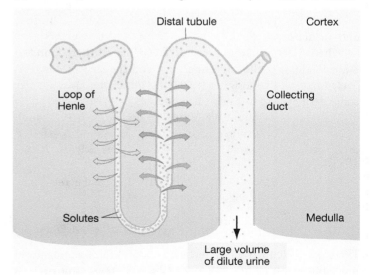

**FIGURE 43.17 ADH Regulates Water Reabsorption by the Collecting Duct.**

**Structure and Function of the Nephron and Collecting Duct**

| Structure | Function |
|---|---|
| **Renal Corpuscle** (Bowman's capsule and glomerulus) | Size-selective filtration: forms filtrate from blood (water and other small substances enter nephron) |
| **Proximal Tubule** | Reabsorbs electrolytes (active transport), nutrients, water |
| **Loop of Henle** | Maintains osmotic gradient in interstitial fluid from outer to inner medulla |
| • Descending limb | • Permeable to water (passive transport out of filtrate) |
| • Thin ascending limb | • Permeable to $Na^+$, $Cl^-$ (passive transport out of filtrate) |
| • Thick ascending limb | • Active transport of $Na^+$, $Cl^-$ out of filtrate |
| **Distal Tubule** | With aldosterone: Reabsorbs $Na^+$. Without aldosterone: Does not reabsorb $Na^+$. |
| **Collecting Duct** | Regulates water retention and loss |
| • Main portion | • With ADH: Water leaves filtrate; produces small volume of urine that is hyperosmotic to blood |
| | Without ADH: Water stays in filtrate; produces large volume of urine that is hyposmotic to blood |
| • Innermost portion | • Urea leaks out by passive transport to establish and/or maintain high osmolarity of inner medulla |

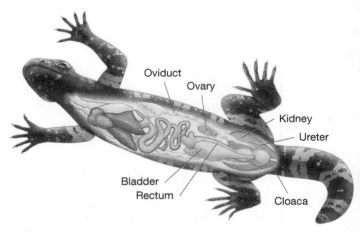

**FIGURE 43.18 The Cloaca Is a Cavity into Which the Urinary, Gastrointestinal, and Reproductive Tracts Empty.**

the loop of Henle. When ADH is present, water is conserved and urine is strongly hyperosmotic relative to blood. The collecting duct is the final place in which the composition of the filtrate can be altered. Urine exiting the collecting ducts moves from the kidneys into ureters and then is stored in the bladder until urination.

When ADH is absent, however, few aquaporins are found in the epithelium of the collecting duct, and the structure is relatively impermeable to water (**FIGURE 43.17b**). In this case, a larger quantity of hyposmotic urine is produced.

✓ If you understand ADH's effect on the collecting duct, you should be able to predict how urine formation is affected by ingestion of ethanol, which inhibits ADH release, versus nicotine, which stimulates ADH release.

**TABLE 43.2** reviews the functions of the four major regions of the nephron and the collecting duct.

## Urine Formation in Nonmammalian Vertebrates

The loop of Henle is an important adaptation in mammals and some birds. Water loss is reduced because these animals can produce urine that is hyperosmotic to their blood. In contrast, fishes, amphibians, and non-avian reptiles lack loops of Henle, and their kidneys are therefore unable to produce concentrated urine.

Many fishes and amphibians do not need to produce concentrated urine. But conserving water is important in reptiles, especially those inhabiting deserts. Recall that reptiles produce nitrogenous wastes in the form of uric acid, which is excreted with very little water and is therefore hyperosmotic to their body tissues. If reptiles' kidneys produce isosmotic urine, how does it become hyperosmotic?

In most reptiles, the ureters empty isosmotic urine into the **cloaca,** a cavity into which the urinary, gastrointestinal, and reproductive tracts all empty (**FIGURE 43.18**). Reptiles are able to absorb water from urine across the wall of the cloaca into the bloodstream. Eventually, a semisolid uric acid paste is excreted along with the feces.

check your understanding

**If you understand that . . .**
- The mammalian kidney is specialized for the production of hyperosmotic urine.
- The loop of Henle is a countercurrent system that maintains a strong osmotic gradient in the medulla.
- The characteristics of urine change in response to hormonal signals. The signals trigger changes in the nephron and collecting duct that either save or eliminate water and solutes.

✓ **You should be able to . . .**

Predict how the following events would affect urine production: drinking massive amounts of water, eating large amounts of salt, and refraining from drinking water for 48 hours.

*Answers are available in Appendix A.*

**(a)** Change following injection of radioactive water into bladder

**(b)** Change following injection of pure water into bladder or stomach

- Bladder
- Stomach

©2007 The Company of Biologists

**FIGURE 43.19 Gila Monsters Can Reabsorb Water from Their Bladders.**
**(a)** Radioactively labeled water passes from bladder into bloodstream. **(b)** Pure water reduces blood osmolarity at a similar rate in dehydrated lizards whether added to stomach or to bladder.

DATA: Davis, J. R., and D. F. DeNardo. 2007. *The Journal of Experimental Biology* 210: 1472–1480.

✓**QUESTION** What physiological trade-offs might be imposed by carrying a large amount of water in the bladder?

Some reptiles also have a bladder that collects the isosmotic urine from the ureters and stores it before emptying it into the cloaca. When water is available, these reptiles drink a lot, and their bladders fill up with dilute urine. Researchers hypothesized that the bladder acts as a "canteen" to store water during times when water is unavailable.

To test this hypothesis, the investigators injected the bladders of dehydrated Gila monsters—a large desert lizard—with radioactively labeled water and drew blood samples over time. The radioactivity of the lizards' blood increased within a half hour, which meant that the radioactively labeled water from the bladder was being absorbed into the bloodstream (**FIGURE 43.19a**).

The researchers also examined whether water in the bladder can rehydrate lizards to the same extent as drinking water.

Working with two groups of dehydrated Gila monsters, they injected water into the bladders of one group, and—to mimic drinking—they injected water into the stomachs of the second group. They found that the osmolarity of the plasma decreased at the same rate in both groups (**FIGURE 43.19b**).

So, the bladder can indeed act as a "canteen," allowing lizards to carry a water supply that they can access when water is scarce. As water is reabsorbed from the bladder, the urine becomes more and more concentrated, but the osmolarity of the blood remains low.

Whether considering the mammalian nephron or the Gila monster bladder, the vertebrate urinary system is remarkably effective in regulating water and electrolyte balance and achieving homeostasis.

---

## CHAPTER 43 REVIEW

*For media, go to MasteringBiology*

## If you understand . . .

### 43.1 Osmoregulation and Excretion

- Solutes move across membranes via passive transport, facilitated diffusion, or active transport. Water moves across membranes by osmosis.

- In most animals, epithelial cells that selectively transport water and electrolytes are responsible for homeostasis.

- The mechanisms involved in regulating water and electrolyte balance vary widely among animal groups because different habitats present different types of osmotic stress.

- The type of nitrogenous waste excreted by an animal is affected by its phylogeny and its habitat type. Most fishes excrete ammonia; mammals and most adult amphibians excrete urea; and insects, reptiles, and birds excrete uric acid.

✓ You should be able to explain how an electrochemical gradient for sodium ions makes it possible for other ions and water to move across a membrane passively.

### 43.2 Water and Electrolyte Balance in Marine Fishes

- Seawater is strongly hyperosmotic in relation to the tissues of marine bony fishes, so the fishes tend to lose water by osmosis and gain electrolytes by diffusion.

- Marine bony fishes are osmoregulators, whereas cartilaginous fishes such as sharks are osmoconformers.

- Epithelial cells in the shark rectal gland and in the gills of marine bony fishes excrete excess salt using sodium–potassium pumps and sodium–potassium–chloride cotransporters located in the basolateral membrane.

- Salt-excreting cells similar to those found in the shark rectal gland occur in the gills of marine fishes, the salt glands of marine birds and other reptiles, and the kidneys of mammals.

✓ You should be able to compare and contrast the mechanisms by which cartilaginous and bony fishes achieve water and electrolyte balance in the ocean.

## 43.3 Water and Electrolyte Balance in Freshwater Fishes

- Freshwater is strongly hyposmotic in relation to the tissues of freshwater fishes, so the fishes tend to gain water by osmosis and lose electrolytes by diffusion.

- Epithelial cells in the gills of freshwater fishes import ions using sodium–potassium pumps ($Na^+/K^+$-ATPases) located in the basolateral membrane and sodium–potassium–chloride cotransporters located in the apical membrane.

✓ You should be able to describe the evidence for the hypothesis that new chloride cells form when salmon migrate from the ocean to freshwater.

## 43.4 Water and Electrolyte Balance in Terrestrial Insects

- A waxy coating on the insect exoskeleton limits evaporative water loss. The openings to insect respiratory organs close when osmotic stress is severe.

- The Malpighian tubules of insects form a filtrate that is isosmotic with the hemolymph. If pumps in the epithelium of the hindgut are activated, then electrolytes and water are reabsorbed from the filtrate and returned to the hemolymph.

- Insects can form hyperosmotic urine that minimizes water loss during the excretion of nitrogenous wastes.

✓ You should be able to predict what type of nitrogenous waste is excreted by aquatic insects.

## 43.5 Water and Electrolyte Balance in Terrestrial Vertebrates

- Nephrons in the vertebrate kidney form a filtrate in the renal corpuscle and then reabsorb valuable nutrients, electrolytes, and water in the proximal tubule.

- A solution containing urea and electrolytes flows through the loop of Henle of mammalian kidneys, where changes in the permeability of epithelial cells to water and salt—along with active transport of salt—create a steep osmotic gradient.

- If antidiuretic hormone (ADH) increases the water permeability of the collecting duct, water is reabsorbed along the osmotic gradient and hyperosmotic urine is produced.

- The nephrons of fishes, amphibians, and reptiles do not have loops of Henle and therefore cannot produce urine that is hyperosmotic to the body fluids. Some of these vertebrates are able to reabsorb water from the cloaca or bladder to produce hyperosmotic urine.

✓ You should be able to explain why desert-dwelling kangaroo rats, which are under extreme osmotic stress due to lack of drinking water, have extremely long loops of Henle relative to their body size.

## You should be able to . . .

## ✓TEST YOUR KNOWLEDGE
*Answers are available in Appendix A*

1. True or False: Sodium–potassium ATPase pumps move three sodium molecules out of a cell in exchange for two potassium ions, establishing an electrochemical gradient.

2. Which one of the following statements is true of fishes that live in freshwater?
   a. The environment is isosmotic with respect to their tissues. As a result, they do not require a specialized organ to maintain water and electrolyte balance.
   b. They lose water to their environment primarily through the gills. They replace this water by drinking.
   c. Water enters epithelial cells in their gills via osmosis. Electrolytes leave the same cells via diffusion.
   d. They have specialized cells that actively pump $Na^+$ and $Cl^-$ from blood into epithelial cells, so the ions can be excreted.

3. Which of the following organisms would lose the most water by osmosis across its gills?
   a. marine bony fish
   b. shark
   c. freshwater bony fish
   d. freshwater invertebrate

4. Which of the following gives the correct sequence of the regions of the nephron with respect to fluid flow?
   a. distal tubule → ascending limb of loop of Henle → descending limb of loop of Henle → proximal tubule → collecting duct
   b. ascending limb of loop of Henle → descending limb of loop of Henle → proximal tubule → distal tubule → collecting duct
   c. proximal tubule → ascending limb of loop of Henle → descending limb of loop of Henle → distal tubule → collecting duct
   d. proximal tubule → descending limb of loop of Henle → ascending limb of loop of Henle → distal tubule → collecting duct

5. What effect does antidiuretic hormone (ADH) have on the nephron?
   a. It increases water permeability of the descending limb of the loop of Henle.
   b. It decreases water permeability of the descending limb of the loop of Henle.
   c. It increases water permeability of the collecting duct.
   d. It decreases water permeability of the collecting duct.

6. Fill in the blank: In Gila monsters, the organ in which water from urine is reabsorbed into the bloodstream is the _____.

✓ TEST YOUR UNDERSTANDING                Answers are available in Appendix A

7. Which of the following organisms would you expect to have the highest concentrations of proteins that protect cells from the toxic effects of ammonia?
   a. shark
   b. freshwater bony fish
   c. terrestrial reptile
   d. mammal

8. Compare and contrast the types of nitrogenous wastes observed in animals. Identify which compound can be excreted with a minimum of water, which is most toxic, and which waste product is found in fishes, in mammals, and in insects. Which type of nitrogenous waste would you expect to find produced by embryos inside eggs laid on land?

9. The chloride cells of fish gills are sometimes called mitochondria-rich cells due to their high density of mitochondria. How does high mitochondrial density relate to the functional role of chloride cells? Would you expect other epithelial cells involved in ion transport to contain large numbers of mitochondria? Explain.

10. This chapter introduced a number of features that help terrestrial animals reduce water loss, including the layer of wax found on insect exoskeletons, the ability of insects to close spiracles, the excretion of nitrogenous wastes as insoluble uric acid, and long loops of Henle in the mammalian kidney. Predict how each of these traits differs in animals that live in very humid versus very dry habitats. How would you test your predictions?

11. Explain why mammals would not be able to produce concentrated urine if they lacked loops of Henle.

12. Scientists have noted that marine invertebrates tend to be osmoconformers, while freshwater invertebrates tend to be osmoregulators. Suggest an explanation for this phenomenon.

✓ TEST YOUR PROBLEM-SOLVING SKILLS                Answers are available in Appendix A

13. Biologists recently have been able to produce mice that lack functioning genes for aquaporins. How does their urine compare to that of individuals with normal aquaporins?
    a. lower volume and lower osmolarity
    b. lower volume and higher osmolarity
    c. higher volume and lower osmolarity
    d. higher volume and higher osmolarity

14. Suppose a grazing mammal ingested the leaves of a plant containing the toxin ouabain. What effect would this toxin have on the mammal's urine volume? Explain.

15. You have isolated a segment of a rat nephron and introduced a solution of known composition. When you compare the fluid collected at the end of the segment with the test solution introduced at the beginning, you find that the volume has decreased by 30 percent and the $Na^+$ concentration has decreased by 30 percent, but the urea concentration has increased by 50 percent. What processes in this segment might account for these changes?

16. QUANTITATIVE To test the hypothesis that mussels are osmoconformers, researchers exposed mussels to water of varying osmolarities and then drew hemolymph samples from the mussels. Is the researchers' hypothesis supported by the data, shown below? Explain.

| Water Osmolarity | Hemolymph Osmolarity |
|---|---|
| 250 | 261 |
| 500 | 503 |
| 750 | 746 |
| 1000 | 992 |

# 45 Gas Exchange and Circulation

**In this chapter you will learn that**

Animals have adaptations for gas exchange across body surfaces and circulation within their bodies

via ↓

Respiratory and circulatory systems  **45.1**

comparing ↓         exploring ↓

$O_2$ and $CO_2$ exchange in air vs. water  **45.2**

$O_2$ and $CO_2$ transport in blood  **45.4**

asking ↓         asking ↓

How do different gas exchange organs work?  **45.3**

How do different circulatory systems work?  **45.5**

During intense exercise, animal circulatory systems deliver large amounts of oxygen to tissues and remove large amounts of carbon dioxide. This chapter explores how gas exchange occurs in animals that live in aquatic or terrestrial environments.

This chapter is part of the Big Picture. See how on pages 840–841.

Animal cells are like factories that run 24 hours a day. Inside the plasma membrane, the chemical reactions that sustain life require a steady input of raw materials. Those reactions also produce a steady stream of wastes. Earlier in this unit, you learned how solid and liquid waste materials are removed from the cells and excreted from the body (see Chapter 43). You also examined how nutrients enter the body (see Chapter 44). Let's now turn our attention to two other major questions:

1. How are two of the most important molecules in the economy of the cell—the oxygen ($O_2$) required for cellular respiration and the carbon dioxide ($CO_2$) produced by cellular respiration—exchanged with the environment?

✔ When you see this checkmark, stop and test yourself. Answers are available in Appendix A.

2. How are these gases—along with wastes, nutrients, and other types of molecules—transported throughout the body?

Understanding gas exchange and circulation is fundamental to understanding how animals work. If either process fails, the consequences are dire. Consider the maladies that can develop when gas exchange or circulation is disrupted in humans: anemia, pneumonia, tuberculosis, malaria, heart disease, and stroke are just a few examples.

Let's begin with an overview of animal respiratory and circulatory systems and then plunge into the details of how gases are exchanged and transported.

## 45.1 The Respiratory and Circulatory Systems

When the mitochondria inside animal cells are producing ATP via cellular respiration, they consume oxygen and produce carbon dioxide. To support continued ATP production, cells have to obtain oxygen and expel excess carbon dioxide continuously (see The Big Picture: Energy, pages 198–199).

How does this gas exchange occur between an animal's environment and its mitochondria? In most cases, gas exchange involves the four steps illustrated in **FIGURE 45.1**:

1. *Ventilation,* the movement of air or water through a specialized gas exchange organ, such as lungs or gills.

2. *Gas exchange,* the diffusion of $O_2$ and $CO_2$ between air or water and the blood at the respiratory surface.

3. *Circulation,* the transport of dissolved $O_2$ and $CO_2$ throughout the body—along with nutrients, wastes, and other types of molecules—via the circulatory system.

4. *Cellular respiration,* the cell's use of $O_2$ and production of $CO_2$. In tissues, where cellular respiration has led to low $O_2$ levels and high $CO_2$ levels, gas exchange occurs between blood and cells.

Steps 1 and 2 are accomplished by the **respiratory system,** the collection of cells, tissues, and organs responsible for gas exchange between the individual animal and its environment. In essence, a respiratory system consists of structures for conducting air or water to a surface where gas exchange takes place.

In some animals the gas exchange surface is the skin, but in most species it is located in a specialized organ like the lungs of tetrapods, the tracheae of insects, or the gills found in mollusks, arthropods, and fishes. Section 45.3 analyzes the structure and function of gills, tracheae, and lungs in detail.

Step 3 in Figure 45.1 is usually accomplished by a **circulatory system,** which moves $O_2$, $CO_2$, and other materials around the body. In many cases, a muscular heart propels a specialized, liquid transport tissue throughout the body via a system of vessels.

Keeping in mind this broad overview of gas exchange and circulatory systems, let's dive into the details by exploring how oxygen and carbon dioxide move between an animal's body and its environment.

## 45.2 Air and Water as Respiratory Media

Gas exchange between the environment and cells is based on diffusion. Under normal conditions, oxygen concentrations are relatively high in the environment (for example, in air that you inhale or in ocean water) and low in tissues, while carbon dioxide levels are relatively high in tissues and low in the environment. Thus oxygen tends to move from the environment into tissues, and carbon dioxide tends to move from tissues into the environment.

How much oxygen and carbon dioxide are present in the atmosphere versus the ocean? What factors in air and water influence how quickly these gases move by diffusion?

### How Do Oxygen and Carbon Dioxide Behave in Air?

The atmosphere is composed primarily of nitrogen (76%) and oxygen (21%) and has trace amounts of argon (0.93%) and $CO_2$ (0.03%). Nitrogen ($N_2$) and argon are not important to animals living at sea level and are usually ignored in analyses of gas exchange.

However, the data are actually a little misleading. To understand why, consider that the *percentage* of $O_2$ in the atmosphere does not vary with elevation. The atmosphere at the top of Mt. Everest is

**1. Ventilation**

Environment

Air or water

Respiratory surface

**2. Gas exchange**

$O_2$

$CO_2$

**3. Circulation**

Blood

**4. Cellular respiration**

$O_2$

$CO_2$

Mitochondria

Respiratory system

Circulatory system

**FIGURE 45.1 Gas Exchange Involves Ventilation, Circulation, and Respiration.** In animals, oxygen and carbon dioxide are exchanged across the surface of a lung, a gill, the skin, or some other gas exchange organ. In many species these gases are then transported to and from cells—where gas exchange again takes place—in a fluid tissue such as blood.

**FIGURE 45.2 Oxygen Makes Up 21 Percent of the Atmosphere, but Its Partial Pressure Depends on Altitude.** Atmospheric pressure, and thus oxygen partial pressure ($P_{O_2}$), fall with increasing elevation.

composed of 21 percent oxygen, just as it is at sea level. The key difference is that far fewer molecules of oxygen and other atmospheric gases are present at high elevations than at sea level. Air at the top of Mt. Everest is less dense than air at sea level, so less oxygen is present. To understand how gases move by diffusion, it is important to express their presence in terms of partial pressures instead of percentages. Pressure is a type of force. A **partial pressure** is the pressure of a particular gas in a mixture of gases.

To calculate the partial pressure of a particular gas, multiply the fractional composition (the fraction of air the gas comprises) by the total pressure exerted by the entire mixture (atmospheric pressure). The calculation is valid because the total pressure of a mixture of gases is the sum of the partial pressures of all the individual gases. This relationship is called Dalton's law.

For example, **FIGURE 45.2** shows that the total atmospheric pressure at sea level is 760 mm Hg (millimeters of mercury). If you multiply this value by 0.21, which is the fraction of air that is $O_2$, you obtain a partial pressure of oxygen, abbreviated $P_{O_2}$, at sea level of 160 mm Hg. Because the atmospheric pressure is only about 250 mm Hg at the top of Mt. Everest, the $P_{O_2}$ there is only $0.21 \times 250 = 53$ mm Hg.

Oxygen and carbon dioxide diffuse between the environment and cells along their respective partial pressure gradients, just as solutes diffuse along their electrochemical gradients. In both air and water, $O_2$ and $CO_2$ move from regions of high partial pressure to regions of low partial pressure. It is hard to breathe at the top of Mt. Everest because the partial pressure of oxygen is low there—meaning that the diffusion gradient between the atmosphere and your lung tissues is small, so fewer molecules of $O_2$ diffuse into your tissues when you take a breath.

## How Do Oxygen and Carbon Dioxide Behave in Water?

To obtain oxygen, water breathers face a much more challenging environment than air breathers do. Aquatic animals live in an environment that contains much less oxygen than the environments inhabited by terrestrial animals. At 15°C, a liter of air can contain up to 209 milliliters (mL) of $O_2$, while a liter of water may contain a maximum of only 7 mL of $O_2$. To extract a given amount of oxygen, an aquatic animal has to process 30 times more water than the amount of air a terrestrial animal breathes.

In addition, water is about a thousand times denser than air and flows much less easily. As a result, water breathers have to expend much more energy to ventilate their respiratory surfaces than do air breathers.

**What Affects the Amount of Gas in a Solution?** Oxygen and carbon dioxide diffuse into water from the atmosphere, but the amount of gas that dissolves in water depends on several factors:

- *Solubility of the gas in water* Oxygen has very low solubility in water. Only 0.003 mL of oxygen dissolves in 100 mL of water for each increase of 1 mm Hg in oxygen partial pressure. Because of this low solubility, blood contains a molecule that binds to oxygen and delivers it to tissues. Without this carrier molecule, the rate of blood flow to tissues would have to increase dramatically to meet oxygen demand.

- *Temperature of the water* As the temperature of water increases, the amount of gas that dissolves in it decreases. Other things being equal, warm-water habitats have much less oxygen available than cold-water habitats do. For a fish, breathing in warm water is comparable to a land-dwelling animal breathing at high elevation.

- *Presence of other solutes* Because seawater has a much higher concentration of solutes than does freshwater, seawater can hold less dissolved gas. At 10°C, up to 8.02 mL of $O_2$ can be present per liter of freshwater versus only 6.35 mL of $O_2$ per liter of seawater. As a result, freshwater habitats tend to be more oxygen rich than marine environments.

- *Partial pressure of the gas in contact with the water* Gases move from regions of high partial pressure to regions of low partial pressure. So if the partial pressure in a liquid exceeds that in the adjacent gas, the gas will bubble up out of the liquid. This is what happens when the cap is removed from a bottle of carbonated beverage. The partial pressure of carbon dioxide in the newly opened drink is much higher than it is in the atmosphere.

**What Affects the Amount of Oxygen Available in an Aquatic Habitat?** The partial pressure of oxygen varies in different types of aquatic habitats, just as it varies with altitude on land. In addition to the four factors just listed, other important considerations affect oxygen's availability in water. These include the presence of photosynthetic organisms and decomposers, the amount of mixing that occurs, and the surface area of the body of water. For example,

- Habitats with large numbers of photosynthetic organisms tend to be relatively oxygen rich. In contrast, oxygen content is extremely low in bogs and other stagnant-water habitats because oxygen is quickly depleted by decomposers that use it as an electron acceptor in cellular respiration.

- Unless currents mix water almost continuously, water near the surface has much higher oxygen content than water near the bottom of the same habitat.

- Shallow ponds and streams tend to be much better oxygenated than deep bodies of water because shallower bodies have a higher ratio of surface area to volume.

- Rapids, waterfalls, and other types of whitewater are the most highly oxygenated of all aquatic environments because a large surface area is exposed to the atmosphere as water splashes over rocks and logs and because air bubbles are incorporated into the water.

Now let's consider the structure and function of ventilatory organs. How do the gills of fishes, the tracheae of insects, and the lungs of mammals cope with the differences between air and water?

## check your understanding

**If you understand that . . .**
- $O_2$ and $CO_2$ move from regions of high partial pressure to regions of low partial pressure.
- The partial pressure of oxygen in a body of water depends on the water's temperature, surface area, and amount of mixing, and on the impacts of photosynthetic organisms and decomposers, among other factors.
- Water breathing is much more difficult than air breathing, in part because the partial pressure of oxygen in water is much lower than its partial pressure in air.

✔ **You should be able to . . .**

1. Explain why oxygen partial pressures are relatively high in mountain streams and relatively low at the ocean bottom.

2. For each of three aquaria, decide whether a large or a small amount of air should be bubbled in. One contains warm-water species, one contains vigorous algal growth, and one contains sedentary animals.

*Answers are available in Appendix A.*

---

## 45.3 Organs of Gas Exchange

Many small animals lack specialized gas exchange organs, such as gills or lungs. Instead, they obtain $O_2$ and eliminate $CO_2$ by diffusion across the body surface. This is possible because their size and shape give them an extraordinarily high ratio of surface area to volume (see Chapter 42). In sponges, jellyfish, flatworms, and other species, diffusion across the body surface is rapid enough to fulfill their requirements for taking in $O_2$ and expelling $CO_2$.

Most of these animals are restricted to living in wet environments, however. For gas exchange to take place efficiently, the surface where it occurs has to be thin, and thin tissues are prone to water loss. Living in wet or humid environments allows animals to exchange gases across their outer surface while avoiding dehydration.

In contrast, animals that are large or that live in dry habitats need some sort of specialized respiratory organ. Respiratory organs provide a greater surface area for gas exchange—enough to meet the demands of a large body filled with cells. In terrestrial animals, respiratory organs are located inside the body, which helps minimize water loss.

Biologists have long marveled at the efficiency of gills and lungs. To appreciate why, let's examine the physical factors that control diffusion rates and then look at the structure and function of these respiratory organs.

### Physical Parameters: The Law of Diffusion

In 1855 Adolf Fick derived an equation regarding diffusion, based on the results of experiments he had performed on the behavior of gases. **Fick's law of diffusion** states that the rate of diffusion of a gas depends on five parameters: the solubility of the gas in the aqueous film lining the gas exchange surface; the temperature; the surface area available for diffusion; the difference in partial pressures of the gas across the gas exchange surface; and the thickness of the barrier to diffusion (**FIGURE 45.3**).

Fick's law identifies traits that allow animals to maximize the rate at which oxygen and carbon dioxide diffuse across surfaces. Specifically, Fick's law states that gases diffuse at the highest rates when three conditions are met:

1. *A* is large, meaning a large area is available for gas exchange. Based on Fick's law, it is not surprising that the respiratory surface in the human lungs would cover about 140 m$^2$— about a quarter of a basketball court—if the epithelium were spread flat.

2. *D* is small, meaning the respiratory surface is extremely thin. In the human lung, this barrier to diffusion is only 0.2 μm thick—about 1/200th of the thickness of this page.

3. $P_2 - P_1$ is large, meaning the partial pressure gradient of the gas across the surface is large. High partial pressure gradients are maintained in part by having an efficient circulatory

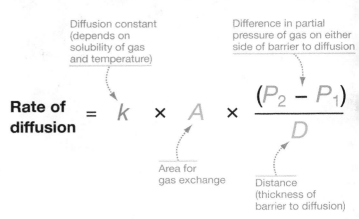

Diffusion constant (depends on solubility of gas and temperature)

Difference in partial pressure of gas on either side of barrier to diffusion

$$\text{Rate of diffusion} = k \times A \times \frac{(P_2 - P_1)}{D}$$

Area for gas exchange

Distance (thickness of barrier to diffusion)

**FIGURE 45.3 Fick's Law Describes the Rate of Diffusion.**

system in close contact with the gas exchange surface. When blood flows close to the respiratory surface, oxygen is rapidly taken away from the area where inward diffusion is occurring, and carbon dioxide is rapidly brought into the area where outward diffusion is occurring. As a result, $P_2 - P_1$ stays high.

What other aspects of gill and lung structure affect diffusion rate? To answer this question, let's delve into the anatomy of these respiratory organs.

## How Do Gills Work?

Gills are outgrowths of the body surface or throat that are used for gas exchange in aquatic animals. Gills are efficient solutions to the problems posed by water breathing, primarily because they present a large surface area for the diffusion of gases across a thin epithelium.

In some species of invertebrates, such as the red tubeworm (**FIGURE 45.4a**), gills project from the body surface and contact the surrounding water directly. In other invertebrate species, such as the crayfish (**FIGURE 45.4b**), gills are located inside the exoskeleton or body wall. If gills are internal, water must be driven over them by cilia, the limbs, or other specialized structures.

In contrast to the diversity of gills found in invertebrates, the gills of bony fishes are all similar in structure. Fish gills are located on both sides of the head and in teleosts (see Chapter 35) consist of four arches, as **FIGURE 45.5** shows.

**How Do Fishes Ventilate Their Gills?** To move water through their gills so gas exchange can take place, most fishes open and close their mouth and **operculum,** the stiff flap of tissue that covers the gills. The pumping action of the mouth and operculum creates a pressure gradient that moves water over the gills.

In contrast, tuna and other fishes that are particularly fast swimmers force water through their gills by swimming with their mouths open. This process is called ram ventilation.

Regardless of how fish gills are ventilated, water flows in one direction through gills, passing over long, thin structures called **gill filaments** that extend from each gill arch. Each gill filament is composed of hundreds or thousands of **gill lamellae.** Gill lamellae are sheetlike structures, shown in detail at the bottom of Figure 45.5. Note that a bed of small blood vessels called capillaries runs through each lamella.

**The Fish Gill Is a Countercurrent System** The one-way flow of water through gill lamellae has a profound impact on gill function, for a simple reason: The flow of blood through the capillary bed in each lamella is in the opposite direction to the flow of water. As a result, each lamella functions as a countercurrent exchanger.

Recall that countercurrent exchangers are based on two adjacent fluids flowing in opposite directions (see Chapter 42). **FIGURE 45.6** illustrates why the countercurrent flow is so critical.

Note two key points about the left side of the figure, where water and blood flow in opposite directions:

1. A slight gradient in partial pressure of oxygen (here, 10 percent) exists along the entire length of the lamella.

2. A large difference in oxygen partial pressure exists between the start and end of the system. In this example, the difference is 100% − 15% = 85% in the water and 90% − 5% = 85% in the blood.

The upshot? Most of the oxygen in the incoming water has diffused into the blood.

Now look at the right side of the figure, where water and blood flow in the same direction.

1. A large gradient in partial pressure of oxygen (here, 100 percent) exists at the start of the system. The gradient in oxygen partial pressures declines rapidly and eventually disappears.

**a)** External gills are in direct contact with water.

External gills

5 mm

**(b)** Internal gills must have water brought to them.

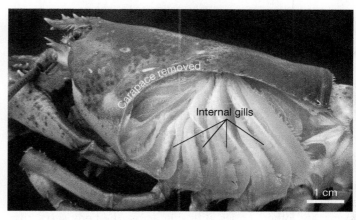

Carapace removed

Internal gills

1 cm

**FIGURE 45.4 Gills Can Be External or Internal. (a)** Red tubeworms are marine polychaetes with gills that protrude from the body. **(b)** Lobster gills are located inside the main body wall. A portion of the crayfish exoskeleton has been removed to expose the gills.

**QUESTION** Predict what the advantages and disadvantages of external versus internal gills might be in terms of fitness.

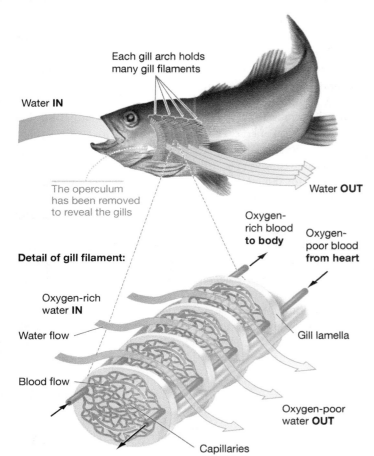

FIGURE 45.5 **Fish Gills Are a Countercurrent Exchange System.** In fish gills, water and blood flow in opposite directions. In the blood vessels, red represents oxygenated blood, blue represents deoxygenated blood, and purple represents mixed blood.

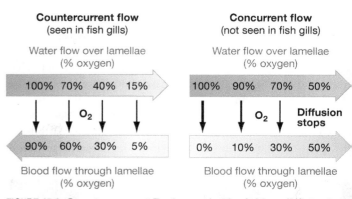

FIGURE 45.6 **Countercurrent Exchange Is Much More Efficient than Concurrent Exchange.** In the countercurrent system of fish gills, oxygen is transferred along the entire length of the capillaries.

✔QUESTION If you understand this concept, you should be able to predict what would happen to oxygen transfer from water to blood if flow were concurrent.

2. A relatively small difference in oxygen partial pressure exists between the start and end of the system. In this example, the difference is 100% − 50% = 50% in the water and 50% − 0% = 50% in the blood.

With this arrangement, only half of the oxygen in the incoming water has diffused into the blood.

Countercurrent flow makes fish gills extremely efficient at extracting oxygen from water because it ensures that a difference in the partial pressure of oxygen and carbon dioxide in water versus blood is maintained over the entire gas exchange surface.

The effect of countercurrent exchange is to maximize the $P_2 − P_1$ term in Fick's law of diffusion, averaged over the entire gill surface. Based on this observation, biologists cite countercurrent exchange as another example of how gills are optimized for efficient gas exchange.

## How Do Insect Tracheae Work?

As noted earlier, air and water are dramatically different ventilatory media, because they have different densities, viscosities, and abilities to hold oxygen and carbon dioxide. In addition, the consequences of exposing the gas exchange surface to air versus water differ.

In aquatic habitats, ventilation tends to disrupt water and electrolyte balance, and homeostasis must be maintained by an active osmoregulatory system. Osmosis causes marine animals to lose water across their gas exchange surface and freshwater animals to gain water (see Chapter 43). Diffusion tends to cause marine animals to gain sodium, chloride, and other ions, and freshwater animals to lose them.

In contrast, breathing leads to a loss of water by evaporation in terrestrial environments. How do terrestrial animals minimize water loss while maximizing the efficiency of gas exchange?

To answer this question, consider the tracheal system of insects. Recall that insects have an extensive system of air-filled tubes called **tracheae** located within the body (see Chapter 43). These connect to the exterior through openings called **spiracles,** which can be closed to minimize the loss of water by evaporation. The ends of tracheae are tiny and highly branched. This design allows the tracheal system to transport air close enough to cells for gas exchange to take place directly across their plasma membranes.

Air moves from the atmosphere into the tracheae and then through the tracheae to the tissues in the insect's body. Is simple diffusion efficient enough to ventilate the system, or is some type of breathing mechanism involved?

If insects ventilate their tracheal system with simple diffusion, then according to Fick's law, the distance that the air would have to diffuse down the tracheae would be very important. In other words, the rate of diffusion of air down the tracheae would be limited in part by the length of the tracheae. In effect, only very small insects have tracheae that are short enough to be efficiently ventilated by simple diffusion.

Many insects are far too large to deliver gases to and from their tissues by simple diffusion alone. How do these large insects ventilate their tracheal system?

Consider a study on the sweet potato hawkmoth. Yutaka Komai set out to investigate how the amount of $O_2$ delivered to the wing muscles changes during flight. To document the partial pressure of oxygen in these muscles, he inserted a needlelike electrode into the flight muscles of a hawkmoth. The electrode was attached to an instrument that measured the partial pressure of oxygen, and the hawkmoth was tethered to a stand (**FIGURE 45.7**).

Komai recorded $P_{O_2}$ as the insect rested and then stimulated the moth to fly by exposing it to wind. The "Results" section of

Figure 45.7 shows how $P_{O_2}$ changed during one such experiment. (The procedure was repeated on several individuals, and the same pattern was observed.)

To read this graph, put your finger on the left-hand end of the orange line and move it toward the right, to where the insect started flying and the line changes to red. Note that $P_{O_2}$ levels in the flight muscles dropped initially. This is not surprising, because flight is an energetically demanding activity. As flying continued, however, $P_{O_2}$ levels recovered until they were nearly as high as when they were at rest.

To explain this observation, biologists propose that the tracheae are alternately compressed and dilated as the muscles around them contract and relax. The muscle contractions and relaxations produce pressure changes that cause the volume of space inside the tracheal system to change (**FIGURE 45.8**). This is a key point: If the volume occupied by a fixed amount of gas expands, the gas pressure decreases. But if the volume that a fixed amount of gas occupies declines, the gas pressure increases.

The volume of the tracheal system increases when muscles relax, causing pressure inside the system to go down and air from the atmosphere to rush in. What happens when muscles

## RESEARCH

**QUESTION:** Does physical activity affect air movement through the tracheal system?

**HYPOTHESIS:** Air moves through the tracheal system faster during physical activity.

**NULL HYPOTHESIS:** Physical activity does not affect the rate of air movement.

**EXPERIMENTAL SETUP:**

Measure oxygen in hawkmoth flight muscle during rest and during flight.

Tether

**PREDICTION:** Flying will increase ventilation of tracheal system, causing increase in $P_{O_2}$ in wing muscle.

**PREDICTION OF NULL HYPOTHESIS:** Flying will not increase ventilation of tracheal system; $P_{O_2}$ in flight muscle will decline steadily during flight.

**RESULTS:**

Flight

Initial drop in oxygen

Recovery of oxygen levels as flying continues

Rest    Rest

$P_{O_2}$ (kPa) — y-axis values: 0, 2, 4, 6, 8, 10, 12

Time (min) — x-axis values: 4, 5, 6, 7, 8, 9

**CONCLUSION:** Muscular contractions may help ventilate the tracheal system in at least some insects.

**FIGURE 45.7 Research Suggests the Tracheal System Is Ventilated during Movement.** On the graph's y-axis, kPa stands for kilopascal, a unit of pressure (or force per unit area).
SOURCE: Komai, Y. 1998. *The Journal of Experimental Biology* 201: 2359–2366.

✔**QUESTION** Why was it important for the researcher to repeat this experiment with several different individuals?

Ground beetle

Tracheae

1 mm

Tracheae dilate when muscles relax

Tracheae compress when muscles contract

200 μm

**FIGURE 45.8 Tracheae Are Dilated and Compressed during Ventilation.** Muscle relaxation and contraction during flight or other activity alternately dilates and compresses tracheae, causing pressure changes that promote air flow in and out of the tracheae. Asterisks in the left image mark tracheal tubes that are compressed in the right image.

contract? The opposite—the volume of the tracheae decreases, pressure inside the system increases, and gas moves out of the tracheae into the atmosphere.

The action of the abdominal and flight muscles therefore stimulates air flow through the insect tracheal system, causing gases to move more quickly than they would by diffusion alone.

In large insects, the movement of gases is further promoted by larger tracheae diameters. These larger diameters increase another variable in Fick's law, the cross-sectional area for gas exchange. As evidence, researchers have shown that the diameter of the tracheae in large beetles is proportionally much larger than that of small beetles. Disproportionally large tracheae allow effective ventilation even in the largest living beetles, which can reach impressive lengths of over 15 cm (6 inches) and weigh over 50 g (3 ounces), the size of a submarine sandwich!

Why don't beetles get even larger than this? Researchers hypothesize that if they did, the size of their tracheae would be so large that there would not be enough space in their limbs for much else. The beetles would lack sufficient muscles and other tissues to support their huge bodies.

In the Paleozoic era about 300 million years ago (mya), however, giant insects flourished. While the largest dragonflies today are about 15 cm in wingspan, during the Paleozoic they grew to be as large as 70 cm (2.3 feet)! How can this be explained?

One major hypothesis posits that giant insects evolved during the Paleozoic era because the atmospheric oxygen concentration was much higher than it is today (**FIGURE 45.9**). Recall that according to Fick's law, the rate of diffusion of a gas from one point to another is affected by the difference in partial pressures of the gas at the two points. During the latter part of the Paleozoic, the value of $P_2 - P_1$ was increased in the equation shown in Figure 45.3. This may have increased the rate of movement of gases through the tracheal system, permitting efficient ventilation in extremely large insects.

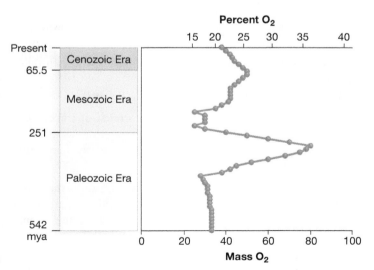

**FIGURE 45.9 Atmospheric Oxygen Levels Peaked during the Paleozoic Era.**

DATA: Berner, R. A. 1999. *Proceedings of the National Academy of Sciences* 96: 10955–10957.

About 50 to 100 million years later, at the start of the Mesozoic era, atmospheric oxygen concentrations declined precipitously. Giant insects went extinct, likely in part because they could no longer supply their tissues with enough oxygen.

## How Do Vertebrate Lungs Work?

In most terrestrial vertebrates, air enters the body through both the nose and mouth. A tube known as the **trachea** (not to be confused with the tracheae of insects) carries the inhaled air to narrower tubes called **bronchi** (singular: **bronchus**). The bronchi branch off into yet narrower tubes, the **bronchioles.** The organs of ventilation, the lungs, enclose the bronchioles and part of the bronchi (**FIGURE 45.10a**, see page 910).

**Lungs** are internal organs that are used for gas exchange. In addition to being found in terrestrial vertebrates—amphibians, reptiles (including birds), and mammals—they occur in many fishes and certain invertebrates.

### Lung Structure and Ventilation Vary among Species

The amount of lung surface area available for gas exchange varies a great deal among species. In frogs and other amphibians, the lung is a simple sac lined with blood vessels. The lungs of mammals, in contrast, are finely divided into tiny sacs called **alveoli** (singular: **alveolus; FIGURE 45.10b**).

Each human lung contains approximately 150 million alveoli, which give mammalian lungs about 40 times more surface area for gas exchange than an equivalent volume of frog lung tissue. As **FIGURE 45.10c** shows, an alveolus provides an interface between air and blood that consists of a thin aqueous film, a layer of epithelial cells, some extracellular matrix (ECM) material, and the wall of a capillary.

In addition to total surface area, the other major feature of lungs that varies among species is mode of ventilation. In the lungs of snails and spiders, air movement takes place by diffusion only. Vertebrates, in contrast, actively ventilate their lungs by pumping air via muscular contractions.

One mechanism for pumping air is **positive pressure ventilation,** used by frogs and related animals. A frog lowers the floor of its throat, increasing the volume there and thus drawing in air from the atmosphere through the nasal passages and into the oral cavity. The animal then closes the nasal passages and contracts its throat muscles. These actions increase the pressure on air in the oral cavity and force it into the lungs.

In effect, frogs push air into their lungs. In contrast, humans and other mammals pull air into their lungs. How does this **negative pressure ventilation** work?

### Ventilation of the Human Lung

The pressure inside the human chest cavity is about 5 mm Hg less than atmospheric pressure. This negative pressure surrounding the lung is just enough to keep the lung expanded. If a wound penetrates the chest wall and the pressure differential between the chest cavity and the atmosphere disappears, the lung on the side of the injury will collapse like a deflated balloon.

**(a)** Airways into the human lungs

Trachea
Lung
Bronchi
Bronchioles

**(b)** Alveoli

Smallest bronchiole
Air
Oxygen-poor blood in
Oxygen-rich blood out
Alveolus
Capillaries

**(c)** The alveolar gas-exchange surface

Air
Oxygen
Aqueous film
Epithelium of alveolus
ECM
Wall of capillary
0.2 μm
Blood

**FIGURE 45.10 Lungs Offer a Thin Membrane with a Large Surface Area for Gas Exchange between Air and Blood. (a)** The human respiratory tract branches repeatedly from the largest airway, the trachea, to the smallest, called bronchioles. The system of airways ends in clusters of tiny sacs called alveoli. **(b)** Alveoli are covered with capillary networks and are **(c)** the site of gas exchange.

Humans ventilate their lungs by changing the pressure within their chest cavity between about −5 mm Hg and −8 mm Hg relative to the atmosphere. As **FIGURE 45.11a** shows, inhalation is based on increasing the volume of the chest cavity and thus lowering the pressure. The change is caused by a downward motion of the thin muscular sheet called the **diaphragm** and an outward motion of the ribs. As the pressure surrounding the lungs drops, air flows into the airways along a pressure gradient.

Exhalation, in contrast, is a passive process—the volume of the chest cavity decreases as the diaphragm and rib muscles relax. Because the lung is elastic, it returns automatically to its original, collapsed shape if it is not stretched or compressed. During exercise, though, exhalation is an energy-demanding, active process.

The changes in pressure that occur during negative pressure ventilation are analogous to changing the pressure within a jar, as shown in **FIGURE 45.11b**.

About 450 mL of air moves into and out of the lungs in an average breath. Only about two-thirds of this volume actually participates in gas exchange, however, because 150 mL of the air occupies **dead space**— air passages that are not lined by a respiratory surface. The trachea and bronchi shown in Figure 45.10a, for example, represent dead space.

Breathing is much more efficient during exercise, when the chest cavity undergoes larger changes in volume. When a person is breathing hard, over 2500 mL of air can move with each inhalation–exhalation cycle, but the 150 mL of dead space stays the same.

**Ventilation of the Bird Lung**  Flight is one of the most energy-demanding activities performed by animals. Even so, some birds fly tens of thousands of kilometers during annual migrations.

Even more impressive, geese regularly fly over the top of Mt. Everest. At this elevation, the partial pressure of oxygen is so low that most humans would immediately black out if they were flown there and dropped off. How are birds able to extract enough oxygen from the atmosphere to support long flights and to fly at high elevations?

**FIGURE 45.12** provides a diagram of ventilation in birds.

1. During inhalation, air flows through the trachea and enters two large air sacs posterior to the lungs.

2. During exhalation, air leaves the posterior air sacs and enters tiny, branching airways, called parabronchi, in the posterior portion of the lungs.

3. During the next inhalation, air moves into parabronchi in the anterior part of the lungs and on to a system of air sacs anterior to the lungs.

4. During the next exhalation, air moves out of the anterior sacs, through the trachea, and out to the atmosphere. Meanwhile, air from the second inhalation is now flowing through the lungs.

The key conclusion from these observations? Airflow through the avian lung is unidirectional.

Why is the avian respiratory system so efficient?

• Dead space is restricted to the short stretch of trachea between the mouth and the opening of the anterior air sacs. As a result, birds use inhaled air much more efficiently than mammals do.

• Gas exchange occurs during both inhalation and exhalation. In contrast, no gas exchange occurs during the exhalation half of the respiratory cycle in mammals. Bird ventilation resembles the continuous ventilation of fish gills in this respect.

• Blood circulates through the bird lung in capillaries that cross the parabronchi perpendicularly. This crosscurrent pattern is less efficient than the countercurrent circulation of fish gills but far more efficient than the weblike arrangement of capillaries that surrounds mammalian alveoli.

**(a)** Lungs expand and contract in response to changes in pressure inside the chest cavity.

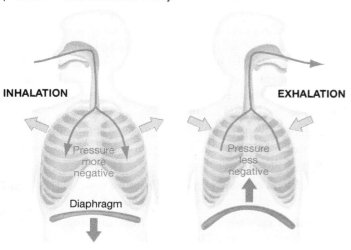

INHALATION

EXHALATION

Pressure more negative

Pressure less negative

Diaphragm

**(b)** Ventilatory forces can be modeled by a balloon in a jar.

Pressure more negative

Pressure less negative

When the diaphragm is pulled down, the balloon inflates.

When the diaphragm is released, the balloon deflates.

**FIGURE 45.11 Changes in the Volume of the Chest Cavity Drive Negative Pressure Ventilation. (a)** Inhalation: When the diaphragm and rib muscles contract, the volume of the lung cavity increases, lowering pressure. In response, air flows into the lungs. Exhalation: When the diaphragm and rib muscles relax, the volume of the lung cavity decreases, causing internal pressure to increase. In response, lung volume decreases—due to elasticity of the lungs—and air flows out. **(b)** A model of negative pressure ventilation.

## Homeostatic Control of Ventilation

An animal is in trouble if its mechanisms of homeostasis fail to maintain blood oxygenation or to eliminate carbon dioxide. Adequate adenosine triphosphate (ATP) production depends on maintaining the partial pressures of oxygen and carbon dioxide within a narrow range, both during rest and vigorous exercise. How is ventilation controlled to achieve this critical homeostasis?

Lung, where gas exchange occurs

Air sacs enable one-way airflow through lung

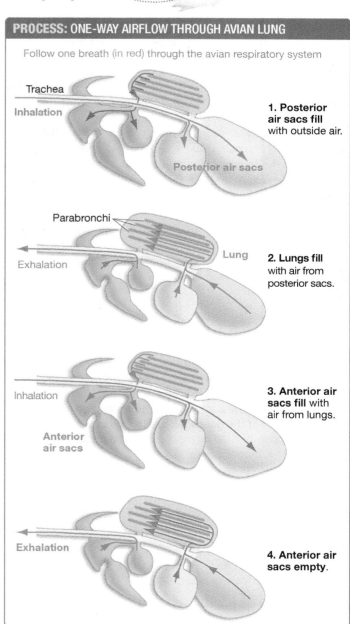

**PROCESS: ONE-WAY AIRFLOW THROUGH AVIAN LUNG**

Follow one breath (in red) through the avian respiratory system

Trachea

Inhalation

Posterior air sacs

**1. Posterior air sacs fill** with outside air.

Parabronchi

Lung

Exhalation

**2. Lungs fill** with air from posterior sacs.

Inhalation

Anterior air sacs

**3. Anterior air sacs fill** with air from lungs.

Exhalation

**4. Anterior air sacs empty.**

**FIGURE 45.12 Air Flows in One Direction through the Bird Lung, Maximizing Gas Exchange.**

When mammals are resting, the rate of breathing is established by the medullary respiratory center, an area at the base of the brain, just above the spinal cord. This center stimulates the rib and diaphragm muscles to contract about 12 to 14 times per minute in humans.

But during exercise, things change. Active muscle tissue takes up more oxygen from the blood. As a result, the partial pressure of oxygen ($P_{O_2}$) in blood drops. Those same muscles release larger quantities of carbon dioxide to the blood, raising its partial pressure ($P_{CO_2}$) in blood. When carbon dioxide reaches the brain, it rapidly diffuses from the blood into the cerebrospinal fluid that bathes the brain. In both blood and cerebrospinal fluid, $CO_2$ reacts with water to form carbonic acid ($H_2CO_3$), which then dissociates to release a hydrogen ion ($H^+$) and a bicarbonate ion ($HCO_3^-$):

$$CO_2 + H_2O \rightleftharpoons H_2CO_3 \rightleftharpoons H^+ + HCO_3^-$$

The result is a slight drop in the pH of blood and cerebrospinal fluid. The change in blood pH is sensed by specialized neurons located near the large arteries that travel from the heart into the neck and to the base of the brain.

Signals from these neurons or from pH detectors in the medullary respiratory center cause the breathing rate to increase. The resulting rise in ventilation rate increases the rate of oxygen delivery to the tissues and the rate at which carbon dioxide is eliminated from the body, restoring $P_{O_2}$ and $P_{CO_2}$ to their resting levels. This control system is so effective that it can maintain stable blood levels of oxygen and carbon dioxide even during intense exercise.

Now let's look more closely at how blood transports oxygen and carbon dioxide between the gas exchange surface and an animal's tissues.

## check your understanding

**If you understand that . . .**

- The rate of diffusion of gases across a respiratory surface depends on the area of the surface, the thickness of the surface, and the difference in partial pressures of the gases across the surface.
- Most large-bodied animals exchange gases via gills, tracheae, or lungs.

✔ **You should be able to . . .**

1. Identify two features that are common to gills, tracheae, and lungs, as well as one trait that is unique to each.
2. When you hold your breath, what happens to the $P_{O_2}$, $P_{CO_2}$, and pH of your blood?

*Answers are available in Appendix A.*

## 45.4 How Are Oxygen and Carbon Dioxide Transported in Blood?

Blood is a connective tissue that consists of cells in a watery extracellular matrix. Besides carrying oxygen and carbon dioxide between cells and the lungs, blood transports nutrients from the digestive tract to other tissues in the body, moves waste products to the kidney and liver for processing, conveys hormones from glands to target tissues, delivers immune system cells to sites of infection, and distributes heat throughout the body.

Given the wide variety of functions that blood serves, it is not surprising that it is a complex tissue. In an average human, 50–65 percent of the blood volume is composed of an extracellular matrix called **plasma.** The remainder of the volume comprises cells and cell fragments that are collectively called formed elements.

The formed elements in blood include platelets, several types of white blood cells, and red blood cells.

- **Platelets** are cell fragments that act to minimize blood loss from ruptured blood vessels. They do so by releasing material that helps form the blockages known as clots.

- **White blood cells** are part of the immune system. They fight infections (as Chapter 51 will explain in detail).

- **Red blood cells** transport oxygen from the lungs to tissues throughout the body. They also play a role in transporting carbon dioxide from tissues to the lungs. In humans, red blood cells make up 99.9 percent of the formed elements.

The human body synthesizes new red blood cells at the rate of 2.5 million per second to replace old red blood cells, which die at the same rate. These red blood cells last for about 120 days. Red blood cells, white blood cells, and platelets develop from stem cells located in the tissue inside bone (bone marrow).

Vertebrates other than mammals transport oxygen in red blood cells that retain their nuclei. But in mammals, red blood cells lose their nuclei as they mature, along with their mitochondria and most other organelles. Mammalian red blood cells are essentially bags filled with approximately 280 million copies of the oxygen-carrying molecule **hemoglobin.**

### Structure and Function of Hemoglobin

Even though oxygen is not highly soluble in water, it is often found in high concentrations in blood. Blood has a high oxygen-carrying capacity because $O_2$ readily binds to the hemoglobin molecules in red blood cells.

The evolution of hemoglobin was a key event in the diversification of animals. By increasing the oxygen-carrying capacity of blood, hemoglobin made it possible for cellular respiration rates to increase. High rates of ATP production, in turn, support high rates of growth, movement, digestion, and other activities.

Hemoglobin is a tetramer, meaning that it consists of four polypeptide chains (**FIGURE 45.13**). Each of the four polypeptide chains binds to a nonprotein group called **heme** (represented by black circles in the figure). Each heme molecule, in turn, contains an iron ion ($Fe^{2+}$) that can bind to an oxygen molecule. As a result, each hemoglobin molecule can bind up to four oxygen molecules. In blood, 98.5 percent of the oxygen is bound to hemoglobin; only 1.5 percent is dissolved in plasma.

**What Is Cooperative Binding?** Blood leaving the human lungs has a $P_{O_2}$ of about 100 mm Hg, while at rest the muscles and other tissues have a $P_{O_2}$ of about 40 mm Hg. This partial pressure difference creates a diffusion gradient that unloads $O_2$ from hemoglobin to the tissues.

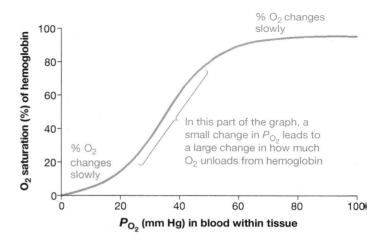

Hemoglobin

Each hemoglobin molecule can bind up to four molecules of oxygen

$O_2$

$O_2$

$O_2$

$O_2$

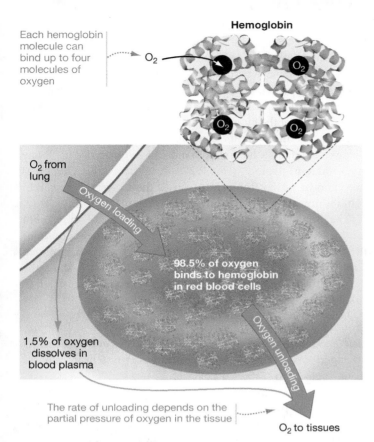

$O_2$ from lung

Oxygen loading

98.5% of oxygen binds to hemoglobin in red blood cells

1.5% of oxygen dissolves in blood plasma

Oxygen unloading

The rate of unloading depends on the partial pressure of oxygen in the tissue

$O_2$ to tissues

**FIGURE 45.13 Hemoglobin Transports Oxygen to Tissues.**

**FIGURE 45.14 The Oxygen–Hemoglobin Equilibrium Curve Is Sigmoidal.** A sigmoidal curve has three distinct regions.

*(Graph: y-axis "$O_2$ saturation (%) of hemoglobin" 0–100; x-axis "$P_{O_2}$ (mm Hg) in blood within tissue" 0–100. Annotations: "% $O_2$ changes slowly", "In this part of the graph, a small change in $P_{O_2}$ leads to a large change in how much $O_2$ unloads from hemoglobin", "% $O_2$ changes slowly".)*

Researchers who studied the dynamics of $O_2$ unloading in tissues found the pattern shown in **FIGURE 45.14**. This graph plots the percentage of $O_2$ saturation of hemoglobin in red blood cells versus the $P_{O_2}$ in the blood within tissues. If saturation of hemoglobin is 100 percent, it means that every possible binding site in hemoglobin contains an oxygen molecule.

The graph in Figure 45.14 is called an **oxygen–hemoglobin equilibrium curve,** or an oxygen dissociation curve or hemoglobin saturation curve. Note that the x-axis plots the partial pressure of oxygen in tissues. In effect, this represents "demand." Oxygen-depleted tissues, where demand for oxygen is high, are on the left-hand part of the horizontal axis; oxygen-rich tissues are toward the right. The y-axis, in contrast, plots the percentage of hemoglobin molecules in blood that are saturated with oxygen—a measure of "supply," or how many oxygen molecules on average are bound to hemoglobin. Each 25 percent change in saturation corresponds to an average of one additional oxygen molecule bound per hemoglobin molecule or one oxygen molecule delivered to tissues.

The most remarkable feature of the oxygen–hemoglobin equilibrium curve is that it is sigmoidal, or S-shaped. The pattern occurs because the binding of each successive oxygen molecule to a subunit of the hemoglobin molecule causes a conformational change in the protein that makes the remaining subunits much more likely to bind oxygen.

This phenomenon is called **cooperative binding.** Conversely, the loss of a bound oxygen molecule changes hemoglobin's conformation in a way that makes the loss of additional oxygen molecules more likely.

**Why Is Cooperative Binding Important?** To understand why cooperative binding is important, use **FIGURE 45.15a** (see page 914) to figure out what happens to hemoglobin saturation when oxygen demand in tissues changes.

Let's begin with some basic observations. When blood arrives at tissues from the lungs, hemoglobin saturation is close to 100 percent. At rest, tissue $P_{O_2}$ is typically about 40 mm Hg. But during exercise, cells are using so much oxygen in cellular respiration that tissue $P_{O_2}$ drops to about 30 mm Hg. Now,

- Put your finger on the x-axis at 40 mm Hg, trace the dashed line up until it hits the equilibrium curve, and check where this point is on the y-axis. The answer is about 52 percent. This means that when tissues are at rest, hemoglobin unloads about half of its oxygen (about 48 percent) to the tissues.

- Now put your finger on the x-axis at 30 mm Hg, trace the dashed line up, and check hemoglobin saturation at this point on the curve. The answer is about 22 percent. This means that when tissues are exercising, hemoglobin unloads about 78 percent of its oxygen to tissues.

Here's the punch line: In response to a relatively small change in tissue $P_{O_2}$, there is a relatively large change in the percentage of saturation of hemoglobin. The large change occurs because the equilibrium curve is extremely steep in the range of $P_{O_2}$ values commonly observed in tissues. The curve is steep because of cooperative binding. Cooperative binding is important because it makes hemoglobin exquisitely sensitive to changes in the of $P_{O_2}$ tissues.

✔ If you understand this concept, you should be able to explain the consequences of an oxygen–hemoglobin equilibrium curve with a middle section that is even steeper than the one shown in Figure 45.15a.

**(a) With cooperative binding,** large amounts of $O_2$ are delivered to resting and exercising tissues.

**(b) Without cooperative binding,** smaller amounts of $O_2$ would be delivered to resting and exercising tissues.

**FIGURE 45.15 Cooperative Binding of $O_2$ by Hemoglobin Results in Greater $O_2$ Delivery than Noncooperative Binding.** The hemoglobin is almost 100 percent saturated with oxygen until it arrives at tissues.

If cooperative binding did not occur, all four subunits of hemoglobin would load or unload oxygen independently of each other. They would lose or gain oxygen in direct proportion to the partial pressure of oxygen in the blood, until the molecule was either completely saturated or unsaturated with oxygen. There would be a linear relationship between hemoglobin saturation and tissue $P_{O_2}$—not a sigmoidal one.

**FIGURE 45.15b** shows noncooperative binding. As the dashed lines on this graph indicate, a relatively small change in oxygen delivery would occur when tissue $P_{O_2}$ changes from its resting level of about 40 mm Hg to 30 mm Hg. Specifically, hemoglobin would unload about 100% − 68% = 32% of its oxygen when tissues are at rest, and about 100% − 52% = 48% of its oxygen during exercise. This difference—about 16 percent—is much less than the 30 percent change observed with cooperative binding.

**How Do Temperature and pH Affect Oxygen Unloading from Hemoglobin?** Cooperative binding is only part of the story behind

oxygen delivery. Hemoglobin—like other proteins—is sensitive to changes in pH and temperature.

As noted above, the temperature and partial pressure of $CO_2$ rise in active muscle tissue during exercise. The $CO_2$ produced by exercising muscle reacts with the water in blood to form carbonic acid, which dissociates and releases a hydrogen ion. As a result, the pH of the blood in exercising muscle drops.

Decreases in pH alter hemoglobin's conformation. These shape changes make hemoglobin more likely to unload $O_2$ at any given value of tissue $P_{O_2}$. As **FIGURE 45.16** shows, this phenomenon, known as the **Bohr shift,** causes the oxygen–hemoglobin equilibrium curve to shift to the right when pH declines.

The Bohr shift is important because it makes hemoglobin more likely to release oxygen during exercise or other conditions in which $P_{CO_2}$ is high, pH is low, and tissues are under oxygen stress. Increasing temperature has the same result: It shifts the curve to the right, representing a greater unloading of oxygen to tissues at any given $P_{O_2}$.

**Oxygen Delivery by Hemoglobin Is Extremely Efficient** To appreciate cooperative binding and the Bohr shift in action, consider an experiment on how the oxygen transport system in rainbow trout responds to sustained exercise.

To begin, biologists had fish swim continuously against a current in a water tunnel. As the researchers increased the speed of the current and thus the swimming speed of the fish, they periodically sampled the $O_2$ content of arterial and venous blood. Arterial blood is freshly oxygenated and moving away from the gills; venous blood is returning to the gills from the rest of the body.

Not surprisingly, the biologists found that arterial $O_2$ levels remained fairly constant as swimming speed increased—meaning the gills continued to work efficiently enough to saturate hemoglobin with oxygen.

**FIGURE 45.16 The Bohr Shift Makes Hemoglobin More Likely to Release Oxygen to Tissues with Low pH.** As pH drops, oxygen becomes less likely to stay bound to hemoglobin at all values of tissue $P_{O_2}$. Exercising tissues have lower pH than resting tissues and thus receive more oxygen from hemoglobin.

✓**QUANTITATIVE** Estimate how much more oxygen is unloaded from hemoglobin at pH 7.2 than at pH 7.4 when the tissue has a $P_{O_2}$ of 30 mm Hg.

In contrast, the $O_2$ content of venous blood, which had undergone gas exchange with the tissues, dropped steadily as swimming speed increased. When the fish had reached their maximum sustainable speed, virtually all the oxygen that had been available in the blood had been extracted.

The data show that in hard-working tissues, the combination of increased temperature, lower pH, and lower $P_{O_2}$ caused hemoglobin to become almost completely deoxygenated. Oxygen-delivery systems based on hemoglobin are extremely efficient.

**Comparing Hemoglobins**  Hemoglobin molecules from different individuals or species may vary in ways that affect fitness—the ability to survive and produce viable offspring. As an example, consider the oxygen–hemoglobin equilibrium curves in **FIGURE 45.17**. The curve in dark red is from a pregnant woman; the curve in light red is from a fetus she is carrying.

The hemoglobin found in fetuses is encoded by different genes than adult hemoglobin and has a distinctive structure and function. Specifically, the oxygen–hemoglobin equilibrium curve for fetal hemoglobin is shifted to the left with respect to the curve for adult hemoglobin.

Recall that the rightward shift of the curve means that hemoglobin is more likely to release oxygen. The leftward shift in Figure 45.17 means that fetal hemoglobin is less likely to give up oxygen—it binds oxygen more tightly. Stated another way, fetal hemoglobin has a higher affinity for oxygen than adult hemoglobin does at every $P_{O_2}$.

This shift is crucial. In the placenta, hemoglobin from the mother's blood gets close to hemoglobin from the fetus's blood. Because fetal hemoglobin has such a high affinity for oxygen, there is a transfer of oxygen from the mother's blood to the fetus's blood. The difference in hemoglobin structure and function ensures an adequate supply of oxygen as the fetus develops.

## $CO_2$ Transport and the Buffering of Blood pH

The carbon dioxide that is produced by cellular respiration in the tissues enters the blood, where it reacts with water to form carbonic acid, which dissociates into bicarbonate and hydrogen ions. Recall that the resulting drop in blood pH stimulates an increase in breathing rate. Rapid exhalation of $CO_2$ then counteracts the drop in blood pH.

Homeostasis with respect to blood pH is reinforced by an elegant series of events that take place inside red blood cells. Biologists were able to work out what was happening when they discovered large amounts of the enzyme **carbonic anhydrase** in red blood cells.

**The Role of Carbonic Anhydrase and Hemoglobin**  Recall that carbonic anhydrase catalyzes the formation of carbonic acid from carbon dioxide in water (see Chapter 44). Consequently, $CO_2$ that diffuses into red blood cells is quickly converted to bicarbonate ions and protons. The same reaction occurs in the plasma surrounding red blood cells, although much more slowly in the absence of the enzyme.

Why is the carbonic anhydrase activity in red blood cells so important? The answer has two parts.

1. The protons produced by the enzyme-catalyzed reaction induce the Bohr shift, which makes hemoglobin more likely to release oxygen.

2. The partial pressure of $CO_2$ in blood drops when carbon dioxide is converted to soluble bicarbonate ions, maintaining a strong partial pressure gradient favoring the entry of $CO_2$ into red blood cells.

Thus, carbonic anhydrase activity makes $CO_2$ uptake from tissues more efficient (**FIGURE 45.18**).

**FIGURE 45.18 Carbonic Anhydrase Is Key to $CO_2$ Transport in Blood.** When $CO_2$ diffuses into red blood cells, carbonic anhydrase quickly converts it to carbonic acid, which dissociates into a bicarbonate ion ($HCO_3^-$) and a proton ($H^+$). This reaction maintains the partial pressure gradient favoring the entry of $CO_2$ into red blood cells. The protons produced by the reaction bind to deoxygenated hemoglobin. Most $CO_2$ in blood is transported to the lungs in the form of $HCO_3^-$.

✔ **QUESTION** This diagram shows the sequence of events in tissues. After reading the rest of Section 45.4, explain what happens when the red blood cell in the diagram reaches the lungs.

**FIGURE 45.17 Fetal Hemoglobin Binds Oxygen More Tightly than Maternal Hemoglobin.**

Once bicarbonate ions form in the red blood cell, they are transported into the blood plasma. The outcome is that most $CO_2$ is transported in blood (specifically in plasma) in the form of $HCO_3^-$—the bicarbonate ion. In contrast, the protons produced by the reaction stay inside red blood cells.

What ultimately happens to these protons? When hemoglobin is carrying few oxygen molecules, it has a high affinity for protons. As a result, it takes up much of the $H^+$ that is produced by the dissociation of carbonic acid. The hemoglobin acts as a **buffer**—a compound that minimizes changes in pH.

**What Happens When Blood Returns to the Lungs?** When deoxygenated blood reaches the alveoli, its environment changes dramatically. In the lungs, a partial pressure gradient favors the diffusion of $CO_2$ from plasma and red blood cells to the atmosphere within the alveoli. As $CO_2$ diffuses from the blood into the alveoli, $P_{CO_2}$ in blood declines.

The drop in blood $P_{CO_2}$ reverses the chemical reactions that occurred in tissues:

1. Hydrogen ions (protons) leave their binding sites on hemoglobin.

2. Protons react with bicarbonate to form $CO_2$.

3. $CO_2$ diffuses into the alveoli and is exhaled from the lungs.

In the meantime, hemoglobin has picked up $O_2$. Hemoglobin's affinity for oxygen is high in the alveoli because blood pH rises as $P_{CO_2}$ declines.

When blood leaves the lungs, it has unloaded its carbon dioxide, and its hemoglobin is saturated with oxygen. The cycle begins anew.

## check your understanding

**If you understand that . . .**

- In blood, oxygen is bound to hemoglobin and transported inside red blood cells. Carbon dioxide is converted to bicarbonate ions and transported in plasma.
- Hemoglobin has several properties that make it an effective transport protein, including cooperative binding of oxygen, the Bohr shift response to low pH, and the ability to bind the protons that are generated when carbon dioxide is converted to bicarbonate ions.

✔ **You should be able to . . .**

Predict how the oxygen–hemoglobin equilibrium curves measured in Tibetan people, whose ancestors have lived at high elevations for thousands of years, compare to curves from people whose ancestors have lived at sea level for many generations.

*Answers are available in Appendix A.*

## 45.5 Circulation

According to Fick's law, differences in the partial pressure of gases are only part of the story when it comes to understanding diffusion rates. Surface area—$A$ in the equation featured in Figure 45.3—also plays a key role.

Animals without circulatory systems have various ways of maximizing the surface area available for diffusion of gases and other key solutes:

- Animals that are only a few millimeters in size, like rotifers and tardigrades, have a small enough volume that diffusion over their body surface is adequate to keep them alive.

- The flattened bodies of flatworms and tapeworms give these animals a high surface-area-to-volume ratio (see Chapter 42). In these species, too, molecules are exchanged with the environment directly across the outer body surface.

- Diffusion across the body wall also occurs in roundworms, where gas exchange is facilitated by muscular contractions in the body wall. Diffusion is enhanced as roundworms circulate fluids by sloshing them back and forth.

- Jellyfish and corals have a large, highly folded gastrovascular cavity that offers a large surface area for exchange of molecules with the environment.

In larger animals, however, the problem of providing a large enough surface area for diffusion is solved by a circulatory system. A circulatory system carries transport tissues called blood or hemolymph into close contact with every cell in the body. In this case, "close contact" is a distance of about 0.1 mm between the smallest blood vessels and cells within tissues. Diffusion is efficient at this scale.

To explore how circulatory systems work, let's start by distinguishing the two most basic types—open and closed. Open circulatory systems occur in most invertebrates, while all vertebrates have closed systems.

### What Is an Open Circulatory System?

In an **open circulatory system,** a fluid connective tissue called hemolymph is actively pumped throughout the body in vessels. The hemolymph is not confined exclusively to the vessels, however. Instead, hemolymph comes into direct contact with tissues. As a result, the molecules being exchanged between hemolymph and tissues do not have to diffuse across the wall of a vessel. Hemolymph transports wastes and nutrients and may also contain oxygen-carrying pigments, some cells, and clotting agents.

**FIGURE 45.19** illustrates the open circulatory system in a clam. Note that a muscular organ called the **heart** pumps hemolymph into vessels that empty into an open, fluid-filled space. Hemolymph is returned to vessels and then the heart when the heart relaxes and its internal pressure drops below that in the body cavity. General body movements also move hemolymph to and from the heart.

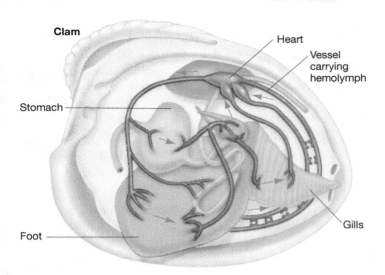

**Clam**

Heart

Vessel carrying hemolymph

Stomach

Foot

Gills

**FIGURE 45.19 Clams Have Open Circulatory Systems.** This drawing shows a clam with the top of the shell removed. Red arrows show the direction of hemolymph flow.

Because it moves throughout the volume of the body, hemolymph is under relatively low pressure in open circulatory systems. As a result, hemolymph flow rates may also be low. These features make open circulatory systems most suitable for relatively sedentary organisms, which do not have high oxygen demands.

Insects, with their rapid movements and more active lifestyles, are an exception to this rule. In the open circulatory systems of insects, the limitations imposed by low hemolymph pressure are overcome by their tracheal respiratory system, which delivers oxygen directly to the tissues.

Another characteristic of open circulatory systems, because they lack discrete, continuous vessels, is that the flow of hemolymph cannot be directed toward tissues that have a high oxygen demand and $CO_2$ buildup. An open circulatory system moves hemolymph throughout an animal's body in much the same way that a ceiling fan moves air throughout a room in a house.

Crustaceans are an important exception to this rule, however. Even though their circulatory system is classified as open, these species have a network of small vessels that can preferentially send hemolymph to tissues with the highest oxygen demands.

## What Is a Closed Circulatory System?

In a **closed circulatory system,** blood flows in a continuous circuit through the body, under pressure generated by a heart. Because the blood is confined to vessels, a closed system can generate enough pressure to maintain a high flow rate.

In a closed circulatory system, blood flow can also be directed in a precise way in response to the tissues' needs. For example, blood can be shunted to leg muscles during exercise, to the intestines after a meal, or to regions of the brain engaged in particular mental tasks.

**Which Lineages Have Closed Circulatory Systems?** Closed circulatory systems are found in vertebrates and a few other lineages where individuals tend to be active. Earthworms and other annelids, for example, have a closed circulatory system and exchange gases with the environment across their thin, moist skin, which has a dense supply of capillaries. As a result, annelids are able to obtain and circulate enough oxygen to support intense muscular activity. Most live as active burrowers and hunters.

A similar situation occurs in squid, octopuses, and other cephalopods that hunt down prey. The closed circulatory system of these mollusks generates high rates of blood flow, which oxygenates their muscles well enough to support rapid movements and a predatory lifestyle.

Closed circulatory systems contain various types of blood vessels, each having a distinct structure and function. Let's review the major types of blood vessels and then consider how the vessels of a closed circulatory system interact with the lymphatic system.

**Types of Blood Vessels** An enormous amount of tubing is required to distribute blood within "diffusion distance" of every cell in the body. If all the blood vessels in a human body were laid end to end, they would stretch about 100,000 km (over 60,000 miles).

Blood vessels are classified as follows:

- **Arteries** are tough, thick-walled vessels that take blood away from the heart. Small arteries are called **arterioles.**

- **Capillaries** are vessels whose walls are just one cell thick, allowing exchange of gases and other molecules between blood and tissues. Networks of capillaries are called **capillary beds.**

- **Veins** are thin-walled vessels that return blood to the heart. Small veins are called **venules.**

The structure of arteries, capillaries, and veins correlates closely with their functions in a closed circulatory system. For example, the heart ejects blood into a large artery, usually called the **aorta.** All arteries have both muscle fibers and elastic fibers in their walls, but elastic fibers dominate the walls of the aorta. As a result, the aorta can expand when blood enters it under high pressure from the heart.

When a contraction of the heart ends, the diameter of the aorta returns to its resting state. This elastic response propels blood away from the heart and augments the force generated by the heart contraction. Similar types of secondary pumping action occur to some extent in other arteries as well. This feature helps maintain forward blood flow in the period between heart contractions.

The walls of arteries and arterioles have a thick layer composed of smooth muscle fibers. When the muscle fibers relax, the vessel diameter increases, resistance to flow is reduced, and blood flow increases in the tissues served by the vessel. But when these muscle fibers contract, the vessel diameter decreases, increasing resistance to flow and slowing the flow of blood in the vessel. In this way, blood flow to tissues can be carefully regulated by signals from the nervous system.

Capillaries are the smallest blood vessels. Their walls are only one cell layer thick, and they are just wide enough to let red blood cells through one at a time (**FIGURE 45.20a**). The extreme thinness of capillaries and the dense network they form throughout the body make them suitable sites for the exchange of gases, nutrients, and wastes between blood and the other tissues.

In some organs, such as the liver, the walls of capillaries contain many small openings that further diminish the barrier to diffusion between blood and the tissues. Despite their thinness, it is rare for capillaries to rupture, because blood pressure drops dramatically as blood passes through arterioles on its way to capillary beds.

After blood from arteries and arterioles passes through capillaries, veins carry it back to the heart. Because blood is under relatively low pressure by the time it exits the tissues, veins have thinner walls and larger interior diameters than arteries do (**FIGURE 45.20b**).

Blood flow in veins is speeded by muscle activity in the extremities, which compresses large veins. Larger veins also contain one-way **valves,** which are thin flaps of tissue that prevent any backflow of blood.

All veins contain some muscle fibers, which contract in response to signals from the nervous system, decreasing the diameter and overall volume of the vessels. Blood pressure in a closed circulatory system is regulated, in part, by actively adjusting the volume of blood contained within the veins.

**What Is Interstitial Fluid?** The relatively high operating pressure of closed circulatory systems, combined with the thinness of capillaries, produces a small but steady leakage of fluid from these blood vessels into the surrounding space. The area between cells is called interstitial space; the fluid that fills it is **interstitial fluid.** Blood cells are retained within capillaries, so interstitial fluid resembles plasma in its electrolyte composition.

Why does interstitial fluid build up? In 1896 Ernest Starling proposed that two forces were at work (**FIGURE 45.21**):

1. There is an outward-directed hydrostatic force in capillaries, created by the pressure on blood generated by the heart. This force is analogous to the pressure that drives water through the wall of a leaky garden hose.

2. There is also an inward-directed osmotic force across the capillary walls, created by the higher concentration of solutes in the blood plasma than in the interstitial space.

Starling reasoned that at the end of the capillary nearest to an arteriole, the hydrostatic force (the blood pressure) would exceed the osmotic force. If so, then in that location fluid would move out of the capillary into the interstitial space. But because blood pressure drops as fluid passes through a long, thin tube, Starling proposed that at the venous end of the capillary, the inward-directed osmotic force would exceed the outward-directed hydrostatic force. Thus, the fluid that was lost at the arteriolar end of the capillary would be largely reclaimed at the venous end.

Note the adverb "largely," however—not all interstitial fluid is reabsorbed by capillaries. In Figure 45.21, not all of the fluid entering the interstitial space at the arteriolar end of the capillary

**(a)** Capillaries are small and extremely thin walled.

Red blood cells

10 µm

**Capillary**

Nucleus

Endothelial cells

Basement membrane

**(b)** Veins and arteries differ in structure.

Red blood cells

Red blood cells

20 µm

**Vein**
(Small-sized)

**Artery**
(Small-sized)

Fibrous tissue

Muscle tissue

Elastic tissue

Endothelium

**FIGURE 45.20 The Structures of Capillaries, Veins, and Arteries Reflect Their Different Functions.**
Notice the differences in relative wall thickness and overall size.

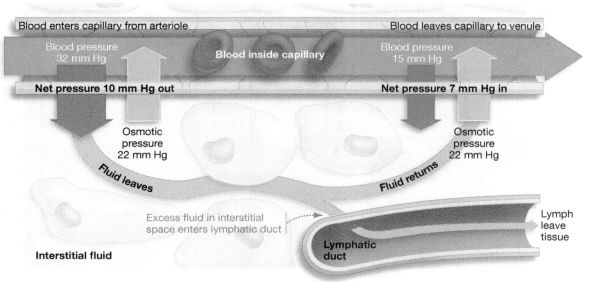

The balance of blood pressure and osmotic forces favors fluid loss from the beginning (inflow end) of capillaries and fluid recovery at the other (outflow) end. Fluid that is not recovered by the capillaries is transported out of the tissue as lymph, which eventually rejoins the blood circulation.

Labels in figure: Blood enters capillary from arteriole · Blood pressure 32 mm Hg · Net pressure 10 mm Hg out · Osmotic pressure 22 mm Hg · Fluid leaves · Interstitial fluid · Blood inside capillary · Excess fluid in interstitial space enters lymphatic duct · Blood leaves capillary to venule · Blood pressure 15 mm Hg · Net pressure 7 mm Hg in · Osmotic pressure 22 mm Hg · Fluid returns · Lymphatic duct · Lymph leave tissue

bed has reentered the bloodstream at the venous end—there is a net buildup of interstitial fluid. What happens to this fluid?

**The Role of the Lymphatic System** Starling proposed that because interstitial fluid is continually added to the interstitial space, there must be a mechanism for draining the excess fluid. In fact, the fluid is collected in the **lymphatic system:** a collection of thin-walled, branching tubules called lymphatic vessels that permeate all tissues. Interstitial fluid that enters the lymphatic ducts is called **lymph.** Lymphatic vessels join with one another, like the tributaries of a river, to form larger vessels. The largest lymphatic vessels return excess interstitial fluid, in the form of lymph, to the major veins entering the heart.

The importance of the lymphatic system becomes evident when lymphatic vessels are damaged or blocked. For example, a disease called elephantiasis results when the lymphatic vessels in the extremities are blocked by parasitic worms that are transmitted from person to person via mosquito bites. The affected limbs swell dramatically because the lymph cannot be drained, and the skin thickens, cracks, and becomes very painful.

## How Does the Heart Work?

In animals with closed circulatory systems, the heart contains at least two chambers: There is at least one thin-walled **atrium** (plural: **atria**), which receives blood, and at least one thick-walled **ventricle,** which generates the force required to propel blood out of the heart and through the circulatory system. Atria are separated from ventricles by atrioventricular valves.

The phylogenetic tree in **FIGURE 45.22** (see page 920) shows the evolutionary relationships among some major vertebrate groups and a simplified sketch of the heart and circulatory system for each lineage. Two points are particularly important to note:

1. The number of atria and ventricles in the heart increased as vertebrates diversified. Fish hearts have one atrium and one ventricle; amphibians, turtles, lizards, and snakes have two atria and one ventricle; crocodilians, birds, and mammals have two atria and two ventricles. It is common to refer to these as two-, three-, and four-chambered hearts, respectively.

2. In fishes, the circulatory system forms a single circuit—one loop services the gills and the body. In other lineages, there are separate circuits to the lungs and to the body.

**Why Did Multichambered Hearts and Multiple Circulations Evolve?** To understand these evolutionary patterns, let's first consider the relatively simple heart and circulatory system found in fishes. A single atrium and ventricle and single circuit are adequate in fishes. Even though blood pressure drops as blood passes through the gills—due to the mechanical resistance to flow that occurs in the gills' capillary beds—blood pressure stays high enough to move blood throughout the body. This is largely because fishes live in the neutrally buoyant environment of water, where gravity does not have a large impact on blood flow.

In contrast, gravity has a much larger effect on circulation in land-dwelling vertebrates. Gravity has a particularly antagonistic effect on the flow of blood to elevated portions of the body. To overcome gravity in terrestrial environments, blood must be pumped at high pressure. However, the capillaries and alveoli of the lungs are too thin to withstand high pressures.

The successful solution in terrestrial vertebrates was the evolution of two separate pumping circuits:

1. The **pulmonary circulation** is a lower-pressure circuit to and from the lung.

2. The **systemic circulation** is a higher-pressure circuit to and from the rest of the body.

The pulmonary and systemic circulations are completely separated in the four-chambered hearts of crocodilians, birds, and mammals. On the other hand, the pulmonary and systemic

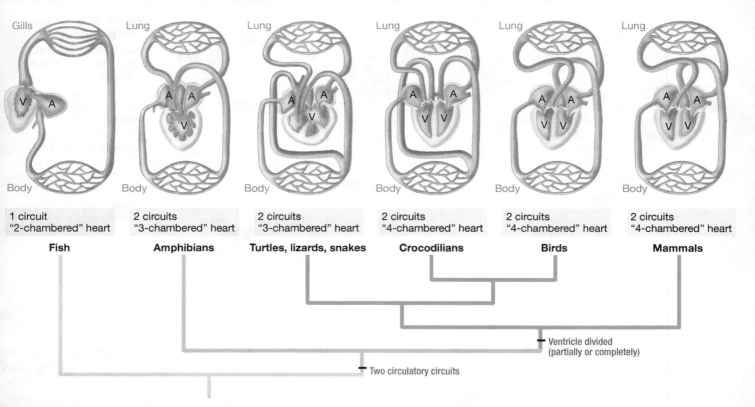

**FIGURE 45.22 As Vertebrate Circulatory Systems Evolved, the Number of Atria and Ventricles Increased.**
"A" denotes the atria—chambers that receive blood coming into the heart from the body and the gills or lungs.
"V" denotes the ventricles—chambers that pump blood out to the gills or lungs and the body.

circulations are only partially separated in the hearts of amphibians, turtles, lizards, and snakes. In these lineages, blood from the right and left atria may mix in the common ventricle before being expelled from the heart to the lungs or to the body. Turtles, lizards, and snakes, however, have partially divided ventricles that can limit the amount of mixing that occurs there (Figure 45.22).

In addition, turtles, lizards, and snakes have a bypass vessel running from the right side of the ventricle directly into the

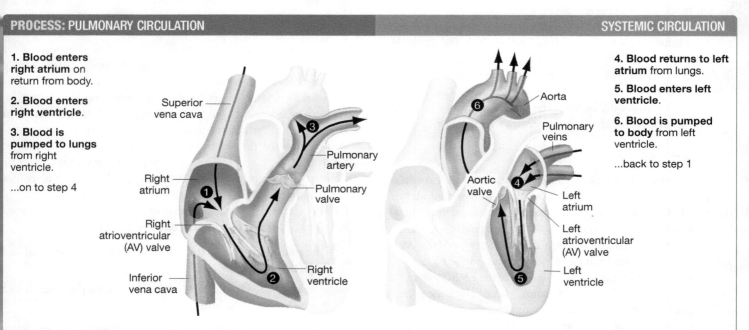

**PROCESS: PULMONARY CIRCULATION**

**SYSTEMIC CIRCULATION**

**1. Blood enters right atrium** on return from body.

**2. Blood enters right ventricle.**

**3. Blood is pumped to lungs** from right ventricle.

...on to step 4

**4. Blood returns to left atrium** from lungs.

**5. Blood enters left ventricle.**

**6. Blood is pumped to body** from left ventricle.

...back to step 1

Superior vena cava

Pulmonary artery

Pulmonary valve

Right atrium

Pulmonary valve

Right atrioventricular (AV) valve

Inferior vena cava

Right ventricle

Aorta

Pulmonary veins

Aortic valve

Left atrium

Left atrioventricular (AV) valve

Left ventricle

**FIGURE 45.23 The Human Heart Maintains Separation of Oxygenated and Deoxygenated Blood.** Blood flows through the chambers in the sequence shown.

systemic circulation. This bypass vessel is also observed in the unusual four-chambered hearts of crocodilians. The bypass vessels have an important function: They shunt blood from the pulmonary to the systemic circulation when the animal is underwater and not breathing. The result is a great reduction in blood flow to the lungs at those times.

Unlike reptiles, the hearts of birds and mammals have completely divided ventricles and lack a bypass vessel. This configuration completely separates the pulmonary and systemic circuits.

**The Human Heart** Your heart is located in the chest cavity, between your lungs, and is roughly the size of your fist. As **FIGURE 45.23** shows, the human circulatory system returns blood from the body to the right atrium of the heart. This blood is low in oxygen, and it arrives via two large veins called the inferior (lower) and superior (upper) **venae cavae** (singular: **vena cava**).

When the muscles that line the right atrium contract, they send deoxygenated blood to the right ventricle. The right ventricle, in turn, contracts and sends blood out to the lungs, via the **pulmonary artery.** In this way, the right ventricle powers the movement of blood through the pulmonary circulation.

Blood flows from atrium to ventricle to artery in only one direction, because one-way valves separate the heart's chambers from each other and from the adjacent arteries. As Figure 45.23 indicates, the valves are flaps, oriented to ensure a one-way flow of blood with little or no backflow. If heart valves are damaged or defective, the resulting backflow can be heard through a stethoscope. The backflow reduces the organ's efficiency and is called a **heart murmur.**

After blood circulates through the capillary beds in the lung's alveoli and becomes oxygenated, it returns to the heart through the **pulmonary veins.** The oxygenated blood enters the left atrium.

When the left atrium contracts, it pushes blood into the left ventricle. The walls of the left ventricle are so thick with muscle cells that their contraction sends oxygenated blood at high pressure through the aorta and into the arteries and capillaries that make up the systemic circulation.

**FIGURE 45.24** summarizes the flow pattern through the human circulatory system and the blood gas concentrations at various points in the pulmonary and systemic circulations. Notice that blood vessels are called arteries or veins according to the direction of blood flow relative to the heart, not because of the oxygen content of the blood in them. Thus, the pulmonary artery is called an artery because it takes blood away from the heart, even though this blood is low in oxygen.

In healthy individuals, gas exchange in the lungs and tissues is rapid relative to the rate at which blood flows through capillaries. This situation is beneficial: It ensures that the maximum amount of oxygen is taken up and the maximum amount of carbon dioxide is released.

Similarly, the slow passage of blood through capillaries means that a maximum amount of oxygen is released from blood to tissues and a maximum amount of carbon dioxide is taken up. As

**FIGURE 45.24 Partial Pressures of Gases Vary throughout the Human Circulatory System.**

✔**QUESTION** Why are the partial pressures of oxygen and carbon dioxide in exhaled air intermediate in magnitude between the partial pressures in inhaled and alveolar air?

a result, partial pressures for oxygen and carbon dioxide in the tissues and the systemic veins are equal.

**Electrical Activation of the Heart** Like other muscle cells, cardiac muscle cells contract in response to electrical signals. In invertebrates, the electrical impulses that trigger contraction come directly from the nervous system. But in vertebrates, a group of cells in the heart itself is responsible for generating the initial signal.

The cells that initiate contraction in the vertebrate heart are known as **pacemaker cells.** They are located in a region of the right atrium called the **sinoatrial (SA) node.**

The SA node and the muscle cells of the heart receive input from the nervous system and from chemical messengers carried in the blood. These inputs are important for regulating both the heart rate and the strength of ventricular contraction. In this way, the amount of blood moving through the circulatory system varies in response to electrical signals and hormones. During the "fight or flight" response (introduced in Chapter 49), for example, a chemical signal called epinephrine causes both heart rate and contraction strength to increase—sending more blood through the body in preparation for rapid movement.

As carefully regulated as the heart rate and contraction strength may be, a vertebrate heart will continue to beat even if all nerves supplying it are severed. Why? An electrical impulse that stimulates contraction is generated in the SA node and rapidly conducted throughout the right and left atria. The signal spreads quickly from cell to cell because of a striking property of cardiac muscle cells: They form physical and electrical connections with each other.

All cardiac muscle cells branch to contact several other cardiac muscle cells, join end to end with these neighboring cells (see Figure 42.5), and connect to them by specialized structures called **intercalated discs.** Because these discs contain many gap junctions (cell-to-cell connections described in Chapter 11), electrical signals pass directly from one cardiac muscle cell to the next.

The electrical activation of the heart is reflected in the orange line on the bottom of **FIGURE 45.25**. This line is an **electrocardiogram,** or **EKG**—a recording of the electrical events that occur over the course of a cardiac cycle. An EKG recording is generated by amplifying the overall electrical signal conducted from the heart to the chest wall through the tissues of the body. By inspecting an EKG, physicians can diagnose disturbances of heart rhythm and detect damage to the heart muscle.

The drawings above the graph in Figure 45.25 show where the key electrical events are happening.

1. The SA node generates an electrical signal.

2. The signal from the SA node is quickly propagated to atrial muscle cells. As a result, the atria contract simultaneously and eject blood into the ventricles.

3. As the atria begin to contract, the signal is conducted to an area of the heart called the **atrioventricular (AV) node.** The AV node delays the signal slightly before passing it to the ventricles. The delay allows the ventricles to fill completely with blood from the atria before they contract.

4. After the delay, the electrical impulse is rapidly transmitted through specialized fibers in the muscular wall that separates the ventricles. The impulse spreads through both ventricles, causing them to contract as the atria relax. The ventricles empty efficiently because the signal and the resulting muscular contraction move from the bottom up to the top of each ventricle—toward the arteries that allow blood to exit.

5. The final electrical event occurs as the ventricles relax and their cells recover—restoring their electrical state before contraction.

✔ If you understand these concepts, you should be able to predict how the amount of blood ejected from the ventricles would change if there were no delay at the AV node.

**PROCESS: ELECTRICAL ACTIVATION OF THE HEART**

1. Signal originates at SA node.
2. Signal spreads over atria; atria contract.
3. Signal delays at AV node.
4. Signal spreads down conducting fibers to bottom of ventricles; ventricles contract.
5. Ventricles relax.

**FIGURE 45.25 Sequential Electrical Activation Leads to Coordinated Contraction of the Heart.** The rate and strength of contractions control the pressure in the chambers and arteries.

**The Cardiac Cycle** The electrical signals originating from the SA node ensure that the atria contract simultaneously, and the delay at the AV node ensures that the atria are relaxed by the time the ventricles contract. The contraction phases of the atria and the ventricles, called **systole,** are therefore closely coordinated with their relaxation phases, or **diastole.**

This sequence of contraction and relaxation is called the **cardiac cycle.** It consists of one diastole and one systole for both atria and ventricles.

Ventricular contraction (ventricular systole) leads to a rapid increase in pressure within both ventricles, as recorded in the dark purple line in **FIGURE 45.26.** Blood is ejected into the pulmonary artery and the aorta when ventricular pressure exceeds the pressure within each respective artery. Blood pressure measured in the systemic arterial circulation at the peak of ventricular ejection into the aorta is called the **systolic blood pressure.** Blood pressure measured just before ventricular ejection is called the **diastolic blood pressure.**

Clinicians report blood pressure measurements in fractional notation, where systolic pressure is the numerator and diastolic pressure is the denominator. People with blood pressures consistently higher than 140/90 mm Hg have high blood pressure, or **hypertension.**

Hypertension is a serious concern to physicians because it can lead to a variety of defects in the heart and circulatory system. Abnormally high blood pressure puts mechanical stress on arteries. If the walls of an artery fail, the individual may experience heart attack, stroke, kidney failure, and burst or damaged vessels.

## Patterns in Blood Pressure and Blood Flow

As blood moves through capillaries, blood pressure drops dramatically—as the top graph in **FIGURE 45.27** indicates. The bottom graph on this figure shows why. Trace the line labeled "Total area" on this graph to see that as arteries branch, rebranch, and eventually form networks of capillaries, the total cross-sectional area of blood vessels in the circulatory system increases—even though the size of individual blood vessels decreases as blood moves away from the heart. Note two key points:

1. Blood pressure in the capillaries drops dramatically (on the top graph) because the amount of mechanical resistance to flow is a function of total cross-sectional area of the vessels—meaning that friction losses are high in capillary beds. The pulsing nature of the pressure observed in the larger arteries diminishes as a result of this pressure drop.

2. As the line labeled "Velocity" in the bottom graph indicates, the velocity of blood flow also decreases significantly in capillary beds relative to arteries and veins, because the same

**FIGURE 45.26 Blood Pressure Changes during the Cardiac Cycle.** These data show the pressures created by the left ventricle and left atrium in the course of a cardiac cycle. In this example, the blood pressure measured in the upper arm would be 120/80 mm Hg. Right ventricle and pulmonary artery pressures would produce a similar pattern except that the blood pressure in the pulmonary artery would be much lower—closer to 25/8 mm Hg.

**FIGURE 45.27 Blood Pressure Drops Dramatically in the Circulatory System.** The top graph shows how blood pressure changes as blood leaves the heart and travels through arteries, capillaries, and veins, as in the branching pattern of the middle diagram. In arteries near the heart, each heartbeat causes fluctuations in blood pressure. These pressure pulses disappear in the capillaries, so blood flows there at a steady speed. The bottom graph plots the total area of blood vessels shown in the diagram, as well as the velocity of blood flow through the vessels.

amount of fluid is passing through a much larger area. Recall that the slow rate of blood flow through capillaries is important: It provides sufficient time for gases, nutrients, and wastes to diffuse between tissues and blood.

## Why Is Regulation of Blood Pressure and Blood Flow Important?
The general patterns of blood pressure and blood flow diagrammed in Figure 45.27 don't tell the entire story, however. Blood movement is carefully regulated at an array of points throughout the circulatory system.

Recall that the walls of arterioles are comprised partially of smooth muscle. Contraction or relaxation of this muscle can constrict or allow blood flow to specific regions of the body. This means that the nervous system, along with certain chemical messengers in the circulation, can accurately control blood flow to various tissues by contracting or relaxing the muscle. For example, arterioles in the skin may dilate during exercise, diverting blood flow to the skin to eliminate excess heat. This accounts for the flushed facial appearance induced by vigorous exercise. Regulating blood flow is important for maintaining homeostasis with respect to body temperature.

As another example of how blood pressure and blood flow are regulated, consider what happens if you sit long enough for blood to pool in your lower extremities, under the influence of gravity. If you stand up rapidly, your blood pressure can drop enough to reduce blood flow to the brain and cause dizziness or even a blackout. More serious drops in blood pressure, due to severe dehydration or blood loss, can be fatal. Fortunately, decreases in blood pressure elicit a powerful homeostatic response.

**Homeostatic Control of Blood Pressure** Recall that all homeostatic responses involve (1) sensors that detect the change in condition, (2) an integrator that processes information about the change, and (3) effectors that diminish the impact of the change (see Chapter 42).

Specialized pressure-sensing receptors called **baroreceptors** detect changes in blood pressure. Baroreceptors are found in the walls of the heart and the major arteries, both as they leave the heart and as they enter the neck. This distribution is logical, because the head tends to be the most elevated part of terrestrial animals, and preserving blood flow to the brain is the highest priority.

When baroreceptors transmit nerve signals to the brain (the integrator) indicating a serious fall in blood pressure, a rapid, three-component effector response ensues:

1. Cardiac output—the volume of blood leaving the left ventricle—increases. This is due to an increase in heart rate and an increase in stroke volume, which is the amount of blood ejected from the ventricles during each cardiac cycle. (Cardiac output = heart rate × stroke volume.)

2. Arterioles serving the capillaries of certain tissues constrict to divert blood to more critical organs. (This occurs in tissues like the skin and intestines, which can endure short-term restrictions in their blood supply without damage.)

3. Veins constrict, decreasing their overall volume. Because more than half of the blood in the circulatory system is contained within the veins, constriction of these vessels shifts blood volume toward the heart and arteries to maintain blood pressure and flow to vital organs.

This coordinated response is mediated both by a portion of the nervous system called the sympathetic nervous system (Chapter 46) and by hormones (Chapter 49) produced by the adrenal glands. Sympathetic nerves and the hormones involved in blood pressure regulation deliver their messages directly to (1) the SA node to increase heart rate, (2) the ventricles of the heart to increase stroke volume, and (3) the muscular walls of the arteries and veins to modify their total volume.

**Cardiovascular Disease** A healthy circulatory system is obviously critical to your well-being. Indeed, **cardiovascular disease,** which is a group of ailments collectively affecting the heart and blood vessels, is the number one cause of death in humans worldwide.

Many factors contribute to cardiovascular disease, including age, tobacco use, poor diet, obesity, inactivity, and genetics. As people age, their blood vessels harden and lose elasticity—a condition called **arteriosclerosis.** Nicotine in tobacco causes constriction of blood vessels, further reducing the diameter of blood vessels and increasing blood pressure.

High-fat diets and lack of physical activity can compound the problem by leading to the deposition of fatty plaques on the walls of blood vessels, which effectively reduces their diameter. The loss of elasticity and the decline in the diameter of the vessels combine to cause increased blood pressure, which can weaken the walls of arteries.

## check your understanding

**If you understand that . . .**
- Animal circulatory systems may be open or closed, but both types of systems circulate blood or hemolymph via pressure generated by one or more hearts.
- In closed systems, regulated changes in the diameter of blood vessels can direct blood to specific regions, and overall blood pressure is carefully regulated through changes in cardiac output.

✔ **You should be able to . . .**
1. Explain how the mammalian lymphatic system and circulatory system interact.
2. Make a labeled diagram showing how blood circulates through the mammalian heart.

*Answers are available in Appendix A.*

If the arteries that deliver blood to the heart muscle become completely blocked, a **myocardial infarction,** or heart attack, can occur. In a myocardial infarction, a portion of heart tissue dies within minutes when it is deprived of oxygen. Depending on the location and extent of damage, myocardial infarction can lead to rapid death.

Over 17 million people worldwide died from cardiovascular disease in 2004, and this number is projected to reach 23 million by the year 2030. With the incidence of obesity and diabetes reaching epidemic proportions, these numbers may become even higher. Effectively combating cardiovascular disease will require improved diet, reduced tobacco use, greater amounts of physical activity, and better access to healthcare across the globe.

## CHAPTER 45 REVIEW

For media, go to MasteringBiology

## If you understand . . .

### 45.1 The Respiratory and Circulatory Systems

- Animal gas exchange involves ventilation, exchange of gases between the environment and the blood, and exchange of gases between blood and tissues.
- Animal circulation involves transportation of gases, nutrients, wastes, and other substances throughout the body.

✓ You should be able to identify the process that uses oxygen inside animal cells.

### 45.2 Air and Water as Respiratory Media

- As media for exchanging oxygen and carbon dioxide, air and water are dramatically different.
- Compared with water, air contains much more oxygen and is much less dense and viscous. As a result, terrestrial animals have to process a much smaller volume of air to extract the same amount of $O_2$, and the amount of work required to do so is less than in aquatic animals.
- Both terrestrial and aquatic animals pay a price for exchanging gases: Land-dwellers lose water to evaporation; freshwater animals lose ions and gain excess water; marine animals gain sodium and chloride and lose water.

✓ You should be able to explain why no water breathers have the extremely high rates of metabolism required for endothermy.

### 45.3 Organs of Gas Exchange

- The structure of gills, tracheae, lungs, and other gas exchange organs minimizes the cost of ventilation while maximizing the rate at which $O_2$ and $CO_2$ diffuse.
- Consistent with predictions made by Fick's law of diffusion, respiratory epithelia tend to be extremely thin and to be folded to increase surface area.
- In fish gills, countercurrent exchange ensures that the differences in $O_2$ and $CO_2$ partial pressures between water and blood are high over the entire length of the ventilatory surface.

- Insect tracheae carry air directly to and from tissues.
- In bird lungs, structural adaptations lead to a high ratio of useful ventilatory space to dead space.
- Breathing rate is regulated to keep the carbon dioxide content of the blood stable during both rest and exercise.

✓ You should be able to explain why no large animals have gas exchange occurring only across the skin.

### 45.4 How Are Oxygen and Carbon Dioxide Transported in Blood?

- The tendency of hemoglobin to give up oxygen varies as a function of the $P_{O_2}$ in surrounding tissue in a sigmoidal fashion. As a result, a relatively small change in tissue $P_{O_2}$ causes a large change in the amount of oxygen released from hemoglobin.
- Oxygen binds less tightly to hemoglobin when pH is low. Because $CO_2$ tends to react with water to form carbonic acid, the existence of high $CO_2$ partial pressures in exercising muscle tissues lowers their pH and makes oxygen less likely to stay bound to hemoglobin and more likely to be unloaded into tissues.
- The $CO_2$ that diffuses into red blood cells from tissues is rapidly converted to carbonic acid by the enzyme carbonic anhydrase. The protons that are released as carbonic acid dissociates bind to deoxygenated hemoglobin. In this way, hemoglobin acts as a buffer that takes protons out of solution and prevents large fluctuations in blood pH.

✓ You should be able to explain why exposure to large doses of carbon monoxide (CO) can lead to suffocation. (The CO found in furnace and engine exhaust and in cigarette smoke binds to the heme groups in hemoglobin 210 times more tightly than does oxygen.)

### 45.5 Circulation

- In many animals, blood or hemolymph moves through the body via a circulatory system consisting of a pump (heart) and vessels.
- In open circulatory systems, overall pressure is low and tissues are bathed directly in hemolymph.

- In closed circulatory systems, blood is contained in vessels that form a continuous circuit. Containment of blood allows higher pressures and flow rates, as well as the ability to direct blood flow accurately to tissues that need it the most.

- In organisms with a closed circulatory system, a lymphatic system returns excess fluid that leaks from the capillaries back to the circulation.

- In amphibians and some reptiles, blood from the pulmonary and systemic circuits may be mixed in the single ventricle.

- In mammals and birds, a four-chambered heart pumps blood into two circuits, which separately serve the lungs and the rest of the body. Crocodilians have a similar heart with a bypass vessel that can shunt blood from the pulmonary to the systemic circuit.

- The cardiac cycle is controlled by electrical signals that originate in the heart itself.

- Heart rate, cardiac output, and contraction of both arterioles and veins are regulated by chemical signals and by electrical signals from the brain.

- Cardiovascular disease is the leading cause of death in humans.

✔ You should be able to predict the characteristics of the circulatory systems of terrestrial animals with high activity rates.

 **MasteringBiology**

**1. MasteringBiology Assignments**

**Tutorials and Activities** Gas Exchange; Gas Exchange in the Lungs and Tissues; Gas Transport in Blood; Human Heart; Human Respiratory System; Mammalian Cardiovascular System Function; Mammalian Cardiovascular System Structure; Path of Blood Flow in Mammals; Transport of Respiratory Gases

**Questions** Reading Quizzes, Blue-Thread Questions, Test Bank

**2. eText** Read your book online, search, take notes, highlight text, and more.

**3. The Study Area** Practice Test, Cumulative Test, BioFlix® 3-D Animations, Videos, Activities, Audio Glossary, Word Study Tools, Art

## You should be able to . . .

✔ **TEST YOUR KNOWLEDGE**     *Answers are available in Appendix A*

1. $O_2$ will diffuse from blood to tissue faster in response to which of the following conditions?
   a. an increase in the $P_{O_2}$ of the tissue
   b. a decrease in the $P_{O_2}$ of the tissue
   c. an increase in the thickness of the capillary wall
   d. a decrease in the surface area of the capillary

2. Which of the following does blood *not* do?
   a. transport $O_2$ and $CO_2$
   b. distribute body heat
   c. produce new red blood cells and other formed elements
   d. buffer against pH changes

3. In insects, what is the adaptive significance of spiracles?
   a. They dilate and constrict during flight or other types of movement, functioning as a "breathing" mechanism.
   b. They open into the body cavity, allowing direct contact between hemolymph and tissues.
   c. They are thin and highly branched, offering a large surface area for gas exchange.
   d. They close off tracheae to minimize water loss.

4. Which of the following is *not* an advantage of breathing air over breathing water?
   a. Air is less dense than water, so it takes less energy to move during ventilation.
   b. Oxygen diffuses faster through air than it does through water.
   c. The oxygen content of air is greater than that of an equal volume of water.
   d. Air breathing leads to high evaporation rates from the respiratory surface.

5. Which of the following promotes oxygen release from hemoglobin?
   a. a decrease in temperature
   b. a decrease in $CO_2$ levels
   c. a decrease in pH
   d. a decrease in carbonic anhydrase

6. Describe the ways in which an open circulatory system is less efficient than a closed circulatory system.

✔ **TEST YOUR UNDERSTANDING**     *Answers are available in Appendix A*

7. Describe the changes in oxygen delivery that occur as a person proceeds from a resting state to intense exercise.

8. Explain how most carbon dioxide is transported in the blood. In humans, why don't intense exercise and rapid production of $CO_2$ lead to a rapid reduction in blood pH?

9. Why is ventilation in birds considered much more efficient than the respiratory system of humans and other mammals?

10. Explain how each parameter in Fick's law of diffusion is reflected in the structure of the mammalian lung.

11. Carp are fishes that thrive in stagnant-water habitats with low oxygen partial pressures. Compared with the hemoglobin of many other fish species, carp hemoglobin has an extremely high affinity for $O_2$. Is this trait adaptive? Explain your answer.

12. Frog lungs have lower surface area for gas exchange than mammalian lungs. Which of the following observations explains this?

a. Frog tissue needs more oxygen than mammalian tissue.
b. Frogs breathe more quickly than mammals.
c. Frogs also obtain oxygen via diffusion across the skin.
d. Frog lung tissue has a greater density of capillary beds than mammalian lung tissue.

13. Predict how the icefish native to the Antarctic are able to transport oxygen and carbon dioxide in their blood even though they lack hemoglobin.

14. Compare and contrast the respiratory and circulatory systems of an insect and a human.

15. Why did separate systemic and pulmonary circulations evolve in species that have the high-pressure circulatory system required for rapid movement of blood?

16. Under certain conditions, cells produce a metabolic byproduct called 2,3-diphosphoglycerate (DPG). Which of the following would support the hypothesis that DPG helps increase oxygen unloading from tissues?

a. DPG shifts the oxygen–hemoglobin equilibrium curve to the left.
b. DPG decreases percentage saturation of hemoglobin with oxygen at a $P_{O_2}$ of 30 mm Hg.
c. DPG increases the pH of the tissues.
d. DPG is produced in greater quantity at low altitude than at high altitude.

# 46 Animal Nervous Systems

**In this chapter you will learn how**

Animals use electrical signaling along neurons for internal communication

*beginning with*

Principles of electrical signaling   **46.1**

*then asking*

How does the action potential work?   **46.2**

*finally looking at*

Synapses—the interface between neurons   **46.3**

*then exploring*

The vertebrate nervous system   **46.4**

*including*

The brain, learning, and memory

Diffusion spectrum imaging reveals the activity and trajectory of neurons in the brain. Such advances in brain imaging are allowing neurobiologists to study how neurons in the brain communicate with one another.

**BIG PICTURE**

This chapter is part of the Big Picture. See how on pages 840–841.

Most students and professional biologists are attracted to the study of neurobiology because they want to understand the human brain as well as higher-order processes like consciousness, intelligence, emotion, learning, and memory. But early in the history of neurobiology, researchers realized that the human brain—with its billions of cells—was much too complex to study productively.

Instead biologists did the same thing they did in the early days of studying cells, genetics, and evolution: They started simply. Early research in neurobiology focused on the function of individual nerve cells, or **neurons,** the cells mainly responsible for the working of the brain and the rest of the nervous system. Neurons conduct information in the form of electrical signals from point to point

✔ When you see this checkmark, stop and test yourself. Answers are available in Appendix A.

in the body at speeds of up to 200 m/sec (450 mph). Thus electrical signaling is a crucial aspect of information processing—one of the five attributes of life (introduced in Chapter 1).

Initial research on the electrical properties of single neurons laid a broad foundation for more recent studies of how the human brain works. This chapter proceeds in the same way. Let's begin by focusing on the neurons themselves and how they use electrical signaling to communicate within the body and with each other. By the end of the chapter, you'll be considering how the brain is organized and how phenomena like memory work.

## 46.1 Principles of Electrical Signaling

The evolution of neurons was a key event in the diversification of animals, along with the evolution of muscles (see Chapter 33). All animals except sponges have neurons and muscle cells. Neurons transmit electrical signals; muscles can respond to signals from neurons by contracting.

Neurons and muscle cells made rapid movement possible. These innovations in cell structure and function enabled animals to evolve into today's flatworms, squid, beetles, sharks, and birds.

Recall that neurons are organized into two basic types of nervous systems:

1. The diffuse arrangement of cells called a **nerve net,** found in cnidarians (jellyfish, hydra, anemones) and ctenophores (comb jellies).

2. A **central nervous system (CNS)** that includes large numbers of neurons aggregated into clusters called ganglia.

In most cases, animals with a CNS have a large cerebral ganglion, or brain, located in their anterior end. You also might recall that this phenomenon—the evolution of a bilaterally symmetric body with structures for information gathering and processing located at the head end—is known as cephalization (see Chapter 33).

Cephalization made animals into efficient eating and moving machines: They face the environment in one direction, and sensory appendages take in information and send it to a nearby brain for processing. After integrating information from an array of sensory cells, the brain sends electrical signals to muscles and other tissues that respond to the sensory stimuli.

### Types of Neurons in the Nervous System

The sensory cells that are responsible for gathering information respond to light, sound, touch, or other stimuli. Sensory cells in the animal's skin, eyes, ears, mouth, and nose transmit information about the environment. Sensory cells inside the body monitor conditions that are important in homeostasis, such as blood pH and temperature. In this way, sensory cells monitor conditions both outside and inside the body. Many sensory cells are **sensory neurons** (**FIGURE 46.1**), which carry information to the brain and spinal cord.

**FIGURE 46.1 The Brain Integrates Sensory Information and Sends Signals to Effector Cells.** In most cases, sensory neurons send information to the brain, where it is integrated with information from other sources. Once integration is complete, a response is sent to effector cells through motor neurons.

Together, the brain and spinal cord form the CNS of vertebrates. One function of the CNS is to integrate information from many sensory neurons. Cells in the CNS called **interneurons** (literally, "between-neurons"), which pass signals from one neuron to another, perform this integration.

Interneurons also make connections between sensory neurons and **motor neurons,** which are nerve cells that send signals to effector cells in glands or muscles. Motor neurons and sensory neurons are bundled together into long, tough strands of nervous tissue called **nerves.** Recall that effectors are structures that bring about a physiological change in an organism (see Chapter 42).

All neurons and other components of the nervous system that are outside the CNS are considered part of the **peripheral nervous system,** or **PNS.** Section 46.4 describes the structure and function of the PNS in more detail.

Typically, sensory information from receptors in the PNS is sent to the CNS, where it is processed. Then a response is transmitted back to appropriate parts of the body via motor neurons. When you stub your toe, pain receptors in your toe relay sensory information to the brain, which then modifies your movements to avoid further injury. You might hop a bit, for example, and then limp to avoid further pressure on that toe.

### The Anatomy of a Neuron

Neurons are difficult to study because they are small, transparent, and morphologically complex. So when Camillo Golgi discovered that some neurons become visible when samples of preserved tissue are treated with a solution containing silver nitrate, his finding was a major advance. The year was 1898.

**(a)** Information flows from dendrites to the axon.

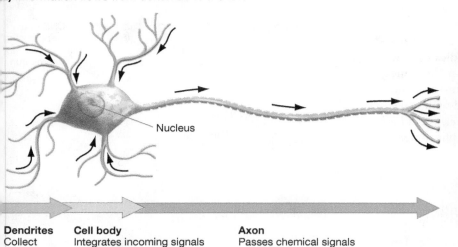

| Dendrites | Cell body | Axon |
|---|---|---|
| Collect chemical signals | Integrates incoming signals and generates outgoing electrical signal to axon | Passes chemical signals to dendrites of another cell or to an effector cell |

**(b)** Neurons form networks for information flow.

Synapses

**FIGURE 46.2 How Does Information Flow in a Neuron? (a)** The structure of a generalized neuron. **(b)** Most neurons receive inputs from many different neurons and send projections to several different neurons.

Through the early decades of the twentieth century, the work of Golgi and Santiago Ramón y Cajal revealed several important points about the anatomy of neurons. Most neurons have the same three parts, shown in **FIGURE 46.2a**:

1. A cell body, which contains the nucleus

2. A highly branched group of relatively short projections called dendrites

3. One or more relatively long projections called axons

Dendrites are rarely more than 2 mm long, but axons can be over a meter in length. The number of dendrites and their arrangement vary greatly from cell to cell. Further, many neurons in the brain have only dendrites and lack axons.

A **dendrite** receives a signal from the axons of adjacent cells; a neuron's **axon** sends a signal to the dendrites and cell bodies of other neurons (**FIGURE 46.2b**). In short, dendrites receive signals; axons pass them on. The **cell body,** or **soma,** also receives signals from axons of other cells. Incoming signals are integrated in the dendrites and cell body, and an outgoing signal is sent to the axon.

Ramón y Cajal maintained that the plasma membrane of each neuron is separated from those of adjacent neurons. This hypothesis was confirmed in the 1950s, when images from electron microscopes showed that most neurons are separated from one another at their junctions by tiny spaces called synapses.

Given that neurons transmit electrical signals, how do they produce them?

## An Introduction to Membrane Potentials

Ions carry an electric charge. In virtually all cells, the cytoplasm and extracellular fluids adjacent to the plasma membrane contain unequal distributions of ions. As a result, cells are inherently electrical in nature.

A difference of electrical charge between any two points creates an **electrical potential,** or a **voltage.** If the positive and negative charges of the ions on each side of a plasma membrane do not balance each other, the membrane will have an electrical potential.

When an electrical potential exists across a plasma membrane, the separation of charges is called a **membrane potential.** If there is a large separation of charges across the membrane, the membrane potential is large.

It is important to remember that membrane potentials refer only to a separation of charge immediately adjacent to the plasma membrane, on either side of the membrane. Even if there is a large membrane potential, there may be no charge separation slightly farther away from the membrane.

**Units and Signs**   Membrane potentials are measured in units called millivolts. The **volt** is the standard unit of electrical potential, and a **millivolt (mV)** is 1/1000 of a volt. As a comparison, an AA battery that you buy in the store has an electrical potential of 1500 mV between its + and − terminals. In neurons, membrane potentials are typically about 65 to 80 mV.

By convention, membrane potentials are always expressed in terms of inside relative to outside (the outside value is defined as 0). Because there are usually more negatively charged ions and fewer positively charged ions on the inside surface of a membrane relative to its outside surface, membrane potentials are usually negative in sign.

**Electrical Potential, Electric Currents, and Electrical Gradients**   Membrane potentials are a form of potential energy. Recall that potential energy is energy based on the position of matter.

To convince yourself that ions have potential energy when a membrane potential exists, consider what would happen if the membrane were removed. Ions would spontaneously move from the region of like charge to the region of unlike charge—causing a flow of charge. This flow of charge, called an **electric current,** would occur because like charges repel and unlike charges attract.

However, charge is not the only form of potential energy. Ions also have different concentrations across membranes. Therefore, a membrane potential also includes energy stored as the concentration gradients of charged ions on the two sides of the membrane. Recall that the combination of an electrical gradient and a concentration gradient is an **electrochemical gradient** (see Chapter 6).

What do all these facts have to do with neuron function? Neurons use the electrochemical gradient of ions across their membranes to power the signals that allow neurons to communicate with one another and with other tissues.

## How Is the Resting Potential Maintained?

When a neuron is not communicating with other cells or tissues, the difference in charge across its membrane is called the **resting potential.** To understand why the resting potential exists, consider the distribution of the various ions and other charged molecules on the two sides of the neuron's plasma membrane, shown in **FIGURE 46.3**:

- The interior side of the membrane has relatively low concentrations of sodium ($Na^+$) and chloride ($Cl^-$) ions, a relatively high concentration of potassium ions ($K^+$), and some organic anions—amino acids and other organic molecules that have dropped a proton and thus carry a negative charge.

- In the extracellular fluid, sodium and chloride ions predominate.

If each type of ion diffused across the membrane in accordance with its concentration gradient, organic anions and $K^+$ would leave the cell, while $Na^+$ and $Cl^-$ would enter.

Ions cannot cross phospholipid bilayers readily, however. They cross plasma membranes efficiently in only three ways (see Chapter 6):

1. Flowing along their electrochemical gradient through an **ion channel**—a protein that forms a pore in the membrane and allows a specific ion to diffuse along its gradient

2. Carried, via a membrane cotransporter protein, with another ion that diffuses along its electrochemical gradient

3. Pumped against an electrochemical gradient by a membrane protein that hydrolyzes adenosine triphosphate (ATP)

How does the distribution of ions illustrated in Figure 46.3 come to be? The answer hinges on two types of membrane proteins: an ion channel that allows potassium ions to diffuse along their gradient, and a pump that actively transports sodium and potassium ions against their gradients. Let's consider each in turn.

**The $K^+$ Leak Channel** At rest, the plasma membrane of neurons is relatively impermeable to most cations. However, neurons have a relatively high number of potassium channels, called $K^+$ **leak channels,** that allow $K^+$ to leak out of the cell. $K^+$ ions slowly

**FIGURE 46.3 Neurons Have a Resting Potential.** In resting neurons, the membrane is selectively permeable to $K^+$. As $K^+$ leaves the cell along its concentration gradient, the inside of the membrane becomes negatively charged relative to the outside. To measure a neuron's membrane potential, researchers insert a microelectrode into the cell and compare that reading with the reading outside the cell.

✔ **QUESTION** Will $K^+$ continue to leave the cell indefinitely? Explain why or why not.

exit the neuron through the leak channels along their electrochemical gradient.

As $K^+$ moves from the interior of the cell to the exterior through leak channels, the inside of the cell becomes more and more negatively charged relative to the outside. This buildup of negative charge inside the cell begins to attract $K^+$ and counteract the concentration gradient that had favored the movement of $K^+$ out.

As a result of the counteracting influences, the membrane reaches a voltage at which equilibrium exists between the concentration gradient that favors movement of $K^+$ out and the electrical gradient that favors movement of $K^+$ in. At this voltage, there is no longer a net movement of $K^+$. This voltage is called the **equilibrium potential** for $K^+$. **Quantitative Methods 46.1** (see page 932) shows how equilibrium potentials for individual ions are calculated.

Although $Cl^-$ and $Na^+$ cross the plasma membrane much less readily than does $K^+$, some movement of these ions also occurs through a small number of leak channels that are selective for each of them. As a result, each type of ion has an equilibrium potential. The membrane as a whole has a membrane potential that combines the effects of the individual ions.

**The Role of the $Na^+/K^+$-ATPase** What is responsible for the higher concentration of $Na^+$ on the outside and $K^+$ on the inside in the first place? It is the sodium–potassium pump, $Na^+/K^+$-ATPase, which actively pumps $Na^+$ out of the cell and $K^+$ into

An equilibrium potential exists whenever there is a concentration gradient for an ion across a membrane and the membrane is permeable to that ion. At the equilibrium potential, the rate at which an ion moves across the membrane down its concentration gradient is equal to the rate at which the ion moves, in the opposite direction, down its electrical gradient. It's the voltage at which the concentration and electrical gradients acting on an ion balance out.

The ion concentration gradients that contribute to equilibrium potentials are produced by the action of Na+/K+-ATPase. This membrane protein converts chemical energy in the form of ATP to electrical energy in the form of a membrane potential.

To calculate an equilibrium potential, biologists use the Nernst equation—a formula that converts the energy stored in a concentration gradient to the energy stored as an electrical potential. The concentration gradient for an ion is symbolized

as $[ion]_o/[ion]_i$, where $[ion]_o$ and $[ion]_i$ are the concentrations of the ion outside and inside the cell, respectively. The equilibrium potential for that ion is symbolized as $E_{ion}$. The Nernst equation specifies the equilibrium potential for a given ion as

$$E_{ion} = 2.3 \frac{RT}{zF} \log \frac{[ion]_o}{[ion]_i}$$

In this expression, $z$ is the valence of the ion (for instance, +1 for potassium) and the expression $RT/F$ is known as the thermodynamic potential. The three terms in the thermodynamic potential are the gas constant ($R$), which acts as a constant of proportionality; the absolute temperature ($T$), measured in Kelvins; and the Faraday constant ($F$), which specifies the amount of charge carried by 1 mol of an ion with a valence of +1 or −1.

Note that the Nernst equation is based on the base-10 logarithm of the ion concentration ratio, $[ion]_o/[ion]_i$. Thus, the thermodynamic potential specifies the voltage required to balance a tenfold concentration ratio

across the membrane. (For more on using logarithms, see **BioSkills 6** in Appendix B.)

The Nernst equation applies to only a single ion. For example, suppose that the potassium concentration inside the axon of a squid neuron has been measured as 400 mM, yet the outside concentration for this ion is only 20 mM (**Table 46.1**). Potassium has a charge of +1, so at 20°C the $RT/zF$ part of the equation yields +25 mV. In this case, the equilibrium potential for potassium becomes

$$E_K = 2.3 \times 25\text{ mV} \times \log \frac{20\text{ mM}}{400\text{ mM}}$$

$$E_K = 58\text{ mV} \times \log 0.05 = -75\text{ mV}$$

The minus sign indicates that the interior of the axon is negatively charged with respect to the exterior.

Repeating this process for Na+ ions and Cl− ions yields the following results for the squid axon:

$$E_{Na} = 58\text{ mV} \times \log \frac{440\text{ mM}}{50\text{ mM}} = +54.8\text{ mV}$$

$$E_{Cl} = -58\text{ mV} \times \log \frac{560\text{ mM}}{51\text{ mM}} = -60\text{ mV}$$

Again, notice that the equilibrium potential given by the Nernst equation is calculated independently for each ion.

✔QUANTITATIVE If you understand this concept, you should be able to calculate the equilibrium potential at 20°C for calcium ($Ca^{2+}$) in a cell where the intracellular concentration is 0.0001 mM and the extracellular concentration is 1 mM.

**TABLE 46.1 Concentration of Important Ions across a Squid Neuron's Plasma Membrane at Rest**

| Ions | Cytoplasm Concentration | Extracellular Concentration | Equilibrium Potential |
|---|---|---|---|
| Na+ | 50 mM | 440 mM | +54.8 mV |
| K+ | 400 mM | 20 mM | −75 mV |
| Cl− | 51 mM | 560 mM | −60 mV |
| Organic anions | 385 mM | — | — |

the cell. More specifically, the energy gained by the sodium–potassium pump when it receives a phosphate group from one ATP is used to move three Na+ ions out of the cell and two K+ ions into the cell (**FIGURE 46.4**).

Active transport via Na+/K+-ATPase ensures that eventually the concentration of K+ is much higher on the inside of the plasma membrane than outside, while the concentration of Na+ is lower inside than outside. In addition to setting up concentration gradients of K+ and Na+, the pump establishes an electrical gradient: The outward movement of three positive charges and inward movement of two positive charges each time the ATPase pumps makes the interior of the membrane less positive (more negative) than the outside.

To summarize, the neuron has a negative resting membrane potential because the Na+/K+-ATPase pumps three cations out for only two cations in, and because K+ exits the neuron through

leak channels along its electrochemical gradient. The resting potential represents energy stored as concentration and electrical gradients in various ions. ✔ If you understand this concept, you should be able to predict what would happen to the membrane potential if Na+ or K+ were allowed to diffuse freely across the membrane.

## Using Microelectrodes to Measure Membrane Potentials

During the 1930s and 1940s, A. L. Hodgkin and Andrew Huxley focused on what has become a classic model system in the study of electrical signaling: the axons of squid.

Squid live in the ocean and are preyed on by fishes and whales. When a squid is threatened, electrical signals travel down the axons to muscle cells. When these muscles contract,

**PROCESS: HOW THE SODIUM–POTASSIUM PUMP (Na⁺/K⁺-ATPase) WORKS**

**1. Sodium loaded.**
Three sodium ions
(Na⁺) enter the protein
from within the cell.

**2. Sodium released.**
ATP phosphorylates the pump,
which changes shape and releases
3 Na⁺ to the outside of the cell.

**3. Potassium loaded.**
Two potassium ions
(K⁺) enter the protein
from outside the cell.

**4. Potassium released.**
The phosphate group drops
off the pump. The protein
changes shape and releases
2 K⁺ to the interior of the cell.

**FIGURE 46.4 In Neuron Membranes, Na⁺/K⁺-ATPase Imports Potassium Ions and Exports Sodium Ions.** By following radioactive Na⁺ and K⁺, biologists found that the pump transports 3 Na⁺ out of the cell for every 2 K⁺ brought in. Notice that this pump operates via a conformational change.

water is expelled from a cavity in the squid's body. As a result, the squid lurches away from danger by jet propulsion (see Chapter 34). The extremely rapid electrical signal produced in the squid is an adaptation that helps avoid predation.

Hodgkin and Huxley decided to study the squid's axon simply because it is so large. Many of the axons found in humans are a mere 2 μm in diameter, but the squid axon is about 500 μm in diameter—large enough that the researchers could record membrane potentials by inserting a wire down its length.

By measuring the voltage difference between the wire inside the cell and an electrode outside the cell, Hodgkin and Huxley could record the voltage across the plasma membrane and observe how it changed in response to stimuli. Later researchers developed glass microelectrodes that were tiny enough to be inserted into smaller neurons to record membrane voltage.

With their relatively simple early equipment, Hodgkin and Huxley were able to record the axon's resting potential. They documented that it can be disrupted by an event called the action potential when the axon is stimulated.

## What Is an Action Potential?

An **action potential** is a rapid, temporary change in a membrane potential. It may qualify as the most important type of electrical signal in cells. When stimulated, neurons mount action potentials that allow them to communicate with other neurons, muscles, or glands.

Although Hodgkin and Huxley initially studied action potentials in the squid giant axon, subsequent work has shown that the action potential has the same general characteristics in all species and in all types of neurons.

**A Three-Phase Signal** **FIGURE 46.5** shows the form of the action potential that Hodgkin and Huxley recorded from the squid's

giant axon—the signal that allows the squid to jet away from predators. The action potential has three distinct phases:

1. **Depolarization** of the membrane. In its resting state, a membrane is said to be polarized because the charges on the two sides are different. Depolarization means that the membrane becomes less polarized than before. During the depolarization phase, the membrane potential becomes less polarized as it moves from highly negative toward zero and then is briefly positive.

2. A rapid **repolarization,** which changes the membrane potential back to negative.

3. A **hyperpolarization** phase, when the membrane is slightly more negative than the resting potential.

**FIGURE 46.5 Action Potentials Have the Same General Shape.** An action potential is a stereotyped change in membrane potential—meaning that it occurs the same way every time.

Together, all three phases of an action potential occur within a few milliseconds.

For an action potential to begin in a squid giant axon, the membrane potential must shift from its resting potential of −65 mV to about −55 mV. If the membrane depolarizes less than that, an action potential does not occur. But if this **threshold potential** is reached, certain channels in the axon membrane open and ions rush into the axon, following their electrochemical gradients. The inside of the membrane becomes less negative and then positive with respect to the outside.

When the membrane potential reaches about +40 mV, an abrupt change occurs and the repolarization phase begins. The change is triggered by the closing of certain ion channels and the opening of other ion channels in the membrane.

To summarize, an action potential occurs because specific ion channels in the plasma membrane open or close in response to changes in voltage. An action potential always has the same three-phase form, even though the size of the resting potential, threshold potential, and peak depolarization may vary among species or even among types of neurons in one species.

**An "All-Or-None" Signal That Propagates**  Hodgkin and Huxley made other important observations about the action potential. Besides being fast and having three distinct phases, it is an all-or-none event.

- There is no such thing as a partial action potential.
- All action potentials for a given neuron are identical in magnitude and duration.
- Action potentials are always propagated down the entire length of the axon.

For example, when an action potential was recorded at a particular point on a squid axon, an action potential that was identical in shape and size would be observed farther down the same axon soon afterward. Neurons are said to have **excitable membranes** because they are capable of generating action potentials that propagate rapidly along the length of the axons.

Taken together, these observations suggested a mechanism for electrical signaling. In the nervous system, information is coded in the form of action potentials that propagate along axons. The frequency of action potentials—not their size—is the meaningful signal. In the squid's giant axon, increased frequency of action potentials signals muscles to contract. As a result, the animal escapes from danger.

## 46.2  Dissecting the Action Potential

Of $Na^+$, $Cl^-$, and $K^+$, which ion or ions are most important in the currents that form the action potential? Are different ions responsible for the depolarization and repolarization phases of the event?

Hodgkin made a crucial start in answering this question when he realized that +40 mV was close to the equilibrium potential for $Na^+$ in the squid giant axon (see **Quantitative Methods 46.1**). If sodium channels opened early in the action potential, then $Na^+$ should flow into the neuron until the membrane potential was about +40 mV. How could this hypothesis be tested?

### Distinct Ion Currents Are Responsible for Depolarization and Repolarization

To understand the currents responsible for the action potential, Hodgkin and Huxley recorded electrical activity in squid axons that were bathed in solutions containing different concentrations of ions.

- Removing $Na^+$ from the solution surrounding the axon abolished the production of action potentials.
- When axons were bathed in solutions with various concentrations of $Na^+$, the peak membrane potential paralleled the concentration of $Na^+$. If $Na^+$ concentration outside the cell was high, the peak was high. If $Na^+$ concentration outside the cell was low, the peak was low.

These experiments furnished strong support for the hypothesis that the action potential begins when $Na^+$ flows into the neuron. In other words, sodium ions are responsible for the depolarization phase.

What happens during the repolarization phase? Using radioactive $K^+$, Hodgkin and Huxley showed that there was a strong flow of potassium ions out of the cell during the repolarization phase.

The action potential consists of a strong inward flow of sodium ions followed by a strong outward flow of potassium ions.
✓ If you understand this concept, you should be able to add labels that read, "Sodium channels open—$Na^+$ enters" and "Potassium channels open—$K^+$ leaves" to Figure 46.5.

### How Do Voltage-Gated Channels Work?

The action potential depends on **voltage-gated channels**—membrane proteins that open and close in response to changes

At the resting potential, voltage-gated Na⁺ channels are closed

Conformational changes open voltage-gated channels when the membrane is depolarized

**FIGURE 46.6 The Shape of a Voltage-Gated Channel Depends on the Membrane Potential.** Changes in the conformation of voltage-gated channels are responsible for changes in a neuron's permeability to ions.

in membrane voltage. The shape of a voltage-gated channel, and thus its ability to admit ions, changes in response to the charges present at the inside of the membrane. **FIGURE 46.6** shows a simple model of how voltage-gated sodium channels change as a function of membrane potential.

Hodgkin and Huxley confirmed that voltage-gated channels exist using a technique called voltage clamping. **Voltage clamping** allows researchers to hold the voltage of a region of an axon at any desired level and record the electrical currents that occur at that voltage. When the researchers held the squid axon at various voltages, different currents resulted. These experiments supported the hypothesis that the behavior of the ion channels depends on voltage.

**Patch Clamping and Studies of Single Channels** Studying individual ion channels became possible in the 1980s when Erwin Neher and Bert Sakmann perfected a technique known as **patch clamping.** As **FIGURE 46.7** shows, the researchers touched a membrane with a fine-tipped microelectrode and applied suction to capture a single ion channel within the electrode's tip.

Using this technique, the researchers were able to document for the first time the currents that flowed through individual

Tip of microelectrode

Axon membrane

Single Na⁺ or K⁺ channel

**FIGURE 46.7 Patch Clamping Provided Insights into the Action Potential.** Patch clamping makes use of extremely fine-tipped microelectrodes. The goal is to isolate one channel and record from it.

channels, and they showed that different ion channels behave differently:

- Voltage-gated channels are either open or closed. There is no gradation in channel behavior. This conclusion is based on the shape of the recorded current: Current flow starts and stops instantly, and the size of the current is always the same.

- Sodium channels open quickly after depolarization. They stay open for about a millisecond, close, and remain inactive for 1 to 2 msec. That explains why the cell can repolarize: Once the sodium channels close, there is a lag before they can open again.

- Potassium channels open with a delay after depolarization. They continue to flip open and closed until the membrane repolarizes. Once the membrane returns to the resting potential, these channels remain closed.

**Positive Feedback Occurs during Depolarization** More detailed experiments on Na⁺ channels also explained why the action potential is an all-or-none event. The key observation was that Na⁺ channels become more likely to open as a membrane depolarizes. As a result, an initial depolarization leads to the opening of more Na⁺ channels, which depolarizes the membrane further, which leads to the opening of additional Na⁺ channels.

The opening of Na⁺ channels exemplifies **positive feedback**—meaning that the occurrence of an event makes the same event more likely to recur. When a fuse is lit, for example, the heat generated by the oxidation reaction accelerates the reaction itself, which generates still more heat and leads to additional oxidation reactions and keeps the fuse burning. Positive feedback is rare in organisms: It cannot be employed as a feedback mechanism under many circumstances because it often leads to uncontrolled events. The opening of Na⁺ channels during an action potential is one of the few examples known.

✔ If you understand how voltage-gated sodium and potassium channels work, you should be able to (1) explain how positive feedback occurs in the opening of Na⁺ channels, and (2) predict what would happen if Na⁺ and K⁺ channels were open at the same time.

**Using Neurotoxins to Identify Channels and Dissect Currents** In addition to using voltage clamping and patch clamping, researchers have used neurotoxins to explore the dynamics of voltage-gated channels. **Neurotoxins** are poisons that affect neuron function—often resulting in convulsions, paralysis, or unconsciousness. They come from sources as diverse as venomous snakes and foxglove plants.

For example, when biologists treated giant axons from lobsters with tetrodotoxin from puffer fish, they found that the resting potential in treated neurons was normal, but action potentials were abolished. More specifically, the flow of K⁺ out of the cell was normal but the influx of Na⁺ was wiped out. Researchers concluded that tetrodotoxin blocks the voltage-gated Na⁺ channel, probably by binding to a specific site on the channel protein.

# How Is the Action Potential Propagated?

To explain how action potentials propagate down an axon, Hodgkin and Huxley suggested the model illustrated in **FIGURE 46.8a**.

**Step 1** The influx of Na$^+$ at the start of an action potential repels intracellular cations, causing them to spread away from the sodium channels.

**Step 2** As positive charges are pushed farther from the initial sodium channels, they depolarize adjacent portions of the membrane.

**Step 3** Nearby voltage-gated Na$^+$ channels open when the membrane reaches threshold, resulting in an action potential.

In this way, action potentials are continuously regenerated at adjacent areas of the plasma membrane (**FIGURE 46.8b**). The response is all or none because action potentials are always regenerated along the entire length of the axon.

Why don't action potentials propagate back up the axon in the direction of the cell body? To answer this question, recall that once Na$^+$ sodium channels have opened and closed, they are less likely to open again for a short period. This is known as the **refractory** state. Action potentials are propagated in one direction only, because "upstream" sodium channels, in the direction of the cell body, are in the refractory state.

The hyperpolarization phase, in which the membrane is more negative than the resting potential, also keeps the charge that spreads upstream from triggering an action potential in that direction, because a much stronger stimulus would be necessary to raise the membrane potential to threshold potential.

**Axon Diameter Affects Speed** Understanding how the action potential propagates helped researchers explain why the squid's axons are so large. When sodium ions enter the axon interior at the start of an action potential, they repulse intracellular cations, causing them to flow along the inside of the membrane. Cations moving down axons with larger diameters meet less resistance to flow than those moving down narrow axons. As a result, the charge spreads down the membrane more quickly.

The upshot is that the squid's giant axon and other large-diameter neurons transmit action potentials much faster than small axons can. The squid axon's large size is an adaptation that makes particularly rapid signaling possible.

## (a) PROCESS: PROPAGATION OF ACTION POTENTIAL

Neuron    Axon

**1. Na$^+$ enters** axon.

**2. Charge spreads;** membrane "downstream" depolarizes.

Depolarization at next ion channel

**3. Downstream voltage-gated channel opens** in response to depolarization.

**FIGURE 46.8 Action Potentials Propagate because Charge Spreads Down the Membrane. (a)** An action potential starts with an inflow of Na$^+$. The influx of positive charge attracts negative charges inside the cell and repels positive charges. As a result, cations spread away from the channel where the Na$^+$ enters and depolarize nearby regions of the neuron. Voltage-gated Na$^+$ channels open in response. **(b)** The action potential is propagated down the axon as a wave of depolarization, but there is no loss of signal because action potentials at one area of the membrane always stimulate action potentials at adjacent areas of the membrane.

**(b)** Action potential spreads as a wave of depolarization.

**Myelination Affects Speed** Relatively few vertebrates have giant axons. Instead, vertebrates—and some invertebrates—have specialized accessory cells whose membranes wrap around the axons of certain neurons and increase the efficiency of action potential propagation.

In the central nervous system, the specialized accessory cells are called **oligodendrocytes.** In the peripheral nervous system, described in Section 46.4, the cells are **Schwann cells (FIGURE 46.9a).** Oligodendrocytes and Schwann cells are two of several types of nervous system cells that support neurons. Collectively, these accessory cells are called **glia.**

When oligodendrocytes or Schwann cells wrap around an axon, they form a **myelin sheath,** which acts as a type of electrical insulation. As action potentials spread down an axon, the myelin sheath prevents charge in the form of ions from leaking back out across the plasma membrane of the neuron.

Consequently, the cations moving down the membrane are able to spread until they hit an unmyelinated section of the axon,

called a **node of Ranvier (FIGURE 46.9b).** The node has a dense concentration of voltage-gated $Na^+$ and $K^+$ channels, so new action potentials can occur at the node.

Electrical signals "jump" from node to node down a myelinated axon much faster than they can move down an unmyelinated axon of the same diameter. In an unmyelinated axon, sodium and potassium channels are found in all locations, and action potentials occur continuously down its length. Myelination is interpreted as an adaptation that makes rapid transmission of electrical signals possible in axons that have a small diameter.

To appreciate the importance of myelination, consider what happens when it is disrupted. If myelin degenerates, the transmission of electrical signals slows considerably. The autoimmune disease **multiple sclerosis (MS)** develops when the immune system mistakenly targets the oligodendrocytes that make up the myelin sheath in the CNS. As damage to myelin increases and electrical signaling is impaired, coordination among neurons is

**(a)** Myelinated axons are wrapped by a series of accessory cells.

Action potentials jump from node to node

Nodes of Ranvier

Schwann cells (glia) wrap around axon, forming myelin sheath

Axon

Schwann cell membrane wrapped around axon

0.5 μm

**(b) PROCESS: WHY ACTION POTENTIALS JUMP DOWN MYELINATED AXONS**

Schwann cell

$Na^+$

**1. Myelination prevents ions from leaking** out through a membrane as the charge spreads down the axon.

Node of Ranvier

$K^+$ $Na^+$

**2. Charge spreads unimpeded until reaching the node of Ranvier,** which is packed with $Na^+$ and $K^+$ channels.

$K^+$ $Na^+$

**3. Signals continue to jump down the axon** in this way, much faster than down an unmyelinated cell.

**FIGURE 46.9 Action Potentials Propagate Quickly in Myelinated Axons.**

affected and muscles weaken. The symptoms of MS are highly variable; in severe cases, the disease progresses and can be crippling.

What happens once an action potential has traveled the length of the axon? In most neurons, the membrane at the end of the axon is adjacent to the membrane of another neuron's dendrite but separated from its surface by a tiny gap. Let's investigate what happens when an action potential arrives at this interface between cells.

## check your understanding

**If you understand that . . .**

- During an action potential, membrane voltage undergoes rapid changes due to an inflow of sodium ions followed by an outflow of potassium ions.
- Action potentials propagate down an axon because inrushing sodium ions repel intracellular cations that move down the membrane and depolarize adjacent portions of the membrane.

✔ **You should be able to . . .**

1. Explain why the action potential is an all-or-none phenomenon.
2. Predict what would happen if batrachotoxin, the poison produced by some species of poison dart frogs, were applied to the membrane. (Batrachotoxin binds to voltage-gated sodium channels and maintains them in an open state.)

*Answers are available in Appendix A.*

## 46.3 The Synapse

The cytoplasm of most neurons is not directly connected to the cytoplasm of other neurons, yet neurons are able to communicate with one another. Based on this observation, there must be some indirect mechanism that transmits signals from cell to cell, across their plasma membranes.

In the 1920s, Otto Loewi showed that this indirect mechanism involves **neurotransmitters.** Neurotransmitters are chemical messengers that transmit information from one neuron to another neuron, or from a neuron to a target cell in a muscle or gland.

Loewi knew that signals from the vagus nerve slow the heart. To test the hypothesis that the signal from nerve to heart muscle is delivered by a chemical, he performed the experiment diagrammed in **FIGURE 46.10.**

First, Loewi isolated the vagus nerve and heart of a frog. As predicted, the heart rate slowed when he stimulated the vagus nerve electrically. Next, he took the solution that bathed the first heart, applied it to another heart—this time one that was not

EXPERIMENTAL SETUP:

Frog heart 1

**1. Stimulate vagus nerve electrically.**

Frog heart 1 | Stimulus

**2. Heartbeat slows** after stimulus.

Frog heart 1

**3. Collect solution** surrounding nerve end.

Frog heart 2

**4. Add solution to second heart.**

PREDICTION: The heartbeat will slow.

PREDICTION OF NULL HYPOTHESIS: There will be no change in heartbeat.

RESULTS:

Frog heart 2 | Stimulus

**Heartbeat slows** after solution is added.

CONCLUSION: The vagus nerve releases molecules that slow heartbeat. Neurotransmitters carry information.

**FIGURE 46.10 Experimental Evidence for the Existence of Neurotransmitters.**

SOURCE: Loewi, O. 1921. Über humorale Übertragbarkeit der Herznervenwirkung. *Pflügers Archiv European Journal of Physiology* 189: 239–242.

✔ QUESTION What would be an appropriate control for this experiment?

accompanied by a vagus nerve—and showed that the second heart rate slowed as well.

This result provided strong evidence for the chemical transmission of electrical signals. The vagus nerve had released a neurotransmitter into the bath.

## Synapse Structure and Neurotransmitter Release

When transmission electron microscopy became available in the 1950s, biologists finally understood the physical nature of the interface, or **synapse,** between neurons. As **FIGURE 46.11** shows, (1) the membranes of axons and dendrites are separated by a tiny space, the **synaptic cleft,** and (2) the ends of axons contain numerous sac-like structures, called **synaptic vesicles.** Synaptic vesicles were hypothesized to be storage sites for neurotransmitters.

Anatomical observations such as these, combined with chemical studies of the synapse, led to the model of synaptic transmission illustrated in **FIGURE 46.12.** Notice that the "sending" cell is the **presynaptic neuron** and the "receiving" cell is the **postsynaptic neuron.**

**Step 1** An action potential arrives at the end of the axon.

**Step 2** The depolarization created by the action potential opens voltage-gated calcium channels located near the synapse, in the presynaptic membrane. The electrochemical gradient for $Ca^{2+}$ results in the inflow of calcium ions through the open channels.

**Step 3** In response to the increased calcium concentration inside the axon, synaptic vesicles fuse with the membrane and release neurotransmitters into the gap between the cells, the synaptic cleft. The delivery of neurotransmitters into the cleft is an example of exocytosis (see Chapter 7).

FIGURE 46.11 **Synaptic Vesicles Cluster Near Synapses.** A cross section of the site where an axon meets a dendrite.

**Step 4** Neurotransmitters bind to receptors on the postsynaptic cell, leading to changes in the membrane potential of the postsynaptic cell. The combined effect on membrane potential of many neurotransmitters binding may trigger an action potential in the postsynaptic cell.

FIGURE 46.12 **Neurons Meet and Transfer Information at Synapses.** The sequence of events that occurs when an action potential arrives at a synapse.

**Step 5** The response ends as the neurotransmitter is broken down and taken back up by the presynaptic cell.

Is the model correct? Let's begin by analyzing the role of neurotransmitters.

## What Do Neurotransmitters Do?

Researchers can look for neurotransmitters by stimulating a neuron, collecting the molecules that are released, and analyzing them chemically. To find the receptor for a particular neurotransmitter, researchers can attach a radioactive atom or other type of label to the neurotransmitter and add it to neurons. Once the labeled transmitter has bound to its receptor, the receptor protein can be isolated and analyzed.

Using techniques such as these, biologists have discovered and characterized a wide array of neurotransmitters and receptors. Some of them are listed in **TABLE 46.2**.

By patch-clamping receptors, biologists confirmed that many neurotransmitters function as ligands. A **ligand** is a molecule that binds to a specific site on a receptor molecule. Many neurotransmitters are ligands that bind to receptors called **ligand-gated channels**. These are channel proteins that open in response to binding by a specific ligand—just as voltage-gated channels open in response to a change in voltage.

When a neurotransmitter binds to a ligand-gated ion channel in the postsynaptic membrane, the channel opens and admits a flow of ions along an electrochemical gradient. In this way, the neurotransmitter's chemical signal is transduced to an electrical signal—a change in the membrane potential of the postsynaptic cell. ✔ If you understand this concept, you should be able to envision a membrane with a resting potential of −65 mV and explain what happens to the membrane potential when a ligand-gated ion channel opens and allows chloride ions to leave the cell. How does this affect the likelihood that the postsynaptic cell will mount an action potential?

Not all neurotransmitters bind to ion channels, however. Some bind to receptors that activate enzymes whose action leads to the production of a second messenger in the postsynaptic cell. Recall that **second messengers** are chemical signals produced

inside a cell in response to a chemical signal that arrives at the cell surface (see Chapter 11).

The second messengers induced by neurotransmitters may trigger changes in enzyme activity, gene transcription, or membrane potential. (Chapter 49 explores the cellular role of second messengers in detail.)

## Postsynaptic Potentials

What happens when a neurotransmitter binds to a ligand-gated ion channel in the postsynaptic cell?

Ligand-gated sodium channels on the membranes of dendrites are in particularly high concentration near synapses. When neurotransmitters bind, these channels open to let sodium into the cell, causing depolarization (**FIGURE 46.13a**). In most cases, depolarization makes an action potential in the postsynaptic cell more likely because the membrane potential approaches threshold. Changes in the postsynaptic cell that bring the membrane potential closer to threshold are called **excitatory postsynaptic potentials (EPSPs)**.

If the receptor activity at the synapse leads to an outflow of potassium ions or an inflow of chloride ions or other anions in the postsynaptic cell, the postsynaptic membrane hyperpolarizes—making action potentials less likely to occur in the postsynaptic cell (**FIGURE 46.13b**). Changes in the postsynaptic cell that make the membrane potential more negative are called **inhibitory postsynaptic potentials (IPSPs)**.

If an EPSP and an IPSP occur at the same time in the same place, they cancel each other out (**FIGURE 46.13c**). Synapses also can be modulatory—meaning that their activity modifies a neuron's response to other EPSPs or IPSPs.

**Postsynaptic Potentials Are Graded** It is critical to realize that, unlike action potentials, EPSPs and IPSPs are not all-or-none events. Instead, they are graded in size.

The size of an EPSP or IPSP depends on the amount of neurotransmitter that is released at the synapse at a given time. A higher concentration of neurotransmitter in the synaptic cleft leads to a larger EPSP or IPSP. Both types of signal are short lived because neurotransmitters do not bind irreversibly to channels

**(a) EPSPs** bring the membrane potential closer to the threshold.

**(b) IPSPs** take the membrane potential farther from threshold.

**(c) Simultaneous EPSPs and IPSPs** cancel each other out.

Depolarization, Na⁺ inflow

Resting potential

EPSP

Hyperpolarization, K⁺ outflow or Cl⁻ inflow

IPSP

Simultaneous Na⁺ inflow plus K⁺ outflow or Cl⁻ inflow

EPSP + IPSP

Membrane potential (mV)

Time

**FIGURE 46.13 Events at the Synapse May Lead to Depolarization or Hyperpolarization of the Postsynaptic Membrane.** These recordings show what happens to the membrane potential of a postsynaptic neuron with the arrival of signals that cause **(a)** depolarization, **(b)** hyperpolarization, or **(c)** no change. The last result occurs because simultaneous depolarizing and hyperpolarizing signals cancel each other out.

**TABLE 46.2 Categories of Neurotransmitters**

| Neurotransmitter | Site of Action | Action* | Drugs That Interfere† |
|---|---|---|---|
| Acetylcholine | Neuromuscular junction, some CNS pathways | Excitatory (inhibitory in some parasympathetic neurons) | • Botulism toxin blocks release<br>• Black widow spider venom increases, then eliminates, release<br>• Alpha-bungarotoxin (in some snake venoms) binds to and blocks receptor |
| **Monoamines** | | | |
| Norepinephrine | Sympathetic neurons, some CNS pathways | Excitatory or inhibitory | • Ritalin (used for attention deficit hyperactivity disorder) increases release<br>• Some antidepressants prevent reuptake |
| Dopamine | Many CNS pathways | Excitatory or modulatory | • Cocaine prevents reuptake<br>• Amphetamine prevents reuptake |
| Serotonin | Many CNS pathways | Inhibitory or modulatory | • MDMA (ecstasy) causes increased release |
| **Amino Acids** | | | |
| Glutamate | Many CNS pathways | Excitatory | • PCP (angel dust) blocks receptor |
| Gamma-aminobutyric acid (GABA) | Some CNS pathways | Inhibitory | • Ethanol mimics response to GABA |
| **Peptides** | | | |
| Endorphins, enkephalins, substance P | Sensory pathways (pain) | Excitatory, modulatory, or inhibitory | |

*Excitatory neurotransmitters make action potentials more likely in postsynaptic cells; inhibitory neurotransmitters make action potentials less likely; modulatory neurotransmitters modify the response at other synapses.

† Drugs that prevent reuptake of neurotransmitters increase their activity.

in the postsynaptic cell. Instead, they are quickly inactivated by enzymes or taken up by the presynaptic cell and recycled.

If either the amount or life span of neurotransmitters is artificially altered, the normal functioning of neurons is altered. The drugs cocaine and amphetamine, for example, exert their effects by inhibiting the uptake and recycling of particular neurotransmitters (see Table 46.2).

**Summation and Threshold** How do EPSPs and IPSPs affect the postsynaptic cell? As **FIGURE 46.14a** shows, the dendrites and the cell body of a neuron typically make hundreds or thousands of synapses with other cells. At any instant, the EPSPs and IPSPs that occur at each of these synapses lead to short-lived changes in membrane potential in the dendrites and cell body of the postsynaptic cell.

**(a)** Most neurons receive information from many other neurons.

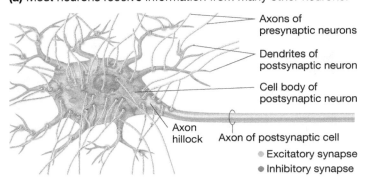

Axons of presynaptic neurons

Dendrites of postsynaptic neuron

Cell body of postsynaptic neuron

Axon hillock — Axon of postsynaptic cell

• Excitatory synapse
• Inhibitory synapse

**(b)** Postsynaptic potentials sum.

FIGURE 46.14 **Neurons Integrate Information from Many Synapses. (a)** The dendrites and cell body of a neuron typically receive signals from hundreds or thousands of other neurons. **(b)** When action potentials arrive close together in time, the postsynaptic potentials sum. Here the first EPSP is insufficient to generate an action potential; two EPSPs arriving close together undergo summation but do not reach threshold; the summing of three EPSPs arriving close together does exceed the threshold. This example is simplified—in reality, hundreds or thousands of IPSPs and EPSPs sum to determine action potential frequency.

If an IPSP and EPSP occur close together in space or time, the changes in membrane potential tend to cancel each other out. But if several EPSPs occur close together in space or time, they sum and make the neuron more likely to reach threshold and fire an action potential (**FIGURE 46.14b**). The additive nature of post-synaptic potentials is termed **summation**.

The sodium channels that trigger action potentials in the postsynaptic cell are located near the start of the axon at a site called the **axon hillock** (see Figure 46.14a). As IPSPs and EPSPs are received and interact throughout the dendrites and cell body, charge spreads to the axon hillock. If the membrane at the axon hillock depolarizes past the threshold potential, enough voltage-gated sodium channels open to trigger positive feedback and an action potential. Once an action potential starts at the axon hillock, it propagates down the axon to the next synapse.

Summation is critically important. Because neurons receive input from many synapses, and because IPSPs and EPSPs sum, information in the form of electrical signals is modified at the synapse before being passed along. An action potential in a presynaptic neuron does not always lead to an action potential in a postsynaptic neuron—the response by the postsynaptic cell depends on the information it receives from a wide array of neurons.

## check your understanding

**If you understand that . . .**

- At a synapse, electrical information in the form of changes in membrane voltage is transduced to chemical information in the form of released neurotransmitters.
- Binding of a neurotransmitter to its receptor causes a change in the membrane potential of the postsynaptic cell.

✔ **You should be able to . . .**

Predict the effect on an EPSP of an increase in the concentration of a synaptic enzyme that breaks down an excitatory neurotransmitter.

*Answers are available in Appendix A.*

## 46.4 The Vertebrate Nervous System

The first three sections of this chapter examined electrical signaling at the level of molecules, membranes, and individual cells. This section discusses electrical signaling at the levels of tissues, organs, and systems.

To begin, let's consider the overall anatomy of the vertebrate nervous system, and how researchers explore the function of the most complex organ known: the human brain. The chapter concludes by returning to the molecular level (and to studies of invertebrates) to introduce recent work on learning and memory.

## What Does the Peripheral Nervous System Do?

Recall from Section 46.1 that the central nervous system (CNS) is made up of the brain and spinal cord and is concerned primarily with integrating information. The peripheral nervous system (PNS) is made up of neurons outside the CNS.

What functions do the cells of the PNS control? Anatomical and functional studies indicate that the PNS consists of two divisions with distinct functions:

1. The **afferent division** transmits sensory information to the CNS.

2. The **efferent division** carries commands from the CNS to the body.

Neurons in the afferent division monitor conditions inside and outside the body. Once information from afferent neurons has been processed in the CNS, neurons in the efferent division carry signals that allow the body to respond to changed conditions in an appropriate way.

As **FIGURE 46.15** shows, the afferent and efferent divisions are part of a hierarchy of PNS functions. The efferent division is further divided into a **somatic nervous system,** which controls voluntary movements, and an **autonomic nervous system,** which controls internal processes such as digestion and heart rate.

- The somatic nervous system carries out voluntary responses, which are under conscious control. Skeletal muscles serve as the effectors.

- The autonomic nervous system carries out involuntary responses, which are not under conscious control. Smooth muscle, cardiac muscle, and glands serve as the effectors.

Many organs and glands are served by two functionally distinct types of autonomic nerves, summarized in **FIGURE 46.16**: One type inhibits activity, whereas the other promotes it.

1. Nerves in the **parasympathetic nervous system** promote "rest and digest" functions that conserve or restore energy.

**FIGURE 46.15 The Nervous System Has Several Functional Divisions.**

For example, the parasympathetic nerves that synapse on the heart slow it down, while those that serve the digestive tract stimulate its activity.

2. Nerves in the **sympathetic nervous system** typically prepare organs for stressful "fight or flight" situations. Sympathetic nerves speed up the heart rate, stimulate the release of glucose from the liver, and inhibit action by digestive organs.

## Functional Anatomy of the CNS

Parasympathetic nerves originate at the base of the brain or the base of the spinal cord. Most sympathetic nerves also originate in the spinal cord, but they emerge along the middle of its length. Similarly, most sensory neurons project axons to the spinal cord, and most somatic motor neurons project from the spinal cord.

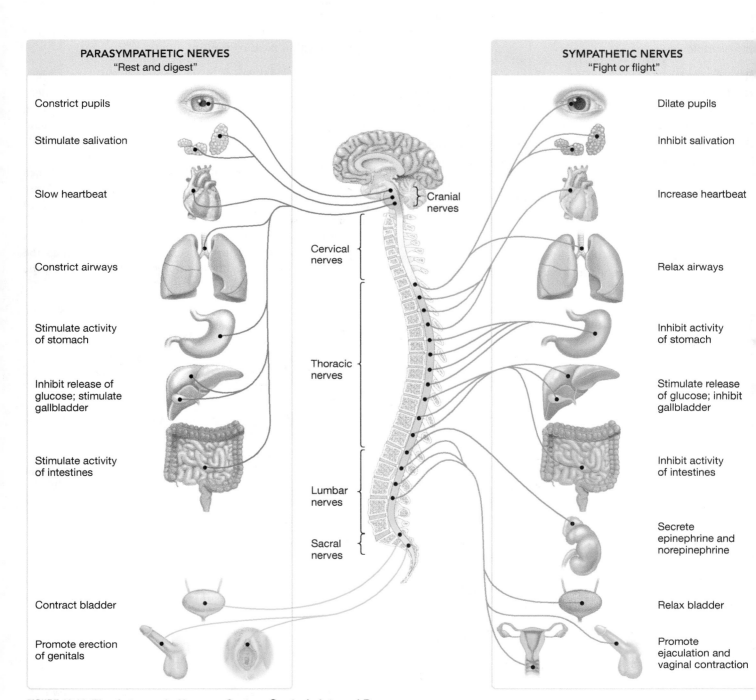

**PARASYMPATHETIC NERVES**
"Rest and digest"

Constrict pupils

Stimulate salivation

Slow heartbeat

Constrict airways

Stimulate activity of stomach

Inhibit release of glucose; stimulate gallbladder

Stimulate activity of intestines

Contract bladder

Promote erection of genitals

**SYMPATHETIC NERVES**
"Fight or flight"

Dilate pupils

Inhibit salivation

Increase heartbeat

Relax airways

Inhibit activity of stomach

Stimulate release of glucose; inhibit gallbladder

Inhibit activity of intestines

Secrete epinephrine and norepinephrine

Relax bladder

Promote ejaculation and vaginal contraction

Cranial nerves

Cervical nerves

Thoracic nerves

Lumbar nerves

Sacral nerves

**FIGURE 46.16  The Autonomic Nervous System Controls Internal Processes.**

✔**QUESTION** Explain how the responses listed here for pupils, heartbeat, and liver support the rest-and-digest versus fight-or-flight functions.

In effect, then, the spinal cord serves as an information conduit. It collects and transmits information throughout the body. Virtually all the information that travels to or from the spinal cord is sent to the brain for processing. An exception is a spinal **reflex,** in which sensory neurons stimulate interneurons in the spinal cord that then directly stimulate motor neurons. This process allows you to withdraw your hand rapidly from a hot burner before your brain becomes aware of the pain.

What happens once sensory signals arrive at the brain? How are thousands of signals integrated to allow an animal to respond to stimuli? Let's begin our exploration of the brain by delving into its anatomy.

**General Anatomy of the Human Brain**   Nineteenth-century anatomists established that the human brain is made up of the four structures labeled in **FIGURE 46.17**: the cerebrum, cerebellum, diencephalon, and brain stem. Each has a distinct function.

- The **cerebrum** makes up the bulk of the human brain. It is divided into left and right hemispheres and is the seat of conscious thought and memory.

- The **cerebellum** coordinates complex motor patterns.

- The **diencephalon** relays sensory information to the cerebrum and controls homeostasis.

- The **brain stem** connects the brain to the spinal cord. It is the autonomic center for regulating cardiovascular, digestive, and other involuntary functions.

Each cerebral hemisphere has four major areas, or lobes: the **frontal lobe,** the **parietal lobe,** the **occipital lobe,** and the **temporal lobe** (**FIGURE 46.18**). The two hemispheres are connected by a thick band of axons called the **corpus callosum.**

The relative size of the entire brain, and of its component structures, varies greatly among vertebrates (**FIGURE 46.19**). For example, compare the size of the cerebrum in fishes and mammals. In fishes, the cerebrum is quite small and is involved mainly in olfactory sensation. In mammals it is very large and contains regions specialized for memory and reasoning, in addition to the processing of multiple sensory and motor functions. Your own cerebrum is three times bigger than in other species of comparably sized mammals, reflecting its role in the higher brain functions that are so advanced in humans.

What methods do researchers use to explore the function of each area within the cerebrum?

**Mapping Functional Areas in the Cerebrum I: Lesion Studies**
Early work on brain function studied people with specific mental deficits caused by areas of brain damage, or lesions. Paul Broca, for example, studied an individual who could understand language but could not speak. After the person's death in 1861, Broca examined the patient's brain and discovered a damaged area, or lesion, in the left frontal lobe of the cerebrum. Broca hypothesized that this region is responsible for speech. More generally, he formulated the hypothesis that specific regions of the brain are specialized for coordinating particular functions.

Broca's claim that functions are localized to specific brain areas has been verified through extensive efforts to map the cerebrum. In some cases, advances were made by studying the

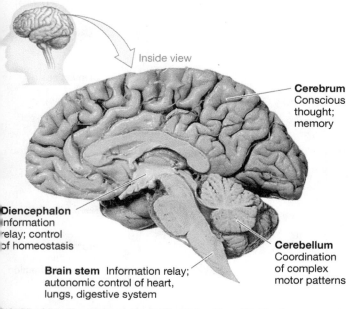

Inside view

**Cerebrum**
Conscious thought; memory

**Diencephalon** Information relay; control of homeostasis

**Cerebellum** Coordination of complex motor patterns

**Brain stem**  Information relay; autonomic control of heart, lungs, digestive system

**FIGURE 46.17  The Human Brain Contains Four Distinct Structures.**

Inside view

**Frontal lobe**

**Parietal lobe**

**Occipital lobe**

**Temporal lobe**

**Corpus callosum:** neurons that connect the two hemispheres

Rear view

Left cerebral hemisphere

Right cerebral hemisphere

**FIGURE 46.18  The Human Cerebrum Has Four Lobes and Two Hemispheres.**

✔**EXERCISE**  On your own head, point to each of the labeled areas.

**FIGURE 46.19 The Relative Sizes of Brain Regions Differ among Vertebrate Lineages.** For example, the cerebrum (in orange) tends to be larger in birds and mammals than in basal vertebrates.

behavior of people known to have had lesions to specific brain regions or to have had specific portions of their brains removed.

In 1848, for example, Phineas Gage was working on a railroad construction site when an iron rod over an inch in diameter was blasted through his skull. The rod entered beneath his left eye, exited through his forehead (**FIGURE 46.20**), and landed some 80 feet away. Miraculously, Gage survived this accident. However, his personality did not fare as well. After the accident, Gage's physician reported him to be "fitful," "irreverent," and "obstinate," a dramatic change from his previous personality. The iron rod had damaged Gage's frontal lobe, providing some of the first clues that this part of the brain plays a role in personality and emotion.

Another fascinating case is that of a 27-year-old man named Henry Gustav Molaison (referred to as "H.M." until his death). In 1953, surgeons treated him for life-threatening seizures by removing a small portion of his temporal lobe and about two thirds of his hippocampus, a structure at the inner edge of the temporal lobe. The man recovered (he died in December 2008, at age 83),

had normal intelligence, and vividly remembered his childhood, but he had no short-term memory. Brenda Milner, who studied this individual for over 40 years, had to introduce herself to him every time they met; he could not even recognize a recent picture of himself. Based on case histories like Molaison's and studies of memory in laboratory animals, a consensus has emerged that several aspects of memory are governed by the hippocampus and interior sections of the temporal lobe.

**Mapping Functional Areas in the Cerebrum II: Electrical Stimulation of Conscious Patients** While working with severe epileptics (people suffering from seizures), Wilder Penfield pioneered a different approach to studying brain function. These individuals were scheduled to have seizure-prone areas of their brains surgically removed. While the patients were awake and under a local anesthetic, Penfield electrically stimulated portions of their cerebrums. His immediate goal was to map essential areas that should be spared from removal if possible.

When Penfield stimulated specific areas, patients reported sensations or experienced movement in particular regions of the body. From these responses, Penfield was able to map the sensory regions of the cerebrum shown in **FIGURE 46.21** (see page 946), as well as the adjacent motor regions. Brain surgeons still use this technique to map critical areas near tumors and seizure-prone areas.

Perhaps the most striking of Penfield's findings was that, on occasion, patients would respond to stimulation of their temporal lobe by having what appeared to be flashbacks. After one region was stimulated, a woman said, "I hear voices. It is late at night around the carnival somewhere—some sort of traveling circus. . . . I just saw lots of big wagons that they used to haul animals in."

Was this a memory, stored in a small set of neurons that Penfield happened to stimulate? The hypothesis that memories are somehow stored in specialized cells is controversial. However, a recent study provided support for it.

Researchers attached tiny electrodes that recorded the electrical activity of individual neurons in the temporal lobes and hippocampi of study subjects. They then showed each subject a set of images of celebrities, places, and objects. In one subject,

**FIGURE 46.20 The Frontal Lobe Injury of Phineas Gage Affected His Personality.** In 1848 a railroad worker named Phineas Gage recovered from a brain injury in which an iron rod was blasted through the frontal lobe of his cerebrum. The resulting change in his personality cued scientists that the frontal lobe plays a role in emotion and temperament.

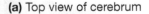

**(a)** Top view of cerebrum

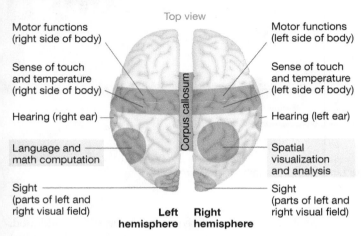

Top view

Motor functions
(right side of body)

Sense of touch
and temperature
(right side of body)

Hearing (right ear)

Language and
math computation

Sight
(parts of left and
right visual field)

Corpus callosum

Motor functions
(left side of body)

Sense of touch
and temperature
(left side of body)

Hearing (left ear)

Spatial
visualization
and analysis

Sight
(parts of left and
right visual field)

**Left
hemisphere**   **Right
hemisphere**

**(b)** Cross section through area responsible for sense of touch
and of temperature

Head
Trunk
Hip
Leg
Arm
Hand
Fingers
Thumb
Eye
Nose
Lips
Teeth
Jaw
Tongue
Genitals

Left
hemisphere

**FIGURE 46.21  Specific Brain Areas Have Specific Functions.**
**(a)** Map of the brain, in top view (as if the person is looking at the
top of the page), showing the functions of some major regions.
The map was compiled from studies of people with damaged brain
areas or in whom brain regions had been removed surgically. Note
that the corpus callosum is not actually as wide as shown here.
**(b)** Researchers mapped the area responsible for the sense of
touch and of temperature by stimulating neurons in the brains of
patients who were awake. The size of the icons corresponds to the
amount of brain area devoted to sensing those parts.

✔**QUESTION**  Is there a correlation between the size of the brain area
devoted to sensing a particular body part and the size of that body
part? Explain.

a specific neuron fired when the subject viewed any of several
images of the actress Jennifer Aniston (**FIGURE 46.22**). The neuron
did not fire for other images showing spiders, buildings, other
actresses, or even Aniston with another person. It appeared that,
through experience, at least one of this patient's neurons became
singularly devoted to the concept of Jennifer Aniston.

It is important to note that the researchers were testing only a
tiny subset of the neurons present in the human brain, so there

may be more than one "Jennifer Aniston neuron" in the brain.
But the take-home message is that the formation or retrieval of
memories associated with specific concepts involves specific
neurons. Researchers are still examining exactly how these neurons interact with other parts of the brain during the processes of
learning and remembering.

Have other approaches to studying memory been productive?

## How Does Memory Work?

**Learning** is an enduring change in behavior that results from a
specific experience in an individual's life. **Memory** is the retention of learned information. Learning and memory are thus
closely related and are often studied in tandem. As an introduction to how researchers explore these phenomena, let's first examine work that focuses on neurons and then review research at
the molecular level.

**Recording from Single Neurons during Memory Tasks**  How do
the action potentials generated by a cell change as learning and
memory take place? Researchers have attempted to answer this
question by recording from individual neurons in the temporal
lobes of humans.

Before operating on patients who were still awake and about
to undergo surgery to remove seizure-prone areas of their brains,
physicians placed electrodes in specific brain regions. Then they
projected words or names of objects on a screen and asked the
individuals to read them silently, read them aloud, or remember them and repeat them later. The data showed that individual
neurons in the cerebrum's temporal lobe are relatively quiet while
patients identify objects but extremely active when the individual
remembers the objects and repeats their names aloud.

What do such data mean? Neurons in the temporal lobe are
most active during memory tasks. So how could action potentials from particular cells make memory possible?

**Documenting Changes in Synapses**  Research on the molecular
basis of memory is based on the idea that learning and memory
must involve some type of short-term or long-term change in
the neurons responsible for these processes. This change could
be structural or chemical in nature. Structural changes might include modifications in the number of synapses that a particular
neuron makes, or even the destruction and creation of neurons.
Chemical changes might involve alterations in the amount of
neurotransmitter released at certain synapses or changes in the
number of receptors present in postsynaptic cells.

To explore the molecular basis of learning and memory, Eric
Kandel's group has focused on an animal much easier to study
than any vertebrate, the sea slug *Aplysia californica* (**FIGURE 46.23a**).
Much of their work has explored the reflex diagrammed in
**FIGURE 46.23b:** When the siphon, a structure on the animal's back,
is touched—for example, by a stream of water—the sea slug
responds by withdrawing its gill. The reflex is produced by a
sensory neuron that is activated by touch and a motor neuron
that projects to a gill muscle. Retracting the gill protects it from
predators.

| 0 action potentials/sec | 8 action potentials/sec | 0 action potentials/sec | 6 action potentials/sec | 0 action potentials/sec |

**FIGURE 46.22 Single-Neuron Recording Reveals that Some Neurons in the Brain Recognize Specific Concepts.** The graphs below each image show how a single neuron fires in response to images of actress Jennifer Aniston but not to other images.

DATA: Quiroga, R. Q., L. Reddy, G. Kreiman, et al. 2005. *Nature* 435: 1102–1107.

Early work established that this simple reflex is modified by learning. For example, *Aplysia* also withdraw their gills when their tails are given an electrical shock. If shocks to the tail are repeatedly combined with a very light touch to the siphon—too light to normally get a response on its own—an *Aplysia* will learn to withdraw its gills in response to a light siphon touch alone.

Follow-up studies on this reflex showed that the neurons involved in learning release the neurotransmitter **serotonin,** which causes an EPSP in the motor neuron to the gill. Repeated application of serotonin mimics what happens at the synapse during learning, when the neurons fire repeatedly. As **FIGURE 46.24a** (see page 948) shows, experimental application of serotonin leads to higher EPSPs, meaning that the motor neuron is more likely to generate action potentials. These results suggest that in *Aplysia*, changes in the nature of the synapse form the molecular basis of learning and memory. This change in responsiveness of the synapse is termed **synaptic plasticity.**

Recently Kandel's team replicated these results with sensory and motor neurons growing in culture. **FIGURE 46.24b** shows two *Aplysia* motor neurons on a culture plate. Each motor neuron synapses with the same sensory neuron. To mimic the learning process, the investigators applied serotonin to one synapse five times over a short period. When they stimulated the sensory neuron a day later, they found a huge increase in EPSPs in the motor neuron postsynaptic to that synapse (**FIGURE 46.24c**). The experimental postsynaptic cells had also established additional synapses. The structure and behavior of the experimental

**(a)** Sea slug *Aplysia californica*

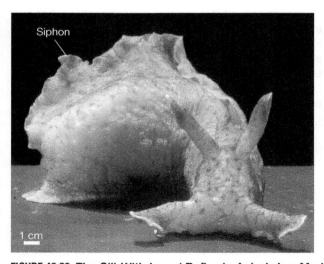

**(b)** Gill-withdrawal reflex protects the gills during an attack.

**FIGURE 46.23 The Gill-Withdrawal Reflex in *Aplysia* Is a Model System in Learning and Memory.**

**(a)** Postsynaptic potentials changing as a result of learning

**(b)** Applying neurotransmitters to neurons in culture

**(c)** Repeating *Aplysia* experiment in culture

**FIGURE 46.24 Learning and Memory Involve Changes in Synapses. (a)** Experiment showing that repeated application of serotonin changes the behavior of postsynaptic neurons. **(b)** An in vitro study of interactions between *Aplysia* motor neurons and sensory neurons. **(c)** Histogram depicting the percentage increase in postsynaptic potentials that occurs after repeated application of serotonin, as in part **(a)**.

DATA: Martin, K. C., A. Casadio, H. Zhu, et al. 1997. *Cell* 91: 927–938.

postsynaptic motor neuron had changed, based on its experience. Neurons that had not received the repeated stimulation with serotonin had normal postsynaptic responses and numbers of synapses.

**Documenting Changes in Neurons** Synapses change over time, but what about the cells of the central nervous system themselves? When early neurobiologists dissected adult cadaver brains, they found that none of the neurons showed signs of mitosis. From these observations they concluded that **neurogenesis**—the formation of new neurons—does not occur in adults.

In 1983, Steven Goldman and Fernando Nottebohm revisited this long-standing theory. They examined whether new neurons can be formed in the brains of songbirds. Songbirds were chosen because in their brains, specific regions that control singing behavior undergo dramatic seasonal changes in size. The researchers hypothesized that these changes result from an increased rate of neurogenesis during the reproductive season.

To test this hypothesis, the researchers injected canaries (**FIGURE 46.25a**) with radiolabeled thymidine, which becomes incorporated into newly synthesized DNA. The researchers later collected the birds' brains, cut them into very thin slices, mounted the slices onto microscope slides, and brought them into contact with photographic film. In this technique, called autoradiography (see **BioSkills 9** in Appendix B), any new cells with radiolabeled thymidine in their DNA would expose the film, thereby indicating the presence and location of cells that were produced after the bird was injected.

The researchers found that adult songbirds are indeed able to produce large numbers of new neurons. Dozens of studies since Goldman and Nottebohm's experiment have confirmed that new neurons are incorporated into the song-control regions of the brain each spring, causing them to grow dramatically in size (**FIGURE 46.25b**). The new neurons promote learning and memory in the song-control system.

Other scientists around the same time and, indeed, even earlier obtained autoradiographic evidence of neurogenesis in adult mammals. However, the sheer number of new cells was much lower in mammals than in birds, so these reports did

check your understanding

**If you understand that . . .**

- The CNS and PNS work together to gather information about the external and internal environments, process that information, and signal muscles, glands, and other tissues to make appropriate responses to the information.
- Brain regions have specific functions.
- Changes in synapses and neurogenesis allow animals to learn and create memories.

✔ **You should be able to . . .**

1. Describe the research strategies that allowed biologists to localize particular functions to specific regions in the brain.
2. Identify the key mechanisms behind learning and memory.

*Answers are available in Appendix A.*

**(a)** Male canaries (left) sing to attract females (right).

**(b)** In songbirds, the size of the brain's song-control region increases in spring.

Winter

Spring

**FIGURE 46.25 Neurogenesis Occurs in the Adult Songbird Brain.**

not convince all researchers. Skeptics initially suggested that the labeled cells in mammals might actually be glia rather than neurons.

A breakthrough came in the early 1990s with the development of new techniques that specifically label neurons. The markers used in these techniques bind to proteins that are found only in neurons and not in glial cells. Since that time, adult neurogenesis has been definitively shown to occur in all vertebrates, including humans.

Scientists are only beginning to understand the functional role of these new neurons. Is it the same as that of neurons made during development? Can neurogenesis be used to help heal brain injuries? Some studies have even suggested that chronic stress during childhood (the stress of poverty or bullying, for example) can reduce the ability to make new neurons, thereby negatively affecting learning in adults.

Results like these reinforce a growing consensus that learning, memory, and the control of complex behaviors involve not only molecular and structural changes in synapses but also changes in the number of neurons. Further, most researchers now agree that at least some aspects of long-term memory involve changes in gene expression. Chemical messengers called hormones also cause changes in gene expression in target cells (see Chapter 49). But before investigating how hormones work, let's focus on the electrical signals involved in vision, hearing, taste, and movement—the subject of Chapters 47 and 48.

---

## CHAPTER 46 REVIEW

*For media, go to MasteringBiology*

### If you understand . . .

#### 46.1 Principles of Electrical Signaling

- All neurons have a cell body and multiple short dendrites that receive signals from other cells. Most neurons also have a single axon that transmits electrical signals to other neurons or to effector cells in glands or muscles.

- Studies of the squid giant axons established that neurons have a resting potential created by the sodium–potassium pump and potassium leak channels. When $Na^+/K^+$-ATPase hydrolyzes ATP, it transports 3 $Na^+$ out of the cell and 2 $K^+$ in.

✔ You should be able to diagram the plasma membrane of a neuron. Add symbols to show the relative concentrations of $Na^+$, $K^+$, and $Cl^-$. Add labels indicating the role of $K^+$ leak channels and the $Na^+/K^+$-ATPase.

#### 46.2 Dissecting the Action Potential

- Studies of the squid axon established that the action potential is a rapid, all-or-none change in membrane potential.

- An action potential begins with an inflow of $Na^+$ that depolarizes the membrane. An outflow of $K^+$ follows and repolarizes the membrane.

- Both $Na^+$ and $K^+$ flow through voltage-gated channels.

- As $Na^+$ flows in, it repulses cations that spread from the site of the action potential, causing the nearby membrane to depolarize enough to trigger an action potential in that adjacent portion of the membrane.

- Propagation takes place most rapidly in large axons or myelinated axons.

✔ You should be able to explain why every action potential in a given neuron is identical.

## 46.3 The Synapse

- When action potentials arrive at a synapse, synaptic vesicles fuse with the axon's membrane and deliver neurotransmitters into the synapse that bind to receptors on the membrane of a postsynaptic cell.

- One class of receptors functions as ligand-gated channels. In response to binding by a neurotransmitter, these channels open and admit ions that depolarize or hyperpolarize the postsynaptic cell's membrane.

- Postsynaptic potentials sum.

- If the membrane at the axon hillock of the postsynaptic neuron depolarizes to a threshold value, an action potential is triggered.

✓ You should be able to explain how summation in the postsynaptic cell relates to the claim that the cell body integrates information from many different synapses.

## 46.4 The Vertebrate Nervous System

- The CNS consists of the brain and spinal cord (in vertebrates); the PNS consists of all nervous system components outside the CNS.

- In vertebrates, the PNS contains somatic and autonomic components. The somatic PNS signals the effector cells producing movement; the autonomic PNS monitors internal conditions and signals the effector cells that change the activity of tissues and organs.

- Early efforts to map functional regions of the brain were based on analyzing deficits in individuals with brain lesions or on stimulating certain regions of the cerebrum.

- Research has established that learning and memory involve modifications in synapses. After learning takes place, certain neurons release more or less neurotransmitter, or make additional synapses, in response to stimulation.

- Recent research shows that vertebrates are capable of adult neurogenesis, which may be an important component of learning and memory.

✓ You should be able to predict the effects of a brain stem lesion in an animal.

(MB) **MasteringBiology**

1. **MasteringBiology Assignments**

   **Tutorials and Activities** Action Potentials, How Neurons Work (1 of 3): Neuron Structure and Resting Potential; How Neurons Work (2 of 3): The Action Potential; How Neurons Work (3 of 3): Conduction of an Action Potential; How Synapses Work (1 of 2): Chemical Synapses; How Synapses Work (2 of 2): Postsynaptic Potentials; Membrane Potentials; Nerve Signals: Action Potentials; Neuron Structure; Signal Transmission at a Chemical Synapse; The Vertebrate Nervous System

   **Questions** Reading Quizzes, Blue-Thread Questions, Test Bank

2. **eText** Read your book online, search, take notes, highlight text, and more.

3. **The Study Area** Practice Test, Cumulative Test, BioFlix® 3-D Animations, Videos, Activities, Audio Glossary, Word Study Tools, Art

## You should be able to . . .

### ✓ TEST YOUR KNOWLEDGE

*Answers are available in Appendix A*

1. Which ion leaks across a neuron's membrane to help create the resting potential?
   a. $Ca^{2+}$
   b. $K^+$
   c. $Na^+$
   d. $Cl^-$

2. Why did the squid axon become a model system for studying electrical signaling in animals?
   a. Its action potentials are particularly large and frequent.
   b. It is the tissue from which researchers initially isolated $Na^+/K^+$-ATPase.
   c. Squids are abundant and easy to obtain.
   d. It was large enough to support intracellular recording by the first microelectrodes.

3. How does myelination affect the propagation of an action potential?
   a. It speeds propagation by increasing the density of voltage-gated channels.
   b. It speeds propagation by increasing electrochemical gradients favoring $Na^+$ entry.

   c. It speeds propagation because cations do not leak out of the membrane as they spread down the axon.
   d. It slows down propagation because $Na^+$ channels exist only at unmyelinated nodes (nodes of Ranvier).

4. In a neuron, what creates the electrochemical gradient favoring the outflow of $K^+$ when the cell is at rest?
   a. $Na^+/K^+$-ATPase
   b. voltage-gated $K^+$ channels
   c. voltage-gated $Na^+$ channels
   d. ligand-gated $Na^+/K^+$ channels

5. Which of the following brain regions is responsible for formation of new memories?
   a. brain stem
   b. hippocampus
   c. frontal lobe
   d. cerebellum

6. Draw a graph of an action potential and label the axes. Label the parts of the graph, and explain which ion flow or flows are responsible for each part.

7. Explain why the Na⁺/K⁺-ATPase is "electrogenic"—meaning that it creates a voltage across a membrane.

8. Explain the difference between a ligand-gated $K^+$ channel and a voltage-gated $K^+$ channel.

9. Describe the role of summation in postsynaptic cells.

10. Compare and contrast the somatic and autonomic components of the PNS.

11. Predict the effect on heart rate of a drug that activates sympathetic nervous system activity.

12. Why is memory thought to involve changes in particular synapses?
   a. In some systems, an increased release of neurotransmitters occurs after learning takes place.
   b. In some systems, the type of neurotransmitter released at the synapse changes after learning takes place.
   c. When researchers stimulated certain neurons electrically, individuals replayed memories.
   d. People who lack short-term memory have specific deficits in synapses within the brain regions responsible for memory.

13. Explain why drugs that prevent neurotransmitters from being taken back up by the presynaptic cell have dramatic effects on the activity of postsynaptic neurons.

14. Discuss the pros and cons of lesion studies and electrical stimulation of conscious patients in determining the functions of particular brain structures.

15. QUANTITATIVE The data points on the graph record the movement of potassium ions (in μSiemens, a unit of conductance) observed when neuron membranes were voltage-clamped at the array of voltages indicated on the *x*-axis. The "Neuron with venom" data were generated by adding black mamba venom to the solution bathing the neuron (black mambas are snakes). Which of these conclusions can you draw from the data?

   a. The venom opens all potassium channels.
   b. The venom blocks all potassium channels.
   c. There is more than one type of potassium channel; at least one is affected by the venom while others are not.
   d. Black mamba venom does not affect potassium ion movement.

16. Studies of the brain show that mature neurons do not undergo mitosis to give rise to new neurons, yet adult neurogenesis occurs in all vertebrates. Suggest a hypothesis as to the source of these new neurons.

# 47 Animal Sensory Systems

**In this chapter you will learn how**

**Animals transform sound, smell, and other stimuli into signals the brain can understand**

↓ by asking

**How do sensory organs convey information to the brain?** 47.1

→ then looking closer at

- **Mechanoreception** 47.2
- **Photoreception** 47.3
- **Chemoreception** 47.4
- **Sensing temperature and electric and magnetic fields** 47.5

which is part of ↓

**The nervous system Ch. 46**

In many species of moth, males have much larger antennae than females do. Receptor cells on the males' feathery antennae detect airborne chemical signals that are produced by sexually mature females. As a result, males can locate females in total darkness.

This chapter is part of the Big Picture. See how on pages 840–841.

Many adult moths are active at night, when it is difficult or impossible to see. Instead of *looking* for a mate under these challenging circumstances, sexually mature female moths release a chemical attractant into the air. Male moths can detect even a single molecule of the attractant, due to receptor cells located on their large, feathery antennae. Guided by an airborne gradient of attractant molecules, a male moth flies unerringly toward a female.

As they patrol in search of these airborne molecules, however, male moths are hunted by bats. Like moths, bats are active almost exclusively at night. Instead of hunting by sight, like a falcon or a cheetah, bats hunt with the aid of sonar: They emit a train of high-pitched sounds as they fly and then listen for echoes that indicate the direction and shape of objects in their path. If the object is a moth, the bat flies toward it, catches the moth in its mouth, and eats it.

✓ When you see this checkmark, stop and test yourself. Answers are available in Appendix A.

But some moth species can hear bat calls. When moths detect sounds from an onrushing bat, they tumble out of the sky in chaotic escape flights.

If you were out at night as these dramas unfolded, at best you might be dimly aware that bats and moths were flying about. Humans cannot smell moth attractants or hear the sounds that most bats emit when flying. It took decades of careful experimentation for biologists to understand how moths and bats sense the world around them and respond to the information they receive.

Sensing and interpreting changes in the environment are fundamental to how animals work. Let's begin with a basic question: How are sounds, smells, and other stimuli transformed into a signal that the brain can understand?

## 47.1 How Do Sensory Organs Convey Information to the Brain?

As a moth flies through the night, its brain receives streams of signals from an array of sensory organs. Antennae provide information about the concentration of female attractant molecules; ears located on various parts of the body send data on the presence of high-pitched sounds; detectors for balance and gravity transmit signals about the body's orientation in space.

Each type of sensory information is detected by a sensory neuron or by a specialized receptor cell that makes a synapse with a sensory neuron. As **FIGURE 47.1** shows, the moth's nervous system integrates the sensory input—the information from sensory neurons—and responds with motor output, via electrical signals, to specific muscle groups (effectors).

The ability to sense a change in the environment depends on three processes:

1. *Transduction,* the conversion of an external stimulus to an internal signal in the form of action potentials along sensory neurons
2. *Amplification* of the signal
3. *Transmission* of the signal to the central nervous system (CNS)

The first step in the sequence, transduction, requires a sensory receptor cell specialized for converting light, sound, touch, or some other signal into an electrical signal. Sensory receptors are located throughout the body and are categorized by type of stimulus:

- **Mechanoreceptors** respond to distortion caused by pressure.
- **Photoreceptors** respond to particular wavelengths of light.
- **Chemoreceptors** perceive specific molecules.
- **Thermoreceptors** detect changes in temperature.
- **Nociceptors** sense harmful stimuli such as tissue injury.
- **Electroreceptors** detect electric fields.
- **Magnetoreceptors** detect magnetic fields.

With such a broad range of possible sensory detectors, it is no wonder that animals can monitor and respond to a wide array of changes in their environments.

Now, how do sensory cells receive information from the environment and report it to the brain, so an appropriate response can occur?

### Sensory Transduction

During the resting state in most sensory cells, the inside of the plasma membrane is more negative than the exterior (see Chapter 46). When ion flows cause the interior to become more positive (less negative), the membrane is **depolarized.** When ions cause the cell interior to become more negative than the resting potential, the membrane is **hyperpolarized.**

Although sensory receptors can detect a remarkable variety of stimuli, they all transduce sensory input—such as light, sounds, touch, and odors—to a change in membrane potential. In this way, different types of information are transduced to a common type of signal—one that can be interpreted by the brain.

If a sensory stimulus induces a large change in a sensory receptor's membrane potential, there is a change in the firing rate of action potentials sent to the brain. The amount of depolarization that occurs in a sound-receptor cell, for example, is proportional to the loudness of the sound. If the depolarization passes

**FIGURE 47.1 Sensory Systems, the CNS, and Effectors Are Linked.** Sensory neurons relay information about conditions inside and outside an animal to the central nervous system. After integrating information from many sensory neurons, the CNS sends signals to muscles.

**(a)** Sound-receptor cells depolarize in response to sound.

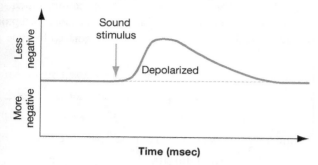

**(b)** Sound-receptor cells respond more strongly to louder sounds.

IGURE 47.2 Sensory Inputs Change the Membrane Potential
f Receptor Cells. **(a)** In response to sensory stimuli, ions flow
cross the membranes of receptor cells and either depolarize or
yperpolarize the membrane. **(b)** The rate at which action potentials
ccur in an auditory neuron transmits information about the nature
nd intensity of the sensory stimulus. (The frequency of a sound,
neasured in hertz, determines its pitch.)

ATA: Rose, J. E., J. E. Hind, D. J. Anderson, et al. 1971. *Journal of Neurophysiology* 34: 685–699.

hreshold, enough voltage-gated sodium channels open to trig-
er action potentials that are relayed to the brain.

**FIGURE 47.2a** shows the membrane potential from a sound-
eceptor cell. If you put your finger on the red line and trace
o the right, you'll notice that when the experimenter played a
ound, the sound-receptor cell depolarized for a short time in re-
ponse. Other sensory cells work in a similar way.

Recall that all action potentials from a given neuron are iden-
ical in size and shape (see Chapter 46). **FIGURE 47.2b** graphs the
ction potential "firing rate" recorded from a sound-receptor cell
hen sounds at various frequencies were played at two distinct
ntensities. Notice that loud sounds induce a higher rate of action
otentials than do soft sounds. In this way receptor cells provide
nformation about the intensity of a stimulus.

But if all types of external stimuli are converted to electrical
ignals in the form of action potentials, and if all action poten-
als are alike in size and duration, how does the brain interpret
e incoming signals properly?

## ansmitting Information to the Brain

here are two keys to understanding how the brain interprets
nsory information. First, receptor cells tend to be highly spe-
fic. For example, each receptor cell in a human ear responds best

to certain pitches of sound. Some receptors are more sensitive
to low-pitched sounds, and others respond best to high-pitched
sounds. The pattern of action potentials from a cell contains information about the pitch of the sound that is being received, its
intensity, and how long the stimulus lasts.

The second key point: Each type of sensory neuron sends its
signal to a specific portion of the brain. Axons from sensory neurons in the human ear project to the temporal lobes at the sides
of the brain, but axons from sensory receptors in the eye deliver
action potentials to the occipital lobe at the back of the brain.
Different regions of the brain are specialized for interpreting different types of stimuli.

Now that the basic principles of sensory reception and transduction have been introduced, let's delve into the details of the
major sensory systems.

## 47.2 Mechanoreception: Sensing Pressure Changes

Animals have a variety of mechanisms for **mechanoreception**—
the sensation of pressure changes. Crabs, for example, have a
fluid-filled organ that helps them sense the pressure created by
gravity. The organ, known as a **statocyst,** is lined with pressure-
receptor cells and contains a small calcium-rich particle that normally rests on the bottom of the organ. But if the crab is tipped or
flipped over, this particle presses against receptors that are *not* on
the bottom of the organ. When the brain receives action potentials from these receptors, it responds by activating muscles that
restore the animal to its normal posture.

It's also common for animals to have cells that are responsible
for detecting direct physical pressure on skin, as well as pressure-
receptor cells that monitor how far muscles or blood vessels are
stretched. Animals detect sound waves, which produce pressure
in air, with hearing, and some aquatic animals detect pressure
waves in water via a lateral line system. These pressure-sensing
systems are all based on the same mechanism.

Let's briefly examine the general design of a mechanoreceptor
cell and its response to pressure, then investigate the specific structures involved in vertebrate hearing and the lateral line system.

### How Do Sensory Cells Respond to Sound Waves and Other Forms of Pressure?

The mechanoreceptors responsible for sensing sound, vibrations, and other pressure waves in the environment are relatively
simple. In every case, direct physical pressure on a plasma membrane or distortion of membrane structures by bending changes
the conformation of ion channels in the membrane and causes
the channels to open or close.

The consequent change in ion flow through the channel proteins results either in a depolarization or a hyperpolarization.
This changes the pattern of action potentials in a sensory neuron.

**The Structure of Hair Cells** In vertebrates, ion channels that
respond to pressure are often found in hair cells. **Hair cells** are

**(a)** Hair cells have many stereocilia and one kinocilium.

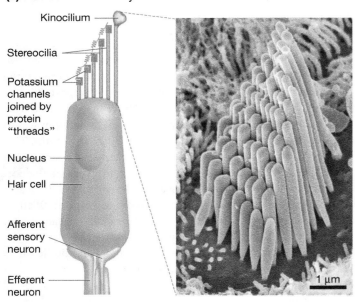

Kinocilium

Stereocilia

Potassium channels joined by protein "threads"

Nucleus

Hair cell

Afferent sensory neuron

Efferent neuron

1 µm

**(b) PROCESS: BENDING OPENS ION CHANNELS**

Pressure wave

K+

K+

Depolarization

Synaptic vesicle

Calcium channel

Ca²⁺          Ca²⁺

Neurotransmitter released into synapse

Afferent neuron (to brain)

1. **Pressure wave bends stereocilia.**

2. **Potassium channels open** in response to bending.

3. **Membrane depolarizes** due to influx of K⁺.

4. **Depolarization triggers inflow of calcium ions.**

5. **Synaptic vesicles fuse with plasma membrane.**

6. **Neurotransmitter is released** and diffuses to afferent neuron.

**FIGURE 47.3 Hair Cells Transduce Sound Waves to Electrical Signals.**

pressure-receptor cells, illustrated in **FIGURE 47.3a**, named for their stiff outgrowths called **stereocilia** (singular: **stereocilium**). The "hairy-looking" stereocilia are microvilli that are reinforced by actin filaments.

Many hair cells also have a single **kinocilium,** a true cilium that contains a 9 + 2 arrangement of microtubules (introduced in Chapter 7). Hair cells are found in the ears of land-dwelling vertebrates and the lateral line system in many species of fishes and some amphibians.

As Figure 47.3a shows, the stereocilia in hair cells are arranged in order of increasing height; if a kinocilium is present, it is the tallest of all the projections. These structures extend into a fluid-filled chamber.

**Signal Transduction in Hair Cells** If stereocilia are bent in the direction of the kinocilium in response to pressure (**FIGURE 47.3b**), the distortion causes potassium ion (K⁺) channels in the stereocilia to open. This is the common theme connecting pressure-sensing cells: Bending opens ion channels.

Recall that the opening of K⁺ channels usually causes an outflow of K⁺ that hyperpolarizes neurons (see Chapter 46). Hair cell plasma membranes respond differently, however, because they are bathed by extracellular fluid with an extraordinarily high K⁺ concentration. As a result, the equilibrium potential for K⁺ in hair cells is 0 mV instead of the −85 mV in a typical neuron. The resting potential of the hair cell plasma membrane is −70 mV, so when the channels open, K⁺ rushes in and causes a depolarization of approximately 20 mV.

In hair cells, depolarization causes an inflow of calcium ions, which triggers an increase in the amount of neurotransmitter released at the synapse between the hair cell and a sensory neuron. The end result is excitation of the postsynaptic cell, meaning that it becomes more likely to fire an action potential to the brain via an afferent sensory neuron. You might recall that afferent neurons are part of the peripheral nervous system and conduct information to the CNS (see Chapter 46).

If sound pressure waves bend stereocilia the other way, however, the K⁺ channels close, and the cell hyperpolarizes by 5 mV. Hyperpolarization of the hair cell decreases the amount of neurotransmitter released at the synapse and inhibits the postsynaptic sensory neuron, making it less likely to trigger action potentials.

How can bending affect ion channels? Electron micrographs show that tiny threads connect the tips of stereocilia to each other. One hypothesis contends that when the stereocilia are bent, the threads somehow pull on the ion channels in the wall of the next tallest stereocilium and open them like tiny trapdoors (see Figure 47.3b, step 2). This hypothesis remains to be confirmed, however. Researchers still do not fully understand how the ion channels involved in pressure reception work.

## Hearing: The Mammalian Ear

**Hearing** is the sensation produced by the wavelike changes in air pressure called sound. A sound consists of waves of pressure in air or in water. The number of pressure waves that occur in 1 second is called the **frequency** of the sound, reported in units called hertz (Hz), or cycles per second. When you hear different sound frequencies, you perceive them as different **pitches.** A high-pitched sound may have a frequency in the range of 8000 Hz, whereas a low-pitched sound frequency might be 1000 Hz.

The ear transduces sound waves into action potentials that send information to the brain. To understand how changes in the membrane potential of hair cells result in hearing, let's focus on the human ear as a case study. The human ear has three sections:

the **outer ear, middle ear,** and **inner ear** (**FIGURE 47.4**). A membrane separates each section from the next.

The path of sound through the ear is traced in Figure 47.4. The outer ear, which projects from the head, collects incoming pressure waves and funnels them into a tube known as the ear canal. At the inner end of the ear canal (see the lower part of Figure 47.4), the waves strike the **tympanic membrane,** or eardrum, which separates the outer ear from the middle ear.

The repeated cycles of air compression cause the tympanic membrane to vibrate back and forth with the same frequency as the sound wave. The vibrations are passed to three tiny bones in the middle ear called the **ear ossicles,** which vibrate against one another in response. The last ossicle, the **stapes** (pronounced *STAY-peez*), vibrates against a membrane called the **oval window,** which separates the middle ear from the inner ear. The oval window oscillates in response and generates waves in the fluid inside a chamber known as the **cochlea** (pronounced *KOK-lee-ah*). These pressure waves are sensed by hair cells in the cochlea.

In effect, the ear translates airborne waves into fluid-borne waves. The system seems extraordinarily complex, though, for

such a simple result. Why doesn't the outer ear canal lead directly to the oval window? Why have a middle ear at all?

**The Middle Ear Amplifies Sounds**  Biologists began to understand the function of the middle ear when they recognized two key aspects of its structure. First, the size difference between the tympanic membrane and the oval window is important. The tympanic membrane is about 15 times larger than the oval window, causing the amount of vibration induced by sound waves to increase by a factor of 15 when it reaches the oval window. This phenomenon is similar to taking the same amount of force used to bang on a very large door and applying it to a very small door.

In addition, the three ossicles act as levers that further amplify vibrations from the tympanic membrane. The overall effect in mammals is to amplify sound by a factor of 22—meaning that soft sounds are amplified enough to stimulate hair cells in the cochlea. Thus, biologists interpret the mammalian middle ear as an adaptation for increasing sensitivity to sound.

To summarize, the mammalian outer ear transmits sound waves from the environment to the middle ear; the middle ear amplifies these waves enough to stimulate the hair cells within the cochlea of the inner ear.

If all hair cells responded equally to all frequencies of sound, you would be able to perceive only one pitch. Everyone's voice—indeed, every noise—would sound the same. How can hair cells distinguish different frequencies?

**The Cochlea Detects the Frequency of Sounds**  As **FIGURE 47.5a** shows, the cochlea is a coiled tube with a set of internal membranes that divide it into three chambers. Hair cells, forming rows in the middle chamber, are embedded in a tissue that sits atop the **basilar membrane** (**FIGURE 47.5b**). In addition, the hair cells' stereocilia touch yet another, smaller surface called the **tectorial membrane.** (The kinocilium is not present in a mature cochlear hair cell.) In effect, hair cells are sandwiched between membranes.

Researchers struggled for decades to understand how these membranes affect hair cell function. It is virtually impossible to study cochleas in living organisms, because the cochleas are tiny, complex, coiled, and buried deep inside the skull. During the 1920s and 1930s, however, Georg von Békésy pioneered work on the structure and function of these organs by performing experiments on cochleas that he had dissected from fresh human cadavers.

Von Békésy was able to vibrate the oval window and record how the cochlea's internal membranes moved in response. He found that when a pressure wave traveled down the fluid in the upper and lower chambers, the basilar membrane vibrated in response. His key finding, though, was that sounds of different frequencies caused the basilar membrane to vibrate maximally at specific points along its length (**FIGURE 47.6**). When the basilar membrane vibrated in a particular location, the stereocilia of the hair cells there were bent one way and then the other by the tectorial membrane.

Von Békésy also noted that the basilar membrane is stiff near the oval window and flexible at the other end. This is why each

**FIGURE 47.4 Mammals Have an Outer Ear, Middle Ear, and Inner Ear.** The middle ear starts with the tympanic membrane and ends in the oval window of the cochlea.

**(a)** The middle chamber of the fluid-filled cochlea contains hair cells.

Cochlea

Auditory nerve (to brain)

Three fluid-filled chambers

Tectorial membrane

Hair cells

Neurons (of auditory nerve)

**(b)** Hair cells are sandwiched between membranes.

Stereocilia

Tectorial membrane

Hair cells

Basilar membrane

Axons of sensory neurons

**FIGURE 47.5 The Human Cochlea Contains Fluid-Filled Chambers Separated by Membranes.**

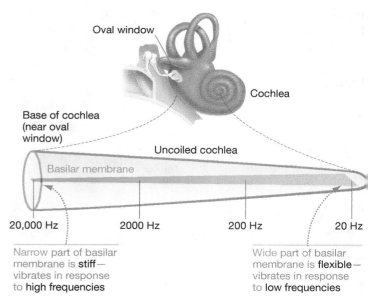

Oval window

Cochlea

Base of cochlea (near oval window)

Uncoiled cochlea

Basilar membrane

20,000 Hz   2000 Hz   200 Hz   20 Hz

Narrow part of basilar membrane is **stiff**—vibrates in response to high frequencies

Wide part of basilar membrane is **flexible**—vibrates in response to low frequencies

**FIGURE 47.6 The Basilar Membrane Varies in Stiffness.** Different parts of the basilar membrane respond to different sound frequencies.

segment vibrates in response to a different frequency of sound. Just as a stiff drumhead produces a high-pitched sound and a loose drumhead yields a low-pitched sound, high-frequency sounds cause the stiff part of the basilar membrane to vibrate; low-frequency sounds cause the flexible part to vibrate.

To summarize, certain portions of the basilar membrane vibrate in response to specific frequencies and result in the bending of hair cell stereocilia. In this way, hair cells in a particular place on the membrane respond to sounds of a certain frequency. When the occipital lobe of the cerebrum receives action potentials from neurons associated with specific hair cells, it interprets them as a particular pitch—meaning a specific frequency of sound. The result is the sense called hearing.

Complex sounds contain a wide variety of frequencies and trigger particular combinations of hair cells. Through experience, the brain learns which combinations of frequencies represent music, a fire alarm, or a best friend's voice.

Compared with the hearing of many mammals, human hearing is not particularly acute. Humans can hear sounds between 20 Hz and 20,000 Hz (20,000 Hz is equal to 20 kHz, or kilohertz). But some mammals can sense low-frequency infrasounds that are too low for humans to hear (*infra–* means below or under); others are aware of high-frequency ultrasounds that are above the range of human hearing (*ultra–* means beyond).

**Elephants Detect Infrasound**   When Katherine Payne was observing elephants at a zoo in the mid-1980s, she noticed a subtle throbbing in the air. Payne knew that infrasound can produce such sensations.

To test the hypothesis that the elephants were producing infrasonic vocalizations, Payne returned to the zoo with microphones that could pick up sounds at extremely low frequency. At normal speed, the tape she made was silent. But when she raised the pitch of the sounds by speeding up the tape, she heard a chorus of cow-like noises. The elephants were calling to each other, using low-frequency sounds.

According to follow-up research, elephants have the best infrasonic hearing of any land mammal. Because infrasound can travel exceptionally long distances, biologists hypothesize that infrasonic calls allow wild elephants to coordinate their movements when they are miles apart.

Recent research suggests that in addition to detecting infrasound via their large ears, elephants use their feet to detect a by-product of infrasound: seismic vibrations traveling in the ground.

**Bats Detect Ultrasound**   Ultrasonic hearing in bats was discovered in the late 1930s, when Donald Griffin borrowed the only ultrasonic apparatus then in existence from Robert Galambos,

- Bat sonar
- Returning sound waves

**FIGURE 47.7 Bats Emit Ultrasonic Sound Waves That Bounce Off Surfaces.** Returning sound waves are sensed by the bat's inner ear.

echoes. Similarly, the part of the brain used to process sound is unusually large in bats, highlighting the extremely important role of echolocation in their navigation and hunting.

More recent research has shown that dolphins, shrews, and certain other animals besides bats use sonar. In fact, it is likely that at least some of these species perceive shapes with their ears better than they do with their eyes.

## The Lateral Line System in Fishes and Amphibians

Hair cells in the ear allow mammals to sense changes in air pressure that are perceived as sound. But in fishes and aquatic amphibians, hair cells in a different organ allow the perception of pressure changes in water. In most fishes and larval amphibians, groups of hair cells are embedded in gel-like domed structures called cupulae inside canals that run the length of the body (**FIGURE 47.8a**), forming a sensory organ called the **lateral line system.**

Pressure changes in the surrounding water—whether resulting from waves, an animal swimming nearby, or some other force—cause changes in the pressure of water moving through the lateral line system (**FIGURE 47.8b**). These changes cause kinocilia and stereocilia on the hair cells to bend, and the distortion leads to a change in action potentials along sensory neurons to the brain. In this way, most aquatic animals get information about pressure changes at specific points along the head and body.

What use do fishes make of the lateral line system? It seems reasonable that the lateral line system could be helpful for identifying mates, locating prey, or avoiding predators. However, fishes could also use vision, smell, or other senses for these functions. How important is the lateral line system?

To answer this question, Kirsten Pohlmann, Jelle Atema, and Thomas Breithaupt studied how nocturnal catfish locate prey. At night, the catfish cannot use vision to hunt smaller fishes, so they must use stimuli that persist in the wake of their prey after it has moved on. The researchers hypothesized that the nocturnal catfish hunt smaller fishes using the lateral line system.

a fellow graduate student. Griffin used the machine to demonstrate that flying bats constantly emit ultrasounds. In follow-up experiments, he documented that a bat with cotton in its ears, or with its mouth taped shut, crashed into walls when released in a room. Blindfolded bats, in contrast, never crashed.

Griffin and Galambos concluded that bats use sound echoes (sonar) to navigate. This concept, termed **echolocation,** was an outlandish idea at the time. When Galambos described it at a meeting in 1940, another scientist shook him by the shoulders and said, "You can't really mean that!"

Bats generate high-frequency sound waves with the larynx, or voice box. These waves "bounce" off of surfaces (including those of insects), producing echoes that the bat perceives in its inner ear (**FIGURE 47.7**). Recall that different sections of the basilar membrane are specialized for sensing sound waves of different frequencies. In bats, a huge area of the basilar membrane is specialized for sensing the high-frequency sounds of the returning

**(a)** The lateral line system consists of a series of canals running along the head and body.

**(b)** Water enters the canals through pores and bends kinocilia on hair cells, activating sensory neurons.

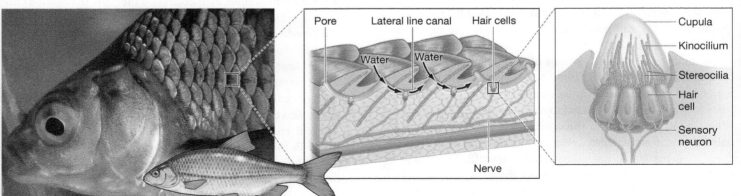

**FIGURE 47.8 The Lateral Line System Detects Pressure Waves in Water. (a)** Lateral line canals lie just under the fish's epidermis. **(b)** Hair cells within the canals have kinocilia and stereocilia embedded in a gel-like cupula.

To test this hypothesis, the researchers conducted an ablation experiment on the catfish (**FIGURE 47.9**). Ablation is the removal or blocking of a process. In this case, the researchers ablated the lateral line system in one group of catfish, using a chemical that blocks the hair cells from responding to pressure waves. In another group of catfish, they ablated the ability to smell or taste the water by surgically removing the lobes of the brain responsible for these senses.

While the catfish whose smell and taste were ablated took the same amount of time as the non-ablated control group to locate and capture prey, it took the catfish whose lateral line was ablated over twice as long. The researchers concluded that the lateral line system is much more important than other senses in the successful hunting of nocturnal fishes.

check your understanding

**RESEARCH**

**QUESTION:** What cues do predatory fish use to detect prey at night?

**HYPOTHESIS:** Predatory fish detect prey using the lateral line system.

**ALTERNATE HYPOTHESIS:** Predatory fish detect prey using smell and taste.

**NULL HYPOTHESIS:** Predatory fish use neither sense to detect prey.

**EXPERIMENTAL SETUP:**

1. Three experimental groups of catfish ($n=16$ for each group):

| Lateral line ablated | Smell and taste ablated | Control fish |
|---|---|---|

2. Acclimate catfish to dark tank at night.

3. Add guppies to tank and record capture success rate.

**PREDICTION:** Fish with their lateral line ablated will have lower capture success than control fish.

**PREDICTION OF ALTERNATE HYPOTHESIS:** Fish with smell and taste ablated will have lower capture success than control fish.

**PREDICTION OF NULL HYPOTHESIS:** There will be no capture success difference among groups.

**RESULTS:**

**Percentage of Guppies Captured**

| Lateral line ablated | Smell and taste ablated | Control fish |
|---|---|---|
| 17% | 60% | 65% |

**CONCLUSION:** Nocturnal predatory catfish use the lateral line system to detect prey.

**FIGURE 47.9 The Lateral Line System Is Used for Predation.**

✔**QUESTION** If you wanted to conduct a study similar to this one on a diurnal species of catfish, what other sense would you need to control for, and how would you do it?

SOURCE: Pohlmann, K., J. Atema, and T. Breithaupt. 2004. The importance of the lateral line in nocturnal predation of piscivorous catfish. *The Journal of Experimental Biology* 207: 2971–2978.

**C Y U**
**If you understand that . . .**

- Mechanoreception is a type of pressure detection that begins when the stereocilia on hair cells bend in response to changes in pressure. The bending movement opens ion channels and results in a change in membrane potential.
- The mammalian ear consists of specialized structures that function in transmitting and amplifying sound and in responding to specific frequencies as well as recognizing changes in intensity.
- The lateral line system in fishes and aquatic amphibians allows them to sense pressure waves in water caused by prey, predators, and potential mates.

✔ **You should be able to . . .**

1. Predict and explain the effect on hearing in each of the following cases: a punctured eardrum, a mutation that results in dramatically shortened stereocilia, and an age-related loss of flexibility in the basilar membrane.

2. Describe the function of the lateral line system in fishes.

*Answers are available in Appendix A.*

## 47.3 Photoreception: Sensing Light

Most animals have a way to sense light. The organs involved in **photoreception** range from simple light-sensitive eyespots in flatworms to the sophisticated, image-forming eyes of vertebrates, cephalopod mollusks, and arthropods.

Variation in the structure of light-sensing organs illustrates an important general principle about the sensory abilities of animals: In most cases, a species' sensory abilities correlate with the environment it lives in and its mode of life—how it finds food and mates. Eyes and other sensory structures are adaptations that allow individuals to thrive in a particular environment. Salamander species that live in meadows and forests have sophisticated eyes; those that live in lightless caves have no functional eyes at all.

Keep this point in mind as you delve into the details of how insects and vertebrates see.

## The Insect Eye

Insects have a **compound eye,** composed of hundreds or thousands of light-sensing columns called **ommatidia.** As **FIGURE 47.10** shows, each ommatidium has a lens that focuses light onto a small number of receptor cells—usually four. The receptor cells, in turn, send axons to the brain.

Each ommatidium contributes information about one small piece of the visual field, not unlike the contribution of a single pixel on a computer monitor. Thus, the more ommatidia in a compound eye, the better the resolution—meaning the resolving power, or ability to distinguish objects.

In addition, the presence of many light-sensing columns makes species with compound eyes particularly good at detecting movement. Insects that hunt by sight, such as damselflies and dragonflies, have particularly large numbers of ommatidia.

## The Vertebrate Eye

Compound eyes are found in insects, crustaceans, and certain other arthropods. Because they appear only in species that are part of the same monophyletic group (see Chapter 28), researchers conclude that this type of eye structure evolved just once—in an ancestor of today's arthropods.

In contrast, the **simple eye**—a structure with a single lens that focuses incoming light onto a layer of many receptor cells—evolved independently in several widely divergent groups, including annelids, cephalopod mollusks (squid and octopuses), and vertebrates. Let's examine the vertebrate version of the simple eye more closely.

**The Structure of the Vertebrate Eye**   **FIGURE 47.11a** shows the major structures in a typical vertebrate eye:

- The outermost layer of the structure is a tough rind of white tissue called the sclera. This is the "white of the eye."

- The front of the sclera forms the **cornea,** a transparent sheet of connective tissue.

- The **iris** is a pigmented, round muscle just inside the cornea. The iris can contract or expand to control the amount of light entering the eye.

- The **pupil** is the hole in the center of the iris.

- Light enters the eye through the cornea and passes through the pupil and a curved, clear **lens.**

- Together, the cornea and lens focus incoming light onto the retina in the back of the eye. The **retina** contains a thin layer of cells with photoreceptors and several layers of neurons.

**FIGURE 47.11b** provides a closer look at the retina, which is attached to the rest of the eye by a single layer of pigmented epithelial cells. From back to front, the retina comprises three distinct cell layers:

1. The photoreceptors, sensory cells that respond to light, are held in place by the pigmented epithelium.

2. Photoreceptors synapse with an intermediate layer of connecting neurons called **bipolar cells.**

3. Bipolar cells in the intermediate neuron layer connect with one another and with neurons called **ganglion cells,** which form the innermost layer of the retina. The axons of the ganglion cells project to the brain via the **optic nerve.**

Note that vertebrate eyes—including yours—have a blind spot because there are no photoreceptor cells where the optic nerve leaves the retina. If light falls in this area, there are no sensory cells available to respond. No signal is sent to the brain, so the stimulus isn't seen.

**What Do Rods and Cones Do?**   Early anatomists established that the photoreceptors in vertebrate eyes come in two distinct types: small rod-shaped cells and cone-shaped cells, called **rods** and **cones,** respectively (**FIGURE 47.12a**). When technical advances allowed changes in the membrane potentials of these cells to be recorded, it became clear that rods and cones differ in function as well as structure.

**(a)** Ommatidia are the functional units of insect eyes.   **(b)** Each ommatidium contains receptor cells that send axons to the CNS.

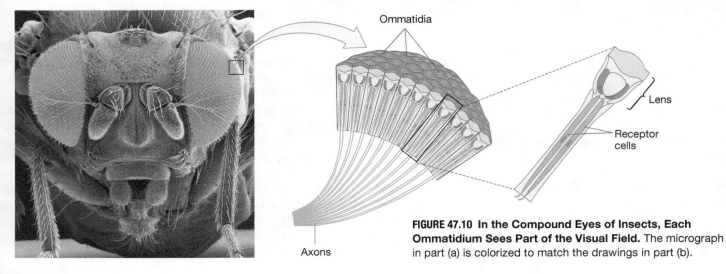

Ommatidia

Lens

Receptor cells

Axons

**FIGURE 47.10 In the Compound Eyes of Insects, Each Ommatidium Sees Part of the Visual Field.** The micrograph in part (a) is colorized to match the drawings in part (b).

**(a)** The structure of the vertebrate eye

**(b)** In the retina, cells are arranged in layers.

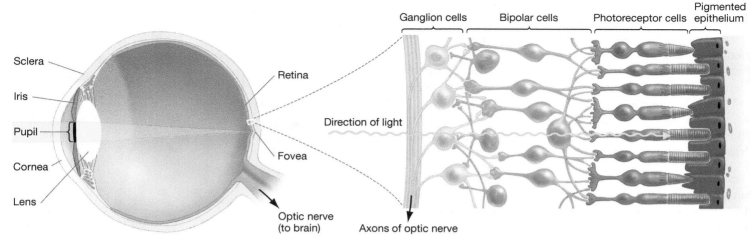

FIGURE 47.11 **Simple Eyes Have a Single Lens That Focuses Incoming Light on Receptor Cells. (a)** Light passes through the pupil of the eye and is focused onto the retina by the cornea and lens. **(b)** The photoreceptor cells that respond to light are in the "outermost" layer of the retina, furthest from the light source.

**(a)** Rods and cones contain stacks of membranes.

**(b)** Rhodopsin is a transmembrane protein complex.

**(c)** The retinal molecule inside rhodopsin changes shape when retinal absorbs light.

FIGURE 47.12 **Rods and Cones Are Packed with Transmembrane Proteins That Contain the Pigment Retinal.**
**(a)** Rods and cones have membranous disks containing thousands of opsin molecules (called rhodopsin in rods).
**(b)** Each opsin holds one retinal molecule. **(c)** Retinal changes conformation when it absorbs light. In response, opsin also changes shape.

✓QUESTION Explain why the change from *cis* to *trans* shown in part (c) would affect opsin's function.

Rods are sensitive to dim light but not to color. Cones, in contrast, are much less sensitive to faint light but are stimulated by different wavelengths (i.e., by colors). These discoveries explained why night vision is largely black and white—at night, the rods do most of the work.

Rods dominate most of the retina, but one small spot in the center of the retina has only cones. This is the **fovea** (see Figure 47.11a). When people focus on an object, their eyes move so that the image falls on the fovea of each eye. Based on these observations, biologists concluded that the high density of cones in the fovea maximizes the resolution of the image.

### How Do Rods and Cones Detect Light?

As Figure 47.12a shows, rods and cones have segments that are packed with membrane-rich disks. The membranes contain large quantities of a transmembrane protein called **opsin**. Each opsin molecule is associated with a molecule of the pigment **retinal**. In rod cells, the two-molecule complex is called **rhodopsin** (**FIGURE 47.12b**).

Experiments with isolated retinal, opsin, and rhodopsin molecules confirmed that retinal changes shape when it absorbs light. Specifically, the number-11 carbon in the retinal molecule changes from the *cis* conformation to the *trans* conformation (**FIGURE 47.12c**). Retinal is a light switch.

The shape change that occurs in retinal triggers a series of events that culminate in a different stream of action potentials being sent to the brain. The sequence of events is unusual, though, because the receipt of a light stimulus does not open ion channels or trigger the release of a neurotransmitter to a sensory neuron.

In vertebrates, the molecular basis of vision is a shape change in retinal that closes ion channels and decreases the amount of neurotransmitter being released to the sensory neuron. In rod cells, electrical activity across the membrane, as well as neurotransmitter release, are maximized in the dark. When retinal has not been activated by light, sodium channels in the rod's plasma membrane are open (**FIGURE 47.13a**), and entry of sodium continually depolarizes the rod cells. Exposure to light transmits information by *inhibiting* both processes.

**FIGURE 47.13b** shows how shutting down happens:

1. Rhodopsin is activated when light causes retinal to change shape from the *cis* to *trans* conformation.

2. Rhodopsin activation causes a membrane-bound molecule called transducin to activate the enzyme phosphodiesterase (PDE).

3. PDE breaks down a nucleotide called cyclic guanosine monophosphate (cGMP) to guanosine monophosphate (GMP).

4. As cGMP levels decline, cGMP-gated sodium channels in the plasma membrane of the rod cell close.

5. When sodium channels close, $Na^+$ entry decreases and the membrane hyperpolarizes.

✔ If you understand this sequence of events, you should be able to explain why cGMP acts as both a second messenger and a ligand in this system, and how transducin compares to G

**(a)** Before stimulation (no light)

Rod

Disk membranes

*cis*

Rhodopsin (inactive)

GDP — Transducin (inactive)

PDE (inactive)

$Na^+$

cGMP — cGMP-gated sodium channel (open)

Plasma membrane of rod

$Na^+$ current depolarizes membrane

**(b)** After stimulation (light)

Light

*trans* — Rhodopsin (activated)

GTP

Transducin (activated)

PDE (activated)

cGMP   **GMP**

cGMP-gated sodium channel (closed)

Lack of $Na^+$ current hyperpolarizes membrane

**FIGURE 47.13 A Signal-Transduction Pathway Connects Light Absorption to Changes in Membrane Potential. (a)** An unstimulated photoreceptor. Notice that sodium ions flow into the cell when light is *not* being received. **(b)** A stimulated photoreceptor. Activation of rhodopsin leads to a reduction in cGMP concentration. With less cGMP available, cGMP-gated sodium channels close, and the membrane hyperpolarizes.

✔**QUESTION** The inflow of sodium ions into a photoreceptor cell is called "the dark current." Why?

proteins (introduced in Chapter 11). You should also be able to explain why shutting $Na^+$ channels results in hyperpolarization.

In response to the ensuing change in membrane potential, smaller quantities of the neurotransmitter glutamate are discharged at the synapse. The decrease in neurotransmitter indicates to the postsynaptic bipolar cell that the rod has absorbed

No color deficiency

Red–green color deficiency

**FIGURE 47.14 People with Red–Green Color Blindness Cannot Distinguish Red from Green.** These images show what a person with red–green color blindness would see, compared to a person with normal color vision.

light. As a result, a new pattern of action potentials is sent to the brain, via neurons called ganglion cells. Axons from ganglion cells are bundled into the optic nerve.

This system is exquisitely sensitive: Biologists have recorded a measurable change in the membrane potentials of rod cells in response to a single photon of light. But how do humans and other animals perceive color?

**Color Vision: The Puzzle of Dalton's Eye** To answer this question, consider the research program initiated by John Dalton[1] in the late eighteenth century. At the age of 26, Dalton realized that he and his brother saw colors differently than other people did. To them, red sealing wax and green laurel leaves appeared to be the same color, and a rainbow exhibited only two hues. Dalton and his brother could not differentiate the colors red and green. This condition is called red–green color blindness (**FIGURE 47.14**).

In a lecture delivered in 1794, Dalton explained his perceptions by hypothesizing that red wavelengths failed to reach his retinas. Further, he hypothesized that because a normal eyeball is filled with clear fluid, and because blue fluids absorb red light, his defective vision resulted from the presence of bluish fluid rather than clear fluid in his eyes.

---

[1]Dalton was an accomplished physicist. He was the first proponent of the atomic theory of matter and formulated Dalton's law on the partial pressures of gases (introduced in Chapter 45). Red–green color blindness is sometimes called daltonism in his honor.

To test this hypothesis, Dalton left instructions that his eyes should be removed after his death and examined to see if the fluid inside was blue. When he died 50 years later, an assistant dutifully removed the eyes from Dalton's corpse and examined them. The fluid inside the eye was not blue at all, however, but slightly yellow—the normal color for an older person. Further, when the back was cut off one eye and colored objects were viewed through the lens, the objects looked perfectly normal. Dalton's hypothesis was incorrect.

**Color Vision: Multiple Opsins** What, then, caused Dalton's color blindness? The key to answering this question was the discovery that the human retina contains three types of color-sensitive photoreceptors: blue, green, and red cones, named for the colors that they best perceive.

To follow up on this result, biologists analyzed opsin molecules from the three cell types and found that each had a distinct amino acid sequence. The three proteins are now called the blue, green, and red opsins (or S, M, and L, for short, medium, and long wavelengths, respectively). Although retinal is the light-absorbing molecule in all photoreceptor cells, the different opsin molecules cause each type to respond to a different range of wavelengths of light.

Based on these results, biologists hypothesized that the brain distinguishes colors by combining signals initiated by the three classes of opsins. **FIGURE 47.15**, for example, graphs how much light is absorbed across a range of wavelengths by the S, M, and

**FIGURE 47.15 Color Vision Is Possible because Different Opsins Absorb Different Wavelengths of Light.** Each human cone cell contains one of three different types of opsin. Each opsin absorbs a different range of wavelengths.

✔**QUESTION** The retinal molecules in S, M, and L opsins are identical. What is the likely reason that they respond to different wavelengths of light?

L opsins of humans. Notice that a wavelength of 560 nanometers (nm) stimulates L cones strongly, M cones to an intermediate degree, and S cones not at all. In response to the corresponding signals from these cells, the brain perceives the color yellow.

Does this hypothesis explain Dalton's color blindness? According to the data in Figure 47.15, wavelengths from green to red do not stimulate S opsin at all. It is thus unlikely that S opsin is involved in red–green color blindness. Did Dalton fail to distinguish red and green because his M or L cones were defective? Research has shown that red–green color-blind people lack either functional M or L cones, or both. Was the same true of Dalton?

This question was answered in the 1990s, when the genes for the M and L opsins were sequenced. Remarkably, Dalton's eyes had been preserved. Researchers managed to extract DNA from the 150-year-old tissue and analyze his M opsin genes and L opsin genes. They found that Dalton had a normal *L* allele but lacked a functional *M* allele. As a result, he did not have green-sensitive cones. The puzzle of Dalton's color vision was solved.

Red–green color blindness, or the inability to distinguish red and green due to an absence of either M or L cones, is estimated to affect about 5 to 10 percent of men and less than 0.5 percent of women. It is more prevalent in men than in women because it is an X-linked trait (see Chapter 14). In contrast, the inability to distinguish blue from other colors, which would result from absence of the S cone, is an extremely rare, autosomal dominant trait.

**Do Other Animals See Color?** What about other animals—do they see color the way humans do? The answer is, probably not. Animals that are active at night have relatively few cone cells and many rods, giving them high sensitivity to light but poor color vision. On the other hand, many vertebrate and invertebrate species have four or more types of opsins and probably perceive a world of colors that is much richer than ours.

In general, the types of opsins found in a species correlate with the environment it inhabits and its mode of life. For example,

- A marine fish called the coelacanth (pronounced *SEE-luh-kanth*), which lives in water 200 m deep, has two opsins that respond to the blue region of the spectrum (wavelengths of 478 nm and 485 nm). As a result, coelacanths perceive several distinct hues of blue that we would perceive as a single color. These opsins offered an adaptive advantage to coelacanths because wavelengths in the yellow and red parts of the spectrum do not penetrate well into deep water—only blue light exists in the coelacanth's habitat.

- In humans and other primates that eat fruit, two of the three opsins are sensitive to wavelengths around 550 nm. The presence of these opsins allows individuals to distinguish between the greens, yellows, and reds of unripe and ripe fruits.

- Many animals (for example, some insects and birds) can see ultraviolet light, which has shorter wavelengths than humans can see. This ability can be vital. Certain flowers have ultraviolet patterns that serve as signals for insect pollinators. Also, many birds have strong ultraviolet patterns in their plumage

that are invisible to us but are important criteria used by females of some species for selecting mates.

**If you understand that . . .**
- In vertebrates, light detection begins when retinal changes shape after absorbing light.
- Stimulation of rhodopsin or the photopsins by light causes conformation changes in retinal, which triggers a series of events resulting in the closing of sodium channels in the membrane of a photoreceptor cell. The resulting change in membrane voltage triggers a change in neurotransmitter release from the receptor cell.

✔ **You should be able to . . .**
1. Explain why retinal can be thought of as a "light switch."
2. Predict the type of vision loss that results from each of the following: detachment of the retina following a car accident, a mutation that knocks out the gene for S opsin, and an age-related clouding of the lens.

*Answers are available in Appendix A.*

## 47.4 Chemoreception: Sensing Chemicals

**Chemoreception** occurs when chemicals bind to chemoreceptors to initiate action potentials in sensory neurons. The sense of taste, called **gustation,** and the sense of smell, called **olfaction,** originate in chemoreceptors. Chemoreceptors detect the presence of particular molecules by undergoing a change in membrane potential when a specific compound is present. In this way, information about the presence of a particular chemical is transduced to an electrical signal in the body.

Until recently, taste and smell were poorly understood in comparison with vision and hearing. It is easy to see why. Eyes and ears respond to relatively simple stimuli—light and sound waves. The tongue and nose, in contrast, respond to thousands of different chemicals. Consequently, taste and smell were difficult to study until techniques became available for identifying how particular molecules bind to certain receptors. But in the past 20 years, research on the chemosenses has exploded.

### Taste: Detecting Molecules in the Mouth

The chemoreceptor cells that sense taste are clustered in structures known as **taste buds.** Although humans have taste buds scattered around the mouth and throat, most taste buds are located on the tongue (**FIGURE 47.16**). A taste bud contains about 100 spindle-shaped taste cells, which contain taste receptors and synapse onto sensory neurons.

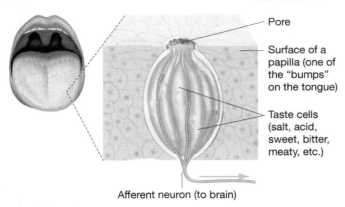

Pore

Surface of a papilla (one of the "bumps" on the tongue)

Taste cells (salt, acid, sweet, bitter, meaty, etc.)

Afferent neuron (to brain)

**FIGURE 47.16 Taste Buds Contain Many Types of Chemoreceptors.**

How do these receptors work on a molecular level, and how do they produce the sensation of taste? Early taste research focused on the hypothesis that four "basic tastes" existed: salty, sour, bitter, and sweet.

**Salt and Sour**   Researchers who analyzed the membrane proteins in taste cells found strong evidence that salt and sour sensations result from the activity of ion channels.

- The sensation of saltiness is due primarily to sodium ions ($Na^+$) dissolved in food. These ions flow into certain taste cells through open $Na^+$ channels and depolarize the cells' membranes.

- Sourness is due in part to the presence of protons ($H^+$), which flow directly into certain taste cells through $H^+$ channels and depolarize the membrane.

The sour taste of grapefruit and other citrus fruits, for example, results from the release of protons by citric acid. In general, the lower the pH of a food, the more it depolarizes a taste cell's plasma membrane, and the more sour the food tastes.

Compared to salt and sour, the molecular mechanisms responsible for the sensations of bitterness and sweetness have been much more difficult to identify. Researchers have only recently been able to document that certain food molecules actually bind to specific receptors on taste cells to cause bitter and sweet tastes.

**Why Do Many Different Foods Taste Bitter?**   Bitterness has been difficult to understand because molecules with very different structures, such as orange peel or unsweetened cocoa, are all perceived as bitter. How is this possible?

An answer began to emerge after researchers confirmed that some humans genetically lack the ability to taste certain bitter substances. In 1931, Arthur Fox was synthesizing phenylthiocarbamide (PTC) and accidentally blew some of it into the air. A nearby colleague complained of a bitter taste in his mouth, but Fox could not taste anything. Follow-up research confirmed that the ability to taste PTC is inherited and polymorphic. About 25 percent of Americans cannot sense the molecule.

To find the gene responsible for this trait, biologists compared the distribution of genetic markers observed in "tasters"

and "nontasters." The mapping effort recently narrowed down this gene's location to several candidate chromosomal segments. (Chapter 20 introduced this type of gene hunt.) In one of the regions, researchers found a family of 40 to 80 genes that encode transmembrane receptor proteins.

Follow-up work has documented that each protein in the family binds to a different type of bitter molecule. A taste cell, however, can have many different receptor proteins from this family. As a result, many different molecules can depolarize the same cell and cause the sensation of bitterness.

Why are so many genes devoted to detecting bitterness? Many of the molecules that bind to these receptors are found in toxic plants; most animals react to bitter foods by spitting them out and avoiding them in the future. In essence, bitterness indicates, "This food is dangerous; don't swallow it."

The proliferation of genes responsible for detecting bitterness hints that the trait is extremely adaptive—meaning that individuals with the capacity to detect a wide array of bitter compounds produce more offspring than do individuals that lack this ability.

**What Is the Molecular Basis of Sweetness and Other Tastes?**   Inspired by progress on bitter receptors, research teams used a similar approach—analyzing mutant mice that could *not* sense sweetness—to understand how the sweet receptor works.

In humans and mice, three closely related membrane receptors are responsible for detecting sweetness as well as glutamate and other amino acids. Glutamate triggers the sensation called **umami,** which is the meaty taste of the molecule monosodium glutamate (MSG). Glutamate is sensed by one particular pair of the three receptors. Sweetness is sensed by a different pair of receptors.

Recent work has solved a long-standing question about sweet sensation—why so many different types of sugars trigger the same sensation. As it turns out, a single receptor has binding sites for multiple types of sweet compounds, meaning that a variety of molecules can stimulate action potentials from the same receptor.

Currently, several teams are studying how the different taste sensations are conveyed to the brain and interpreted. Although taste is beginning to reveal its secrets, the complete story will probably not be known for many years.

## Olfaction: Detecting Molecules in the Air

Taste allows animals to assess the quality of their food before swallowing it. Olfaction, in contrast, allows animals to monitor airborne molecules that convey information. Wolves and domestic dogs, for example, can distinguish millions of different airborne molecules at vanishingly small concentrations. The molecules that constitute odor contain information about the movements and activities of prey and other members of their own species.

**Odorants Provide Information about the Environment**   Airborne molecules that convey information about food or the environment are called **odorants**. When they reach the nose, they diffuse

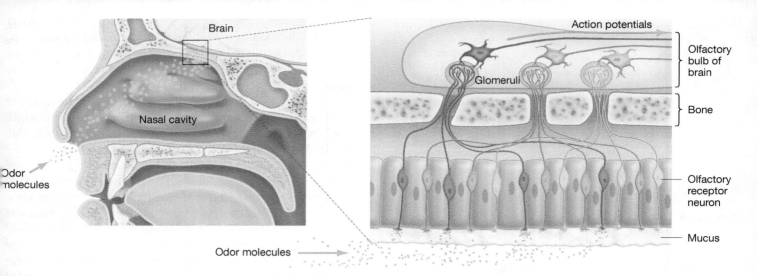

**FIGURE 47.17 In Mammals, Chemoreceptor Cells in the Nose Respond to Specific Odorants.** Each of the chemosensory neurons in the nose has one type of odor receptor protein on its dendrites. Sensory neurons with the same receptor project to the same glomerulus, or section within the olfactory bulb of the brain.

into a mucus layer in the roof of the nose (**FIGURE 47.17**). There, they activate olfactory neurons by binding to membrane-bound receptor proteins. Axons from these neurons project up to the **olfactory bulb,** the part of the brain where olfactory signals are processed and interpreted.

Understanding the anatomy of the odor-recognition system was a relatively simple task. Understanding how receptor neurons distinguish one molecule from another was much more difficult. Initially, investigators hypothesized that receptors respond to a small set of "basic odors," such as musky, floral, minty, and so on. The idea was that each basic odor would be detected by its own type of receptor, much like the way gustation works.

In 1991, Linda Buck and Richard Axel discovered a gene family in mice that comprises hundreds of distinct coding regions and encodes receptor proteins on the surface of olfactory receptor neurons. Follow-up experiments confirmed that each receptor protein binds to a small set of molecules.

Further work established that most, if not all, vertebrates possess this family of genes. Mammals typically have 800 to 1500 of these genes, meaning mammals could produce at least 800 to 1500 different olfactory receptor proteins. In humans, however, about half of these genes have mutations that probably render them nonfunctional. This observation may explain why the sense of smell is so poor in humans compared with that of most other mammals. But the sense of smell is even worse in whales and dolphins—70% to 80% of their olfactory receptor genes are nonfunctional. These animals rely far more on hearing and vision than on smell to sense their environment.

Buck and Axel's announcement inspired a series of questions. How many different receptors occur in the membrane of each neuron involved in odor reception? How does the brain make sense of the input from so many different receptors?

Recently, scientists determined that each olfactory neuron has only one type of receptor, and neurons with the same type of

receptor are linked to distinct regions in the olfactory bulb of the brain. These regions are called **glomeruli** (meaning little balls).

Follow-up work from Axel's lab indicated that each smell recognized by mice is associated with the activation of a different subset of the 2000 glomeruli in the brain. For example, the activation of clumps 130, 256, and 1502 might be perceived as the smell "cinnamon." In essence, then, the sensing of odorants is similar to the visual system's use of three cones to perceive many colors; but odor reception works on a much larger scale.

Interestingly, odorant receptors recently have been identified in locations other than the typical olfactory epithelium—for example, in tissues of the heart and pancreas. Receptors have also been identified in the cell membranes of sperm cells, where they appear to play an important role in guiding the sperm toward the egg. Research on this complex and impressive sense continues at a furious pace.

**Pheromones Provide Information about Members of the Same Species** Recall from the introduction to this chapter that male silk moths are able to locate female moths from miles away. Males have much larger antennae than females, suggesting that they use these antennae in a sex-specific manner.

These factors led scientists to hypothesize that female moths release a chemical into the environment that binds to chemoreceptors on the males' antennae and acts as an attractant. In 1959, scientists identified this chemical and named it bombykol, after the scientific name of the silk moth (*Bombyx mori*). Bombykol was the first chemically characterized **pheromone,** meaning a chemical that is secreted into the environment and that affects the behavior or physiology of animals of the same species.

Thousands of pheromones have since been identified in invertebrates and vertebrates alike, performing such roles as alerting other members of a beehive to an intruder or signaling a male rodent that a female is ovulating. In insects, pheromones typically bind to receptors on the antennae. In tetrapod vertebrates, pheromone receptors are often localized in the **vomeronasal organ,** a sensory organ in the nasal region but distinct from the olfactory bulb. The vomeronasal organ and the olfactory bulb send signals to different parts of the brain, although some animals also sense odorants with the vomeronasal organ. For example, a snake may follow a scent trail of prey using its vomeronasal organ.

Do humans release pheromones? This is a hotly debated question. In 1971, Martha McClintock demonstrated that the menstrual cycles of women living in close contact with one another become synchronized as a result of a secretion from the women's armpits, but the responsible chemical has yet to be identified. Other studies have suggested that secretions from men's armpits can alter hormone levels in women, but both the amount of the chemical secreted and the reaction to it vary dramatically among men and women. Until scientists more fully understand the mechanisms by which these human "pheromones" achieve their effects, the jury is out.

check your understanding

**If you understand that . . .**
- In most cases, chemoreception occurs when a specific molecule in air or food binds to a specific receptor in the nose or mouth and the binding event is transduced to a change in membrane voltage.
- Odorants bind to chemoreceptors to initiate action potentials to the brain, where action potentials from specific receptors are interpreted as particular smells.
- Pheromones bind to chemoreceptors that send action potentials to brain regions that then affect the behavior or physiology of the animal.

✔ **You should be able to . . .**
1. Discuss why a loss in chemosensory ability occurs when you burn your tongue with extremely hot food.
2. Develop a hypothesis to explain why the vomeronasal organ appears to be vestigial in most primates.

*Answers are available in Appendix A.*

## 47.5 Other Sensory Systems

The stimuli and senses discussed so far are the ones you are likely most familiar with. But animals can sense much more than pressure waves, light, and chemicals. All animals can sense temperature and painful stimuli, and some can even perceive electric or magnetic fields. Let's start with temperature and examine each of these other stimuli and senses in turn.

### Thermoreception: Sensing Temperature

Recall that many animals thermoregulate to maintain body temperature within an acceptable range (see Chapter 42). Virtually every physiological process, from digestion to metabolic rate, is temperature-dependent, so the ability to sense temperature changes in the environment and respond accordingly is crucial.

**Thermoreception Helps Animals Thermoregulate** Animals detect heat energy by **thermoreception** and adjust their behaviors or physiological processes, such as shivering and sweating, in response.

Some thermoreceptors are located in the central nervous system. In mammals, the hypothalamus is the brain region that senses departures from homeostatic body temperature and sends signals to effectors to restore homeostasis (see Figure 42.16).

Thermoreceptors also are commonly found on skin and other outer surfaces of animals, so that changes in the temperature of the environment can be sensed. As an example, several types of thermoreceptors have been identified in mammals. Some receptors depolarize in response to cooling, and others depolarize in response to heating. Picking up a cold object stimulates "cold receptors" in your skin, resulting in an increase in the rate of action potentials in sensory neurons that inform your brain that the object is cold.

Interestingly, extreme temperatures are sensed by a different type of receptor, called a nociceptor, that also senses other painful stimuli such as those produced by certain chemicals, excessive pressure, and tissue damage. If you touch a hot stove burner, the pain you feel arises primarily via stimulation of nociceptors.

**Pit Vipers Have Extremely Sensitive Thermoreceptors** The pit vipers are a group of snakes named after the two temperature-sensitive pits just beneath their nostrils (**FIGURE 47.18a**, see page 968). Inside each pit is a membrane lined with exquisitely sensitive thermoreceptors—a rattlesnake's thermoreceptors can sense changes in temperature as little as 0.003°C.

Pit vipers use these thermoreceptors to sense the heat energy given off by prey, predators, and even possible burrows in which to hide. The brains of these snakes may combine visual and thermal stimuli into a "thermal image" that might look something like an image from an infrared camera (**FIGURE 47.18b**). Even in complete darkness, rattlesnakes can strike prey with deadly precision.

✔ If you understand this, you should be able to predict whether a rattlesnake could strike effectively at its prey with (1) its eyes covered but pits exposed, (2) its eyes and pits covered with cotton cloth, and (3) its eyes and pits covered with an opaque heat-blocking material.

### Electroreception: Sensing Electric Fields

All animals give off weak electrical impulses that arise from the activity of their nerves and muscles. Since water is a good conductor of these electrical impulses, many kinds of fishes use **electroreception,** or sensation of electric fields, to locate prey, detect predators, and navigate.

**Sharks Use Electroreception to Hunt and Navigate** In sharks, some parts of the lateral line system are specialized to detect electrical fields rather than pressure. Tiny pores scattered across a shark's head contain structures called **ampullae of Lorenzini**

**(a)** Pit vipers have temperature-sensitive pits.

**(b)** Warm animals emit infrared radiation.

**FIGURE 47.18 Pit Vipers Use Thermoreception to Detect Prey. (a)** Pits are lined with extremely sensitive thermoreceptors. **(b)** Pit vipers can detect infrared radiation given off by rodents and other prey.

(**FIGURE 47.19**). These ampullae are lined with hair cells that depolarize in response to a change in electrical polarity and send signals to the shark's brain via sensory neurons.

The sensitivity of these ampullae is remarkable—sharks can detect electrical currents as weak as a nanovolt (a billionth of a volt). This ability allows sharks to detect prey that are far away or even buried in the sand at the ocean floor. Combined with their exquisite sense of olfaction—sharks can detect a single drop of blood in a million drops of ocean water—electroreception makes them finely tuned predators.

Although data are scarce, scientists have some evidence to suggest that sharks also use electroreception to navigate. Ocean currents moving through the Earth's magnetic field generate weak electrical currents. Sharks have been observed in the ocean orienting themselves to these fields as well as to artificially created fields in the laboratory.

**Electrogenic Fishes Generate Electric Fields** **Electrogenic fishes** have specialized organs near their tails that generate electric fields stronger than those of regular nerves or muscles. The currents generated by the electric organ move in an arc through the water (**FIGURE 47.20**). Any item located within that arc will disrupt the currents, allowing the fish's electroreceptors to detect it. In this way, electrogenic fishes use their electric organs to locate prey, sense predators, navigate through murky water, and even communicate with other fishes.

Some electrogenic fishes have the ability to produce extremely strong currents that stun or kill their prey. The electric organs of electric eels take up over 80 percent of their body mass and can generate a 500-volt change in electrical potential and 1 ampere of current in the water around them. This amount of current is enough to kill a person swimming in water with an electric eel.

## Magnetoreception: Sensing Magnetic Fields

The Earth produces a magnetic field as it rotates on its axis. Just as a compass uses this magnetic field to determine direction, animals may home in on magnetic fields while navigating. **Magnetoreception** has been described in many groups of organisms, including bacteria, fungi, invertebrates, and all vertebrate classes.

In general, studies of the mechanisms by which animals sense the Earth's magnetic fields are in their infancy. However, scientists are confident that at least several distinct mechanisms have evolved. Recall that sharks can sense magnetic fields indirectly via electric fields produced by ocean currents. Terrestrial organisms, in contrast, have the ability to sense magnetic fields directly.

In 1968, German scientists noticed that European robins being kept in the laboratory with no visual cues to the outside began to sit at one end of their cages at the beginning of the migratory season. This behavior led the scientists to hypothesize that birds use magnetoreception to determine direction as they migrate.

Since then, support for this hypothesis has accumulated. Application of artificial magnetic fields changes the robins' orientation. For example, when placed into circular chambers with artificial magnetic fields, birds always orient themselves in relation to the artificial field. Furthermore, disruption of the

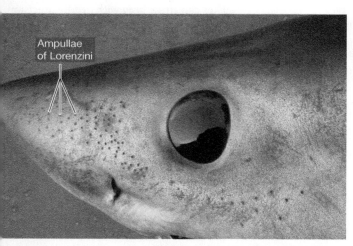

**FIGURE 47.19 Ampullae of Lorenzini on Sharks' Heads Detect Electrical Fields to Help Locate Prey and Navigate.**

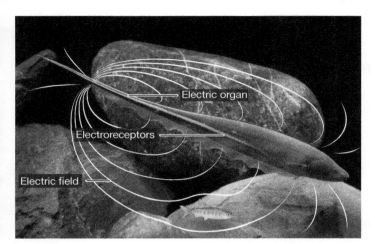

**FIGURE 47.20 Electrogenic Fishes Can Create Strong Electric Fields.** The fish emits an electric current with its electric organ. When a prey object disrupts the electric field, the fish detects its presence using electroreceptors.

magnetic field prevents birds from navigating properly. When scientists fitted homing pigeons with little caps that reversed the polarity of the magnetic field, the pigeons flew in the direction opposite to the one they were trained to fly in.

What enables birds to sense magnetic fields? It is likely a combination of factors. One hypothesis is that deposits of iron inside sensory neurons in the beak play a role in stimulating a response to changes in the magnetic field. In support of this hypothesis, cutting these neurons prevents birds from responding to artificial changes in the magnetic field in the lab. To complicate matters, however, magnetoreception in birds is apparently also dependent on vision. Covering the right eye—but not the

left eye—of migrating birds interferes with their ability to navigate using magnetic cues.

This complication highlights a key feature of sensory perception: Animals do not use individual senses in isolation, but rather combine sensations of many types when locating prey, evading predation, or communicating with other animals. Whether it is a homing pigeon using magnetoreception and photoreception to find its way home, or a rattlesnake using a visual and thermal image to strike at a mouse, all animals depend on sensory systems that work together to provide the animal with the information it requires to survive.

 **If you understand that . . .**

- Thermoreceptors, nociceptors, electroreceptors, and magnetoreceptors convey information about temperature, painful stimuli, electric fields, and magnetic fields, respectively.
- Animals combine input from multiple senses to locate prey, escape from predators, and communicate with other animals.

✔ **You should be able to . . .**

1. Identify one or more habitat types in which electrogenic fishes may have a survival advantage.
2. Propose a mechanism by which a female sea turtle migrates to lay eggs on the beach she was born on decades earlier.

*Answers are available in Appendix A.*

---

**CHAPTER 47 REVIEW** *For media, go to MasteringBiology*

## If you understand . . .

### 47.1 How Do Sensory Organs Convey Information to the Brain?

- If the membrane potential of a sensory cell is altered substantially enough in response to a stimulus, the pattern of action potentials that it sends to the brain changes. In this way, sensory stimuli as different as sound and light are transduced to electrical signals.
- The brain is able to distinguish different types of stimuli because axons from different types of sensory neurons project to different regions of the brain.

✔ You should be able to suggest a hypothesis to explain why people who have had limbs amputated experience "phantom pain"—the perception that their missing tissue hurts.

### 47.2 Mechanoreception: Sensing Pressure Changes

- Pressure receptors detect direct physical stimulation, including stimulation from sound.
- Hair cells, the major sensory detectors in the vertebrate ear, undergo a change in membrane potential in response to bending of their stereocilia.
- Sound waves of a certain frequency cause a certain part of the cochlea's basilar membrane to vibrate. Hair cells at this location stimulate action potentials in sensory neurons in response to the vibration.
- Hair cells in the lateral line systems of fishes and aquatic amphibians are stimulated by pressure changes in the water.

- You should be able to identify the key feature common to gravity sensing, hearing, and the lateral line system.

## 47.3 Photoreception: Sensing Light

- In the vertebrate eye, photoreceptors are located in rods and cones. Although these two cell types differ in structure and function, both contain molecules that consist of retinal paired with opsin (called rhodopsin in rod cells).
- The rhodopsin found in rods is stimulated by even the faintest light.
- Color vision is possible because cones contain opsins that respond to specific wavelengths of light absorbed by retinal.
- Humans distinguish colors based on the pattern of stimulation of three types of opsins found in cones. People who lack one of the functional cone opsins are color blind, meaning they cannot distinguish as many colors as people with all three opsins can.

✓ You should be able to explain how different animal species are able to see different colors.

## 47.4 Chemoreception: Sensing Chemicals

- Chemoreceptors detect the presence of certain foodborne or airborne molecules.
- Taste buds contain taste cells with membrane proteins that respond to toxins, salt, acid, and other types of molecules in food. Sodium ions and protons enter taste cells via channels and depolarize the membrane directly, producing the sensations of saltiness and acidity. Sugars and some toxic compounds bind to membrane receptors and trigger action potentials that are interpreted by the brain as sweet and bitter flavors, respectively.
- Smell, or olfaction, is used to scan molecules from the outside environment. Airborne chemicals are detected by hundreds of different odor-receptor proteins located in the membranes of receptor cells in the nose.

✓ You should be able to explain why people with nasal congestion complain that food tastes bland, and why the brain can perceive so many different flavors based on inputs from just four or five basic types of taste receptors.

## 47.5 Other Sensory Systems

- Thermoreceptors respond to changes in temperature.
- Nociceptors respond to painful stimuli, including extreme temperatures, certain chemicals, excessive pressure, and tissue damage.
- Electroreceptors contain modified hair cells that respond to electric fields.
- Magnetoreceptors respond to magnetic fields and are often used in navigation and orientation.

✓ You should be able to explain why the chemical capsaicin, found in chili peppers, feels hot on the tongue.

### (MB) MasteringBiology

1. **MasteringBiology Assignments**

   **Tutorials and Activities** Structure and Function of the Eye; Vertebrate Eye

   **Questions** Reading Quizzes, Blue-Thread Questions, Test Bank

2. **eText** Read your book online, search, take notes, highlight text, and more.

3. **The Study Area** Practice Test, Cumulative Test, BioFlix® 3-D Animations, Videos, Activities, Audio Glossary, Word Study Tools, Art

# You should be able to . . .

## ✓TEST YOUR KNOWLEDGE

1. What is echolocation?
   a. use of echoes from high-frequency vocalizations to detect objects
   b. use of extremely low-frequency vocalizations to communicate over long distances
   c. vision based on input from many independent lenses, functioning like pixels on a computer screen
   d. variation in the structure of opsin proteins, which allows animals to see different colors

2. In the human ear, how do different hair cells respond to different frequencies of sound?
   a. Waves of pressure move through the fluid in the cochlea.
   b. Hair cells are "sandwiched" between membranes.
   c. Receptors in the stereocilia of each hair cell are different; each receptor protein responds to a certain range of frequencies.
   d. Because the basilar membrane varies in stiffness, it vibrates in certain places in response to certain frequencies.

3. Which of the following comparisons of rods and cones is *false*?
   a. Most human eyes have one type of rod and three types of cones.
   b. Rods are more sensitive to dim light than cones are.
   c. Nocturnal animals have fewer rods than diurnal animals.
   d. Both rods and cones use retinal and opsins to detect light.

4. Which of the following statements about taste is *true*?
   a. Sweetness is a measure of the concentration of hydrogen ions in food.
   b. Sodium ions from foods can directly depolarize certain taste cells.
   c. All bitter-tasting compounds have a similar chemical structure.
   d. Membrane receptors are involved in detecting acids.

5. True or false: A rattlesnake's facial pits detect the presence of prey using photoreception.

6. What type of sensory system do migrating birds use to detect direction?

7. Considering that sounds and odors both trigger changes in the patterns of action potentials from sensory cells, how does the brain perceive which sense is which when the action potentials reach the brain?

   a. The action potentials stimulated by sounds are different in size and shape from those stimulated by an odor.

   b. The axons from different sensory neurons go to different areas of the brain.

   c. Mechanoreception is not consciously perceived by the brain, whereas chemoreception is.

   d. Chemoreception is not consciously perceived by the brain, whereas mechanoreception is.

8. Give three examples of how the sensory abilities of an animal correlate with its habitat or method of finding food and mates.

9. QUANTITATIVE Scientists collected data on the date of onset of the menstrual cycles of a group of women who moved into a college dormitory together in the fall. The *y*-axis of the graph shows the average difference (in days) between the onset of a woman's cycle and the average onset date of the rest of the women. Describe how these data provide evidence for the existence of a human pheromone.

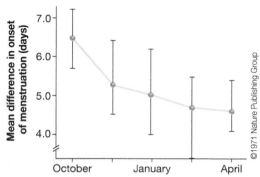

DATA: McClintock, M. K. 1971. *Nature* 229: 244–245, Figure 1.

10. Explain how the bending of stereocilia in a hair cell and binding by a bitter-tasting molecule can both result in an ion channel opening.

11. Scientists generally think that a "good hypothesis" is one that is reasonable and testable and inspires further research into the phenomenon. Using these criteria, was Dalton's hypothesis about color vision a good hypothesis? Was it correct? Explain your answer.

12. Design experiments to test the hypothesis that electric eels are both electrogenic and electroreceptive.

13. Which of the following animals is *least* likely to have a well-developed vomeronasal organ?

    a. fish

    b. salamander

    c. rodent

    d. snake

14. Compare and contrast the lateral line system of fishes with electroreception in sharks.

15. A company is marketing perfumes that it claims are attractive to the opposite sex because they contain "pure reaction-grade human pheromones." Explain why this is unlikely to be truth in advertising.

16. Houseflies have about 800 ommatidia in each of their compound eyes. Dragonflies, in contrast, have up to 10,000 ommatidia per eye. Houseflies feed by lapping up watery material from piles of excrement or rotting carcasses, which they locate by scent. Dragonflies are aerial predators and hunt by sight. How would you test the hypothesis that the large numbers of ommatidia in dragonflies make them more efficient hunters?

## CHAPTER 1

### IN-TEXT QUESTIONS AND EXERCISES

**p. 4 Fig. 1.2** [analyze] If Pasteur had done any of the things listed, he would have had more than one variable in his experiment. This would allow critics to claim that he got different results because of the differences in broth types, heating, or flask types—not the difference in exposure to preexisting cells. The results would not be definitive.
**p. 6** [apply] The average kernel protein content would decline, from 11 percent to a much lower value over time.
**p. 6 CYU** [apply] The data points would all be about 11 percent, indicating no change in average kernel protein content over time.
**p. 7 Fig. 1.4** [apply] Molds and other fungi are more closely related to green algae because they differ from plants at two positions (5 and 8 from left) but differ from green algae at only one position (8).
**p. 8 Fig. 1.6** [apply] The eukaryotic cell is roughly 10 times the size of the prokaryotic cell.
**p. 9 CYU** [evaluate] From the sequence data provided, species A and B differ only in one ribonucleotide of the rRNA sequence (position 10 from left). Species C differs from species A and B in four ribonucleotides (positions 1, 2, 9, and 10). A correctly drawn phylogenetic tree would indicate that species A and B appear to be closely related, and species C is more distantly related. See FIGURE A1.1.
**p. 13 (1)** [analyze] You could conclude that the ants weren't navigating normally, because they had been caught and released and transferred to a new channel. **(2)** [analyze] You could conclude that the ants can't navigate normally on their manipulated legs.
**p. 13 CYU** The key here is to test predation rates during the hottest part of the day (when desert ants actually feed) versus other parts of the day. The experiment would best be done in the field, where natural predators are present. One approach would be to capture a large number of ants, divide the group in two, and measure predation rates (number of ants killed per hour) when they are placed in normal habitat during the hottest part of the day versus an hour before (or after). **(1)** [analyze] The control group here is the normal condition—ants out during the hottest part of the day. If you didn't include a control, a critic could argue that predation did or did not occur because of your experimental setup or manipulation, not because of differences in temperature. **(2)** [analyze] You would need to make sure that there is no difference in body size, walking speed, how they were captured and maintained, or other traits that might make the ants in the two groups more or less susceptible to predators. They should also be put out in the same habitat, so the presence of predators is the same in the two treatments.
**p. 13 Fig. 1.10** [analyze] The interpretation of the experiment would not likely change, but your confidence in the conclusions drawn would be reduced if you used just one ant.

### IF YOU UNDERSTAND . . .

**1.1.** [understand] Dead cells cannot regulate the passage of materials between exterior and interior spaces, replicate, use energy, or process information. **1.2** [understand] Observations on thousands of diverse species supported the claim that all organisms consist of cells. The hypothesis that all cells come from preexisting cells was supported when Pasteur showed that new cells do not arise and grow in a boiled liquid unless they are introduced from the air. **1.3** [understand] If seeds with higher protein content leave the most

offspring, then individuals with low protein in their seeds will become rare over time. **1.4** [understand] A newly discovered species can be classified as a member of the Bacteria if the sequence of its rRNA contains some features found only in Bacteria. The same logic applies to classifying a new species in the Archaea or Eukarya. **1.5** [understand] (1) A hypothesis is an explanation of how the world works; a prediction is an outcome you should observe if the hypothesis is correct. (2) Experiments are convincing because they measure predictions from two opposing hypotheses. Both predicted actions cannot occur, so one hypothesis will be supported while the other will not.

### YOU SHOULD BE ABLE TO . . .

#### ✔ Test Your Knowledge

**1.** [remember] d **2.** [understand] d **3.** [remember] populations **4.** [understand] b **5.** [understand] An individual's ability to survive and reproduce **6.** [understand] c

#### ✔ Test Your Understanding

**7.** [evaluate] That the entity they discovered replicates, processes information, acquires and uses energy, is cellular, and that its populations evolve. **8.** [understand] a **9.** [understand] Over time, traits that increased the fitness of individuals in this habitat became increasingly frequent in the population. **10.** [understand] Individuals with certain traits are selected, in the sense that they produce the most offspring. **11.** [analyze] Yes. If evolution is defined as "change in the characteristics of a population over time," then those organisms that are most closely related should have experienced less change over time. On a phylogenetic tree, species with substantially similar rRNA sequences would be diagrammed with a closer common ancestor—one that had the sequences they inherited—than the ancestors shared between species with dissimilar rRNA sequences. **12.** [understand] A null hypothesis specifies what a researcher should observe when the hypothesis being tested isn't correct.

#### ✔ Test Your Problem-Solving Skills

**13.** [analyze] A scientific theory is not a guess—it is an idea whose validity can be tested with data. Both the cell theory and the theory of evolution have been validated by large bodies of observational and experimental data. **14.** [apply] If all eukaryotes living today have a nucleus, then it is logical to conclude that the nucleus arose in a common ancestor of all eukaryotes, indicated by the arrow you should have added to the figure. See FIGURE A1.2. If it had arisen in a common ancestor of Bacteria or Archaea, then species in those groups would have had to lose the trait—an unlikely event. **15.** [evaluate] The data set was so large and diverse that it was no longer reasonable to argue that noncellular life-forms would be discovered. **16.** [apply] b

### BIG PICTURE Doing Biology

**p. 16 CYU (1)** [understand] Biologists design and carry out a study, either observational or experimental, to test their ideas. As part of this process, they state their ideas as a hypothesis and null hypothesis and make predictions. They analyze and interpret the data they have gathered, and determine whether the data support their ideas. If not, they revisit their ideas and come up with an alternative hypothesis and design another study to test these new predictions. **(2)** [understand] There are many

possible examples. Consider, for example, the experiment on navigation in foraging desert ants (Chapter 1). In addition to testing how the ants use information on stride length and number to calculate how far they are from the nest (multicellular organism and population levels), researchers also could test how the "pedometer" works at the level of cells and molecules. **(3)** [analyze] A hypothesis is a testable statement to explain a specific phenomenon or a set of observations. The word theory refers to proposed explanations for very broad patterns in nature that are supported by a wide body of evidence. A theory serves as a framework for the development of new hypotheses. **(4)** [analyze] The next step is to relate your findings to existing theories and the current scientific literature, and then to communicate your findings to colleagues through informal conversations, presentations at scientific meetings, and eventually publication in peer-reviewed journals.

## CHAPTER 2

### IN-TEXT QUESTIONS AND EXERCISES

**p. 20 Fig. 2.3** [apply] There are 15 electrons in phosphorus, so there must be 15 protons, which is the atomic number. Since the mass number is 31, then the number of neutrons is 16.
**p. 23** [understand] *Water:* arrows pointing from hydrogens to oxygen atom; *ammonia:* arrows pointing from hydrogens to nitrogen atom; *methane:* double arrows between carbons and hydrogens; *carbon dioxide:* arrows pointing from carbon to oxygens; *molecular nitrogen:* double arrows between nitrogens.
**p. 23 Fig. 2.7** [understand] Oxygen and nitrogen have high electronegativities. They hold shared electrons more tightly than C, H, and many other atoms, resulting in polar bonds.
**p. 24 CYU** [evaluate] See FIGURE A2.1.

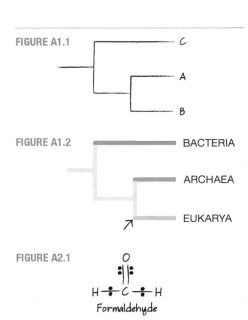

FIGURE A1.1

FIGURE A1.2

FIGURE A2.1

Formaldehyde

**p. 25 (1)** evaluate $^{\delta+}H-O^{\delta-}-H^{\delta+}$ **(2)** apply If water were linear, the partial negative charge on oxygen would have partial positive charges on either side. Compared to the actual, bent molecule, the partial negative charge would be much less exposed and less able to participate in hydrogen bonding.

**p. 26 Fig. 2.14** understand Oils are nonpolar. They have long chains of carbon atoms bonded to hydrogen atoms, which share electrons evenly because their electronegativities are similar. When an oil and water are mixed, the polar water molecules interact with each other via hydrogen bonding rather than with the nonpolar oil molecules, which interact with themselves instead.

**p. 28 Table 2.2** understand "Cause" (Row 1): electrostatic attractions between partial charges on water and opposite charges on ions; hydrogen bonds; water and other polar molecules. "Biological Consequences" (Row 2): ice to float; freezing solid. "Cause" (Row 4): lots of heat energy; break hydrogen bonds and change water to a gas.

**p. 29** apply The proton concentration would be $3.2 \times 10^{-9}$ M.

**p. 29 Fig. 2.17** apply The concentration of protons would decrease because milk is more basic (pH 6.5) than black coffee (pH 5).

**p. 30** apply The bicarbonate concentration would increase. The protons ($H^+$) released from carbonic acid would react with the hydroxide ions ($OH^-$) dissociated from NaOH to form $H_2O$, leaving fewer protons free to react with bicarbonate to reform carbonic acid.

**p. 32 CYU (1)** apply The reaction would be spontaneous based on the change in potential energy; the reactants have higher chemical energy than the products. The entropy, however, is not increased based on the number of molecules, although heat given off from the reaction still results in increased entropy. **(2)** understand The electrons are shifted farther from the nuclei of the carbon and hydrogen atoms and closer to the nuclei of the more electronegative oxygen atoms.

**p. 32 Fig. 2.19** remember See **FIGURE A2.2**.

**p. 33 Fig. 2.21** analyze The water-filled flask is the ocean; the gas-filled flask is the atmosphere; the condensed water droplets are rain; the electrical sparks are lightning.

**p. 37 Table 2.3** understand All the functional groups in Table 2.3, except the sulfhydryl group (−SH), are highly polar. The sulfhydryl group is only very slightly polar.

## IF YOU UNDERSTAND . . .

**2.1.** understand The bonds in methane and ammonia are all covalent, but differ in polarity: Methane has nonpolar covalent bonds while ammonia has polar covalent bonds. Sodium chloride does not have covalent bonds; instead, ionic bonds hold the ionized sodium and chloride together. **2.2** understand Assuming neutral pH, amino and hydroxyl groups would interact with the partial negative charge on water's oxygen, because they both carry a positive charge (partial for the hydrogen in the hydroxyl). The carboxyl group would interact with the partial positive charges on water's hydrogens, since it would carry a negative charge after losing the proton from its hydroxyl. **2.3** understand Like solar radiation, the energy in electricity generates free radicals that would promote the reaction. **2.4** understand "Top-down" approach: The reaction responsible for synthesizing acetic acid is observed in cells and can serve as an intermediate for the formation of a more complex molecule (acetyl CoA) that is used by cells throughout the tree of life. "Bottom-up" approach: This reaction can also occur under conditions that mimic the early Earth environment in deep-sea vents. **2.5** apply The hydroxyls would increase the solubility of octane by introducing polar covalent bonds, which would make the molecule more hydrophilic. The high electronegativity of oxygen would decrease the potential energy of the modified molecule.

## YOU SHOULD BE ABLE TO . . .

### ✔ Test Your Knowledge

**1.** understand b **2.** remember a **3.** remember c **4.** remember d **5.** remember Potential energy and entropy. **6.** remember The prebiotic soup model and the surface metabolism model.

### ✔ Test Your Understanding

**7.** apply c. Acetic acid has more highly electronegative oxygen atoms than the other molecules. When bonded to carbon or hydrogen, each oxygen will result in a polar covalent bond. **8.** apply Relative electronegativities would be F > O > H > Na. One bond would form with sodium, and it would be ionic. **9.** understand When oxygen is covalently bonded to hydrogen, the difference in electronegativities between the atoms causes the electrons to spend more time near the oxygen. In contrast, the atoms in $H_2$ and $O_2$ have the same electronegativities, so they equally share electrons in their covalent bonds. **10.** apply See **FIGURE A2.3**. **11.** apply The dissociation reaction of carbonic acid lowers the pH of the solution by releasing extra $H^+$ into the solution. If additional $CO_2$ is added, the sequence of reactions would be driven to the right, which would make the ocean more acidic. **12.** understand The carbon framework determines the overall shape of an organic molecule. The functional groups attached to the carbons determine the molecule's chemical behavior, because these groups are likely to interact with other molecules.

### ✔ Test Your Problem-Solving Skills

**13.** analyze b. **14.** analyze No, they don't conflict. Shells that are farther from the protons (positive charges) in the nucleus house electrons that have greater potential energy than shells closer to the nucleus. **15.** analyze One possible concept map relating the structure of water to its properties is shown below (see **FIGURE A2.4**). **16.** create In hot weather, water absorbs large amounts of heat due to its high specific heat and high heat of vaporization. In cold weather, water releases the large amount of heat that it has absorbed.

**FIGURE A2.2**

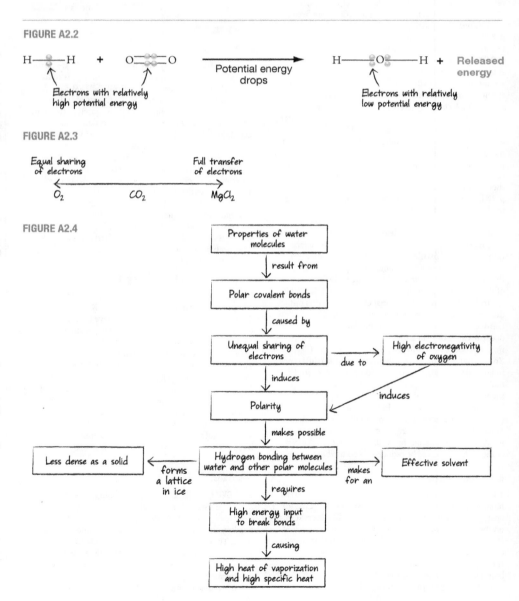

H—H + O=O → H—O—H + Released energy

Electrons with relatively high potential energy

Potential energy drops

Electrons with relatively low potential energy

**FIGURE A2.3**

Equal sharing of electrons ← → Full transfer of electrons

$O_2$     $CO_2$     $MgCl_2$

**FIGURE A2.4**

Properties of water molecules

↓ result from

Polar covalent bonds

↓ caused by

Unequal sharing of electrons → due to → High electronegativity of oxygen

↓ induces        induces ↙

Polarity

↓ makes possible

Less dense as a solid ← forms a lattice in ice — Hydrogen bonding between water and other polar molecules — makes for an → Effective solvent

↓ requires

High energy input to break bonds

↓ causing

High heat of vaporization and high specific heat

# CHAPTER 3

## IN-TEXT QUESTIONS AND EXERCISES

**p. 43 Fig. 3.2** [understand] The green R-groups contain mostly C and H, which have roughly equal electronegativities. Electrons are evenly shared in C−H bonds and C−S bonds, so the groups are nonpolar. Cysteine has a sulfur that is slightly more electronegative than hydrogen, so it will be less nonpolar than the other green groups. All of the pink R-groups have a highly electronegative oxygen atom with a partial negative charge, making them polar. **p. 44** [apply] From most hydrophilic to most hydrophobic: (1) aspartate, (2) asparagine, (3) tyrosine, (4) valine. The most hydrophilic amino acids will have side chains with full charges (ionized), like aspartate, followed by those with the largest number of highly electronegative atoms, like oxygen or nitrogen. Highly electronegative atoms produce polar covalent bonds with carbon or hydrogen. The most hydrophobic will not have oxygen or nitrogen in their side chains, but instead will have the largest number of C−H bonds, which are nonpolar covalent. **p. 47 CYU** [understand] See **FIGURE A3.1**. **p. 52 CYU (1)** [understand] Secondary, tertiary, and quaternary structure all depend on bonds and other interactions between amino acids that are linked in a chain in a specific order (primary structure). **(2)** [apply] There would be $20^5$ different peptides, or $3.2 \times 10^6$ different primary sequences. **p. 55 CYU** [apply] Amino acid changes would be expected to be in the active site or in regions that affect the folded structure of this site. Either of these changes could result in a different active site that either binds a new substrate or catalyzes a different reaction.

## IF YOU UNDERSTAND . . .

**3.1.** [understand] Look at the R-group of the amino acid. If there is a positive charge, then it is basic. If there is a negative charge, then it is acidic. If there is not a charge, but there is an oxygen atom, then it is polar uncharged. If there is no charge or oxygen, then it is nonpolar. **3.2** [apply] Nonpolar amino acid residues would be found in the interior of a globular protein, grouped with other nonpolar residues due to hydrophobic interactions. **3.3** [analyze] Both calmodulin and infectious prions require some form of induction to achieve their active conformations. Calcium ions are required for calmodulin to fold into its functional structure while prions are induced to change their shape by other, improperly folded prion proteins. **3.4** [analyze] *Catalysis:* Proteins are made of amino acids, which have many reactive functional groups, and can fold into different shapes that allow the formation of active sites. *Defense:* Similar to catalysis, the chemical properties and capacity for different shapes allows proteins to be made that can attach to virtually any type of invading virus or cell. *Signaling:* The flexibility in protein structure allows protein activities to be quickly turned on or off based on binding to signal molecules or ions.

## YOU SHOULD BE ABLE TO . . .

### ✔ Test Your Knowledge

**1.** [remember] d **2.** [remember] The atoms and functional groups found in the side chains. **3.** [remember] b **4.** [remember] b **5.** [understand] The order and type of amino acids (i.e., the primary structure) contains the information that directs folding. **6.** [understand] a

### ✔ Test Your Understanding

**7.** [understand] Because the nonpolar amino acid residues are not able to interact with the water solvent, they are crowded together in the interior of a protein and surrounded by a network of hydrogen-bonded water molecules. This crowding leads to the development of van der Waals interactions that help glue the nonpolar

side chains together. **8.** [understand] No, polymerization is a nonspontaneous reaction because the product molecules have lower entropy than the free form of the reactants and there would be nothing to prevent hydrolysis from reversing the reaction. **9.** [understand] Many possible correct answers, including (1) the presence of an active site in an enzyme that is precisely shaped to fit a substrate or substrates in the correct orientation for a reaction to occur; (2) the doughnut shape of porin that allows certain substances to pass through it; (3) the cable shape of collagen to provide structural support for cells and tissues. **10.** [create] Proteins are highly variable in overall shape and chemical properties due to variation in the composition of R-groups and the array of secondary through quaternary structures that are possible. This variation allows them to fulfill many different roles in the cell. Diversity in the shape and reactivity of active sites also makes them effective catalysts. **11.** [understand] c **12.** [create] In many proteins, especially those involved in cell signaling, their structure is affected by binding to other molecules or ions. Since the shape of the protein is directly involved in its function, the protein's activity is regulated by controlling how it is folded. If proteins were inflexible, this type of control could not occur.

### ✔ Test Your Problem-Solving Skills

**13.** [analyze] The side chain of proline is a cyclic structure that is covalently bonded to the nitrogen in the core amino group. This restricts the movement of the side chain relative to the core nitrogen, which further restricts the backbone when the nitrogen participates in a peptide bond with a neighboring amino acid. **14.** [create] See **FIGURE A3.2 15.** [apply] b. Phosphates have a negative charge, so they are most likely to form ionic bonds with the positively-charged side chains of basic amino acid residues. **16.** [apply] The inherited forms likely have some alteration in the primary structure such that the infectious form is spontaneously generated at a higher rate than normal. The amino acid sequence in these prions would likely differ from those transmitted between animals.

# CHAPTER 4

## IN-TEXT QUESTIONS AND EXERCISES

**p. 59** [understand] See **FIGURE A4.1**.

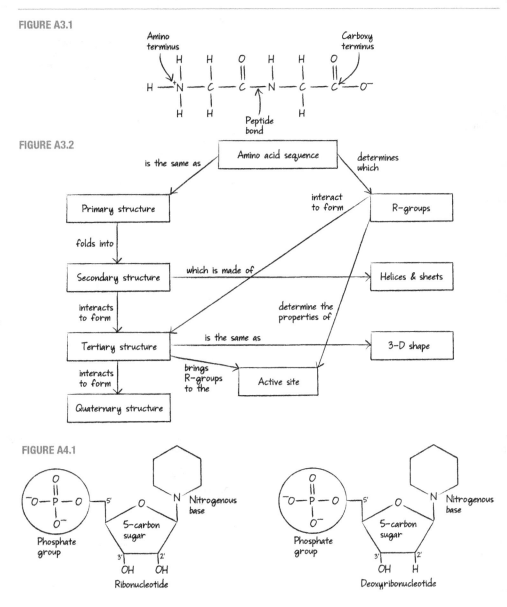

**FIGURE A3.1**

**FIGURE A3.2**

**FIGURE A4.1**

**p. 60 Fig. 4.3** (understand) 5′-UAGC-′3
**p. 61 CYU** (understand) See **FIGURE A4.2**.
**p. 63** (understand) If the two strands were parallel, the G-C pairing would align N−H groups together and C=O groups together, which would not allow hydrogen bonds to form.
**p. 64 Fig. 4.8** (analyze) It is not spontaneous—energy must be added (as heat) for the reaction to occur.
**p. 65 CYU** (remember) See **FIGURE A4.3**.

## IF YOU UNDERSTAND . . .

**4.1.** (understand) Cells activate nucleotides by linking additional phosphates to an existing 5′ phosphate. Activation increases the chemical energy in the nucleotides enough to offset the decrease in entropy that will result from the polymerization reaction. **4.2** (understand) C-G pairs involve three hydrogen bonds, so they are more stable than A-T pairs with just two hydrogen bonds. **4.3** (analyze) A single-stranded RNA molecule has unpaired bases that can pair with other bases on the same RNA strand, thereby folding the molecule into stem-and-loop configurations. These secondary structures can further fold on themselves, giving the molecule a tertiary structure. Because DNA molecules are double stranded, with no unpaired bases, further internal folding is not possible. **4.4** (understand) Examples would include (1) the production of nucleotides, and (2) polymerization of RNA. It is thought that nucleotides were scarce during chemical evolution, so their catalyzed synthesis by a ribozyme would have been advantageous. Catalysis by an RNA replicase would have dramatically increased the reproductive rate of RNA molecules.

## YOU SHOULD BE ABLE TO . . .

### ✔ Test Your Knowledge

**1.** (remember) c **2.** (remember) c **3.** (remember) a **4.** (remember) d **5.** (remember) One end has a free phosphate group on the 5′ carbon; the other end has a free hydroxyl group bonded to the 3′ carbon. **6.** (understand) DNA is a more stable molecule than RNA because it lacks a hydroxyl group on the 2′ carbon and is therefore more resistant to cleavage, and because the two sugar-phosphate backbones are held together by many hydrogen bonds between nitrogenous bases.

### ✔ Test Your Understanding

**7.** (apply) In DNA, the secondary structure requires that every guanine pairs with a cytosine and every thymine pairs with an adenine, resulting in consistent ratios between the nucleotides. Chargaff's rules do not apply to RNA, since it is single-stranded and the pairing is not consistent throughout the molecules. **8.** (apply) a; if 30 percent is adenine, then 30 percent would be thymine, since they are base-paired together. This means that 40 percent consists of G-C base pairs, which would be equally divided between the two bases. **9.** (apply) The DNA sequence of the new strand would be 5′-ATCGATATC-3′. The RNA sequence would be the same, except each T would be replaced by a U. **10.** (understand) DNA has limited catalytic ability because it (1) lacks functional groups that can participate in catalysis and (2) has a regular structure that is not conducive to forming shapes required for catalysis. RNA molecules can catalyze some reactions because they (1) have exposed hydroxyl functional groups and (2) can fold into shapes that that can function in catalysis. **11.** (apply) No. Catalytic activity in ribozymes depends on the tertiary structure generated from single-stranded molecules. Double-stranded nucleic acids do not form tertiary structures. **12.** (understand) An RNA replicase would undergo replication and be able to evolve. It would process information in the sense of copying itself, and it would use energy to drive polymerization reactions. It would not be bound by a membrane and considered a cell, however, and it would not be able to acquire energy. It would best be considered as an intermediate step between nonlife and true life (as outlined in Chapter 1).

### ✔ Test Your Problem-Solving Skills

**13.** (create) See **FIGURE A4.4** **14.** (apply) Yes—if the complementary bases lined up over the entire length of the two strands, they would twist into a double helix analogous to a DNA molecule. The same types of hydrogen bonds and hydrophobic interactions would occur as observed in the "stem" portion of hairpins in single-stranded RNA. **15.** (apply) In a triple helix, the bases are unlikely to align properly for hydrogen bonding to occur, so hydrophobic interactions would probably be more important. **16.** (apply) b; the high temperature would make it more likely that the secondary and tertiary structures would be denatured in the ribozymes. To overcome this effect, you would expect the hairpins to possess more G-C pairs, since they consist of three hydrogen bonds compared to the two found in A-T pairs.

## CHAPTER 5

### IN-TEXT QUESTIONS AND EXERCISES

**p. 73 Fig. 5.2** (understand) See the structure of mannose in **FIGURE A5.1**.
**p. 75 CYU** (apply) See **FIGURE A5.2**.
**p. 78 CYU** (remember) They could differ in (1) location of linkages (e.g., 1,4 or 1,6); (2) types of linkages (e.g., α or β); (3) the sequence of the monomers (e.g., two galactose and then two glucose, versus alternating galactose and glucose); and/or (4) whether the four monomers are linked in a line or whether they branch.
**p. 79 Fig. 5.6** (apply) The percentage of inhibition would not change for the intact glycoprotein bar. The purified

---

**FIGURE A4.3**

**FIGURE A5.1**

**FIGURE A4.2**

**FIGURE A4.4**

carbohydrate bar would be at zero inhibition, and the glycoprotein with digested carbohydrate bar would be similar to the intact glycoprotein bar.

**p. 80 Fig. 5.7** (understand) All of the C—C and C—H bonds should be circled.

**p. 81 CYU (1)** (understand) *Aspect 1:* The β-1,4-glycosidic linkages in these molecules result in insoluble fibers that are difficult to degrade. *Aspect 2:* When individual molecules of these carbohydrates align, bonds form between them and produce fibers or sheets that resist pulling and pushing forces. **(2)** (apply) Most are probably being broken down into glucose, some of which in turn is being broken down in reactions that lead to the synthesis of ATP. Some will be resistant to digestion, such as the insoluble cellulose that makes up dietary fiber. This will help retain water and support the digestion and passage of fecal material.

## IF YOU UNDERSTAND . . .

**5.1.** (understand) Molecules have to interact in an extremely specific orientation in order for a reaction to occur. Changing the location of a functional group by even one carbon can mean that the molecule will undergo completely different types of reactions. **5.2** (analyze) Glycosidic linkages can vary more in location and geometry than linkages between amino acids and nucleotides do. This variability increases the structural diversity possible in carbohydrates compared to proteins and nucleic acids. **5.3** (understand) (1) Polysaccharides used for energy storage are formed entirely from glucose monomers joined by α-glycosidic linkages; structural polysaccharides are made up of glucose or other sugars joined by β-glycosidic linkages. (2) The monomers in energy-storage polysaccharides are linked in a helical arrangement; the monomers in structural polysaccharides are linked in a linear arrangement. (3) Energy-storage polysaccharides may branch; structural polysaccharides do not. (4) Individual chains of energy-storage polysaccharides do not associate with each other; adjacent chains of structural polysaccharides are linked by hydrogen bonds or covalent bonds.

## YOU SHOULD BE ABLE TO . . .

### ✓ Test Your Knowledge

**1.** (remember) d **2.** (remember) Monosaccharides can differ from one another in three ways: (1) the location of their carbonyl group; (2) the number of carbon atoms they contain; and (3) the orientations of their hydroxyl groups. **3.** (remember) a **4.** (remember) c **5.** (remember) a **6.** (understand) The electrons in the C=O bonds of carbon dioxide molecules are held tightly by the highly electronegative oxygen atoms, so they have low potential energy. The electrons in the C—C and C—H bonds of carbohydrates are shared equally, so they have much higher potential energy.

### ✓ Test Your Understanding

**7.** (understand) c. **8.** (apply) a; lactose is a disaccharide formed from a β-1,4-glycosidic linkage, so if two glucose molecules were linked with this bond, they would resemble units of cellulose and not be digested by human infants or adults. **9.** (understand) Carbohydrates are ideal for displaying the identity of the cell because they are so diverse structurally. This diversity enables them to serve as very specific identity tags for cells. **10.** (understand) When you compare the glucose monomers in an α-1,4-glycosidic linkage versus in a β-1,4-glycosidic linkage, the linkages are located on opposite sides of the plane of the glucose rings, and the glucose monomers are linked in the same orientation versus having every other glucose flipped in orientation. β-1,4-glycosidic linkages are much more likely to form linear fibers and sheets, so they resist degradation. **11.** (remember) Because (1) no mechanism is

known for the prebiotic polymerization of sugars; (2) no catalytic carbohydrates have been discovered that can perform polymerization reactions; and (3) sugar residues in a polysaccharide are not capable of complementary base pairing. **12.** (understand) Starch and glycogen both consist of glucose monomers joined by α-1,4-glycosidic linkages, and both function as storage carbohydrates. Starch is a mixture of unbranched and branched polysaccharides—called amylose and amylopectin, respectively. All glycogen polysaccharides are branched.

### ✓ Test Your Problem-Solving Skills

**13.** (analyze) Carbohydrates are energy-storage molecules, so minimizing their consumption may reduce total energy intake. Lack of available carbohydrate also forces the body to use fats for energy, reducing the amount of fat that is stored. **14.** (apply) d; lactose is a disaccharide of glucose and galactose, which can be cleaved by enzymes expressed in the human gut to release galactose. **15.** (analyze) Amylase breaks down the starch in the cracker into glucose monomers, which stimulate the sweet receptors in your tongue. **16.** (apply) When bacteria contact lysozyme, the peptidoglycan in their cell walls begins to degrade, leading to the death of the bacteria. Lysozyme therefore helps protect humans against bacterial infections.

## CHAPTER 6

### IN-TEXT QUESTIONS AND EXERCISES

**p. 87** (understand) Fatty acids are amphipathic because their hydrocarbon tails are hydrophobic but their carboxyl functional groups are hydrophilic.

**p. 87 Fig. 6.4** (apply) At the polar hydroxyl group in cholesterol and the polar head group in phospholipids.

**p. 88 CYU (1)** (analyze) Fats consist of three fatty acids linked to glycerol; steroids have a distinctive four-ring structure with variable side groups attached; phospholipids have a hydrophilic, phosphate-containing "head" region and a hydrocarbon tail. **(2)** (understand) In cholesterol, the hydrocarbon steroid rings and isoprenoid chain are hydrophobic; the hydroxyl group is hydrophilic. In phospholipids, the phosphate-containing head group is hydrophilic; the hydrocarbon chains are hydrophobic.

**p. 89** (apply) Amino acids have amino and carboxyl groups that are ionized in water and nucleotides have negatively charged phosphates. Due to their charge and larger size, both would be placed below the small ions at the bottom of the scale (permeability $< 10^{-12}$ cm/sec).

**p. 90 CYU** (create) See TABLE A6.1.

**p. 91 Fig. 6.10** (apply) Increasing the number of phospholipids with polyunsaturated tails would increase permeability of the liposomes. Starting from the left, the first line (no cholesterol) would represent liposomes with 50% polyunsaturated phospholipids, the second line would be 20% polyunsaturated phospholipids, and the third line would contain only saturated phospholipids.

**p. 92** (apply) If there is a difference in temperature, then there would be a difference in thermal motion. The solute concentration on the side with a higher temperature would decrease because the solute particles would be moving faster and hence be more likely to move to the cooler side of the membrane, where they would slow down.

**p. 93 Fig. 6.13** (apply) Higher, because less water would have to move to the right side to achieve equilibrium.

---

**FIGURE A5.2**

Start with a monosacchride. This one is a 3-carbon aldose (carbonyl group at end)

Variation 1: 3-carbon ketose (carbonyl group in middle)

Variation 2: 4-carbon aldose

Variation 3: 3-carbon aldose with different arrangement of hydroxyl group

---

**TABLE A6.1**

| Factor | Effect on permeability | Reason |
|---|---|---|
| Temperature | Decreases as temperature decreases. | Lower temperature slows movement of hydrocarbon tails, allowing more interactions (membrane is more dense). |
| Cholesterol | Decreases as cholesterol content increases. | Cholesterol molecules fill in the spaces between the hydrocarbon tails, making the membrane more tightly packed. |
| Length of hydrocarbon tails | Decreases as length of hydrocarbon tails increases. | Longer hydrocarbon tails have more interactions (membrane is more dense). |
| Saturation of hydrocarbon tails | Decreases as degree of saturation increases. | Saturated fatty acids have straight hydrocarbon tails that pack together tightly, leaving few gaps. |

**p. 94 CYU** create See **FIGURE A6.1**.

**p. 96 Fig. 6.18** create Repeat the procedure using a lipid bilayer that is free of membrane proteins, such as synthetic liposomes constructed from only phospholipids. If proteins were responsible for the pits and mounds, then this control would not show these structures.

**p. 97** apply Your arrow should point out of the cell. There is no concentration gradient for chloride, but the outside has a net positive charge, which favors outward movement of negative ions.

**p. 97 Fig. 6.21** analyze No—the 10 replicates where no current was recorded probably represent instances where the CFTR protein was damaged and not functioning properly. (In general, no experimental method works perfectly.")

**p. 101 CYU** understand Passive transport does not require an input of energy—it happens as a result of energy already present in existing concentration or electrical gradients. Active transport is active in the sense of requiring an input of energy from, for example, ATP. In cotransport, a second ion or molecule is transported against its concentration gradient along with (i.e., "co") an ion that is transported along its concentration gradient.

**p. 101 Fig. 6.26** understand *Diffusion:* description as given; no proteins involved. *Facilitated diffusion:* Passive movement of ions or molecules that cannot cross a phospholipid bilayer readily along a concentration gradient; facilitated by channel or carrier proteins. *Active transport:* Active movement of ions or molecules that will build a gradient; facilitated by pump proteins powered by an energy source such as ATP.

**YOU UNDERSTAND . . .**

**1.** analyze Adding $H_2$ increases the saturation of the oil by converting C=C bonds into C–C bonds with added hydrogens. Lipids with more C–H bonds tend to be solid at room temperature. **6.2** understand Highly permeable and fluid bilayers possess short, unsaturated hydrocarbon tails while those that are highly impermeable and less fluid contain long, saturated hydrocarbon tails.

**3** apply (1) The solute will diffuse until both sides are at equal concentrations. (2) Water will diffuse toward the side with the higher solute concentration. **6.4** apply See FIGURE A6.2.

**YOU SHOULD BE ABLE TO . . .**

**Test Your Knowledge**

understand c **2.** remember a **3.** understand b **4.** understand d understand For osmosis to occur, a concentration gradient and membrane that allows water to pass, but not the solute, must be present. **6.** analyze Channel proteins form pores in the membrane and carrier proteins undergo conformational changes to shuttle molecules or ions across the membrane.

**Test Your Understanding**

apply b **8.** analyze No, because they have no polar end to interact with water. Instead, these lipids would float on the surface of water, or collect in droplets suspended in water, reducing their interaction with water to a minimum. **9.** understand Hydrophilic, phosphate-containing head groups interact with water; hydrophobic hydrocarbon tails associate with each other. A bilayer is more stable than are independent phospholipids in solution. **10.** apply Ethanol's polar hydroxyl group reduces the speed at which it can cross a membrane, but its small size and lack of charge would allow it to slowly cross membranes—between the rates of water and glucose transport. **11.** understand Only nonpolar, hydrophobic amino acid residues would be found in the portion of a protein that crosses the membrane. In the interior of the bilayer, these residues would be hidden from the water solvent and interact with the nonpolar lipid tails. apply Chloride ions from sodium chloride will move from the left side to the right through the CFTR. Water

will initially move from the right side to the left by osmosis, but as chloride ions move to the right, water will follow. $Na^+$ and $K^+$ ions will not move across the membrane.

✔ **Test Your Problem-Solving Skills**

**13.** apply c **14.** create Flip-flops should be rare, because they require a polar head group to pass through the hydrophobic portion of the lipid bilayer. To test this prediction, you could monitor the number of dyed phospholipids that transfer from one side of the membrane to the other in a given period of time. **15.** apply Organisms that live in very cold environments are likely to have highly unsaturated phospholipids. The kinks in unsaturated hydrocarbon tails keep membranes fluid and permeable, even at low temperature. Organisms that live in very hot environments would likely have phospholipids with saturated tails, to prevent membranes from becoming too fluid and permeable. **16.** analyze Adding a methyl group makes a drug more hydrophobic and thus more likely to pass through a lipid bilayer. Adding a charged group makes it hydrophilic and reduces its ability to pass through the lipid bilayer. These modifications would help target the drug to either the inside or outside of cells, respectively.

**BIG PICTURE Chemistry of Life**

**p. 104 CYU (1)** understand Oxygen is much more electronegative than hydrogen, so within water, the electrons are unequally shared in the O—H covalent bonds. The resulting partial negative charge around the oxygen and partial positive charges around the hydrogen atoms allow for hydrogen bonds to form among water molecules. **(2)** analyze Unlike other macromolecules, nucleic acids can serve as templates for their own replication. RNA is generally single-stranded and can adopt many different

three-dimensional structures. The flexibility in structure, combined with the presence of reactive hydroxyl groups, contribute to the formation of active sites that catalyze chemical reactions. One or more of these catalytic RNA molecules may have evolved the ability to self-replicate. DNA is not likely to have catalyzed its own replication, as it is most often double-stranded, with no clear tertiary structure, and it lacks the reactive hydroxyl groups. **(3)** remember In the amino acid, the nitrogen in the amino ($NH_3^+$) group and the carbon in the carboxyl ($COO^-$) group should be circled. In the nucleotide, the oxygen in the hydroxyl (OH) group and the phosphorus in the phosphate ($PO_4^{2-}$) group on the nucleotide should be circled. **(4)** understand A line representing a protein should be drawn such that it completely crosses the lipid bilayer at least once. The protein could be involved in a variety of different roles, including transport of substances across the membrane in the form of a channel, carrier, or pump.

## CHAPTER 7

**IN-TEXT QUESTIONS AND EXERCISES**

**p. 110 CYU** remember (1) The nucleoid compacts the chromosome to fit inside the cell via supercoiling while still keeping it accessible for replication and transmission of information. (2) Photosynthetic membranes increase food production by providing a large surface area to hold the pigments and enzymes required for photosynthesis. (3) Flagella propel cells through liquid, often toward a food source. (4) The layer of thick, strong material stiffens the cell wall and provides protection from mechanical damage.
**p. 114 Fig. 7.12** create Storing the toxins in vacuoles prevents the toxins from damaging the plant's own organelles and cells.

**FIGURE A6.1**

**FIGURE A6.2**

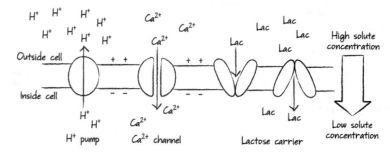

**p. 116 CYU (1)** [understand] Both organelles contain specific sets of enzymes. Lysosomal enzymes digest macromolecules in the acidic lumen of this organelle, releasing monomers that can be recycled into new macromolecules. Peroxisomes contain catalase and other enzymes that process fatty acids and toxins via oxidation reactions. **(2)** [understand] From top to bottom: administrative/information hub, protein factory, large molecule manufacturing and shipping (protein synthesis and folding center, lipid factory, protein finishing and shipping line, waste processing and recycling center), warehouse, fatty-acid processing and detox center, power station, food-manufacturing facility, support beams, perimeter fencing with secured gates, and leave blank.

**p. 118 Fig. 7.16** [remember] See FIGURE A7.1.

**p. 121** [analyze] (1) Nucleotides are small enough that they would diffuse through the nuclear pore complex along their gradients—a passive process that would not require energy. (2) Large proteins must be escorted through the nuclear pore complex, which is directional and requires energy, since the protein is concentrated inside the nucleus.

**p. 121 Fig. 7.18** [apply] "Prediction": The labeled tail region fragments or the labeled core region fragments of the nucleoplasmin protein will be found in the cell nucleus. "Prediction of null hypothesis": Either both the fragments (no required signal) or neither of them (whole protein signal) will be found in the nucleus of the cell. "Conclusion": The send-to-nucleus signal is in the tail region of the nucleoplasmin protein.

**p. 123** [apply] During the chase period, proteins appear to have first entered the Golgi after 7 minutes and then started to move into secretory granules after 37 minutes. This means that in this experiment, it took approximately 30 minutes for the fastest-moving proteins to pass through the Golgi.

**p. 126** [apply] In receptor-mediated endocytosis, the conversion of a late endosome to a lysosome is dependent on receiving acid hydrolases from the Golgi. If this receptor is not present, then the enzymes will not be sent and the late endosome will not mature into a lysosome to digest the endocytosed products.

**p. 126 CYU (1)** [apply] Proteins that enter the nucleus are fully synthesized and have an NLS that interacts with another protein to get it into the organelle. The NLS is not removed. Proteins that enter the ER have a signal sequence that interacts with the SRP during translation. The ribosome is moved to the ER and synthesis continues, moving the protein into the ER. The signal is removed once it enters the organelle. **(2)** [apply] The protein would be in the lysosome. The ER signal would direct the protein into the ER before it is completely synthesized. The M-6-P tag will direct the protein from the Golgi to the late endosome to the lysosome. Thus the complete protein is never free in the cytosol, where the NLS could direct it into the nucleus.

**p. 132 CYU** [analyze] Actin filaments are made up of two strands of actin monomers, microtubules are made up of tubulin protein dimers that form a tube, and intermediate filaments are made up of a number of different protein subunits. Actin filaments and microtubules exhibit polarity (or directionality), and new subunits are constantly being added or subtracted at either end (but added faster to the plus end). All three elements provide structural support, but only actin filaments and microtubules serve as tracks for motors involved in movement and cell division.

**p. 132 Fig. 7.30** [apply] The microtubule doublets of the axoneme would slide past each other completely, but the axoneme would not bend.

## IF YOU UNDERSTAND . . .

**7.1** [understand] (1) Cells will be unable to synthesize new proteins and will die. (2) In many environments, cells will be unable to resist the osmotic pressure of water entering the cytoplasm and will burst. (3) The cell shape will be different, and cells will not be able to divide.
**7.2** [understand] (1) The cell will be unable to produce a sufficient amount of ATP and will die. (2) Reactive molecules, like hydrogen peroxide, will damage the cell, and it will likely die. (3) Nothing will happen, since plants do not have centrioles. **7.3** [analyze] The liver cell would be expected to have more peroxisomes and less rough endoplasmic reticulum than the salivary cells would.
**7.4** [create] The addition or removal of phosphates would change the folded structure of the protein, exposing the NLS for nuclear transport. **7.5** [create] As a group, proteins have complex and highly diverse shapes and chemical properties that allow them to recognize a great number of different zip codes in a very specific manner. **7.6** [apply] The Golgi is positioned near the microtubule organizing center, which has microtubules running from the minus end out to the plus end (near the plasma membrane). Kinesin would be used to move these vesicles as it walks toward the plus end.

## YOU SHOULD BE ABLE TO . . .

### ✔ Test Your Knowledge

**1.** [understand] b **2.** [remember] They have their own small, circular chromosomes; they produce their own ribosomes; and they divide in a manner that is similar to bacterial fission, independent of cellular division. **3.** [remember] c **4.** [remember] b **5.** [remember] a **6.** [understand] The phosphate links to the motor protein and causes it to change shape, which results in the protein moving along the filament.

### ✔ Test Your Understanding

**7.** [analyze] All cells are bound by a plasma membrane, are filled with cytoplasm, carry their genetic information (DNA) in chromosomes, and contain ribosomes

---

**FIGURE A7.1**

### (a) Animal pancreatic cell: Exports digestive enzymes.

Rough ER — Secretory vesicles

### (b) Animal testis cell: Exports lipid-soluble signals.

Smooth ER

### (c) Plant leaf cell: Manufactures ATP and sugar.

Chloroplasts — Nucleus
Vacuole

### (d) Brown fat cells: Burn fat to generate heat in lieu of ATP.

Mitochondria

(the sites of protein synthesis). Some prokaryotes have organelles not found in plants or animals, such as a magnetite-containing structure. Plant cells have chloroplasts, vacuoles, and a cell wall. Animal cells contain lysosomes and lack a cell wall. **8.** analyze a; the endoplasmic reticulum is responsible for synthesizing the membrane proteins required for the transport of solutes across the plasma membrane. **9.** create The NLS will be used to actively import the protein into the nucleus, leaving very little of the protein in the cytoplasm. Diffusion alone would not drive all the protein into the nucleus. **10.** create Ribosome in cytoplasm (signal is synthesized) → Ribosome at rough ER (protein is completed, folded, and glycosylated) → Transport vesicle → Golgi apparatus (protein is processed; has molecular zip code indicating destination) → Transport vesicle → Plasma membrane → Extracellular space. **11.** create This occurs in microfilaments and microtubules because they have ends that differ structurally and functionally—they have different filament growth rates. Intermediate filaments have identical ends, so there is no difference in the rate of assembly between the two ends. **12.** understand Polarized cytoskeletal filaments (microtubules or microfilaments) are present between the organelles. End-directed motor proteins use ATP to move these transport vesicles between them.

✓ **Test Your Problem-Solving Skills**

**13.** understand b; fimbriae are involved in bacterial attachment to surfaces and other cells, which would be important in the ability to grow on teeth. **14.** create The proteins must receive a molecular zip code that binds to a receptor on the surface of peroxisomes. They could diffuse randomly to peroxisomes or be transported in a directed way by motor proteins. **15.** create The tails cleaved from nucleoplasmin could be attached to the gold particles that were excluded from crossing the pore complex owing to their size. If these modified particles entered the nucleus, then the tail is not limited to the nucleoplasmin transport alone. **16.** create The proteins would likely be found in the cytoplasm (e.g., actin and myosin) or imported into the mitochondria. Since there is a high energy demand, you would predict that there are many active mitochondria.

# CHAPTER 8

## IN-TEXT QUESTIONS AND ANSWERS

**p. 139** apply (1) If $\Delta S$ is positive (products have more disorder than reactants), then according to the free energy equation, $\Delta G$ is more likely to be negative as temperature ($T$) increases even if $\Delta H$ is positive. The increased temperature represents added heat energy that may be used to drive an endothermic reaction to completion, making the reaction spontaneous. (2) Exothermic reactions may be nonspontaneous if they result in a decrease in entropy—meaning that the products are more ordered than the reactants ($\Delta S$ is negative).

**p. 139 CYU (1)** understand Gibbs equation: $\Delta G = \Delta H - T \Delta S$. $\Delta G$ symbolizes the change in the Gibbs free energy. $\Delta H$ represents the difference in enthalpy (heat, pressure, and volume) between the products and the reactants. $T$ represents the temperature (in degrees Kelvin) at which the reaction is taking place. $\Delta S$ symbolizes the change in entropy (amount of disorder). (2) understand When $\Delta H$ is negative—meaning that the reactants have lower enthalpy than the products—and when $\Delta S$ is positive, meaning that the products have higher entropy (are more disordered) than the reactants.

**p. 140 Fig. 8.4** understand Each point represents the data from a single test, not an average of many experiments, so it is not possible to calculate the standard error of the average.

**p. 144** analyze Redox reactions transfer energy between molecules or atoms via electrons. When oxidized molecules are reduced, their potential energy increases. ATP

hydrolysis is often coupled with the phosphorylation of another molecule. This phosphorylation increases the potential energy of the molecule.

**p. 144 CYU (1)** understand Electrons in C−H bonds are not held as tightly as electrons in C−O bonds, so they have higher potential energy. **(2)** understand In part, because its three phosphate groups have four negative charges in close proximity. The electrons repulse each other, raising their potential energy.

**p. 144 Fig. 8.9** understand The $\Delta G$ in the uncoupled reaction would be positive (>0), and each of the steps in the coupled reaction would have a negative (<0) $\Delta G$.

**p. 147** remember (1) binding substrates, (2) transition state, (3) R-groups, (4) structure

**p. 146 Fig. 8.12** understand No—a catalyst affects only the activation energy, not the overall change in free energy.

**p. 147 Fig. 8.14** analyze See FIGURE A8.1.

**p. 149 CYU (1)** create The rate of the reaction is based primarily on the activity of the enzyme. Once the temperature reaches a level that causes unfolding and inactivation of the enzyme, the rate decreases to the uncatalyzed rate. **(2)** apply The shape change would most likely alter the shape of the active site. If phosphorylation activates catalytic activity, the change to the active site would allow substrates to bind and be brought to their transition state. If phosphorylation inhibits catalytic activity, the shape change to the active site would likely prevent substrates from binding or no longer orient them correctly for the reaction to occur.

**p. 150** apply The concentration of A and B would be higher than in the fully functional pathway since they are not depleted to produce C. If D is not being depleted by other reactions, then equilibrium would be established between C and D, resulting in lower concentrations of both.

## IF YOU UNDERSTAND . . .

**8.1** understand Reactions are spontaneous when the free energy in the products is lower than that of the reactants ($\Delta G$ is negative). Enthalpy and entropy are measures used to determine free-energy changes. Enthalpy measures the potential energy of the molecules, and entropy measures the disorder. For exergonic, spontaneous reactions, disorder normally increases and the potential energy stored in the products normally decreases relative to the reactants. **8.2** understand Energetic coupling transfers free energy released from exergonic reactions to drive endergonic reactions. Since endergonic reactions are required for sustaining life, without energetic coupling, life would not exist. **8.3** understand Amino acid R-groups lining the active site interact with the substrates, orienting them in a way that stabilizes the transition state, thereby lowering the activation energy needed for the reaction to proceed. **8.4** analyze Allosteric regulation and phosphorylation cause changes in the conformation of the enzyme that affects its catalytic function. Allosteric regulation involves non-covalent bonding, while phosphorylation is a covalent modification of the enzyme's primary structure. **8.5** apply In the first step of the pathway, the rate would increase as the intermediate, which is the product of the first reaction, is removed. In the last step, the rate would decrease due to the loss of the intermediate, which serves as the substrate for the last reaction.

## YOU SHOULD BE ABLE TO . . .

✓ **Test Your Knowledge**

**1.** remember c **2.** remember a **3.** remember a **4.** remember The enzyme changes shape, but the change is not permanent. The enzyme shape will return to its original conformation after releasing the products. **5.** remember d **6.** remember When the product of a pathway feeds back to interact with an enzyme early in the same pathway to inhibit its function.

✓ **Test Your Understanding**

**7.** understand The shape of reactant molecules (the key) fits into the active site of an enzyme (the lock). Fischer's

original model assumed that enzymes were rigid; in fact, enzymes are flexible and dynamic. **8.** understand d. Energy, such as the thermal energy in fire, must be provided to overcome the activation energy barrier before the reaction can proceed. **9.** understand The phosphorylation reaction is exergonic because the electrons in ADP and the phosphate added to the substrate experience less electrical repulsion, and thus have less potential energy, than they did in ATP. A phosphorylated reactant (i.e., an activated intermediate) gains enough potential energy to shift the free energy change for the reaction from endergonic to exergonic. **10.** apply For the coupled reaction, step 1 has a $\Delta G$ of about −3 kcal/mol and step 2 has a $\Delta G$ of about −3 kcal/mol. The uncoupled reaction has a $\Delta G$ of about +1.3 kcal/mol. **11.** analyze Both are mechanisms that regulate enzymes; the difference is whether the regulatory molecule binds at the active site (competitive inhibition) or away from the active site (allosteric regulation). **12.** apply Catabolic reactions will often have a negative $\Delta G$ based on a decrease in enthalpy and increase in entropy. Anabolic reactions are the opposite—a positive $\Delta G$ that is based on an increase in enthalpy and decrease in entropy.

✓ **Test Your Problem-Solving Skills**

**13.** create See FIGURE A8.2. **14.** apply Without the coenzyme, the free-radical-containing transition state would not be stabilized and the reaction rate would drop dramatically. **15.** analyze The data suggest that the enzyme and substrate form a transition state that requires a change in the shape of the active site, and that each movement corresponds to one reaction. **16.** apply b. The sugar likely functions as an allosteric regulator to activate the enzyme.

# CHAPTER 9

## IN-TEXT QUESTIONS AND EXERCISES

**p. 156 Fig. 9.2** remember Glycolysis: "What goes in" = glucose, NAD⁺, ADP, inorganic phosphate; "What comes out" = pyruvate, NADH, ATP. Pyruvate processing: "What goes in" = pyruvate, NAD⁺; "What comes out" = NADH, $CO_2$, acetyl CoA. Citric acid cycle: "What goes in" = acetyl CoA, NAD⁺, FAD, GDP or ADP, inorganic phosphate; "What comes out" = NADH, $FADH_2$, ATP or GTP, $CO_2$. Electron transport and oxidative phosphorylation: "What goes in" = NADH, $FADH_2$, $O_2$, ADP, inorganic phosphate; "What comes out" = ATP, $H_2O$, NAD⁺, FAD.

FIGURE A8.1

FIGURE A8.2

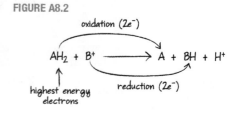

**p. 161** (apply) If the regulatory site had a higher affinity for ATP than the active site, then ATP would always be bound at the regulatory site, and glycolysis would always proceed at a very slow rate.

**p. 161 Fig. 9.9** (remember) "Positive control": AMP, NAD$^+$, CoA (reaction substrates). "Negative control by feedback inhibition": acetyl CoA, NADH, ATP (reaction products).

**p. 165 CYU** (remember) (1) and (2) are combined with the answer to p. 171 CYU (3) Start with 12 triangles on glucose. (These triangles represent the 12 pairs of electrons that will be moved to electron carriers during redox reactions throughout glycolysis and the citric acid cycle.) Move two triangles to the NADH circle generated by glycolysis and the other 10 triangles to the pyruvate circle. Then move these 10 triangles through the pyruvate dehydrogenase square, placing two of them in the NADH circle next to pyruvate dehydrogenase. Add the remaining eight triangles in the acetyl CoA circle. Next move the eight triangles in the acetyl CoA circle through the citric acid cycle, placing six of them in the NADH circle and two in the FADH$_2$ circle generated during the citric acid cycle. (4) These boxes are marked with stars in the diagram.

**p. 165 Fig. 9.13** (apply) NADH would be expected to have the highest amount of chemical energy since its production is correlated with the largest drop in free energy in the graph.

**p. 167 Fig. 9.15** (understand) The proton gradient arrow should start above in the inner membrane space and point down across the membrane into the mitochondrial matrix. *Complex I:* "What goes in" = NADH; "What comes out" = NAD$^+$, e$^-$, transported H$^+$. *Complex II:* "What goes in" = FADH$_2$; "What comes out" = FAD, e$^-$, H$^+$. *Complex III:* "What goes in" = e$^-$, H$^+$; "What comes out" = e$^-$, transported H$^+$. *Complex IV:* "What goes in" = e$^-$, H$^+$, O$_2$; "What comes out" = H$_2$O, transported H$^+$.

**p. 169** (explain) "Indirect" is accurate because most of the energy released during glucose oxidation is not used to produce ATP directly. Instead, this energy is stored in reduced electron carriers that are used by the ETC to generate a proton gradient across a membrane. These protons then diffuse down their concentration gradient across the inner membrane through ATP synthase, which drives ATP synthesis.

**p. 169 Fig. 9.17** (create) They could have placed the vesicles in an acidic solution that has a pH below that of the solution in the vesicle. This would set up a proton gradient across the membrane to test for ATP synthesis.

**p. 171 CYU** (understand) See FIGURE A9.1. To illustrate the chemiosmotic mechanism, take the triangles (electrons) piled on the NADH and FADH$_2$ circles and move them through the ETC. While moving these triangles, also move dimes from the mitochondrial matrix to the intermembrane space. As the triangles exit the ETC, add them to the oxygen to water circle. Once all the dimes have been pumped by the ETC into the intermembrane space, move them through ATP synthase back into the mitochondrial matrix to fuel the formation of ATP.

**p. 173 CYU** (understand) Electron acceptors such as oxygen have a much higher electronegativity than pyruvate. Donating an electron to O$_2$ causes a greater drop in potential energy, making it possible to generate much more ATP per molecule of glucose.

## IF YOU UNDERSTAND . . .

**9.1** (understand) The radioactive carbons in glucose can be fully oxidized by the central pathways to generate CO$_2$, which would be radiolabeled. Other molecules, like lipids and amino acids, would also be expected to be radiolabeled since they are made using intermediates from the central pathways in other anabolic pathways. **9.2** (apply) See FIGURE A9.2. **9.3** (understand) Pyruvate dehydrogenase accomplishes three different tasks that would be expected to require multiple enzymes and active sites: CO$_2$ release, NADH production, and linking of an acetyl group to CoA. **9.4** (apply) NADH would decrease if a drug poisoned the acetyl CoA and oxaloacetate-to-citrate enzyme, since the citric acid cycle would no longer be able to produce NADH in the steps following this reaction in the pathway. **9.5** (apply) The ATP synthase allows protons to reenter the mitochondrial matrix after they have been pumped out by the ETC. By blocking ATP synthase, you would expect the pH of the matrix to increase (decreased proton concentration). **9.6** (understand) Organisms that produce ATP by fermentation would be expected to grow more slowly than those that produce ATP via cellular respiration simply because fermentation produces fewer ATP molecules per glucose molecule than cellular respiration does.

## YOU SHOULD BE ABLE TO . . .

### ✔ Test Your Knowledge

**1.** (understand) Glycolysis → Pyruvate processing → citric acid cycle → ETC and chemiosmosis. The first three steps are responsible for glucose oxidation; the final step produces the most ATP. **2.** (remember) b **3.** (understand) d **4.** (understand) Most of the energy is stored in the form of NADH. **5.** (remember) c **6.** (remember) a

### ✔ Test Your Understanding

**7.** (understand) Stored carbohydrates can be broken down into glucose that enters the glycolytic pathway. If carbohydrates are absent, products from fat and protein catabolism can be used to fuel cellular respiration or fermentation. If ATP is plentiful, anabolic reactions use

FIGURE A9.1

FIGURE A9.2

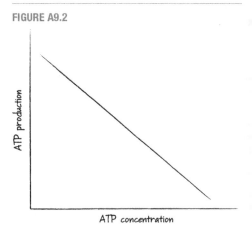

intermediates of the glycolytic pathway and the citric acid cycle to synthesize carbohydrates, fats, and proteins. **8.** (analyze) Both processes produce ATP from ADP and $P_i$, but substrate-level phosphorylation occurs when enzymes remove a "high-energy" phosphate from a substrate and directly transfer it to ADP, while oxidative phosphorylation occurs when electrons move through an ETC and produce a proton-motive force that drives ATP synthase. **9.** (understand) Aerobic respiration is much more productive because oxygen has extremely high electronegativity compared with other electron acceptors, resulting in a greater release of energy during electron transport and more proton pumping. **10.** (apply) b **11.** (analyze) Both phosphofructokinase and isocitrate dehydrogenase are regulated by feedback inhibition, where the product of the reaction or series of reactions inhibits the enzyme activity. They differ in that phosphofructokinase is regulated by allosteric inhibition while isocitrate dehydrogenase is controlled by competitive inhibition. **12.** (understand) Oxidative phosphorylation is possible via a proton gradient that is established by redox reactions in the ETC. ATP synthase consists of a membrane-associated $F_o$ unit and a $F_1$ unit joined by a rotor shaft. When protons flow through the $F_o$ unit, it spins the rotor shaft within the fixed $F_1$ unit. This spinning shaft causes structural changes in the $F_1$ that drives the synthesis of ATP from ADP and $P_i$.

### ✔ Test Your Problem-Solving Skills

**13.** (create) When complex IV is blocked, electrons can no longer be transferred to oxygen, the final acceptor, and cellular respiration stops. Fermentation could keep glycolysis going, but it is inefficient and unlikely to fuel a cell's energy needs over the long term. Cells that lack the enzymes required for fermentation would die first. **14.** (apply) Because mitochondria with few cristae would have fewer electron transport chains and ATP synthase molecules, they would produce much less ATP than mitochondria with numerous cristae. **15.** (apply) For each glucose molecule, two ATP are produced in glycolysis and two ATP are produced in the citric acid cycle via substrate-level phosphorylation. A total of 10 NADH and 2 $FADH_2$ molecules are produced from glycolysis, pyruvate oxidation, and the citric acid cycle. If each NADH were to yield 3 ATP, and each $FADH_2$ were to yield 2 ATP, then a total of 34 ATP would be produced via oxidative phosphorylation. Adding these totals would result in 38 ATP. A cell will not produce this much ATP, because the proton-motive force is used in other transport steps and because of other issues that may reduce the overall efficiency. **16.** (apply) b

# CHAPTER 11

## IN-TEXT QUESTIONS AND EXERCISES

**p. 204 CYU** (analyze) Plant cell walls and animal ECMs are both fiber composites. In plant cell walls the fiber component consists of cross-linked cellulose fibers, and the ground substance is pectin. In animal ECMs the fiber component consists of collagen fibrils, and the ground substance is proteoglycan.
**p. 207** (apply) Developing muscle cells could not adhere normally, and muscle tissue would not form properly. The embryo would die.

**p. 207 Fig. 11.9** (create) "Prediction": Cells treated with an antibody that blocks membrane proteins involved in adhesion will not adhere. "Prediction of null hypothesis": All cells will adhere normally.
**p. 209 CYU (1)** (analyze) The three structures differ in composition, but their function is similar. The middle lamella in plants is composed of pectins that glue adjacent cells together. Tight junctions are made up of membrane proteins that line up and "stitch" adjacent cells together. Desmosomes are "rivet-like" structures composed of proteins that link the cytoskeletons of adjacent cells. **(2)** (understand) The plasma membranes of adjacent plant cells are continuous at plasmodesmata and share portions of the smooth endoplasmic reticulum. Gap junctions connect adjacent animal cells by forming protein-lined pores. Both structures result in openings between the cells that allow cytosol, including ions and small molecules, to be shared.
**p. 211 Fig. 11.12** (create) The steroid hormone likely changes the structure of the receptor such that it now exposes a nuclear localization signal, which is required for the protein to be transported into the nucleus.
**p. 213** (analyze) The spy is the signaling molecule that arrives at the cell surface (the castle gate). The guard is the G-protein-coupled receptor in the plasma membrane, and the queen is the G protein. The commander of the guard is the enzyme that is activated by the G protein to produce second messengers (the soldiers).
**p. 214** (apply) **(1)** The red dominos (RTK components) would be the first two dominos in the chain, followed by the black domino (Ras). This black domino would start two or more new branches, each one represented by a single domino of one color (e.g., green) to represent the activation of one type of kinase. Each of these green dominos would then again branch out, knocking down two or more branches consisting of single dominos of a different color (blue). The same branching pattern would result from each blue domino knocking down two or more yellow dominos. **(2)** Each single black domino (Ras) would require 10 green dominos, 100 blue dominos, and 1000 yellow dominos.
**p. 215 CYU (1)** (understand) Each cell–cell signaling molecule binds to a specific receptor protein. A cell can respond to a signal only if it has the appropriate receptor. Only certain cell types will have the appropriate receptor for a given signaling molecule. **(2)** (understand) Signals are amplified if one or more steps in a signal transduction pathway, involving either second messengers or a phosphorylation cascade, result in the activation of multiple downstream molecules.
**p. 215 Fig. 11.16** (apply) **(1)** cell responses A and C **(2)** cell responses A, B, and C **(3)** cell responses B and C.

## IF YOU UNDERSTAND . . .

**11.1** (apply) **(1)** Cells without functional integrin molecules would likely die as a result of not being able to send the appropriate anchorage-dependent survival signals. **(2)** Cells would be more sensitive to pulling or shearing forces; both cells and tissues would be weaker and more susceptible to damage. **11.2** (apply) Cells would not be coordinated in their activity, so the heart tissue would not contract in unison and the heart would not beat.
**11.3** (analyze) Adrenalin binds to both heart and liver cells, but the activated receptors trigger different signal transduction pathways and lead to different cell responses.
**11.4** (analyze) The signal transduction pathways are similarly organized in both unicellular and multicellular organisms—consisting of signaling molecules, receptors, and second messengers. There is more variety in the means of transmitting the signal between cells in multicellular organisms compared to unicellular organisms. For example, there are no direct connections such as gap junctions or plasmodesmata in unicellular organisms.

## YOU SHOULD BE ABLE TO . . .

### ✔ Test Your Knowledge

**1.** (remember) Fiber composites consist of cross-linked fiber components that withstand tension and a ground substance that withstands compression. The cellulose microfibrils in plants and collagen fibrils in animals functionally resemble the steel rods in reinforced concrete. The pectin in plants and proteoglycan in animals functionally resemble the concrete ground substance. **2.** (remember) b **3.** (remember) a **4.** (understand) a **5.** (remember) d **6.** (remember) Responses that affect which proteins are produced and those that affect the activity of existing proteins.

### ✔ Test Your Understanding

**7.** (understand) b **8.** (understand) If each enzyme in the cascade phosphorylates many copies of the enzyme in the next step of the cascade, the initial signal will be amplified many times over. **9.** (analyze) All three are made up of membrane-spanning proteins that directly interact between adjacent cells. Tight junctions seal adjacent animal cells together; gap junctions allow a flow of material from the cytosol of one to the other. Desmosomes firmly secure adjacent cells to one another but do not affect the movement of substances between cells or into the cells. **10.** (understand) When dissociated cells from two sponge species were mixed, the cells sorted themselves into distinct aggregates that contained only cells of the same species. By blocking membrane proteins with antibodies and isolating cells that would not adhere, researchers found that specialized groups of proteins, including cadherins, are responsible for selective adhesion. **11.** (create) Signaling molecule crosses plasma membrane and binds to intracellular receptor (reception) → Receptor changes conformation, and the activated receptor complex moves to target site (processing) → Activated receptor complex binds to a target molecule (e.g., a gene or membrane pump), which changes its activity (response) → Signaling molecule falls off receptor or is destroyed; receptor changes to inactive conformation (deactivation). **12.** (understand) Information from different signals may conflict or be reinforcing. "Crosstalk" between signaling pathways allows cells to integrate information from many signals at the same time instead of responding to each signal in isolation.

### ✔ Test Your Problem-Solving Skills

**13.** (apply) d **14.** (analyze) (a) The response would have to be extremely local—the activated receptor complex would have to affect nearby proteins. (b) No amplification could occur, because the number of signaling molecules dictates the amount of the response. (c) The only way to regulate the response would be to block the receptor or make it more responsive to the signaling molecule. **15.** (create) Chitin forms chains that can cross-link with one another. This fungal cell wall would likely need to be either relaxed or destroyed, and new cell wall synthesis would be coordinated with the directional growth.

**16.** create Antibody binding to the two parts of the receptor may be causing them to dimerize. Since dimerization normally results after the signaling molecule binds to the receptor, the antibodies could be activating the receptor by mimicking this interaction. The result would be signal transduction even in the absence of the signaling molecule.

# CHAPTER 12

## IN-TEXT QUESTIONS AND EXERCISES

**p. 223** understand **(1)** Genes are segments of chromosomes that code for RNAs and proteins. **(2)** Chromosomes are made of chromatin. **(3)** Sister chromatids are identical copies of the same chromosome, joined together.
**p. 224 Fig. 12.5** apply **(1)** prophase cells would have 4 chromosomes with $2x$ DNA. **(2)** Anaphase cells would

have 8 chromosomes and $2x$ DNA. **(3)** Each daughter cell will have 4 chromosomes with $x$ DNA.
**p. 226** apply See **TABLE A12.1**.
**p. 227 Fig. 12.6** apply The chromosome and black bar would move at the same rate toward the spindle pole.
**p. 229 CYU (1)** apply See **FIGURE A12.1**. **(2)** apply Loss of the motors would result in two problems: (1) It would reduce the ability of chromosomes to attach to microtubules via their kinetochores; (2) cytokinesis would be inhibited since the Golgi-derived vesicles would not be moved to the center of the spindle to build the cell plate.
**p. 230 Fig. 12.10** create Inject cytoplasm from an M-phase frog egg into a somatic cell that is in interphase. If the somatic cell starts mitosis, then the meiotic factor is not limited to gametes.
**p. 230 Fig. 12.11** analyze In effect, MPF turns itself off after it is activated. If this didn't happen, the cell might undergo mitosis again before the cell has replicated its DNA.

**p. 231** understand MPF activates proteins that get mitosis under way. MPF consists of a cyclin and a Cdk, and it is turned on by phosphorylation at the activating site and dephosphorylation at the inhibitory site. Enzymes that degrade cyclin reduce MPF levels.
**p. 232 CYU (1)** remember $G_1 \rightarrow S \rightarrow G_2 \rightarrow M$. Checkpoints occur at the end of $G_1$ and $G_2$ and during M phase.
**(2)** understand Cdk levels are fairly constant throughout the cycle, but cyclin increases during interphase and peaks in M phase. This accumulation of cyclin is a prerequisite for MPF activity, which turns on at the end of $G_2$, initiating M phase, and declines at the end of M phase.

## IF YOU UNDERSTAND . . .

**12.1** understand The $G_1$ and $G_2$ phases give the cell time to replicate organelles and grow before division as well as perform the normal functions required to stay alive. Chromosomes replicate during S phase and are separated from one another during M phase. Cytokinesis also occurs during M phase, when the parent cell divides into two daughter cells. **12.2** apply In cells that do not dissolve the nuclear envelope, the spindle must be constructed inside the nucleus to attach to the chromosomes and separate them. **12.3** apply Cells would prematurely enter M phase, shortening the length of $G_2$ and resulting in the daughter cells' being smaller than normal.
**12.4** analyze The absence of growth factors in normal cells would cause them to arrest in the $G_1$ phase—eventually all the cells in the culture would be in $G_1$. The cancerous cells are not likely to be dependent on these growth factors, so the cells would not arrest and would continue through the cell cycle.

## YOU SHOULD BE ABLE TO . . .

### ✔ Test Your Knowledge
**1.** remember b **2.** remember d **3.** remember d **4.** remember c
**5.** understand Daughter chromosomes were observed to move toward the pole faster than do the marked regions of fluorescently labeled kinetochore microtubules.
**6.** remember The cycle would arrest in M phase, and cytokinesis would not occur.

### ✔ Test Your Understanding
**7.** apply For daughter cells to have identical complements of chromosomes, all the chromosomes must be replicated during the S phase, the spindle apparatus must connect with the kinetochores of each sister chromatid in prometaphase, and the sister chromatids of each replicated chromosome must be partitioned in anaphase and fully separated into daughter cells by cytokinesis. **8.** create One possible concept map is shown in **FIGURE A12.2**. **9.** understand Microinjection experiments suggested that something in the cytoplasm of M-phase cells activated the transition from interphase to M phase. The control for this experiment was to inject cytoplasm from a $G_2$-arrested oocyte into another $G_2$-arrested oocyte. **10.** apply Protein kinases phosphorylate proteins. Phosphorylation changes a protein's shape, altering its function (activating or inactivating it). As a result, protein kinases regulate the function of proteins. **11.** understand Cyclin concentrations change during the cell cycle. At high concentration, cyclins bind to a specific cyclin-dependent kinase (or Cdk), forming a dimer. This dimer becomes active MPF by changing its shape through the phosphorylation (activating site) and dephosphorylation (inhibitory site) of Cdk. **12.** analyze b.

### ✔ Test Your Problem-Solving Skills
**13.** analyze a; adding up each phase allows you to determine that the cell cycle is 8.5 hours long. After 9 hours, the radiolabeled cells would have passed through a full cycle and be in either S phase or $G_2$—none would have entered M phase. **14.** apply The embryo passes through multiple rounds of the cell cycle, but cytokinesis does

**FIGURE A12.1**

**FIGURE A12.2**

**TABLE A12.1**

| | Prophase | Prometaphase | Metaphase | Anaphase | Telophase |
|---|---|---|---|---|---|
| Spindle apparatus | Starts to form | Contacts and moves chromosomes | Anchors poles to membrane and produces tension at kinetochores | Pulls chromatids apart | Defines site of cytokinesis |
| Nuclear envelope | Present | Disintegrates | Nonexistent | Nonexistent | Re-forms |
| Chromosomes | Condense | Attach to microtubules | Held at metaphase plate | Sister chromatids separate into daughter chromosomes | Collect at opposite poles |

not occur during M phases. **15.** apply Early detection of cancers leads to a greater likelihood of survival. The widespread implementation of breast and prostate exams allows for the identification and removal of benign tumors before they become malignant. **16.** analyze Cancer requires many defects. Older cells have had more time to accumulate defects. Individuals with a genetic predisposition to cancer start out with some cancer-related defects, but this does not mean that the additional defects required for cancer to occur will develop.

# CHAPTER 13

## IN-TEXT QUESTIONS AND EXERCISES

**p. 239** apply $n = 4$; the organism is diploid with $2n = 8$.
**p. 240** remember See FIGURE A13.1. Because the two sister chromatids are identical and attached, it is sensible to consider them as parts of a single chromosome.
**p. 242** apply There will be four DNA molecules in each gamete because the 8 replicated chromosomes in a diploid cell are reduced to 4 replicated chromosomes per cell at the end of meiosis I. In meiosis II, the sister chromatids of each replicated chromosome are separated. Each cell now contains 4 unreplicated chromosomes, each with a single molecule of DNA.
**p. 245** apply Crossing over would not occur and the daughter cells produced by meiosis would be diploid, not haploid. There would be no reduction division.
**p. 246 CYU (1)** understand Use four long and four short pipe cleaners (or pieces of cooked spaghetti) to represent the chromatids of two replicated homologous chromosomes (four total chromosomes). Mark two long and two short ones with a colored marker pen to distinguish maternal and paternal copies of these chromosomes. Twist identical pipe cleaners (e.g., the two long colored ones) together to simulate replicated chromosomes. Arrange the pipe cleaners to depict the different phases of meiosis I as follows: *Early prophase I:* Align sister chromatids of each homologous pair to form two tetrads. *Late prophase I:* Form one or more crossovers between non-sister chromatids in each tetrad. (This is hard to simulate with pipe cleaners—you'll have to imagine that each chromatid now contains both maternal and paternal segments.) *Metaphase I:* Line up homologous pairs (the two pairs of short pipe cleaners and the two pairs of long pipe cleaners) at the metaphase plate. *Anaphase I:* Separate homologs. Each homolog still consists of sister chromatids joined at the centromere. *Telophase I and cytokinesis:* Move homologs apart to depict formation of two haploid cells, each containing a single replicated copy of two different chromosomes. **(2)** understand During anaphase I, homologs (not sister chromatids, as in mitosis) are separated, making the cell products of meiosis I haploid. **(3)** understand The pairing of homologs in metaphase I and their separation in anaphase I so that one goes to one daughter cell and the other to the other daughter cell means that each daughter cell obtains precisely one copy of each type of chromosome.
**p. 248** apply Each gamete would inherit either all maternal or all paternal chromosomes. This would limit genetic variation in the offspring by precluding the many possible gametes containing various combinations of maternal and paternal chromosomes.
**p. 248 CYU (1)** apply See FIGURE A13.2. Maternal chromosomes are white and paternal chromosomes are black. Daughter cells with other possible combinations of chromosomes than shown could result from meiosis of this parent cell. **(2)** understand Crossing over would increase the genetic diversity of these gametes by creating many different combinations of maternal and paternal alleles along each of the chromosomes. **(3)** analyze Asexual reproduction generates no appreciable genetic diversity. Self-fertilization is preceded by meiosis so it generates gametes, through crossing over and independent

assortment, that have combinations of alleles not present in the parent. Outcrossing generates the most genetic diversity among offspring because it produces new combinations of alleles from two different individuals.
**p. 249 Fig. 13.11** apply See FIGURE A13.3.
**p. 251 Fig. 13.14** apply Asexually: 64 (16 individuals from generation three produce 4 offspring per individual). Sexually: 16 (8 individuals from generation three form 4 couples; each couple produces 4 offspring).
**p. 252 Fig. 13.15** apply The rate of outcrossing is predicted to rise initially, as the pathogen selects for resistant roundworms, and then to fall as the roundworms in the population gain resistance and take advantage of the increased numbers of offspring offered by having more hermaphrodites that can reproduce by self-fertilization.

## IF YOU UNDERSTAND . . .

**13.1** remember See the right panel of Figure 13.7 and note how the cells transition from diploid to haploid in meiosis I. Also note that each chromosome contains two sister chromatids before and after meiosis I.
**13.2** understand (a) See Figure 13.10 and note how the two different ways of aligning two homologous pairs of chromosomes at metaphase I of meiosis can create four different combinations of maternal and paternal chromosomes in daughter cells. (b) See Figure 13.11. Note that for each homologous pair with one crossover, two chromatids are recombinant and two are unaltered. Since each chromatid will produce a chromosome at the end of meiosis II, your drawing should show that two out of four of these chromosomes are recombinant.
**13.3** apply (a) Your model should show events similar to those of Figure 13.12. (b) Your model should show two cells with one of each type of chromosome ($n$), one cell with an extra copy of one chromosome ($n + 1$), and one gamete without any copies of one chromosome ($n - 1$).
**13.4** remember Sexual reproduction will likely occur during times when conditions are changing rapidly, because genetically diverse offspring may have an advantage in the new conditions.

## YOU SHOULD BE ABLE TO . . .

### ✔ Test Your Knowledge

**1.** remember b **2.** remember a **3.** remember b **4.** understand b
**5.** remember 1/2 **6.** remember mitosis.

### ✔ Test Your Understanding

**7.** remember Homologous chromosomes are similar in size, shape, and gene content, and originate from different parents. Sister chromatids are exact copies of a chromosome that are generated when chromosomes are replicated (S phase of the cell cycle). **8.** understand Refer to Figure 13.7 as a guide for this exercise. The four pens represent the chromatids in one replicated homologous pair; the four pencils, the chromatids in a different homologous pair. To simulate meiosis II, make two "haploid cells"—each with a pair of pens and a pair of pencils representing two replicated chromosomes (one of each type in this species). Line them up in the middle of the cell; then separate the two pens and the two pencils in each cell such that one pen and one pencil go to each of four daughter cells. **9.** understand Meiosis I is a reduction division because homologs separate—daughter cells have just one of each type of chromosome instead of two. Meiosis II is not a reduction division because sister chromatids separate— daughter cells have unreplicated chromosomes instead of replicated chromosomes, but still just one of each type. **10.** apply b. **11.** apply Tetraploids produce diploid gametes, which combine with a haploid gamete from a diploid individual to form a triploid offspring. Mitosis proceeds normally in triploid cells because mitosis doesn't require forming pairs of chromosomes. But during meiosis in a triploid, homologous chromosomes can't pair up correctly. The third set of chromosomes does not have a homologous partner to pair with. **12.** understand Asexually produced individuals are genetically identical, so if one is susceptible to a new disease, all are. Sexually produced individuals are genetically unique, so if a new disease strain evolves, at least some plants are likely to be resistant.

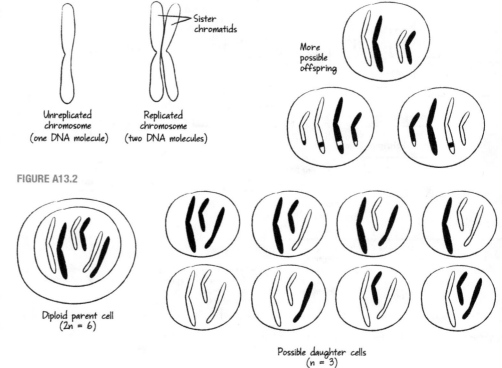

FIGURE A13.1

Sister chromatids

Unreplicated chromosome (one DNA molecule)

Replicated chromosome (two DNA molecules)

FIGURE A13.2

Diploid parent cell ($2n = 6$)

Possible daughter cells ($n = 3$)

FIGURE A13.3

More possible offspring

✔ **Test Your Problem-Solving Skills**

**13.** `apply` The gibbon would have 22 chromosomes in each gamete, and the siamang would have 25. Each somatic cell of the offspring would have 47 chromosomes. The offspring should be sterile because it has some chromosomes that would not form homologous pairs at prophase I of meiosis. **14.** `apply` c **15.** `apply` Aneuploidy is the major cause of spontaneous abortion. If spontaneous abortion is rare in older women, it would result in a higher incidence of aneuploid conditions such as Down syndrome in older women, as recorded in the Figure 13.13. **16. (a)** `create` Such a study might be done in the laboratory, controlling conditions in identical dishes. A population of rotifers infected with fungus could be established in each dish. One dish of rotifers would be kept moist; the other dishes of rotifers would be allowed to dry out. After various periods of time, water would be added to each dish and then the rotifers would be observed to see if fungal infections reappeared. **(b)** `create` Wind disperses the rotifer to new and often pathogen-free environments. In this case, the ticket to a sex-free existence is not genetic diversity but the evolution of an alternative means of evading pathogens made possible by fungus-infected rotifers ridding themselves of the pathogen when they dry.

# CHAPTER 14

## IN-TEXT QUESTIONS AND EXERCISES

**p. 260 Fig. 14.3** `evaluate` An experiment is a failure if you didn't learn anything from it. That is not the case here.
**p. 261 Table 14.2** `analyze` *Row 6:* 3.14 : 1; *Row 7:* 266.
**p. 262** `apply` Filling in the top and side of a Punnett square requires writing out the types and ratios of gametes. For a cross involving one gene (monohybrid cross), this amounts to applying the principle of segregation as one allele is segregated from another. The phenotype ratios are 1 : 1 round : wrinkled; the genotype ratios are 1 : 1 *Rr* : *rr*.
**p. 262 Fig. 14.4** `understand` No—the outcome (the expected offspring genotypes that the Punnett square generates) will be the same.

**p. 263 CYU (1)** `apply` See answer to Problem 13 in Test Your Problem-Solving Skills, below. **(2)** `apply` See answer to Problem 15 in Test Your Problem-Solving Skills.
**p. 265** `apply` *AABb* → *AB* and *Ab. PpRr* → *PR, Pr, pR,* and *pr. AaPpRr* → *APR, APr, ApR, Apr, aPR, aPr, apr,* and *aPr.*
**p. 265 CYU (1)** `apply` See answer to Problem 14 in Test Your Problem-Solving Skills. **(2)** `apply` See answer to Problem 16 in Test Your Problem-Solving Skills.
**p. 269 CYU (1)** `understand` See **FIGURE A14.1**. Segregation of alleles occurs when homologs that carry those alleles are separated during anaphase I. One allele ends up in each daughter cell. **(2)** `understand` See **FIGURE A14.2**. Independent assortment occurs because homologous pairs line up randomly at the metaphase plate during metaphase I. The figure shows two alternative arrangements of homologs in metaphase I. As a result, it is equally possible for a gamete to receive the following four combinations of alleles: *YR, Yr, yR, yr.*
**p. 270 Fig. 14.12** `apply` X*WY,* X*Wy,* X*wY,* X*wy.*

**p. 271 Fig. 14.13** `analyze` Random chance (or perhaps red-eyed, gray-bodied males don't survive well).
**p. 273 Fig. 14.16** `analyze` The gene colored orange is *ruby;* the gene colored blue is *miniature wings.*
**p. 275 Fig. 14.19** `understand` In this case of gene-by-gene interaction, the 9 : 3 : 3 : 1 ratio comes from four different forms of one trait (comb shape), whereas in a standard dihybrid cross, the four different phenotypes come from two different phenotypes for each of two genes.
**p. 276 CYU (1)** `apply` The comb phenotype results from interactions between alleles at two different genes, not a single gene. Matings between rose- and pea-comb chickens produce F₂ offspring that may have a new combination of alleles and thus new phenotypes. **(2)** `apply` Kernel color in wheat is influenced by alleles at many different genes, not a single gene. F₂ offspring have a normal distribution of phenotypes, not a 3 : 1 ratio.
**p. 276 Fig. 14.21** `understand` Because there are many different genotypes that can produce intermediate coloration and fewer that can produce the extremes of coloration.

**FIGURE A14.1**

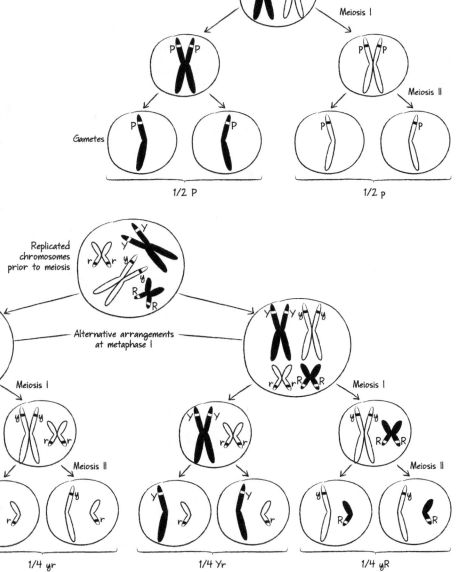

**FIGURE A14.2**

**p. 279 Fig. 14.23** A heterozygous female and a color-blind male. 1 color-blind male : 1 color-blind female.

## IF YOU UNDERSTAND . . .

**14.1** (understand) Because crosses within a pure line never produce individuals with a different phenotype, this indicates that there must be only one allele in pure-line individuals. **14.2** (apply) $B$ and $b$. **14.3** (apply) $BR$, $Br$, $bR$, and $br$, in equal proportions. The $B$ and $b$ alleles are located on different but homologous chromosomes, which separate into different daughter cells during meiosis I. The $BbRr$ notation indicates that the $B$ and $R$ genes are on different chromosomes. As a result, the chromosomes line up independently of each other in metaphase of meiosis I. The $B$ allele is equally likely to go to a daughter cell with $R$ as with $r$; likewise, the $b$ allele is equally likely to go to a daughter cell with $R$ as with $r$. **14.4** (apply) There are many ways to show this. If eye color in *Drosophila* is chosen as an example, then a pair of Punnett squares like those in Figure 14.11 illustrate how reciprocal crosses involving an X-linked recessive gene give different results. **14.5** (understand) Linkage refers to the physical connection of two alleles on the same chromosome. Crossing over breaks this linkage between particular alleles as segments of maternal and paternal homologs are exchanged. **14.6** (apply) See **FIGURE A14.3** for the pedigree. Note that the birth order of daughters and sons is arbitrary; other birth orders are equally valid. A Punnett square will show that all the sons are predicted to be $X^+Y$ and all the daughters $X^+X^c$, where $X^+$ shows the dominant, X-linked allele for normal color vision and $X^c$ shows the X-linked recessive color blindness allele.

## YOU SHOULD BE ABLE TO . . .

### ✔ Test Your Understanding

1. (understand) d  2. (understand) b  3. (understand) a  4. (understand) d
5. (understand) a  6. (understand) a  7. (evaluate) d  8. (remember) b  9. (apply) b
10. (understand) d

### ✔ Test Your Problem-Solving Skills

**11.** (apply) **Example Solution** Here you're given offspring phenotypes and you're asked to infer parental genotypes. To do this you have to propose hypothetical parental genotypes to test, make a Punnett square to predict the offspring genotypes, and then see if the predicted offspring phenotypes match the data. In this case, coming up with a hypothesis for the parental genotypes is relatively straightforward because the problem states that the trait is due to one gene and two alleles. No information on sex is given, so assume the gene is autosomal (the simplest case). Now look at the second entry in the chart. It shows a 3 : 1 ratio of offspring from a winged individual that self-fertilizes. This result is consistent with the hypothesis that $W^+$ is dominant and $W^-$ recessive and that this parent's genotype is $W^+W^-$. Now let's look at the first cross in the chart. If $W^+$ is dominant, then a wingless parent must be $W^-W^-$. When you do the Punnett square to predict offspring genotypes from selfing, you find that all the offspring will produce wingless fruits, consistent with the data. In the third cross, all the offspring make winged fruits even though one of the parents produces wingless

**FIGURE A14.3**

fruits and thus is $W^-W^-$. This would happen only if the winged parent is $W^+W^+$. (If this reasoning isn't immediately clear to you, work the Punnett square.) In the fourth cross, you could get offspring that all make winged fruits if the parents were $W^+W^+$ and $W^+W^+$, or if the parents were $W^+W^+$ and $W^+W^-$. Either answer is correct. Again, you can write out the Punnett squares to see that this statement is correct.

**12.** (apply) **Example Solution** Here you are given parental and offspring phenotypes and are asked to infer the parental genotypes. As a starting point, assume that the coat colors are due to the simplest genetic system possible: one autosomal gene with two alleles, where one allele is dominant and the other recessive. Because female II produces only black offspring, it's logical to suppose that black is dominant to brown. Let's use $B$ for black and $b$ for brown. Then the male parent is $bb$. To produce offspring with a 1 : 1 ratio of black : brown coats, female I must be $Bb$. But to produce all black offspring, female II must be $BB$. This model explains the data, so you can accept it as correct.

**13.** (apply) 3/4; 1/256 (see BioSkills 5 in Appendix B); 1/2 (the probabilities of transmitting the alleles or having sons does not change over time). **14.** (apply) Your answer to the first three parts should conform to the $F_1$ and $F_2$ crosses diagrammed in Figure 14.5b, except that different alleles and traits are being analyzed. The recombinant gametes would be $Yi$ and $yI$. Yes—there would be some individuals with yellow seeds and constricted pods and with green seeds and inflated pods. **15.** (apply) Cross 1: non-crested ($Cc$) × non-crested ($Cc$) = 22 non-crested ($C\_$); 7 crested ($cc$). Cross 2: crested ($cc$) × crested ($cc$) = 20 crested ($cc$). Cross 3: non-crested ($Cc$) × crested ($cc$) = 7 non-crested ($Cc$); 6 crested ($cc$). Non-crested ($C$) is the dominant allele. **16.** (apply) This is a dihybrid cross that yields progeny phenotypes in a 9 : 3 : 3 : 1 ratio. Let $O$ stand for the allele for orange petals and $o$ allele for yellow petals; let $S$ stand for the allele for spotted petals and $s$ the allele for unspotted petals. Start with the hypothesis that $O$ is dominant to $o$, that $S$ is dominant to $s$, that the two genes are found on different chromosomes so they assort independently, and that the parent individual's genotype is $OoSs$. If you do a Punnett square for the $OoSs × OoSs$ mating, you'll find that progeny phenotypes should be in the observed 9 : 3 : 3 : 1 proportions. **17.** (analyze) Let $D$ stand for the normal allele and $d$ for the allele responsible for Duchenne-type muscular dystrophy. The woman's family has no history of the disease, so her genotype is almost certainly $DD$. The man is not afflicted, so he must be $DY$. (The trait is X-linked, so he has only one allele; the "Y" stands for the Y chromosome.) Their children are not at risk. The man's sister could be a carrier, however—meaning she has the genotype $Dd$. If so, then half of the second couple's male children are likely to be affected. **18.** (understand) Your stages of meiosis should look like a simplified version of Figure 13.7, except with $2n = 4$ instead of $2n = 6$. The $A$ and $a$ alleles could be on the red and blue versions of the longest chromosome, and the $B$ and $b$ alleles could be on the red and blue versions of the smallest chromosome, similar to the way the hair- and eye-color genes are shown in Figure 13.10. The places you draw them are the locations of the $A$ and $B$ genes, but each chromosome has only one allele. Each pair of red and blue chromosomes is a homologous pair. Sister chromatids bear the same allele (e.g., both sister chromatids of the long blue chromosomes might bear the $a$ allele). Chromatids from the longest and shortest chromosomes are not homologous. To identify the events that result in the principles of segregation and independent assortment, see Figures 14.7 and 14.8 and substitute $A$, $a$, and $B$, $b$ for $R$, $r$ and $Y$, $y$. **19.** (apply) Half their offspring should have the genotype $iI^A$ and the type A blood phenotype. The other half of their offspring should have the genotype $iI^B$ and the type B blood

phenotype. Second case: the genotype and phenotype ratios would be 1 : 1 : 1 : 1 $I^AI^B$ (type AB) : $I^Ai$ (type A) : $I^Bi$ (type B) : $ii$ (type O). **20.** (apply) Because the children of Tukan and Valco had no eyes and smooth skin, you can conclude that the allele for eyelessness is dominant to eyes and the allele for smooth skin is dominant to hooked skin. $E$ = eyeless, $e$ = two eye sets, $S$ = smooth skin, $s$ = hooked skin. Tukan is $eeSS$; Valco is $EEss$. The children are all $EeSs$. Grandchildren with eyes and smooth skin are $eeS$-. Assuming that the genes are on different chromosomes, one-fourth of the children's gametes are $ee$ and three-fourths are $S$-. So 1/4 $ee$ × 3/4 $S$- × 32 = 6 children would be expected to have two sets of eyes and smooth skin. **21.** (create) Although the mothers were treated as children by a reduction of dietary phenylalanine, they would have accumulated phenylalanine and its derivatives once they went off the low-phenylalanine diet as young adults. Children born of such mothers were therefore exposed to high levels of phenylalanine during pregnancy. For this reason, a low-phenylalanine diet is recommended for such mothers throughout the pregnancy. **22.** (apply) According to Mendel's model, palomino individuals should be heterozygous at the locus for coat color. If you mated palomino individuals, you would expect to see a combination of chestnut, palomino, and cremello offspring. If blending inheritance occurred, however, all the offspring should be palomino. **23.** (apply) Because this is an X-linked trait, the father who has hemophilia could not have passed the trait on to his son. Thus, the mother in couple 1 must be a carrier and must have passed the recessive allele on to her son, who is XY and affected. To educate a jury about the situation, you should draw what happens to the X and Y during meiosis and then make a drawing showing the chromosomes in couple 1 and couple 2, with a Punnett square showing how these chromosomes are passed to the affected and unaffected children. **24.** (apply) The curved-wing allele is autosomal recessive; the lozenge-eyed allele is sex-linked (specifically, X-linked) recessive. Let $L$ be the allele for long wings and $l$ be the allele for curved wings; let $X^R$ be the allele for red eyes and $X^r$ the allele for lozenge eyes. The female parent is $LlX^RX^r$; the male parent is $LlX^RY$. **25.** (apply) Albinism indicates the absence of pigment, so let $b$ stand for an allele that gives the absence of blue and $y$ for an allele that gives the absence of yellow pigment. If blue and yellow pigment blend to give green, then both green parents are $BbYy$. The green phenotype is found in $BBYY$, $BBYy$, $BbYY$, and $BbYy$ offspring. The blue phenotype is found in $BByy$ or $Bbyy$ offspring. The yellow phenotype is observed in $bbYY$ or $bbYy$ offspring. Albino offspring are $bbyy$. The phenotypes of the offspring should be in the ratio 9 : 3 : 3 : 1 as green : blue : yellow : albino. Two types of crosses yield $BbYy$ $F_1$ offspring: $BByy × bbYY$ (blue × yellow) and $BBYY × bbyy$ (green × albino). **26.** (apply) The chance that their first child will have hemophilia is 1/2. This is because all sons will have the disease and there is a 1/2 chance of having a firstborn son. The chance of having a carrier as their first child is also 1/2. This is because all daughters and none of the sons will be carriers and there is a 1/2 chance of having a firstborn daughter. (Recall that males cannot carry an X-linked recessive trait—with only one X chromosome, males either have the trait or not.) **27.** (apply) Autosomal dominant.

## CHAPTER 15

### IN-TEXT QUESTIONS AND EXERCISES

**p. 286 Fig. 15.2** (analyze) The lack of radioactive protein in the pellet (after centrifugation) is strong evidence; they could also make micrographs of infected bacterial cells before and after agitation.

**p. 287 Fig. 15.3** (apply) 5'-TAG-3'.

**p. 288 Fig. 15.5** (apply) The same two bands should appear, but the upper band (DNA containing only $^{14}$N) should get bigger and darker and the lower band (hybrid DNA)

should get smaller and lighter in color since each succeeding generation has relatively less heavy DNA.
**p. 290** (apply) See FIGURE A15.1. The new strands grow in opposite directions, each in the $5' \rightarrow 3'$ direction.
**p. 292** (apply) Helicase, topoisomerase, single-strand DNA-binding proteins, primase, and DNA polymerase are all required for leading-strand synthesis. If any one of these proteins is nonfunctional, DNA replication will not occur.
**p. 293** (apply) See FIGURE A15.2. If DNA ligase were defective, then the leading strand would be continuous, and the lagging strand would have gaps in it where the Okazaki fragments had not been joined.
**p. 294 CYU (1)** (understand) DNA polymerase adds nucleotides only to the free $3'$ —OH on a strand. Primase synthesizes a short RNA sequence that provides the free $3'$ end necessary for DNA polymerase to start working. **(2)** (understand) The need to begin DNA synthesis many times on the lagging strand requires many new primers. Since DNA polymerase I is needed to remove primers, it is required predominantly on the primer-rich lagging strand.
**p. 296 Fig. 15.13** (apply) As long as the RNA template could bind to the "overhanging" section of single-stranded DNA, any sequence could produce a longer strand. For example, $5'$-CCCAUUCCC-$3'$ would work just as well.
**p. 297 CYU (1)** (understand) This is because telomerase is needed only to replicate one end of a linear DNA and bacterial DNAs lack ends because they are circular.
**(2)** (understand) Since telomerase works by extending one strand of DNA without any external template and because DNA synthesis requires a template, telomerase must contain an internal template to allow it to extend a DNA chain.
**p. 299 Fig. 15.16** (analyze) They are lower in energy and not absorbed effectively by the DNA bases.
**p. 300 CYU (1)** (apply) The mutation rate would be predicted to rise because differences in base-pair stability and shape make it possible for DNA polymerase to distinguish correct from incorrect base pairs during DNA replication. **(2)** (apply) The mutation rate should increase because without a way to distinguish which strand to use as a template for repair, about half of mismatches on average would be repaired using the incorrect strand as a template. **(3)** (remember) The enzyme that removes the dimer and surrounding DNA is specific to nucleotide excision repair. DNA polymerase and DNA ligase work in both nucleotide excision repair and normal DNA synthesis.
**p. 300 Fig. 15.18** (apply) Exposure to UV radiation can cause formation of thymine dimers. If thymine dimers are not repaired, they represent mutations. If such mutations occur in genes controlling the cell cycle, cells can grow abnormally, resulting in cancers.

## IF YOU UNDERSTAND . . .

**15.1** (apply) These results would not allow distinguishing whether DNA or protein was the genetic material.
**15.2** (understand) The bases added during DNA replication are shown in red type.

|  |  |
|---|---|
| Original DNA: | **CAATTACGGA** |
|  | **GTTAATGCCT** |
| Replicated DNA: | **CAATTACGGA** |
|  | GTTAATGCCT |
|  | CAATTACGGA |
|  | **GTTAATGCCT** |

**15.3** (understand) See FIGURE A15.3. **15.4** (understand) Because cancer cells divide nearly without limit, it's important for these cells to have active telomerase so that chromosomes don't shorten to the point where cell division becomes impossible. **15.5** (understand) If errors in DNA aren't corrected, they represent mutations. When DNA repair systems fail, the mutation rate increases. As the mutation rate increases, the chance that one or more cell-cycle genes will be mutated increases. Mutations in these genes often result in uncontrolled cell division, ultimately leading to cancer.

## YOU SHOULD BE ABLE TO . . .

### ✔ Test Your Knowledge
**1.** (remember) d **2.** (understand) a **3.** (remember) topoisomerase
**4.** (remember) b **5.** (remember) c **6.** (remember) telomerase

### ✔ Test Your Understanding
**7.** (remember) Labeling DNA or labeling proteins. **8.** (understand) DNA is constantly damaged, and many pathways have evolved to repair this onslaught of damage. If a DNA repair pathway is inactivated by mutation, damage is inefficiently repaired. Consequently mutation rates increase, and the increased number of mutations increases the probability that cancer-causing mutations will occur.
**9.** (understand) On the lagging strand, DNA polymerase moves away from the replication fork. When helicase unwinds a new section of DNA, primase must build a new primer on the template for the lagging strand (closer to the fork) and another polymerase molecule must begin synthesis at this point. This makes the lagging-strand synthesis discontinuous. On the leading strand, DNA polymerase moves in the same direction as helicase, so synthesis can continue, without interruption, from a single primer (at the origin of replication).
**10.** (understand) Telomerase binds to the overhang at the end of a chromosome. Once bound, it begins catalyzing the addition of deoxyribonucleotides to the overhang in the

$5' \rightarrow 3'$ direction, lengthening the overhang. This allows primase, DNA polymerase, and ligase to catalyze the addition of deoxyribonucleotides to the lagging strand in the $5' \rightarrow 3'$ direction, restoring the lagging strand to its original length. **11.** (apply) a (Because the ability to distinguish which strand contains the incorrect base would be lost). **12.** (analyze) d (The regularity of DNA's structure allows enzymes to recognize any type of damage that distorts this regular structure.)

### ✔ Test Your Problem-Solving Skills
**13.** (analyze) c (If DNA polymerase could synthesize DNA $3' \rightarrow 5'$ as well as the normal $5' \rightarrow 3'$, then both newly synthesized DNA strands could be extended to follow the replication fork.) **14.** (apply) (a) In FIGURE A15.4, the gray lines represent DNA strands containing radioactivity. (b) After one round of replication in radioactive solution, one double-stranded DNA would be radioactive in both strands and the other would not be radioactive in either strand. After another round of DNA synthesis, this time in nonradioactive solution, one of the four DNA molecules would be radioactive in both strands and the other three DNA molecules would contain no radioactivity in any strand. **15.** (analyze) (a) The double mutant of both *uvrA* and *recA* is most sensitive to UV light; the single mutants are in between; and the wild type is

FIGURE A15.1

Direction of new strand synthesis

Direction of new strand synthesis

FIGURE A15.2

Okazaki fragments

FIGURE A15.3

Lagging    Leading

Leading    Lagging

FIGURE A15.4

Chromosome

Sister chromatids

Replication in radioactive solution

Mitosis

Replication in nonradioactive solution

least sensitive. (b) The *recA* gene contributes more to UV repair through most of the UV dose levels. But at very high UV doses, the *uvrA* gene is somewhat more important than the *recA* gene. **16.** apply About 4600 seconds or 77 minutes. This answer comes from knowing that replication proceeds bidirectionally, so replication from each fork is predicted to replicate half the chromosome. This is 4.6 million base pairs/2 = 2.3 million base pairs. At 500 base pairs per second, this requires 2.3 million base pairs/500 base pairs per second = 4600 seconds. To obtain the time in minutes, divide 4600 seconds by 60 seconds per minute.

# CHAPTER 16

## IN-TEXT QUESTIONS AND EXERCISES

**p. 305 Fig. 16.1** apply No, it could not make citrulline from ornithine without enzyme 2. Yes, it would no longer need enzyme 2 to make citrulline.

**p. 306 Fig. 16.2** create Many possibilities: strain of fungi used, exact method for creating mutants and harvesting spores to grow, exact growing conditions (temperature, light, recipe for growth medium—including concentrations of supplements), objective criteria for determining growth or no growth.

**p. 309 CYU** remember Change in DNA sequence, change in sequence of transcribed mRNA, potential change in amino acid sequence of protein, likely altered protein function (if amino acid sequence was altered), likely change in phenotype.

**p. 312** analyze (1) The codons in Figure 16.4 are translated correctly. (2) See FIGURE A16.1. (3) There are many possibilities (just pick alternative codons for one or more of the amino acids); one is an mRNA sequence (running 5′ → 3′): 5′ GCG-AAC-GAU-UUC-CAG 3′. To get the corresponding DNA sequence, write this sequence but substitute Ts for Us: 5′ GCG-AAC-GAT-TTC-CAG 3′. Now write the complementary bases, which will be in the 3′ → 5′ direction: 3′ CGC-TTG-CTA-AAG-GTC 5′. When this second strand is transcribed by RNA polymerase, it will produce the mRNA given with the proper 5′ → 3′ orientation.

**p. 312 CYU (1)** apply Note the 3′ → 5′ polarity of the DNA sequences in the accompanying table, and in the subsequent answer. This means that the complementary mRNA codon will read 5′ → 3′. U (rather than T) is the base transcribed from A.

| DNA | mRNA Codon | Amino Acid |
|-----|-----------|------------|
| ATA | UAU | Tyrosine |
| ATG | UAC | Tyrosine |
| ATT | UAA | Stop |
| GCA | UGC | Cysteine |

**(2)** understand The ATA → ATG mutation would have no effect on the protein. The ATA → ATT mutation introduces a stop codon, so the resulting polypeptide would be shortened. This would result in synthesis of a mutant protein much shorter than the original protein. The ATA → GCA mutation might have a profound effect on the protein's conformation because cysteine's structure is different from tyrosine's.

**p. 312 Fig. 16.7** apply See FIGURE A16.1.

**p. 314 Fig. 16.9** analyze Chromosomes 2, 3, 6, 10, 13, 14, 15, 18, 19, 21, 22, and the X chromosome show aneuploidy. Virtually every chromosome has structural rearrangements, and translocations are the most obvious. These are seen when two or more different colors occur on the same chromosome.

## IF YOU UNDERSTAND . . .

**16.1** understand Ornithine, citrulline or arginine could be added to allow growth. As Figure 16.1 shows, these

compounds are made after the steps catalyzed by the enzymes 1, 2, and 3 that are needed to produce arginine. **16.2** understand An inhibitor of RNA synthesis will eventually prevent the synthesis of new proteins because newly synthesized mRNA is needed for translation. **16.3** apply AUG UGG AAA/AAG CAA/CAG **16.4** understand Since redundancy is having more than one codon specify a particular amino acid, redundancy makes it possible for there to be a point mutation without altering the amino acid. This is a silent mutation. A silent mutation is likely to be neutral because there is no change in amino acid sequence.

## YOU SHOULD BE ABLE TO . . .

### ✓ Test Your Knowledge

**1.** remember d **2.** understand a **3.** understand d **4.** remember Because there is no chemical complementarity between nucleotides and amino acids; and because in eukaryotes, DNA is in the nucleus but translation occurs in the cytoplasm. **5.** understand d **6.** remember A codon that signals the end of translation.

### ✓ Test Your Understanding

**7.** understand Because the Morse code and genetic code both use simple elements (dots and dashes; 4 different bases) in different orders to encode complex information (words; amino acid sequences).

**8.**

Substrate 1 →A Substrate 2 →B Substrate 3 →C
Substrate 4 →D ... →E Substrate 5 →  Biological Sciazine

apply Substrate 3 would accumulate. Hypothesis: The individuals have a mutation in the gene for enzyme D.

**9.** understand They supported an important prediction of the hypothesis: Losing a gene (via mutation) resulted in loss of an enzyme. **10.** understand c **11.** understand In a triplet code, addition or deletion of 1–2 bases disrupts the reading frame "downstream" of the mutation site(s), resulting in a dysfunctional protein. But addition or deletion of 3 bases restores the reading frame—the normal sequence is disrupted only between the first and third mutation. The resulting protein is altered but may still be able to function normally. Only a triplet code would show these patterns. **12.** understand A point mutation changes the nucleotide sequence of an existing allele, creating a new one, so it always changes the genotype. But because the genetic code is redundant, and because point mutations can occur in DNA sequences that do not code for amino acids, these point mutations do not change the protein product and therefore do not change the phenotype.

### ✓ Test Your Problem-Solving Skills

**13.** apply See FIGURE A16.2. **14.** analyze Every copying error would result in a mutation that would change the amino

acid sequence of the protein and would likely affect its function. **15.** analyze Before the central dogma was understood, DNA was known to be the hereditary material, but no one knew how particular sequences of bases resulted in the production of RNA and protein products. The central dogma clarified how genotypes produce phenotypes. **16.** analyze c

# CHAPTER 17

## IN-TEXT QUESTIONS AND EXERCISES

**p. 318 Fig. 17.1** remember RNA is synthesized in the 5′ → 3′ direction; the DNA template is "read" 3′ → 5′.

**p. 321 CYU (1)** apply Transcription would be reduced or absent because the missing nucleotides are in the −10 region, one of the two critical parts of the promoter. **(2)** understand NTPs are required because the three phosphate groups raise the monomer's potential energy enough to make the polymerization reaction exergonic.

**p. 322 Fig. 17.5** apply There would be no loops—the molecules would match up exactly.

**p. 323 CYU (1)** understand The subunits contain both RNA (the *ribonucleo–* in the name) and proteins. **(2)** understand The cap and tail protect mRNAs from degradation and facilitate translation.

**p. 326 Fig. 17.11** analyze If the amino acids stayed attached to the tRNAs, the gray line in the graph would stay high and the green line low. If the amino acids were transferred to some other cell component, the gray line would decline but the green line would be low.

**p. 327** understand (1) The amino acid attaches on the top right of the L-shaped structure. (2) The anticodon is antiparallel in orientation to the mRNA codon, and it contains the complementary bases.

**p. 332 CYU** understand E is for exit—the site where uncharged tRNAs are ejected; P is for peptidyl (or peptide bond)—the site where peptide bond formation takes place; A is for aminoacyl—the site where aminoacyl tRNAs enter.

## IF YOU UNDERSTAND . . .

**17.1** apply Transcription would continue past the normal point because the insertion of nucleotides would disrupt the structure of the RNA hairpin that functions as a terminator. **17.2** apply The protein-coding segment of the gene is predicted to be longer in eukaryotes because of the presence of introns. **17.3** understand The tRNAs act as adaptors because they couple the information contained in the nucleotides of mRNA to that contained in the amino acid sequence of proteins. **17.4** apply An incorrect amino acid would appear often in proteins. This is because the altered synthetase would sometimes add the correct amino acid for a particular tRNA and at other

---

**FIGURE A16.1**

mRNA sequence:
5′ AUG-CUG-GAG-GGG-GUU-AGA-CAU 3′

Amino acid sequence:
Met-Leu-Glu-Gly-Val-Arg-His

**FIGURE A16.2**

Bottom DNA strand:
3′ AACTT-TAC(start)-GGG-CAA-ACC-TCT-AGC-CCA-ATG-TCG-ATC(stop)-AGTTTC 5′

mRNA sequence:
5′ AUG-CCC-GUU-UGG-AGA-UCG-GGU-UAC-AGC-UAG 3′

Amino acid sequence:
Met-Pro-Val-Trp-Arg-Ser-Gly-Tyr-Ser

times add the incorrect amino acid. **17.5** create One possible concept map is shown in **FIGURE A17.1**.

#### YOU SHOULD BE ABLE TO . . .

✔ **Test Your Knowledge**

**1.** understand c **2.** remember c **3.** understand To speed the correct folding of newly synthesized proteins **4.** remember d **5.** remember At the 3′ end **6.** apply b

✔ **Test Your Understanding**

**7.** understand Basal transcription factors bind to promoter sequences in eukaryotic DNA and facilitate the binding of RNA polymerase. As part of the RNA polymerase holoenzyme, sigma binds to a promoter sequence in bacterial DNA and to allow RNA polymerase to initiate at the start of genes. **8.** analyze The wobble rules allow a single tRNA to pair with more than one type of mRNA codon. This is distinct from redundancy, in which more than one codon can specify a single amino acid. If the wobble rules did not exist, there would need to be one tRNA for each amino-acid-specifying codon in the redundant genetic code. **9.** apply b **10.** apply After a peptide bond forms between the polypeptide and the amino acid held by the tRNA in the A site, the ribosome moves down the mRNA. As it does, an uncharged tRNA leaves the E site. The now-uncharged tRNA that was in the P site enters the E site; the tRNA holding the polypeptide chain moves from the A site to the P site, and a new aminoacyl tRNA enters the A site. **11.** apply The ribosome's active site is made up of RNA, not protein. **12.** understand The separation allows the aminoacyl tRNA to place the amino acid into the ribosome's active site while reaching to the distant codon on the mRNA.

✔ **Test Your Problem-Solving Skills**

**13.** create Ribonucleases degrade mRNAs that are no longer needed by the cell. If an mRNA for a hormone that increased heart rate were never degraded, the hormone would be produced continuously and heart rate would stay elevated—a dangerous situation. **14.** apply d **15.** analyze The regions most crucial to the ribosome's function should be the most highly conserved: the active site, the E, P, and A sites, and the site where mRNAs initially bind. **16.** analyze The most likely locations are one of the grooves or channels where RNA, DNA, and ribonucleotides move through the enzyme—plugging one of them would prevent transcription.

## CHAPTER 19

### IN-TEXT QUESTIONS AND EXERCISES

**p. 352 Fig. 19.4** analyze Acetylation of histones decondenses chromatin and allows transcription to begin, so HATs are elements in positive control. Deacetylation condenses chromatin and inactivates transcription, so HDACs are elements in negative control.
**p. 353 CYU (1)** apply Many more genes than normal are predicted to be expressed because the inability to methylate DNA would lead to more decondensed chromatin.
**(2)** understand Addition of acetyl groups to histones or methyl groups to DNA can cause chromatin to decondense or condense, respectively. Different patterns of acetylation or methylation will determine which genes in muscle cells versus brain cells can be transcribed and which are not available for transcription.
**p. 353 Fig. 19.5** create They could do something to change histone modifications to see how this affects gene transcription instead of just making the observation that certain histone modifications and low rates of transcription go together.
**p. 355 Fig. 19.6** analyze A typical eukaryotic gene usually contains introns and is regulated by multiple enhancers. Bacterial operons lack introns and enhancers. The

promoter-proximal element found in some eukaryotic genes is comparable to the *araC* binding site in the *ara* operon of bacteria. Bacterial operons have a single promoter but code for more than one protein; eukaryotic genes code for a single product.
**p. 356** analyze The basal transcription factors found in muscle and nerve cells are similar or identical; the regulatory transcription factors found in each cell type are different.
**p. 356** understand DNA forms loops when distant regulatory regions, such as silencers and enhancers, are brought close to the promoter through binding of regulatory transcription factors to mediator.
**p. 356 CYU (1)** analyze Bacterial regulatory sequences are found close to the promoter; eukaryotic regulatory sequences can be close to the promoter or far from it. Bacterial regulatory proteins interact directly with RNA polymerase to initiate or prevent transcription; eukaryotic regulatory proteins influence transcription by altering chromatin structure or binding to the basal transcription complex through mediator proteins.
**(2)** understand Certain regulatory proteins decondense chromatin at muscle- or brain-specific genes and then activate or repress the transcription of cell-type-specific genes. Muscle-specific genes are expressed only if muscle-specific regulatory proteins are produced and activated.
**p. 358** understand Alternative splicing does not occur in bacteria because bacterial genes do not contain introns—in bacteria, each gene codes for a single product. Alternative splicing is part of step 3 in Figure 19.1.

**p. 359** remember Step 4 and step 5. RNA interference either **(1)** decreases the life span of mRNAs or **(2)** inhibits translation.
**p. 360 CYU (1)** understand It became clear that a single gene can code for multiple products instead of a single one.
**(2)** understand The miRNAs interfere with mRNAs by targeting them for destruction or preventing them from being translated.
**p. 362 CYU (1)** understand Many different types of mutations can disrupt control of the cell cycle and initiate cancer. These mutations can affect any of the six levels of control over gene regulation outlined in Figure 19.1.
**(2)** understand The p53 protein is responsible for shutting down the cell cycle in cells with damaged DNA. If the protein does not function, then cells with damaged DNA—and thus many mutations—continue to divide. If these cells have mutations in genes that regulate the cell cycle, then they may continue to divide in an uncontrolled fashion.

### IF YOU UNDERSTAND . . .

**19.1** understand Because eukaryotic RNAs are not translated as soon as transcription occurs, it is possible for RNA processing to occur, which creates variation in the mRNAs produced from a primary RNA transcript and in their life spans. **19.2** understand The default state of eukaryotic genes is "off," because the highly condensed state of the chromatin makes DNA unavailable to RNA polymerase. **19.3** understand See **FIGURE A19.1**. **19.4** understand Alternative splicing makes it possible for a single gene to

**FIGURE A17.1**

**FIGURE A19.1**

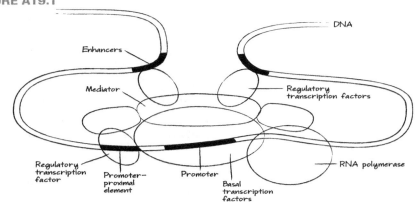

code for multiple products. **19.5** [analyze] One difference is that, in bacteria, genes that need to be turned on together are often clustered together in operons. Eukaryotes do not use operons. A similarity is in the way eukaryotes turn on many genes together and the strategy of bacterial regulons. Here, genes that are in many different locations share a DNA regulatory sequence and are activated when a regulatory transcription factor binds to the regulatory sequence. **19.6** [understand] In mutant cells that lack a form of p53 that can bind to enhancers, DNA damage cannot arrest the cell cycle, the cell cannot kill itself, and damaged DNA is replicated. This leads to mutations that can move the cell farther down the road to cancer.

## YOU SHOULD BE ABLE TO . . .

### ✓ Test Your Knowledge

[remember] c **2.** [remember] A tumor suppressor is a gene or protein that holds cell division in check unless conditions are right for the cell to divide. **3.** [understand] d [remember] The set of regulatory transcription factors present in a particular cell, not differences in DNA sequence, are largely responsible for which genes are expressed. **5.** [remember] b **6.** [remember] d

### ✓ Test Your Understanding

[analyze] (a) Enhancers and the *araC* site are similar because both are sites in DNA where regulatory proteins bind. They are different because enhancers generally are located at great distances from the promoter, whereas the *araC* site is located nearer the promoter. (b) Promoter-proximal elements and the *lac* operon operator are both regulatory sites in DNA located close to the promoter. (c) Basal transcription factors and sigma are proteins that must bind to the promoter before RNA polymerase can initiate transcription. They differ because sigma is part of the RNA polymerase holoenzyme, while the basal transcription complex recruits RNA polymerase to the promoter. **8.** [understand] If changes in the environment cause changes in how spliceosomes function, then the RNAs and proteins produced from a particular gene could change in a way that helps the cell cope with the new environmental conditions. **9.** [analyze] Enhancers and silencers are both regulatory sequences located at a distance from the promoter. Enhancers bind regulatory proteins that activate transcription; silencers bind regulatory proteins that shut down transcription. (b) Promoter-proximal elements and enhancers are both regulatory sequences that bind positive regulatory transcription factors. Promoter-proximal elements are located close to the promoter; enhancers are far from the promoter. Transcription factors bind to regulatory sites in DNA; mediator does not bind to DNA but instead forms a bridge between regulatory transcription factors and

basal transcription factors. **10.** [apply] Inhibition of a histone deacetylase is predicted to leave acetyl groups on histones longer than normal. This is predicted to keep gene transcription going longer than normal, leading to higher levels of particular proteins and a change in the phenotype of the cell. **11.** [analyze] c; this is because there are many more modifications in the histone code relative to the genetic code. **12.** [apply] The cell is predicted to arrest in the cell cycle and most likely will commit suicide through activation of apoptosis genes because of the continually active *p53*.

### ✓ Test Your Problem-Solving Skills

**13.** [apply] c; This is because promoters and enhancers are brought into close physical proximity when transcription begins (see Figure 19.8). Since rats of malnourished mothers initiate *Hnf4a* gene transcription infrequently, the promoter and enhancer will be together less often in these animals compared with rats born to well-nourished mothers. **14.** [understand] See **FIGURE A19.2**. The value for the normal diet should be shown as 1.0 and the value for the low-protein diet should be shown as 0.64 (0.64 comes from the ratio of the cpm of the low-protein diet divided by the cpm of the normal diet, or 7368/11,478). **15.** [create] You could treat a culture of DNA-damaged cells with a drug that stops transcription and then compare them with untreated DNA-damaged cells. If transcriptional control regulates p53 levels, then the p53 level would be lower in the treated cells versus control cells. If control of p53 levels is post-translational, then in both cultures the p53 level would be the same. *Other approaches:* Add labeled NTPs to damaged cells and see if they are incorporated into mRNAs for p53; or add labeled amino acids to damaged cells and see if they are incorporated into completed p53 proteins; or add labeled phosphate groups and see if they are added to p53 proteins. **16.** [create] The double-stranded RNA could be cut by the same enzyme that creates double-stranded miRNAs from miRNA precursors. This double-stranded RNA may be incorporated into RISC and converted into a single-stranded RNA. The single-stranded RNA held by RISC would work in RNA interference to trigger the destruction of the complementary viral mRNA.

## BIG PICTURE Genetic Information

**p. 366 CYU (1)** [remember] Star = DNA, mRNA, proteins. **(2)** [understand] RNA "is reverse transcribed by" reverse transcriptase "to form" DNA. **(3)** [analyze] E = splicing, etc.; E = meiosis and sexual reproduction (along with their links). **(4)** [analyze] Chromatin "makes up" chromosomes; independent assortment and recombination "contribute to" high genetic diversity.

## CHAPTER 20

### IN-TEXT QUESTIONS AND EXERCISES

**p. 372** [understand] Isolate the DNA and cut it into small fragments with EcoRI, which leaves sticky ends. Cut copies of a plasmid or other vector with EcoRI. Mix the fragments and plasmids under conditions that promote complementary base pairing by sticky ends of fragments and plasmids. Use DNA ligase to catalyze formation of phosphodiester bonds and seal the sequences.
**p. 372 Fig. 20.4** [apply] No—many times, because many copies of each type of mRNA were present in the pituitary cells, and many pituitary cells were used to prepare the library.
**p. 373** [apply] The probe must be single stranded so that it will bind by complementary base pairing to the target DNA, and it must be labeled so that it can be detected. The probe will base-pair only with fragments that include a sequence complementary to the probe's sequence. A probe with the sequence 5′ AATCG 3′ will

bind to the region of the target DNA that has the sequence 5′ CGATT 3′ as shown here:

5′ AATCG 3′
3′ TCCGGTTAGCATTACCATTTT 5′

**p. 374 CYU (1)** [understand] When the endonuclease makes a staggered cut in a palindromic sequence and the strands separate, the single-stranded bases that are left will bind ("stick") to the single-stranded bases left where the endonuclease cut the same palindrome at a different location. **(2)** [understand] The word probe means to examine thoroughly. A DNA probe "examines" a large set of sequences thoroughly and binds to one—the one that has a complementary base sequence.
**p. 375 Fig. 20.7** [analyze] The polymerase will begin at the 3′ end of each primer. On the top strand in part (b), it will move to the left; on the bottom strand, it will move to the right. As always, synthesis is in the 5′-to-3′ direction.
**p. 376 CYU (1)** [understand] Denaturation makes DNA single stranded so the primer can bind to the sequence during the annealing step. Once the primer is in place, *Taq* polymerase can synthesize the rest of the strand during the extension step. It is a "chain reaction" because the products of each reaction cycle are used in the next reaction cycle—this is why the number of copies doubles in each cycle. **(2)** [apply] One of many possible answers is shown in **FIGURE A20.1**.
**p. 378 CYU** [understand] If ddNTPs were present at high concentration, they would almost always be incorporated—meaning that only fragments from the first complementary base in the sequence would be produced.
**p. 379** [understand] Using a map with many markers makes it more likely that there will be one marker that is very tightly linked to the gene of interest—meaning that a form of the marker will almost always be associated with the phenotype you are tracking.
**p. 382 CYU** [create] Start with a genetic map with as many polymorphic markers as possible. Determine the genotype at these markers for a large number of individuals who have the same type of alcoholism—one that is thought to have a genetic component—as well as a large number of unaffected individuals. Look for particular versions of a marker that is almost always found in affected individuals. Genes that contribute to a predisposition to alcoholism will be near that marker.
**p. 383 Fig. 20.11** [apply] The insertion will probably disrupt the gene and have serious consequences for the cell and potentially the individual.

### IF YOU UNDERSTAND . . .

**20.1** [understand] Special features of DNA are needed to allow replication in a cell. It is unlikely that any DNA fragment generated by cutting the DNA of one species with a restriction enzyme would replicate when inserted into a bacterial cell. By placing DNA fragments within plasmids that normally replicate in a bacterial cell, the inserted DNA can be replicated along with the plasmid.
**20.2** [analyze] Advantages of cloning in cells: No knowledge of the sequence is required. Disadvantages of cloning in cells: It is slower and technically more difficult than PCR. PCR advantages: It is fast and easy, and it can amplify a DNA sequence that is rare in the sample. PCR disadvantage: It requires knowledge of sequences on either side of the target gene, so primers can be designed.
**20.3** [understand] The length of each fragment is dictated by where a ddNTP was incorporated into the growing strand, and each ddNTP corresponds to a base on the template strand. Thus the sequence of fragment sizes corresponds to the sequence on the template DNA.
**20.4** [understand] In this case, both affected and unaffected individuals would have the same marker, so there would be no way to associate a particular form of the marker with the gene and phenotype you are interested in.
**20.5** [understand] An advantage of using retrovirus vectors is that any foreign genes they carry are integrated into

**FIGURE A19.2**

Relative Hnf4a transcription levels — y-axis from 0 to 1.2; bars for Normal (1.0) and Low-protein (~0.64).

human chromosomes, so delivered genes become a permanent feature of the cell's genome. The concern is that they may integrate at sites that alter gene function in ways that harm cell function, or even worse, lead to cancer. **20.6** [understand] Genes can be inserted into the Ti plasmids carried by *Agrobacterium*, and the recombinant plasmids transferred to plant cells infected by the bacterium.

### YOU SHOULD BE ABLE TO . . .

#### ✔ Test Your Knowledge

**1.** [understand] They cut DNA at specific sites, known as recognition sites, to produce DNA fragments useful for cloning. **2.** [remember] b **3.** [understand] ddNTPs lack the —OH (hydroxyl) group on the 3′ carbon of deoxyribose sugar that is required to extend the DNA chain during synthesis. **4.** [understand] a **5.** [remember] b **6.** [understand] d

#### ✔ Test Your Understanding

**7.** [understand] When a restriction endonuclease cuts a "foreign gene" sequence and a plasmid, the same sticky ends are created on the excised foreign gene and the cut plasmid. After the sticky ends on the foreign gene and the plasmid anneal, DNA ligase catalyzes closure of the DNA backbone, sealing the foreign gene into the plasmid DNA (see **FIGURE A20.2**). **8.** [apply] If the DNA at each cycle steadily doubles, it is predicted to yield a 33.6 million-fold increase (a $2^{25}$-fold increase). **9.** [understand] A cDNA library is a collection of complementary DNAs made from all the mRNAs present in a certain group of cells. A cDNA library from a human nerve cell would be different from one made from a human muscle cell, because nerve cells and muscle cells express many different genes that are specific to their cell type. **10.** [remember] Genetic markers are genes or other loci that have known locations in the genome. When these locations are diagrammed, they represent the physical

relationships between landmarks—in other words, they form a map. **11.** [understand] d; these regulatory sequences promote expression of introduced genes in the endosperm—the rice grain eaten as food. **12.** [analyze] PCR and cellular DNA synthesis are similar in the sense of producing copies of a template DNA. Both rely on primers and DNA polymerase. The major difference between the two is that PCR copies only a specific target sequence, but the entire genome is copied during cellular DNA synthesis.

#### ✔ Test Your Problem-Solving Skills

**13.** [create] You could use a computer program to identify likely promoter sequences in the sequence data and then look for sequences just downstream that have an AUG start codon and codons that could be part of the protein-coding exons of a potential protein about 500 amino acids (500 codons or 1500 bases) long. **14.** [analyze] False. Since somatic-cell modifications cannot be passed on to future generations, but germ-line modifications may be passed on to offspring, germ-line modification opens a new set of ethical questions. **15.** [analyze] In both techniques, researchers use an indicator to identify either a gene of interest or a colony of bacteria with a particular trait. The problem is the same—picking one particular thing (a certain gene or a cell with a particular mutation) out of a large collection. **16.** [analyze] (a) Primer 1b binds to the top right strand and would allow DNA polymerase to synthesize the top strand across the target gene. Primer 1a, however, binds to the upper left strand and would allow DNA polymerase to synthesize the upper strand *away* from the target gene. Primer 2a binds to the bottom left strand and would allow DNA polymerase to synthesize the bottom strand across the target gene. Primer 2b, however, binds to the bottom right strand and would allow DNA polymerase to synthesize away from the target gene. (b) She could use primer 1b with primer 2a.

### IN-TEXT QUESTIONS AND EXERCISES

**p. 410 CYU** [understand] Biologists have been able to grow entire plants from a single differentiated cell taken from an adult. They have also succeeded in producing animals by transferring the nucleus of a fully differentiated cell to an egg whose nucleus has been removed.

**p. 411 Fig. 22.4** [apply] Anterior structures are predicted to be shifted farther back in the embryo, since higher-than-normal levels of the anterior-specifying Bicoid protein would be present in posterior regions.

**p. 412 Fig. 22.6** [apply] Since Bicoid is located in the anterior cytoplasm and works to turn on genes that produce anterior structures, a prediction is that this manipulation would create a concentration gradient of Bicoid with its highest point in the middle of the mutant embryo. This would lead to the most anterior-like structures in the center of the embryo and more posterior structures forming on either side.

**p. 414 Fig. 22.10** [create] Genes are usually considered homologous if they have similar DNA sequence and exon–intron structure.

**p. 415 CYU (1)** [understand] Bicoid is a transcription factor, and cells that experience a high versus medium versus low concentrations of Bicoid express Bicoid-regulated genes at different levels. **(2)** [understand] Bicoid proteins control the expression of gap genes, which—in effect—tell cells which third of the embryo they are in along the anterior–posterior axis. Gap genes control the expression of pair-rule genes, which organize the embryo into individual segments. Pair-rule genes control expression of segment polarity genes, which establish an anterior-posterior polarity to each individual segment. Segment polarity genes turn on homeotic genes, which then trigger genes for producing segment-specific structures like wings or legs.

### IF YOU UNDERSTAND . . .

**22.1** [apply] The seedling would be misshapen because controlling the plane of cleavage is essential for formation of normal structures in plants. **22.2.** [understand] Cells in the stem contain a complete set of genes, so if they can be de-differentiated and receive appropriate signals from other cells, they could differentiate into any cell type and cooperate to form any structure of the plant, including roots. **22.3** [analyze] Because segmentation genes work in a cascade, mutation of a pair-rule gene is expected to influence the expression of genes in the next level, segment polarity genes, but not affect the expression of earlier acting genes, such as gap genes. **22.4** [apply] This procedure is predicted to lead to the loss of limbs because the regulatory sequence replacement will cause the regions of expression of *Hoxc8* and *Hoxc6* to overlap.

### YOU SHOULD BE ABLE TO . . .

#### ✔ Test Your Knowledge

**1.** [remember] b **2.** [remember] stem cells **3.** [understand] a **4.** [remember] True **5.** [remember] a **6.** [remember] a conserved gene that can be expressed at different times and places during development to produce different types of structures in different organisms.

#### ✔ Test Your Understanding

**7.** [understand] They occur in both plants and animals, and are responsible for the changes that occur as an embryo develops. **8.** [understand] If an adult cell used for cloning had some permanent change or loss of genetic information during development, it should not be able to direct the development of a viable adult. But if the adult cell is genetically equivalent to a fertilized egg, then it should

---

**FIGURE A20.1**

5′ CATGACTATTACGTATCGGGTACTATGCTATCGATCTAGCTACGCTAGCT 3′
3′ GTACTGATAATGCATAGCCCATGATACGATAGCTAGATCGATGCGATCGA 5′

Primer #1, which will anneal to the 3′ end of the top strand:

5′ AGCTAGCGTAGCTAGATCGAT 3′

Primer #2, which will anneal to the 3′ end of the bottom strand:

5′ CATGACTATTACGTATCGGGT 3′

The primers will bind to the separated strands of the parent DNA sequence as follows:

5′ CATGACTATTACGTATCGGGTACTATGCTATCGATCTAGCTACGCTAGCT 3′
                                    3′ TAGCTAGATCGATGCGATCGA 5′

5′ CATGACTATTACGTATCGGGT 3′
3′ GTACTGATAATGCATAGCCCATGATACGATAGCTAGATCGATGCGATCGA 5′

**FIGURE A20.2**

Sticky ends on cut plasmid and gene to be inserted are complementary and can base pair

DNA ligase forms four phosphodiester bonds between gene and plasmid DNA at the points indicated by arrows

be capable of directing the development of a new individual. **9.** (understand) The researchers exposed adult flies to treatments that induce mutations and then looked for embryos with defects in the anterior–posterior body axis or body segmentation. The embryos had mutations in genes required for body axis formation and segmentation. **10.** (understand) Development—specifically differentiation—depends on changes in gene expression. Changes in gene expression depend on differences in regulatory transcription factors. **11.** (create) Differentiation is triggered by the production of transcription factors, which induce other transcription factors, and so on—a sequence that constitutes a regulatory cascade—as development progresses. At each step in the cascade, a new subset of genes is activated—resulting in a step-by-step progression from undifferentiated to fully differentiated cells. **12.** (analyze) c. This result shows that a mouse tool-kit gene is similar enough (conserved) to a fly gene to be able to take over its function.

#### ✔ Test Your Problem-Solving Skills

**13.** (apply) There would be more Bicoid protein farther toward the posterior and less in the anterior—meaning that the anterior segments would be "less anterior" in their characteristics and the posterior segments would be "more anterior." **14.** (analyze) The result means that the human gene was expressed in worms and that its protein product has performed the same function in worms as in humans. This is strong evidence that the genes are homologous and that their function has been evolutionarily conserved. **15.** (apply) c. Since the morphogen concentration is halved every 100 μm away from the posterior pole, dropping to 1/16 the highest concentration would require 4 "halvings" of the initial concentration ($1/2 \times 1/2 \times 1/2 \times 1/2 = 1/16$), and this would take place in 4 steps of 100 μm each—or 400 μm from the morphogen source. This is where the leg is predicted to be formed. **16.** (create) Tool-kit genes—such as *Hox* genes—are responsible for triggering the production of structures like wings or legs in particular segments. One hypothesis to explain the variation is that changes in gene expression of tool-kit genes led to different numbers of segments that express leg-forming *Hox* genes.

## CHAPTER 28

### IN-TEXT QUESTIONS AND EXERCISES

**p. 507 Fig. 28.1** (apply) Many trees are possible. See **FIGURE A28.1.**

**p. 510** (understand) Because whales and hippos share SINEs 4–7 and no other species has these four, they are synapomorphies that define them as a monophyletic group. The similarity is unlikely to be due to homoplasy because the chance of four SINEs inserting in exactly the same place in two different species, independently, is very small. **p. 510 CYU** (analyze) Hair and limb structures in humans and whales are examples of homology because they are traits that can be traced to a common ancestor. All mammals have hair and similar limb bone structure. However, extensive hair loss and advanced social behavior in whales and humans are examples of homoplasy. These traits are not common to all mammalian species and likely arose independently during the evolution of specific mammalian lineages. **p. 511 Fig. 28.4** (apply) See **FIGURE A28.2.** SINEs group (19, 20) identifies peccaries and pigs as a monophyletic group. **p. 513** (apply) Since some organisms fossilize better than others—such as mollusks with hard shells—a paleontologist would be mistaken to conclude that mollusks were more abundant than other organisms at a certain time just because mollusks are more abundant in the fossil

record. Similarly, a paleontologist would be mistaken to conclude that no organisms occupied an ancient desert based on the lack of fossil evidence; organisms in deserts do not fossilize well. Several other examples are possible. **p. 517** (create) In habitats on the mainland, complex communities have been established for a long time, so tarweeds in California and *Anolis* lizards on the mainland experience greater competition for resources and are limited to specific niches. **p. 520 CYU** (understand) In terms of ecological opportunity, many resources were available because no other animals (or other types of organisms) existed to exploit them. Also, the evolution of new species in new niches made new niches available for predators. Morphological innovations like limbs and complex mouthparts were important because they made it possible for animals to live in habitats other than the benthic area, and to consume new types of food. **p. 520 Fig. 28.14** (analyze) The dinosaurs went extinct during the end-Cretaceous. About 15 percent of families went extinct.

### IF YOU UNDERSTAND . . .

**28.1** (apply) Humans are the only mammal that walks upright on two legs, so this character is a synapomorphy that defines the hominins. **28.2** (apply) Snail shells are hard structures, and snails often live in marine environments that fossilize readily, so snail fossils are relatively abundant. Abundant fossils are more helpful than rare fossils for estimating changes in relative abundance over time. **28.3** (analyze) They could eat food that was available off the substrate. And once animals lived off (and away from) the bottom, it created an opportunity for other animals who could eat them to evolve. **28.4** (evaluate) This statement is false. Human-induced extinctions today are not due to poor adaptation to the normal environment. Humans are changing habitats rapidly and in unusual ways (such as clear-cutting forests), so most species cannot adapt to these changes rapidly enough to avoid going extinct. In this way, human-induced extinctions are more similar to mass extinctions than to background extinctions.

### YOU SHOULD BE ABLE TO . . .

#### ✔ Test Your Knowledge

**1.** (remember) c **2.** (understand) a **3.** (understand) b **4.** (understand) False **5.** (understand) d **6.** (remember) True

#### ✔ Test Your Understanding

**1.** (evaluate) The fossil record is biased because recent, abundant organisms with hard parts that live underground or in environments where sediments are being deposited are most likely to fossilize. Even so, it is the only data available on what organisms that lived in the past looked like, and where they lived. **2.** (create) An enormous amount of animal diversity appeared in a time frame that was short compared to the sweep of earlier Earth history. The most common analogy is to an explosion, referring to the sudden and spectacular radiation of lineages. Another analogy is your hand, where one line (your arm) comes into a node (your palm) and several lineages (your fingers) come out. Many other answers are possible. **3.** (understand) Homoplasy is rare relative to homology, so phylogenetic trees that minimize the total change required are usually more accurate. In the case of the artiodactyl astragalus, parsimony was misleading because the astragalus was lost when whales evolved limblessness—creating two changes (a loss following a gain) instead of one (a gain). **4.** (create) (Many answers are possible.) Adaptive radiation of *Anolis* lizards after they colonized new islands in the Caribbean. *Hypothesis:* After lizards arrived on each new island, where there were no predators or competitors, they rapidly diversified to occupy four distinct types of habitats on each island. Adaptive radiation during the Cambrian period

following a morphological innovation. *Hypothesis:* Additional *Hox* genes made it possible to organize a large, complex body; the evolution of complex mouthparts and limbs made it possible for animals to move and find food in new ways. **5.** (apply) About 90 percent of species went extinct during the end-Permian, so about 10 percent survived, written as 0.1 in decimals. $1880 \times 0.1 = 188$ would make it to graduation. **6.** (apply) d

#### ✔ Test Your Problem-Solving Skills

**1.** (understand) b **2.** (evaluate) Many trees are possible. See **FIGURE A28.3.** Sponges are the outgroup. The most parsimonious tree has the fewest number of changes (five in this case). Adding more characters to the matrix can improve the reliability of the results. **3.** (understand) It would be helpful to have (1) a large crater or other physical evidence from a major impact dated at 251 mya, (2) shocked quartz and microtektites in rock layers dating to the end-Permian era, and (3) high levels of iridium or other elements common in space rocks and rare on Earth, dated to the time of the extinctions. **4.** (create) Many concept map topologies are possible. Maps should follow this logic: Oxygen is an effective final electron acceptor in cellular respiration because of its high electronegativity. Organisms that use it as a final electron acceptor can produce more usable energy than organisms that do not use oxygen, but only if it is available. With more available energy, aerobic organisms can grow larger and move faster.

### BIG PICTURE Evolution

**p. 526 CYU (1)** (understand) Circle = inbreeding, sexual selection, nonrandom mating, natural selection, genetic drift,

**FIGURE A28.1**

**FIGURE A28.2**

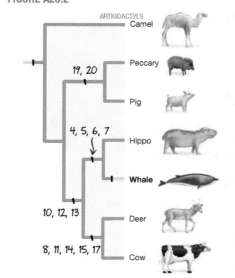

mutation, and gene flow. **(2)** `analyze` Adaptation "increases" fitness; synapomorphies "identify branches on" the tree of life. **(3)** `analyze` Several answers possible, e.g., adaptive radiations and mass extinctions → can be studied using → the fossil record. **(4)** `analyze` Genetic drift, mutation, and gene flow "are random with respect to" fitness.

# CHAPTER 29

## IN-TEXT QUESTIONS AND EXERCISES

**p. 529 Fig. 29.1** `analyze` Prokaryotic—it would require just one evolutionary change, the origin of the nuclear envelope in Eukarya. If it were eukaryotic, it would require that the nuclear envelope was lost in both Bacteria and Archaea—two changes are less parsimonious (see Chapter 28).

**p. 529 Table 29.1** `apply` See **FIGURE A29.2**.

**p. 534 Fig. 29.5** `analyze` Weak—different culture conditions may have revealed different species.

**p. 535 CYU (1)** `create` Conditions should mimic a spill—sand or stones with a layer of crude oil, or seawater with oil floating on top. Add samples, from sites contaminated with oil, that might contain cells capable of using molecules in oil as electron donors or electron acceptors. Other conditions (temperature, pH, etc.) should be realistic. **(2)** `create` Use metagenomic analysis. After isolating DNA from a soil sample, fragment and sequence the DNA. Compare the sequences to those from known organisms and use the data to place the species on the tree of life.

**p. 538** `apply` cyanobacteria—photoautotrophs; *Clostridium aceticum*—chemoorganoautotroph; *Nitrosopumilus* sp.—chemolithoautotrophs; helicobacteria— photoheterotrophs; *Escherichia coli*—chemoorganoheterotroph; *Beggitoa*—chemolithotrophic heterotrophs.

**p. 539 Fig. 29.10** `apply` Table 29.5 contains the answers. For example, for organisms called sulfate reducers you would have $H_2$ as the electron donor, $SO_4^{2-}$ as the electron acceptor, and $H_2S$ as the reduced by-product. For humans the electron donor is glucose ($C_6H_{12}O_6$), the electron acceptor is $O_2$, and the reduced by-product is water ($H_2O$).

**p. 541** `understand` Different species of bacteria that have different forms of bacterial chlorophyll will not absorb the same wavelengths of light and will therefore not compete.

**p. 542 Fig. 29.12** `apply` Aerobic respiration. More free energy is released when oxygen is the final electron acceptor than when any other molecule is used, so more ATP can be produced and used for growth.

**p. 543** `apply` If bacteria and archaea did not exist, then (1) the atmosphere would have little or no oxygen, and (2) almost all nitrogen would exist in molecular form (the gas $N_2$).

**p. 543 Fig. 29.13** `apply` Add a label for "animals" in the upper right quarter of the circle, and draw arrows leading from "Organic compounds with amino groups" to "animals" and from "animals" to "$NH_3$."

**p. 544 CYU** `evaluate` Eukaryotes can only (1) fix carbon via the Calvin–Benson pathway, (2) use aerobic respiration with organic compounds as electron donors, and (3) perform oxygenic photosynthesis. Among bacteria and archaea, there is much more diversity in pathways for carbon fixation, respiration, and photosynthesis, along with many more fermentation pathways.

**p. 545a, p. 545b, p. 546a, p. 546b, p. 547** `apply` See **FIGURE A29.1**.

**p. 548 Fig. 29.21** `apply` About 600,000 *N. maritimus* cells would fit end to end on a meter stick.

## IF YOU UNDERSTAND . . .

**29.1** `analyze` Eukaryotes have a nuclear envelope that encloses their chromosomes; bacteria and archaea do not. Bacteria have cell walls that contain peptidoglycan, and archaea have phospholipids containing isoprene subunits in their plasma membranes. Thus, the exteriors of a bacterium and archaeon are radically different. Archaea and eukaryotes also have similar machinery for processing genetic information. **29.2** `apply` After extracting and sequencing DNA from bacteria that live in an insect gut, analyze the resulting sequences for genes that are similar to known genes involved in nitrogen fixation. **29.3** `understand` They are compatible, and thrive in each others' presence—one species' waste product is the other species' food.

## YOU SHOULD BE ABLE TO . . .

### ✔ Test Your Knowledge

**1.** `understand` c **2.** `remember` b **3.** `remember` d **4.** `remember` d **5.** `remember` False—the enzyme nitrogenase is poisoned by oxygen. **6.** `remember` peptidoglycan

### ✔ Test Your Understanding

**1.** `understand` c **2.** `understand` An electron donor provides the potential energy required to produce ATP. **3.** `evaluate` Yes. The array of substances that bacteria and archaea can use as electron donors, electron acceptors, and fermentation substrates, along with the diversity of ways that they can fix carbon and perform photosynthesis, allows them to live just about anywhere. **4.** `apply` They should get energy from reduced organic compounds "stolen" from their hosts. **5.** `understand` Large amounts of potential energy are released and ATP produced when oxygen is the electron acceptor, because oxygen is so electronegative.

---

**FIGURE A28.3**

**FIGURE A29.1**

**FIGURE A29.2**

Large body size and high growth rates are not possible without large amounts of ATP. **6.** [understand] They are paraphyletic because the prokaryotes include some (bacteria and archaea) but not all (eukaryotes) groups derived from the common ancestor of all organisms living today.

### ✓ Test Your Problem-Solving Skills

**1.** [understand] c (It is pathogenic on a wide variety of organisms). **2.** [analyze] This result supports their hypothesis because the drug poisons the enzymes of the electron transport chain and prevents electron transfer to $Fe^{3-}$, which is required to drive magnetite synthesis. If magnetite had still formed, another explanation would have been needed. **3.** [create] Hypothesis: A high rate of tooth cavities in Western children is due to an excess of sucrose in the diet, which is absent from the diets of East African children. To test this hypothesis, switch a group of East African children to a diet that contains sucrose, switch a group of Western children to a diet lacking sucrose, and monitor the presence of *S. mutans* in both groups of children. **4.** [create] Look in waters or soil polluted with benzene-containing compounds. Put samples from these environments in culture tubes where benzene is the only source of carbon. Monitor the cultures and study the cells that grow efficiently.

## CHAPTER 30

### IN-TEXT QUESTIONS AND EXERCISES

**p. 529 CYU (1)** [understand] Opisthokonts have a flagellum at the base or back of the cell; alveolate cells contain unique support structures called alveoli; stramenopiles—meaning "straw hairs"—have straw-like hairs on their flagella. **(2)** [understand] In direct sequencing, DNA is isolated directly from the environment and analyzed to place species on the tree of life. It is not necessary to actually see the species being studied.
**p. 557 CYU (1)** [understand] *Plasmodium* species are transmitted to humans by mosquitoes. If mosquitoes can be prevented from biting people, they cannot spread the disease. **(2)** [apply] Iron added → primary producers (photosynthetic protists and bacteria) bloom → more carbon dioxide taken up from atmosphere during photosynthesis → consumers bloom, eat primary producers → bodies of primary producers and consumers fall to bottom of ocean → large deposits of carbon-containing compounds form on ocean floor.
**p. 560** [apply] See FIGURE A30.1.
**p. 560 Fig. 30.8** [analyze] Two—one derived from the original bacterium and one derived from the eukaryotic cell that engulfed the bacterium.
**p. 561** [apply] A photosynthetic bacterium (e.g., a cyanobacterium) could have been engulfed by a larger eukaryotic cell. If it was not digested, it could continue to photosynthesize and supply sugars to the host cell.
**p. 562** [apply] Membrane infoldings observed in bacterial species today support the hypothesis's plausibility—they confirm that the initial steps actually could have happened. The continuity of the nuclear envelope and ER are consistent with the hypothesis, which predicts that the two structures are derived from the same source (infolded membranes).
**p. 564** [apply] The chloroplast genes label should come off of the branch that leads to cyanobacteria. (If you had a phylogeny of just the cyanobacteria, the chloroplast branch would be located somewhere inside.)
**p. 565** [analyze] The acquisition of the mitochondrion and the chloroplast represent the transfer of entire genomes, and not just single genes, to a new organism.
**p. 566** [apply] Yes—when food is scarce or population density is high, the environment is changing rapidly (deteriorating). Offspring that are genetically unlike their parents may be better able to cope with the new and challenging environment.

**p. 569a** [understand] (1) Alternation of generations refers to a life cycle in which there are multicellular haploid phases and multicellular diploid phases. A gametophyte is the multicellular haploid phase that produces gametes; the sporophyte is the multicellular diploid phase that produces spores. A spore is a cell that grows into a multicellular individual but is not produced by fusion of two cells. A zygote is a cell that grows into a multicellular individual but *is* produced by fusion of two cells (gametes). Gametes are haploid cells that fuse to form a zygote. (2) See FIGURE A30.2.
**p. 569b** [apply] Most likely, the two types of amoebae evolved independently. The alternative hypothesis is that the common ancestor of alveolates, stramenopiles, rhizarians, plants, opisthokonts, and amoebozoa were amoeboid and that this growth form was lost many times. See FIGURE A30.1.
**p. 569c, p. 569d, p. 569e, p. 570a, p. 570b, p. 570c** [apply] See FIGURE A30.1.
**p. 571** [analyze] If euglenids could take in food via phagocytosis (ingestive feeding), then that would have provided a mechanism by which a smaller photosynthetic protist could have been engulfed and incorporated into the cell via secondary endosymbiosis.
**p. 572a, p. 572b, p. 573, p 574.** [apply] See FIGURE A30.1.

### IF YOU UNDERSTAND . . .

**30.1** [understand] Photosynthetic protists use $CO_2$ and light to produce sugars and other organic compounds, so they furnish the first or primary source of organic material in an ecosystem. **30.2** [remember] Eukaryotic cells contain many organelles, including a nucleus, endomembrane system, and an extensive cytoskeleton. Most prokaryotic cells contain few or no organelles, and no nucleus or endomembrane system and lack a complex cytoskeleton. **30.3** [understand] (1) Outside membrane was from host eukaryote; inside from engulfed cyanobacterium. (2) From the outside in, the four membranes are derived from the eukaryote that engulfed a chloroplast-containing eukaryote, the plasma membrane of the eukaryote that was engulfed, the outer membrane of the engulfed cell's chloroplast, and the inner membrane of its chloroplast.

### YOU SHOULD BE ABLE TO . . .

### ✓ Test Your Knowledge

**1.** [understand] b **2.** [remember] b **3.** [remember] a **4.** [remember] b **5.** [remember] False. **6.** [remember] diatoms.

### ✓ Test Your Understanding

**1.** [understand] a **2.** [understand] Because all eukaryotes living today have cells with a nuclear envelope, it is valid to infer that their common ancestor also had a nuclear envelope. Because bacteria and archaea do not have a nuclear envelope, it is valid to infer that the trait arose in the common ancestor of eukaryotes. **3.** [understand] The host cell provided a protected environment and carbon compounds for the endosymbiont; the endosymbiont provided increased ATP from the carbon compounds **4.** [understand] It confirmed a fundamental prediction made by the hypothesis and could not be explained by any alternative hypothesis. **5.** [understand] All alveolates have alveoli, which are unique structures that function in supporting the cell. Among alveolates there are species that are (1) ingestive feeders, photosynthetic, or parasitic, and that (2) move using cilia, flagella, or a type of amoeboid movement.

### ✓ Test Your Problem-Solving Skills

**1.** [analyze] d **2.** [analyze] If the apicoplast that is found in *Plasmodium* (the organism that causes malaria) is genetically similar to chloroplasts, and if glyphosate poisons chloroplasts, it is reasonable to hypothesize that glyphosate will poison the apicoplast and potentially kill the *Plasmodium*. This would be a good treatment strategy

for malaria because humans have no chloroplasts, provided that the glyphosate produces no other effects that would be detrimental to humans. **3.** [evaluate] Primary producers usually grow faster when $CO_2$ concentration increases, but to date they have not grown fast enough to make $CO_2$ levels drop—$CO_2$ levels have been increasing steadily over decades. **4.** [analyze] Given that lateral gene transfer can occur at different points in a phylogenetic history, specific genes can become part of a lineage by a different route from that taken by other genes of the organism. In the case of chlorophyll *a*, its history traces back to a bacterium being engulfed by a protist and forming a chloroplast.

---

**FIGURE A30.1**

**FIGURE A30.2**

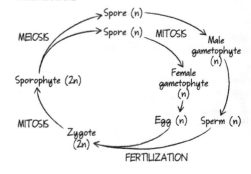

# CHAPTER 33

## IN-TEXT QUESTIONS AND EXERCISES

**p. 639 Fig. 33.2** `apply` The label and bar for "Segmentation?" should go on the branch to the left of the clam shell and "Mollusca" label. The label and bar for "Toolkit genes for segmentation?" should go on the same branch as cephalization, CNS, and coelom.

**p. 640** `apply` The genetic tool kit required for multicellularity includes genes that regulate the cell cycle, and thus cell division. When something goes wrong in this process, uncontrolled growth called cancer can result. Thus, cancer may be as ancient as multicellularity itself.

**p. 642 Fig. 33.7** `analyze` Stained *Hox* and *dpp* gene products would either not be found in *Nematostella* at all or would not occur in the same anterior–posterior and dorsal–ventral pattern as observed in bilaterians.

**p. 646 CYU (1)** `apply` Yes, your body has a tube-within-a-tube design. Humans are vertebrates, vertebrates are chordates, chordates are bilaterians, and all bilaterians have a tube-within-a-tube design, consisting of a bilaterally symmetrical, slender body with an inner tube (gut), an outer tube (mostly skin), muscles and organs derived from mesoderm in between, and one end (head) cephalized with sensory organs and brain. **(2)** `understand` When an animal moves through an environment in one direction, its ability to acquire food and perceive and respond to threats is greater if its feeding, sensing, and information-processing structures are at the leading end.

**p. 651 Fig. 33.14** `evaluate` The larva and metamorphosis arrow should be circled in the life cycle. It might be adaptive to skip the feeding larval stage if more food resources are available for the mother (who must expend energy to produce the yolk) than for the larva, if predation pressure on larvae is high, or if other environmental factors for larvae are unfavorable, resulting in high mortality of the larvae.

**p. 652 CYU (1)** `understand` The mouthparts of deposit feeders are relatively simple because these animals simply gulp relatively soft material. The mouthparts of mass feeders are more complex because they have to tear off and process chunks of relatively hard material. **(2)** `create` Gametes that are shed into aquatic environments can float or swim. This cannot happen on land, so internal fertilization is more common there. Also, gametes are more at risk of drying out on land, and internal fertilization eliminates that risk.

**p. 653** `apply` The origin of cilia-powered swimming should be marked on the Ctenophora branch.

**p. 654** `apply` The origin of cnidocytes should be marked on the Cnidaria branch.

## IF YOU UNDERSTAND . . .

**33.1** `apply` It should increase dramatically—animals would no longer be consuming plant material. **33.2** `understand` Your drawing should show the tube-within-a-tube design of a worm, with one end labeled head and containing the mouth and brain. From the brain, one or two major nerve tracts should run the length of the body. The gut should go from the mouth to the other end, ending in the anus. In between the gut and outer body wall, there should be blocks or layers of muscle. **33.3** `apply` There are many possible answers. For example, within the phylum Arthropoda: The sensory systems have diversified (e.g., eyes are important for sight in flies, antennae are important for smelling in moths); feeding strategies have diversified (e.g., butterflies are fluid feeders but caterpillars are mass feeders); ecological roles have diversified (e.g., butterflies are herbivores but spiders are carnivores); limbs have diversified (e.g., butterflies have legs and wings but caterpillars have lobe-like limbs); and some insects, like grasshoppers, have direct development whereas others, like mosquitoes, have indirect development. **33.4** `remember` If you see a

---

sessile, multicellular animal with no symmetry or radial symmetry, with outcurrent holes, and choanocytes, it is a sponge. If you see a radially symmetric, transparent, planktonic organism moving via rows of cilia, it is a ctenophore. If you see a diploblastic, outwardly radially symmetric animal that is either a single polyp or colony of multiple polyps, or it is a medusa, then the animal is a cnidarian.

## YOU SHOULD BE ABLE TO . . .

### ✔ Test Your Knowledge

**1.** `remember` a **2.** `remember` True **3.** `remember` protostomes, deuterostomes **4.** `understand` a **5.** `remember` d **6.** `remember` d

### ✔ Test Your Understanding

**1.** `understand` Diploblasts have two types of embryonic tissue (ectoderm, endoderm); triploblasts have three (ectoderm, mesoderm, endoderm). Mesoderm made it possible for an enclosed, mesoderm-lined cavity to develop, creating a coelom. **2.** `analyze` Many unicellular organisms are heterotrophic, but they can consume only small bits of food. Animals are multicellular, so they are larger and can consume larger amounts of food—making them important consumers in food webs. **3.** `apply` There are about 18.4 named arthropods for every named species of chordate (1,160,000/63,000), about 1.3 named mollusks for every named species of chordate (85,000/63,000), and about 0.4 named species of nematode worm for every named species of chordate (25,000/63,000). These numbers are likely to be underestimates because there are probably many more arthropods, mollusks, and nematode worms than have been described, yet relatively few of the larger, more familiar chordates (including vertebrates) left to be described. **4.** `understand` In oviparous species, the mother adds nutrient-rich yolk to the egg that nourishes the developing embryo. In viviparous species, the mother transfers nutrients directly from her body to the growing embryo. **5.** `evaluate` You could stain the gene products of the segmentation genes in chordates (such as a mouse embryo) and observe whether the expression pattern correlates with the expression pattern observed in arthropods (such as a fly embryo). **6.** `apply` c

### ✔ Test Your Problem-Solving Skills

**1.** `analyze` Yes—if the same gene is found in nematodes and humans, it was likely found in the common ancestor of protostomes and deuterostomes. If so, then fruit flies should also have this gene. **2.** `apply` Asexual reproduction is likely to be favored when the sea anemones have plenty of resources such as space and food. Sexual reproduction is likely to be favored when the sea anemones are stressed due to lack of resources, predation, infection, or other factors. In this case, it is adaptive to reproduce in a way that enables dispersal to a new site and/or genetically diverse offspring, some of which will be more likely to survive selection than a clone of identical animals would. **3.** `apply` Since echinoderms evolved from bilaterally symmetric ancestors with nerve cords, they should have nerve cords too. However, the organization of the nerve cords should be more diffuse, because echinoderms need to take in and process information from multiple directions—not just one. **4.** `apply` d

# CHAPTER 34

## IN-TEXT QUESTIONS AND EXERCISES

**p. 659 Fig. 34.3** `apply` We know that aquatic living was the ancestral trait because the outgroups (e.g., Cnidaria, Porifera) were aquatic. We also have fossil evidence that the aquatic lifestyle was ancestral.

**p. 660, p. 662, p. 665, p. 666, p. 667, p. 671, p. 674** `apply` See FIGURE A34.1.

---

**p. 662 Fig. 34.6** `evaluate` Different phyla of worms have different feeding strategies and mouthparts, and they eat different foods, so they are not all in direct competition for food.

**p. 664 CYU (1)** `apply` Snails on land would be expected to have gills or lungs inside the body or otherwise protected from drying out, thinner shells so that they are not as heavy, and desiccation-resistant eggs. **(2)** `evaluate` The tentacles of the octopus could be probed during development for *Hox* genes known to be important in establishing the foot of snails. If the expression pattern is similar, homology would be supported.

**p. 664 Fig. 34.10** `apply` You should have drawn a circle around all the tentacles.

## IF YOU UNDERSTAND . . .

**34.1** `remember` Ecological opportunity was important in the diversification of protostomes because many lineages made the transition from water to land, radiating into new niches. Genetic opportunity was important because changes in the expression of developmental tool-kit genes enabled diverse modifications of body plans based on existing genes. **34.2** `understand` One source of diversification is the loss of ancestral traits; just because a species does not possess a trait does not mean that its ancestor didn't. **34.3** `analyze` Both arthropods and vertebrates have segmented bodies, which are especially amenable to modularity since a change in the expression pattern of developmental tool-kit genes can change the number, size, and type of segments, exposing morphological diversity to the adaptive forces of natural selection.

## YOU SHOULD BE ABLE TO . . .

### ✔ Test Your Knowledge

**1.** `remember` False **2.** `remember` a **3.** `remember` c **4.** `understand` c **5.** `remember` Both groups are bilaterally symmetric triploblasts with the protostome pattern of development. **6.** `remember` b

### ✔ Test Your Understanding

**1.** `remember` d **2.** `apply` Both annelids and arthropods have segmented bodies, unlike other protostomes such as flatworms and nematodes. **3.** `evaluate` Clams are relatively sessile as adults. Because larvae can swim, they provide a mechanism to disperse to new locations. To test this idea, you could measure the distance traveled by clam larvae and measure their success in recruiting to new habitats compared to larvae that are artificially limited to stay near their parents. **4.** `apply` Land plants would require cuticles or other mechanisms to keep their tissues from drying out, a mechanism of keeping gametes from

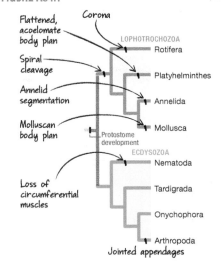

FIGURE A34.1

drying out, and structural support to retain body shape despite the effects of gravity. **5.** (evaluate) The ability to fly allowed insects to disperse to new habitats and find new food sources efficiently. **6.** (analyze) It might be adaptive for juveniles of hemimetabolous individuals to use the same food source as the adults when the food source is plentiful.

### ✓ Test Your Problem-Solving Skills

**1.** (analyze) See FIGURE A34.2. **2.** (analyze) If the ancestors of brachiopods and mollusks lived in similar habitats and experienced natural selection that favored similar traits, then they would have evolved to have similar forms and habitats. This is called convergent evolution (see Chapter 28). **3.** (evaluate) This hypothesis is reasonable because simple characteristics often occur before more elaborate ones; this could be true for the radula and foot in aplacophorans. An alternate hypothesis would be that these structures' simple forms are derived characteristics that are adaptations for parasitism, but the evidence suggests that aplacophorans are carnivores and detritivores, not parasites. The position of the aplacophorans in the phylogeny could be tested by using DNA sequence data rather than morphological characters in a phylogenetic analysis. **4.** (apply) b

## CHAPTER 35

### IN-TEXT QUESTIONS AND EXERCISES

**p. 682 Fig. 35.1** (apply) Invertebrates are a paraphyletic group. The group does not include all the descendants of the common ancestor because vertebrates are excluded.
**p. 684 CYU** (understand) If it's an echinoderm, it should have five-part radial symmetry, a calcium carbonate endoskeleton just underneath the skin, and a water vascular system (e.g., visible tube feet).
**p. 684, p. 685a, p. 685b** (apply) See FIGURE A35.1.
**p. 690 Fig. 35.12** (apply) Mammals and birds are equally related to amphibians. Because birds and mammals share a common ancestor, and this ancestor shares a common ancestor with amphibians.
**p. 691** (apply) See FIGURE A35.2.
**p. 693 Fig. 35.16** (analyze) If this phylogeny were estimated on the basis of limb traits, it would be based on the *assumption* that the limb evolved from fish fins in a series of steps. But because the phylogeny was estimated from other types of data, it is legitimate to use it to analyze the evolution of the limb without making a circular argument.
**p. 694 Fig. 35.18** (analyze) The yolk sac is smaller here—their function in an amniotic egg has been taken over by the placenta.
**p. 695 CYU (1)** (understand) Jaws allow animals to capture food efficiently and process it by crushing or tearing. The ability to process food more efficiently increased the importance of jawed vertebrates as herbivores and carnivores. The tetrapod limb enables vertebrates to locomote on land. The amniotic egg enables vertebrates to lay eggs on land; amniotic eggs are resistant to drying out. The placenta protects the growing fetus and enables the mother

to be mobile. Parental care reduces the number of offspring that can be raised, but increases their survivorship. Flight enabled pterosaurs, bats, and birds to expand into new habitats. **(2)** (analyze) Protostomes and deuterostomes living on land both have mechanisms for preventing their eggs from drying out (e.g., thick membranes in snail and insect eggs; amniotic egg in tetrapods), preventing their skin from drying out (e.g., waxy cuticle in insects, scaly skin in reptiles), and keeping their respiratory surfaces from drying out (e.g., lungs in land snails and tracheal system in insects; lungs in tetrapods).
**p. 696** (apply) See FIGURE A35.3.
**p. 698a, p. 698b, p. 699, p. 700** (apply) See FIGURE A35.4.
**p. 701a, p. 701b, p. 702a, p. 702b, p. 703a, p. 703b** (apply) See FIGURE A35.3.
**p. 705 Table 35.1** (analyze) 44 percent, 26 percent; relative to body size, *H. floresiensis* has a smaller brain than *H. sapiens.*
**p. 706 Fig. 35.37** (apply) Five hominin species existed 1.8 mya, and three existed 100,000 years ago.
**p. 706 Fig. 35.38** (analyze) The forehead became much larger, and the face became "flatter"; the brow ridges are less prominent in later skulls than in earlier skulls.

### IF YOU UNDERSTAND . . .

**35.1** (apply) (1) Mussels and clams will increase dramatically; (2) kelp density will increase.
**35.2** (understand) Your cartoon should have a dorsal hollow nerve chord along the top, dorsal edge; another line representing the notochord below the nerve cord; a tail

labeled at one end; and a series of lines or bumps representing pharyngeal gill slits near the other end.
**35.3** (understand) Like today's lungfish, the earliest tetrapods could have used their limbs for pulling themselves along the substrate in shallow-water habitats. **35.4** (understand) The earliest fossils of *H. sapiens* are found in Africa, and phylogenetic analyses of living human populations indicate that the most basal groups are all African.

**FIGURE A35.3**

**FIGURE A35.1**

**FIGURE A35.2**

**FIGURE A35.4**

### ✔ Test Your Knowledge

1. [remember] True 2. [remember] a 3. [understand] d 4. [remember] mammals 5. [understand] d 6. [remember] b

### ✔ Test Your Understanding

1. [understand] c 2. [understand] Pharyngeal gill slits function in suspension feeding. The notochord furnishes a simple endoskeleton that stiffens the body; electrical signals that coordinate movement are carried by the dorsal hollow nerve cord to the muscles in the post-anal tail, which beats back and forth to make swimming possible. Cephalochordates and Urochordates are chordates, but they are not vertebrates. 3. [analyze] If jaws are derived forms of gill arches, then the same genes and the same cells should be involved in the development of the jaw and the gill arches. 4. [understand] Increased parental care allows offspring to be better developed, and thus have increased chances of survival, before they have to live on their own. 5. [evaluate] Yes: Over a short time interval, many species that occupy an array of foods and habitats evolved. Changes in tooth and jaw structure, tool use, and body size suggest that different hominin species exploited different types of food. 6. [evaluate] A phylogeny of modern humans would reject the out-of-Africa hypothesis if the most ancestral lineages in the phylogeny were from any other region but Africa, such as Asia or Europe.

### ✔ Test Your Problem-Solving Skills

1. [apply] b 2. [evaluate] Xenoturbellidans either retain traits that were present in the common ancestor of all deuterostomes, or they have lost many complex morphological characteristics. 3. [evaluate] Vertebrate limbs are diverse in form and function (they can serve as arms, flippers, wings, etc.) but have homologous bones within. Molecular probes could be used to visualize the expression patterns of tool-kit genes like *Hox* in the embryonic limbs of different vertebrate species to show how changes in the expression of homologous genes can cause changes to the structure and function of limbs. 4. [analyze] See FIGURE A35.5. It is important to use indigenous people for this study to minimize the amount of gene flow (transfer of alleles from one population to another) that occurred during the history of the study populations due to immigration and interbreeding.

**FIGURE A35.5**

## CHAPTER 42

### IN-TEXT QUESTIONS AND EXERCISES

**p. 844 Fig. 42.2** [create] There would be no difference between experimental and control males.
**p. 847 Fig. 42.4** [analyze] Based on the projections called axons that go to specific cells and tissues, neurons transmit signals to specific tissues rather than broadly throughout the body.

**p. 850 CYU** [analyze] *Connective tissues* consist of cells embedded in a matrix. The density of the matrix determines the rigidity of the connective tissue and its function in padding/protection, structural support, or transport. *Nervous tissue* is composed of neurons and support cells. Neurons have long projections that function as "biological wires" for transmitting electrical signals. *Muscle tissue* has cells that can contract and functions in movement. *Epithelial tissue* has tightly packed layers of cells with distinct apical and basal surfaces. They protect underlying tissues and regulate the entry and exit of materials into these tissues.
**p. 850** [apply] A newborn.
**p. 851 Fig. 42.10** [create] The puppy has to eat relatively more because it has a higher mass-specific metabolic rate than an adult dog.
**p. 852 Fig. 42.11** [apply] There should be no oxygen uptake on either side of the chamber.
**p. 853 CYU (1)** [understand] As three-dimensional size increases, volume increases more quickly than does surface area, so the surface area/volume ratio decreases.
**(2)** [analyze] The squirrel has a higher mass-specific metabolic rate because it is a smaller animal. It therefore needs more energy per unit body mass than a bear.
**p. 858 CYU (1)** [analyze] Endotherms can remain active during the winter and at night and sustain high levels of aerobic activities such as running or flying, but they require large amounts of food energy. Ectotherms need much less food and can devote a larger proportion of their food intake to reproduction, but they have a hard time maintaining high activity levels at night or in cold weather. **(2)** [apply] The whale's tongue would become colder because not as much heat would be transferred from warm arterial blood to cool venous blood with concurrent flow as with countercurrent flow, and as a result more heat from the arterial blood would be lost to the environment.

### IF YOU UNDERSTAND . . .

**42.1** [understand] Some adaptations to cold environments in mammals include the evolution of thick coats of hair, countercurrent heat exchangers in the extremities, and dark coloration to absorb radiation. Acclimatization may include further thickening and darkening of hair upon exposure to cold. **42.2** [apply] Loosening tight junctions would compromise the barrier between the external and internal environments. It would allow water and other substances (including toxins) to pass more readily across the epithelial boundary. **42.3** [create] King Kong is endothermic, and his huge mass would generate a great deal of heat. His relatively small surface area, especially as compared to a normal-sized gorilla, would not be able to dissipate the heat—especially if it were covered with fur. **42.4** [create] Individuals could acclimatize by normal homeostatic mechanisms (increased sweating, seeking shade, etc.). Individuals with alleles that allowed them to function better at higher temperatures would produce more offspring than individuals without those alleles. Over time, this would lead to adaptation via natural selection. **42.5** [create] *Apatosaurus* was likely a homeotherm because of its huge size. Because of its low surface area/volume ratio, metabolically produced heat would be trapped inside the dinosaur's body. Even if exposed to cold or warm temperatures, the dinosaur's temperature would not change much because it takes a long time for it to lose or gain heat across such a relatively small surface area.

### YOU SHOULD BE ABLE TO . . .

### ✔ Test Your Knowledge

1. [understand] True 2. [remember] Epithelial 3. [understand] b
4. [understand] d 5. [understand] a 6. [analyze] a

### ✔ Test Your Understanding

7. [understand] It is where environmental changes are sensed first. As an effector, it has a large surface area for losing or gaining heat. 8. [analyze] A warm frog can move, breathe, and digest much faster than a cold frog, because enzymes work faster (rates of chemical reactions increase) at 35°C than at 5°C. A warm frog needs much more food, though, to support this high metabolic rate. 9. [understand] *Absorptive sections* have many folds and projections that increase their surface area for absorption. *Capillaries* have a high surface area because they are thin and highly branched, making exchange of fluids and gases efficient. *Beaks of Galápagos finches* have sizes and shapes that correlate with the type of food each species eats. Large beaks are used to crack large seeds; long, thin beaks are used to pick insects off surfaces; etc. *Fish gills* are thin, flattened structures with a large surface area, which facilitates the efficient exchange of gases and wastes. 10. [analyze] A larger sphere has a relatively smaller surface area for its interior volume than does a smaller sphere, because surface area increases with size at a lower rate than volume does. Diffusion will be more efficient in the smaller sphere. 11. [apply] See FIGURE A42.1. The graph shows that as size (length) increases, the volume increases more rapidly than than the surface area. 12. [understand] c. This is an example of negative feedback because insulin is released in response to an increase in a parameter (blood sugar concentration)

**FIGURE A42.1**

and acts to reduce that parameter so that homeostasis is maintained. In the other examples, homeostasis is not maintained.

### ✔ Test Your Problem-Solving Skills

13. [create] Large individuals require more food, so are more susceptible to starvation if food sources can't be defended (e.g., when seeds are scattered around). They may also be slower and/or more visible to predators. 14. [create] You would have to show changes in the frequencies of alleles whose products are affected by temperature—for example, increases in the frequencies of alleles for enzymes that operate best at higher temperature. 15. [create] The heat-dissipating system should have a very high surface area/volume ratio. Based on biological structures, it should be flattened (thin) and highly folded and branched, and/or contain tubelike projections. 16. [understand] a. Turtles are ectothermic, so they do not expend much energy to produce body heat. Mice are endothermic, and expend energy to regulate body temperature. Mice will therefore have a higher basal metabolic rate and consume more food.

# CHAPTER 43

## IN-TEXT QUESTIONS AND EXERCISES

**p. 863 Fig. 43.1** (understand) The black and white molecules are moving down their concentration gradients, and the concentration of red molecules does not affect the concentration of black or white molecules.

**p. 867 Fig. 43.6** (understand) The sodium–potassium ATPase performs primary active transport; the sodium–chloride–potassium cotransporter performs secondary active transport; the chloride and potassium channels are involved in passive transport.

**p. 869 CYU** (apply) The osmolarity of the fish's tissue would decrease because the pumps would no longer be able to import sodium.

**p. 869 Fig. 43.8** (analyze) The underside of the abdomen is shaded by the grasshopper's body. This location is relatively cool and should reduce the loss of water during respiration.

**p. 871 CYU (1)** (understand) Uric acid is insoluble in water and can be excreted without much water loss. **(2)** (understand) When electrolytes are reabsorbed in the hindgut epithelia, water follows along an osmotic gradient.

**p. 873** (understand) Blood contains cells and large molecules as well as ions, nutrients, and wastes; the filtrate contains only ions, nutrients, and wastes.

**p. 876** (apply) (1) Less water reabsorption will occur because the osmotic gradient is not as steep. (2) Filtrate osmolarity will be lower because less water has been reabsorbed. (3) Salt reabsorption will be reduced because the concentration of NaCl in the filtrate is lower.

**p. 878** (create) Ethanol consumption inhibits water reabsorption, leading to a larger volume of less concentrated urine. Nicotine consumption increases water reabsorption, leading to a smaller volume of more concentrated urine.

**p. 878 CYU** (apply) Water intake increases blood pressure and filtration rate in the renal corpuscle. It leads to lowered electrolyte concentration in the blood and filtrate and the production of large volumes of dilute urine. Eating large amounts of salt results in concentrated, hyperosmotic urine. Water deprivation triggers ADH release and the production of concentrated, hyperosmotic urine.

**p. 879 Fig. 43.19** (create) Carrying a large volume of water in the bladder may be energetically costly to the animal. The animal also might not be able to run as quickly and may have an increased predation risk.

## IF YOU UNDERSTAND . . .

**43.1** (understand) A sodium gradient establishes an osmotic gradient that moves water. It also sets up an electrochemical gradient that can move ions against their electrochemical gradient by secondary active transport through a cotransporter, or with their electrochemical gradient by passive diffusion through a channel.

**43.2** (analyze) Cartilaginous fishes such as sharks maintain a high concentration of urea in their blood, which raises their osmolarity to about the same as seawater. Therefore, they lose very little water to the environment. Bony fishes drink seawater and maintain their osmolarity lower than that of seawater by actively transporting excess ions out of the gills. Sharks actively excrete sodium chloride through a rectal gland. **43.3** (understand) When comparing chloride cells in gills of salmon in the ocean versus freshwater, the cells are in different locations on the gills, different forms of $Na^+/K^+$-ATPase exist, and $Na^+K^+Cl^-$ transporters are located on the basolateral side of the membrane in ocean salmon and on the apical side of the membrane in freshwater salmon. **43.4** (apply) Aquatic insects produce more urea, and especially more ammonia, than terrestrial insects because these nitrogenous wastes are energetically less expensive to produce than uric acid. Ammonia and urea require more water to be excreted, but aquatic insects have access to plenty of water. **43.5** (create) The longer the loop of Henle, the steeper the osmotic gradient in the interstitial fluid in the medulla. Steep osmotic gradients allow a great deal of water to be reabsorbed as urine passes through the collecting duct, resulting in highly concentrated urine.

## YOU SHOULD BE ABLE TO . . .

### ✓ Test Your Knowledge

**1.** (remember) True **2.** (understand) c **3.** (apply) a **4.** (remember) d **5.** (understand) c **6.** (remember) bladder

### ✓ Test Your Understanding

**7.** (create) b. Fishes excrete nitrogenous wastes in the form of ammonia. Although the ammonia can easily diffuse across the fish's gills into the water, freshwater ponds are often small and ammonia can build up to potentially toxic levels. **8.** (analyze) Ammonia is toxic and must be diluted with large amounts of water to be excreted safely. Urea and uric acid are safer and do not have to be excreted with large amounts of water but are more expensive to produce in terms of energy expenditure. Fish excrete ammonia; mammals excrete urea; insects excrete uric acid. You would expect the embryos inside terrestrial eggs to excrete uric acid, since it is the least toxic and is insoluble in water. **9.** (understand) Mitochondria are needed to produce ATP. A key component of salt regulation in fish is the $Na^+/K^+$-ATPase, which requires ATP to function. Because ATP fuels establishment of the ion gradients necessary for the cotransport mechanisms used by chloride cells as well as other epithelial cells, an abundance of mitochondria would be expected in a chloride cell. **10.** (create) The wax layer should be thicker in insects inhabiting dry habitats, because the animals there are under more osmotic stress (more evaporation due to low humidity; less available drinking water). Insects that live in extremely humid habitats may lack the ability to close their spiracles; animals that live in humid habitats may excrete primarily ammonia or urea and have relatively short loops of Henle. In each case, you could test these predictions by comparing individuals of closely related species that live in dry versus humid habitats. **11.** (create) Without a loop of Henle, there would be no concentration gradient in the medullary interstitial fluid, so water would not be absorbed from the pre-urine in the collecting duct; concentrated urine could not be formed. **12.** (create) Freshwater has such a low osmolarity that if invertebrates osmoconformed to it, they would lack sufficient quantities of ions to conduct electrical currents in their excitable tissues.

### ✓ Test Your Problem-Solving Skills

**13.** (apply) c. Without aquaporins in the collecting duct, water cannot be reabsorbed, which would result in increased urine volume and decreased urine osmolarity. **14.** (create) The mammal's urine volume would increase dramatically. Ouabain would poison $Na^+/K^+$-ATPase pumps in the nephron, which would prevent reabsorption of ions and nutrients. Without the osmotic gradient established by reabsorption of ions and nutrients, the water would remain in the nephron and exit as urine.

**15.** (analyze) The observation that the $Na^+$ concentration decreased by 30 percent, even as volume also decreased, indicates that $Na^+$ ions were reabsorbed to a greater degree than water. The observation that the urea concentration increased by 50 percent indicates that urea was not reabsorbed. **16.** (analyze) The hypothesis that the mussels are osmoconformers is supported because their hemolymph is very close in osmolarity to that of the wide range of water osmolarities into which they are placed.

# CHAPTER 45

## IN-TEXT QUESTIONS AND EXERCISES

**p. 905 CYU (1)** (analyze) Oxygen partial pressure is high in mountain streams because the water is cold, mixes constantly, and has a high surface area (due to white water). Oxygen partial pressure is low at the ocean bottom because that is far from the surface, where gas exchange takes place, and there is relatively little mixing. **(2)** (create) *Warm-water species:* Large amount of air, because the oxygen-carrying capacity of warm water is low. *Vigorous algal growth:* Small amount of air, because algae contribute oxygen to the water through photosynthesis. *Sedentary animals:* Small amount of air, because sedentary animals require relatively little oxygen.

**p. 906 Fig. 45.4** (analyze) External gills are ventilated passively and are efficient because they are in direct contact with water. They are exposed to predators and mechanical damage, however. Internal gills are protected but have to be ventilated by some type of active mechanism for water flow.

**p. 907 Fig. 45.6** (apply) If "concurrent flow" occurred, oxygen transfer would stop, because the partial pressure gradient driving diffusion would fall to zero partway along the length of the capillary.

**p. 909 Fig. 45.7** (analyze) Using many animals increases confidence that the results are true for most or all members of the population and are not due to one or a few unusual individuals or circumstances.

**p. 912 CYU (1)** (analyze) Common features include large surface area, short diffusion distance (a thin gas exchange membrane), and a mechanism that keeps fresh air or water moving over the gas exchange surface. Only fish gills use a countercurrent exchange mechanism; only tracheae deliver oxygen directly to cells without using a circulatory system; only lungs (mammalian) contain "dead space"—areas that are not involved in gas exchange. **(2)** (apply) The $P_{O_2}$ would go down as oxygen is used up, the $P_{CO_2}$ would go up as $CO_2$ diffuses into the blood but cannot be exhaled, and pH would drop as the $CO_2$ dissolves in blood to form bicarbonate and $H^+$ ions.

**p. 913** (create) There would be an even larger change in the oxygen saturation of hemoglobin in response to an even smaller change in the partial pressure of oxygen.

**p. 914 Fig. 45.16** (analyze) According to the data in the figure, when the tissue $P_{O_2}$ is 30 mm Hg, the oxygen saturation of hemoglobin is about 15 percent for blood at pH 7.2 and about 25 percent at pH 7.4. Therefore, about 85 percent of the oxygen is released from hemoglobin at pH 7.2, but only about 75 percent of the oxygen is released at pH 7.4.

**p. 915 Fig. 45.18** (analyze) In the lungs, a strong partial pressure gradient favors diffusion of dissolved $CO_2$ from blood into the alveoli. As the partial pressure of $CO_2$ in the blood declines, hydrogen ions leave hemoglobin and react with bicarbonate to form more $CO_2$, which then diffuses into the alveoli and is exhaled from the lungs.

**p. 916 CYU** analyze The curve for Tibetans should be shifted to the left relative to people adapted to sea level—meaning that their hemoglobin has a higher affinity for oxygen at all partial pressures.

**p. 921 Fig. 45.24** analyze Air from the alveoli mixes with air in the "dead space" in the bronchi and trachea on its way out of the body. This dead space air is from the previous inhalation ($P_{O_2}$ = 160 mm Hg; $P_{CO_2}$ = 0.3), so when the alveolar air mixes with the dead space air, the partial pressures in the exhaled air achieve levels intermediate between that of inhaled and alveolar air.

**p. 922** apply Without the delay at the AV node, the ventricles would not have the chance to fully fill with blood from the atria. As a consequence, the volume of blood ejected from the ventricles would decline.

**p. 924 CYU (1)** understand Blood plasma that leaks out of the capillaries and is not reabsorbed into capillaries enters lymphatic vessels that eventually merge with blood vessels. **(2)** understand See FIGURE A45.1.

## IF YOU UNDERSTAND . . .

**45.1** understand Cellular respiration. **45.2** create It is harder to extract oxygen from water than it is to extract it from air. This limits the metabolic rate of water breathers. **45.3** analyze Large animals have a relatively small body surface area relative to their volume. If they had to rely solely on gas exchange across their skin, the skin surface area would not be large enough to exchange the volume of oxygen needed to meet their metabolic needs. **45.4** create Since $O_2$ cannot compete as well as CO for binding sites in hemoglobin, $O_2$ transport decreases. As oxygen levels in the blood drop, tissues (most crucially in the brain) become deprived of oxygen, and suffocation occurs. **45.5** apply Their circulatory systems should have relatively high pressures—achieved by independent systemic and pulmonary circulations powered by a four-chambered heart—to maximize the delivery of oxygenated blood to metabolically active tissues.

## YOU SHOULD BE ABLE TO . . .

### ✔ Test Your Knowledge

**1.** understand b **2.** remember c **3.** understand d **4.** understand d **5.** remember c **6.** understand An open circulatory system is less efficient than a closed circulatory system because it is not capable of directing the hemolymph toward specific organs, and because the pressure is lower, resulting in slower flow of hemolymph.

### ✔ Test Your Understanding

**7.** understand During exercise, $P_{O_2}$ decreases in the tissues and $P_{CO_2}$ increases. The increase in $P_{CO_2}$ lowers tissue pH. The drop in $P_{O_2}$ and pH causes more oxygen to be released from hemoglobin. **8.** understand In blood, $CO_2$ is converted to carbonic acid, which dissociates into a proton and a bicarbonate ion. Because the protons bind to deoxygenated hemoglobin, they do not cause a dramatic drop in blood pH (hemoglobin acts as a buffer). Also, small decreases in blood pH trigger a homeostatic response that increases breathing rate and expulsion of $CO_2$. **9.** understand Because airflow through bird lungs is unidirectional, the gas exchange surfaces are continuously ventilated with fresh, oxygenated air. The trachea and bronchi in a mammalian lung do not have a gas exchange surface, and bidirectional airflow in these species means that "stale" air has to be expelled before "fresh" air can be inhaled. As a result, the alveoli are not ventilated continuously. **10.** understand Lungs increase the temperature of the air and are moist to allow greater solubility of gases (increasing $k$); alveoli present a large

surface area (large $A$); the epithelium of alveoli is thin (small $D$); and constant delivery of deoxygenated blood to alveoli maintains a steep partial pressure gradient, favoring diffusion of oxygen into the body ($P_2 - P_1$ is high). **11.** analyze Yes—the trait compensates for the small $P_{O_2}$ gradient between stagnant water and the blood of the carp. **12.** analyze c

### ✔ Test Your Problem-Solving Skills

**13.** create Cold water carries more oxygen than warm water does, so icefish blood can carry enough oxygen to supply the tissues with oxygen even in the absence of hemoglobin. The oxygen and carbon dioxide are simply dissolved in the blood. **14.** analyze The insect tracheal system delivers $O_2$ directly to respiring cells; in humans, $O_2$ is first taken up by the blood of the circulatory system, which then delivers it to the cells. The human respiratory system also has specialized muscles devoted to ventilating the lungs. The open circulatory system of the insect is a low-pressure system, which makes use of pumps (hearts) and body movements to circulate hemolymph. The closed circulatory system of humans is a high-pressure system, which can respond to rapid changes in $O_2$ demand by tissues. **15.** understand If the pulmonary circulation were under pressure as high as that found in the systemic circulation, large amounts of fluid would be forced out of capillaries in the lungs. There is a conflict between the thin surface required for efficient gas exchange and the thickness needed in blood vessels to withstand high pressure. **16.** analyze b

## CHAPTER 46

### IN-TEXT QUESTIONS AND EXERCISES

**p. 931 Fig. 46.3** apply No—as $K^+$ leaves the cell along its concentration gradient, the interior of the cell becomes more negative. As a result, an electrical gradient favoring movement of $K^+$ into the cell begins to counteract the concentration gradient favoring movement of $K^+$ out of the cell. Eventually, the two opposing forces balance out, and there is no net movement of $K^+$.

**p. 932a** apply $E_{Ca2+}$ = 58 mV × log 1 mM/0.0001 mM)/ (+2) = 116 mV.

**p. 932b** apply The membrane potential would be near zero because the $Na^+$ and $K^+$ would diffuse across the membrane along their concentration gradients.

**p. 934 CYU (1)** apply The resting potential would fall (be much less negative) because $K^+$ could no longer leak out of the cell. **(2)** understand The size of an action potential from a particular neuron does not vary, so it cannot contain information. Only the frequency of action potentials from the same neuron varies.

**FIGURE A45.1**

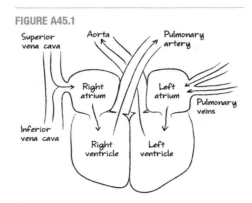

**p. 934** understand See FIGURE A46.1.

**p. 935 (1)** understand $Na^+$ channels open when the cell membrane depolarizes, and as more channels open, more $Na^+$ flows into the cell, further depolarizing the cell, causing more voltage-gated $Na^+$ channels to open. **(2)** apply Sodium would flow inward as potassium flowed outward, and their charges would cancel each other out. The membrane would not depolarize.

**p. 938 CYU (1)** understand Once the threshold level of depolarization is attained, the probability that the voltage-gated sodium channels will open approaches 100 percent. But below threshold, the massive opening of $Na^+$ channels does not occur. This is why the action potential is all or none. **(2)** apply The membrane would depolarize and stay depolarized.

**p. 938 Fig. 46.10** understand Get a solution taken from the synapse between the heart muscle and the vagus nerve *without* the nerve being stimulated. Expose a second heart to this solution. There should be no change in heart rate.

**p. 940** analyze The inside of the cell becomes more positive (depolarized). This shifts the membrane potential closer to the threshold, making it more likely that the postsynaptic cell will fire an action potential.

**p. 942 CYU** apply The EPSP would not be as strong if an enzyme that broke down excitatory neurotransmitter increased in concentration.

**p. 943 Fig. 46.16** analyze In the rest-and-digest mode, pupils take in less light stimulation, the heartbeat slows to conserve energy, liver conserves glucose, and digestion is promoted by release of gallbladder products. In the fight-or-flight mode, the pupils open to take in more light, the heartbeat increases to support muscle activity, and the liver releases glucose into the blood to fuel the fight or the flight (for example, from a predator).

**p. 944 Fig. 46.18** understand Point to your forehead and top of your head for the frontal lobe, the top and top rear of your head for the parietal lobe, the back of your head for the occipital lobe, and the sides of your head (just above your ear openings) for the temporal lobes.

**p. 946 Fig. 46.21** analyze No—for example, part (b) indicates that the size of the brain area devoted to the trunk is no bigger than the size of the brain area devoted to the thumb.

**FIGURE A46.1**

**p. 948 CYU (1)** understand One method is to study individuals with known brain lesions and correlate the location of the defect with a deficit in mental or physical function. Another is to directly stimulate brain areas in conscious patients during brain surgery and record the response. **(2)** remember Learning and memory involve changes in the number, sensitivity, and placement of synapses and neurons.

### IF YOU UNDERSTAND . . .

**46.1** understand See **FIGURE A46.2**. **46.2** understand Because the behavior of voltage-gated Na⁺ and K⁺ channels does not change. Every time a membrane depolarizes past the threshold and all of the voltage-gated Na⁺ channels are open, the same amount of Na⁺ will enter the cell, and the cell will depolarize to the same extent. In addition, K⁺ channels open at the same time and allow the same amount of K⁺ to leave the cell, so that it repolarizes to the same extent. **46.3** understand Summation means that EPSPs and IPSPs produced at various sites combine to determine the response or lack of response in a postsynaptic cell. Thus the behavior of a postsynaptic cell depends on the integration of input from many synapses. **46.4** apply The animal would likely die because its basic bodily functions (circulation, breathing, digestion, etc.) would be disrupted.

### YOU SHOULD BE ABLE TO . . .

#### ✔ Test Your Knowledge

**1.** remember b **2.** remember d **3.** understand c **4.** remember a **5.** remember b **6.** understand See **FIGURE A46.3**.

#### ✔ Test Your Understanding

**7.** understand The Na⁺/K⁺-ATPase pumps 3 Na⁺ out of the cell for every 2 K⁺ it brings in. Since more positive charges leave the cell than enter it, there is a difference in charge on the two sides of the membrane and thus a voltage. **8.** analyze The ligand-gated channel opens or closes in response to binding by a small molecule (for example, a neurotransmitter); the voltage-gated channel opens or closes in response to changes in membrane potential. **9.** understand EPSPs and IPSPs are produced by flow of ions through channels in the membrane, which change the membrane potential in the postsynaptic cell. If a flow of ions at one point depolarizes the cell but a nearby flow of ions hyperpolarizes the cell, then in combination the flows of ions cancel each other out. But if two adjacent flows of ions depolarize the cell, then

their effects are additive and sum to produce a total that is more likely to reach threshold. **10.** analyze The somatic system responds to external stimuli and controls voluntary skeletal muscle activity, such as movement of arms and legs. The autonomic system controls internal involuntary activities, such as digestion, heart rate, and gland activities. **11.** apply A drug that activates the sympathetic nervous system would increase heart rate. **12.** understand a

#### ✔ Test Your Problem-Solving Skills

**13.** apply The neurotransmitters will stay in the synaptic cleft longer, so the amount of binding to ligand-gated channels will increase. Ion flows into the postsynaptic cell will increase dramatically, affecting its membrane potential and likelihood of firing action potentials. **14.** analyze The benefit of these approaches is that they allow the specific role of the brain region to be assessed in a living person. However, diseased or damaged brains may not respond like healthy and undamaged brains. Also, the extent of lesions and the exact location of electrical stimulation may be difficult to determine, making correlations between the regions affected and the response imprecise. **15.** analyze c (Because the current is reduced from normal levels, but not eliminated completely, there must be more than one type of potassium channel present. The venom probably knocks out just one specific type of channel.) **16.** create A reasonable hypothesis is that the new neurons arise from stem cells in the brain.

## CHAPTER 47

### IN-TEXT QUESTIONS AND EXERCISES

**p. 959 CYU (1)** apply A punctured eardrum wouldn't vibrate correctly and would result in hearing loss at all frequencies in the affected ear. If the stereocilia are too short to come into contact with the tectorial membrane, vibration of the basilar membrane will not cause them to bend, and sound will not be detected. A loss in basilar membrane flexibility would result in the inability to hear lower-pitched sounds, such as human speech. **(2)** understand The lateral line system senses pressure waves in the water, allowing fishes to detect the presence of such objects as prey, predators, or potential mates.

**p. 959 Fig. 47.9** create Vision could potentially be used to detect prey in diurnal catfish. To control for this, catfish could be blinded or "blindfolded" with an opaque material over their eyes to permit study of the lateral line system.

**p. 961 Fig. 47.12** create The change in retinal's shape would induce a change in opsin's shape. A protein's function correlates with its shape, so opsin's function is likely to change as well.

**p. 962** analyze cGMP is a second messenger in the sense that it signals the sodium channel that transducing is inactive, and it is also a ligand that opens sodium channels. Transducin is like a G protein because it switches from "off" to "on" in response to a receptor protein, activating a key protein as a result. Closing Na⁺ channels stops the entry of positive charges into the cell, making the inside of the cell more negative relative to the outside.

**p. 962** understand This ion flow occurs when the photoreceptor cell is not receiving light—when the cell is in the dark.

**p. 963 Fig. 47.15** create The S, M, and L opsin proteins are each different in structure. These structural differences affect the ability of retinal to absorb specific frequencies of light and change shape.

**p. 964 CYU (1)** understand Retinal acts like an on-off switch that indicates whether light has fallen on a rod cell. When retinal absorbs light, it changes shape. The shape change triggers events that result in a change in action potentials, signaling that light has been absorbed. **(2)** apply Retina detachment from a jarring car accident would separate the retina from the optic nerve, resulting in blindness. The mutation would produce blue–purple color blindness, because the S opsin responds to wavelengths in that region of the spectrum. A clouded lens would reduce the amount of light that reaches the retina, reducing visual sensitivity.

**p. 967 CYU (1)** understand Extremely hot food damages taste receptors, so those proteins would no longer be able to respond to their chemical triggers. **(2)** create One hypothesis to explain why the vomeronasal organ is vestigial in most primates is that primates have evolved other complex methods of communication, including gestures, facial expressions, and language, that render sensation with the vomeronasal organ less important.

**p. 967** apply (1) A rattlesnake with its eyes covered will strike effectively because its pits will sense the prey. (2) A rattlesnake with its eyes and pits covered with cotton cloth will strike effectively. The cloth will block vision but the heat from the animal will penetrate the cloth to stimulate the thermoreceptors in the pits. (3) A rattlesnake with its eyes and pits covered with an opaque heat-blocking material will not be able to strike effectively, because the material blocks vision and heat energy.

**p. 969 CYU (1)** create Electrogenic fishes may have a survival advantage over other fishes in murky water, where vision would be compromised. **(2)** create Female sea turtles likely use magnetic cues to locate their natal beaches.

### IF YOU UNDERSTAND . . .

**47.1** create The sensory neurons that used to serve that limb are cut, but may still fire action potentials that stimulate brain areas associated with awareness of pain in the missing limb. **47.2** analyze Each of these senses involves ion channels that open in response to application of pressure to cell membranes. **47.3** understand Because different animal species have different sets of opsin molecules that respond to different wavelengths of light absorbed by retinal they see different colors. **47.4** create Smells are part of the sensation of flavor, and people

**FIGURE A46.2**

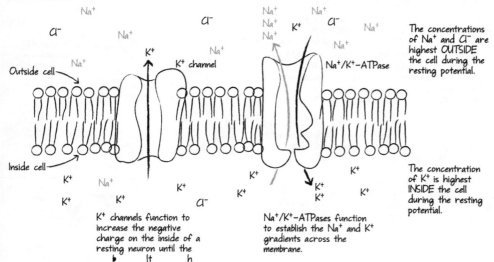

The concentrations of Na⁺ and Cl⁻ are highest OUTSIDE the cell during the resting potential.

The concentration of K⁺ is highest INSIDE the cell during the resting potential.

K⁺ channels function to increase the negative charge on the inside of a resting neuron until the ♭ It h

Na⁺/K⁺-ATPases function to establish the Na⁺ and K⁺ gradients across the membrane.

## FIGURE A46.3

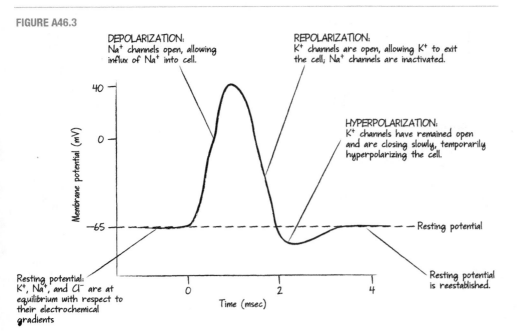

**DEPOLARIZATION:**
Na⁺ channels open, allowing influx of Na⁺ into cell.

**REPOLARIZATION:**
K⁺ channels are open, allowing K⁺ to exit the cell; Na⁺ channels are inactivated.

**HYPERPOLARIZATION:**
K⁺ channels have remained open and are closing slowly, temporarily hyperpolarizing the cell.

Resting potential

Resting potential:
K⁺, Na⁺, and Cl⁻ are at equilibrium with respect to their electrochemical gradients

Resting potential is reestablished.

Membrane potential (mV)

Time (msec)

---

with nasal congestion cannot smell. In addition to smell being important, the small number of taste receptors can send many different frequencies of action potentials to the brain, and the taste receptors can be stimulated in many different combinations. **47.5** *understand* Capsaicin binds to thermoreceptors that are also activated at high temperatures, leading to the perception of heat. It can also bind to some nociceptors.

### ✓ YOU SHOULD BE ABLE TO . . .

#### ✓ Test Your Knowledge

**1.** *understand* a **2.** *remember* d **3.** *understand* c **4.** *remember* b **5.** *remember* false **6.** *remember* magnetoreception

#### ✓ Test Your Understanding

**7.** *understand* b **8.** *understand* The many possible examples include several blue opsins allowing coelacanths to distinguish the blue wavelengths present in their deep-sea habitat, infrasound hearing allowing elephants to hear over long distances, ultrasonic hearing allowing bats to hunt by echolocation and moths to avoid bat predators, red and yellow opsins allowing fruit-eating mammals to distinguish ripe from unripe fruit. **9.** *analyze* The data provide evidence that a pheromone acted to synchronize the women's menstrual cycles because the average time between onset of a woman's cycle and that of the rest of the women declined over time following move-in to the dorms in fall. It declined most rapidly after they first moved in together. The leveling of the graph over time shows that the onset dates became more synchronized. **10.** *understand* Ion channels in hair cells are thought to open in response to physical distortion caused by the bending of stereocilia. Ion channels in taste receptors, in contrast, change shape and open when certain bitter-tasting molecules bind to them. **11.** *evaluate* Dalton's hypothesis was reasonable because blue fluid absorbs red light and would prevent it from reaching the retina, and this could be tested by dissecting his eyes. Although the

hypothesis was rejected, it inspired a rigorous test and required researchers to think of alternative explanations. **12.** *create* To determine whether electric eels are electrogenic, place an eel in a tank and measure the electricity of water to determine if the eel is emitting an electric field. To determine whether they are electroreceptive, place an eel in a tank in the dark and add an object the size and shape of a prey item that emits no scent or taste. Block the lateral line system with a chemical as in Figure 47.9. If the eel locates the object, it must do so using electroreception.

#### ✓ Test Your Problem-Solving Skills

**13.** *understand* a; vomeronasal organs evolved in tetrapods, presumably as an adaptation for communication in terrestrial habitats. **14.** *analyze* Both the lateral line system and electroreceptors use hair cells to sense changes in the water. Hair cells in the lateral line system contain mechanoreceptors that are depolarized in response to changes in water pressure. In contrast, electroreceptors cause hair cells to depolarize in response to changes in the electric field. **15.** *evaluate* It is unlikely that a perfume contains human pheromones because they have never actually been characterized, although their presence is suspected. **16.** *create* Block all but a few hundred ommatidia in the center of each compound eye of many dragonflies with an opaque material, and observe any differences that might occur in their ability to detect and pursue prey compared to individuals whose ommatidia had been covered by a transparent material.

## Bioskills

**BIOSKILLS 1; p. B:2 CYU (1)** *apply* 3.1 miles **(2)** *apply* 37°C **(3)** *apply* Multiply your weight in pounds by 1/2.2 (0.45). **(4)** *apply* 4 **(5)** *apply* 4 **(6)** Two significant figures. When you multiply, the answer can have no more significant

---

figures than the least accurate measurement—in this case, 1.6.

**BIOSKILLS 2; p. B:3 CYU (1)** *apply* "different-yoked-together" **(2)** *apply* "sugary-loosened" **(3)** *apply* "study-of-form" **(4)** *apply* "three-bodies"

**BIOSKILLS 3; p. B:6 CYU (1)** *apply* about 18% **(2)** *apply* a dramatic drop (almost 10%) **(3)** *understand* No—the order of presentation in a bar chart does not matter (though it's convenient to arrange the bars in a way that reinforces the overall message). **(4)** *apply* 11 **(5)** *apply* 68 inches

**BIOSKILLS 4; p. B:7 CYU** *apply* Test 2, the estimate based on the larger sample—the more replicates or observations you have, the more precise your estimate of the average should be.

**BIOSKILLS 5; p. B:8 CYU (1)** *apply* $1/2 \times 1/2 \times 1/2 \times 1/2 = 1/16$ **(2)** *apply* $1/6 + 1/6 + 1/6 = 1/2$

**BIOSKILLS 6; p. B:9 CYU (1)** *understand* exponential **(2)** *apply* $\ln N_t = \ln N_0 + rt$

**BIOSKILLS 7; p. B:9 Fig. B7.1.** *analyze* See FIGURE BA.1. **p. B:10 Fig. B7.2.** *analyze* See FIGURE BA.2. **p. B:11 Fig. B7.3.** *analyze* Figure B7.3d is different.

---

## FIGURE BA.1

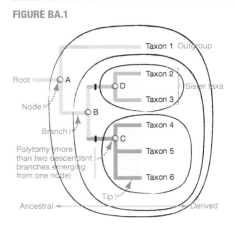

Taxon 1 Outgroup
Taxon 2
Taxon 3
Taxon 4
Taxon 5
Taxon 6
Sister taxa
Root — A
Node — D — B — C
Branch
Polytomy (more than two descendant branches emerging from one node)
Tip
Ancestral — Derived

## FIGURE BA.2

Common chimp
A
Outgroup to humans
B
Origin of walking on two legs
C
D
E
F
*Australopithecus afarensis*
*Paranthropus robustus*
*Paranthropus boisei*
*Homo erectus*
*Homo neanderthalensis*
*Homo sapiens*
Sister species
Sister species
Humans

OSKILLS 9; p. B:13 Fig. B9.1 `understand` DNA and RNA
e acids that tend to drop a proton in solution, giving
em a negative charge.

B:15 CYU `analyze` The lane with no band comes from a
mple where RNA X is not present. The same size RNA
is present in the next two lanes, but the faint band has
ry few copies while the dark band has many. In the
urth lane, the band is formed by a smaller version of
NA X, and relatively few copies are present.

OSKILLS 10; p. B:17 CYU (1) `understand` size and/or den-
ty. (2) `apply` Mitochondria, because they are larger in
ze compared with ribosomes.

OSKILLS 11; p. B:19 CYU (1) `analyze` No—it's just that
mitochondria happened to be present in this section

sliced through the cell. (2) `explain` Understanding a molecule's structure is often critical to understanding how it
functions in cells.

BIOSKILLS 12; p. B:21 CYU (1) `analyze` It may not be clear
that the results are relevant to noncancerous cells that
are not growing in cell culture—that is, that the artificial
conditions mimic natural conditions. (2) `analyze` It may
not be clear that the results are relevant to individuals
that developed normally, from an embryo—that is, that
the artificial conditions mimic natural conditions.

BIOSKILLS 13; p. B:23 Fig. B13.1 `analyze` This is human
body temperature—the natural habitat of E. coli.
p. B:24 CYU (1) `analyze` Caenorhabditis elegans would be a
good possibility, because the cells that normally die have
already been identified. You could find mutant individuals that lacked normal cell death; you could compare

the resulting embryos to normal embryos and be able to
identify exactly which cells change as a result. (2) `analyze`
Any of the multicellular organisms in the list would
be a candidate, but Dictyostelium discoideum might be
particularly interesting because cells stick to each other
only during certain points in the life cycle. (3) `analyze` Mus
musculus—as the only mammal in the list, it is the organism most likely to have a gene similar to the one you
want to study.

BIOSKILLS 14; p. B:26 CYU `synthesize` Many examples are
possible. See Figure 1.9 in Chapter 1, as an example of
the format to use for your Research Box.

BIOSKILLS 15; p. B:27 CYU (1) `analyze` See FIGURE BA.4.
(2) `analyze` See FIGURE BA.4.

---

**IGURE BA.3**

| Molecular formula: | $CO_2$ |
| Structural formula: | $O=C=O$ |
| Ball-and-stick model: | |
| Space-filling model: | |

**FIGURE BA.4**

## BIOSKILL the metric system and significant figures

Scientists ask questions that can be answered by observing or measuring things—by collecting data. What units are used to make measurements? When measurements are reported, how can you tell how reliable the data are?

### The Metric System

The metric system is the system of units of measure used in every country of the world but three (Liberia, Myanmar, and the United States). It is also the basis of the SI system—the International System of Units (abbreviated from the French, *Système international d'unités*)—used in scientific publications.

The popularity of the metric system is based on its consistency and ease of use. These attributes, in turn, arise from the system's use of the base 10. For example, each unit of length in the system is related to all other measures of length in the system by a multiple of 10. There are 10 millimeters in a centimeter; 100 centimeters in a meter; 1000 meters in a kilometer.

Measures of length in the English system, in contrast, do not relate to each other in a regular way. Inches are routinely divided into 16ths; there are 12 inches in a foot; 3 feet in a yard; 5280 feet (or 1760 yards) in a mile.

If you have grown up in the United States and are accustomed to using the English system, it is extremely important to begin developing a working familiarity with metric units and values. **Tables B1.1** and **B1.2** (see B:2) should help you get started with this process.

As an example, consider the following question: An American football field is 120 yards long, while rugby fields are 144 meters

TABLE B1.1 **Metric System Units and Conversions**

| Measurement | Unit of Measurement and Abbreviation | Metric System Equivalent | Converting Metric Units to English Units |
|---|---|---|---|
| Length | kilometer (km) | $1\ km = 1000\ m = 10^3\ m$ | 1 km = 0.62 mile |
| | meter (m) | 1 m = 100 cm | 1 m = 1.09 yards = 3.28 feet = 39.37 inches |
| | centimeter (cm) | $1\ cm = 0.01\ m = 10^{-2}\ m$ | 1 cm = 0.3937 inch |
| | millimeter (mm) | $1\ mm = 0.001\ m = 10^{-3}\ m$ | 1 mm = 0.039 inch |
| | micrometer (μm) | $1\ \mu m = 10^{-6}\ m = 10^{-3}\ mm$ | |
| | nanometer (nm) | $1\ nm = 10^{-9}\ m = 10^{-3}\ \mu m$ | |
| Area | hectare (ha) | $1\ ha = 10{,}000\ m^2$ | 1 ha = 2.47 acres |
| | square meter (m²) | $1\ m^2 = 10{,}000\ cm^2$ | $1\ m^2 = 1.196$ square yards |
| | square centimeter (cm²) | $1\ cm^2 = 100\ mm^2 = 10^{-4}\ m^2$ | $1\ cm^2 = 0.155$ square inch |
| Volume | liter (L) | 1 L = 1000 mL | 1 L = 1.06 quarts |
| | milliliter (mL) | $1\ mL = 1000\ \mu L = 10^{-3}\ L$ | 1 mL = 0.034 fluid ounce |
| | microliter (μL) | $1\ \mu L = 10^{-6}\ L$ | |
| Mass | kilogram (kg) | 1 kg = 1000 g | 1 kg = 2.20 pounds |
| | gram (g) | 1 g = 1000 mg | 1 g = 0.035 ounce |
| | milligram (mg) | $1\ mg = 1000\ \mu g = 10^{-3}\ g$ | |
| | microgram (μg) | $1\ \mu g = 10^{-6}\ g$ | |
| Temperature | Kelvin (K)* | | $K = °C + 273.15$ |
| | degrees Celsius (°C) | | $°C = \frac{5}{9}(°F - 32)$ |
| | degrees Fahrenheit (°F) | | $°F = \frac{9}{5}°C + 32$ |

*Absolute zero is −273.15 °C = 0 K.

## TABLE B1.2 Prefixes Used in the Metric System

| Prefix | Abbreviation | Definition |
|--------|--------------|------------|
| nano– | n | $0.000\,000\,001 = 10^{-9}$ |
| micro– | μ | $0.000\,001 = 10^{-6}$ |
| milli– | m | $0.001 = 10^{-3}$ |
| centi– | c | $0.01 = 10^{-2}$ |
| deci– | d | $0.1 = 10^{-1}$ |
| – | – | $1 = 10^{0}$ |
| kilo– | k | $1000 = 10^{3}$ |
| mega– | M | $1\,000\,000 = 10^{6}$ |
| giga– | G | $1\,000\,000\,000 = 10^{9}$ |

long. In yards, how much longer is a rugby field than an American football field? To solve this problem, first convert meters to yards: 144 m × 1.09 yards/m = 157 yards (note that the unit "m" cancels out). The difference in yards is thus: 157 – 120 = 37 yards. If you did these calculations on a calculator, you might have come up with 36.96 yards. Why has the number of yards been rounded off? The answer lies in significant figures. Let's take a closer look.

## Significant Figures

Significant figures or "sig figs"—the number of digits used to report the measurement—are critical when reporting scientific data. The number of significant figures in a measurement, such as 3.524, is the number of digits that are known with some degree of confidence (3, 5, and 2) plus the last digit (4), which is an estimate or approximation. How do scientists know how many digits to report?

## Rules for Working with Significant Figures

The rules for counting significant figures are summarized here:

- All nonzero numbers are always significant.

- Leading zeros are never significant; these zeros do nothing but set the decimal point.

- Embedded zeros are always significant.

- Trailing zeros are significant *only* if the decimal point is specified (Hint: Change the number to scientific notation. It is easier to see the "trailing" zeros.)

**Table B1.3** provides examples of how to apply these rules. The bottom line is that significant figures indicate the precision of measurements.

## Precision versus Accuracy

If biologists count the number of bird eggs in a nest, they report the data as an exact number—say, 3 eggs. But if the same biologists are measuring the diameter of the eggs, the numbers will be inexact. Just how inexact they are depends on the equipment used to make the measurements. For example, if you measure the width of your textbook with a ruler several times, you'll get essentially the same measurement again and again. Precision refers to how closely individual measurements agree with each other. So, you have determined the length with precision, but how do you know if the ruler was accurate to begin with?

Accuracy refers to how closely a measured value agrees with the correct value. You don't know the accuracy of a measuring device unless you calibrate it, by comparing it against a ruler that is known to be accurate. As the sensitivity of equipment used to

## check your understanding

**If you understand BioSkill 1**

✔ You should be able to . . .

1. **QUANTITATIVE** Calculate how many miles a runner completes in a 5.0-kilometer run.

2. **QUANTITATIVE** Calculate your normal body temperature in degrees Celsius (Normal body temperature is 98.6°F.).

3. **QUANTITATIVE** Calculate your current weight in kilograms.

4. **QUANTITATIVE** Calculate how many liters of milk you would need to buy to get approximately the same volume as a gallon of milk.

5. **QUANTITATIVE** Multiply the measurements 2.8723 and 1.6. How many significant figures does your answer have? Why?

## TABLE B1.3 Rules for Working with Significant Figures

| Example | Number of Significant Figures | Scientific Notation | Rule |
|---------|-------------------------------|---------------------|------|
| 35,200 | 5 | $3.52 \times 10^{4}$ | All nonzero numbers are always significant |
| 0.00352 | 3 | $3.52 \times 10^{-3}$ | Leading zeros are not significant |
| 1.035 | 4 | $1.035\,(\times 10^{0})$ | Imbedded zeros are always significant |
| 200 | 1 | $2 \times 10^{2}$ | Trailing zeros are significant only if the decimal point is specified |
| 200.0 | 4 | $2.000 \times 10^{2}$ | Trailing zeros are significant only if the decimal point is specified |

make a measurement increases, the number of significant figures increases. For example, if you used a kitchen scale to weigh out some sodium chloride, it might be accurate to $3 \pm 1$ g (1 significant figure); but an analytical balance in the lab might be accurate to $3.524 \pm 0.001$ g (4 significant figures).

In science, only the numbers that have significance—that are obtained from measurement—are reported. It is important to follow the "sig fig rules" when reporting a measurement, so that data do not appear to be more accurate than the equipment allows.

## Combining Measurements

How do you deal with combining measurements with different degrees of accuracy and precision? The simple rule to follow is that the accuracy of the final answer can be no greater than the least accurate measurement. So, when you multiply or divide measurements, the answer can have no more significant figures than the least accurate measurement. When you add or subtract measurements, the answer can have no more decimal places than the least accurate measurement.

As an example, consider that you are adding the following measurements: 5.9522, 2.065, and 1.06. If you plug these numbers into your calculator, the answer your calculator will give you is 9.0772. However, this is incorrect—you must round your answer off to the nearest value, 9.08, to the least number of decimal places in your data.

It is important to nail down the concept of significant figures and to practice working with metric units and values. The Check Your Understanding questions in this BioSkill should help you get started with this process.

---

**BIOSKILL 2** some common Latin and Greek roots used in biology

| Greek or Latin Root | English Translation | Example Term |
|---|---|---|
| a, an | not | anaerobic |
| aero | air | aerobic |
| allo | other | allopatric |
| amphi | on both sides | amphipathic |
| anti | against | antibody |
| auto | self | autotroph |
| bi | two | bilateral symmetry |
| bio | life, living | bioinformatics |
| blast | bud, sprout | blastula |
| co | with | cofactor |
| cyto | cell | cytoplasm |
| di | two | diploid |
| ecto | outer | ectoparasite |
| endo | inner, within | endoparasite |
| epi | outer, upon | epidermis |
| exo | outside | exothermic |
| glyco | sugary | glycolysis |
| hetero | different | heterozygous |
| homo | alike | homozygous |
| hydro | water | hydrolysis |
| hyper | over, more than | hypertonic |
| hypo | under, less than | hypotonic |
| inter | between | interspecific |
| intra | within | intraspecific |
| iso | same | isotonic |
| logo, logy | study of | morphology |
| lyse, lysis | loosen, burst | glycolysis |
| macro | large | macromolecule |

| Greek or Latin Root | English Translation | Example Term |
|---|---|---|
| meta | change, turning point | metamorphosis |
| micro | small | microfilament |
| morph | form | morphology |
| oligo | few | oligopeptide |
| para | beside | parathyroid gland |
| photo | light | photosynthesis |
| poly | many | polymer |
| soma | body | somatic cells |
| sym, syn | together | symbiotic, synapsis |
| trans | across | translation |
| tri | three | trisomy |
| zygo | yoked together | zygote |

check your understanding

**If you understand BioSkill 2**

✔ **You should be able to . . .**

Provide literal translations of the following terms:

1. heterozygote
2. glycolysis
3. morphology
4. trisomy

Graphs are the most common way to report data, for a simple reason. Compared to reading raw numerical values in a table or list, a graph makes it much easier to understand what the data mean.

Learning how to read and interpret graphs is one of the most basic skills you'll need to acquire as a biology student. As when learning piano or soccer or anything else, you need to understand a few key ideas to get started and then have a chance to practice—a lot—with some guidance and feedback.

## Getting Started

To start reading a graph, you need to do three things: read the axes, figure out what the data points represent—that is, where they came from—and think about the overall message of the data. Let's consider each step in turn.

### What Do the Axes Represent?

Graphs have two axes: one horizontal and one vertical. The horizontal axis of a graph is also called the *x*-axis or the abscissa. The vertical axis of a graph is also called the *y*-axis or the ordinate. Each axis represents a variable that takes on a range of values. These values are indicated by the ticks and labels on the axis. Note that each axis should *always* be clearly labeled with the unit or treatment it represents.

**FIGURE B3.1** shows a scatterplot—a type of graph where continuous data are graphed on each axis. Continuous data can take an array of values over a range. In contrast, discrete data can take only a restricted set of values. If you were graphing the average height of men and women in your class, height is a continuous variable, but gender is a discrete variable.

For the example in this figure, the *x*-axis represents time in units of generations of maize; the *y*-axis represents the average percentage of the dry weight of a maize kernel that is protein.

To create a graph, researchers plot the independent variable on the *x*-axis and the dependent variable on the *y*-axis (Figure B3.1a). The terms independent and dependent are used because the values on the *y*-axis depend on the *x*-axis values. In our example, the researchers wanted to show how the protein content of maize kernels in a study population changed over time. Thus, the protein concentration plotted on the *y*-axis depended on the year (generation) plotted on the *x*-axis. The value on the *y*-axis always depends on the value on the *x*-axis, but not vice versa.

In many graphs in biology, the independent variable is either time or the various treatments used in an experiment. In these cases, the *y*-axis records how some quantity changes as a function of time or as the outcome of the treatments applied to the experimental cells or organisms.

**(a) Read the axes**—what is being plotted?

**(b) Look at the bars or data points**—what do they represent?

**(c) What's the punchline?**

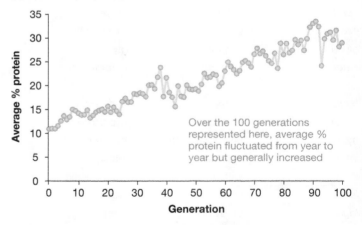

**FIGURE B3.1  Scatterplots Are Used to Graph Continuous Data.**

## What Do the Data Points Represent?

Once you've read the axes, you need to figure out what each data point is. In our maize kernel example, the data point in Figure B3.1b represents the average percentage of protein found in a sample of kernels from a study population in a particular generation.

If it's difficult to figure out what the data points are, ask yourself where they came from—meaning, how the researchers got them. You can do this by understanding how the study was done and by understanding what is being plotted on each axis. The y-axis will tell you what they measured; the x-axis will usually tell you when they measured it or what group was measured. In some cases—for example, in a plot of average body size versus average brain size in primates—the x-axis will report a second variable that was measured.

In other cases, a data point on a graph may represent a relative or arbitrary unit of measurement. The data point shows the ratio of the amount of a substance, intensity, or other quantities, relative to a predetermined reference measurement. For example, the y-axis might show the percentage of relative activity of an enzyme—the rate of the enzyme-catalyzed reaction, scaled to the highest rate of activity observed (100 percent)—in experiments conducted under conditions that are identical except for one variable, such as pH or temperature (see Figure 8.14).

## What Is the Overall Trend or Message?

Look at the data as a whole, and figure out what they mean. Figure B3.1c suggests an interpretation of the maize kernel example. If the graph shows how some quantity changes over time, ask yourself if that quantity is increasing, decreasing, fluctuating up and down, or staying the same. Then ask whether the pattern is the same over time or whether it changes over time.

When you're interpreting a graph, it's extremely important to limit your conclusions to the data presented. Don't extrapolate beyond the data, unless you are explicitly making a prediction based on the assumption that present trends will continue. For example, you can't say that the average percentage of protein content was increasing in the population before the experiment started, or that it will continue to increase in the future. You can say only what the data tell you.

## Types of Graphs

Many of the graphs in this text are scatterplots like the one shown in Figure B3.1c, where individual data points are plotted. But you will also come across other types of graphs in this text.

### Scatterplots, Lines, and Curves

*Scatterplots* sometimes have data points that are by themselves, but at other times data points will be connected by dot-to-dot lines to help make the overall trend clearer, as in Figure B3.1c, or may have a smooth line through them.

A *smooth line* through data points—sometimes straight, sometimes curved—is a mathematical "line of best fit." A line of best fit represents a mathematical function that summarizes the relationship between the x and y variables. It is "best" in the sense of fitting the data points most precisely. The line may pass through some of the points, none of the points, or all of the points.

*Curved lines* often take on characteristic shapes depending on the relationships between the x and y variable. For example, a bell-shaped curve depicts a normal distribution in which most data points are clumped near the middle, while a sigmoid or S-shaped curve exhibits small changes at first, which then accelerate and approach maximal value over time. Data from studies on population growth (see Chapter 54), enzyme kinetics (see Chapter 8), and oxygen–hemoglobin dissociation (see Chapter 45) typically fall on a curved line.

### Bar Charts, Histograms, and Box-and-Whisker Plots

Scatterplots, or line-of-best-fit graphs, are the most appropriate type of graph when the data have a continuous range of values and you want to show individual data points. But other types of graphs are used to represent different types of distributions:

- *Bar charts* plot data that have discrete or categorical values instead of a continuous range of values. In many cases the bars might represent different treatment groups in an experiment, as in **FIGURE B3.2a** (see B:6). In this graph, the height of the bar indicates the average value. Statistical tests can be used to determine whether a difference between treatment groups is significant (see **BIOSKILLS 4**).

- *Histograms* illustrate frequency data and can be plotted as numbers or percentages. **FIGURE B3.2b** shows an example where height is plotted on the x-axis, and the number of students in a population is plotted on the y-axis. Each rectangle indicates the number of individuals in each interval of height, which reflects the relative frequency, in this population, of people whose heights are in that interval. The measurements could also be recalculated so that the y-axis would report the proportion of people in each interval. Then the sum of all the bars would equal 100 percent. Note that if you were to draw a smooth curve connecting the top of the bars on this histogram, the smooth curve would represent the shape of a bell.

- *Box-and-whisker plots* allow you to easily see where most of the data fall. Each box indicates where half of the data numbers are. The whiskers indicate the lower extreme and the upper extreme of the data. The vertical line inside each box indicates the median—meaning that half of the data are above this value and half are below (see Figure 1.9 for an example).

When you are looking at a bar chart that plots values from different treatments in an experiment, ask yourself if these values are the same or different. If the bar chart reports averages over discrete ranges of values, ask what trend is implied—as you would for a scatterplot.

**(a)** Bar chart

**(b)** Histogram

**FIGURE B3.2 Bar Charts and Histograms.** **(a)** Bar charts are used to graph data that are discontinuous or categorical. **(b)** Histograms show the distribution of frequencies or values in a population.

When you are looking at a histogram, ask whether there is a "hump" in the data—indicating a group of values that are more frequent than others. Is the hump in the center of the distribution of values, toward the left, or toward the right? If so, what does it mean?

Similarly, when you are looking at a box-and-whisker plot, ask yourself what information the graph gives you. What is the range of values for the data? Where are half the data points? Below what value is three quarters of the data?

## Getting Practice

Working with this text will give you lots of practice with reading graphs—they appear in almost every chapter. In many cases we've inserted an arrow to represent your instructor's hand at the whiteboard, with a label that suggests an interpretation or draws your attention to an important point on the graph. In other cases, you should be able to figure out what the data mean on your own or with the help of other students or your instructor.

check your understanding

**If you understand BioSkill 3**
✔ You should be able to . . .

1. **QUANTITATIVE** Determine the total change in average percentage of protein in maize kernels, from the start of the experiment until the end.

2. **QUANTITATIVE** Determine the trend in average percentage of protein in maize kernels between generation 37 and generation 42.

3. Explain whether the conclusions from the bar chart in Figure B3.2a would be different if the data and label for Treatment 3 were put on the far left and the data and label for Treatment 1 on the far right.

4. **QUANTITATIVE** Determine approximately how many students in this class are 70 inches tall, by using Figure B3.2b.

5. **QUANTITATIVE** Determine the most common height in the class graphed in Figure B3.2b.

---

# BIOSKILL 4 — using statistical tests and interpreting standard error bars

When biologists do an experiment, they collect data on individuals in a treatment group and a control group, or several such comparison groups. Then they want to know whether the individuals in the two (or more) groups are different. For example, in one experiment student researchers measured how fast a product formed when they set up a reaction with three different concentrations of reactants (introduced in Chapter 8). Each treatment—meaning, each combination of reactant concentrations—was replicated many times.

**FIGURE B4.1** graphs the average reaction rate for each of the three treatments in the experiment. Note that Treatments 1, 2, and 3 represent increasing concentrations of reactants. The thin

"I-beams" on each bar indicate the standard error of each average. The standard error is a quantity that indicates the uncertainty in the calculation of an average.

For example, if two trials with the same concentration of reactants had a reaction rate of 0.075 and two trials had a reaction rate of 0.025, then the average reaction rate would be 0.050. In this case, the standard error would be large. But if two trials had a reaction rate of 0.051 and two had a reaction rate of 0.049, the average would still be 0.050, but the standard error would be small.

In effect, the standard error quantifies how confident you are that the average you've calculated is the average you'd observe if

FIGURE B4.1 **Standard Error Bars Indicate the Uncertainty in an Average.**

you did the experiment under the same conditions an extremely large number of times. It is a measure of precision (see **BIOSKILLS 1**).

Once they had calculated these averages and standard errors, the students wanted to answer a question: Does reaction rate increase when reactant concentration increases?

After looking at the data, you might conclude that the answer is yes. But how could you come to a conclusion like this objectively, instead of subjectively?

The answer is to use a statistical test. This can be thought of as a three-step process.

1. Specify the null hypothesis, which is that reactant concentration has no effect on reaction rate.

2. Calculate a test statistic, which is a number that characterizes the size of the difference among the treatments. In this case, the test statistic compares the actual differences in reaction rates among treatments to the difference predicted by the null hypothesis. The null hypothesis predicts that there should be no difference.

3. The third step is to determine the probability of getting a test statistic at least as large as the one calculated just by chance. The answer comes from a reference distribution—a mathematical function that specifies the probability of getting various values of the test statistic if the null hypothesis is correct. (If you take a statistics course, you'll learn which test

statistics and reference distributions are relevant to different types of data.)

You are very likely to see small differences among treatment groups just by chance—even if no differences actually exist. If you flipped a coin 10 times, for example, you are unlikely to get exactly five heads and five tails, even if the coin is fair. A reference distribution tells you how likely you are to get each of the possible outcomes of the 10 flips if the coin is fair, just by chance.

In this case, the reference distribution indicated that if the null hypothesis of no actual difference in reaction rates is correct, you would see differences at least as large as those observed only 0.01 percent of the time just by chance. By convention, biologists consider a difference among treatment groups to be statistically significant if there is less than a 5 percent probability of observing it just by chance. Based on this convention, the student researchers were able to claim that the null hypothesis is not correct for reactant concentration. According to their data, the reaction they studied really does happen faster when reactant concentration increases.

You'll likely be doing actual statistical tests early in your undergraduate career. To use this text, though, you only need to know what statistical testing does. And you should take care to inspect the standard error bars on graphs in this book. As a *very* rough rule of thumb, averages often turn out to be significantly different, according to an appropriate statistical test, if there is no overlap between two times the standard errors.

In several cases in this text, you'll need to combine probabilities from different events in order to solve a problem. One of the most common applications is in genetics problems. For example, Punnett squares work because they are based on two fundamental rules of probability. Each rule pertains to a distinct situation.

## The Both-And Rule

The both-and rule—also known as the product rule or multiplication rule—applies when you want to know the probability that two or more independent events occur together. Let's use the rolling of two dice as an example. What is the probability of rolling two sixes? These two events are independent, because the probability of rolling a six on one die has no effect on the probability of rolling a six on the other die. (In the same way, the probability of getting a gamete with allele R from one parent has no effect on the probability of getting a gamete with allele R from the other parent. Gametes fuse randomly.)

The probability of rolling a six on the first die is 1/6. The probability of rolling a six on the second die is also 1/6. The probability of rolling a six on *both* dice, then, is $1/6 \times 1/6 = 1/36$. In other words, if you rolled two dice 36 times, on average you would expect to roll two sixes once.

In the case of a cross between two parents heterozygous at the R gene, the probability of getting allele R from the father is 1/2 and the probability of getting R from the mother is 1/2. Thus, the probability of getting both alleles and creating an offspring with genotype RR is $1/2 \times 1/2 = 1/4$.

## The Either-Or Rule

The either-or rule—also known as the sum rule or addition rule—applies when you want to know the probability of an event happening when there are several different ways for the same event or outcome to occur. In this case, the probability that the event will occur is the sum of the probabilities of each way that it can occur.

For example, suppose you wanted to know the probability of rolling either a one or a six when you toss a die. The probability of drawing each is 1/6, so the probability of getting one or the other is $1/6 + 1/6 = 1/3$. If you rolled a die three times, on average you'd expect to get a one or a six once.

In the case of a cross between two parents heterozygous at the R gene, the probability of getting an R allele from the father and an r allele from the mother is $1/2 \times 1/2 = 1/4$. Similarly, the probability of getting an r allele from the father and an R allele from the mother is $1/2 \times 1/2 = 1/4$. Thus, the combined probability of getting the Rr genotype in either of the two ways is $1/4 + 1/4 = 1/2$.

## check your understanding

**If you understand BioSkill 5**

✔ **You should be able to . . .**

1. **QUANTITATIVE** Calculate the probability of getting four "tails" if four students each toss a coin.

2. **QUANTITATIVE** Calculate the probability of getting a two, a three, or a six after a single roll of a die.

You have probably been introduced to logarithms and logarithmic notation in algebra courses, and you will encounter logarithms at several points in this course. Logarithms are a way of working with powers—meaning, numbers that are multiplied by themselves one or more times.

Scientists use exponential notation to represent powers. For example,

$$a^x = y$$

means that if you multiply $a$ by itself $x$ times, you get $y$. In exponential notation, $a$ is called the base and $x$ is called the exponent. The entire expression is called an exponential function.

What if you know $y$ and $a$, and you want to know $x$? This is where logarithms come in. You can solve for exponents using logarithms. For example,

$$x = \log_a y$$

This equation reads, $x$ is equal to the logarithm of $y$ to the base $a$. Logarithms are a way of working with exponential functions. They are important because so many processes in biology (and chemistry and physics, for that matter) are exponential. To understand what's going on, you have to describe the process with an exponential function and then use logarithms to work with that function.

Although a base can be any number, most scientists use just two bases when they employ logarithmic notation: 10 and $e$ (sometimes called Euler's number after Swiss mathematician Leonhard Euler). What is $e$? It is a rate of exponential growth shared by many natural processes, where $e$ is the limit of $(1 + \frac{1}{n})^n$ (as $n$ tends to infinity). Mathematicians have shown that the base $e$ is an irrational number (like $\pi$) that is approximately equal to 2.718. Like 10, $e$ is just a number; $10^0 = 1$ and, likewise, $e^0 = 1$. But both 10 and $e$ have qualities that make them convenient to use in biology (as well as chemistry and physics).

Logarithms to the base 10 are so common that they are usually symbolized in the form $\log y$ instead of $\log_{10} y$. A logarithm to the base $e$ is called a natural logarithm and is symbolized ln (pronounced *EL-EN*) instead of log. You write "the natural logarithm of $y$" as ln $y$.

Most scientific calculators have keys that allow you to solve problems involving base 10 and base $e$. For example, if you know $y$, they'll tell you what $\log y$ or $\ln y$ are—meaning that they'll solve for $x$ in our first example equation. They'll also allow you to find a number when you know its logarithm to base 10 or base $e$. Stated another way, they'll tell you what $y$ is if you know $x$, and $y$ is equal to $e^x$ or $10^x$. This is called taking an antilog. In most cases, you'll use the inverse or second function button on your calculator to find an antilog (above the log or ln key).

To get some practice with your calculator, consider this equation:

$$10^2 = 100$$

If you enter 100 in your calculator and then press the log key, the screen should say 2. The logarithm tells you what the exponent is. Now press the antilog key while 2 is on the screen. The calculator screen should return to 100. The antilog solves the exponential function, given the base and the exponent.

If your background in algebra isn't strong, you'll want to get more practice working with logarithms—you'll see them frequently during your undergraduate career. Remember that once you understand the basic notation, there's nothing mysterious about logarithms. They are simply a way of working with exponential functions, which describe what happens when something is multiplied by itself a number of times—like cells that divide and then divide again and then again.

Using logarithms will also come up when you are studying something that can have a large range of values, like the concentration of hydrogen ions in a solution or the intensity of sound that the human ear can detect. In cases like this, it's convenient to express the numbers involved as exponents. Using exponents makes a large range of numbers smaller and more manageable. For example, instead of saying that hydrogen ion concentration in a solution can range from 1 to $10^{-14}$, the pH scale allows you to simply say that it ranges from 1 to 14. Instead of giving the actual value, you're expressing it as an exponent. It just simplifies things.

## check your understanding

**If you understand BioSkill 6**

✔ **You should be able to . . .**

Use the equation $N_t = N_0 e^{rt}$ (see Chapter 54).

1. Explain what type of function this equation describes.

2. **QUANTITATIVE** Determine how you would write the equation, after taking the natural logarithm of both sides.

Phylogenetic trees show the evolutionary relationships among species, just as a genealogy shows the relationships among people in your family. They are unusual diagrams, however, and it can take practice to interpret them correctly.

To understand how evolutionary trees work, consider **FIGURE B7.1**. Notice that a phylogenetic tree consists of a root (the most ancestral branch in the tree), branches, nodes, and tips.

- Branches represent populations through time. In this text, branches are drawn as horizontal lines. In most cases the length of the branch is arbitrary and has no meaning, but in some cases branch lengths are proportional to time or the extent of genetic difference among populations (if so, there will be a scale at the bottom of the tree). The vertical lines on the tree represent splitting events, where one group broke into two independent groups. Their length is arbitrary—chosen simply to make the tree more readable.

- Nodes (also called forks) occur where an ancestral group splits into two or more descendant groups (see point A in Figure B7.1). Thus, each node represents the most recent common ancestor of the two or more descendant populations that emerge from it. If more than two descendant groups emerge from a node, the node is called a polytomy (see node C). A polytomy usually means that the populations split from one another so quickly that it is not possible to tell which split off earlier or later.

- Tips (also called terminal nodes) are the tree's endpoints, which represent groups living today or a dead end—a branch

ending in extinction. The names at the tips can represent species or larger groups such as mammals or conifers.

Recall that a taxon (plural: taxa) is any named group of organisms (see Chapter 1). A taxon could be a single species, such as *Homo sapiens*, or a large group of species, such as Primates. Tips connected by a single node on a tree are called sister taxa.

The phylogenetic trees used in this text are all rooted. This means that the first, or most basal, node on the tree—the one on the far left in this book—is the most ancient. To determine where the root on a tree occurs, biologists include one or more outgroup species when they are collecting data to estimate a particular phylogeny. An outgroup is a taxonomic group that is known to have diverged before the rest of the taxa in the study. Outgroups are used to establish whether a trait is ancestral or derived. An ancestral trait is a characteristic that existed in an ancestor; a derived trait is a characteristic that is a modified form of the ancestral trait, found in a descendant.

In Figure B7.1, Taxon 1 is an outgroup to the monophyletic group consisting of taxa 2–6. A monophyletic group consists of an ancestral species and all of its descendants. The root of a tree is placed between the outgroup and the monophyletic group being studied. This position in Figure B7.1 is node A. Note that black hash marks are used to indicate a derived trait that is shared among the red branches, and another derived trait that is shared among the orange branches.

Understanding monophyletic groups is fundamental to reading and estimating phylogenetic trees. Monophyletic groups may also be called lineages or clades and can be identified using the "one-snip test": If you cut any branch on a phylogenetic tree, all of the branches and tips that fall off represent a monophyletic group. Using the one-snip test, you should be able to convince yourself that the monophyletic groups on a tree are nested. In Figure B7.1, for example, the monophyletic group comprising node A and taxa 1–6 contains a monophyletic group consisting of node B and taxa 2–6, which includes the monophyletic group represented by node C and taxa 4–6.

To put all these new terms and concepts to work, consider the phylogenetic tree in **FIGURE B7.2**, which shows the relationships between common chimpanzees and six human and humanlike species that lived over the past 5–6 million years. Chimps functioned as an outgroup in the analysis that led to this tree, so the root was placed at node A. The branches marked in red identify a monophyletic group called the hominins.

To practice how to read a tree, put your finger at the tree's root, at the far left, and work your way to the right. At node A, the ancestral population split into two descendant populations. One of these populations eventually evolved into today's chimps; the other gave rise to the six species of hominins pictured. Now

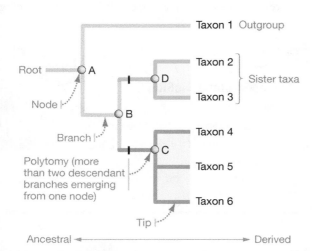

**FIGURE B7.1 Phylogenetic Trees Have Roots, Branches, Nodes, and Tips.**

✔**EXERCISE** Circle all four monophyletic groups present.

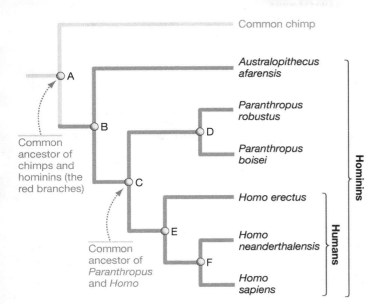

**FIGURE B7.2 An Example of a Phylogenetic Tree.** A phylogenetic tree showing the relationships of species in the monophyletic group called hominins.

✔**EXERCISE** All of the hominins walked on two legs—unlike chimps and all of the other primates. Add a mark on the phylogeny to show where upright posture evolved, and label it "origin of walking on two legs." Circle and label a pair of sister species. Label an outgroup to the monophyletic group called humans (species in the genus *Homo*).

continue moving your finger toward the tips of the tree until you hit node C. It should make sense to you that at this splitting event, one descendant population eventually gave rise to two *Paranthropus* species, while the other became the ancestor of humans—species in the genus *Homo*. As you study Figure B7.2, consider these two important points:

1. There are many equivalent ways of drawing this tree. For example, this version shows *Homo sapiens* on the bottom. But the tree would be identical if the two branches emerging from node E were rotated 180°, so that the species appeared in the order *Homo sapiens*, *Homo neanderthalensis*, *Homo erectus*. Trees are read from root to tips, not from top to bottom or bottom to top.

2. No species on any tree is any higher or lower than any other. Chimps and *Homo sapiens* have been evolving exactly the same amount of time since their divergence from a common ancestor—neither species is higher or lower than the other. It is legitimate to say that more ancient groups like *Australopithecus afarensis* have traits that are ancestral or more basal—meaning, that appeared earlier in evolution—compared to traits that appear in *Homo sapiens*, which are referred to as more derived.

**FIGURE B7.3** presents a chance to test your tree-reading ability. Five of the six trees shown in this diagram are identical in terms of the evolutionary relationships they represent. One differs. The key to understanding the difference is to recognize that the ordering of tips does not matter in a tree—only the ordering of nodes (branch points) matters. You can think of a tree as being like a mobile: The tips can rotate without changing the underlying relationships.

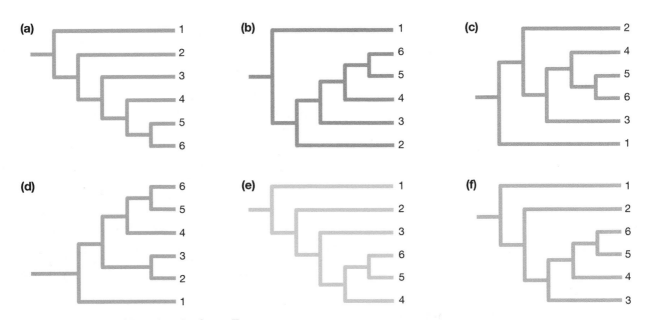

**FIGURE B7.3 Alternative Ways of Drawing the Same Tree.**

✔**QUESTION** Five of these six trees describe exactly the same relationships among taxa 1 through 6. Identify the tree that is different from the other five.

If you haven't had much chemistry yet, learning basic biological chemistry can be a challenge. One stumbling block is simply being able to read chemical structures efficiently and understand what they mean. This skill will come much easier once you have a little notation under your belt and you understand some basic symbols.

Atoms are the basic building blocks of everything in the universe, just as cells are the basic building blocks of your body. Every atom has a one- or two-letter symbol. **Table B8.1** shows the symbols for most of the atoms you'll encounter in this book. You should memorize these. The table also offers details on how the atoms form bonds as well as how they are represented in some visual models.

When atoms attach to each other by covalent bonding, a molecule forms. Biologists have a couple of different ways of representing molecules—you'll see each of these in the book and in class.

- Molecular formulas like those in **FIGURE B8.1a** simply list the atoms present in a molecule. Subscripts indicate how many of each atom are present. If the formula has no subscript, only one atom of that type is present. A methane (natural gas) molecule, for example, can be written as $CH_4$. It consists of one carbon atom and four hydrogen atoms.

TABLE B8.1 **Some Attributes of Atoms Found in Organisms**

| Atom | Symbol | Number of Bonds It Can Form | Standard Color Code* |
|---|---|---|---|
| Hydrogen | H | 1 | white |
| Carbon | C | 4 | black |
| Nitrogen | N | 3 | blue |
| Oxygen | O | 2 | red |
| Sodium | Na | 1 | — |
| Magnesium | Mg | 2 | — |
| Phosphorus | P | 5 | orange or purple |
| Sulfur | S | 2 | yellow |
| Chlorine | Cl | 1 | — |
| Potassium | K | 1 | — |
| Calcium | Ca | 2 | — |

*In ball-and-stick or space-filling models.

- Structural formulas like those in **FIGURE B8.1b** show which atoms in the molecule are bonded to each other. Each bond is indicated by a dash. The structural formula for methane in-

|  | Methane | Ammonia | Water | Oxygen |
|---|---|---|---|---|
| **a)** Molecular formulas: | $CH_4$ | $NH_3$ | $H_2O$ | $O_2$ |
| **b)** Structural formulas: | | | | |
| **c)** Ball-and-stick models: | | | | |
| **d)** Space-filling models: | | | | |

**FIGURE B8.1 Molecules Can Be Represented in Several Different Ways.**

✓**EXERCISE** Carbon dioxide consists of a carbon atom that forms a double bond with each of two oxygen atoms, for a total of four bonds. It is a linear molecule. Write carbon dioxide's molecular formula and then draw its structural formula, a ball-and-stick model, and a space-filling model.

dicates that each of the four hydrogen atoms forms one covalent bond with carbon, and that carbon makes a total of four covalent bonds. Single covalent bonds are symbolized by a single dash; double bonds are indicated by two dashes.

Even simple molecules have distinctive shapes, because different atoms make covalent bonds at different angles. Ball-and-stick and space-filling models show the geometry of the bonds accurately.

- In a ball-and-stick model, a stick is used to represent each covalent bond (see **FIGURE B8.1c**).
- In space-filling models, the atoms are simply stuck onto each other in their proper places (see **FIGURE B8.1d**).

To learn more about a molecule when you look at a chemical structure, ask yourself three questions:

1. *Is the molecule polar—meaning that some parts are more negatively or positively charged than others?* Molecules that contain nitrogen or oxygen atoms are often polar, because these atoms have such high electronegativity (see Chapter 2). This trait is important because polar molecules dissolve in water.

2. *Does the structural formula show atoms that might participate in chemical reactions?* For example, are there charged atoms or amino or carboxyl ($-COOH$) groups that might act as a base or an acid?

3. *In ball-and-stick and especially space-filling models of large molecules, are there interesting aspects of overall shape?* For example, is there a groove where a protein might bind to DNA, or a cleft where a substrate might undergo a reaction in an enzyme?

# BIOSKILL 9 separating and visualizing molecules

To study a molecule, you have to be able to isolate it. Isolating a molecule is a two-step process: the molecule has to be separated from other molecules in a mixture and then physically picked out or located in a purified form. **BIOSKILLS 9** focuses on the techniques that biologists use to separate nucleic acids and proteins and then find the particular one they are interested in.

## Using Electrophoresis to Separate Molecules

In molecular biology, the standard technique for separating proteins and nucleic acids is called gel electrophoresis or, simply, electrophoresis (literally, "electricity-moving"). You may be using electrophoresis in a lab for this course, and you will certainly be analyzing data derived from electrophoresis in this text.

The principle behind electrophoresis is simple. Proteins (when denatured and coated with a special detergent) and nucleic acids carry a charge. As a result, these molecules move when placed in an electric field. Negatively charged molecules move toward the positive electrode; positively charged molecules move toward the negative electrode.

To separate a mixture of macromolecules so that each one can be isolated and analyzed, researchers place the sample in a gelatinous substance. More specifically, the sample is placed in a "well"—a slot in a sheet or slab of the gelatinous substance. The "gel" itself consists of long molecules that form a matrix of fibers. The gelatinous matrix has pores that act like a sieve through which the molecules can pass.

When an electrical field is applied across the gel, the molecules in the well move through the gel toward an electrode. Molecules that are smaller or more highly charged for their size move faster than do larger or less highly charged molecules. As they move, then, the molecules separate by size and by charge. Small and highly charged molecules end up at the bottom of the gel; large, less-charged molecules remain near the top.

### An Example "Run"

**FIGURE B9.1** (see B:14) shows the electrophoresis setup used in an experiment investigating how RNA molecules polymerize. In this case, the investigators wanted to document how long RNA molecules became over time, when ribonucleoside triphosphates were present in a particular type of solution.

Step 1 shows how they loaded samples of macromolecules, taken on different days during the experiment, into wells at the top of the gel slab. This is a general observation: Each well holds a different sample. In this and many other cases, the researchers also filled a well with a sample containing fragments of known size, called a size standard or "ladder."

In step 2, the researchers immersed the gel in a solution that conducts electricity and applied a voltage across the gel. The molecules in each well started to run down the gel, forming a lane. After several hours of allowing the molecules to move, the researchers removed the electric field (step 3). By then, molecules of different size and charge had separated from one another. In this case, small RNA molecules had reached the bottom of the gel. Above them were larger RNA molecules, which had run more slowly.

**FIGURE B9.1 Macromolecules Can Be Separated via Gel Electrophoresis.**

✔**QUESTION** DNA and RNA run toward the positive electrode. Why are these molecules negatively charged?

## Why Do Separated Molecules Form Bands?

When researchers visualize a particular molecule on a gel, using techniques described in this section, the image that results consists of bands: shallow lines that are as wide as a lane in the gel. Why?

To understand the answer, study **FIGURE B9.2**. The left panel shows the original mixture of molecules. In this cartoon, the size of each dot represents the size of each molecule. The key is to realize that the original sample contains many copies of each specific molecule, and that these copies run down the length of the gel together—meaning, at the same rate—because they have the same size and charge.

It's that simple: Molecules that are alike form a band because they stay together.

## Using Thin Layer Chromatography to Separate Molecules

Gel electrophoresis is not the only way to separate molecules. Researchers also use a method called thin layer chromatography. This method was developed in the early 1900s by botanists who were analyzing the different-colored pigments from leaves of a plant (see Chapter 10), hence the name chromatography from the Greek words khroma for "color" and graphein, "to write."

In this method, rather than loading the sample into the well of a gel, the samples are deposited or "spotted" near the bottom of a stiff support, either glass or plastic, that is coated with a thin layer of silica gel, cellulose, or a similar porous material. The coated support is placed in a solvent solution. As the solvent

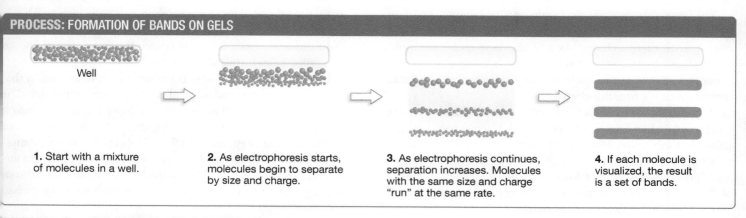

**FIGURE B9.2 On a Gel, Molecules That Are Alike Form Bands.**

wicks upward through the coating by capillary action, it carries the molecules in the mixture with it. Molecules are carried at different rates, based on their size and solubility in the solvent.

## Visualizing Molecules

Once molecules have been separated using electrophoresis or thin layer chromatography, they have to be detected. Unfortunately, although plant pigments are colored, proteins and nucleic acids are invisible unless they are tagged in some way. Let's first look at two of the most common tagging systems and then consider how researchers can tag and visualize specific molecules of interest and not others.

### Using Radioactive Isotopes and Autoradiography

When molecular biology was getting under way, the first types of tags in common use were radioactive isotopes—forms of atoms that are unstable and release energy in the form of radiation.

In the polymerization experiment diagrammed in Figure B9.1, for example, the researchers had attached a radioactive phosphorus atom to the monomers—ribonucleoside triphosphates—used in the original reaction mix. Once polymers formed, they contained radioactive atoms. When electrophoresis was complete, the investigators visualized the polymers by laying X-ray film over the gel. Because radioactive emissions expose film, a black dot appears wherever a radioactive atom is located in the gel. So many black dots occur so close together that the collection forms a dark band.

This technique for visualizing macromolecules is called autoradiography. The autoradiograph that resulted from the polymerization experiment is shown in **FIGURE B9.3**. The samples, taken on days 2, 4, 6, 8, and 14 of the experiment, are noted along the bottom. The far right lane contains macromolecules of known size; this lane is used to estimate the size of the molecules in the experimental samples. The bands that appear in each sample lane represent the different polymers that had formed.

### Reading a Gel

One of the keys to interpreting or "reading" a gel, or the corresponding autoradiograph, is to realize that darker bands contain more radioactive markers, indicating the presence of many radioactive molecules. Lighter bands contain fewer molecules.

To read a gel, then, you look for (1) the presence or absence of bands in some lanes—meaning, some experimental samples—versus others, and (2) contrasts in the darkness of the bands—meaning, differences in the number of molecules present.

For example, several conclusions can be drawn from the data in Figure B9.3. First, a variety of polymers formed at each stage. After the second day, for example, polymers from 12 to 18 monomers long had formed. Second, the overall length of polymers produced increased with time. At the end of the fourteenth day, most of the RNA molecules were between 20 and 40 monomers long.

**Polymerization of RNA**

Day:  2  4  6  8  14  Size standard

Number of nucleotides in RNA fragments: 40, 30, 20, 10

**FIGURE B9.3 Autoradiography Is a Technique for Visualizing Macromolecules.** The molecules in a gel can be visualized in a number of ways. In this case, the RNA molecules in the gel exposed an X-ray film because they had radioactive atoms attached. When developed, the film is called an autoradiograph.

Starting in the late 1990s and early 2000s, it became much more common to tag nucleic acids with fluorescent tags. Once electrophoresis is complete, fluorescence can be detected by exposing the gel to an appropriate wavelength of light; the fluorescent tag fluoresces or glows in response (fluorescence is explained in Chapter 10).

Fluorescent tags have important advantages over radioactive isotopes: (1) They are safer to handle. (2) They are faster—you don't have to wait hours or days for the radioactive isotope to expose a film. (3) They come in multiple colors, so you can tag several different molecules in the same experiment and detect them independently.

### Using Nucleic Acid Probes

In many cases, researchers want to find one specific molecule—a certain DNA sequence, for example—in the collection of molecules on a gel. How is this possible? The answer hinges on using a particular molecule as a probe.

You'll learn in more detail about how probes work in this text (Chapter 20). Here it's enough to get the general idea: A probe is a marked molecule that binds specifically to your molecule of interest. The "mark" is often a radioactive atom, a fluorescent tag, or an enzyme that catalyzes a color-forming or light-emitting reaction.

If you are looking for a particular DNA or RNA sequence on a gel, for example, you can expose the gel to a single-stranded probe that binds to the target sequence by complementary base pairing. Once it has bound, you can detect the band through autoradiography or fluorescence.

- *Southern blotting* is a technique for making DNA fragments that have been run out on a gel single stranded, transferring them from the gel to a nylon membrane, and then probing them to identify segments of interest. The technique was named after its inventor, Edwin Southern.

- *Northern blotting* is a technique for transferring RNA fragments from a gel to a nylon membrane and then probing them to detect target segments. The name is a lighthearted play on Southern blotting—the protocol from which it was derived.

## Using Antibody Probes

How can researchers find a particular protein out of a large collection of different proteins? The answer is to use an antibody. An antibody is a protein that binds specifically to a section of a different protein (see Chapter 51 if you want more detail on the structure of antibodies and their function in the immune system).

To use an antibody as a probe, investigators attach a tag molecule—often an enzyme that catalyzes a color-forming reaction—to the antibody and allow it to react with proteins in a mixture. The antibody will stick to the specific protein that it binds to and then can be visualized thanks to the tag it carries.

If the proteins in question have been separated by gel electrophoresis and transferred to a membrane, the result is called a western blot. The name western is an extension of the Southern and northern patterns.

## Using Radioimmunoassay and ELISA to Measure Amounts of Molecules

Another important method that makes use of antibodies is called a radioimmunoassay. This method is used when investigators want to measure tiny amounts of a molecule, such as a hormone in the blood. In this case, a known quantity of a hormone is labeled with a radioactive tag. This tagged hormone is then mixed with a known amount of antibody, and the two bind to one another. Next, a sample of blood, containing an unknown quantity of that same hormone, is added. The hormone from the blood and the radiolabeled hormone compete for antibody binding sites. As the concentration of unlabeled hormone increases, more of it binds to the antibody, displacing more of the radiolabeled hormone. The amount of unbound radiolabeled hormone is then measured. Using known standards as a reference, the amount of hormone in the blood can be determined.

Another commonly used technique based on similar principles is called ELISA (enzyme-linked immunosorbent assay). In this case, the amount of a particular molecule is measured using colorimetric signals instead of a radioactive signal.

check your understanding

**If you understand BioSkill 9**

✔ You should be able to . . .

Interpret a gel that has been stained for "RNA X." One lane contains no bands. Two lanes have a band in the same location, even though one of the bands is barely visible and the other is extremely dark. The fourth lane has a faint band located below the bands in the other lanes.

Biologists use a technique called differential centrifugation to isolate specific cell components. Differential centrifugation is based on breaking cells apart to create a complex mixture and then separating components in a centrifuge. A centrifuge accomplishes this task by spinning cells in a solution that allows molecules and other cell components to separate according to their density or size and shape. The individual parts of the cell can then be purified and studied in detail, in isolation from other parts of the cell.

The first step in preparing a cell sample for centrifugation is to release the cell components by breaking the cells apart. This can be done by putting them in a hypotonic solution, by exposing them to high-frequency vibration, by treating cells with a detergent, or by grinding them up. Each of these methods breaks apart plasma membranes and releases the contents of the cells.

The resulting pieces of plasma membrane quickly reseal to form small vesicles, often trapping cell components inside. The solution that results from the homogenization step is a mixture of these vesicles, free-floating macromolecules released from the cells, and organelles. A solution like this is called a cell extract or cell homogenate.

When a cell homogenate is placed in a centrifuge tube and spun at high speed, the components that are in solution tend to move outward, along the red arrow in **FIGURE B10.1a**. The effect is similar to a merry-go-round, which seems to push you outward in a straight line away from the spinning platform. In response to this outward-directed force, the cell homogenate exerts a centripetal (literally, "center-seeking") force that pushes the homogenate away from the bottom of the tube. Larger, denser molecules or particles resist this inward force more readily than do smaller, less dense ones and so reach the bottom of the centrifuge tube faster.

To separate the components of a cell extract, researchers often perform a series of centrifuge runs. Steps 1 and 2 of

**(a)** How a centrifuge works

When the centrifuge spins, the macromolecules tend to move toward the bottom of the centrifuge tube (red arrow)

The solution in the tube exerts a centripetal force, which resists movement of the molecules to the bottom of the tube (blue arrow)

Motor

Very large or dense molecules overcome the centripetal force more readily than smaller, less dense ones. As a result, larger, denser molecules move toward the bottom of the tube faster.

**(b) PROCESS: DIFFERENTIAL CENTRIFUGATION**

Low-speed centrifugation → Medium-speed centrifugation → High-speed centrifugation

Supernatant

Pellet

**1.** Start with uniform cell homogenate in centrifuge tube.

**2.** After low-speed spin, pellet contains large components. Transfer supernatant to new tube.

**3.** After medium-speed spin, pellet contains medium components. Transfer supernatant to new tube.

**4.** After high-speed spin, pellet contains small components.

**(c) PROCESS: SUCROSE DENSITY–GRADIENT CENTRIFUGATION**

Lower-density solution

Higher-density solution

Sample

**1.** Add sample to tube of variable-density solution.

**2.** Run centrifuge. Cell components are separated into distinct bands based on size and/or density.

**3.** To extract specific cell components for analysis, puncture bottom of tube with needle and collect drops from specific bands.

**FIGURE B10.1 Cell Components Can Be Separated by Centrifugation. (a)** The forces inside a centrifuge tube allow cell components to be separated. **(b)** Through a series of centrifuge runs made at increasingly higher speeds, an investigator can separate fractions of a cell homogenate by size via differential centrifugation. **(c)** A high-speed centrifuge run can achieve extremely fine separation among cell components by sucrose density–gradient centrifugation.

**FIGURE B10.1b** illustrate how an initial treatment at low speed causes larger, heavier parts of the homogenate to move below smaller, lighter parts. The material that collects at the bottom of the tube is called the pellet, and the solution and solutes left behind form the supernatant ("above-swimming"). The supernatant is placed in a fresh tube and centrifuged at increasingly higher speeds and longer durations. Each centrifuge run continues to separate cell components based on their size and density.

To accomplish separation of macromolecules or organelles, researchers frequently follow up with centrifugation at extremely high speeds. One strategy is based on filling the centrifuge tube with a series of sucrose solutions of increasing density (**FIGURE B10.1c**). The density gradient allows cell components to separate on the basis of small differences in size, shape, and density. When the centrifuge run is complete, each cell component occupies a distinct band of material in the tube, based on how quickly each component moves through the increasingly dense gradient of sucrose solution during the centrifuge run. A researcher can then collect the material in each band for further study.

# BIOSKILL  biological imaging: microscopy and x-ray crystallography

A lot of biology happens at levels that can't be detected with the naked eye. Biologists use an array of microscopes to study small multicellular organisms, individual cells, and the contents of cells. And to understand what individual macromolecules or macromolecular machines like ribosomes look like, researchers use data from a technique called X-ray crystallography.

You'll probably use dissecting microscopes and compound light microscopes to view specimens during your labs for this course, and throughout this text you'll be seeing images generated from other types of microscopy and from X-ray crystallographic data. Among the fundamental skills you'll be acquiring as an introductory student, then, is a basic understanding of how these techniques work. The key is to recognize that each approach for visualizing microscopic structures has strengths and weaknesses. As a result, each technique is appropriate for studying certain types or aspects of cells or molecules.

## Light and Fluorescence Microscopy

If you use a dissecting microscope during labs, you'll recognize that it works by magnifying light that bounces off a whole specimen—often a live organism. You'll be able to view the specimen in three dimensions, which is why these instruments are sometimes called stereomicroscopes, but the maximum magnification possible is only about 20 to 40 times normal size (20× to 40×).

To view smaller objects, you'll probably use a compound microscope. Compound microscopes magnify light that is passed *through* a specimen. The instruments used in introductory labs are usually capable of 400× magnifications; the most sophisticated compound microscopes available can achieve magnifications of about 2000×. This is enough to view individual bacterial or eukaryotic cells and see large structures inside cells, like condensed chromosomes (see Chapter 12). To prepare a specimen for viewing under a compound light microscope, the tissues or cells are usually sliced to create a section thin enough for light to pass through efficiently. The section is then dyed to increase contrast and make structures visible. In many cases, different types of dyes are used to highlight different types of structures.

To visualize specific proteins, researchers use a technique called immunostaining. After preparing tissues or cells for viewing, the specimen is stained with fluorescently tagged antibodies. In this case, the cells are viewed under a fluorescence microscope. Ultraviolet or other wavelengths of light are passed through the specimen. The fluorescing tag emits visible light in response. The result? Beautiful cells that glow green, red, or blue.

## Electron Microscopy

Until the 1950s, the compound microscope was the biologist's only tool for viewing cells directly. But the invention of the electron microscope provided a new way to view specimens. Two basic types of electron microscopy are now available: one that allows researchers to examine cross sections of cells at extremely high magnification, and one that offers a view of surfaces at somewhat lower magnification.

### Transmission Electron Microscopy

The transmission electron microscope (TEM) is an extraordinarily effective tool for viewing cell structure at high magnification. TEM forms an image from electrons that pass through a specimen, just as a light microscope forms an image from light rays that pass through a specimen.

Biologists who want to view a cell under a transmission electron microscope begin by "fixing" the cell, meaning that they treat it with a chemical agent that stabilizes the cell's structure and contents while disturbing them as little as possible. Then the researcher permeates the cell with an epoxy plastic that stiffens the structure. Once this epoxy hardens, the cell can be cut into extremely thin sections with a glass or diamond knife. Finally, the sectioned specimens are impregnated with a metal—often lead. (The reason for this last step is explained shortly.)

**FIGURE B11.1a** outlines how the transmission electron microscope works. A beam of electrons is produced by a tungsten filament at the top of a column and directed downward. (All of the air is pumped out of the column, so that the electron beam isn't scattered by collisions with air molecules.) The electron beam passes through a series of lenses and through the specimen. The lenses are actually electromagnets, which alter the path of the beam much like a glass lens in a dissecting or compound microscope bends light. The electromagnet lenses magnify and focus the image on a screen at the bottom of the column. There the electrons strike a coating of fluorescent crystals, which emit visible light in response—just like a television screen. When the microscopist moves the screen out of the way and allows the electrons to expose a sheet of black-and-white film or to be detected by a digital camera, the result is a micrograph—a photograph of an image produced by microscopy.

The image itself is created by electrons that pass through the specimen. If no specimen were in place, all the electrons would pass through and the screen (and micrograph) would be uniformly bright. Unfortunately, cell materials by themselves would also appear fairly uniform and bright. This is because an atom's ability to deflect an electron depends on its mass. In turn, an atom's mass is a function of its atomic number. The hydrogen, carbon, oxygen, and nitrogen atoms that dominate biological molecules have low atomic numbers. This is why cell biologists must saturate cell sections with lead solutions. Lead has a high atomic number and scatters electrons effectively. Different macromolecules take up lead atoms in different amounts, so the metal acts as a "stain" that produces contrast. With TEM, areas of dense metal scatter the electron beam most, producing dark areas in micrographs.

The advantage of TEM is that it can magnify objects up to $250,000\times$—meaning that intracellular structures are clearly visible. The downsides are that researchers are restricted to observing dead, sectioned material, and they must take care that the preparation process does not distort the specimen.

## Scanning Electron Microscopy

The scanning electron microscope (SEM) is the most useful tool biologists have for looking at the surfaces of structures. Materials are prepared for scanning electron microscopy by coating their surfaces with a layer of metal atoms. To create an image of this surface, the microscope scans the surface with a narrow beam of electrons. Electrons that are reflected back from the surface or that are emitted by the metal atoms in response to the beam then strike a detector. The signal from the detector controls a second electron beam, which scans a TV-like screen and forms an image magnified up to 50,000 times the object's size.

Because SEM records shadows and highlights, it provides images with a three-dimensional appearance (**FIGURE B11.1b**). It cannot magnify objects nearly as much as TEM can, however.

---

**(a) Transmission electron microscopy:** High magnification of cross sections

Tungsten filament
(source of electrons)

Condenser lens

Specimen

Objective lens

Projector lens

Image on
fluorescent screen

0.2 μm

Cross section of *E. coli* bacterium

**(b) Scanning electron microscopy:**
Lower magnification of surfaces

1 μm

Surface view of *E. coli* bacteria

**FIGURE B11.1 There Are Two Basic Types of Electron Microscopy.**

## Studying Live Cells and Real-Time Processes

Until the 1960s, biologists were unable to get clear, high-magnification images of living cells. But a series of innovations over the past 50 years has made it possible to observe organelles and subcellular structures in action.

The development of video microscopy, where the image from a light microscope is captured by a video camera instead of by an eye or a film camera, proved revolutionary. It allowed specimens to be viewed at higher magnification, because video cameras are more sensitive to small differences in contrast than are the human eye or still cameras. It also made it easier to keep live specimens functioning normally, because the increased light sensitivity of video cameras allows them to be used with low illumination, so specimens don't overheat. And when it became possible to digitize video images, researchers began using computers to remove out-of-focus background material and increase image clarity.

A more recent innovation was the use of a fluorescent molecule called green fluorescent protein, or GFP, which allows researchers to tag specific molecules or structures and follow their movement in live cells over time. This was a major advance over immunostaining, in which cells have to be fixed. GFP is naturally synthesized in jellyfish that fluoresce, or emit light. By affixing GFP to another protein (using genetic engineering techniques described in Chapter 20) and then inserting it into a live cell, investigators can follow the protein's fate over time and even videotape its movement. For example, researchers have videotaped GFP-tagged proteins being transported from the rough ER through the Golgi apparatus and out to the plasma membrane. This is cell biology: the movie.

GFP's influence has been so profound that the researchers who developed its use in microscopy were awarded the 2008 Nobel Prize in Chemistry.

## Visualizing Structures in 3-D

The world is three-dimensional. To understand how microscopic structures and macromolecules work, it is essential to understand their shape and spatial relationships. Consider three techniques currently being used to reconstruct the 3-D structure of cells, organelles, and macromolecules.

- *Confocal microscopy* is carried out by mounting cells that have been treated with one or more fluorescing tags on a microscope slide and then focusing a beam of ultraviolet or other wavelengths of light at a specific depth within the specimen. The fluorescing tag emits visible light in response. A detector for this light is then set up at exactly the position where the emitted light comes into focus. The result is a sharp image of a precise plane in the cell being studied (**FIGURE B11.2a**). Note that if you viewed the same specimen under a conventional fluorescence microscope, the image would be blurry because it results from light emitted by the entire cell (**FIGURE B11.2b**). By altering the focal plane, a researcher can record images from

**(a)** Confocal fluorescence image of single cell    **(b)** Conventional fluorescence image of same cell

25 µm

FIGURE B11.2 **Confocal Microscopy Provides Sharp Images of Living Cells. (a)** The confocal image of this mouse intestinal cell is sharp, because it results from light emitted at a single plane inside the cell. **(b)** The conventional image of this same cell is blurred, because it results from light emitted by the entire cell.

an array of depths in the specimen; a computer can then be used to generate a 3-D image of the cell.

- *Electron tomography* uses a transmission electron microscope to generate a 3-D image of an organelle or other subcellular structure. The specimen is rotated around a single axis while the researcher takes many "snapshots." The individual images are then pieced together with a computer. This technique has provided a much more accurate view of mitochondrial structure than was possible using traditional TEM (see Chapter 7).

- *X-ray crystallography, or X-ray diffraction analysis*, is the most widely used technique for reconstructing the 3-D structure of molecules. As its name implies, the procedure is based on bombarding crystals of a molecule with X-rays. X-rays are scattered in precise ways when they interact with the electrons surrounding the atoms in a crystal, producing a diffraction pattern that can be recorded on X-ray film or other types of detectors (**FIGURE B11.3**). By varying the orientation of the X-ray beam as it strikes a crystal and documenting the

## check your understanding

**If you understand BioSkill 11**

✔ You should be able to . . .

1. Interpret whether the absence of mitochondria in a transmission electron micrograph of a cancerous human liver means that the cell lacks mitochondria.

2. Explain why the effort to understand the structure of biological molecules is worthwhile even though X-ray crystallography is time consuming and technically difficult. What's the payoff?

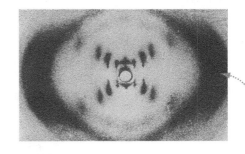

The patterns are determined by the structure of the molecules within the crystal

FIGURE B11.3 **X-Ray Crystallography.** When crystallized molecules are bombarded with X-rays, the radiation is scattered in distinctive patterns. The photograph at the right shows an X-ray film that recorded the pattern of scattered radiation from DNA molecules.

diffraction patterns that result, researchers can construct a map representing the density of electrons in the crystal. By relating these electron-density maps to information about the primary structure of the nucleic acid or protein, a 3-D model of the molecule can be built. Virtually all of the molecular models used in this book were built from X-ray crystallographic data.

# BIOSKILL 12  cell and tissue culture methods

For researchers, there are important advantages to growing plant and animal cells and tissues outside the organism itself. Cell and tissue cultures provide large populations of a single type of cell or tissue and the opportunity to control experimental conditions precisely.

## Animal Cell Culture

The first successful attempt to culture animal cells occurred in 1907, when a researcher cultivated amphibian nerve cells in a drop of fluid from the spinal cord. But it was not until the 1950s and 1960s that biologists could routinely culture plant and animal cells in the laboratory. The long lag time was due to the difficulty of re-creating conditions that exist in the intact organism precisely enough for cells to grow normally.

To grow in culture, animal cells must be provided with a liquid mixture containing the nutrients, vitamins, and hormones that stimulate growth. Initially, this mixture was serum, the liquid portion of blood; now, serum-free media are available for certain cell types. Serum-free media are preferred because they are much more precisely defined chemically than serum.

In addition, many types of animal cells will not grow in culture unless they are provided with a solid surface that mimics the types of surfaces that enable cells in the intact organisms to adhere. As a result, cells are typically cultured in flasks (**FIGURE B12.1a**, left; see B:22).

Even under optimal conditions, though, normal cells display a finite life span in culture. In contrast, many cultured cancerous cells grow indefinitely. This characteristic correlates with a key feature of cancerous cells in organisms: Their growth is continuous and uncontrolled.

Because of their immortality and relative ease of growth, cultured cancer cells are commonly used in research on basic aspects of cell structure and function. For example, the first human cell type to be grown in culture was isolated in 1951 from a malignant tumor of the uterine cervix. These cells are called HeLa cells in honor of their donor, Henrietta Lacks, who died soon thereafter from her cancer. HeLa cells continue to grow in laboratories around the world (Figure B12.1a, right).

## Plant Tissue Culture

Certain cells found in plants are totipotent—meaning that they retain the ability to divide and differentiate into a complete, mature plant, including new types of tissue. These cells, called parenchyma cells, are important in wound healing and asexual reproduction. But they also allow researchers to grow complete adult plants in the laboratory, starting with a small number of parenchyma cells.

Biologists who grow plants in tissue culture begin by placing parenchyma cells in a liquid or solid medium containing all the

**(a) Animal cell culture:** immortal HeLa cancer cells

**(b) Plant tissue culture:** tobacco callus

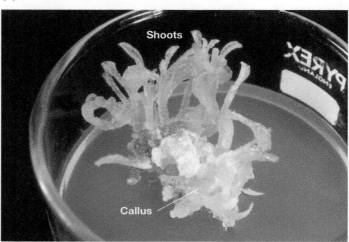

FIGURE B12.1 **Animal and Plant Cells Can Be Grown in the Lab.**

nutrients required for cell maintenance and growth. In the early days of plant tissue culture, investigators found not only that specific growth signals called hormones were required for successful growth and differentiation but also that the relative abundance of hormones present was critical to success.

The earliest experiments on hormone interactions in tissue cultures were done with tobacco cells in the 1950s by Folke Skoog and co-workers. These researchers found that when the hormone called auxin was added to the culture by itself, the cells enlarged but did not divide. But if the team added roughly equal amounts of auxin and another growth signal called cytokinin to the cells, the cells began to divide and eventually formed a callus, or an undifferentiated mass of parenchyma cells.

By varying the proportion of auxin to cytokinins in different parts of the callus and through time, the team could stimulate the growth and differentiation of root and shoot systems and produce whole new plants (**FIGURE B12.1b**). A high ratio of auxin to cytokinin led to the differentiation of a root system, while a high ratio of cytokinin to auxin led to the development of a shoot system. Eventually Skoog's team was able to produce a complete plant from just one parenchyma cell.

The ability to grow whole new plants in tissue culture from just one cell has been instrumental in the development of genetic engineering (see Chapter 20). Researchers insert recombinant genes into target cells, test the cells to identify those that successfully express the recombinant genes, and then use tissue culture techniques to grow those cells into adult individuals with a novel genotype and phenotype.

check your understanding

**C Y U**

**If you understand BioSkill 12**

✔ **You should be able to . . .**

1. Identify a limitation of how experiments on HeLa cells are interpreted.

2. State a disadvantage of doing experiments on plants that have been propagated from single cells growing in tissue culture.

Research in biological science starts with a question. In most cases, the question is inspired by an observation about a cell or an organism. To answer it, biologists have to study a particular species. Study organisms are called model organisms, because investigators hope that they serve as a model for what is going on in a wide array of species.

Model organisms are chosen because they are convenient to study and because they have attributes that make them appropriate for the particular research proposed. They tend to have some common characteristics:

- *Short generation time and rapid reproduction*  This trait is important because it makes it possible to produce offspring quickly and perform many experiments in a short amount of time—you don't have to wait long for individuals to grow.

- *Large numbers of offspring*  This trait is particularly important in genetics, where many offspring phenotypes and genotypes need to be assessed to get a large sample size.

- *Small size, simple feeding and habitat requirements*  These attributes make it relatively cheap and easy to maintain individuals in the lab.

The following notes highlight just a few model organisms supporting current work in biological science.

## Escherichia coli

Of all model organisms in biology, perhaps none has been more important than the bacterium *Escherichia coli*—a common inhabitant of the human gut. The strain that is most commonly worked on today, called K-12 (**FIGURE B13.1a**; see B:24), was originally isolated from a hospital patient in 1922.

During the last half of the twentieth century, key results in molecular biology originated in studies of *E. coli*. These results include the discovery of enzymes such as DNA polymerase, RNA polymerase, DNA repair enzymes, and restriction endonucleases; the elucidation of ribosome structure and function; and the initial characterization of promoters, regulatory transcription factors, regulatory sites in DNA, and operons. In many cases, initial discoveries made in *E. coli* allowed researchers to confirm that homologous enzymes and processes existed in an array of organisms, often ranging from other bacteria to yeast, mice, and humans.

The success of *E. coli* as a model for other species inspired Jacques Monod's claim that "Once we understand the biology of *Escherichia coli*, we will understand the biology of an elephant." The genome of *E. coli* K-12 was sequenced in 1997, and the strain continues to be a workhorse in studies of gene function, biochemistry, and particularly biotechnology. Much remains to

be learned, however. Despite over 60 years of intensive study, the function of about a third of the *E. coli* genome is still unknown.

In the lab, *E. coli* is usually grown in suspension culture, where cells are introduced to a liquid nutrient medium, or on plates containing agar—a gelatinous mix of polysaccharides. Under optimal growing conditions—meaning before cells begin to get crowded and compete for space and nutrients—a cell takes just 30 minutes on average to grow and divide. At this rate, a single cell can produce a population of over a million descendants in just 10 hours. Except for new mutations, all of the descendant cells are genetically identical.

## Dictyostelium discoideum

The cellular slime mold *Dictyostelium discoideum* is not always slimy, and it is not a mold—meaning a type of fungus. Instead, it is an amoeba. Amoeba is a general term that biologists use to characterize a unicellular eukaryote that lacks a cell wall and is extremely flexible in shape. *Dictyostelium* has long fascinated biologists because it is a social organism. Independent cells sometimes aggregate to form a multicellular structure.

Under most conditions, *Dictyostelium* cells are haploid (*n*) and move about in decaying vegetation on forest floors or other habitats. They feed on bacteria by engulfing them whole. When these cells reproduce, they can do so sexually by fusing with another cell then undergoing meiosis, or asexually by mitosis, which is more common. If food begins to run out, the cells begin to aggregate. In many cases, tens of thousands of cells cohere to form a 2-mm-long mass called a slug (**FIGURE B13.1b**). (This is not the slug that is related to snails.)

After migrating to a sunlit location, the slug stops and individual cells differentiate according to their position in the slug. Some form a stalk; others form a mass of spores at the tip of the stalk. (A spore is a single cell that develops into an adult organism, but it is not formed from gamete fusion like a zygote is.) The entire structure, stalk plus mass of spores, is called a fruiting body. Cells that form spores secrete a tough coat and represent a durable resting stage. The fruiting body eventually dries out, and the wind disperses the spores to new locations, where more food might be available.

*Dictyostelium* has been an important model organism for investigating questions about eukaryotes:

- Cells in a slug are initially identical in morphology but then differentiate into distinctive stalk cells and spores. Studying this process helped biologists better understand how cells in plant and animal embryos differentiate into distinct cell types.

**(a)** Bacterium *Escherichia coli* (strain K-12)

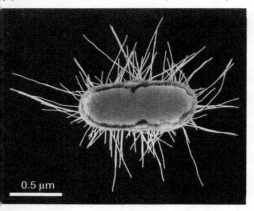

0.5 μm

**(b)** Slime mold *Dictyostelium discoideum*

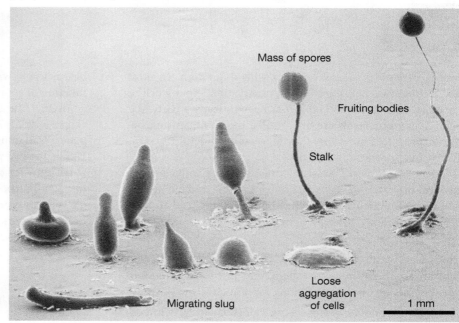

Mass of spores

Fruiting bodies

Stalk

Loose aggregation of cells

Migrating slug

1 mm

**(c)** Thale cress *Arabidopsis thaliana*

5 cm

**(e)** Fruit fly *Drosophila melanogaster*

0.5 mm

**(f)** Roundworm *Caenorhabditis elegans*

0.1 mm

**(d)** Yeast *Saccharomyces cerevisiae*

5 μm

**(g)** Mouse *Mus musculus*

1 cm

**FIGURE B13.1 Model Organisms.**

**QUESTION** *E. coli* is grown at a temperature of 37°C. Why?

- The process of slug formation has helped biologists study how animal cells move and how they aggregate as they form specific types of tissues.
- When *Dictyostelium* cells aggregate to form a slug, they stick to each other. The discovery of membrane proteins responsible for cell–cell adhesion helped biologists understand some of the general principles of multicellular life (highlighted in Chapter 11).

## *Arabidopsis thaliana*

In the early days of biology, the best-studied plants were agricultural varieties such as maize (corn), rice, and garden peas. When biologists began to unravel the mechanisms responsible for oxygenic photosynthesis in the early to mid-1900s, they relied on green algae that were relatively easy to grow and manipulate in the lab—often the unicellular species *Chlamydomonas reinhardii*—as an experimental subject.

Although crop plants and green algae continue to be the subject of considerable research, a new model organism emerged in the 1980s and now serves as the preeminent experimental subject in plant biology. That organism is *Arabidopsis thaliana*, commonly known as thale cress or wall cress (**FIGURE B13.1c**).

*Arabidopsis* is a member of the mustard family, or Brassicaceae, so it is closely related to radishes and broccoli. In nature it is a weed—meaning a species that is adapted to thrive in habitats where soils have been disturbed.

One of the most attractive aspects of working with *Arabidopsis* is that individuals can grow from a seed into a mature, seed-producing plant in just four to six weeks. Several other attributes make it an effective subject for study: It has just five chromosomes, has a relatively small genome with limited numbers of repetitive sequences, can self-fertilize as well as undergo cross-fertilization, can be grown in a relatively small amount of space and with a minimum of care in the greenhouse, and produces up to 10,000 seeds per individual per generation.

*Arabidopsis* has been instrumental in a variety of studies in plant molecular genetics and development, and it is increasingly popular in ecological and evolutionary studies. In addition, the entire genome of the species has now been sequenced, and studies have benefited from the development of an international "*Arabidopsis* community"—a combination of informal and formal associations of investigators who work on *Arabidopsis* and use regular meetings, e-mail, and the Internet to share data, techniques, and seed stocks.

## *Saccharomyces cerevisiae*

When biologists want to answer basic questions about how eukaryotic cells work, they often turn to the yeast *Saccharomyces cerevisiae*.

*S. cerevisiae* is unicellular and relatively easy to culture and manipulate in the lab (**FIGURE B13.1d**). In good conditions, yeast cells grow and divide almost as rapidly as bacteria. As a result,

the species has become the organism of choice for experiments on control of the cell cycle and regulation of gene expression in eukaryotes. For example, research has confirmed that several of the genes controlling cell division and DNA repair in yeast have homologs in humans; and when mutated, these genes contribute to cancer. Strains of yeast that carry these mutations are now being used to test drugs that might be effective against cancer.

*S. cerevisiae* has become even more important in efforts to interpret the genomes of organisms like rice, mice, zebrafish, and humans. It is much easier to investigate the function of particular genes in *S. cerevisiae* by creating mutants or transferring specific alleles among individuals than it is to do the same experiments in mice or zebrafish. Once the function of a gene has been established in yeast, biologists can look for the homologous gene in other eukaryotes. If such a gene exists, they can usually infer that it has a function similar to its role in *S. cerevisiae*. It was also the first eukaryote with a completely sequenced genome.

## *Drosophila melanogaster*

If you walk into a biology building on any university campus around the world, you are almost certain to find at least one lab where the fruit fly *Drosophila melanogaster* is being studied (**FIGURE B13.1e**).

*Drosophila* has been a key experimental subject in genetics since the early 1900s. It was initially chosen as a focus for study by T. H. Morgan, because it can be reared in the laboratory easily and inexpensively, matings can be arranged, the life cycle is completed in less than two weeks, and females lay a large number of eggs. These traits made fruit flies valuable subjects for breeding experiments designed to test hypotheses about how traits are transmitted from parents to offspring (see Chapter 14).

More recently, *Drosophila* has also become a key model organism in the field of developmental biology. The use of flies in developmental studies was inspired largely by the work of Christianne Nüsslein-Volhard and Eric Wieschaus, who in the 1980s isolated flies with genetic defects in early embryonic development. By investigating the nature of these defects, researchers have gained valuable insights into how various gene products influence the development of eukaryotes (see Chapter 22). The complete genome sequence of *Drosophila* has been available to investigators since the year 2000.

## *Caenorhabditis elegans*

The roundworm *Caenorhabditis elegans* emerged as a model organism in developmental biology in the 1970s, due largely to work by Sydney Brenner and colleagues. (*Caenorhabditis* is pronounced *see-no-rab-DIE-tiss*.)

*C. elegans* was chosen for three reasons: (1) Its cuticle (soft outer layer) is transparent, making individual cells relatively easy to observe (**FIGURE B13.1f**); (2) adults have exactly 959 nonreproductive cells; and, most important, (3) the fate of each cell in an embryo can be predicted because cell fates are invariant among individuals. For example, when researchers examine a 33-cell *C. elegans* embryo, they know exactly which of the 959 cells in the adult will be derived from each of those 33 embryonic cells.

In addition, *C. elegans* are small (less than 1 mm long), are able to self-fertilize or cross-fertilize, and undergo early development in just 16 hours. The entire genome of *C. elegans* has now been sequenced.

## *Mus musculus*

The house mouse *Mus musculus* is the most important model organism among mammals. For this reason, it is especially prominent in biomedical research, where researchers need to work on individuals with strong genetic and developmental similarities to humans.

The house mouse was an intelligent choice of model organism in mammals because it is small and thus relatively inexpensive to maintain in captivity, and because it breeds rapidly. A litter can contain 10 offspring, and generation time is only 12 weeks—meaning that several generations can be produced in a year. Descendants of wild house mice have been selected for docility and other traits that make them easy to handle and rear; these populations are referred to as laboratory mice (**FIGURE B13.1g**).

Some of the most valuable laboratory mice are strains with distinctive, well-characterized genotypes. Inbred strains are

virtually homogenous genetically (see Chapter 26) and are useful in experiments where gene-by-gene or gene-by-environment interactions have to be controlled. Other populations carry mutations that knock out genes and cause diseases similar to those observed in humans. These individuals are useful for identifying the cause of genetic diseases and testing drugs or other types of therapies.

## check your understanding

**If you understand BioSkill 13**

✔ **You should be able to . . .**

Determine which model organisms described here would be the best choice for the following studies. In each case, explain your reasoning.

1. A study of why specific cells in an embryo die at certain points in normal development. One goal is to understand the consequences for the individual when programmed cell death does not occur when it should.

2. A study of proteins that are required for cell–cell adhesion.

3. Research on a gene suspected to be involved in the formation of breast cancer in humans.

# BIOSKILL 14 — primary literature and peer review

As part of the process of doing science, biologists communicate their results to the scientific community through publications in scientific journals that report on their original research discoveries (see Chapter 1). These published reports are referred to, interchangeably, as the primary literature, research papers, or primary research articles.

## What Is the Primary Literature?

Scientists publish "peer-reviewed" papers. This means that several experts in the field have carefully read the paper and considered its strengths and weaknesses. Reviewers write a critique of the paper and make a recommendation to the journal editor as to whether the paper should be published. Often reviewers will suggest additional experiments that need to be completed before a paper is considered acceptable for publication. The peer review process means that research discoveries are carefully vetted before they go to press.

A primary research paper can be distinguished from secondary sources—such as review articles, textbooks, and magazine articles—by looking for key characteristics. A primary research paper includes a detailed description of methods and results,

written by the researchers who did the work. A typical paper contains a Title, Abstract, Introduction, Materials and Methods (or Experimental Design), Results and Discussion (**Table B14.1**), although the order and name of the sections varies among journals.

## Getting Started

At first, trying to read the primary literature may seem like a daunting task. A paper may be peppered with unfamiliar terms and acronyms. If you tried to read a research paper from start to finish, like you might read a chapter in this textbook, it would be a frustrating experience. But, with practice, the scientific literature becomes approachable, and it is well worth the effort. The primary literature is the cutting edge, the place to read firsthand about the process of doing science. Becoming skilled at reading and evaluating scientific reports is a powerful way to learn how to think critically—to think like a biologist.

To get started, try breaking down reading the primary research article into a series of steps:

1. Read the authors' names. Where are they from? Are they working as a team or alone? After delving into the literature,

**TABLE B14.1  Sections of a Primary Research Paper**

| Section | Characteristics |
|---|---|
| Title | Short, succinct, eye-catching |
| Abstract | Summary of Methods, Results, Discussion. Explains why the research was done and why the results are significant. |
| Introduction | Background information (what past work was done, why the work was important). States the objectives and hypotheses of the study and explains why the study is important. |
| Materials and Methods | Explains how the work was done and where it was done. |
| Results | Explains what the data show. |
| Discussion | Explains why the data show what they show, how the analysis relates to the objectives from the Introduction, and the significance of findings and how they advance the field. |

certain familiar names will crop up again and again. You'll begin to recognize the experts in a particular field.

2. Read the title. It should summarize the key finding of the paper and tell you what you can expect to learn from the paper.

3. Read the abstract. The abstract summarizes the entire paper in a short paragraph. At this point, it might be tempting to stop reading. But sometimes authors understate or overstate the significance and conclusions of their work. You should never cite an article as a reference after having read only the abstract.

4. Read the Introduction. The first couple of paragraphs should make it clear what the objectives or hypotheses of the paper are; the remaining paragraphs will give you the background information you need to understand the point of the paper.

5. Flip through the article and look at the figures, illustrations, and tables, including reading the legends.

6. Read the Results section carefully. Ask yourself these questions: Do the results accurately describe the data presented in the paper? Were all the appropriate controls carried out in an experiment? Are there additional experiments that you think should have been performed? Are the figures and tables clearly labeled?

7. Consult the Materials and Methods section to help understand the research design and the techniques used.

8. Read the Discussion. The first and last paragraphs usually summarize the key findings and state their significance. The Discussion is the part of the paper where the results are explained in the context of the scientific literature. The authors should explain what their results mean.

## Getting Practice

The best way to get practice is to start reading the scientific literature as often as possible. You could begin by reading some of the references cited in this textbook. You can get an electronic copy of most articles through online databases such as PubMed, Science-Direct, or Google Scholar, or through your institution's library.

After reading a primary research paper, you should be able to paraphrase the significance of the paper in a few sentences, free of technical jargon. You should also be able to both praise and criticize several points of the paper. As you become more familiar with reading the scientific literature, you're likely to start thinking about what questions remain to be answered. And, you may even come up with "the next experiment."

check your understanding

**If you understand BioSkill 14**

✔ **You should be able to . . .**

After choosing a primary research paper on a topic in biology that you would like to know more about, select one figure in the Results section that reports on the experiment and construct a Research box (like the ones in this textbook) that depicts this experiment.

A concept map is a graphical device for organizing and expressing what you know about a topic. It has two main elements: **(1)** concepts that are identified by words or short phrases and placed in a box or circle, and **(2)** labeled arrows that physically link two concepts and explain the relationship between them. The concepts are arranged hierarchically on a page with the most general concepts at the top and the most specific ideas at the bottom.

The combination of a concept, a linking word, and a second concept is called a proposition. Good concept maps also have cross-links—meaning, labeled arrows that connect different elements in the hierarchy as you read down the page.

Concept maps, initially developed by Joseph Novak in the early 1970s, have proven to be an effective studying and learning tool. They can be particularly valuable if constructed by a group, or when different individuals exchange and critique concept maps they have created independently. Although concept maps vary widely in quality and can be graded using objective criteria, there are many equally valid ways of making a high-quality concept map on a particular topic.

When you are asked to make a concept map in this text, you will usually be given at least a partial list of concepts to use. As an example, suppose you were asked to create a concept map on experimental design and were given the following concepts: results, predictions, control treatment, experimental treatment, controlled (identical) conditions, conclusions, experiment, hypothesis to be tested, null hypothesis. One possible concept map is shown in **FIGURE B15.1**.

Good concept maps have four qualities:

1. They exhibit an organized hierarchy, indicating how each concept on the map relates to larger and smaller concepts.

2. The concept words are specific—not vague.

3. The propositions are accurate.

4. There is cross-linking between different elements in the hierarchy of concepts.

As you practice making concept maps, go through these criteria and use them to evaluate your own work as well as the work of fellow students.

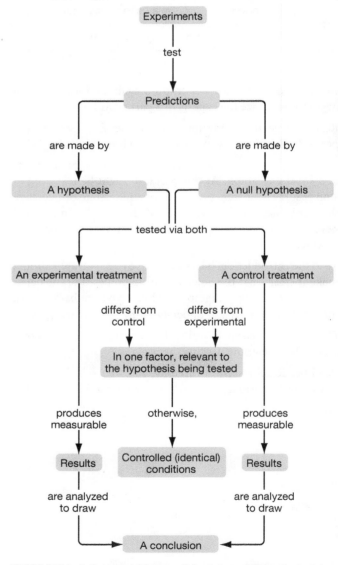

**FIGURE B15.1 A Concept Map on Principles of Experimental Design.**

Most students have at one time or another wondered why a particular question on an exam seemed so hard, while others seemed easy. The explanation lies in the type of cognitive skills required to answer the question. Let's take a closer look.

## Categories of Human Cognition

Bloom's Taxonomy is a classification system that instructors use to identify the cognitive skill levels at which they are asking students to work, particularly on practice problems and exams. Bloom's Taxonomy is also a very useful tool for students to know—it can help you to figure out the appropriate level at which you should be studying to succeed in a course.

Bloom's Taxonomy distinguishes six different categories of human thinking: remember, understand, apply, analyze, evaluate, and create. One of the most useful distinctions lies not in the differences among the six categories, but rather in the difference between high-order cognitive (HOC) and low-order cognitive (LOC) skills. **FIGURE B16.1** shows how the different levels of the taxonomy can be broken into HOC and LOC skills.

Skills that hallmark LOCs include recall, explanation, or application of knowledge in the exact way that you have before (remember, understand, apply), while skills that typify HOCs include the application of knowledge in a new way, as well as the breakdown, critique, or creation of information (analyze, evaluate, and create). Most college instructors will assume students are proficient at solving LOC questions and will expect you to frequently work at the HOC levels. HOC problems usually require use of basic vocabulary and applying knowledge—working at this level helps students to master the LOC levels.

## Six Study Steps to Success

Bloom's Taxonomy provides a useful guide for preparing for an exam, using the following six steps:

1. *Answer in-chapter questions while reading the chapter.* All questions in this book have been assigned Bloom's levels, so you can review the question answers and the Bloom's level while you study.

2. *Identify the Bloom's level(s) of the questions that you are having greatest difficulty answering.* While working through

FIGURE B16.1 **Bloom's Taxonomy.**

the text, take note of the content and Bloom's level(s) that you find the most challenging.

3. *Use the Bloom's Taxonomy Study Guide* (**Table B16.1;** see B:30) *to focus your study efforts at the appropriate Bloom's level.* Table B16.1 lists specific study methods that can help you practice your understanding of the material at both the LOC and HOC levels, whether you are studying alone or with a study group.

4. *Complete the end-of-chapter questions as if you're taking an exam, without looking for the answers.* If you look at the chapter text or jump to the answers, then you really aren't testing your ability to work with the content and have reduced the questions to the lowest Bloom's level of remember.

5. *Grade your answers and note the Bloom's level of the questions you got wrong.* At what level of Bloom's Taxonomy were the questions you missed?

6. *Use the Bloom's Taxonomy Study Guide to focus your study efforts at the appropriate Bloom's level.* If you missed a lot of questions, then spend more time studying the material and find other resources for quizzing yourself.

By following these steps and studying at the HOC levels, you should succeed in answering questions on in-class exams.

**TABLE B16.1 Bloom's Taxonomy Study Guide**

| | Individual Study Activities | Group Study Activities |
|---|---|---|
| **Create (HOC)**<br>Generate something new | • Generate a hypothesis or design an experiment based on information you are studying<br>• Create a model based on a given data set<br>• Create summary sheets that show how facts and concepts relate to each other<br>• Create questions at each level of Bloom's Taxonomy as a practice test and then take the test | • Each student puts forward a hypothesis about biological process and designs an experiment to test it. Peers critique the hypotheses and experiments<br>• Create a new model/summary sheet/concept map that integrates each group member's ideas |
| **Evaluate (HOC)**<br>Defend or judge a concept or idea | • Provide a written assessment of the strengths and weaknesses of your peers' work or understanding of a given concept based on previously determined criteria | • Provide a verbal assessment of the strengths and weaknesses of your peers' work or understanding of a given concept based on previously described criteria, and have your peers critique your assessment |
| **Analyze (HOC)**<br>Distinguish parts and make inferences | • Analyze and interpret data in primary literature or a textbook without reading the author's interpretation and then compare the authors' interpretation with your own<br>• Analyze a situation and then identify the assumptions and principles of the argument<br>• Compare and contrast two ideas or concepts<br>• Construct a map of the main concepts by defining the relationships of the concepts using one- or two-way arrows | • Work together to analyze and interpret data in primary literature or a textbook without reading the author's interpretation, and defend your analysis to your peers<br>• Work together to identify all of the concepts in a paper or textbook chapter, construct individual maps linking the concepts together with arrows and words that relate the concepts, and then grade each other's concept maps |
| **Apply (HOC or LOC)**<br>Use information or concepts in new ways (HOC) or in the same ways (LOC) | • Review each process you have learned and then ask yourself: What would happen if you increase or decrease a component in the system, or what would happen if you alter the activity of a component in the system?<br>• If possible, graph a biological process and create scenarios that change the shape or slope of the graph | • Practice writing out answers to old exam questions on the board, and have your peers check to make sure you don't have too much or too little information in your answer<br>• Take turns teaching your peers a biological process while the group critiques the content |
| **Understand (LOC)**<br>Explain information or concepts | • Describe a biological process in your own words without copying it from a book or another source<br>• Provide examples of a process<br>• Write a sentence using the word<br>• Give examples of a process | • Discuss content with peers<br>• Take turns quizzing each other about definitions, and have your peers check your answer |
| **Remember (LOC)**<br>Recall information | • Practice labeling diagrams<br>• List characteristics<br>• Identify biological objects or components from flash cards<br>• Quiz yourself with flash cards<br>• Take a self-made quiz on vocabulary<br>• Draw, classify, select, or match items<br>• Write out the textbook definitions | • Check a drawing that another student labeled<br>• Create lists of concepts and processes that your peers can match<br>• Place flash cards in a bag and take turns selecting one for which you must define a term<br>• Do the preceding activities, and have peers check your answers |

# Periodic Table of Elements

| | | |
|---|---|---|
| **1** | | Atomic number |
| **H** | | Atomic symbol |
| Hydrogen | | Name |
| 1.008 | | Atomic weight* |

- Most common elements in living things
- Other major elements (minerals) found in living things
- Important trace elements (minerals) found in living things
- Elements mostly found in non-living things
- Elements not found in nature (synthesized by scientists)

| 1 | 2 | | | | | | | | | | | 13 | 14 | 15 | 16 | 17 | 18 |
|---|---|---|---|---|---|---|---|---|---|---|---|---|---|---|---|---|---|
| **1**<br>**H**<br>Hydrogen<br>1.008 | | | | | | | | | | | | | | | | | **2**<br>**He**<br>Helium<br>4.003 |
| **3**<br>**Li**<br>Lithium<br>6.941 | **4**<br>**Be**<br>Beryllium<br>9.012 | | | | | | | | | | | **5**<br>**B**<br>Boron<br>10.81 | **6**<br>**C**<br>Carbon<br>12.01 | **7**<br>**N**<br>Nitrogen<br>14.01 | **8**<br>**O**<br>Oxygen<br>16.00 | **9**<br>**F**<br>Fluorine<br>19.00 | **10**<br>**Ne**<br>Neon<br>20.18 |
| **11**<br>**Na**<br>Sodium<br>22.99 | **12**<br>**Mg**<br>Magnesium<br>24.31 | 3 | 4 | 5 | 6 | 7 | 8 | 9 | 10 | 11 | 12 | **13**<br>**Al**<br>Aluminum<br>26.98 | **14**<br>**Si**<br>Silicon<br>28.09 | **15**<br>**P**<br>Phosphorus<br>30.97 | **16**<br>**S**<br>Sulfur<br>32.07 | **17**<br>**Cl**<br>Chlorine<br>35.45 | **18**<br>**Ar**<br>Argon<br>39.95 |
| **19**<br>**K**<br>Potassium<br>39.10 | **20**<br>**Ca**<br>Calcium<br>40.08 | **21**<br>**Sc**<br>Scandium<br>44.96 | **22**<br>**Ti**<br>Titanium<br>47.87 | **23**<br>**V**<br>Vanadium<br>50.94 | **24**<br>**Cr**<br>Chromium<br>52.00 | **25**<br>**Mn**<br>Manganese<br>54.94 | **26**<br>**Fe**<br>Iron<br>55.85 | **27**<br>**Co**<br>Cobalt<br>58.93 | **28**<br>**Ni**<br>Nickel<br>58.69 | **29**<br>**Cu**<br>Copper<br>63.55 | **30**<br>**Zn**<br>Zinc<br>65.38 | **31**<br>**Ga**<br>Gallium<br>69.72 | **32**<br>**Ge**<br>Germanium<br>72.64 | **33**<br>**As**<br>Arsenic<br>74.92 | **34**<br>**Se**<br>Selenium<br>78.96 | **35**<br>**Br**<br>Bromine<br>79.90 | **36**<br>**Kr**<br>Krypton<br>83.80 |
| **37**<br>**Rb**<br>Rubidium<br>85.47 | **38**<br>**Sr**<br>Strontium<br>87.61 | **39**<br>**Y**<br>Yttrium<br>88.91 | **40**<br>**Zr**<br>Zirconium<br>91.22 | **41**<br>**Nb**<br>Niobium<br>92.91 | **42**<br>**Mo**<br>Molybdenum<br>95.96 | **43**<br>**Tc**<br>Technetium<br>[98]† | **44**<br>**Ru**<br>Ruthenium<br>101.1 | **45**<br>**Rh**<br>Rhodium<br>102.9 | **46**<br>**Pd**<br>Palladium<br>106.4 | **47**<br>**Ag**<br>Silver<br>107.9 | **48**<br>**Cd**<br>Cadmium<br>112.4 | **49**<br>**In**<br>Indium<br>114.8 | **50**<br>**Sn**<br>Tin<br>118.7 | **51**<br>**Sb**<br>Antimony<br>121.8 | **52**<br>**Te**<br>Tellurium<br>127.6 | **53**<br>**I**<br>Iodine<br>126.9 | **54**<br>**Xe**<br>Xenon<br>131.3 |
| **55**<br>**Cs**<br>Cesium<br>132.9 | **56**<br>**Ba**<br>Barium<br>137.3 | * | **72**<br>**Hf**<br>Hafnium<br>178.5 | **73**<br>**Ta**<br>Tantalum<br>180.9 | **74**<br>**W**<br>Tungsten<br>183.8 | **75**<br>**Re**<br>Rhenium<br>186.2 | **76**<br>**Os**<br>Osmium<br>190.2 | **77**<br>**Ir**<br>Iridium<br>192.2 | **78**<br>**Pt**<br>Platinum<br>195.1 | **79**<br>**Au**<br>Gold<br>197.0 | **80**<br>**Hg**<br>Mercury<br>200.6 | **81**<br>**Tl**<br>Thallium<br>204.4 | **82**<br>**Pb**<br>Lead<br>207.2 | **83**<br>**Bi**<br>Bismuth<br>209.0 | **84**<br>**Po**<br>Polonium<br>[209] | **85**<br>**At**<br>Astatine<br>[210] | **86**<br>**Rn**<br>Radon<br>[222] |
| **87**<br>**Fr**<br>Francium<br>[223] | **88**<br>**Ra**<br>Radium<br>[226] | ** | **104**<br>**Rf**<br>Rutherfordium<br>[265] | **105**<br>**Db**<br>Dubnium<br>[268] | **106**<br>**Sg**<br>Seaborgium<br>[271] | **107**<br>**Bh**<br>Bohrium<br>[270] | **108**<br>**Hs**<br>Hassium<br>[277] | **109**<br>**Mt**<br>Meitnerium<br>[276] | **110**<br>**Ds**<br>Darmstadtium<br>[281] | **111**<br>**Rg**<br>Roentgenium<br>[280] | **112**<br>**Cn**<br>Copernicium<br>[285] | **113**<br>**Uut**<br>Ununtrium<br>[284] | **114**<br>**Fl**<br>Flerovium<br>[289] | **115**<br>**Uup**<br>Ununpentium<br>[288] | **116**<br>**Lv**<br>Livermorium<br>[293] | **117**<br>**UUs**<br>Ununseptium<br>[294] | **118**<br>**UUo**<br>Ununoctium<br>[294] |

| *Lanthanides | **57**<br>**La**<br>Lanthanum<br>138.9 | **58**<br>**Ce**<br>Cerium<br>140.1 | **59**<br>**Pr**<br>Praseodymium<br>140.9 | **60**<br>**Nd**<br>Neodymium<br>144.2 | **61**<br>**Pm**<br>Promethium<br>[145] | **62**<br>**Sm**<br>Samarium<br>150.4 | **63**<br>**Eu**<br>Europium<br>152.0 | **64**<br>**Gd**<br>Gadolinium<br>157.3 | **65**<br>**Tb**<br>Terbium<br>158.9 | **66**<br>**Dy**<br>Dysprosium<br>162.5 | **67**<br>**Ho**<br>Holmium<br>164.9 | **68**<br>**Er**<br>Erbium<br>167.3 | **69**<br>**Tm**<br>Thulium<br>168.9 | **70**<br>**Yb**<br>Ytterbium<br>173.1 | **71**<br>**Lu**<br>Lutetium<br>175.0 |
|---|---|---|---|---|---|---|---|---|---|---|---|---|---|---|---|
| **Actinides | **89**<br>**Ac**<br>Actinium<br>[227] | **90**<br>**Th**<br>Thorium<br>232.0 | **91**<br>**Pa**<br>Protactinium<br>231.0 | **92**<br>**U**<br>Uranium<br>238.0 | **93**<br>**Np**<br>Neptunium<br>[237] | **94**<br>**Pu**<br>Plutonium<br>[244] | **95**<br>**Am**<br>Americium<br>[243] | **96**<br>**Cm**<br>Curium<br>[247] | **97**<br>**Bk**<br>Berkelium<br>[247] | **98**<br>**Cf**<br>Californium<br>[251] | **99**<br>**Es**<br>Einsteinium<br>[252] | **100**<br>**Fm**<br>Fermium<br>[257] | **101**<br>**Md**<br>Mendelevium<br>[258] | **102**<br>**No**<br>Nobelium<br>[259] | **103**<br>**Lr**<br>Lawrencium<br>[262] |

DATA: Wieser, M. E., and M. Berglund. 2009. *Pure and Applied Chemistry* 81: 2131–2156.

*Atomic weights are reported to four significant figures.

†For elements with a variable number of protons and/or neutrons, the mass number of the longest-lived isotope of the element is reported in brackets.

# Glossary

**5′ cap** A modified guanine (G) nucleotide (7-methylguanylate) added to the 5′ end of eukaryotic mRNAs. Helps protect the mRNA from being degraded and promotes efficient initiation of translation.

**abdomen** A region of the body; in insects, one of the three prominent body regions called tagmata.

**abiotic** Not alive (e.g., air, water, and some components of soil). Compare with **biotic**.

**aboveground biomass** The total mass of living plants in an area, excluding roots.

**abscisic acid (ABA)** A plant hormone that inhibits growth; it stimulates stomatal closure and triggers dormancy.

**abscission** In plants, the normal (often seasonal) shedding of leaves, fruits, or flowers.

**abscission zone** The region at the base of a petiole where cell wall degradation occurs; results in the dropping of leaves.

**absorption** In animals, the uptake of ions and small molecules, derived from food, across the lining of the intestine and into the bloodstream.

**absorption spectrum** The amount of light of different wavelengths absorbed by a pigment. Usually depicted as a graph of light absorbed versus wavelength. Compare with **action spectrum**.

**acclimation** A change in a study organism's phenotype that occurs in response to laboratory conditions.

**acclimatization** A change in an individual's phenotype that occurs in response to a change in natural environmental conditions.

**acetyl CoA** A molecule produced by oxidation of pyruvate (the final product of glycolysis) in a reaction catalyzed by pyruvate dehydrogenase. Can enter the citric acid cycle and is used as a carbon source in the synthesis of fatty acids, steroids, and other compounds.

**acetylation** Addition of an acetyl group ($-COCH_3$) to a molecule. Acetylation of histone proteins is important in controlling chromatin condensation.

**acetylcholine (Ach)** A neurotransmitter, released by nerve cells at neuromuscular junctions, that triggers contraction of skeletal muscle cells but slows the rate of contraction in cardiac muscle cells. Also used as a neurotransmitter between neurons.

**acid** Any compound that gives up protons or accepts electrons during a chemical reaction or that releases hydrogen ions when dissolved in water.

**acid-growth hypothesis** The hypothesis that auxin triggers elongation of plant cells by increasing the activity of proton pumps, making the cell wall more acidic and leading to expansion of the cell wall and an influx of water.

**acoelomate** A bilaterian animal that lacks an internal body cavity (coelom). Compare with **coelomate** and **pseudocoelomate**.

**acquired immune deficiency syndrome (AIDS)** A human disease characterized by death of immune system cells (in particular helper T cells) and subsequent vulnerability to other infections. Caused by the human immunodeficiency virus (HIV).

**acrosome** A caplike structure, located on the head of a sperm cell, that contains enzymes capable of dissolving the outer coverings of an egg.

**ACTH** See **adrenocorticotropic hormone**.

**actin** A globular protein that can be polymerized to form filaments. Actin filaments are part of the cytoskeleton and constitute the thin filaments in skeletal muscle cells.

**actin filament** A long fiber, about 7 nm in diameter, composed of two intertwined strands of polymerized actin protein; one of the three types of cytoskeletal fibers. Involved in cell movement. Also called a *microfilament*. Compare with **intermediate filament** and **microtubule**.

**action potential** A rapid, temporary change in electrical potential across a membrane, from negative to positive and back to negative. Occurs in cells, such as neurons and muscle cells, that have an excitable membrane.

**action spectrum** The relative effectiveness of different wavelengths of light in driving a light-dependent process such as photosynthesis. Usually depicted as a graph of some measure of the process versus wavelength. Compare with **absorption spectrum**.

**activation energy** The amount of energy required to initiate a chemical reaction; specifically, the energy required to reach the transition state.

**activator** A protein that binds to a DNA regulatory sequence to increase the frequency of transcription initiation by RNA polymerase.

**active site** The location in an enzyme molecule where substrates (reactant molecules) bind and react.

**active transport** The movement of ions or molecules across a membrane against an electrochemical gradient. Requires energy (e.g., from hydrolysis of ATP) and assistance of a transport protein (e.g., pump).

**adaptation** Any heritable trait that increases the fitness of an individual with that trait, compared with individuals without that trait, in a particular environment.

**adaptive immune response** See **adaptive immunity**.

**adaptive immunity** Immunity to a particular pathogen or other antigen conferred by activated B and T cells in vertebrates. Characterized by specificity, diversity, memory, and self–nonself recognition. Also called *adaptive immune response*. Compare with **innate immunity**.

**adaptive radiation** Rapid evolutionary diversification within one lineage, producing many descendant species with a wide range of adaptive forms.

**adenosine triphosphate (ATP)** A molecule consisting of an adenine base, a sugar, and three phosphate groups that can be hydrolyzed to release energy. Universally used by cells to store and transfer energy.

**adhesion** The tendency of certain dissimilar molecules to cling together due to attractive forces. Compare with **cohesion**.

**adipocyte** A fat cell.

**adrenal gland** Either of two small endocrine glands, one above each kidney. The outer portion (cortex) secretes several steroid hormones; the inner portion (medulla) secretes epinephrine and norepinephrine.

**adrenaline** See **epinephrine**.

**adrenocorticotropic hormone (ACTH)** A peptide hormone, produced and secreted by the anterior pituitary, that stimulates release of steroid hormones (e.g., cortisol, aldosterone) from the adrenal cortex.

**adult** A sexually mature individual.

**adventitious root** A root that develops from a plant's shoot system instead of from the plant's root system.

**aerobic** Referring to any metabolic process, cell, or organism that uses oxygen as an electron acceptor. Compare with **anaerobic**.

**afferent division** The part of the nervous system that transmits information about the internal and external environment to the central nervous system. Consists mainly of sensory neurons. Compare with **efferent division**.

**age class** All the individuals of a specific age in a population.

**age-specific fecundity** The average number of female offspring produced by a female in a certain age class.

**age structure** The proportion of individuals in a population that are of each possible age.

**agglutination** Clumping together of cells or viruses by antibodies or other cross-linking molecules.

**aggregate fruit** A fruit (e.g., raspberry) that develops from a single flower that has many separate carpels. Compare with **multiple** and **simple fruit**.

**AIDS** See **acquired immune deficiency syndrome**.

**albumen** A solution of water and protein (particularly albumins), found in amniotic eggs, that nourishes the growing embryo. Also called *egg white*.

**alcohol fermentation** Catabolic pathway in which pyruvate produced by glycolysis is converted to ethanol in the absence of oxygen.

**aldosterone** A hormone that stimulates the kidney to conserve salt and water and promotes retention of sodium; produced in the adrenal cortex.

**allele** A particular version of a gene.

**allergen** Any molecule (antigen) that triggers an allergic response (an allergy).

**allergy** An IgE-mediated abnormal response to an antigen, usually characterized by dilation of blood vessels, contraction of smooth muscle cells, and increased activity of mucus-secreting cells.

**allopatric speciation** Speciation that occurs when populations of the same species become geographically isolated, often due to dispersal or vicariance. Compare with **sympatric speciation**.

**allopatry** Condition in which two or more populations live in different geographic areas. Compare with **sympatry**.

**allopolyploidy** (adjective: allopolyploid) The state of having more than two full sets of chromosomes (polyploidy) due to hybridization between different species. Compare with **autopolyploidy**.

**allosteric regulation** Regulation of a protein's function by binding of a regulatory molecule, usually to a specific site distinct from the active site, that causes a change in the protein's shape.

**α-amylase** See **amylase**.

**α-helix (alpha-helix)** A protein secondary structure in which the polypeptide backbone coils into a spiral shape stabilized by hydrogen bonding.

**alternation of generations** A life cycle involving alternation of a multicellular haploid stage (gametophyte) with a multicellular diploid stage (sporophyte). Occurs in most plants and some protists.

**alternative splicing** In eukaryotes, the splicing of primary RNA transcripts from a single gene in different ways to produce different mature mRNAs and thus different polypeptides.

**altruism** Any behavior that has a fitness cost to the individual (lowered survival and/or reproduction) and a fitness benefit to the recipient. See **reciprocal altruism**.

**alveolus** (plural: alveoli) Any of the tiny air-filled sacs of a mammalian lung.

**ambisense RNA virus** A ssRNA virus whose genome consists of at least one strand that contains both positive-sense and negative-sense regions.

**aminoacyl tRNA** A transfer RNA molecule that is covalently bound to an amino acid.

**aminoacyl-tRNA synthetase** An enzyme that catalyzes the addition of a particular amino acid to its corresponding tRNA molecule.

**ammonia (NH₃)** A small molecule, produced by the breakdown of proteins and nucleic acids, that is very toxic to cells. Is a strong base that gains a proton to form the ammonium ion ($NH_4^+$).

**amnion** The innermost of the membranes surrounding the embryo in an amniotic egg.

**amniotes** A major lineage of vertebrates (Amniota) that reproduce with amniotic eggs. Includes all reptiles (including birds) and mammals—all tetrapods except amphibians.

**amniotic egg** An egg that has a watertight shell or case enclosing a membrane-bound water supply (the amnion), food supply (yolk sac), and waste sac (allantois).

**amoeboid motion** See **cell crawling**.

**amphibians** A lineage of vertebrates, many of which breathe through their skin and feed on land but lay their eggs in water. Represent the earliest tetrapods; include frogs, salamanders, and caecilians.

**amphipathic** Containing hydrophilic and hydrophobic regions.

**ampullae of Lorenzini** Structures on the heads of sharks that contain cells with electroreceptors.

**amylase** Any enzyme that can break down starch by catalyzing hydrolysis of the glycosidic linkages between the glucose residues.

**amyloplasts** Starch-storing organelles (plastids) in plants. In root cap cells, they settle to the bottom of the cell and may be used as gravity detectors.

**anabolic pathway** Any set of chemical reactions that synthesizes large molecules from smaller ones. Generally requires an input of energy. Compare with **catabolic pathway**.

**anadromous** Having a life cycle in which adults live in the ocean (or large lakes) but migrate up freshwater streams to breed and lay eggs.

**anaerobic** Referring to any metabolic process, cell, or organism that uses an electron acceptor other than oxygen, including fermentation or anaerobic respiration. Compare with **aerobic**.

**anaphase** A stage in mitosis or meiosis during which chromosomes are moved to opposite poles of the spindle apparatus.

**anatomy** The study of the physical structure of organisms.

**ancestral trait** A trait found in the ancestors of a particular group.

**aneuploidy** (adjective: aneuploid) The state of having an abnormal number of copies of a certain chromosome.

**angiosperm** A flowering vascular plant that produces seeds within mature ovaries (fruits). The angiosperms form a single lineage. Compare with **gymnosperm**.

**animal** A member of a major lineage of eukaryotes (Animalia) whose members typically have a complex, large, multicellular body; eat other organisms; and are mobile.

**animal model** Any disease that occurs in a nonhuman animal and has parallels to a similar disease of humans. Studied by medical researchers in hopes that findings may apply to human disease.

**anion** A negatively charged ion.

**annelids** Members of the phylum Annelida (segmented worms). Distinguished by a segmented body and a coelom that functions as a hydrostatic skeleton. Annelids belong to the lophotrochozoan branch of the protostomes.

**annual** Referring to a plant whose life cycle normally lasts only one growing season—less than one year. Compare with **perennial**.

**anoxygenic** Referring to any process or reaction that does not produce oxygen. Photosynthesis in purple sulfur and purple nonsulfur bacteria, which does not involve photosystem II, is anoxygenic. Compare with **oxygenic**.

**antagonistic muscle group** A set of two or more muscles that reextend one another by transmitting their forces via the skeleton.

**antenna** (plural: antennae) A long appendage of the head that is used to touch or smell.

**antenna complex** Part of a photosystem, containing an array of chlorophyll molecules and accessory pigments, that receives energy from light and directs the energy to a central reaction center during photosynthesis.

**anterior** Toward an animal's head and away from its tail. The opposite of posterior.

**anterior pituitary** The part of the pituitary gland containing endocrine cells that produce and release a variety of peptide hormones in response to other hormones from the hypothalamus. Compare with **posterior pituitary**.

**anther** The pollen-producing structure at the end of a stamen in flowering plants (angiosperms).

**antheridium** (plural: antheridia) The sperm-producing structure in most land plants except angiosperms.

**anthropoids** One of the two major lineages of primates, including apes, humans, and all monkeys. Compare with **prosimians**.

**antibiotic** Any substance, such as penicillin, that can kill or inhibit the growth of bacteria.

**antibody** A protein produced by B cells that can bind to a specific part of an antigen, tagging it for removal by the immune system. All monomeric forms of antibodies consist of two light chains and two heavy chains, which vary between different antibodies. Also called *immunoglobulin*.

**anticodon** The sequence of three bases (a triplet) in a transfer RNA molecule that can bind to an mRNA codon with a complementary sequence.

**antidiuretic hormone (ADH)** A peptide hormone, secreted from the posterior pituitary gland, that stimulates water retention by the kidney. Also called *vasopressin*.

**antigen** Any foreign molecule, often a protein, that can stimulate an innate or adaptive response by the immune system.

**antigen presentation** Process by which small peptides, derived from ingested particulate antigens (e.g., bacteria) or intracellular antigens (e.g., viruses in infected cell) are complexed with MHC proteins and transported to the cell surface, where they are displayed and can be recognized by T cells.

**antiparallel** Describing the opposite orientation of nucleic acid strands that are hydrogen bonded to one another, with one strand running in the $5' \rightarrow 3'$ direction and the other in the $3' \rightarrow 5'$ direction.

**antiporter** A carrier protein that allows an ion to diffuse down an electrochemical gradient, using the energy of that process to transport a different substance in the opposite direction *against* its concentration gradient. Compare with **symporter**.

**antiviral** Any drug or other agent that can interfere with the transmission or replication of viruses.

**aorta** In terrestrial vertebrates, the major artery carrying oxygenated blood away from the heart.

**aphotic zone** Deep water receiving no sunlight. Compare with **photic zone**.

**apical** Toward the top. In plants, at the tip of a branch. In animals, on the side of an epithelial layer that faces the environment and not other body tissues. Compare with **basal**.

**apical–basal axis** The shoot-to-root axis of a plant.

**apical bud** A bud at the tip of a stem or branch, where growth occurs to lengthen the stem or branch.

**apical dominance** Inhibition of lateral bud growth by the apical meristem at the tip of a plant branch.

**apical meristem** A group of undifferentiated plant cells, at the tip of a shoot or root, that is responsible for primary growth. Compare with **cambium**.

**apodeme** Any of the chitinous ingrowths of the exoskeleton to which muscles attach.

**apomixis** The formation of mature seeds without fertilization occurring; a type of asexual reproduction.

**apoplast** In plants, the region outside plasma membranes consisting of the porous cell walls and the intervening extracellular air space. Compare with **symplast**.

**apoptosis** Series of tightly controlled changes that lead to the self-destruction of a cell. Occurs frequently during embryological development and as part of the immune response to remove infected or cancerous cells. Also called *programmed cell death*.

**appendix** A blind sac (having only one opening) that extends from the cecum in some mammals.

**aquaporin** A type of channel protein through which water can move by osmosis across a plasma membrane.

**aquifer** An underground layer of porous rock, sand, or gravel that is saturated with water.

***ara* operon** A set of three genes in *E. coli* that are transcribed into a single mRNA and required for metabolism of the sugar arabinose. Transcription of the *ara* operon is controlled by the AraC regulatory protein.

***araC*** The regulatory gene (written as *araC*) or regulatory protein (when written as AraC) of the *E. coli ara* operon.

**arbuscular mycorrhizal fungi (AMF)** Fungi from the Glomeromycota lineage whose hyphae enter the root cells of their host plants. Also called *endomycorrhizal fungi*.

**Archaea** One of the three taxonomic domains of life, consisting of unicellular prokaryotes distinguished by cell walls made of certain polysaccharides not found in bacterial or eukaryotic cell walls, plasma membranes composed of unique isoprene-containing phospholipids, and ribosomes and RNA polymerase similar to those of eukaryotes. Compare with **Bacteria** and **Eukarya**.

**archegonium** (plural: archegonia) The egg-producing structure in most land plants except angiosperms.

**arteriole** Any of the many tiny vessels that carry blood from arteries to capillaries.

**arteriosclerosis** Hardening and loss of elasticity of arteries.

**artery** Any thick-walled blood vessel that carries blood (oxygenated or not) under relatively high pressure away from the heart to organs throughout the body. Compare with **vein**.

**arthropods** Members of the phylum Arthropoda. Distinguished by a segmented body; a hard, jointed exoskeleton; paired, jointed appendages; and an extensive body cavity called a hemocoel. Arthropods belong to the ecdysozoan branch of the protostomes.

**articulation** A movable point of contact between two rigid components of a skeleton, such as between bones of a vertebrate endoskeleton or between segments of cuticle in an arthropod exoskeleton. See **joint**.

**artificial selection** Deliberate manipulation by humans, as in animal and plant breeding, of the genetic composition of a population by allowing only individuals with desirable traits to reproduce.

**ascus** (plural: asci) Specialized spore-producing cell found at the ends of hyphae in "sac fungi" (Ascomycota).

**asexual reproduction** Any form of reproduction where offspring inherit DNA from only one parent. Includes binary fission, budding, and parthenogenesis. Compare with **sexual reproduction**.

**astral microtubules** Mitotic and meiotic microtubules that have arisen from the two spindle poles and interact with proteins on the plasma membrane.

**asymmetric competition** Ecological competition between two species in which one species suffers a much greater fitness decline than the other. Compare with **symmetric competition**.

**atomic number** The number of protons in the nucleus of an atom, giving the atom its identity as a particular chemical element.

**atomic weight** The average mass of an element that is based on the relative proportions of all the naturally occurring isotopes.

**ATP synthase** A large membrane-bound protein complex that uses the energy of protons flowing through it to synthesize ATP.

**ATP** See **adenosine triphosphate**.

**atrioventricular (AV) node** A region of the heart between the right atrium and right ventricle where electrical signals from the atrium are slowed briefly before spreading to the ventricle. This delay allows the ventricle to fill with blood before contracting. Compare with **sinoatrial (SA) node**.

**atrium** (plural: atria) A thin-walled chamber of the heart that receives blood from veins and pumps it to a neighboring chamber (the ventricle).

**autocrine** Relating to a chemical signal that affects the same cell that produced and released it.

**autoimmunity** A pathological condition in which the immune system attacks self cells or tissues of an individual's own body.

**autonomic nervous system** The part of the peripheral nervous system that controls internal organs and involuntary processes, such as stomach contraction, hormone release, and heart rate. Includes parasympathetic and sympathetic nerves. Compare with **somatic nervous system**.

**autophagy** The process by which damaged organelles are surrounded by a membrane and delivered to a lysosome to be recycled.

**autopolyploidy** (adjective: autopolyploid) The state of having more than two full sets of chromosomes

(polyploidy) due to a mutation that doubled the chromosome number. All the chromosomes come from the same species. Compare with **allopolyploidy**.

**autosomal inheritance** The inheritance patterns that occur when genes are located on autosomes rather than on sex chromosomes.

**autosome** Any chromosome other than a sex chromosome (i.e,. any chromosome other than the X or Y in mammals).

**autotroph** Any organism that can synthesize reduced organic compounds from simple inorganic sources such as $CO_2$ or $CH_4$. Most plants and some bacteria and archaea are autotrophs. Also called *primary producer*. Compare with **heterotroph**.

**auxin** Indoleacetic acid (IAA), a plant hormone that stimulates phototropism and cell elongation.

**axillary bud** A bud that forms at a node and may develop into a lateral (side) branch. Also called *lateral bud*.

**axon** A long projection of a neuron that can propagate an action potential.

**axon hillock** The site in a neuron where an axon joins the cell body and where action potentials are first triggered.

**axoneme** A structure found in eukaryotic cilia and flagella and responsible for their motion; composed of two central microtubules surrounded by nine doublet microtubules (9 + 2 arrangement).

**B cell** A type of lymphocyte that matures in the bone marrow and, with T cells, is responsible for adaptive immunity. Produces antibodies and also functions in antigen presentation. Also called *B lymphocyte*.

**B-cell receptor (BCR)** An immunoglobulin protein embedded in the plasma membrane of mature B cells and to which antigens bind. Apart from the transmembrane domain, it is identical in structure to antibodies.

**BAC library** A collection of all the sequences found in the genome of a species, inserted into **bacterial artificial chromosomes (BACs)**.

**background extinction** The average rate of low-level extinction that has occurred continuously throughout much of evolutionary history. Compare with **mass extinction**.

**Bacteria** One of the three taxonomic domains of life, consisting of unicellular prokaryotes distinguished by cell walls composed largely of peptidoglycan, plasma membranes similar to those of eukaryotic cells, and ribosomes and RNA polymerase that differ from those in archaeans or eukaryotes. Compare with **Archaea** and **Eukarya**.

**bacterial artificial chromosome (BAC)** An artificial version of a bacterial chromosome that can be used as a cloning vector to produce many copies of large DNA fragments.

**bacteriophage** Any virus that infects bacteria.

**baculum** A bone inside the penis; usually present in mammals with a penis that lacks erectile tissue.

**balancing selection** A mode of natural selection in which no single allele is favored in all populations of a species at all times. Instead, there is a balance among alleles in terms of fitness and frequency.

**ball-and-stick model** A representation of a molecule where atoms are shown as balls—colored and scaled to indicate the atom's identity—and covalent bonds are shown as rods or sticks connecting the balls in the correct geometry.

**bar coding** The use of well-characterized gene sequences to identify species.

**bark** The protective outer layer of woody plants, composed of cork cells, cork cambium, and secondary phloem.

**baroreceptors** Specialized nerve cells in the walls of the heart and certain major arteries that detect changes in blood pressure and trigger appropriate responses by the brain.

**basal** Toward the base. In plants, toward the root or at the base of a branch where it joins the stem. In animals, on the side of an epithelial layer that abuts underlying body tissues. Compare with **apical**.

**basal body** The microtubule organizing center for cilia and flagella in eukaryotic cells. Consists of nine triplets of microtubules arranged in a circle and establishes the structure of axonemes. Structurally identical with a centriole.

**basal lamina** A thick, collagen-rich extracellular matrix that underlies most epithelial tissues in animals and connects it to connective tissue.

**basal metabolic rate (BMR)** The total energy consumption by an organism at rest in a comfortable environment. For aerobes, often measured as the amount of oxygen consumed per hour.

**basal transcription factor** Proteins, present in all eukaryotic cells, that bind to promoters and help initiate transcription. Compare with **regulatory transcription factor**.

**base** Any compound that acquires protons or gives up electrons during a chemical reaction or accepts hydrogen ions when dissolved in water.

**basidium** (plural: basidia) Specialized spore-producing cell at the ends of hyphae in club fungi, members of the Basidiomycota.

**basilar membrane** The membrane on which the bottom portion of hair cells sits in the vertebrate cochlea.

**basolateral** Toward the bottom and sides. In animals, the side of an epithelial layer that faces other body tissues and not the environment.

**Batesian mimicry** A type of mimicry in which a harmless or palatable species resembles a dangerous or poisonous species. Compare with **Müllerian mimicry**.

**beak** A structure that exerts biting forces and is associated with the mouth; found in birds, cephalopods, and some insects.

**behavior** Any action by an organism, often in response to a stimulus.

**behavioral ecology** The study of how organisms respond to particular abiotic and biotic stimuli from their environment.

**beneficial** In genetics, referring to any mutation, allele, or trait that increases an individual's fitness.

**benign tumor** A mass of abnormal tissue that appears due to unregulated growth but does not spread to other organs. Benign tumors are not cancers. Compare with **malignant tumor**.

**benthic** Living at the bottom of an aquatic environment.

**benthic zone** The area along the bottom of an aquatic environment.

**β-pleated sheet (beta-pleated sheet)** A protein secondary structure in which the polypeptide backbone folds into a sheetlike shape stabilized by hydrogen bonding.

**bilateral symmetry** An animal body pattern in which one plane of symmetry divides the body into a left side and a right side. Typically, the body is long and narrow, with a distinct head end and tail end. Compare with **radial symmetry**.

**bilaterian** A member of a major lineage of animals (Bilateria) that are bilaterally symmetrical at some point in their life cycle, have three embryonic germ layers, and have a coelom. All protostomes and deuterostomes are bilaterians.

**bile** A complex solution produced by the liver, stored in the gallbladder, and secreted into the intestine. Contains steroid derivatives called bile salts that are responsible for emulsification of fats during digestion.

**binary fission** The process of cell division used for asexual reproduction of many prokaryotic cells. The genetic material is replicated and partitioned to opposite sides of a growing cell, which is then divided in half to create two genetically identical cells.

**biodiversity** The diversity of life considered at three levels: genetic diversity (variety of alleles and/or genes in a population, species, or group of species); species diversity (variety and relative abundance of species present in a certain area); and ecosystem diversity (variety of communities and abiotic components in a region).

**biodiversity hotspot** A region that is extraordinarily rich in species.

**biofilm** A complex community of bacteria enmeshed in a polysaccharide-rich, extracellular matrix that allows them to attach to a surface.

**biogeochemical cycle** The pattern of circulation of an element or molecule among living organisms and the environment.

**biogeography** The study of how species and populations are distributed geographically.

**bioinformatics** The field of study concerned with managing, analyzing, and interpreting biological information, particularly DNA sequences.

**biological species concept** The definition of a species as a population or group of populations that are reproductively isolated from other groups. Members of a species have the potential to interbreed in nature to produce viable, fertile offspring but cannot interbreed successfully with members of other species. Compare with **morphospecies** and **phylogenetic species concepts**.

**bioluminescence** The emission of light by a living organism via an enzyme-catalyzed reaction.

**biomagnification** In animal tissues, an increase in the concentration of particular molecules that may occur as those molecules are passed up a food chain.

**biomass** The total mass of all organisms in a given population or geographical area; usually expressed as total dry weight.

**biome** A large terrestrial or marine region characterized by distinct abiotic characteristics and dominant types of vegetation.

**biomechanics** A field of biology that applies the principles of physics and engineering to analyze the mechanical structure and function of organisms.

**bioprospecting** The effort to find commercially useful compounds by studying organisms—especially species that are poorly studied to date.

**bioremediation** The use of living organisms, usually bacteria or archaea, to degrade environmental pollutants.

**biosphere** The thin zone surrounding the Earth where all life exists; the sum of all terrestrial and aquatic ecosystems.

**biotechnology** The application of biological techniques and discoveries to medicine, industry, and agriculture.

**biotic** Living, or produced by a living organism. Compare with **abiotic**.

**bipedal** Walking primarily on two legs; characteristic of hominins.

**bipolar cell** A type of cell in the vertebrate retina that receives information from one or more photoreceptors and passes it to other bipolar cells or ganglion cells.

**bivalent** The structure formed by synapsed homologous chromosomes during prophase of meiosis I. Also known as a *tetrad*.

**bivalves** A lineage of mollusks that have shells made of two parts, or valves, such as clams and mussels.

**bladder** A mammalian organ that holds urine until it can be excreted.

**blade** The wide, flat part of a plant leaf.

**blastocoel** Fluid-filled cavity in the blastula of many animal species.

**blastocyst** The mammalian blastula. A roughly spherical structure composed of trophoblast cells on the exterior and a cluster of cells (the inner cell mass) that fills part of the interior space.

**blastomere** A cell created by cleavage divisions in early animal embryos.

**blastopore** An opening (pore) in the surface of some early embryos, through which cells move during gastrulation.

**blastula** In vertebrate development, a ball of cells (blastomere cells) typically surrounding a fluid-filled cavity (the blastocoel). The blastula is formed by cleavage of a zygote and undergoes gastrulation. See **blastocyst**.

**blood** A type of connective tissue consisting of red blood cells and leukocytes suspended in a fluid portion, an extracellular matrix called plasma. Transports materials throughout the vertebrate body.

**body mass index (BMI)** A mathematical relationship of weight and height used to assess obesity in humans. Calculated as weight (kg) divided by the square of height (m²).

**body plan** The basic architecture of an animal's body, including the number and arrangement of limbs, body segments, and major tissue layers.

**bog** A freshwater wetland that has no or almost no water flow, resulting in very low oxygen levels and acidic conditions.

**Bohr shift** The rightward shift of the oxygen–hemoglobin equilibrium curve that occurs with decreasing pH. It results in hemoglobin being more likely to release oxygen in the acidic environment of exercising muscle.

**bone** A type of vertebrate connective tissue consisting of living cells and blood vessels within a hard extracellular matrix composed of calcium phosphate ($CaPO_4$) and small amounts of calcium carbonate ($CaCO_3$) and protein fibers.

**bone marrow** The soft tissue filling the inside of large bones; contains stem cells that develop into red blood cells and leukocytes throughout life.

**Bowman's capsule** The hollow, double-walled, cup-shaped portion of a nephron that surrounds a glomerulus in the vertebrate kidney.

**brain** A large mass of neurons, located in the head region of an animal, that is involved in information processing; may also be called the cerebral ganglion.

**brain stem** The most posterior portion of the vertebrate brain, connecting to the spinal cord and responsible for autonomic body functions such as heart rate, respiration, and digestion.

**braincase** See **cranium**.

**branch** (1) A part of a phylogenetic tree that represents populations through time. (2) Any extension of a plant's shoot system.

**brassinosteroids** A family of steroid hormones found in plants; stimulate growth.

**bronchiole** Any of the small tubes in mammalian lungs that carry air from the bronchi to the alveoli.

**bronchus** (plural: bronchi) In mammals, one of a pair of large tubes that lead from the trachea to each lung.

**bryophyte** See **non-vascular plants**.

**budding** Asexual reproduction in which an outgrowth from the parent breaks free as an independent individual; occurs in yeasts and some invertebrates.

**buffer** A substance that, in solution, acts to minimize changes in the pH of that solution when acid or base is added.

**bulbourethral gland** In male mammals, either of a small pair of glands at the base of the urethra that secrete an alkaline mucus (part of semen), which lubricates the tip of the penis and neutralizes acids in the urethra during copulation. In humans, also called *Cowper's glands*.

**bulk flow** The directional mass movement of a fluid due to pressure differences, such as movement of water through plant xylem and phloem, and movement of blood in animals.

**bulk-phase endocytosis** Nonspecific uptake of extracellular fluid by pinching off the plasma membrane to form small membrane-bound vesicles; considered to be a means of retrieving membrane from the surface following exocytosis. Compare with **receptor-mediated endocytosis**.

**bundle-sheath cell** A type of cell found around the vascular tissue (veins) of plant leaves.

**$C_3$ pathway** The most common form of photosynthesis in which atmospheric $CO_2$ is fixed by rubisco to form 3-phosphoglycerate, a three-carbon molecule. Used in first phase of the Calvin cycle.

**$C_4$ pathway** A variant type of photosynthesis in which atmospheric $CO_2$ is first fixed by PEP carboxylase into four-carbon acids, rather than the three-carbon molecules of the classic $C_3$ pathway. Used to concentrate $CO_2$ to reduce photorespiration in the Calvin cycle while stomata are closed.

**$C_4$ photosynthesis** A variant type of photosynthesis in which atmospheric $CO_2$ is first fixed into four-carbon sugars, rather than the three-carbon sugars of classic $C_3$ photosynthesis. Enhances photosynthetic efficiency in hot, dry environments by reducing loss of oxygen due to photorespiration.

**cadherin** Any of a class of cell-surface proteins involved in selective cell–cell adhesion. Important for coordinating movements of cells and the establishment of tissues during embryological development.

**callus** In plants, a mass of undifferentiated cells that can generate roots and other tissues necessary to create a mature plant.

**Calvin cycle** In photosynthesis, the set of reactions that use NADPH and ATP formed in the light-dependent reactions to drive the fixation of $CO_2$, reduction of the fixed carbon to produce sugar, and the regeneration of the substrate used to fix $CO_2$. Also called *light-independent reactions*.

**calyx** All of the sepals of a flower.

**CAM** See **crassulacean acid metabolism**.

**cambium** (plural: cambia) In woody plants, tissue that consists of two types of cylindrical meristems that increase the width of roots and shoots through the process of secondary growth. See **vascular cambium** and **cork cambium**.

**Cambrian explosion** The rapid diversification of animal body types and lineages that occured between the species present in the Doushantuo faunas (around 570 mya), Ediacaran faunas (565–542 mya), and the Early Cambrian faunas (525–515 mya).

**cancer** General term for any tumor whose cells grow in an uncontrolled fashion, invade nearby tissues, and spread to other sites in the body.

**capillarity** The tendency of water to move up a narrow tube due to adhesion, cohesion, and surface tension (also called capillary action).

**capillary** Any of the many small, thin-walled blood vessels that permeate all tissues and organs, and allow exchange of gases and other molecules between blood and body cells.

**capillary bed** A thick network of capillaries.

**capsid** A shell of protein enclosing the genome of a virus particle.

**carapace** In crustaceans, a large platelike section of the exoskeleton that covers and protects the cephalothorax (e.g., a crab's "shell").

**carbohydrate** Any of a class of molecules that contain a carbonyl group, several hydroxyl groups, and several to many carbon-hydrogen bonds. See **monosaccharide** and **polysaccharide**.

**carbon cycle, global** The worldwide movement of carbon among terrestrial ecosystems, the oceans, and the atmosphere.

**carbon fixation** The process of converting gaseous carbon dioxide into an organic molecule, often associated with photosynthesis. See also **PEP carboxylase** and **rubisco**.

**carbonic anhydrase** An enzyme that catalyzes the formation of carbonic acid ($H_2CO_3$) from carbon dioxide and water.

**carboxylic acids** Organic acids with the form R-COOH (a carboxyl group).

**cardiac cycle** One complete heartbeat cycle, including systole and diastole.

**cardiac muscle** The muscle tissue of the vertebrate heart; responsible for pumping blood. Consists of long, branched fibers that are electrically connected and that initiate their own contractions; not under voluntary control. Compare with **skeletal** and **smooth muscle**.

**cardiovascular disease** A group of diseases of the heart and blood vessels caused by poor diet, obesity, inactivity, genetics, tobacco use, age, and other factors.

**carnivore** (adjective: carnivorous) An animal whose diet consists predominantly of meat, or other animals. Most members of the mammalian taxon Carnivora are carnivores. Some plants are carnivorous, trapping and killing small animals and then absorbing nutrients from the prey's body. Compare with **herbivore** and **omnivore**.

**carotenoid** Any of a class of accessory pigments, found in chloroplasts, that absorb wavelengths of light not absorbed by chlorophyll; typically appear yellow, orange, or red. Includes carotenes and xanthophylls.

**carpel** The female reproductive organ in a flower. Consists of the stigma, to which pollen grains adhere; the style, through which the pollen tube grows; and the ovary, which houses the ovule. Compare with **stamen**.

**carrier protein** A membrane protein that facilitates diffusion of a small molecule (e.g., glucose) across a membrane by a process involving a reversible change in the shape of the protein. Also called *carrier* or *transporter*. Compare with **channel protein**.

**carrier** A heterozygous individual carrying a normal allele and a recessive allele for an inherited trait; does not display the phenotype of the recessive trait but can pass the recessive allele to offspring.

**carrying capacity ($K$)** The maximum population size of a certain species that a given habitat can support.

**cartilage** A type of vertebrate connective tissue that consists of relatively few cells scattered in a stiff matrix of polysaccharides and protein fibers. Provides structural support.

**Casparian strip** In plant roots, a waxy layer containing suberin, a water-repellent substance that prevents movement of water through the walls of endodermal cells, thus blocking the apoplastic pathway of water and ion movement into the vascular tissue.

**cast** A type of fossil, formed when the decay of a body part leaves a void that is then filled with minerals that later harden.

**catabolic pathway** Any set of chemical reactions that breaks down large, complex molecules into smaller ones, releasing energy in the process. Compare with **anabolic pathway**.

**catalysis** (verb: catalyze) Acceleration of the rate of a chemical reaction due to a decrease in the free energy of the transition state, called the activation energy.

**catalyst** Any substance that increases the rate of a chemical reaction without itself undergoing any permanent chemical change.

**catecholamines** A class of small compounds, derived from the amino acid tyrosine, that are used as hormones or neurotransmitters. Include epinephrine, norepinephrine, and dopamine.

**cation** A positively charged ion.

**cation exchange** The release (displacement) of cations, such as magnesium and calcium from soil particles, by protons in acidic soil water. The released cations are available for uptake by plants.

**CD4** A membrane protein on the surface of some T cells in humans. $CD4^+$ T cells can give rise to helper T cells.

**CD8** A membrane protein on the surface of some T cells in humans. $CD8^+$ T cells can give rise to cytotoxic T cells.

**Cdk** See **cyclin-dependent kinase**.

**cDNA** See **complementary DNA**.

**cDNA library** A set of cDNAs from a particular cell type or stage of development. Each cDNA is carried by a plasmid or other cloning vector and can be separated from other cDNAs. Compare with **genomic library**.

**cecum** A blind sac between the small intestine and the colon. Is enlarged in some species (e.g., rabbits) that use it as a fermentation vat for digestion of cellulose.

**cell** A highly organized compartment bounded by a thin, flexible structure (plasma membrane) and containing concentrated chemicals in an aqueous (watery) solution. The basic structural and functional unit of all organisms.

**cell body** The part of a neuron that contains the nucleus; where incoming signals are integrated. Also called the *soma*.

**cell crawling** A form of cellular movement involving actin filaments in which the cell produces bulges (pseudopodia) that stick to the substrate and pull the cell forward. Also called *amoeboid motion*.

**cell cycle** Ordered sequence of events in which a eukaryotic cell replicates its chromosomes, evenly partitions the chromosomes to two daughter cells, and then undergoes division of the cytoplasm.

**cell-cycle checkpoint** Any of several points in the cell cycle at which progression of a cell through the cycle can be regulated.

**cell division** Creation of new cells by division of preexisting cells.

**cell-mediated (immune) response** The type of immune response that involves generation of cytotoxic

T cells from $CD8^+$ T cells. Defends against pathogen-infected cells, cancer cells, and transplanted cells. Compare with **humoral (immune) response**.

**cell membrane** See **plasma membrane**.

**cell plate** A flattened sac-like structure formed in the middle of a dividing plant cell from Golgi-derived vesicles containing cell wall material; ultimately divides the cytoplasm into two separate cells.

**cell sap** An aqueous solution found in the vacuoles of plant cells.

**cell theory** The theory that all organisms are made of cells and that all cells come from preexisting cells.

**cell wall** A fibrous layer found outside the plasma membrane of most bacteria and archaea and many eukaryotes.

**cellular respiration** A common pathway for production of ATP, involving transfer of electrons from compounds with high potential energy through an electron transport chain and ultimately to an electron acceptor (often oxygen).

**cellulase** An enzyme that can break down cellulose by catalyzing hydrolysis of the glycosidic linkages between the glucose residues.

**cellulose** A structural polysaccharide composed of glucose monomers joined by $\beta$-1,4-glycosidic linkages. Found in the cell wall of algae, plants, and some bacteria and fungi.

**Cenozoic era** The most recent interval of geologic time, beginning 65.5 million years ago, during which mammals became the dominant vertebrates and angiosperms became the dominant plants.

**central dogma** The scheme for information flow in the cell: DNA $\rightarrow$ RNA $\rightarrow$ protein.

**central nervous system (CNS)** Large numbers of neurons aggregated into clusters called ganglia in bilaterian animals. In vertebrates, the central nervous system consists of the brain and spinal cord. Compare with **nerve net** and **peripheral nervous system (PNS)**.

**centriole** One of two small cylindrical structures found together within the centrosome near the nucleus of a eukaryotic cell (not found in plants). Consists of microtubule triplets and is structurally identical with a basal body.

**centromere** Constricted region of a replicated chromosome where the two sister chromatids are joined and the kinetochore is located.

**centrosome** Structure in animal and fungal cells, containing two centrioles, that serves as a microtubule organizing center for the cell's cytoskeleton and for the spindle apparatus during cell division.

**cephalization** The formation in animals of a distinct anterior region (the head) where sense organs and a mouth are clustered.

**cephalochordates** One of the three major chordate lineages (Cephalochordata), comprising small, mobile organisms that live in marine sands and suspension feed; also called *lancelets* or *amphioxus*. Compare with **urochordates** and **vertebrates**.

**cephalopods** A lineage of mollusks including the squid, octopuses, and nautiluses. Distinguished by large brains, excellent vision, tentacles, and a reduced or absent shell.

**cerebellum** Posterior section of the vertebrate brain; involved in coordination of complex muscle movements, such as those required for locomotion and maintaining balance.

**cerebrum** The most anterior section of the vertebrate brain. Divided into left and right hemispheres and four lobes: frontal lobe, involved in complex decision making (in humans); occipital lobe, receives and interprets visual information; parietal lobe, involved in integrating sensory and motor functions; and temporal lobe, functions in memory, speech (in humans), and interpreting auditory information.

**cervix** The bottom portion of the uterus, containing a canal that leads to the vagina.

**chaetae** (singular: chaeta) Bristle-like extensions found in some annelids.

**channel protein** A protein that forms a pore in a cell membrane. The structure of most channels allows them to admit just one or a few types of ions or molecules. Compare with **carrier protein**.

**character** Any genetic, morphological, physiological, or behavioral characteristic of an organism to be studied.

**character displacement** The evolutionary tendency for the traits of similar species that occupy overlapping ranges to change in a way that reduces interspecific competition.

**chelicerae** A pair of clawlike appendages found around the mouth of certain arthropods called chelicerates (spiders, mites, and allies).

**chemical bond** An attractive force binding two atoms together. Covalent bonds, ionic bonds, and hydrogen bonds are types of chemical bonds.

**chemical energy** The potential energy stored in covalent bonds between atoms.

**chemical equilibrium** A dynamic but stable state of a reversible chemical reaction in which the forward reaction and reverse reactions proceed at the same rate, so that the concentrations of reactants and products remain constant.

**chemical evolution** A The theory that simple chemical compounds in the early atmosphere and ocean combined via chemical reactions to form larger, more complex substances, eventually leading to the origin of life and the start of biological evolution.

**chemical reaction** Any process in which one compound or element is combined with others or is broken down; involves the making and/or breaking of chemical bonds.

**chemiosmosis** An energetic coupling mechanism whereby energy stored in an electrochemical proton gradient is used to drive an energy-requiring process such as production of ATP.

**chemokine** Any of a subset of cytokines that acts as a chemical signal attracting leukocytes to a site of tissue injury or infection.

**chemolithotroph** An organism (bacteria or archaea) that produces ATP by oxidizing inorganic molecules with high potential energy such as ammonia ($NH_3$) or methane ($CH_4$). Also called *lithotroph*. Compare with **chemoorganotroph**.

**chemoorganotroph** An organism that produces ATP by oxidizing organic molecules with high potential energy such as sugars. Also called *organotroph*. Compare with **chemolithotroph**.

**chemoreception** A sensory system in which receptors are activated in response to the binding of chemicals.

**chemoreceptor** A sensory cell or organ specialized for detection of specific molecules or classes of molecules.

**chiasma** (plural: chiasmata) The X-shaped structure formed during meiosis by crossing over between non-sister chromatids in a pair of homologous chromosomes.

**chitin** A structural polysaccharide composed of *N*-acetyl-glucosamine (NAG) monomers joined end to end by β-1,4-glycosidic linkages. Found in cell walls of fungi and many algae, and in external skeletons of insects and crustaceans.

**chitons** A lineage of marine mollusks that have a protective shell formed of eight calcium carbonate plates.

**chlorophyll** Any of several closely related green pigments, found in chloroplasts, that absorb light during photosynthesis.

**chloroplast** A chlorophyll-containing organelle, bounded by a double membrane, in which photosynthesis occurs; found in plants and photosynthetic protists. Also the location of starch, amino acid, fatty acid, purine, and pyrimidine synthesis.

**choanocyte** A specialized, flagellated feeding cell found in choanoflagellates (protists that are the closest living relatives of animals) and sponges (the most ancient animal phylum).

**cholecystokinin** A peptide hormone secreted by cells in the lining of the small intestine. Stimulates the secretion of digestive enzymes from the pancreas and of bile from the liver and gallbladder.

**chordate** Any member of the phylum Chordata. Chordates are deuterostomes distinguished by a dorsal hollow nerve cord, pharyngeal gill slits, a notochord, and a post-anal tail. Includes vertebrates, cephalochordata, and urochordata.

**chromatid** One of the two identical double-stranded DNAs composing a replicated chromosome that is connected at the centromere to the other strand.

**chromatin** The complex of DNA and proteins, mainly histones, that compose eukaryotic chromosomes. Can be highly compact (heterochromatin) or loosely coiled (euchromatin).

**chromatin remodeling** The process by which the DNA in chromatin is unwound from its associated proteins to allow transcription or replication. May involve chemical modification of histone proteins or reshaping of the chromatin by large multiprotein complexes in an ATP-requiring process.

**chromatin remodeling complexes** Sets of enzymes that use energy from ATP hydrolysis shift nucleosomes on DNA to expose regulatory sequences to transcription factors.

**chromosome theory of inheritance** The principle that genes are located on chromosomes and that patterns of inheritance are determined by the behavior of chromosomes during meiosis.

**chromosome** Gene-carrying structure consisting of a single long molecule of double-stranded DNA and associated proteins (e.g., histones). Most prokaryotic cells contain a single, circular chromosome; eukaryotic cells contain multiple noncircular (linear) chromosomes located in the nucleus.

**cilium** (plural: cilia) One of many short, filamentous projections of some eukaryotic cells, containing a core of microtubules. Used to move the cell as well as to circulate fluid or particles around the surface of a stationary cell. See **axoneme**.

**circadian clock** An internal mechanism found in most organisms that regulates many body processes (sleep–wake cycles, hormonal patterns, etc.) in a roughly 24-hour cycle.

**circulatory system** The system responsible for moving oxygen, carbon dioxide, and other materials (hormones, nutrients, wastes) within the animal body.

**cisternae** (singular: cisterna) Flattened, membrane-bound compartments that make up the Golgi apparatus.

**cisternal maturation** The process of cargo movement through the Golgi apparatus by residing in cisternae that mature from *cis* to *trans* via the import and export of different Golgi enzymes.

**citric acid cycle** A series of eight chemical reactions that start with citrate (deprotonated citric acid) and ends with oxaloacetate, which reacts with acetyl CoA to form citrate—forming a cycle that is part of the pathway that oxidizes glucose to $CO_2$. Also known as the *Krebs cycle* or *tricarboxylic acid (TCA) cycle*.

**clade** See **monophyletic group**.

**cladistic approach** A method for constructing a phylogenetic tree that is based on identifying the unique traits (shared, derived characters, called synapomorphies) of each monophyletic group.

**Class I MHC protein** A type of MHC protein that is present on the plasma membrane of virtually all nucleated cells and functions in presenting antigen to $CD8^+$ T cells.

**Class II MHC protein** A type of MHC protein that is present only on the plasma membrane of certain cells in the immune response, such as dendritic cells, macrophages, and B cells. It functions in presenting epitopes of antigens to $CD4^+$ T cells.

**cleavage** In animal development, the series of rapid mitotic cell divisions, with little cell growth, that produces successively smaller cells (blastomeres) and transforms a zygote into a multicellular blastula.

**cleavage furrow** A pinching in of the plasma membrane that occurs as cytokinesis begins in animal cells and deepens until the cytoplasm is divided into two daughter cells.

**climate** The prevailing, long-term weather conditions in a particular region.

**climax community** The stable, final community that develops from ecological succession.

**clitoris** A rod of erectile tissue in the external genitalia of female mammals. Is formed from the same embryonic tissue as the male penis and has a similar function in sexual arousal.

**cloaca** In a few mammals and many nonmammalian vertebrates, a body cavity opening to the outside and used by both the excretory and reproductive systems.

**clonal selection theory** The dominant explanation of the generation of an adaptive immune response. According to the theory, the immune system retains a vast pool of inactive lymphocytes, each with a unique receptor for a unique epitope. Lymphocytes that encounter their complementary epitopes are stimulated to divide (selected and cloned), producing daughter cells that combat infection and confer immunity.

**clone** (1) An individual that is genetically identical to another individual. (2) A lineage of genetically identical individuals or cells. (3) As a verb, to make one or more genetic replicas of a cell or individual.

**cloning vector** A plasmid or other agent used to transfer recombinant genes into cultured host cells. Also called simply *vector*.

**closed circulatory system** A circulatory system in which the circulating fluid (blood) is confined to blood vessels and flows in a continuous circuit. Compare with **open circulatory system**.

**cnidocyte** A specialized stinging cell found in cnidarians (e.g., jellyfish, corals, and anemones) and used in capturing prey.

**co-receptor** Any membrane protein that acts with some other membrane protein in a cell interaction or cell response.

**cochlea** The organ of hearing in the inner ear of mammals, birds, and crocodilians. A coiled, fluid-filled tube containing specialized pressure-sensing neurons (hair cells) that detect sounds of different pitches.

**coding strand** See **non-template strand**.

**codominance** An inheritance pattern in which heterozygotes exhibit both of the traits seen in each type of homozygous individual.

**codon** A sequence of three nucleotides in DNA or RNA that codes for an amino acid or a start or stop signal for protein synthesis.

**coefficient of relatedness (*r*)** A measure of how closely two individuals are related. Calculated as the probability that an allele in two individuals is inherited from the same ancestor.

**coelom** An internal, usually fluid-filled body cavity that is completely or partially lined with mesoderm.

**coelomate** An animal that has a true coelom, completely lined with mesoderm. Compare with **acoelomate** and **pseudocoelomate**.

**coenocytic** Containing many nuclei and a continuous cytoplasm through a filamentous body, without the body being divided into distinct cells. Some fungi are coenocytic.

**coenzyme** A small organic molecule that is a required cofactor for an enzyme-catalyzed reaction. Often donates or receives electrons or functional groups during the reaction.

**coenzyme A (CoA)** A molecule that is required for many cellular reactions and that is often transiently linked to other molecules, such as acetyl groups (see **acetyl CoA**).

**coenzyme Q** A nonprotein molecule that shuttles electrons between membrane-bound complexes in the mitochondrial electron transport chain. Also called **ubiquinone** or *Q*.

**coevolution** A pattern of evolution in which two interacting species reciprocally influence each other's adaptations over time.

**coevolutionary arms race** A series of adaptations and counter-adaptations observed in species that interact closely over time and affect each other's fitness.

**cofactor** An inorganic ion, such as a metal ion, that is required for an enzyme to function normally. May be bound tightly to an enzyme or associate with it transiently during catalysis.

**cohesion** The tendency of certain like molecules (e.g., water molecules) to cling together due to attractive forces. Compare with **adhesion**.

**cohesion-tension theory** The theory that water movement upward through plant vascular tissues is due to loss of water from leaves (transpiration), which pulls a cohesive column of water upward.

**cohort** A group of individuals that are the same age and can be followed through time.

**coleoptile** A modified leaf that covers and protects the stems and leaves of grass seedlings.

**collagen** A fibrous, pliable, cable-like glycoprotein that is a major component of the extracellular matrix of animal cells. Various subtypes differ in their tissue distribution, some of which are assembled into large fibrils in the extracellular space.

**collecting duct** In the vertebrate kidney, a large straight tube that receives filtrate from the distal tubules of several nephrons. Involved in the regulated reabsorption of water.

**collenchyma cell** In plants, an elongated cell with cell walls thickened at the corners that provides support to growing plant parts; usually found in strands along leaf veins and stalks. Compare with **parenchyma cell** and **sclerenchyma cell**.

**colon** The portion of the large intestine where feces are formed by compaction of wastes and reabsorption of water.

**colony** An assemblage of individuals. May refer to an assemblage of semi-independent cells or to a breeding population of multicellular organisms.

**commensalism** (adjective: commensal) A symbiotic relationship in which one organism (the commensal) benefits and the other (the host) is not harmed. Compare with **mutualism** and **parasitism**.

**communication** In ecology, any process in which a signal from one individual modifies the behavior of another individual.

**community** All of the species that interact with each other in a certain area.

**companion cell** In plants, a cell in the phloem that is connected via many plasmodesmata to adjacent sieve-tube elements. Companion cells provide materials to maintain sieve-tube elements and function in the loading and unloading of sugars into sieve-tube elements.

**compass orientation** A type of navigation in which movement occurs in a specific direction.

**competition** In ecology, the interaction of two species or two individuals trying to use the same limited resource (e.g., water, food, living space). May occur between individuals of the same species

(intraspecific competition) or different species (interspecific competition).

**competitive exclusion principle** The principle that two species cannot coexist in the same ecological niche in the same area because one species will outcompete the other.

**competitive inhibition** Inhibition of an enzyme's ability to catalyze a chemical reaction via binding of a nonreactant molecule that competes with the substrate(s) for access to the active site.

**complement system** A set of proteins that circulate in the bloodstream and can destroy bacteria by forming holes in the bacterial plasma membrane.

**complementary base pairing** The association between specific nitrogenous bases of nucleic acids stabilized by hydrogen bonding. Adenine pairs only with thymine (in DNA) or uracil (in RNA), and guanine pairs only with cytosine.

**complementary DNA (cDNA)** DNA produced in the laboratory using an RNA transcript as a template and reverse transcriptase; corresponds to a gene but lacks introns. Also produced naturally by retroviruses.

**complementary strand** A newly synthesized strand of RNA or DNA that has a base sequence complementary to that of the template strand.

**complete digestive tract** A digestive tract with two openings, usually called a mouth and an anus.

**complete metamorphosis** See **holometabolous metamorphosis**.

**compound eye** An eye formed of many independent light-sensing columns (ommatidia); occurs in arthropods. Compare with **simple eye**.

**concentration gradient** Difference across space (e.g., across a membrane) in the concentration of a dissolved substance.

**condensation reaction** A chemical reaction in which two molecules are joined covalently with the removal of an $-OH$ from one and an $-H$ from another to form water. Also called a *dehydration reaction*. Compare with **hydrolysis**.

**conduction** (1) Direct transfer of heat between two objects that are in physical contact. Compare with **convection**. (2) Transmission of an electrical impulse along the axon of a nerve cell.

**cone cell** A photoreceptor cell with a cone-shaped outer portion that is particularly sensitive to bright light of a certain color. Also called simply *cone*. Compare with **rod cell**.

**connective tissue** An animal tissue consisting of scattered cells in a liquid, jellylike, or solid extracellular matrix. Includes bone, cartilage, tendons, ligaments, and blood.

**conservation biology** The effort to study, preserve, and restore threatened genetic diversity, populations, communities, and ecosystems.

**constant (*C*) region** The invariant amino acid sequence in polypeptides that are used to make antibodies, B-cell receptors, and T-cell receptors. Apart from antibody class types (IgG, IgM, etc.), this region remains constant within an individual. Compare with **variable (*V*) region**.

**constitutive** Always occurring; always present. Commonly used to describe enzymes and other proteins

that are synthesized continuously or mutants in which one or more genetic loci are constantly expressed due to defects in gene control.

**constitutive defense** A defensive trait that is always manifested even in the absence of a predator or pathogen. Also called *standing defense*. Compare with **inducible defenses**.

**constitutive mutant** An abnormal (mutated) strain that produces a product at all times, instead of under certain conditions only.

**consumer** See **heterotroph**.

**consumption** Predation or herbivory.

**continental shelf** The portion of a geologic plate that extends from a continent under seawater.

**continuous strand** See **leading strand**.

**contraception** Any of several methods to prevent pregnancy.

**control** In a scientific experiment, a group of organisms or samples that do not receive the experimental treatment but are otherwise identical to the group that does.

**convection** Transfer of heat by movement of large volumes of a gas or liquid. Compare with **conduction**.

**convergent evolution** The independent evolution of similar traits in distantly related organisms due to adaptation to similar environments and a similar way of life.

**cooperative binding** The tendency of the protein subunits of hemoglobin to affect each other's oxygen binding such that each bound oxygen molecule increases the likelihood of further oxygen binding.

**coprophagy** The eating of feces.

**coral reef** A large assemblage of colonial marine corals that usually serves as shallow-water, sunlit habitat for many other species as well.

**co-receptor** Any membrane protein that acts with some other membrane protein in a cell interaction or cell response.

**core enzyme** The enzyme responsible for catalysis in a multipart holoenzyme.

**cork cambium** One of two types of cylindrical meristem, consisting of a ring of undifferentiated plant cells found just under the cork layer of woody stems and roots; produces new cork cells on its outer side. Compare with **vascular cambium**.

**cork cell** A cell in the protective outermost layer of a woody stem and root that produces and accumulates waxes that make the cell less permeable to water and gases.

**corm** A rounded, thick underground stem that can produce new plants via asexual reproduction.

**cornea** The transparent sheet of connective tissue at the very front of the eye in vertebrates and some other animals. Protects the eye and helps focus light.

**corolla** All of the petals of a flower.

**corona** The cluster of cilia at the anterior end of a rotifer; in many species it facilitates suspension feeding.

**corpus callosum** A thick band of neurons that connects the two hemispheres of the cerebrum in the mammalian brain.

**corpus luteum** A yellowish structure that secretes progesterone in an ovary. Is formed from a follicle that has recently ovulated.

**cortex** (1) In animals, the outermost region of an organ, such as the kidney or adrenal gland. (2) In plants, a layer of ground tissue found outside the vascular bundles of roots and outside the pith of a stem.

**corticotropin-releasing hormone (CRH)** A peptide hormone, produced and secreted by the hypothalamus, that stimulates the anterior pituitary to release ACTH.

**cortisol** A steroid hormone, produced and secreted by the adrenal cortex, that increases blood glucose and prepares the body for stress. The major glucocorticoid hormone in some mammals. Also called *hydrocortisone*.

**cost–benefit analysis** Decisions or analyses that weigh the fitness costs and benefits of a particular action.

**cotransporter** A transmembrane protein that facilitates diffusion of an ion down its previously established electrochemical gradient and uses the energy of that process to transport some other substance, in the same or opposite direction, *against* its concentration gradient. Also called *secondary active transporter*. See **antiporter** and **symporter**.

**cotyledon** The first leaf, or seed leaf, of a plant embryo. Used for storing and digesting nutrients and/or for early photosynthesis.

**countercurrent exchanger** In animals, any anatomical arrangement that allows the maximum transfer of heat or a soluble substance from one fluid to another. The two fluids must be flowing in opposite directions and have a heat or concentration gradient between them.

**covalent bond** A type of chemical bond in which two atoms share one or more pairs of electrons. Compare with **hydrogen bond** and **ionic bond**.

**cranium** A bony, cartilaginous, or fibrous case that encloses and protects the brain of vertebrates. Forms part of the skull. Also called *braincase*.

**crassulacean acid metabolism (CAM)** A variant type of photosynthesis in which $CO_2$ is fixed and stored in organic acids at night when stomata are open and then released to feed the Calvin cycle during the day when stomata are closed. Helps reduce water loss and $CO_2$ loss by photorespiration.

**cristae** (singular: crista) Sac-like invaginations of the inner membrane of a mitochondrion. Location of the electron transport chain and ATP synthase.

**Cro-Magnon** A prehistoric European population of modern humans (*Homo sapiens*) known from fossils, paintings, sculptures, and other artifacts.

**crop** A storage organ in the digestive system of certain vertebrates.

**cross** A mating between two individuals that is used for genetic analysis.

**cross-pollination** Pollination of a flower by pollen from another individual, rather than by self-fertilization. Also called *crossing*.

**cross-talk** Interactions among signaling pathways, triggered by different signals, that modify a cellular response.

**crossing over** The exchange of segments of non-sister chromatids between a pair of homologous chromosomes that occurs during meiosis I.

**crosstalk** Interactions among signaling pathways that modify a cellular response.

**crustaceans** A lineage of arthropods that includes shrimp, lobster, and crabs. Many have a carapace (a platelike portion of the exoskeleton covering the cephalothorax) and mandibles for biting or chewing.

**cryptic species** A species that cannot be distinguished from similar species by easily identifiable morphological traits.

**culture** In cell biology, a collection of cells or a tissue growing under controlled conditions, usually in suspension or on the surface of a dish of solid growth medium.

**Cushing's disease** A human endocrine disorder caused by loss of feedback inhibition of cortisol on ACTH secretion. Characterized by high ACTH and cortisol levels and wasting of body protein reserves.

**cuticle** A protective coating secreted by the outermost layer of cells of an animal or a plant; often functioning to reduce evaporative water loss.

**cyanobacteria** A lineage of photosynthetic bacteria formerly known as blue-green algae. Likely the first life-forms to carry out oxygenic photosynthesis.

**cyclic AMP (cAMP)** Cyclic adenosine monophosphate; a small molecule, derived from ATP, that is widely used by cells in signal transduction and transcriptional control.

**cyclic electron flow** Path of electrons in which excited electrons of photosystem I are transferred back to plastoquinone (PQ), the start of the electron transport chain normally associated with photosystem II. Instead of reducing $NADP^+$ to make NADPH, the electron energy is used to make ATP via photophosphorylation. Compare with **noncyclic electron flow**.

**cyclin** One of several regulatory proteins whose concentrations fluctuate cyclically throughout the cell cycle. Involved in the control of the cell cycle via cyclin-dependent kinases.

**cyclin-dependent kinase (Cdk)** Any of several related protein kinases that are functional only when bound to a cyclin and are activated by other modifications. Involved in control of the cell cycle.

**cytochrome *c* (cyt *c*)** A soluble protein that shuttles electrons between membrane-bound complexes in the mitochondrial electron transport chain.

**cytokine** Any of a diverse group of signaling proteins, secreted largely by cells of the immune system, whose effects include stimulating leukocyte production, recruiting cells to the site of infection, tissue repair, and fever. Generally function to regulate the type, intensity, and duration of an immune response.

**cytokinesis** Division of the cytoplasm to form two daughter cells. Typically occurs immediately after division of the nucleus by mitosis or meiosis.

**cytokinins** A class of plant hormones that stimulate cell division and retard aging.

**cytoplasm** All the contents of a cell, excluding the nucleus, bounded by the plasma membrane.

**cytoplasmic determinant** A regulatory transcription factor or signaling molecule that is distributed unevenly in the cytoplasm of the egg and that directs early pattern formation in an embryo.

**cytoplasmic streaming** The directed flow of cytosol and organelles that facilitates distribution of materials within some large plant and fungal cells. Occurs along actin filaments and is powered by myosin.

**cytoskeleton** In eukaryotic cells, a network of protein fibers in the cytoplasm that are involved in cell shape, support, locomotion, and transport of materials within the cell. Prokaryotic cells have a similar but much less extensive network of fibers.

**cytosol** The fluid portion of the cytoplasm, excluding the contents of membrane-enclosed organelles.

**cytotoxic T cell** A type of $CD8^+$ effector T cell that induces apoptosis in infected and cancerous cells. Recognizes target cells via interactions with complementary class I MHC–peptide complexes. Also called *cytotoxic T lymphocyte (CTL)* and *killer T cell*. Compare with **helper T cell**.

**dalton (Da)** A unit of mass equal to 1/12 the mass of one carbon-12 atom; about the mass of 1 proton or 1 neutron.

**daughter strand** The strand of DNA that is newly replicated from an existing template strand of DNA.

**day-neutral plant** A plant whose flowering time is not affected by the relative length of day and night (the photoperiod). Compare with **long-day** and **short-day plant**.

**dead space** Air passages that are not involved in gas exchange with the blood; examples are the trachea and bronchi.

**deciduous** Describing a plant that sheds leaves or other structures at regular intervals (e.g., each autumn).

**decomposer** See **detritivore**.

**decomposer food chain** An ecological network of detritus, decomposers that eat detritus, and predators and parasites of the decomposers.

**deep sequencing** A method to learn the types of mRNAs or DNA sequences present in cells, and their relative amounts, involving the preparation and sequencing of cDNA libraries.

**definitive host** The host species in which a parasite reproduces sexually. Compare with **intermediate host**.

**dehydration reaction** See **condensation reaction**.

**deleterious** In genetics, referring to any mutation, allele, or trait that reduces an individual's fitness.

**deletion** In genetics, refers to the loss of part of a chromosome.

**demography** The study of factors that determine the size and structure of populations through time.

**dendrite** A short extension from a neuron's cell body that receives signals from other neurons.

**dendritic cell** A type of leukocyte that ingests and digests foreign antigens, moves to a lymph node, and presents the antigens' epitopes, in the context of MHC proteins on its membrane, to $CD4^+$ and $CD8^+$ T cells.

**dense connective tissue** A type of connective tissue, distinguished by having an extracellular matrix dominated by collagen fibers. Found in tendons and ligaments.

**density dependent** In population ecology, referring to any characteristic that varies depending on population density.

**density independent** In population ecology, referring to any characteristic that does not vary with population density.

**deoxyribonucleic acid (DNA)** A nucleic acid composed of deoxyribonucleotides that carries the genetic information of a cell. Generally occurs as two intertwined strands, but these can be separated. See also **double helix**.

**deoxyribonucleoside triphosphate (dNTP)** A monomer used by DNA polymerase to polymerize DNA. Consists of the sugar deoxyribose, a base (A, T, G, or C), and three phosphate groups.

**deoxyribonucleotide** See **nucleotide**.

**depolarization** A change in membrane potential from its resting negative state to a less negative or a positive state; a normal phase in an action potential. Compare with **hyperpolarization**.

**depolarization** Change in membrane potential from its resting negative state to a less negative or to a positive state; a normal phase in an action potential. Compare with **hyperpolarization**.

**deposit feeder** An animal that eats its way through a food-containing substrate.

**derived trait** A trait that is clearly homologous with a trait found in an ancestor of a particular group, but that has a new form.

**dermal tissue system** The tissue forming the outer layer of a plant; also called *epidermis*.

**descent with modification** The phrase used by Darwin to describe his hypothesis of evolution by natural selection.

**desmosome** A type of cell–cell attachment structure, consisting of cadherin proteins, that is anchored to intermediate filaments. Serves to link the cytoskeletons of adjacent animal cells and form strong cell–cell attachments throughout a tissue. Compare with **gap junction** and **tight junction**.

**detergent** A type of small amphipathic molecule used to solubilize hydrophobic molecules in aqueous solution.

**determination** In development, the commitment of a cell to a particular differentiated fate. Once a cell is fully determined, it can differentiate only into a particular cell type (e.g., liver cell, brain cell).

**detritivore** An organism whose diet consists mainly of dead organic matter (detritus). Various bacteria, fungi, protists, and animals are detritivores. Also called *decomposer*.

**detritus** A layer of dead organic matter that accumulates at ground level or on seafloors and lake bottoms.

**deuterostomes** A major lineage of bilaterian animals that share a pattern of embryological development, including formation of the anus earlier than the mouth, and formation of the coelom by pinching off of layers of mesoderm from the gut. Includes echinoderms and chordates. Compare with **protostomes**.

**developmental homology** A similarity in embryonic form, or in the fate of embryonic tissues, that is due to inheritance from a common ancestor.

**diabetes mellitus** A disease caused by defects in insulin production (type 1) or in the response of cells to insulin (type 2). Characterized by abnormally high blood glucose levels and huge amounts of glucose-containing urine.

**diaphragm** An elastic, sheetlike structure. In mammals, the muscular sheet of tissue that separates the chest and abdominal cavities. It contracts and moves downward during inhalation, expanding the chest cavity.

**diastole** The portion of the cardiac cycle during which the atria or ventricles of the heart are relaxed. Compare with **systole**.

**diastolic blood pressure** The force exerted by blood against artery walls during relaxation of the heart's left ventricle. Compare with **systolic blood pressure**.

**dicot** Any flowering plant (angiosperm) that has two cotyledons (embryonic leaves) upon germination. The dicots do not form a monophyletic group. Also called *dicotyledonous plant*. Compare with **eudicot** and **monocot**.

**dideoxy sequencing** A laboratory technique for determining the exact nucleotide sequence of DNA. Relies on the use of dideoxynucleoside triphosphates (ddNTPs), which terminate DNA replication.

**diencephalon** The part of the mammalian brain that relays sensory information to the cerebellum and functions in maintaining homeostasis.

**differential centrifugation** Procedure for separating cellular components according to their size and density by spinning a cell homogenate in a series of centrifuge runs. After each run, the supernatant is removed from the deposited material (pellet) and spun again at progressively higher speeds.

**differential gene expression** Expression of different sets of genes in cells with the same genome. Responsible for creating different cell types.

**differentiation** The process by which any unspecialized cell becomes a distinct specialized cell type (e.g., liver cell, brain cell), usually by changes in gene expression. Also called *cell differentiation*.

**diffusion** Spontaneous movement of a substance from one region to another, often with a net movement from a region of high concentration to one of low concentration (i.e., down a concentration gradient).

**digestion** The physical and chemical breakdown of food into molecules that can be absorbed into the body of an animal.

**digestive tract** The long tube that begins at the mouth and ends at the anus. Also called *alimentary canal* or *gastrointestinal (GI) tract*.

**dihybrid cross** A mating between two parents that are heterozygous for two different genes.

**dikaryotic** Describing a cell or fungal mycelium having two haploid nuclei that are genetically distinct.

**dimer** An association of two molecules that may be identical (homodimer) or different (heterodimer).

**dioecious** Describing an angiosperm species that has male and female reproductive structures on separate plants. Compare with **monoecious**.

**diploblast** (adjective: diploblastic) An animal whose body develops from two basic embryonic cell layers

or tissues—ectoderm and endoderm. Compare with **triploblast**.

**diploid** (1) Having two sets of chromosomes (2*n*). (2) A cell or an individual organism with two sets of chromosomes, one set inherited from the mother and one set from the father. Compare with **haploid**.

**direct sequencing** A technique for identifying and studying microorganisms that cannot be grown in culture. Involves detecting and amplifying copies of certain specific genes in the microorganisms' DNA, sequencing these genes, and then comparing the sequences with the known sequences from other organisms.

**directional selection** A mode of natural selection that favors one extreme phenotype with the result that the average phenotype of a population changes in one direction. Generally reduces overall genetic variation in a population. Compare with **disruptive selection** and **stabilizing selection**.

**disaccharide** A carbohydrate consisting of two monosaccharides (sugar residues) linked together.

**discontinuous strand** See **lagging strand**.

**discrete trait** An inherited trait that exhibits distinct phenotypes rather than the continuous variation characteristic of a quantitative trait such as body height.

**dispersal** The movement of individuals from their place of origin (birth, hatching) to a new location.

**disruptive selection** A mode of natural selection that favors extreme phenotypes at both ends of the range of phenotypic variation. Maintains overall genetic variation in a population. Compare with **stabilizing selection** and **directional selection**.

**distal tubule** In the vertebrate kidney, the convoluted portion of a nephron into which filtrate moves from the loop of Henle. Involved in the regulated reabsorption of sodium and water. Compare with **proximal tubule**.

**disturbance** In ecology, any strong, short-lived disruption to a community that changes the distribution of living and/or nonliving resources.

**disturbance regime** The characteristic disturbances that affect a given ecological community.

**disulfide bond** A covalent bond between two sulfur atoms, typically in the side chains of certain amino acids (e.g., cysteine). Often contributes to tertiary and quaternary levels of protein structure.

**DNA** See **deoxyribonucleic acid**.

**DNA cloning** Any of several techniques for producing many identical copies of a particular gene or other DNA sequence.

**DNA fingerprinting** Any of several methods for identifying individuals by unique features of their genomes. Commonly involves using PCR to produce many copies of certain short tandem repeats (microsatellites) and then analyzing their lengths.

**DNA helicase** An enzyme that breaks hydrogen bonds between nucleotides of DNA, "unzipping" a double-stranded DNA molecule.

**DNA library** See **cDNA library** and **genomic library**.

**DNA ligase** An enzyme that joins pieces of DNA by catalyzing the formation of a phosphodiester bond between the pieces.

**DNA methylation** The addition of a methyl group ($-CH_3$) to a DNA molecule.

**DNA methyltransferase** A class of eukaryotic enzymes that add a methyl group to cytosines in DNA. Methylation of DNA leads to chromatin condensation and is an important means of regulating gene expression in eukaryotes.

**DNA microarray** A set of single-stranded DNA fragments, representing thousands of different genes that are permanently fixed to a small glass slide. Can be used to determine which genes are expressed in different cell types, under different conditions, or at different developmental stages.

**DNA polymerase** Any enzyme that catalyzes synthesis of DNA from deoxyribonucleotide triphosphates (dNTPs).

**domain** (1) A taxonomic category, based on similarities in basic cellular biochemistry, above the kingdom level. The three recognized domains are Bacteria, Archaea, and Eukarya. (2) A section of a protein that has a distinctive tertiary structure and function.

**dominant** Referring to an allele that determines the same phenotype when it is present in homozygous or heterozygous form.. Compare with **recessive**.

**dormancy** A temporary state of greatly reduced metabolic activity and growth in plants or plant parts (e.g., seeds, spores, bulbs, and buds).

**dorsal** Toward an animal's back and away from its belly. The opposite of ventral.

**dorsal hollow nerve chord** See **nerve chord**.

**double fertilization** An unusual form of reproduction seen in flowering plants, in which one sperm cell fuses with an egg to form a zygote and the other sperm cell fuses with two polar nuclei to form the triploid endosperm.

**double helix** The secondary structure of DNA, consisting of two antiparallel DNA strands wound around each other.

**Down syndrome** A human developmental disorder caused by trisomy of chromosome 21.

**downstream** In genetics, the direction in which RNA polymerase moves along a DNA strand. Compare with **upstream**.

**duplication** In genetics, refers to an additional copy of part of a chromosome.

**dynein** A class of motor proteins that uses the chemical energy of ATP to "walk" toward the minus end of a microtubule. Dyneins are responsible for bending of cilia and flagella, play a role in chromosome movement during mitosis, and can transport vesicles and organelles.

**early endosome** A small transient organelle that is formed by the accumulation of vesicles from receptor-mediated endocytosis and is an early stage in the formation of a lysosome.

**ecdysone** An insect hormone that triggers either molting (to a larger larval form) or metamorphosis (to the adult form), depending on the level of juvenile hormone.

**ecdysozoans** A major lineage of protostomes (Ecdysozoa) that grow by shedding their external skeletons (molting) and expanding their bodies. Includes arthropods, nematodes, and other groups. Compare with **lophotrochozoans**.

**echinoderms** A major lineage of deuterostomes (Echinodermata) distinguished by adult bodies with five-sided radial symmetry, a water vascular system, and tube feet. Includes sea urchins, sand dollars, and sea stars.

**echolocation** The use of echoes from vocalizations to obtain information about locations of objects in the environment.

**ecological selection** Also known as environmental selection. A type of natural selection that favors individuals with heritable traits that enhance their ability to survive and reproduce in a certain physical and/or biological environment, excluding their ability to obtain a mate. Compare with **sexual selection**.

**ecology** The study of how organisms interact with each other and with their surrounding environment.

**ecosystem** All the organisms that live in a geographic area, together with the nonliving (abiotic) components that affect or exchange materials with the organisms; a community and its physical environment.

**ecosystem diversity** The variety of biotic components in a region along with abiotic components, such as soil, water, and nutrients.

**ecosystem function** The sum of biological and chemical processes that are characteristic of a given ecosystem—such as primary production, nitrogen cycling, and carbon storage.

**ecosystem services** All of the benefits that humans derive, directly or indirectly, from ecosystem functions.

**ecotourism** Tourism that is based on observing wildlife or experiencing other aspects of natural areas.

**ectoderm** The outermost of the three basic cell layers (germ layers) in most animal embryos; gives rise to the outer covering and nervous system. Compare with **endoderm** and **mesoderm**.

**ectomycorrhizal fungi (EMF)** Fungi whose hyphae form a dense network that covers their host plant's roots but do not enter the root cells.

**ectoparasite** A parasite that lives on the outer surface of the host's body.

**ectotherm** An animal that gains most of its body heat from external sources as opposed to metabolic processes. Compare with **endotherm**.

**effector** Any cell, organ, or structure with which an animal can respond to external or internal stimuli. Usually functions, along with a sensor and integrator, as part of a homeostatic system.

**efferent division** The part of the nervous system that carries commands from the central nervous system to the body. Consists primarily of motor neurons.

**egg** A mature female gamete and any associated external layers (such as a shell). Larger and less mobile than the male gamete. In animals, also called *ovum*.

**ejaculation** The release of semen from the copulatory organ of a male animal.

**ejaculatory duct** A short duct through which sperm move during ejaculation; connects the vas deferens to the urethra.

**electric current** A flow of electrical charge past a point. Also called *current*.

**electrical potential** Potential energy created by a separation of electrical charges between two points. Also called *voltage*.

**electrocardiogram (EKG)** A recording of the electrical activity of the heart, as measured through electrodes on the skin.

**electrochemical gradient** The combined effect of an ion's concentration gradient and electrical (charge) gradient across a membrane that affects the diffusion of ions across the membrane.

**electrogenic fish** Any of various kinds of fishes having specialized electric organs that emit a current into the water to detect objects.

**electrolyte** Any compound that dissociates into ions when dissolved in water. In nutrition, any of the major ions necessary for normal cell function.

**electromagnetic spectrum** The entire range of wavelengths of radiation extending from short wavelengths (high energy) to long wavelengths (low energy). Includes gamma rays, X-rays, ultraviolet, visible light, infrared, microwaves, and radio waves (from short to long wavelengths).

**electron acceptor** A reactant that gains an electron and is reduced in a reduction–oxidation reaction.

**electron carrier** Any molecule that readily accepts electrons from and donates electrons to other molecules. Protons may be transferred with the electrons in the form of hydrogen atoms.

**electron donor** A reactant that loses an electron and is oxidized in a reduction–oxidation reaction.

**electron shell** A group of orbitals of electrons with similar energies. Electron shells are arranged in roughly concentric layers around the nucleus of an atom, and electrons in outer shells have more energy than those in inner shells. Electrons in the outermost shell, the valence shell, often are involved in chemical bonding.

**electron transport chain (ETC)** Any set of membrane-bound protein complexes and mobile electron carriers involved in a coordinated series of redox reactions in which the potential energy of electrons is successively decreased and used to pump protons from one side of a membrane to the other.

**electronegativity** A measure of the ability of an atom to attract electrons toward itself from an atom to which it is bonded.

**electroreception** A sensory system in which receptors are activated by electric fields.

**electroreceptor** A sensory cell or organ specialized to detect electric fields.

**element** A substance, consisting of atoms with a specific number of protons. Elements preserve their identity in chemical reactions.

**elongation** (1) The process by which RNA lengthens during transcription. (2) The process by which a polypeptide chain lengthens during translation.

**elongation factors** Proteins involved in the elongation phase of translation, assisting ribosomes in the synthesis of the growing peptide chain.

**embryo** A young, developing organism; the stage after fertilization and zygote formation.

**embryo sac** The female gametophyte in flowering plants.

**embryogenesis** The production of an embryo from a zygote. Embryogenesis is an early event in development of animals and plants.

**Embryophyta** An increasingly popular name for the lineage called land plants; reflects their retention of a fertilized egg.

**embryophyte** A plant that nourishes its embryos inside its own body. All land plants are embryophytes.

**emergent property** A property that stems from the interaction of simpler elements and that is impossible to predict from the study of individual elements.

**emergent vegetation** Any plants in an aquatic habitat that extend above the surface of the water.

**emerging disease** Any infectious disease, often a viral disease, that suddenly afflicts significant numbers of humans for the first time; often due to changes in the host species for a pathogen or to radical changes in the genetic material of the pathogen.

**emigration** The migration of individuals away from one population to other populations. Compare with **immigration**.

**emulsification** (verb: emulsify) The dispersion of fat into an aqueous solution. Usually requires the aid of an amphipathic substance such as a detergent or bile salts, which can break large fat globules into microscopic fat droplets.

**endangered species** A species whose numbers have decreased so much that it is in danger of extinction throughout all or part of its range.

**endemic species** A species that lives in one geographic area and nowhere else.

**endergonic** Referring to a chemical reaction that requires an input of energy to occur and for which the Gibbs free-energy change ($\Delta G$) is greater than zero. Compare with **exergonic**.

**endocrine** Relating to a chemical signal (hormone) that is released into the bloodstream by a producing cell and acts on a distant target cell.

**endocrine disruptor** An exogenous chemical that interferes with normal hormonal signaling.

**endocrine gland** A gland that secretes hormones directly into the bloodstream or interstitial fluid instead of into ducts. Compare with **exocrine gland**.

**endocrine system** All of the glands and tissues that produce and secrete hormones into the bloodstream.

**endocytosis** General term for any pinching off of the plasma membrane that results in the uptake of material from outside the cell. Includes phagocytosis, pinocytosis, and receptor-mediated endocytosis. Compare with **exocytosis**.

**endoderm** The innermost of the three basic cell layers (germ layers) in most animal embryos; gives rise to the digestive tract and organs that connect to it (liver, lungs, etc.). Compare with **ectoderm** and **mesoderm**.

**endodermis** In plant roots, a cylindrical layer of cells that separates the cortex from the vascular tissue and location of the Casparian strip.

**endomembrane system** A system of organelles in eukaryotic cells that synthesizes, processes, transports, and recycles proteins and lipids. Includes the endoplasmic reticulum (ER), Golgi apparatus, and lysosomes.

**endomycorrhizal fungi** See **arbuscular mycorrhizal fungi (AMF)**.

**endoparasite** A parasite that lives inside the host's body.

**endophyte** (adjective: endophytic) A fungus that lives inside the aboveground parts of a plant in a symbiotic relationship. Compare with **epiphyte**.

**endoplasmic reticulum (ER)** A network of interconnected membranous sacs and tubules found inside eukaryotic cells. See **rough** and **smooth endoplasmic reticulum**.

**endoskeleton** Bony and/or cartilaginous structures within the body that provide support. Examples are the spicules of sponges, the plates in echinoderms, and the bony skeleton of vertebrates. Compare with **exoskeleton**.

**endosperm** A triploid ($3n$) tissue in the seed of a flowering plant (angiosperm) that serves as food for the plant embryo. Functionally analogous to the yolk in some animal eggs.

**endosymbiont** An organism that lives in a symbiotic relationship inside the body of its host.

**endosymbiosis** An association between organisms of two different species in which one lives inside the cell or cells of the other.

**endosymbiosis theory** The theory that mitochondria and chloroplasts evolved from prokaryotes that were engulfed by host cells and took up a symbiotic existence within those cells, a process termed primary endosymbiosis. In some eukaryotes, chloroplasts may have originated by secondary endosymbiosis; that is, when a cell engulfed a chloroplast-containing protist and retained its chloroplasts.

**endotherm** An animal whose primary source of body heat is internally generated. Compare with **ectotherm**.

**endothermic** Referring to a chemical reaction that absorbs heat. Compare with **exothermic**.

**energetic coupling** In cellular metabolism, the mechanism by which energy released from an exergonic reaction (commonly, hydrolysis of ATP) is used to drive an endergonic reaction.

**energy** The capacity to do work or to supply heat. May be stored (potential energy) or available in the form of motion (kinetic energy).

**enhancer** A regulatory sequence in eukaryotic DNA that may be located far from the gene it controls or within introns of the gene. Binding of specific proteins to an enhancer enhances the transcription of certain genes.

**enrichment culture** A method of detecting and obtaining cells with specific characteristics by placing a sample, containing many types of cells, under a specific set of conditions (e.g., temperature, salt concentration, available nutrients) and isolating those cells that grow rapidly in response.

**enthalpy (*H*)** A quantitative measure of the amount of potential energy, or heat content, of a system plus the pressure and volume it exerts on its surroundings.

**entropy (*S*)** A quantitative measure of the amount of disorder of any system, such as a group of molecules.

**envelope (viral)** A membrane that encloses the capsids of some viruses. Normally includes specialized proteins that attach to host-cell surfaces.

**environmental sequencing** See **metagenomics**.

**enzyme** A protein catalyst used by living organisms to speed up and control biological reactions.

**epicotyl** In some embryonic plants, a portion of the embryonic stem that extends above the cotyledons.

**epidemic** The spread of an infectious disease throughout a population in a short time period. Compare with **pandemic**.

**epidermis** The outermost layer of cells of any multicellular organism.

**epididymis** A coiled tube wrapped around each testis in reptiles, birds, and mammals. The site of the final stages of sperm maturation.

**epigenetic inheritance** Pattern of inheritance involving differences in phenotype that are not due to differences in the nucleotide sequence of genes.

**epinephrine** A catecholamine hormone, produced and secreted by the adrenal medulla, that triggers rapid responses related to the fight-or-flight response. Also called *adrenaline*.

**epiphyte** (adjective: epiphytic) A nonparasitic plant that grows on the trunks or branches of other plants and is not rooted in soil.

**epithelial tissues** See **epithelium**.

**epithelium** (plural: epithelia) An animal tissue consisting of sheetlike layers of tightly packed cells that line an organ, a gland, a duct, or a body surface. Also called *epithelial tissue*.

**epitope** A small region of a particular antigen to which an antibody, B-cell receptor, or T-cell receptor binds.

**equilibrium potential** The membrane potential at which there is no net movement of a particular ion into or out of a cell.

**ER signal sequence** A short amino acid sequence that marks a polypeptide for transport to the endoplasmic reticulum, where synthesis of the polypeptide chain is completed and the signal sequence removed. See **signal recognition particle**.

**erythropoietin (EPO)** A peptide hormone, released by the kidney in response to low blood-oxygen levels, that stimulates the bone marrow to produce more red blood cells.

**esophagus** The muscular tube that connects the mouth to the stomach.

**essential amino acid** Any amino acid that an animal cannot synthesize and must obtain from the diet. May refer specifically to one of the eight essential amino acids of adult humans: isoleucine, leucine, lysine, methionine, phenylalanine, threonine, tryptophan, and valine.

**essential nutrient** Any chemical element, ion, or compound that is required for normal growth, reproduction, and maintenance of a living organism and that cannot be synthesized by the organism.

**EST** See **expressed sequence tag**.

**ester linkage** The covalent bond formed by a condensation reaction between a carboxyl group and a hydroxyl group. Ester linkages join fatty acids to glycerol to form a fat or phospholipid.

**estradiol** The major estrogen produced by the ovaries of female mammals and many other vertebrates. Stimulates development of the female reproductive tract, growth of ovarian follicles, and growth of breast tissue in mammals.

**estrogens** A class of steroid hormones, including estradiol, estrone, and estriol, that generally promote female-like traits. Secreted by the gonads, fat tissue, and some other organs.

**estrous cycle** A female reproductive cycle in which the uterine lining is reabsorbed rather than shed in the absence of pregnancy and the female is sexually receptive only briefly during mid-cycle (estrus). It is seen in all mammals except Old World monkeys and apes (including humans). Compare with **menstrual cycle**.

**ethylene** A gaseous plant hormone associated with senescence that induces fruits to ripen and flowers to fade.

**eudicot** A member of a monophyletic group (lineage) of angiosperms that includes complex flowering plants and trees (e.g., roses, daisies, maples). All eudicots have two cotyledons, but not all dicots are members of this lineage. Compare with **dicot** and **monocot**.

**Eukarya** One of the three taxonomic domains of life, consisting of unicellular organisms (most protists, yeasts) and multicellular organisms (fungi, plants, animals) distinguished by a membrane-bound cell nucleus, numerous organelles, and an extensive cytoskeleton. Compare with **Archaea** and **Bacteria**.

**eukaryote** A member of the domain Eukarya; an organism whose cells contain a nucleus, numerous membrane-bound organelles, and an extensive cytoskeleton. May be unicellular or multicellular. Compare with **prokaryote**.

**eusociality** A complex social structure in which workers sacrifice most or all of their direct reproduction to help rear the queen's offspring. Common in insects such as ants, bees, wasps, and termites.

**eutherians** A lineage of mammals (Eutheria) whose young develop in the uterus and are not housed in an abdominal pouch. Also called *placental mammals*.

**evaporation** The energy-absorbing phase change from a liquid state to a gaseous state. Many organisms evaporate water as a means of heat loss.

**evo-devo** Popular term for evolutionary developmental biology, a research field focused on how changes in developmentally important genes have led to the evolution of new phenotypes.

**evolution** (1) The theory that all organisms on Earth are related by common ancestry and that they have changed over time, and continue to change, via natural selection and other processes. (2) Any change in the genetic characteristics of a population over time, especially a change in allele frequencies.

**ex situ conservation** Preserving species outside of natural areas (e.g., in zoos, aquaria, or botanical gardens).

**excitable membrane** A plasma membrane that is capable of generating an action potential. Neurons, muscle cells, and some other cells have excitable membranes.

**excitatory postsynaptic potential (EPSP)** A change in membrane potential, usually depolarization, at a neuron dendrite that makes an action potential more likely.

**exergonic** Referring to a chemical reaction that can occur spontaneously, releasing heat and/or increasing entropy, and for which the Gibbs free-energy change ($\Delta G$) is less than zero. Compare with **endergonic**.

**exocrine gland** A gland that secretes some substance through a duct into a space other than the circulatory system, such as the digestive tract or the skin surface. Compare with **endocrine gland**.

**exocytosis** Secretion of intracellular molecules (e.g., hormones, collagen), contained within membrane-bound vesicles, to the outside of the cell by fusion of vesicles to the plasma membrane. Compare with **endocytosis**.

**exon** A transcribed region of a eukaryotic gene or region of a primary transcript that is retained in the mature RNA. Except for 5′ and 3′ UTRs, mRNA exons code for amino acids. Compare with **intron**.

**exoskeleton** A hard covering secreted on the outside of the body, used for body support, protection, and muscle attachment. Prominent in arthropods. Compare with **endoskeleton**.

**exothermic** Referring to a chemical reaction that releases heat. Compare with **endothermic**.

**exotic species** A nonnative species that is introduced into a new area. Exotic species often are competitors, pathogens, or predators of native species.

**expansins** A class of plant proteins that break hydrogen bonds between components in the primary cell wall to allow it to expand for cell growth.

**exponential population growth** The accelerating increase in the size of a population that occurs when the growth rate is constant and density independent. Compare with **logistic population growth**.

**expressed sequence tag (EST)** A portion of a transcribed gene (synthesized from an mRNA in a cell), used to find the physical location of that gene in the genome.

**extant species** A species that is living today.

**extensor** A muscle that pulls two bones farther apart from each other, increasing the angle of the joint, as in the extension of a limb or the spine. Compare with **flexor**.

**extinct species** A species that has died out.

**extracellular digestion** Digestion that takes place outside of an organism, as occurs in many fungi that make and secrete digestive enzymes.

**extracellular matrix (ECM)** A complex meshwork in which animal cells are embedded, consisting of proteins (e.g., collagen, proteoglycan, laminin) and polysaccharides produced by the cells.

**extremophile** A bacterium or archaean that thrives in an "extreme" environment (e.g., high-salt, high-temperature, low-temperature, or low-pressure).

**F₁ generation** First filial generation. The first generation of offspring produced from a mating (i.e., the offspring of the parental generation).

**facilitated diffusion** Passive movement of a substance across a membrane with the assistance of transmembrane carrier proteins or channel proteins.

**facilitation** In ecological succession, the phenomenon in which early-arriving species make conditions more favorable for later-arriving species. Compare with **inhibition** and **tolerance**.

**facultative anaerobe** Any organism that can survive and reproduce by performing aerobic respiration when oxygen is available or fermentation when it is not.

**FAD/FADH₂** Oxidized and reduced forms, respectively, of flavin adenine dinucleotide. A nonprotein electron carrier that functions in the citric acid cycle and oxidative phosphorylation.

**fallopian tube** A narrow tube connecting the uterus to the ovary in humans, through which the egg travels after ovulation. Site of fertilization and cleavage. In nonhuman animals, called *oviduct*.

**fast muscle fiber** Type of skeletal muscle fiber that is white in color, generates ATP by glycolysis, and contracts rapidly but fatigues easily. Also called *fast glycolytic*, or *Type IIb, fiber*.

**fat** A lipid consisting of three fatty acid molecules joined by ester linkages to a glycerol molecule. Also called *triacylglycerol* or *triglyceride*.

**fatty acid** A lipid consisting of a hydrocarbon chain bonded at one end to a carboxyl group. Used by many organisms to store chemical energy; a major component of animal and plant fats and phospholipids.

**fauna** All the animal species characteristic of a particular region, period, or environment.

**feather** A specialized skin outgrowth, composed of β-keratin, present in all birds as well as in some non-avian dinosaurs. Used for flight, insulation, display, and other purposes.

**feces** The waste products of digestion.

**fecundity** The average number of female offspring produced by a single female in the course of her lifetime.

**feedback inhibition** A type of control in which high concentrations of the product of a metabolic pathway inhibit one of the enzymes early in the pathway. A form of negative feedback.

**fermentation** Any of several metabolic pathways that regenerate oxidizing agents, such as $NAD^+$, by transferring electrons to a final electron acceptor in the absence of an electron transport chain. Allows pathways such as glycolysis to continue to make ATP.

**ferredoxin** In photosynthetic organisms, an iron- and sulfur-containing protein in the electron transport chain of photosystem I. Can transfer electrons to the enzyme $NADP^+$ reductase, which catalyzes formation of NADPH.

**fertility** The average number of surviving children that each woman has during her lifetime.

**fertilization** Fusion of the nuclei of two haploid gametes to form a zygote with a diploid nucleus.

**fertilization envelope** A physical barrier that forms around a fertilized egg in many animals. The fertilization envelope prevents fertilization by more than one sperm (polyspermy).

**fetal alcohol syndrome (FAS)** A condition marked by hyperactivity, severe learning disabilities, and depression. Thought to be caused by exposure of an individual to high blood alcohol concentrations during embryonic development.

**fetus** In live-bearing animals, the unborn offspring after the embryonic stage. It usually is developed sufficiently to be recognizable as belonging to a certain species.

**fiber** In plants, a type of elongated sclerenchyma cell that provides support to vascular tissue. Compare with **sclereid**.

**Fick's law of diffusion** A mathematical relationship that describes the rates of diffusion of gases.

**fight-or-flight response** Rapid physiological changes that prepare the body for emergencies. Includes increased heart rate, increased blood pressure, and decreased digestion.

**filament** Any thin, threadlike structure, particularly (1) the threadlike extensions of a fish's gills or (2) part of a stamen: the slender stalk that bears the anthers in a flower.

**filter feeder** See **suspension feeder**.

**filtrate** Any fluid produced by filtration, in particular the fluid ("pre-urine") in the Malpighian tubules of insects and the nephrons of vertebrate kidneys.

**filtration** A process of removing large components from a fluid by forcing it through a filter. Occurs in a renal corpuscle of the vertebrate kidney, allowing water and small solutes to pass from the blood into the nephron.

**fimbria** (plural: fimbriae) A long, needlelike projection from the cell membrane of prokaryotes that is involved in attachment to nonliving surfaces or other cells.

**finite rate of increase (λ)** The rate of increase of a population over a given period of time. Calculated as the ending population size divided by the starting population size. Compare with **intrinsic rate of increase**.

**first law of thermodynamics** The principle of physics that energy is conserved in any process. Energy can be transferred and converted into different forms, but it cannot be created or destroyed.

**fission** (1) A form of asexual reproduction in which a prokaryotic cell divides to produce two genetically similar daughter cells by a process similar to mitosis of eukaryotic cells. Also called *binary fission*. (2) A form of asexual reproduction in which an animal splits into two or more individuals of approximately equal size; common among invertebrates.

**fitness** The ability of an individual to produce viable offspring relative to others of the same species.

**fitness trade-off** See **trade-off**.

**fixed action pattern (FAP)** Highly stereotyped behavior pattern that occurs in a certain invariant way in a certain species. A form of innate behavior.

**flaccid** Limp as a result of low internal (turgor) pressure (e.g., a wilted plant leaf). Compare with **turgid**.

**flagellum** (plural: flagella) A long, cellular projection that undulates (in eukaryotes) or rotates (in prokaryotes) to move the cell through an aqueous environment. See **axoneme**.

**flatworms** Members of the phylum Platyhelminthes. Distinguished by a broad, flat, unsegmented body

that lacks a coelom. Flatworms belong to the lophotrochozoan branch of the protostomes.

**flavin adenine dinucleotide** See **FAD/FADH₂**.

**flexor** A muscle that pulls two bones closer together, decreasing the joint angle, as in the flexing of a limb or the spine. Compare with **extensor**.

**floral meristem** A group of undifferentiated plant stem cells that can give rise to the four organs making up a flower.

**florigen** In plants, a protein hormone that is synthesized in leaves and transported to the shoot apical meristem, where it stimulates flowering.

**flower** In angiosperms, the part of a plant that contains reproductive structures. Typically includes a calyx, a corolla, and one or more stamens and/or carpels. See **perfect** and **imperfect flower**.

**fluid connective tissue** A type of connective tissue, distinguished by having a liquid extracellular matrix; includes blood.

**fluid feeder** Any animal that feeds by sucking or mopping up liquids such as nectar, plant sap, or blood.

**fluid-mosaic model** The widely accepted hypothesis that the plasma membrane and organelle membranes consist of proteins embedded in a fluid phospholipid bilayer.

**fluorescence** The spontaneous emission of light from an excited electron falling back to its normal (ground) state.

**follicle** In a mammalian ovary, a sac of supportive cells containing an egg cell.

**follicle-stimulating hormone (FSH)** A peptide hormone, produced and secreted by the anterior pituitary; it stimulates (in females) growth of eggs and follicles in the ovaries or (in males) sperm production in the testes.

**follicular phase** In a menstrual cycle, the first major phase, during which follicles grow and estradiol levels increase; ends with ovulation.

**food** Any nutrient-containing material that can be consumed and digested by animals.

**food chain** A relatively simple pathway of energy flow through a few species, each at a different trophic level, in an ecosystem. Might include, for example, a primary producer, a primary consumer, a secondary consumer, and a decomposer. A subset of a **food web**.

**food web** The complex network of interactions among species in an ecosystem formed by the transfer of energy and nutrients among trophic levels. Consists of many food chains.

**foot** One of the three main parts of the mollusk body; a muscular appendage, used for movements such as crawling and/or burrowing into sediment.

**foraging** Searching for food.

**forebrain** One of the three main regions of the vertebrate brain; includes the cerebrum, thalamus, and hypothalamus. Compare with **hindbrain** and **midbrain**.

**fossil** Any physical trace of an organism that existed in the past. Includes tracks, burrows, fossilized bones, casts, and so on.

**fossil record** All of the fossils that have been found anywhere on Earth and that have been formally described in the scientific literature.

**founder effect** A change in allele frequencies that often occurs when a new population is established from a small group of individuals (founder event) due to sampling error (i.e., the small group is not a representative sample of the source population).

**fovea** In the vertebrate eye, a portion of the retina where incoming light is focused; contains a high proportion of cone cells.

**frameshift mutation** The addition or deletion of a nucleotide in a coding sequence that shifts the reading frame of the mRNA.

**free energy** The energy of a system that can be converted into work. It may be measured only through the change in free energy in a reaction. See **Gibbs free-energy change**.

**free radicals** Any substance containing one or more atoms with an unpaired electron. Unstable and highly reactive.

**frequency** The number of wave crests per second traveling past a stationary point. Determines the pitch of sound and the color of light.

**frequency-dependent selection** A pattern of selection in which certain alleles are favored only when they are rare; a form of balancing selection.

**fronds** The large leaves of ferns.

**frontal lobe** In the vertebrate brain, one of the four major areas in the cerebrum.

**fruit** In flowering plants (angiosperms), a mature, ripened plant ovary (or group of ovaries), along with the seeds it contains and any adjacent fused parts; often functions in seed dispersal. See **aggregate**, **multiple**, and **simple fruit**.

**fruiting body** A structure formed in some prokaryotes, fungi, and protists for spore dispersal; usually consists of a base, a stalk, and a mass of spores at the top.

**functional genomics** The study of how a genome works; that is, when and where specific genes are expressed and how their products interact to produce a functional organism.

**functional group** A small group of atoms bonded together in a precise configuration and exhibiting particular chemical properties that it imparts to any organic molecule in which it occurs.

**fundamental niche** The total theoretical range of environmental conditions that a species can tolerate. Compare with **realized niche**.

**fungi** A lineage of eukaryotes that typically have a filamentous body (mycelium) and obtain nutrients by absorption.

**fungicide** Any substance that can kill fungi or slow their growth.

**G protein** Any of various proteins that are activated by binding to guanosine triphosphate (GTP) and inactivated when GTP is hydrolyzed to GDP. In G-protein-coupled receptors, signal binding directly triggers the activation of a G protein, leading to production of a second messenger or initiation of a phosphorylation cascade.

**G₁ phase** The phase of the cell cycle that constitutes the first part of interphase before DNA synthesis (S phase).

**G₂ phase** The phase of the cell cycle between synthesis of DNA (S phase) and mitosis (M phase); the last part of interphase.

**gallbladder** A small pouch that stores bile from the liver and releases it as needed into the small intestine during digestion of fats.

**gametangium** (plural: gametangia) (1) The gamete-forming structure found in all land plants except angiosperms. Contains a sperm-producing antheridium and an egg-producing archegonium. (2) The gamete-forming structure of some chytrid fungi.

**gamete** A haploid reproductive cell that can fuse with another haploid cell to form a zygote. Most multicellular eukaryotes have two distinct forms of gametes: egg cells (ova) and sperm cells.

**gametogenesis** The production of gametes (eggs or sperm).

**gametophyte** In organisms undergoing alternation of generations, the multicellular haploid form that arises from a single haploid spore and produces gametes. Compare with **sporophyte**.

**ganglion** (plural: ganglia) A mass of neurons in a centralized nervous system.

**ganglion cell** In the retina, a type of neuron whose axons form the optic nerves.

**gap junction** A type of cell–cell attachment structure that directly connects the cytosolic components of adjacent animal cells, allowing passage of water, ions, and small molecules between the cells. Compare with **desmosome** and **tight junction**.

**gastrin** A hormone produced by cells in the stomach lining in response to the arrival of food or to a neural signal from the brain. Stimulates other stomach cells to release hydrochloric acid.

**gastropods** A lineage of mollusks distinguished by a large, muscular foot and a unique feeding structure, the radula. Include slugs and snails.

**gastrulation** The process of coordinated cell movements, including the moving of some cells from the outer surface of the embryo to the interior, that results in the formation of three germ layers (endoderm, mesoderm, and ectoderm) and the axes of the embryo.

**gated channel** A channel protein that opens and closes in response to a specific stimulus, such as the binding of a particular molecule or a change in voltage across the membrane.

**gemma** (plural: gemmae) A small reproductive structure that is produced asexually in some plants during the gametophyte phase and can grow into a mature gametophyte; most common in non-vascular plants, particularly liverworts and club mosses, and in ferns

**gene** A section of DNA (or RNA, for some viruses) that encodes information for building one or more related polypeptides or functional RNA molecules along with the regulatory sequences required for its transcription.

**gene duplication** The formation of an additional copy of a gene, typically by misalignment of

chromosomes during crossing over. Thought to be an important evolutionary process in creating new genes.

**gene expression** The set of processes, including transcription and translation, that convert information in DNA into a product of a gene, most commonly a protein.

**gene family** A set of genetic loci whose DNA sequences are extremely similar. Thought to have arisen by duplication of a single ancestral gene and subsequent mutations in the duplicated sequences.

**gene flow** The movement of alleles between populations; occurs when individuals leave one population, join another, and breed.

**gene pool** All the alleles of all the genes in a certain population.

**gene therapy** The treatment of an inherited disease by introducing a normal form of the gene.

**generation** The average time between a mother's first offspring and her daughter's first offspring.

**genetic bottleneck** A reduction in allelic diversity resulting from a sudden reduction in the size of a large population (population bottleneck) due to a random event.

**genetic code** The set of all codons and their meaning.

**genetic correlation** A type of evolutionary constraint in which selection on one trait causes a change in another trait as well; may occur when the same gene(s) affect both traits.

**genetic diversity** The diversity of alleles or genes in a population, species, or group of species.

**genetic drift** Any change in allele frequencies due to random events. Causes allele frequencies to drift up and down randomly over time, and eventually can lead to the fixation or loss of alleles.

**genetic equivalence** Having all different cell types of a multicellular individual possess the same genome.

**genetic homology** Similarity in DNA nucleotide sequences, RNA nucleotide sequences, or amino acid sequences due to inheritance from a common ancestor.

**genetic map** A list of genes on a chromosome that indicates their position and relative distances from one another. Also called a *linkage map*. Compare with **physical map**.

**genetic marker** A genetic locus that can be identified and traced in populations by laboratory techniques or by a distinctive visible phenotype.

**genetic recombination** A change in the combination of alleles on a given chromosome or in a given individual. Also called *recombination*.

**genetic screen** Any technique that identifies individuals with a particular type of mutation.

**genetic variation** (1) The number and relative frequency of alleles present in a particular population. (2) The proportion of phenotypic variation in a trait that is due to genetic rather than environmental influences in a certain population in a certain environment.

**genetics** The study of the inheritance of traits.

**genital** (plural: genitalia) Any external copulatory organ.

**genome** All the hereditary information in an organism, including not only genes but also stretches of DNA that do not contain genes.

**genome annotation** The process of analyzing a genome sequence to identify key features such as genes, regulatory sequences, and splice sites.

**genomic library** A set of DNA segments representing the entire genome of a particular organism. Each segment is carried by a plasmid or other cloning vector and can be separated from other segments. Compare with **cDNA library**.

**genomics** The field of study concerned with sequencing, interpreting, and comparing whole genomes from different organisms.

**genotype** All the alleles of every gene present in a given individual. Often specified only for the alleles of a particular set of genes under study. Compare with **phenotype**.

**genus** (plural: genera) In Linnaeus' system, a taxonomic category of closely related species. Always italicized and capitalized to indicate that it is a recognized scientific genus.

**geologic time scale** The sequence of eons, eras, and periods used to describe the geologic history of Earth.

**germ cell** In animals, any cell that can potentially give rise to gametes. Also called *germ-line cells*.

**germ layer** In animals, one of the three basic types of tissue formed during gastrulation; gives rise to all other tissues. See **endoderm**, **mesoderm**, and **ectoderm**.

**germ line** In animals, any of the cells that are capable of giving rise to reproductive cells (sperm or egg). Compare with **germ cell**.

**germ theory of disease** The theory that infectious diseases are caused by bacteria, viruses, and other microorganisms.

**germination** The process by which a seed becomes a young plant.

**gestation** The period of development inside the mother, from implantation to birth, in those species that have live birth.

**gibberellins** A class of hormones, found in plants and fungi, that stimulate growth. Gibberellic acid (GA) is one of the major gibberellins.

**Gibbs free-energy change (ΔG)** A measure of the change in enthalpy and entropy that occurs in a given chemical reaction. $\Delta G$ is less than 0 for spontaneous reactions and greater than 0 for nonspontaneous reactions.

**gill** Any organ in aquatic animals that exchanges gases and other dissolved substances between the blood and the surrounding water. Typically, a filamentous outgrowth of a body surface.

**gill arch** In aquatic vertebrates, a curved region of tissue between the gills. Gills are suspended from the gill arches.

**gill filament** In fish, any of the many long, thin structures that extend from gill arches into the water and across which gas exchange occurs.

**gill lamella** (plural: gill lamellae) Any of hundreds to thousands of sheetlike structures, each containing a capillary bed, that make up a gill filament.

**gland** An organ whose primary function is to secrete some substance, either into the blood (endocrine gland) or into some other space such as the gut or skin (exocrine gland).

**glia** Collective term for several types of cells in nervous tissue that are not neurons and do not conduct electrical signals but perform other functions, such as providing support, nourishment, or electrical insulation. Also called *glial cells*.

**global carbon cycle** See **carbon cycle, global**.

**global climate change** The global sum of all the local changes in temperature and precipitation patterns that accompany global warming (or in some past events, global cooling).

**global gene regulation** The regulation of multiple bacterial genes that are not part of one operon.

**global nitrogen cycle** See **nitrogen cycle, global**.

**global warming** A sustained increase in Earth's average surface temperature.

**global water cycle** See **water cycle, global**.

**glomalin** A glycoprotein that is abundant in the hyphae of arbuscular mycorrhizal fungi; when hyphae decay, it is an important component of soil.

**glomerulus** (plural: glomeruli) (1) In the vertebrate kidney, a ball-like cluster of capillaries, surrounded by Bowman's capsule, at the beginning of a nephron. (2) In the brain, a ball-shaped cluster of neurons in the olfactory bulb.

**glucagon** A peptide hormone produced by the pancreas in response to low blood glucose. Raises blood glucose by triggering breakdown of glycogen and stimulating gluconeogenesis. Compare with **insulin**.

**glucocorticoids** A class of steroid hormones, produced and secreted by the adrenal cortex, that increase blood glucose and prepare the body for stress. Include cortisol and corticosterone. Compare with **mineralocorticoids**.

**gluconeogenesis** Synthesis of glucose, often from non-carbohydrate sources (e.g., proteins and fatty acids). In plants, used to produce glucose from products of the Calvin cycle. In animals, occurs in the liver in response to low insulin levels and high glucagon levels.

**glucose** Six-carbon monosaccharide whose oxidation in cellular respiration is the major source of ATP in animal cells.

**glyceraldehyde-3-phosphate (G3P)** The phosphorylated three-carbon compound formed as the result of carbon fixation in the first step of the Calvin cycle.

**glycerol** A three-carbon molecule that forms the "backbone" of phospholipids and most fats.

**glycogen** A highly branched storage polysaccharide composed of glucose monomers joined by $\alpha$-1,4- and $\alpha$-1,6-glycosidic linkages. The major form of stored carbohydrate in animals.

**glycolipid** Any lipid molecule that is covalently bonded to a carbohydrate group.

**glycolysis** A series of 10 chemical reactions that oxidize glucose to produce pyruvate, NADH, and ATP.

Used by organisms as part of fermentation or cellular respiration.

**glycoprotein** Any protein with one or more covalently bonded carbohydrates, typically oligosaccharides.

**glycosidic linkage** The covalent linkage formed by a condensation reaction between two sugar monomers; joins the residues of a polysaccharide.

**glycosylation** Addition of a carbohydrate group to a molecule.

**glyoxysome** Specialized type of peroxisome found in plant cells and packed with enzymes for processing the products of photosynthesis.

**gnathostomes** Animals with jaws. Most vertebrates are gnathostomes.

**Golgi apparatus** A eukaryotic organelle, consisting of stacks of flattened membranous sacs (cisternae), that functions in processing and sorting proteins and lipids destined to be secreted or directed to other organelles. Also called *Golgi complex*.

**gonad** An organ, such as a testis or an ovary, that produces reproductive cells.

**gonadotropin-releasing hormone (GnRH)** A peptide hormone, produced and secreted by the hypothalamus, that stimulates release of follicle-stimulating hormone (FSH) and luteinizing hormone (LH) from the anterior pituitary.

**grade** In taxonomy, a group of species that share some, but not all, of the descendants of a common ancestor. Also called a *paraphyletic group*.

**Gram-negative** Describing bacteria that look pink when treated with a Gram stain. These bacteria have a cell wall composed of a thin layer of peptidoglycan and an outer phospholipid layer. Compare with **Gram-positive**.

**Gram-positive** Describing bacteria that look purple when treated with a Gram stain. These bacteria have cell walls composed of a thick layer of peptidoglycan and no outer phospholipid later. Compare with **Gram-negative**.

**Gram stain** A dye that distinguishes the two general types of cell walls found in bacteria. Used to routinely classify bacteria as Gram-negative or Gram-positive.

**granum** (plural: grana) In chloroplasts, a stack of flattened, membrane-bound thylakoid discs where the light reactions of photosynthesis occur.

**gravitropism** The growth or movement of a plant in a particular direction in response to gravity.

**grazing food chain** The ecological network of herbivores and the predators and parasites that consume them.

**great apes** See **hominids**.

**green algae** A paraphyletic group of photosynthetic organisms that contain chloroplasts similar to those in green plants. Often classified as protists, green algae are the closest living relatives of land plants and form a monophyletic group with them.

**greenhouse gas** An atmospheric gas that absorbs and reflects infrared radiation, so that heat radiated from Earth is retained in the atmosphere instead of being lost to space.

**gross primary productivity** In an ecosystem, the total amount of carbon fixed by photosynthesis (or more

rarely, chemosynthesis), including that used for cellular respiration, over a given time period. Compare with **net primary productivity**.

**ground meristem** The middle layer of a young plant embryo. Gives rise to the ground tissue system.

**ground tissue** An embryonic tissue layer that gives rise to parenchyma, collenchyma, and sclerenchyma—tissues other than the epidermis and vascular tissue. Also called *ground tissue system*.

**groundwater** Any water below the land surface.

**growth factor** Any of a large number of signaling molecules that are secreted by certain cells and that stimulate other cells to grow, divide, or differentiate.

**growth hormone (GH)** A peptide hormone, produced and secreted by the mammalian anterior pituitary, that promotes lengthening of the long bones in children and muscle growth, tissue repair, and lactation in adults. Also called *somatotropin*.

**guanosine triphosphate (GTP)** A nucleotide consisting of guanine, a ribose sugar, and three phosphate groups. Can be hydrolyzed to release free energy. Commonly used in RNA synthesis and also functions in signal transduction in association with G proteins.

**guard cell** One of two specialized, crescent-shaped cells forming the border of a plant stoma. Guard cells can change shape to open or close the stoma. See also **stoma**.

**gustation** The perception of taste.

**guttation** Excretion of water droplets from plant leaves; visible in the early morning. Caused by root pressure.

**gymnosperm** A vascular plant that makes seeds but does not produce flowers. The gymnosperms include five lineages of green plants (cycads, ginkgoes, conifers, redwoods, and gnetophytes). Compare with **angiosperm**.

**H⁺-ATPase** See **proton pump**.

**habitat degradation** The reduction of the quality of a habitat.

**habitat destruction** Human-caused destruction of a natural habitat, replaced by an urban, suburban, or agricultural landscape.

**habitat fragmentation** The breakup of a large region of a habitat into many smaller regions, separated from others by a different type of habitat.

**Hadley cell** An atmospheric cycle of large-scale air movement in which warm equatorial air rises, moves north or south, and then descends at approximately 30° N or 30° S latitude.

**hair cell** A pressure-detecting sensory cell that has tiny "hairs" (stereocilia) jutting from its surface. Found in the inner ear, lateral line system, and ampullae of Lorenzini.

**hairpin** A secondary structure in RNA consisting of a stable loop formed by hydrogen bonding between purine and pyrimidine bases on the same strand.

**Hamilton's rule** The proposition that an allele for altruistic behavior will be favored by natural selection only if $Br \, C$, where $B$ = the fitness benefit to the recipient, $C$ = the fitness cost to the actor, and $r$ = the coefficient of relatedness between recipient and actor.

**haploid** (1) Having one set of chromosomes (1*n* or *n* for short). (2) A cell or an individual organism with one set of chromosomes. Compare with **diploid**.

**haploid number** The number of different types of chromosomes in a cell. Symbolized as *n*.

**Hardy–Weinberg principle** A principle of population genetics stating that genotype frequencies in a large population do not change from generation to generation in the absence of evolutionary processes (e.g., mutation, gene flow, genetic drift, and selection), and nonrandom mating.

**haustorium** (plural: haustoria) Highly modified stem or root of a parasitic plant. The haustorium penetrates the tissues of a host and absorbs nutrients and water.

**hearing** The sensation of the wavelike changes in air pressure called sound.

**heart** A muscular pump that circulates blood throughout the body.

**heart murmur** A distinctive sound caused by backflow of blood through a defective heart valve.

**heartwood** The older xylem in the center of an older stem or root, containing protective compounds and no longer functioning in water transport.

**heat** Thermal energy that is transferred from an object at higher temperature to one at lower temperature.

**heat of vaporization** The energy required to vaporize 1 gram of a liquid into a gas.

**heat-shock proteins** Proteins that facilitate refolding of proteins that have been denatured by heat or other agents.

**heavy chain** The larger of the two types of polypeptide chains in an antibody or B-cell receptor molecule; composed of a variable (*V*) region, which contributes to the antigen-binding site, and a constant (*C*) region. Differences in heavy-chain constant regions determine the different classes of immunoglobulins (IgA, IgE, etc.). Compare with **light chain**.

**helper T cell** A CD4$^+$ effector T cell that secretes cytokines and in other ways promotes the activation of other lymphocytes. Activated by interacting with complementary class II MHC–peptide complexes on the surface of antigen-presenting cells such as dendritic cells.

**heme** A small molecule that binds to each of the four polypeptides that combine to form hemoglobin; contains an iron ion that can bind oxygen.

**hemimetabolous metamorphosis** A type of metamorphosis in which the animal increases in size from one stage to the next, but does not dramatically change its body form. Also called *incomplete metamorphosis*.

**hemocoel** A body cavity, present in arthropods and some mollusks, containing a pool of circulatory fluid (hemolymph) bathing the internal organs. Unlike a coelom, a hemocoel is not lined in mesoderm.

**hemoglobin** An oxygen-binding protein consisting of four polypeptide subunits, each containing an oxygen-binding heme group. The major oxygen carrier in mammalian blood.

**hemolymph** The circulatory fluid of animals with open circulatory systems (e.g., insects) in which the fluid is not confined to blood vessels.

**herbaceous** Referring to a plant that is not woody.

**herbivore** (adjective: herbivorous) An animal that eats primarily plants and rarely or never eats meat. Compare with **carnivore** and **omnivore**.

**herbivory** The practice of eating plant tissues.

**heredity** The transmission of traits from parents to offspring via genetic information.

**heritable** Referring to traits that can be transmitted from one generation to the next.

**hermaphrodite** An organism that produces both male and female gametes.

**heterokaryotic** Describing a cell or fungal mycelium containing two or more haploid nuclei that are genetically distinct.

**heterospory** (adjective: heterosporous) In seed plants, the production of two distinct types of spores: microspores, which become the male gametophyte, and megaspores, which become the female gametophyte. Compare with **homospory**.

**heterotherm** An animal whose body temperature varies markedly. Compare with **homeotherm**.

**heterotroph** Any organism that cannot synthesize reduced organic compounds from inorganic sources and that must obtain them from other organisms. Some bacteria, some archaea, and virtually all fungi and animals are heterotrophs. Also called *consumer*. Compare with **autotroph**.

**heterozygote advantage** A pattern of natural selection that favors heterozygous individuals compared with homozygotes. Tends to maintain genetic variation in a population, thus is a form of balancing selection.

**heterozygous** Having two different alleles of a gene.

**hexose** A monosaccharide (simple sugar) containing six carbon atoms.

**hibernation** An energy-conserving physiological state, marked by a decrease in metabolic rate, body temperature, and activity, that lasts for a prolonged period (weeks to months). Occurs in some animals in response to winter cold and scarcity of food. Compare with **torpor**.

**hindbrain** One of the three main regions of the vertebrate brain, responsible for balance and sometimes hearing; includes the cerebellum and medulla oblongata. Compare with **forebrain** and **midbrain**.

**histamine** A molecule released from mast cells during an inflammatory response that, at high concentrations, causes blood vessels to constrict to reduce blood loss from tissue damage.

**histone** One of several positively charged (basic) proteins associated with DNA in the chromatin of eukaryotic cells.

**histone acetyltransferases (HATs)** A class of eukaryotic enzymes that loosen chromatin structure by adding acetyl groups to histone proteins.

**histone code** The hypothesis that specific combinations of chemical modifications of histone proteins contain information that influences chromatin condensation and gene expression.

**histone deacetylases (HDACs)** A class of eukaryotic enzymes that condense chromatin by removing acetyl groups from histone proteins.

**holoenzyme** A multipart enzyme consisting of a core enzyme (containing the active site for catalysis) along with other required proteins.

**holometabolous metamorphosis** A type of metamorphosis in which the animal completely changes its form; includes a distinct larval stage. Also called *complete metamorphosis*.

**homeobox** A DNA sequence of about 180 base pairs that codes for a DNA binding motif called the homeodomain in the resulting protein. Genes containing a homeobox usually play a role in controlling development of organisms from fruit flies to humans.

**homeostasis** (adjective: homeostatic) The array of relatively stable chemical and physical conditions in an animal's cells, tissues, and organs. May be achieved by the body's passively matching the conditions of a stable external environment (conformational homeostasis) or by active physiological processes (regulatory homeostasis) triggered by variations in the external or internal environment.

**homeotherm** An animal that has a constant or relatively constant body temperature. Compare with **heterotherm**.

**homeotic mutation** A mutation that causes one body part to be substituted for another.

**hominids** Members of the family Hominidae, which includes humans and extinct related forms, chimpanzees, gorillas, and orangutans. Distinguished by large body size, no tail, and an exceptionally large brain. Also called *great apes*.

**hominins** Any extinct or living species of bipedal apes, such as *Australopithecus africanus*, *Homo erectus*, and *Homo sapiens*.

**homologous** See **homology**.

**homologous chromosomes** In a diploid organism, chromosomes that are similar in size, shape, and gene content. Also called *homologs*.

**homology** (adjective: homologous) Similarity among organisms of different species due to their inheritance from a common ancestor. Features that exhibit such similarity (e.g., DNA sequences, proteins, body parts) are said to be homologous. Compare with **homoplasy**.

**homoplasy** (adjective: homoplastic) Similarity among organisms of different species due to reasons other than common ancestry, such as convergent evolution. Features that exhibit such similarity (e.g., the wings of birds and bats) are said to be homoplastic, or convergent. Compare with **homology**.

**homospory** (adjective: homosporous) In seedless vascular plants, the production of just one type of spore. Compare with **heterospory**.

**homozygous** Having two identical alleles of a gene.

**hormone** Any of many different signaling molecules that circulate throughout the plant or animal body and can trigger characteristic responses in distant target cells at very low concentrations.

**hormone-response element** A specific sequence in DNA to which a steroid hormone–receptor complex can bind and affect gene transcription.

**host** An individual that has been invaded by an organism such as a parasite or a virus, or that provides habitat or resources to a commensal organism.

**host cell** A cell that has been invaded by a parasitic organism or a virus and provides an environment that is conducive to the pathogen's growth and reproduction.

***Hox* genes** A class of genes found in several animal phyla, including vertebrates, that are expressed in a distinctive pattern along the anterior–posterior axis in early embryos and control formation of specific structures. *Hox* genes code for transcription factors with a DNA-binding sequence called a homeobox.

**human** Any member of the genus *Homo,* which includes modern humans (*Homo sapiens*) and several extinct species.

**human chorionic gonadotropin (hCG)** A glycoprotein hormone produced by a human embryo and placenta from about week 3 to week 14 of pregnancy. Maintains the corpus luteum, which produces hormones that preserve the uterine lining.

**Human Genome Project** The multinational research project that sequenced the human genome.

**human immunodeficiency virus (HIV)** A retrovirus that causes acquired immune deficiency syndrome (AIDS) in humans.

**humoral (immune) response** The type of immune response that is mediated through the production and secretion of antibodies, complement proteins, and other soluble factors that eliminate extracellular pathogens. Compare with **cell-mediated (immune) response**.

**humus** The decayed organic matter in soils.

**hybrid** The offspring of parents from two different strains, populations, or species.

**hybrid zone** A geographic area where interbreeding occurs between two species, sometimes producing fertile hybrid offspring.

**hydrocarbon** An organic molecule that contains only hydrogen and carbon atoms.

**hydrogen bond** A weak interaction between two molecules or different parts of the same molecule resulting from the attraction between a hydrogen atom with a partial positive charge and another atom (usually O or N) with a partial negative charge. Compare with **covalent bond** and **ionic bond**.

**hydrogen ion (H$^+$)** A single proton with a charge of 1+; typically, one that is dissolved in solution or that is being transferred from one atom to another in a chemical reaction.

**hydrolysis** A chemical reaction in which a molecule is split into smaller molecules by reacting with water. In biology, most hydrolysis reactions involve the splitting of polymers into monomers. Compare with **condensation reaction**.

**hydrophilic** Interacting readily with water. Hydrophilic compounds are typically polar compounds containing partially or fully charged atoms. Compare with **hydrophobic**.

**hydrophobic** Not readily interacting with water. Hydrophobic compounds are typically nonpolar compounds that lack partially or fully charged atoms. Compare with **hydrophilic**.

**hydrophobic interactions** Very weak interactions between nonpolar molecules, or nonpolar regions of the same molecule, when exposed to an aqueous

solvent. The surrounding water molecules support these interactions by interacting with one another and encapsulating the nonpolar molecules.

**hydroponic growth** Growth of plants in liquid cultures instead of soil.

**hydrostatic skeleton** A system of body support involving a body wall in tension surrounding a fluid or soft tissue under compression.

**hydroxide ion (OH$^-$)** An oxygen atom and a hydrogen atom joined by a single covalent bond and carrying a negative charge; formed by dissociation of water.

**hygiene hypothesis** The claim that immune disorders arise in individuals less likely to have been exposed to pathogens and parasites, especially in early childhood. Provides an explanation for the increased risk of allergies and autoimmune disease in countries with high levels of sanitation.

**hyperosmotic** Comparative term designating a solution that has a greater solute concentration, and therefore a lower water concentration, than another solution. Compare with **hyposmotic** and **isosmotic**.

**hyperpolarization** A change in membrane potential from its resting negative state to an even more negative state; a normal phase in an action potential. Compare with **depolarization**.

**hypersensitive reaction** An intense allergic response by cells that have been sensitized by previous exposure to an allergen.

**hypersensitive response** In plants, the rapid death of a cell that has been infected by a pathogen, thereby reducing the potential for infection to spread throughout a plant. Compare with **systemic acquired resistance**.

**hypertension** Abnormally high blood pressure.

**hypertonic** Comparative term designating a solution that, if inside a cell or vesicle, results in the uptake of water and swelling or even bursting of the membrane-bound structure. This solution has a greater solute concentration than the solution on the other side of the membrane. Used when the solute is unable to pass through the membrane. Compare with **hypotonic** and **isotonic**.

**hypha** (plural: hyphae) One of the long, branching strands of a fungal mycelium (the mesh-like body of a fungus). Also found in some protists.

**hypocotyl** The stem of a very young plant; the region between the cotyledon (embryonic leaf) and the radicle (embryonic root).

**hyposmotic** Comparative term designating a solution that has a lower solute concentration, and therefore a higher water concentration, than another solution. Compare with **hyperosmotic** and **isosmotic**.

**hypothalamic–pituitary axis** The functional interaction of the hypothalamus and the anterior pituitary gland, which are anatomically distinct but work together to regulate most of the other endocrine glands in the body.

**hypothalamus** A part of the brain that functions in maintaining the body's internal physiological state by regulating the autonomic nervous system, endocrine system, body temperature, water balance, and appetite.

**hypothesis** A testable statement that explains a phenomenon or a set of observations.

**hypotonic** Comparative term designating a solution that, if inside a cell or vesicle, results in the loss of water and shrinkage of the membrane-bound structure. This solution has a lower solute concentration than the solution on the other side of the membrane. Used when the solute is unable to pass through the membrane. Compare with **hypertonic** and **isotonic**.

**immigration** The migration of individuals into a particular population from other populations. Compare with **emigration**.

**immune system** The system whose primary function is to defend the host organism against pathogens. Includes several types of cells (e.g., leukocytes). In vertebrates, several organs are also involved where specialized cells develop or reside (e.g., lymph nodes and thymus).

**immunity** (adjective: immune) State of being protected against infection by disease-causing pathogens.

**immunization** The conferring of immunity to a particular disease by artificial means.

**immunoglobulin (Ig)** Any of the class of proteins that are structurally related to antibodies.

**immunological memory** The ability of the immune system to "remember" an antigen and mount a rapid, effective adaptive immune response to a pathogen encountered years or decades earlier. Based on the formation of memory lymphocytes.

**impact hypothesis** The hypothesis that a collision between the Earth and an asteroid caused the mass extinction at the K–P boundary, 65 million years ago.

**imperfect flower** A flower that contains male parts (stamens) *or* female parts (carpels) but not both. Compare with **perfect flower**.

**implantation** The process by which an embryo buries itself in the uterine or oviductal wall and forms a placenta. Occurs in mammals and some other viviparous vertebrates.

**in situ hybridization** A technique for detecting specific DNAs and mRNAs in cells and tissues by use of labeled complementary probes. Can be used to determine where and when particular genes are expressed in embryos.

**inbreeding** Mating between closely related individuals. Increases homozygosity of a population and often leads to a decline in the average fitness via selection (inbreeding depression).

**inbreeding depression** In inbred offspring, fitness declines due to deleterious recessive alleles that are homozygous, thus exposed to selection.

**inclusive fitness** The combination of (1) direct production of offspring (direct fitness) and (2) extra production of offspring by relatives in response to help provided by the individual in question (indirect fitness).

**incomplete digestive tract** A digestive tract that has just one opening.

**incomplete dominance** An inheritance pattern in which the heterozygote phenotype is in between the homozygote phenotypes.

**incomplete metamorphosis** See **hemimetabolous metamorphosis**.

**independent assortment, principle of** The concept that each pair of hereditary elements (alleles of the same gene) segregates (separates) independently of alleles of other genes during meiosis. One of Mendel's two principles of genetics.

**indeterminate growth** A pattern of growth in which an individual continues to increase its overall body size throughout its life.

**induced fit** Change in the shape of the active site of an enzyme, as the result of initial weak binding of a substrate, so that it binds substrate more tightly.

**inducer** A small molecule that triggers transcription of a specific gene, often by binding to and inactivating a repressor protein.

**inducible defense** A defensive trait that is manifested only in response to the presence of a consumer (predator or herbivore) or pathogen. Compare with **constitutive defense**.

**infection thread** An invagination of the plasma membrane of a root hair through which beneficial nitrogen-fixing bacteria enter the roots of their host plants (legumes).

**inflammatory response** An aspect of the innate immune response, seen in most cases of infection or tissue injury, in which the affected tissue becomes swollen, red, warm, and painful.

**ingestion** The act of bringing food into the digestive tract.

**inhibition** In ecological succession, the phenomenon in which early-arriving species make conditions less favorable for the establishment of certain later-arriving species. Compare with **facilitation** and **tolerance**.

**inhibitory postsynaptic potential (IPSP)** A change in membrane potential, usually hyperpolarization, at a neuron dendrite that makes an action potential less likely.

**initiation** (1) In an enzyme-catalyzed reaction, the stage during which enzymes orient reactants precisely as they bind at specific locations within the enzyme's active site. (2) In DNA transcription, the stage during which RNA polymerase and other proteins assemble at the promoter sequence and open the strands of DNA to start transcription. (3) In translation, the stage during which a complex consisting of initiation factor proteins, a ribosome, an mRNA, and an aminoacyl tRNA corresponding to the start codon is formed.

**initiation factors** A class of proteins that assist ribosomes in binding to a messenger RNA molecule to begin translation.

**innate behavior** Behavior that is inherited genetically, does not have to be learned, and is typical of a species.

**innate immune response** See **innate immunity**.

**innate immunity** A set of barriers to infection and generic defenses against broad types of pathogens. Produces an immediate response that involves many different leukocytes, which often activate an inflammatory response. Compare with **acquired immunity**.

**inner cell mass (ICM)** A cluster of cells, in the interior of a mammalian blastocyst, that eventually develop into the embryo. Contrast with **trophoblast**.

**inner ear** The innermost portion of the mammalian ear, consisting of a fluid-filled system of tubes that includes the cochlea (which receives sound vibrations from the middle ear) and the semicircular canals (which function in balance).

**insects** A terrestrial lineage of arthropods distinguished by three tagmata (head, thorax, abdomen), a single pair of antennae, and unbranched appendages.

**insulin** A peptide hormone produced by the pancreas in response to high levels of glucose (or amino acids) in blood. Enables cells to absorb glucose and coordinates synthesis of fats, proteins, and glycogen. Compare with **glucagon**.

**integral membrane protein** Any membrane protein that spans the entire lipid bilayer. Also called *transmembrane protein*. Compare with **peripheral membrane protein**.

**integrated pest management** In agriculture or forestry, systems for managing insects or other pests that include carefully controlled applications of toxins, introduction of species that prey on pests, planting schemes that reduce the chance of a severe pest outbreak, and other techniques.

**integrator** A component of an animal's nervous system that functions as part of a homeostatic system by evaluating sensory information and triggering appropriate responses. See **effector** and **sensor**.

**integrin** Any of a class of cell-surface proteins that bind to laminins and other proteins in the extracellular matrix, thus holding cells in place.

**intercalated disc** A type of specialized connection between adjacent heart muscle cells that contains gap junctions, allowing electrical signals to pass between the cells.

**intermediate filament** A long fiber, about 10 nm in diameter, composed of one of various proteins (e.g., keratins, lamins); one of the three types of cytoskeletal fibers. Used to form networks that help maintain cell shape and hold the nucleus in place. Compare with **actin filament** and **microtubule**.

**intermediate host** The host species in which a parasite reproduces asexually. Compare with **definitive host**.

**intermediate muscle fiber** Type of skeletal muscle fiber that is pink in color, generates ATP by both glycolysis and aerobic respiration, and has contractile properties that are intermediate between slow fibers and fast fibers. Also called fast oxidative fiber.

**interneuron** A neuron that passes signals from one neuron to another. Compare with **motor neuron** and **sensory neuron**.

**internode** The section of a plant stem between two nodes (sites where leaves attach).

**interphase** The portion of the cell cycle between one M phase and the next. Includes the $G_1$ phase, S phase, and $G_2$ phase.

**intersexual selection** The sexual selection of an individual of one gender for mating by an individual of the other gender (usually by female choice).

**interspecific competition** Competition between members of different species for the same limited resource. Compare with **intraspecific competition**.

**interstitial fluid** The plasma-like fluid found in the region (interstitial space) between cells.

**intertidal zone** The region between the low-tide and high-tide marks on a seashore.

**intrasexual selection** Competition among members of one gender for an opportunity to mate (usually male–male competition).

**intraspecific competition** Competition between members of the same species for the same limited resource. Compare with **interspecific competition**.

**intrinsic rate of increase ($r_{max}$)** The rate at which a population will grow under optimal conditions (i.e., when birthrates are as high as possible and death rates are as low as possible). Compare with **finite rate of increase**.

**intron** A region of a eukaryotic gene that is transcribed into RNA but is later removed. Compare with **exon**.

**invasive species** An exotic (nonnative) species that, upon introduction to a new area, spreads rapidly and competes successfully with native species.

**inversion** A mutation in which a segment of a chromosome breaks from the rest of the chromosome, flips, and rejoins in reversed orientation.

**invertebrates** A paraphyletic group composed of animals without a backbone; includes about 95 percent of all animal species. Compare with **vertebrates**.

**involuntary muscle** Muscle that contracts in response to stimulation by involuntary (parasympathetic or sympathetic), but not voluntary (somatic), neural stimulation.

**ion** An atom or a molecule that has lost or gained electrons and thus carries an electric charge, either positive (cation) or negative (anion), respectively.

**ion channel** A type of channel protein that allows certain ions to diffuse across a plasma membrane down an electrochemical gradient.

**ionic bond** A chemical bond that is formed when an electron is completely transferred from one atom to another so that the atoms remain associated due to their opposite electric charges. Compare with **covalent bond** and **hydrogen bond**.

**iris** A ring of pigmented muscle just behind the cornea in the vertebrate eye that contracts or expands to control the amount of light entering the eye through the pupil.

**isosmotic** Comparative term designating a solution that has the same solute concentration and water concentration as another solution. Compare with **hyperosmotic** and **hyposmotic**.

**isotonic** Comparative term designating a solution that, if inside a cell or vesicle, results in no net uptake or loss of water and thus no effect on the volume of the membrane-bound structure. This solution has the same solute concentration as the solution on the other side of the membrane. Compare with **hypertonic** and **hypotonic**.

**isotope** Any of several forms of an element that have the same number of protons but differ in the number of neutrons.

**joint** A place where two components (bones, cartilages, etc.) of a skeleton meet. May be movable (an articulated joint) or immovable (e.g., skull sutures).

**juvenile** An individual that has adult-like morphology but is not sexually mature.

**juvenile hormone** An insect hormone that prevents larvae from metamorphosing into adults.

**karyogamy** Fusion of two haploid nuclei to form a diploid nucleus. Occurs in many fungi, and in animals and plants during fertilization of gametes.

**karyotype** The distinctive appearance of all of the chromosomes in an individual, including the number of chromosomes and their length and banding patterns (after staining with dyes).

**keystone species** A species that has an exceptionally great impact on the other species in its ecosystem relative to its abundance.

**kidney** In terrestrial vertebrates, one of a paired organ situated at the back of the abdominal cavity that filters the blood, produces urine, and secretes several hormones.

**kilocalorie (kcal)** A unit of energy often used to measure the energy content of food. A kcal of energy raises 1 kg of water 1°C.

**kin selection** A form of natural selection that favors traits that increase survival or reproduction of an individual's kin at the expense of the individual.

**kinesin** A class of motor proteins that uses the chemical energy of ATP to "walk" toward the plus end of a microtubule. Used to transport vesicles, particles, organelles and chromosomes.

**kinetic energy** The energy of motion. Compare with **potential energy**.

**kinetochore** A protein complex at the centromere where microtubules attach to the chromosome. Contains motor proteins and microtubule-binding proteins that are involved in chromosome segregation during M phase.

**kinetochore microtubules** Microtubules in the spindle formed during mitosis and meiosis that are attached to the kinetochore on a chromosome.

**kinocilium** (plural: kinocilia) A single cilium that juts from the surface of many hair cells and functions in detection of sound or pressure.

**knock-out allele** A mutant allele that does not produce a functional product. Also called a *null allele* or *loss-of-function allele*.

**Koch's postulates** Four criteria used to determine whether a suspected infectious agent causes a particular disease.

**labium majus** (plural: labia majora) One of two outer folds of skin that surround the labia minora, clitoris, and vaginal opening of female mammals.

**labium minus** (plural: labia minora) One of two folds of skin inside the labia majora and surrounding the opening of the urethra and vagina.

**labor** The strong muscular contractions of the uterus that expel the fetus during birth.

**lac operon** A set of three genes in *E. coli* that are transcribed into a single mRNA and required for lactose metabolism. Studies of the *lac* operon revealed many insights about gene regulation.

**lactation** (verb: lactate) Production of milk to feed offspring, from mammary glands of mammals.

**lacteal** A small lymphatic vessel extending into the center of a villus in the small intestine. Receives chylomicrons containing fat absorbed from food.

**lactic acid fermentation** Catabolic pathway in which pyruvate produced by glycolysis is converted to lactic acid in the absence of oxygen.

**lagging strand** In DNA replication, the strand of new DNA that is synthesized discontinuously in a series of short pieces that are later joined. Also called *discontinuous strand*. Compare with **leading strand**.

**laminins** An abundant protein in the extracellular matrix that binds to other ECM components and to integrins in plasma membranes; helps anchor cells in place. Predominantly found in the basal lamina; many subtypes function in different tissues.

**large intestine** The distal portion of the digestive tract, consisting of the cecum, colon, and rectum. Its primary function is to compact the wastes delivered from the small intestine and absorb enough water to form feces.

**larva** (plural: larvae) An immature stage of an animal species in which the immature and adult stages have different body forms.

**late endosome** A membrane-bound vesicle that arises from an early endosome, accepts lysosomal enzymes from the Golgi, and matures into a lysosome.

**latency** In viruses that infect animals, the ability to coexist with the host cell in a dormant state without producing new virions. The viral genetic material is replicated as the host cell replicates. Genetic material may or may not be integrated in the host genome, depending on the virus.

**lateral bud** A bud that forms at the nodes of a stem and may develop into a lateral (side) branch. Also called *axillary bud*.

**lateral gene transfer** Transfer of DNA between two different species.

**lateral line system** A pressure-sensitive sensory organ found in many aquatic vertebrates.

**lateral root** A plant root that extends horizontally from another root.

**leaching** Loss of nutrients from soil via percolating water.

**leading strand** In DNA replication, the strand of new DNA that is synthesized in one continuous piece. Also called *continuous strand*. Compare with **lagging strand**.

**leaf** The main photosynthetic organ of vascular plants.

**leak channel** Ion channel that allows ions to leak across the membrane of a neuron in its resting state.

**learning** An enduring change in an individual's behavior that results from specific experience(s).

**leghemoglobin** An iron-containing protein similar to hemoglobin. Found in infected cells of legume root nodules where it binds oxygen, preventing it from poisoning a bacterial enzyme needed for nitrogen fixation.

**legumes** Members of the pea plant family. Many form symbiotic associations with nitrogen-fixing bacteria in their roots.

**lens** A transparent structure that focuses incoming light onto a retina or other light-sensing apparatus of an eye.

**lenticel** Spongy segment in bark that allows gas exchange between cells in a woody stem and the atmosphere.

**leptin** A hormone produced and secreted by fat cells (adipocytes) that acts to stabilize fat-tissue mass partly by inhibiting appetite and increasing energy expenditure.

**leukocyte** Any of several types of blood cells, including neutrophils, macrophages, and lymphocytes, that reside in tissues and circulate in blood and lymph. Functions in tissue repair and defense against pathogens. Also called *white blood cell*.

**lichen** A symbiotic association of a fungus, often in the Ascomycota lineage, and a photosynthetic alga or cyanobacterium.

**life cycle** The sequence of developmental events and phases that occurs during the life span of an organism, from fertilization to offspring production.

**life history** The sequence of events in an individual's life from birth to reproduction to death, including how an individual allocates resources to growth, reproduction, and activities or structures that are related to survival.

**life table** A data set that summarizes the probability that an individual in a certain population will survive and reproduce in any given year over the course of its lifetime.

**ligament** Connective tissue that joins bones of an endoskeleton together.

**ligand** Any molecule that binds to a specific site on a receptor molecule.

**ligand-gated channel** An ion channel that opens or closes in response to binding by a certain molecule. Compare with **voltage-gated channel**.

**light chain** The smaller of the two types of polypeptide chains in an antibody or B-cell receptor molecule; composed of a variable (*V*) region, which contributes to the antigen-binding site, and a constant (*C*) region. Compare with **heavy chain**.

**lignin** A substance, found in the secondary cell walls of some plants, that is exceptionally stiff and strong; a complex polymer built from six-carbon rings. Most abundant in woody plant parts.

**limiting nutrient** Any essential nutrient whose scarcity in the environment significantly reduces growth and reproduction of organisms.

**limnetic zone** Open water (not near shore) that receives enough sunlight to support photosynthesis.

**lineage** See **monophyletic group**.

**LINEs (long interspersed nuclear elements)** The most abundant class of transposable elements in human genomes; can create copies of itself and insert them elsewhere in the genome. Compare with **SINEs**.

**lingual lipase** An enzyme produced by glands in the tongue. It breaks down fat molecules into fatty acids and monoglycerides.

**linkage** In genetics, a physical association between two genes because they are on the same chromosome; the inheritance patterns resulting from this association.

**linkage map** See **genetic map**.

**lipid** Any organic substance that does not dissolve in water, but dissolves well in nonpolar organic solvents. Lipids include fatty acids, fats, oils, waxes, steroids, and phospholipids.

**lipid bilayer** The basic structural element of all cellular membranes; consists of a two-layer sheet of phospholipid molecules with their hydrophobic tails oriented toward the inside and their hydrophilic heads toward the outside. Also called *phospholipid bilayer*.

**littoral zone** Shallow water near shore that receives enough sunlight to support photosynthesis. May be marine or freshwater; often flowering plants are present.

**liver** A large, complex organ of vertebrates that performs many functions, including storage of glycogen, processing and conversion of food and wastes, and production of bile.

**lobe-finned fish** Fish with fins supported by bony elements that extend down the length of the structure.

**locomotion** Movement of an organism under its own power.

**locus** (plural: loci) A gene's physical location on a chromosome.

**logistic population growth** The density-dependent decrease in growth rate as population size approaches the carrying capacity. Compare with **exponential population growth**.

**long interspersed nuclear elements** See **LINEs**.

**long-day plant** A plant that blooms in response to short nights (usually in late spring or early summer in the Northern Hemisphere). Compare with **day-neutral** and **short-day plant**.

**loop of Henle** In the vertebrate kidney, a long U-shaped loop in a nephron that extends into the medulla. Functions as a countercurrent exchanger to set up an osmotic gradient that allows reabsorption of water from the collecting duct.

**loose connective tissue** A type of connective tissue consisting of fibrous proteins in a soft matrix. Often functions as padding for organs.

**lophophore** A specialized feeding structure found in some lophotrochozoans and used in suspension (filter) feeding.

**lophotrochozoans** A major lineage of protostomes (Lophotrochozoa) that grow by extending the size of their skeletons rather than by molting. Many phyla have a specialized feeding structure (lophophore) and/or ciliated larvae (trochophore). Includes rotifers, flatworms, segmented worms, and mollusks. Compare with **ecdysozoans**.

**loss-of-function allele** See **knock-out allele**.

**LUCA** The *l*ast *u*niversal *c*ommon *a*ncestor of cells. This theoretical entity is proposed to be the product of chemical evolution and provided characteristics of life that are shared by all living organisms on Earth today.

**lumen** The interior space of any hollow structure (e.g., the rough ER) or organ (e.g., the stomach).

**lung** Any respiratory organ used for gas exchange between blood and air.

**luteal phase** The second major phase of a menstrual cycle, after ovulation, when the progesterone levels are high and the body is preparing for a possible pregnancy.

**luteinizing hormone (LH)** A peptide hormone, produced and secreted by the anterior pituitary, that stimulates estrogen production, ovulation, and formation of the corpus luteum in females and testosterone production in males.

**lymph** The mixture of fluid and white blood cells that circulates through the ducts and lymph nodes of the lymphatic system in vertebrates.

**lymph node** Any of many small, oval structures that lymph moves through in the lymphatic system. Filters the lymph and screens it for pathogens and other antigens. Major sites of lymphocyte activation.

**lymphatic system** In vertebrates, a body-wide network of thin-walled ducts (or vessels) and lymph nodes, separate from the circulatory system. Collects excess fluid from body tissues and returns it to the blood; also functions as part of the immune system.

**lymphocyte** A cell that circulates through the bloodstream and lymphatic system and is responsible for the development of adaptive immunity. In most cases belongs to one type of leukocyte—either B cells or T cells.

**lysogeny** In viruses that infect bacteria (bacteriophages), the ability to coexist with the host cell in a dormant state without producing new virions. The viral genetic material is integrated in the host chromosome and is replicated as the host cell replicates. Compare with **lytic cycle**.

**lysosome** A small, acidified organelle in an animal cell containing enzymes that catalyze hydrolysis reactions and can digest large molecules. Compare with **vacuole**.

**lysozyme** An enzyme that functions in innate immunity by digesting bacterial cell walls. Occurs in lysosomes of phagocytes and is secreted in saliva, tears, mucus, and egg white.

**lytic cycle** A type of viral replicative growth in which the production and release of virions kills the host cell. Compare with **lysogeny**.

**M phase** The phase of the cell cycle during which cell division occurs. Includes mitosis or meiosis and often cytokinesis.

**M-phase-promoting factor (MPF)** A complex of a cyclin and cyclin-dependent kinase that, when activated, phosphorylates a number of specific proteins needed to initiate mitosis in eukaryotic cells.

**macromolecular machine** A group of proteins that assemble to carry out a particular function.

**macromolecule** Any very large organic molecule, usually made up of smaller molecules (monomers) joined together into a polymer. The main biological macromolecules are proteins, nucleic acids, and polysaccharides.

**macronutrient** Any element (e.g., nitrogen) that is required in large quantities for normal growth, reproduction, and maintenance of a living organism. Compare with **micronutrient**.

**macrophage** A type of leukocyte in the innate immune system that participates in the inflammatory response by secreting cytokines and phagocytizing invading pathogens and apoptotic cells. Also serves as an antigen-presenting cell to activate lymphocytes.

**MADS box** A DNA sequence that codes for a DNA-binding motif in proteins; present in floral organ identity genes in plants. Functionally similar sequences are found in some fungal and animal genes.

**magnetoreception** A sensory system in which receptors are activated in response to magnetic fields.

**magnetoreceptor** A sensory cell or organ specialized for detecting magnetic fields.

**major histocompatibility protein** See **MHC protein**.

**maladaptive** Describing a trait that lowers fitness.

**malaria** A human disease caused by five species of the protist *Plasmodium* and passed to humans by mosquitoes.

**malignant tumor** A tumor that is actively growing and disrupting local tissues or is spreading to other organs. Cancer consists of one or more malignant tumors. Compare with **benign tumor**.

**Malpighian tubules** A major excretory organ of insects, consisting of blind-ended tubes that extend from the gut into the hemocoel. Filter hemolymph to form "pre-urine" and then send it to the hindgut for further processing.

**mammals** One of the two lineages of amniotes (vertebrates that produce amniotic eggs) distinguished by hair (or fur) and mammary glands. Includes the monotremes (platypuses), marsupials, and eutherians (placental mammals).

**mammary glands** Specialized exocrine glands that produce and secrete milk for nursing offspring. A diagnostic feature of mammals.

**mandibles** Any mouthpart used in chewing. In vertebrates, the lower jaw. In insects, crustaceans, and myriapods, the first pair of mouthparts.

**mantle** One of the three main parts of the mollusk body; the thick outer tissue that protects the visceral mass and may secrete a calcium carbonate shell.

**marsh** A wetland dominated by grasses and other nonwoody plants.

**marsupials** A lineage of mammals (Marsupiala) that nourish their young in an abdominal pouch after a very short period of development in the uterus.

**mass extinction** The extinction of a large number of diverse evolutionary groups during a relatively short period of geologic time (about 1 million years). May occur due to sudden and extraordinary environmental changes. Compare with **background extinction**.

**mass feeder** An animal that ingests chunks of food.

**mass number** The total number of protons and neutrons in an atom.

**mast cell** A type of leukocyte that is stationary (embedded in tissue) and helps trigger the inflammatory response, including secretion of histamine, to infection or injury. Particularly important in allergic responses and defense against parasites.

**maternal chromosome** A chromosome inherited from the mother.

**mechanical advantage** The ratio of force exerted on a load to the muscle force of the effort. A measure of the force efficiency of a mechanical system.

**mechanoreception** A sensory system in which receptors are activated in response to changes in pressure.

**mechanoreceptor** A sensory cell or organ specialized for detecting distortions caused by touch or pressure. One example is hair cells in the cochlea.

**mediator** Regulatory proteins in eukaryotes that form a physical link between regulatory transcription factors that are bound to DNA, the basal transcription complex, and RNA polymerase.

**medium** A liquid or solid that supports the growth of cells.

**medulla** The innermost part of an organ (e.g., kidney or adrenal gland).

**medulla oblongata** In vertebrates, a region of the brain stem that along with the cerebellum forms the hindbrain.

**medusa** (plural: medusae) The free-floating stage in the life cycle of some cnidarians (e.g., jellyfish). Compare with **polyp**.

**megapascal (MPa)** A unit of pressure (force per unit area) equivalent to 1 million pascals (Pa).

**megasporangium** (plural: megasporangia) In heterosporous species of plants, a spore-producing structure that produces megaspores, which go on to develop into female gametophytes.

**megaspore** In seed plants, a haploid (*n*) spore that is produced in a megasporangium by meiosis of a diploid (*2n*) megasporocyte; develops into a female gametophyte. Compare with **microspore**.

**meiosis** In sexually reproducing organisms, a special two-stage type of cell division in which one diploid (*2n*) parent cell produces haploid (*n*) cells (gametes); results in halving of the chromosome number. Also called *reduction division*.

**meiosis I** The first cell division of meiosis, in which synapsis and crossing over occur and homologous chromosomes are separated from each other, producing daughter cells with half as many chromosomes (each composed of two sister chromatids) as the parent cell.

**meiosis II** The second cell division of meiosis, in which sister chromatids are separated from each other. Similar to mitosis.

**melatonin** A hormone, produced by the pineal gland, that regulates sleep–wake cycles and seasonal reproduction in vertebrates.

**membrane potential** A difference in electric charge across a cell membrane; a form of potential energy. Also called *membrane voltage*.

**memory** Retention of learned information.

**memory cells** A type of lymphocyte responsible for maintaining immunity for years or decades after an infection. Descended from a B cell or T cell activated during a previous infection or vaccination.

**meniscus** (plural: menisci) The concave boundary layer formed at most air–water interfaces due to adhesion and surface tension.

**menstrual cycle** A female reproductive cycle seen in Old World monkeys and apes (including humans) in which the uterine lining is shed (menstruation) if no pregnancy occurs. Compare with **estrous cycle**.

**menstruation** The periodic shedding of the uterine lining through the vagina that occurs in females of Old World monkeys and apes, including humans.

**meristem** (adjective: meristematic) In plants, a group of undifferentiated cells, including stem cells, which can divide and develop into various adult tissues throughout the life of a plant. See also **apical meristem** and **ground meristem**.

**mesoderm** The middle of the three basic cell layers (germ layers) in most animal embryos; gives rise to muscles, bones, blood, and some internal organs (kidney, spleen, etc.). Compare with **ectoderm** and **endoderm**.

**mesoglea** A gelatinous material, containing scattered ectodermal cells, that is located between the ectoderm and endoderm of cnidarians (e.g., jellyfish, corals, and anemones).

**mesophyll cell** A type of cell, found near the surfaces of plant leaves, that is specialized for the light-dependent reactions of photosynthesis.

**Mesozoic era** The interval of geologic time, from 251 million to 65.5 million years ago, during which gymnosperms were the dominant plants and dinosaurs the dominant vertebrates. Ended with extinction of the dinosaurs (except birds).

**messenger RNA (mRNA)** An RNA molecule transcribed from DNA that carries information (in codons) that specifies the amino acid sequence of a polypeptide.

**meta-analysis** A comparative analysis of the results of many smaller, previously published studies.

**metabolic pathway** A linked series of biochemical reactions that build up or break down a particular molecule; the product of one reaction is the substrate of the next reaction.

**metabolic rate** The total energy use by all the cells of an individual. For aerobic organisms, often measured as the amount of oxygen consumed per hour.

**metabolic water** The water that is produced as a by-product of cellular respiration.

**metagenomics** The inventory of all the genes in a community or ecosystem by sequencing, analyzing, and comparing the genomes of the component organisms. Also called *environmental sequencing*.

**metagenomics** The inventory of all the genes in a community or ecosystem by sequencing, analyzing, and comparing the genomes of the component organisms. Sequencing of all or most of the genes present in an environment directly (also called *environmental sequencing*).

**metallothioneins** Small plant proteins that bind to and prevent excess metal ions from acting as toxins.

**metamorphosis** Transition from one developmental stage to another, such as from the larval to the adult form of an animal.

**metaphase** A stage in mitosis or meiosis during which chromosomes line up in the middle of the cell.

**metaphase plate** The plane along which chromosomes line up in the middle of the spindle during metaphase of mitosis or meiosis; not an actual structure.

**metapopulation** A population made up of many small, physically isolated populations connected by migration.

**metastasis** The spread of cancerous cells from their site of origin to distant sites in the body where they may establish additional tumors.

**methanogen** A prokaryote that produces methane ($CH_4$) as a by-product of cellular respiration.

**methanotroph** An organism (bacteria or archaea) that uses methane ($CH_4$) as its primary electron donor and source of carbon.

**methyl salicylate (MeSA)** A molecule that is hypothesized to function as a signal, transported among tissues, that triggers systematic acquired resistance in plants—a response to pathogen attack.

**MHC protein** Any of a large set of mammalian cell-surface glycoproteins involved in marking cells as self and in antigen presentation to T cells. Also called *MHC molecule*. Compare with **Class I** and **Class II MHC protein**.

**microbe** Any microscopic organism, including bacteria, archaea, and various tiny eukaryotes.

**microbiology** The field of study concerned with microscopic organisms.

**microfibril** Bundled strands of cellulose that serve as the fibrous component in plant cell walls.

**microfilament** See **actin filament**.

**micronutrient** Any element (e.g., iron, molybdenum, magnesium) that is required in very small quantities for normal growth, reproduction, and maintenance of a living organism. Compare with **macronutrient**.

**micropyle** The tiny pore in a plant ovule through which the pollen tube reaches the embryo sac.

**microRNA (miRNA)** A small, single-stranded RNA associated with proteins in an RNA-induced silencing complex (RISC). Processed from a longer premiRNA gene transcript. Can bind to complementary sequences in mRNA molecules, allowing the associated proteins of RISC to degrade the bound mRNA or inhibit its translation. See **RNA interference**.

**microsatellite** A noncoding stretch of eukaryotic DNA consisting of a repeating sequence 2 to 6 base pairs long. Also called *short tandem repeat* or *simple sequence repeat*.

**microsporangium** (plural: microsporangia) In heterosporous species of plants, a spore-producing structure that produces microspores, which go on to develop into male gametophytes.

**microspore** In seed plants, a haploid (*n*) spore that is produced in a microsporangium by meiosis of a diploid (*2n*) microsporocyte; develops into a male gametophyte. Compare with **megaspore**.

**microtubule** A long, tubular fiber, about 25 nm in diameter, formed by polymerization of tubulin protein dimers; one of the three types of cytoskeletal fibers. Involved in cell movement and transport of materials within the cell. Compare with **actin filament** and **intermediate filament**.

**microtubule organizing center (MTOC)** General term for any structure (e.g., centrosome and basal body) that organizes microtubules in cells.

**microvilli** (singular: microvillus) Tiny protrusions from the surface of an epithelial cell that increase the surface area for absorption of substances.

**midbrain** One of the three main regions of the vertebrate brain; includes sensory integrating and relay centers. Compare with **forebrain** and **hindbrain**.

**middle ear** The air-filled middle portion of the mammalian ear, which contains three small bones (ossicles) that transmit and amplify sound from the tympanic membrane to the inner ear. Is connected to the throat via the eustachian tube.

**migration** (1) In ecology, a seasonal movement of large numbers of organisms from one geographic location or habitat to another. (2) In population genetics, movement of individuals from one population to another.

**millivolt (mV)** A unit of voltage equal to 1/1000 of a volt.

**mimicry** A phenomenon in which one species has evolved (or learns) to look or sound like another species. See **Batesian mimicry** and **Müllerian mimicry**.

**mineral** One of various inorganic substances that are important components of enzyme cofactors or of structural materials in an organism.

**mineralocorticoids** A class of steroid hormones, produced and secreted by the adrenal cortex, that regulate electrolyte levels and the overall volume of body fluids. Aldosterone is the principal one in humans. Compare with **glucocorticoids**.

**minisatellite** A noncoding stretch of eukaryotic DNA consisting of a repeating sequence that is 6 to 100 base pairs long. Also called *variable number tandem repeat (VNTR)*.

**mismatch repair** The process by which mismatched base pairs in DNA are fixed.

**missense mutation** A point mutation (change in a single base pair) that changes one amino acid for another within the sequence of a protein.

**mitochondrial matrix** Central compartment of a mitochondrion, which is lined by the inner membrane; contains mitochondrial DNA, ribosomes, and the enzymes for pyruvate processing and the citric acid cycle.

**mitochondrion** (plural: mitochondria) A eukaryotic organelle that is bounded by a double membrane and is the site of aerobic respiration and ATP synthesis.

**mitogen-activated protein kinases (MAPK)** Enzymes that are involved in signal transduction pathways that often lead to the induction of cell replication. Different types are organized in a series, where one kinase activates another via phosphorylation. See also **phosphorylation cascade**.

**mitosis** In eukaryotic cells, the process of nuclear division that results in two daughter nuclei genetically identical with the parent nucleus. Subsequent cytokinesis (division of the cytoplasm) yields two daughter cells.

**mode of transmission** The type of inheritance observed as a trait is passed from parent to offspring. Some common types are autosomal recessive, autosomal dominant, and X-linked recessive.

**model organism** An organism selected for intensive scientific study based on features that make it easy to work with (e.g., body size, life span), in the hope that findings will apply to other species.

**molarity** A common unit of solute concentration equal to the number of moles of a dissolved solute in 1 liter of solution.

**mole** The amount of a substance that contains $6.022 \times 10^{23}$ of its elemental entities (e.g., atoms, ions, or molecules). This number of molecules of a compound will have a mass equal to the molecular weight of that compound expressed in grams.

**molecular chaperone** A protein that facilitates the folding of newly synthesized proteins into their correct three-dimensional shape. Usually works by an ATP-dependent mechanism.

**molecular formula** A notation that indicates only the numbers and types of atoms in a molecule, such as $H_2O$ for the water molecule. Compare with **structural formula**.

**molecular weight** The sum of the atomic weights of all of the atoms in a molecule; roughly, the total number of protons and neutrons in the molecule.

**molecule** A combination of two or more atoms held together by covalent bonds.

**molting** A method of body growth, used by ecdysozoans, that involves the shedding of an external protective cuticle or skeleton, expansion of the soft body, and growth of a new external layer.

**monocot** Any flowering plant (angiosperm) that has a single cotyledon (embryonic leaf) upon germination. Monocots form a monophyletic group. Also called a monocotyledonous plant. Compare with **dicot**.

**monoecious** Describing an angiosperm species that has both male and female reproductive structures on each plant. Compare with **dioecious**.

**monohybrid cross** A mating between two parents that are both heterozygous for one given gene.

**monomer** A small molecule that can covalently bind to other similar molecules to form a larger macromolecule. Compare with **polymer**.

**monophyletic group** An evolutionary unit that includes an ancestral population and all of its descendants but no others. Also called a *clade* or *lineage*. Compare with **paraphyletic group** and **polyphyletic group**.

**monosaccharide** A molecule that has the molecular formula $(CH_2O)_n$ and cannot be hydrolyzed to form any smaller carbohydrates. Also called *simple sugar*. Compare with **oligosaccharide** and **polysaccharide**.

**monosomy** The state of having only one copy of a particular type of chromosome in an otherwise diploid cell.

**monotremes** A lineage of mammals (Monotremata) that lay eggs and then nourish the young with milk. Includes just five living species: the platypus and four species of echidna, all with leathery beaks or bills.

**morphogen** A molecule that exists in a concentration gradient and provides spatial information to embryonic cells.

**morphology** The shape and appearance of an organism's body and its component parts.

**morphospecies concept** The definition of a species as a population or group of populations that have measurably different anatomical features from other groups. Also called *morphological species concept*. Compare with **biological species concept** and **phylogenetic species concept**.

**motor neuron** A nerve cell that carries signals from the central nervous system (brain and spinal cord) to an effector, such as a muscle or gland. Compare with **interneuron** and **sensory neuron**.

**motor protein** A class of proteins whose major function is to convert the chemical energy of ATP into motion. Includes dynein, kinesin, and myosin.

**MPF** See **M-phase-promoting factor**.

**mRNA** See **messenger RNA**.

**mucosal-associated lymphoid tissue (MALT)** Collective term for lymphocytes and other leukocytes associated with skin cells and mucus-secreting epithelial tissues in the gut and respiratory tract. Plays an important role in preventing entry of pathogens into the body.

**mucous cell** A type of cell found in the epithelial layer of the stomach; responsible for secreting mucus into the stomach.

**mucus** (adjective: mucous) A slimy mixture of glycoproteins (called mucins) and water that is secreted in many animal organs for lubrication. Serves as a barrier to protect surfaces from infection.

**Müllerian inhibitory substance** A peptide hormone, secreted by the embryonic testis, that causes regression (withering away) of the female reproductive ducts.

**Müllerian mimicry** A type of mimicry in which two (or more) harmful species resemble each other. Compare with **Batesian mimicry**.

**multicellularity** The state of being composed of many cells that adhere to each other and do not all express the same genes, with the result that some cells have specialized functions.

**multiple allelism** The existence of more than two alleles of the same gene.

**multiple fruit** A fruit (e.g., pineapple) that develops from many separate flowers and thus many carpels. Compare with **aggregate** and **simple fruit**.

**multiple sclerosis (MS)** A human autoimmune disease in which the immune system attacks the myelin sheaths that insulate axons of neurons.

**muscle fiber** A single muscle cell.

**muscle tissue** An animal tissue consisting of bundles of long, thin, contractile cells (muscle fibers). Functions primarily in movement.

**mutagen** Any physical or chemical agent that increases the rate of mutation.

**mutant** An individual that carries a mutation, particularly a new or rare mutation.

**mutation** Any change in the hereditary material of an organism (DNA in most organisms, RNA in some viruses). The only source of new alleles in populations.

**mutualism** (adjective: mutualistic) A symbiotic relationship between two organisms (mutualists) that benefits both. Compare with **commensalism** and **parasitism**.

**mutualist** Organism that is a participant and partner in a mutualistic relationship. See **mutualism**.

**mycelium** (plural: mycelia) A mass of underground filaments (hyphae) that form the body of a fungus. Also found in some protists and bacteria.

**mycorrhiza** (plural: mycorrhizae) A mutualistic association between certain fungi and the roots of most vascular plants, sometimes visible as nodules or nets in or around plant roots.

**myelin sheath** Multiple layers of myelin, derived from the cell membranes of certain glial cells, wrapped around the axon of a neuron and providing electrical insulation.

**myocardial infarction** Death of cardiac muscle cells when deprived of oxygen.

**myoD** A transcription factor that is a master regulator of muscle cell differentiation (short for "*myo*blast *determination*").

**myofibril** Long, slender structure composed of contractile proteins organized into repeating units (sarcomeres) in vertebrate heart muscle and skeletal muscle.

**myosin** Any one of a class of motor proteins that use the chemical energy of ATP to move along actin filaments in muscle contraction, cytokinesis, and vesicle transport.

**myriapods** A lineage of arthropods with long segmented trunks, each segment bearing one or two pairs of legs. Includes millipedes and centipedes.

**NAD$^+$/NADH** Oxidized and reduced forms, respectively, of nicotinamide adenine dinucleotide. A nonprotein electron carrier that functions in many of the redox reactions of metabolism.

**NADP$^+$/NADPH** Oxidized and reduced forms, respectively, of nicotinamide adenine dinucleotide phosphate. A nonprotein electron carrier that is reduced during the light-dependent reactions in photosynthesis and extensively used in biosynthetic reactions.

**natural experiment** A situation in which a natural change in conditions enables comparisons of groups, rather than a manipulation of conditions by researchers.

**natural selection** The process by which individuals with certain heritable traits tend to produce more surviving offspring than do individuals without those traits, often leading to a change in the genetic makeup of the population. A major mechanism of evolution.

**nauplius** A distinct planktonic larval stage seen in many crustaceans.

**Neanderthal** A recently extinct European species of hominin, *Homo neanderthalensis*, closely related to but distinct from modern humans.

**nectar** The sugary fluid produced by flowers to attract and reward pollinating animals.

**nectary** A nectar-producing structure in a flower.

**negative control** Of genes, when a regulatory protein shuts down expression by binding to DNA on or near the gene.

**negative feedback** A self-limiting, corrective response in which a deviation in some variable (e.g., concentration of some compound) triggers responses aimed at returning the variable to normal. Represents a means of maintaining homeostasis. Compare with **positive feedback**.

**negative pressure ventilation** Ventilation of the lungs by expanding the rib cage so as to "pull" air into the lungs. Compare with **positive pressure ventilation**.

**negative-sense RNA virus** An ssRNA virus whose genome contains sequences complementary to those in the mRNA required to produce viral proteins. Compare with **ambisense virus** and **positive-sense virus**.

**nematodes** See **roundworms**.

**nephron** One of many tiny tubules inside the kidney that function in the formation of urine.

**neritic zone** Shallow marine waters beyond the intertidal zone, extending down to about 200 meters, where the continental shelf ends.

**nerve** A long, tough strand of nervous tissue, typically containing thousands of axons, wrapped in connective tissue; carries impulses between the central nervous system and some other part of the body.

**nerve cord** In chordate animals, a hollow bundle of nerves extending from the brain along the dorsal (back) side of the animal, with cerebrospinal fluid inside a central channel. One of the defining features of chordates.

**nerve net** A nervous system in which neurons are diffuse instead of being clustered into large ganglia or tracts; found in cnidarians and ctenophores.

**nervous tissue** An animal tissue consisting of nerve cells (neurons) and various supporting cells.

**net primary productivity (NPP)** In an ecosystem, the total amount of carbon fixed by photosynthesis over a given time period minus the amount oxidized during cellular respiration. Compare with **gross primary productivity**.

**net reproductive rate ($R_0$)** The growth rate of a population per generation; equivalent to the average number of female offspring that each female produces over her lifetime.

**neural tube** A folded tube of ectoderm that forms along the dorsal side of a young vertebrate embryo; gives rise to the brain and spinal cord.

**neuroendocrine** Referring to nerve cells (neurons) that release hormones into the blood or to such hormones themselves.

**neurogenesis** The birth of new neurons from central nervous system stem cells.

**neurohormones** Hormones produced by neurons.

**neuron** A cell that is specialized for the transmission of nerve impulses. Typically has dendrites, a cell body, and a long axon that forms synapses with other neurons. Also called *nerve cell*.

**neurosecretory cell** A nerve cell (neuron) that produces and secretes hormones into the bloodstream. Principally found in the hypothalamus. Also called *neuroendocrine cell*.

**neurotoxin** Any substance that specifically destroys or blocks the normal functioning of neurons.

**neurotransmitter** A molecule that transmits signals from one neuron to another or from a neuron to a muscle or gland. Examples are acetylcholine, dopamine, serotonin, and norepinephrine.

**neutral** In genetics, referring to any mutation or mutant allele that has no effect on an individual's fitness.

**neutrophil** A type of leukocyte, capable of moving through body tissues, that engulfs and digests pathogens and other foreign particles; also secretes various compounds that attack bacteria and fungi.

**niche** The range of resources that a species can use and the range of conditions that it can tolerate. More broadly, the role that species plays in its ecosystem.

**niche differentiation** The evolutionary change in resource use by competing species that occurs as the result of character displacement.

**nicotinamide adenine dinucleotide** See **NAD$^+$/ NADH**.

**nitrogen cycle, global** The movement of nitrogen among terrestrial ecosystems, the oceans, and the atmosphere.

**nitrogen fixation** The incorporation of atmospheric nitrogen ($N_2$) into ammonia ($NH_3$), which can be used to make many organic compounds. Occurs in only a few lineages of bacteria and archaea.

**nociceptor** A sensory cell or organ specialized to detect tissue damage, usually producing the sensation of pain.

**Nod factors** Molecules produced by nitrogen-fixing bacteria that help them recognize and bind to roots of legumes.

**node** (1) In animals, any small thickening (e.g., a lymph node). (2) In plants, the part of a stem where leaves or leaf buds are attached. (3) In a phylogenetic tree, the point where two branches diverge, representing the point in time when an ancestral group split into two or more descendant groups. Also called *fork*.

**node of Ranvier** One of the unmyelinated sections that occurs periodically along a neuron's axon and serves as a site where an action potential can be regenerated.

**nodule** Globular structure on roots of legume plants that contain symbiotic nitrogen-fixing bacteria.

**noncyclic electron flow** Path of electron flow in which electrons pass from photosystem II, through an electron transport chain, to photosystem I, and ultimately to NADP$^+$ during the light-dependent reactions of photosynthesis. See also **Z scheme**.

**nondisjunction** An error that can occur during meiosis or mitosis, in which one daughter cell receives two copies of a particular chromosome and the other daughter cell receives none.

**nonpolar covalent bond** A covalent bond in which electrons are equally shared between two atoms of the same or similar electronegativity. Compare with **polar covalent bond**.

**nonsense mutation** A point mutation (change in a single base pair) that converts an amino-acid-specifying codon into a stop codon.

**non-sister chromatids** The chromatids of a particular type of chromosome (after replication) with respect to the chromatids of its homologous chromosome. Crossing over occurs between non-sister chromatids. Compare with **sister chromatids**.

**non-template strand** The strand of DNA that is not transcribed during synthesis of RNA. Its sequence corresponds to that of the mRNA produced from the other strand. Also called *coding strand*.

**non-vascular plants** A paraphyletic group of land plants that lack vascular tissue and reproduce using spores. The non-vascular plants include three lineages of green plants (liverworts, mosses, and hornworts). These lineages are sometimes called *bryophytes*.

**norepinephrine** A catecholamine used as a neurotransmitter in the sympathetic nervous system. Also is produced by the adrenal medulla and functions as a hormone that triggers rapid responses relating to the fight-or-flight response.

**notochord** A supportive but flexible rod that occurs in the back of a chordate embryo, ventral to the developing spinal cord. Replaced by vertebrae in most adult vertebrates. A defining feature of chordates.

**nuclear envelope** The double-layered membrane enclosing the nucleus of a eukaryotic cell.

**nuclear lamina** A lattice-like sheet of fibrous nuclear lamins, which are one type of intermediate filament. Lines the inner membrane of the nuclear envelope, stiffening the envelope and helping to organize the chromosomes.

**nuclear lamins** Intermediate filaments that make up the nuclear lamina layer—a lattice-like layer inside the nuclear envelope that stiffens the structure.

**nuclear localization signal (NLS)** A short amino acid sequence that marks a protein for delivery to the nucleus.

**nuclear pore** An opening in the nuclear envelope that connects the inside of the nucleus with the cytoplasm and through which molecules such as mRNA and some proteins can pass.

**nuclear pore complex** A large complex of dozens of proteins lining a nuclear pore, defining its shape and regulating transport through the pore.

**nuclease** Any enzyme that can break down RNA or DNA molecules.

**nucleic acid** A macromolecule composed of nucleotide monomers. Generally used by cells to store or transmit hereditary information. Includes ribonucleic acid and deoxyribonucleic acid.

**nucleoid** In prokaryotic cells, a dense, centrally located region that contains DNA but is not surrounded by a membrane.

**nucleolus** In eukaryotic cells, a specialized structure in the nucleus where ribosomal RNA processing occurs and ribosomal subunits are assembled.

**nucleosome** A repeating, bead-like unit of eukaryotic chromatin, consisting of about 200 nucleotides of DNA wrapped twice around eight histone proteins.

**nucleotide excision repair** The process of removing a damaged region in one strand of DNA and replacing it with the correct sequence using the undamaged strand as a template.

**nucleotide** A molecule consisting of a five-carbon sugar (ribose or deoxyribose), a phosphate group, and one of several nitrogen-containing bases. DNA and RNA are polymers of nucleotides containing deoxyribose (deoxyribonucleotides) and ribose (ribonucleotides), respectively. Equivalent to a nucleoside plus one phosphate group.

**nucleus** (1) The center of an atom, containing protons and neutrons. (2) In eukaryotic cells, the large organelle containing the chromosomes and surrounded by a double membrane. (3) A discrete clump of neuron cell bodies in the brain, usually sharing a distinct function.

**null allele** See **knock-out allele**.

**null hypothesis** A hypothesis that specifies what the results of an experiment will be if the main hypothesis being tested is wrong. Often states that there will be no difference between experimental groups.

**nutrient** Any substance that an organism requires for normal growth, maintenance, or reproduction.

**occipital lobe** In the vertebrate brain, one of the four major areas in the cerebrum.

**oceanic zone** The waters of the open ocean beyond the continental shelf.

**odorant** Any volatile molecule that conveys information about food or the environment.

**oil** An unsaturated fat that is liquid at room temperature.

**Okazaki fragment** Short segment of DNA produced during replication of the lagging strand template. Many Okazaki fragments make up the lagging strand in newly synthesized DNA.

**olfaction** The perception of odors.

**olfactory bulb** A bulb-shaped projection of the brain just above the nose. Receives and interprets odor information from the nose.

**oligodendrocyte** A type of glial cell that wraps around axons of some neurons in the central nervous system, forming a myelin sheath that provides electrical insulation. Compare with **Schwann cell**.

**oligopeptide** A chain composed of fewer than 50 amino acids linked together by peptide bonds. Often referred to simply as *peptide*.

**oligosaccharide** A linear or branched polymer consisting of less than 50 monosaccharides joined by glycosidic linkages. Compare with **monosaccharide** and **polysaccharide**.

**ommatidium** (plural: ommatidia) A light-sensing column in an arthropod's compound eye.

**omnivore** (adjective: omnivorous) An animal whose diet regularly includes both meat and plants. Compare with **carnivore** and **herbivore**.

**oncogene** Any gene whose protein product stimulates cell division at all times and thus promotes cancer development. Often is a mutated form of a gene involved in regulating the cell cycle. See **proto-oncogene**.

**one-gene, one-enzyme hypothesis** The hypothesis that each gene is responsible for making one enzyme. This hypothesis has expanded to include genes that produce proteins other than enzymes or that produce RNAs as final products.

**oogenesis** The production of egg cells (ova).

**oogonium** (plural: oogonia) In an ovary, any of the diploid cells that can divide by mitosis to create primary oocytes (which can undergo meiosis) and more oogonia.

**open circulatory system** A circulatory system in which the circulating fluid (hemolymph) is not confined to blood vessels. Compare with **closed circulatory system**.

**open reading frame (ORF)** Any DNA sequence, ranging in length from several hundred to thousands of base pairs long, that is flanked by a start codon and a stop codon. ORFs identified by computer analysis of DNA may be functional genes, especially if they have other features characteristic of genes (e.g., promoter sequence).

**operator** In prokaryotic DNA, a binding site for a repressor protein; located near the start of an operon.

**operculum** The stiff flap of tissue that covers the gills of teleost fishes.

**operon** A region of prokaryotic DNA that codes for a series of functionally related genes and is transcribed from a single promoter into one mRNA.

**opsin** A transmembrane protein that is covalently linked to retinal, the light-detecting pigment in rod and cone cells.

**optic nerve** A bundle of neurons that runs from the eye to the brain.

**optimal foraging** The concept that animals forage in a way that maximizes the amount of usable energy they take in, given the costs of finding and ingesting their food and the risk of being eaten while they're at it.

**orbital** The region of space around an atomic nucleus in which an electron is present most of the time.

**organ** A group of tissues organized into a functional and structural unit.

**organ system** Groups of tissues and organs that work together to perform a function.

**organelle** Any discrete, membrane-bound structure within a cell (e.g., mitochondrion) that has a characteristic structure and function.

**organic** For a compound, containing carbon and hydrogen and usually containing carbon–carbon bonds. Organic compounds are widely used by living organisms.

**organism** Any living entity that contains one or more cells.

**organogenesis** A stage of embryonic development that follows gastrulation and that creates organs from the three germ layers.

**origin of replication** The site on a chromosome at which DNA replication begins.

**osmoconformer** An animal that does not actively regulate the osmolarity of its tissues but conforms to the osmolarity of the surrounding environment.

**osmolarity** The concentration of dissolved substances in a solution, measured in osmoles per liter.

**osmoregulation** The process by which a living organism controls the concentration of water and salts in its body.

**osmoregulator** An animal that actively regulates the osmolarity of its tissues.

**osmosis** Diffusion of water across a selectively permeable membrane from a region of low solute concentration (high water concentration) to a region of high solute concentration (low water concentration).

**ossicles, ear** In mammals, three bones found in the middle ear that function in transferring and amplifying sound from the outer ear to the inner ear.

**ouabain** A plant toxin that poisons the sodium–potassium pumps of animals.

**out-of-Africa hypothesis** The hypothesis that modern humans (*Homo sapiens*) evolved in Africa and spread to other continents, replacing other *Homo* species without interbreeding with them.

**outcrossing** Reproduction by fusion of the gametes of different individuals, rather than by self-fertilization.

**outer ear** The outermost portion of the mammalian ear, consisting of the pinna (ear flap) and the ear canal. Funnels sound to the tympanic membrane.

**outgroup** A taxon that is closely related to a particular monophyletic group but is not part of it.

**oval window** A membrane separating the fluid-filled cochlea from the air-filled middle ear; sound vibrations pass through it from the middle ear to the inner ear in mammals.

**ovary** The egg-producing organ of a female animal, or the fruit- and seed-producing structure in the female part of a flower.

**overexploitation** Unsustainable removal of wildlife from the natural environment for use by humans.

**oviduct** See **fallopian tube**.

**oviparous** In animals, producing eggs that are laid outside the body where they develop and hatch. Compare with **ovoviviparous** and **viviparous**.

**ovoviviparous** In animals, producing eggs that are retained inside the body until they are ready to hatch. Compare with **oviparous** and **viviparous**.

**ovulation** The release of an egg from an ovary of a female vertebrate. In humans, an ovarian follicle releases an egg at the end of the follicular phase of the menstrual cycle.

**ovule** In flowering plants, the structure inside an ovary that contains the female gametophyte and eventually (if fertilized) becomes a seed.

**ovum** (plural: ova) See **egg**.

**oxidation** The loss of electrons from an atom or molecule during a redox reaction, either by donation of an electron to another atom or molecule, or by the shared electrons in covalent bonds moving farther from the atomic nucleus.

**oxidative phosphorylation** Production of ATP molecules by ATP synthase using the proton gradient established via redox reactions of an electron transport chain.

**oxygen–hemoglobin equilibrium curve** The graphed depiction of the percentage of hemoglobin in the blood that is bound to oxygen at various partial pressures of oxygen.

**oxygenic** Referring to any process or reaction that produces oxygen. Photosynthesis in plants, algae, and cyanobacteria, which involves photosystem II, is oxygenic. Compare with **anoxygenic**.

**oxytocin** A peptide hormone, secreted by the posterior pituitary, that triggers labor and milk production in females and that stimulates pair bonding, parental care, and affiliative behavior in both sexes.

**p53** A tumor-suppressor protein (molecular weight of 53 kilodaltons) that responds to DNA damage by stopping the cell cycle, turning on DNA repair machinery, and, if necessary, triggering apoptosis. Encoded by the *p53* gene.

**pacemaker cell** Any of a group of specialized cardiac muscle cells in the sinoatrial (SA) node of the vertebrate heart that have an inherent rhythm and can generate an electrical impulse that spreads to other heart cells.

**paleontologists** Scientists who study the fossil record and the history of life.

**Paleozoic era** The interval of geologic time, from 542 million to 251 million years ago, during which fungi, land plants, and animals first appeared and diversified. Began with the Cambrian explosion and ended with the extinction of many invertebrates and vertebrates at the end of the Permian period.

**pancreas** A large gland in vertebrates that has both exocrine and endocrine functions. Secretes digestive enzymes into a duct connected to the intestine and secretes several hormones (notably, insulin and glucagon) into the bloodstream.

**pancreatic amylase** An enzyme produced by the pancreas that breaks down glucose chains by catalyzing hydrolysis of the glycosidic linkages between the glucose residues.

**pancreatic lipase** An enzyme that is produced in the pancreas and acts in the small intestine to break bonds in complex fats, releasing small lipids.

**pandemic** The spread of an infectious disease in a short time period over a wide geographic area and affecting a very high proportion of the population. Compare with **epidemic**.

**parabiosis** An experimental technique for determining whether a certain physiological phenomenon is regulated by a hormone; consists of surgically uniting two individuals so that hormones can pass between them.

**paracrine** Relating to a chemical signal that is released by one cell and affects neighboring cells.

**paraphyletic group** A group that includes an ancestral population and *some* but not all of its descendants. Compare with **monophyletic group**.

**parapodia** (singular: parapodium) Appendages found in some annelids from which bristle-like structures (chaetae) extend.

**parasite** An organism that lives on a host species (ectoparasite) or in a host species (endoparasite) and that damages its host.

**parasitism** (adjective: parasitic) A symbiotic relationship between two organisms that is beneficial to one organism (the parasite) but detrimental to the other (the host). Compare with **commensalism** and **mutualism**.

**parasitoid** An organism that has a parasitic larval stage and a free-living adult stage. Most parasitoids are insects that lay eggs in the bodies of other insects.

**parasympathetic nervous system** The part of the autonomic nervous system that stimulates responses for conserving or restoring energy, such as reduced heart rate and increased digestion. Compare with **sympathetic nervous system**.

**parenchyma cell** In plants, a general type of cell with a relatively thin primary cell wall. These cells, found in leaves, the centers of stems and roots, and fruits, are involved in photosynthesis, storage, and transport. Compare with **collenchyma cell** and **sclerenchyma cell**.

**parental care** Any action by which an animal expends energy or assumes risks to benefit its offspring (e.g., nest building, feeding of young, defense).

**parental generation** The adults used in the first experimental cross of a breeding experiment.

**parental strand** A strand of DNA that is used as a template during DNA synthesis.

**parietal cell** A cell in the stomach lining that secretes hydrochloric acid.

**parietal lobe** In the vertebrate brain, one of the four major areas in the cerebrum.

**parsimony** The logical principle that the most likely explanation of a phenomenon is the most economical or simplest. When applied to comparison of alternative phylogenetic trees, it suggests that the one requiring the fewest evolutionary changes is most likely to be correct.

**parthenogenesis** Development of offspring from unfertilized eggs; a type of asexual reproduction.

**partial pressure** The pressure of one particular gas in a mixture of gases; the contribution of that gas to the overall pressure.

**particulate inheritance** The observation that genes from two parents do not blend together in offspring, but instead remain separate or particle-like.

**pascal (Pa)** A unit of pressure (force per unit area).

**passive transport** Diffusion of a substance across a membrane. When this event occurs with the assistance of membrane proteins, it is called *facilitated diffusion*.

**patch clamping** A technique for studying the electrical currents that flow through individual ion channels by sucking a tiny patch of membrane to the hollow tip of a microelectrode.

**paternal chromosome** A chromosome inherited from the father.

**pathogen** (adjective: pathogenic) Any entity capable of causing disease, such as a microbe, virus, or prion.

**pattern formation** The series of events that determines the spatial organization of an entire embryo or parts of an embryo, for example, setting the major body axes early in development.

**pattern-recognition receptor** On leukocytes, a class of membrane proteins that bind to molecules commonly associated with foreign cells and viruses and signal responses against broad types of pathogens. Part of the innate immune response.

**peat** Semi-decayed organic matter that accumulates in moist, low-oxygen environments such as *Sphagnum* (moss) bogs.

**pectin** A gelatinous polysaccharide found in the primary cell wall of plant cells. Attracts and holds water, forming a gel that resists compression forces and helps keep the cell wall moist.

**pedigree** A family tree of parents and offspring, showing inheritance of particular traits of interest.

**penis** The copulatory organ of male mammals, used to insert sperm into a female.

**pentose** A monosaccharide (simple sugar) containing five carbon atoms.

**PEP carboxylase** An enzyme that catalyzes addition of $CO_2$ to phosphoenolpyruvate, a three-carbon compound, forming a four-carbon organic acid. See also **$C_4$ pathway** and **crassulacean acid metabolism (CAM)**.

**pepsin** A protein-digesting enzyme present in the stomach.

**peptide** See **oligopeptide**.

**peptide bond** The covalent bond formed by a condensation reaction between two amino acids; links the residues in peptides and proteins.

**peptidoglycan** A complex structural polysaccharide found in bacterial cell walls.

**perennial** Describing a plant whose life cycle normally lasts for more than one year. Compare with **annual**.

**perfect flower** A flower that contains both male parts (stamens) and female parts (carpels). Compare with **imperfect flower**.

**perforation** In plants, a small hole in the primary and secondary cell walls of vessel elements that allows passage of water.

**pericarp** The part of a fruit, formed from the ovary wall, that surrounds the seeds and protects them. Corresponds to the flesh of most edible fruits and the hard shells of most nuts.

**pericycle** In plant roots, a layer of cells just inside the endodermis that give rise to lateral roots.

**peripheral membrane protein** Any membrane protein that does not span the entire lipid bilayer and associates with only one side of the bilayer. Compare with **integral membrane protein**.

**peripheral nervous system (PNS)** All the components of the nervous system that are outside the central nervous system (the brain and spinal cord). Includes the somatic nervous system and the autonomic nervous system.

**peristalsis** Rhythmic waves of muscular contraction. In the digestive tract, pushes food along. In animals with hydrostatic skeletons, enables crawling.

**permafrost** A permanently frozen layer of icy soil found in most tundra and some taiga.

**permeability** The tendency of a structure, such as a membrane, to allow a given substance to diffuse across it.

**peroxisome** An organelle found in most eukaryotic cells that contains enzymes for oxidizing fatty acids and other compounds, including many toxins, rendering them harmless. See **glyoxysome**.

**petal** Any of the leaflike organs arranged around the reproductive organs of a flower. Often colored and scented to attract pollinators.

**petiole** The stalk of a leaf.

**pH** A measure of the concentration of protons in a solution and thus of acidity or alkalinity. Defined as the negative of the base-10 logarithm of the proton concentration: $pH = -\log[H^+]$.

**phagocytosis** Uptake by a cell of small particles or cells by invagination and pinching off of the plasma membrane to form small, membrane-bound vesicles; one type of **endocytosis**.

**pharyngeal gill slits** A set of parallel openings from the throat to the outside that function in both feeding and gas exchange. A diagnostic trait of chordates.

**pharyngeal jaw** A secondary jaw in the back of the throat; found in some fishes, it aids in food processing. Derived from modified gill arches.

**phenology** The timing of events during the year, in environments where seasonal changes occur.

**phenotype** The detectable traits of an individual. Compare with **genotype**.

**phenotypic plasticity** Within-species variation in phenotype that is due to differences in environmental conditions. Occurs more commonly in plants than animals.

**pheophytin** The molecule in photosystem II that accepts excited electrons from the reaction center chlorophyll and passes them to an electron transport chain.

**pheromone** A chemical signal, released by an individual into the external environment, that can trigger changes in the behavior or physiology or both of another member of the same species.

**phloem** A plant vascular tissue that conducts sugars between roots and shoots; contains sieve-tube elements and companion cells. Primary phloem develops from the procambium of apical meristems; secondary phloem, from the vascular cambium. Compare with **xylem**.

**phosphatase** An enzyme that removes phosphate groups from proteins or other molecules. Phosphatases are often used in the inactivation of signaling pathways that involve the phosphorylation and activation of proteins.

**phosphodiester linkage** Chemical linkage between adjacent nucleotide residues in DNA and RNA. Forms when the phosphate group of one nucleotide condenses with the hydroxyl group on the sugar of another nucleotide. Also known as *phosphodiester bond*.

**phosphofructokinase** The enzyme that catalyzes synthesis of fructose-1,6-bisphosphate from fructose-6-phosphate, a key reaction in glycolysis (step 3). Also called *6-phosphofructokinase*.

**phospholipid** A class of lipid having a hydrophilic head (including a phosphate group) and a hydrophobic tail (consisting of two hydrocarbon chains). Major components of the plasma membrane and organelle membranes.

**phosphorylase** An enzyme that breaks down glycogen by catalyzing hydrolysis of the $\alpha$-glycosidic linkages between the glucose residues.

**phosphorylation** (verb: phosphorylate) The addition of a phosphate group to a molecule.

**phosphorylation cascade** A series of enzyme-catalyzed phosphorylation reactions commonly used in signal transduction pathways to amplify and convey a signal inward from the plasma membrane.

**photic zone** In an aquatic habitat, water that is shallow enough to receive some sunlight (whether or not it is enough to support photosynthesis). Compare with **aphotic zone**.

**photon** A discrete packet of light energy; a particle of light.

**photoperiod** The amount of time per day (usually in hours) that an organism is exposed to light.

**photoperiodism** Any response by an organism to the relative lengths of day and night (i.e., photoperiod).

**photophosphorylation** Production of ATP molecules by ATP synthase using the proton-motive force generated as light-excited electrons flow through an electron transport chain during photosynthesis.

**photoreception** A sensory system in which receptors are activated by light.

**photoreceptor** A molecule, a cell, or an organ that is specialized to detect light.

**photorespiration** A series of light-driven chemical reactions that consumes oxygen and releases carbon dioxide, basically undoing photosynthesis. Usually occurs when there are high $O_2$ and low $CO_2$ concentrations inside plant cells; often occurs when stomata must be kept closed to prevent dehydration.

**photoreversibility** A change in conformation that occurs in certain plant pigments when they are exposed to the particular wavelengths of light that they absorb; triggers responses by the plant.

**photosynthesis** The complex biological process that converts the energy of light into chemical energy stored in glucose and other organic molecules. Occurs in most plants, algae, and some bacteria.

**photosystem** One of two types of units, consisting of a central reaction center surrounded by antenna complexes, that is responsible for the light-dependent reactions of photosynthesis.

**photosystem I** A photosystem that contains a pair of P700 chlorophyll molecules and uses absorbed light energy to reduce $NADP^+$ to NADPH.

**photosystem II** A photosystem that contains a pair of P680 chlorophyll molecules and uses absorbed light energy to produce a proton-motive force for the synthesis of ATP. Oxygen is produced as a by-product when water is split to obtain electrons.

**phototroph** An organism (most plants, algae, and some bacteria) that produces ATP through photosynthesis.

**phototropins** A class of plant photoreceptors that detect blue light and initiate various responses.

**phototropism** Growth or movement of an organism in a particular direction in response to light.

**phylogenetic species concept** The definition of a species as the smallest monophyletic group in a phylogenetic tree. Compare with **biological species concept** and **morphospecies concept**.

**phylogenetic tree** A branching diagram that depicts the evolutionary relationships among species or other taxa.

**phylogeny** The evolutionary history of a group of organisms.

**phylum** (plural: phyla) In Linnaeus' system, a taxonomic category above the class level and below the kingdom level. In plants, sometimes called a *division*.

**physical map** A map of a chromosome that shows the number of base pairs between various genetic markers. Compare with **genetic map**.

**physiology** The study of how an organism's body functions.

**phytochrome** A specialized plant photoreceptor that exists in two shapes depending on the ratio of red to far-red light and is involved in the timing of certain physiological processes, such as flowering, stem elongation, and germination.

**pigment** Any molecule that absorbs certain wavelengths of visible light and reflects or transmits other wavelengths.

**piloting** A type of navigation in which animals use familiar landmarks to find their way.

**pineal gland** An endocrine gland, located in the brain, that secretes the hormone melatonin.

**pioneering species** Those species that appear first in recently disturbed areas.

**pit** In plants, a small hole in the secondary cell walls of tracheids and vessel elements that allows passage of water.

**pitch** The sensation produced by a particular frequency of sound. Low frequencies are perceived as low pitches; high frequencies, as high pitches.

**pith** In the shoot systems of plants, ground tissue located to the inside of the vascular bundles.

**pituitary gland** A small gland located directly under the brain and physically and functionally connected to the hypothalamus. Produces and secretes an array of hormones that affect many other glands and organs.

**placenta** A structure that forms in the pregnant uterus from maternal and fetal tissues. Delivers oxygen to the fetus, exchanges nutrients and wastes between mother and fetus, anchors the fetus to the uterine wall, and produces some hormones. Occurs in most mammals and in a few other vertebrates.

**placental mammals** See **eutherians**.

**plankton** Drifting organisms (animals, plants, archaea, or bacteria) in aquatic environments.

**Plantae** The monophyletic group that includes red, green, and glaucophyte algae, and land plants.

**plasma** The non-cellular portion of blood.

**plasma cell** A B cell that produces large quantities of antibodies after being activated by interacting with antigen and a CD4$^+$ T cell via peptide presentation. Also called an *effector B cell*.

**plasma membrane** A membrane that surrounds a cell, separating it from the external environment and selectively regulating passage of molecules and ions into and out of the cell. Also called *cell membrane*.

**plasmid** A small, usually circular, supercoiled DNA molecule independent of the cell's main chromosome(s) in prokaryotes and some eukaryotes.

**plasmodesmata** (singular: plasmodesma) Physical connections between two plant cells, consisting of membrane-lined gaps in the cell walls through which the two cells' plasma membranes, cytoplasm, and smooth ER can connect directly. Functionally similar to gap junctions in animal cells.

**plasmogamy** Fusion of the cytoplasm of two individuals. Occurs in many fungi.

**plastocyanin** A small protein that shuttles electrons originating from photosystem II to the reaction center of photosystem I during photosynthesis.

**plastoquinone (PQ)** A nonprotein electron carrier in the chloroplast electron transport chain. Receives excited electrons from photosystem II (noncyclic) or photosystem I (cyclic) and passes them to more

electronegative molecules in the chain. Also transports protons from the stroma to the thylakoid lumen, generating a proton-motive force.

**platelet** A small membrane-bound cell fragment in vertebrate blood that functions in blood clotting. Derived from large cells in the bone marrow.

**pleiotropy** (adjective: pleiotropic) The ability of a single gene to affect more than one trait.

**ploidy** The number of complete chromosome sets present. *Haploid* refers to a ploidy of 1; *diploid*, a ploidy of 2; *triploid*, a ploidy of 3; and *tetraploid*, a ploidy of 4.

**point mutation** A mutation that results in a change in a single base pair in DNA.

**polar** (1) Asymmetrical or unidirectional. (2) Carrying a partial positive charge on one side of a molecule and a partial negative charge on the other. Polar molecules are generally hydrophilic.

**polar body** Any of the tiny, nonfunctional cells that are made as a by-product during meiosis of a primary oocyte, due to most of the cytoplasm going to the ovum.

**polar covalent bond** A covalent bond in which electrons are shared unequally between atoms differing in electronegativity, resulting in the more electronegative atom having a partial negative charge and the other atom, a partial positive charge. Compare with **nonpolar covalent bond**.

**polar microtubules** Mitotic and meiotic microtubules that have arisen from the two spindle poles and overlap with each other in the middle of the spindle apparatus.

**polar nuclei** In flowering plants, the nuclei in the female gametophyte that fuse with one sperm nucleus to produce the endosperm. Most species have two.

**pollen grain** In seed plants, a male gametophyte enclosed within a protective coat of sporopollenin.

**pollen tube** In flowering plants, a structure that grows out of a pollen grain after it reaches the stigma, extends down the style, and through which two sperm cells are delivered to the ovule.

**pollination** The process by which pollen reaches the carpel of a flower (in flowering plants), transferred from anther to stigma, or reaches the ovule directly (in conifers and their relatives).

**pollination syndrome** Suites of flower characters that are associated with certain types of pollinators and that have evolved through natural selection imposed by the interaction between flowers and pollinators.

**poly(A) signal** In eukaryotes, a short sequence of nucleotides near the 3′ end of pre-mRNAs that signals cleavage of the RNA and addition of the poly(A) tail.

**poly(A) tail** In eukaryotes, a sequence of about 100–250 adenine nucleotides added to the 3′ end of newly transcribed messenger RNA molecules.

**polygenic inheritance** Having many genes influence one trait.

**polymer** Any long molecule composed of small repeating units (monomers) bonded together. The main biological polymers are proteins, nucleic acids, and polysaccharides.

**polymerase chain reaction (PCR)** A laboratory technique for rapidly generating millions of identical

copies of a specific stretch of DNA. Works by incubating the original DNA sequence of interest with primers, nucleotides, and DNA polymerase.

**polymerization** (verb: polymerize) The process by which many identical or similar small molecules (monomers) are covalently bonded to form a large molecule (polymer).

**polymorphic species** A species that has two or more distinct phenotypes in the same interbreeding population at the same time.

**polymorphism** (adjective: polymorphic) (1) The occurrence of more than one allele at a genetic locus in a population. (2) The occurrence of more than two distinct phenotypes of a trait in a population.

**polyp** The immotile (sessile) stage in the life cycle of some cnidarians (e.g., jellyfish). Compare with **medusa**.

**polypeptide** A chain of 50 or more amino acids linked together by peptide bonds. Compare with **oligopeptide** and **protein**.

**polyphyletic group** An unnatural group based on convergent (homoplastic) characteristics that are not present in a common ancestor. Compare with **monophyletic group**.

**polyploidy** (adjective: polyploid) The state of having more than two full sets of chromosomes, either from the same species (autopolyploidy) or from different species (allopolyploidy).

**polyribosome** A messenger RNA molecule along with more than one attached ribosome and their growing peptide strands.

**polysaccharide** A linear or branched polymer consisting of many monosaccharides joined by glycosidic linkages. Compare with **monosaccharide** and **oligosaccharide**.

**polytomy** A node in a phylogenetic tree that depicts an ancestral branch dividing into three or more descendant branches; usually indicates that insufficient data were available to resolve which taxa are more closely related.

**population** A group of individuals of the same species living in the same geographic area at the same time.

**population density** The number of individuals of a population per unit area.

**population dynamics** Changes in the size and other characteristics of populations through time and space.

**population ecology** The study of how and why the number of individuals in a population changes over time and space.

**population thinking** The ability to analyze trait frequencies, event probabilities, and other attributes of populations of molecules, cells, or organisms.

**pore** In land plants, an opening in the epithelium that allows gas exchange. See also **stoma**.

**positive control** Of genes, when a regulatory protein triggers expression by binding to DNA on or near the gene.

**positive feedback** A physiological mechanism in which a change in some variable stimulates a response that increases the change. Relatively rare in organisms but is important in generation of the action potential. Compare with **negative feedback**.

**positive pressure ventilation** Ventilation of the lungs by using positive pressure in the mouth to "push" air into the lungs. Compare with **negative pressure ventilation**.

**positive-sense RNA virus** An ssRNA virus whose genome contains the same sequences as the mRNA required to produce viral proteins. Compare with **ambisense virus** and **negative-sense virus**.

**posterior** Toward an animal's tail and away from its head. The opposite of anterior.

**posterior pituitary** The part of the pituitary gland that contains the ends of hypothalamic neurosecretory cells and from which oxytocin and antidiuretic hormone are secreted. Compare with **anterior pituitary**.

**postsynaptic neuron** A neuron that receives signals, usually via neurotransmitters, from another neuron at a synapse. Compare with **presynaptic neuron**.

**post-translational control** Regulation of gene expression by modification of proteins (e.g., addition of a phosphate group or sugar residues) after translation.

**postzygotic isolation** Reproductive isolation resulting from mechanisms that operate after mating of individuals of two different species occurs. The most common mechanisms are the death of hybrid embryos or reduced fitness of hybrids.

**potential energy** Energy stored in matter as a result of its position or molecular arrangement. Compare with **kinetic energy**.

**prebiotic soup model** Hypothetical explanation for chemical evolution whereby small molecules reacted with one another in a mixture of organic molecules condensed into a body of water, typically in reference to the early oceans.

**Precambrian** The interval between the formation of the Earth, about 4.6 billion years ago, and the appearance of most animal groups about 542 million years ago. Unicellular organisms were dominant for most of this era, and oxygen was virtually absent for the first 2 billion years.

**pre-mRNA** In eukaryotes, the primary transcript of protein-coding genes. Pre-mRNA is processed to form mRNA.

**predation** The killing and eating of one organism (the prey) by another (the predator).

**predator** Any organism that kills other organisms for food.

**prediction** A measurable or observable result of an experiment based on a particular hypothesis. A correct prediction provides support for the hypothesis being tested.

**pressure-flow hypothesis** The hypothesis that sugar movement through phloem tissue is due to differences in the turgor pressure of phloem sap.

**pressure potential** ($\psi_p$) A component of the potential energy of water caused by physical pressures on a solution. It can be positive or negative. Compare with **solute potential** ($\psi_s$).

**presynaptic neuron** A neuron that transmits signals, usually by releasing neurotransmitters, to another neuron or to an effector cell at a synapse.

**prezygotic isolation** Reproductive isolation resulting from any one of several mechanisms that prevent individuals of two different species from mating.

**primary active transport** A form of active transport in which a source of energy like ATP is directly used to move ions against their electrochemical gradients.

**primary cell wall** The outermost layer of a plant cell wall, made of cellulose fibers and gelatinous polysaccharides, that defines the shape of the cell and withstands the turgor pressure of the plasma membrane.

**primary consumer** An herbivore; an organism that eats plants, algae, or other primary producers. Compare with **secondary consumer**.

**primary decomposer** A decomposer (detritivore) that consumes detritus from plants.

**primary growth** In plants, an increase in the length of stems and roots due to the activity of apical meristems. Compare with **secondary growth**.

**primary immune response** An adaptive immune response to a pathogen that the immune system has not encountered before. Compare with **secondary immune response**.

**primary meristem** In plants, three types of partially differentiated cells that are produced by apical meristems, including protoderm, ground meristem, and procambium. Compare with **apical meristem** and **cambium**.

**primary oocyte** Any of the large diploid cells in an ovarian follicle that can initiate meiosis to produce a haploid secondary oocyte and a polar body.

**primary producer** Any organism that creates its own food by photosynthesis or from reduced inorganic compounds and that is a food source for other species in its ecosystem. Also called *autotroph*.

**primary spermatocyte** Any of the diploid cells in the testis that can initiate meiosis I to produce two secondary spermatocytes.

**primary structure** The sequence of amino acid residues in a peptide or protein; also the sequence of nucleotides in a nucleic acid. Compare with **secondary**, **tertiary**, and **quaternary structure**.

**primary succession** The gradual colonization of a habitat of bare rock or gravel, usually after an environmental disturbance that removes all soil and previous organisms. Compare with **secondary succession**.

**primary transcript** In eukaryotes, a newly transcribed RNA molecule that has not yet been processed to a mature RNA. Called *pre-mRNA* when the final product is a protein.

**primase** An enzyme that synthesizes a short stretch of RNA to use as a primer during DNA replication.

**primates** The lineage of mammals that includes prosimians (lemurs, lorises, etc.), monkeys, and great apes (including humans).

**primer** A short, single-stranded RNA molecule that base-pairs with a DNA template strand and is elongated by DNA polymerase during DNA replication.

**probe** A radioactively or chemically labeled single-stranded fragment of a known DNA or RNA sequence that can bind to and detect its complementary sequence in a sample containing many different sequences.

**proboscis** A tubular, often extensible feeding appendage with which food can be obtained.

**procambium** A primary meristem tissue that gives rise to the vascular tissue.

**product** Any of the final materials formed in a chemical reaction.

**progesterone** A steroid hormone produced and secreted by the corpus luteum in the ovaries after ovulation and by the placenta during gestation; protects the uterine lining.

**programmed cell death** Regulated cell death that is used in development, tissue maintainance, and destruction of infected cells. Can occur in different ways; apoptosis is the best-known mechanism.

**prokaryote** A member of the domain Bacteria or Archaea; a unicellular organism lacking a nucleus and containing relatively few organelles or cytoskeletal components. Compare with **eukaryote**.

**prolactin** A peptide hormone, produced and secreted by the anterior pituitary, that promotes milk production in female mammals and has a variety of effects on parental behavior and seasonal reproduction in other vertebrates.

**prometaphase** A stage in mitosis or meiosis during which the nuclear envelope breaks down and microtubules attach to kinetochores.

**promoter** A short nucleotide sequence in DNA that binds a sigma factor (in bacteria) or basal transcription factors (in eukaryotes) to enable RNA polymerase to begin transcription. In bacteria, several contiguous genes are often transcribed from a single promoter. In eukaryotes, each gene generally has its own promoter.

**promoter-proximal element** In eukaryotes, regulatory sequences in DNA that are close to a promoter and that can bind regulatory transcription factors.

**proofreading** The process by which a DNA polymerase recognizes and removes a wrong base added during DNA replication and then continues synthesis.

**prophase** The first stage in mitosis or meiosis during which chromosomes become visible and the spindle apparatus forms. Synapsis and crossing over occur during prophase of meiosis I.

**prosimians** One of the two major lineages of primates, a paraphyletic group including lemurs, pottos, and lorises. Compare with **anthropoids**.

**prostate gland** A gland in male mammals that surrounds the base of the urethra and secretes a fluid that is a component of semen.

**prosthetic group** A non-amino acid atom or molecule that is permanently attached to an enzyme or other protein and is required for its function.

**protease** An enzyme that can break up proteins by cleaving the peptide bonds between amino acid residues.

**proteasome** A macromolecular machine that destroys proteins that have been marked by the addition of ubiquitin.

**protein** A macromolecule consisting of one or more polypeptide chains composed of 50 or more amino acids linked together. Each protein has a unique sequence of amino acids and generally possesses a characteristic three-dimensional shape.

**protein kinase** An enzyme that catalyzes the addition of a phosphate group to another protein, typically activating or inactivating the substrate protein.

**proteinase inhibitors** Defense compounds, produced by plants, that induce illness in herbivores by inhibiting digestive enzymes.

**proteoglycan** A type of highly glycosylated protein found in the extracellular matrix of animal cells that attracts and holds water, forming a gel that resists compression forces.

**proteome** The complete set of proteins produced by a particular cell type.

**proteomics** The systematic study of the interactions, localization, functions, regulation, and other features of the full protein set (proteome) in a particular cell type.

**protist** Any eukaryote that is not a green plant, animal, or fungus. Protists are a diverse paraphyletic group. Most are unicellular, but some are multicellular or form aggregations called colonies.

**protocell** A hypothetical pre-cell structure consisting of a membrane compartment that encloses replicating macromolecules, such as ribozymes.

**protoderm** The exterior layer of a young plant embryo that gives rise to the epidermis.

**proto-oncogene** Any gene that encourages cell division in a regulated manner, typically by triggering specific phases in the cell cycle. Mutation may convert it into an oncogene. See **oncogene**.

**proton pump** A membrane protein that can hydrolyze ATP to power active transport of protons ($H^+$ ions) across a membrane against an electrochemical gradient. Also called $H^+$-ATPase.

**proton-motive force** The combined effect of a proton gradient and an electric potential gradient across a membrane, which can drive protons across the membrane. Used by mitochondria and chloroplasts to power ATP synthesis via the mechanism of chemiosmosis.

**protostomes** A major lineage of animals that share a pattern of embryological development, including formation of the mouth earlier than the anus, and formation of the coelom by splitting of a block of mesoderm. Includes arthropods, mollusks, and annelids. Compare with **deuterostomes**.

**proximal tubule** In the vertebrate kidney, the convoluted section of a nephron into which filtrate moves from Bowman's capsule. Involved in the largely unregulated reabsorption of electrolytes, nutrients, and water. Compare with **distal tubule**.

**proximate causation** In biology, the immediate, mechanistic cause of a phenomenon (how it happens), as opposed to why it evolved. Also called *proximate explanation*. Compare with **ultimate causation**.

**pseudocoelomate** An animal that has a coelom that is only partially lined with mesoderm. Compare with **acoelomate** and **coelomate**.

**pseudogene** A DNA sequence that closely resembles a functional gene but is not transcribed. Thought to have arisen by duplication of the functional gene followed by inactivation due to a mutation.

**pseudopodium** (plural: pseudopodia) A temporary bulge-like extension of certain protist cells used in cell crawling and ingestion of food.

**puberty** The various physical and emotional changes that an immature human undergoes in reaching reproductive maturity. Also the period when such changes occur.

**pulmonary artery** A short, thick-walled artery that carries oxygen-poor blood from the heart to the lungs.

**pulmonary circulation** The part of the circulatory system that sends oxygen-poor blood to the lungs. It is separate from the rest of the circulatory system (the systemic circulation) in mammals and birds.

**pulmonary vein** A short, thin-walled vein that carries oxygen-rich blood from the lungs to the heart. Humans have four such veins.

**pulse–chase experiment** A type of experiment in which a population of cells or molecules at a particular moment in time is marked by means of a labeled molecule (pulse) and then their fate is followed over time (chase).

**pump** Any membrane protein that can hydrolyze ATP and change shape to power active transport of a specific ion or small molecule across a plasma membrane against its electrochemical gradient. See **proton pump**.

**pupa** (plural: pupae) A metamorphosing insect that is enclosed in a protective case.

**pupil** The hole in the center of the iris through which light enters a vertebrate or cephalopod eye.

**pure line** In animal or plant breeding, a strain that produces offspring identical with themselves when self-fertilized or crossed to another member of the same population. Pure lines are homozygous for most, if not all, genetic loci.

**purifying selection** Selection that lowers the frequency of or even eliminates deleterious alleles.

**purines** A class of small, nitrogen-containing, double-ringed bases (guanine, adenine) found in nucleotides. Compare with **pyrimidines**.

**pyrimidines** A class of small, nitrogen-containing, single-ringed bases (cytosine, uracil, thymine) found in nucleotides. Compare with **purines**.

**pyruvate dehydrogenase** A large enzyme complex, located in the mitochondrial matix, that is responsible for converting pyruvate to acetyl CoA during cellular respiration.

**quantitative trait** A trait that exhibits continuous phenotypic variation (e.g., human height), rather than the distinct forms characteristic of discrete traits.

**quaternary structure** In proteins, the overall three-dimensional shape formed from two or more polypeptide chains (subunits); determined by the number, relative positions, and interactions of the subunits. In single stranded nucleic acids, the hydrogen bonding between two or more distinct strands will form this level of structure through hydrophobic interactions between complementary bases. Compare with **primary**, **secondary**, and **tertiary structures**.

**quorum sensing** Cell–cell signaling in unicellular organisms, in which cells of the same species communicate via chemical signals. It is often observed that cell activity changes dramatically when the population reaches a threshold size, or quorum.

**radial symmetry** An animal body pattern that has at least two planes of symmetry. Typically, the body is in the form of a cylinder or disk, and the body parts radiate from a central hub. Compare with **bilateral symmetry**.

**radiation** Transfer of heat between two bodies that are not in direct physical contact. More generally, the emission of electromagnetic energy of any wavelength.

**radicle** The root of a plant embryo.

**radioactive isotope** A version of an element that has an unstable nucleus, which will release radiation energy as it decays to a more stable form. Decay often results in the radioisotope becoming a different element.

**radioimmunoassay** A competitive binding assay in which the quantity of hormone in a sample can be estimated. Uses radioactively labeled hormones that compete with the unknown hormone to bind with an antibody.

**radula** A rasping feeding appendage in mollusks such as gastropods (snails, slugs).

**rain shadow** The dry region on the side of a mountain range away from the prevailing wind.

**range** The geographic distribution of a species.

**Ras protein** A type of G protein that is activated by enzyme-linked cell-surface receptors, including receptor tyrosine kinases. Activated Ras then initiates a phosphorylation cascade, culminating in a cell response.

**ray-finned fishes** Members of the Actinopterygii, a diverse group of fishes with fins supported by bony rods arranged in a ray pattern.

**rays** In plant shoot systems with secondary growth, a lateral row of parenchyma cells produced by vascular cambium. Transport water and nutrients laterally across the stem.

**Rb protein** A tumor suppressor protein that helps regulate progression of a cell from the $G_1$ phase to the S phase of the cell cycle. Defects in Rb protein are found in many types of cancer.

**reactant** Any of the starting materials in a chemical reaction.

**reaction center** Centrally located component of a photosystem containing proteins and a pair of specialized chlorophyll molecules. It is surrounded by antenna complexes that transmit resonance energy to excite the reaction center pigments.

**reading frame** A series of non-overlapping, three-base-long sequences (potential codons) in DNA or RNA. The reading frame for a polypeptide is set by the start codon.

**realized niche** The portion of the fundamental niche that a species actually occupies given limiting factors such as competition with other species. Compare with **fundamental niche**.

**receptor-mediated endocytosis** Uptake by a cell of certain extracellular macromolecules, bound to specific receptors in the plasma membrane, by pinching off the membrane to form small membrane-bound vesicles.

**receptor tyrosine kinase (RTK)** Any of a class of enzyme-linked cell-surface signal receptors that undergo phosphorylation after binding a signaling molecule. The activated, phosphorylated receptor then triggers a signal transduction pathway inside the cell.

**recessive**  Referring to an allele whose phenotypic effect is observed only in homozygous individuals. Compare with **dominant**.

**reciprocal altruism**  Altruistic behavior that is exchanged between a pair of individuals at different times (i.e., sometimes individual A helps individual B, and sometimes B helps A).

**reciprocal cross**  A cross in which the mother's and father's phenotypes are the reverse of that examined in a previous cross.

**recombinant**  Possessing a new combination of alleles. May refer to a single chromosome or DNA molecule, or to an entire organism.

**recombinant DNA technology**  A variety of techniques for isolating specific DNA fragments and introducing them into different regions of DNA or a different host organism.

**rectal gland**  A salt-excreting gland in the digestive system of sharks, skates, and rays.

**rectum**  The last portion of the digestive tract. It is where feces are held until they are expelled.

**red blood cell**  A hemoglobin-containing cell that circulates in the blood and delivers oxygen from the lungs to the tissues.

**redox reaction**  Any chemical reaction that involves either the complete transfer of one or more electrons from one reactant to another, or a reciprocal shift in the position of shared electrons within one or more of the covalent bonds of two reactants. Also called *reduction–oxidation reaction*.

**reduction**  The gain of electrons by an atom or molecule during a redox reaction, either by acceptance of an electron from another atom or molecule, or by the shared electrons in covalent bonds moving closer to the atomic nucleus.

**reduction–oxidation reaction**  See **redox reaction**.

**reflex**  An involuntary response to environmental stimulation. May involve the brain (conditioned reflex) or not (spinal reflex).

**refractory**  No longer responding to stimuli that previously elicited a response. An example is the tendency of voltage-gated sodium channels to remain closed immediately after an action potential.

**regulatory sequence**  Any segment of DNA that is involved in controlling transcription of a specific gene by binding a regulatory transcription factor protein.

**regulatory transcription factor**  General term for proteins that bind to DNA regulatory sequences (eukaryotic enhancers, silencers, and promoter-proximal elements), but not to the promoter itself, leading to an increase or decrease in transcription of specific genes. Compare with **basal transcription factor**.

**regulon**  A large set of genes in bacteria that are controlled by a single type of regulatory molecule. Regulon genes are transcribed in response to environmental cues and allow cells to respond to changing environments.

**reinforcement**  In evolutionary biology, the natural selection for traits that prevent interbreeding between recently diverged species.

**release factors**  Proteins that trigger termination of translation when a ribosome reaches a stop codon.

**renal corpuscle**  In the vertebrate kidney, the ball-like structure at the beginning of a nephron, consisting of a glomerulus and the surrounding Bowman's capsule. Acts as a filtration device.

**replacement rate**  The number of offspring each female must produce over her entire life to "replace" herself and her mate, resulting in zero population growth. The actual number is slightly more than 2 because some offspring die before reproducing.

**replica plating**  A method of identifying bacterial colonies that have certain mutations by transferring cells from each colony on a master plate to a second (replica) plate and observing their growth when exposed to different conditions.

**replication fork**  The Y-shaped site at which a double-stranded molecule of DNA is separated into two single strands for replication.

**replicative growth**  The process by which viruses produce new virions.

**replisome**  The macromolecular machine that copies DNA; includes DNA polymerase, helicase, primase, and other enzymes.

**repolarization**  Return to a resting potential after a membrane potential has changed; a normal phase in an action potential.

**repressor**  (1) In bacteria, a protein that binds to an operator sequence in DNA to prevent transcription when an inducer is not present and that comes off DNA to allow transcription when an inducer binds to the repressor protein. (2) In eukaryotes, a protein that binds to a silencer sequence in DNA to prevent or reduce gene transcription.

**reproductive development**  The phase of plant development that involves development of the flower and reproductive cells. Follows vegetative development and occurs when a shoot apical meristem (SAM) transitions to a flower-producing meristem.

**reptiles**  One of the two lineages of amniotes (vertebrates that produce amniotic eggs) distinguished by adaptations for life and reproduction on land. Living reptiles include turtles, snakes and lizards, crocodiles and alligators, and birds. Except for birds, all are ectotherms.

**resilience, community**  A measure of how quickly a community recovers following a disturbance.

**resistance, community**  A measure of how much a community is affected by a disturbance.

**respiratory system**  The collection of cells, tissues, and organs responsible for gas exchange between an animal and its environment.

**resting potential**  The membrane potential of a cell in its resting, or normal, state.

**restriction endonucleases**  Bacterial enzymes that cut DNA at a specific base-pair sequence (restriction site). Also called *restriction enzymes*.

**retina**  A thin layer of light-sensitive cells (rods and cones) and neurons at the back of a simple eye, such as that of cephalopods and vertebrates.

**retinal**  A light-absorbing pigment that is linked to the protein opsin in rods and cones of the vertebrate eye.

**retrovirus**  A virus with an RNA genome that reverse-transcribes its RNA into a double-stranded DNA sequence, which is then inserted into the host's genome as part of its replicative cycle.

**reverse transcriptase**  An enzyme that can synthesize double-stranded DNA from a single-stranded RNA template.

**rhizobia**  (singular: rhizobium) Members of the bacterial genus *Rhizobium*; nitrogen-fixing bacteria that live in root nodules of members of the pea family (legumes).

**rhizoid**  The hairlike structure that anchors a non-vascular plant to the substrate.

**rhizome**  A modified stem that runs horizontally underground and produces new plants at the nodes (a form of asexual reproduction). Compare with **stolon**.

**rhodopsin**  A transmembrane complex that is instrumental in detection of light by rods of the vertebrate eye. Is composed of the transmembrane protein opsin covalently linked to retinal, a light-absorbing pigment.

**ribonucleic acid (RNA)**  A nucleic acid composed of ribonucleotides that usually is single stranded. Functions include structural components of ribosomes (rRNA), transporters of amino acids (tRNA), and messages of the DNA code required for protein synthesis (mRNA), among others.

**ribonucleotide**  See **nucleotide**.

**ribosomal RNA (rRNA)**  An RNA molecule that forms part of the ribosome.

**ribosome**  A large macromolecular machine that synthesizes proteins by using the genetic information encoded in messenger RNA. Consists of two subunits, each composed of ribosomal RNA and proteins.

**ribosome binding site**  In a bacterial mRNA molecule, the sequence just upstream of the start codon to which a ribosome binds to initiate translation. Also called the *Shine–Dalgarno sequence*.

**ribozyme**  Any RNA molecule that can act as a catalyst, that is, speed up a chemical reaction.

**ribulose bisphosphate (RuBP)**  A five-carbon compound that combines with $CO_2$ in the first step of the Calvin cycle during photosynthesis.

**RNA**  See **ribonucleic acid**.

**RNA interference (RNAi)**  Degradation of an RNA molecule or inhibition of its translation following its binding by a short RNA (microRNA) whose sequence is complementary to a portion of the mRNA.

**RNA polymerase**  An enzyme that catalyzes the synthesis of RNA from ribonucleotides using a DNA template.

**RNA processing**  In eukaryotes, the changes that a primary RNA transcript undergoes to become a mature RNA molecule. For pre-mRNA it includes the addition of a 5′ cap and poly(A) tail and splicing to remove introns.

**RNA replicase**  A viral enzyme that can synthesize RNA from an RNA template. Also called an *RNA-dependent RNA polymerase*.

**RNA world hypothesis**  Proposal that chemical evolution produced RNAs that could catalyze key reactions involved in their own replication and basic

**abolism**, which led to the evolution of proteins the first life-form.

**rod cell** A photoreceptor cell with a rod-shaped outer portion that is particularly sensitive to dim light but not used to distinguish colors. Also called simply **rod**. Compare with **cone cell**.

**root** (1) An underground part of a plant that anchors the plant and absorbs water and nutrients. (2) The most ancestral branch in a phylogenetic tree.

**root apical meristem (RAM)** A group of undifferentiated plant stem cells at the tip of a plant root that can differentiate into mature root tissue.

**root cap** A small group of cells that covers and protects the root apical meristem. Senses gravity and determines the direction of root growth.

**root hair** A long, thin outgrowth of the epidermal cells of plant roots, providing increased surface area for absorption of water and nutrients.

**root pressure** Positive pressure of xylem sap in the vascular tissue of roots. Generated during the night as a result of the accumulation of ions from the soil and subsequent osmotic movement of water into the xylem.

**root system** The belowground part of a plant.

**rotifer** Member of the phylum Rotifera. Distinguished by a cluster of cilia, called a corona, used in suspension feeding in marine and freshwater environments. Rotifers belong to the lophotrochozoan branch of the protostomes.

**rough endoplasmic reticulum (rough ER)** The portion of the endoplasmic reticulum that is dotted with ribosomes. Involved in synthesis of plasma membrane proteins, secreted proteins, and proteins localized to the ER, Golgi apparatus, and lysosomes. Compare with **smooth endoplasmic reticulum**.

**roundworms** Members of the phylum Nematoda. Distinguished by an unsegmented body with a pseudocoelom and no appendages. Roundworms belong to the ecdysozoan branch of the protostomes. Also called *nematodes*.

**rubisco** The enzyme that catalyzes the first step of the Calvin cycle during photosynthesis: the addition of a molecule of $CO_2$ to ribulose bisphosphate. See also **carbon fixation**.

**ruminant** Member of a group of hoofed mammals (e.g., cattle, sheep, deer) that have a four-chambered stomach specialized for digestion of plant cellulose. Ruminants regurgitate cud, a mixture of partially digested food and cellulose-digesting bacteria, from the largest chamber (the rumen) for further chewing.

**salinity** The proportion of solutes dissolved in water in natural environments, often designated in grams of solute per kilogram of water (cited as parts per thousand).

**salivary amylase** An enzyme that is produced by the salivary glands and that can break down starch by catalyzing hydrolysis of the glycosidic linkages between the glucose residues.

**salivary gland** A type of vertebrate gland that secretes saliva (a mixture of water, mucus-forming glycoproteins, and digestive enzymes) into the mouth.

**sampling error** The selection of a nonrepresentative sample from some larger population, due to chance.

**saprophyte** An organism that feeds primarily on dead plant material.

**sapwood** The younger xylem in the outer layer of wood of a stem or root, functioning primarily in water transport.

**sarcomere** The repeating contractile unit of a skeletal muscle cell; the portion of a myofibril located between adjacent Z disks.

**sarcoplasmic reticulum** Sheets of smooth endoplasmic reticulum in a muscle cell. Contains high concentrations of calcium, which can be released into the cytoplasm to trigger contraction.

**saturated** Referring to lipids in which all the carbon-carbon bonds are single bonds. Such compounds have relatively high melting points. Compare with **unsaturated**.

**scanning electron microscope (SEM)** A microscope that produces images of the surfaces of objects by reflecting electrons from a specimen coated with a layer of metal atoms. Compare with **transmission electron microscope**.

**scarify** To scrape, rasp, cut, or otherwise damage the coat of a seed. Necessary in some species to trigger germination.

**Schwann cell** A type of glial cell that wraps around axons of some neurons outside the brain and spinal cord, forming a myelin sheath that provides electrical insulation. Compare with **oligodendrocyte**.

**scientific name** The unique, two-part name given to each species, with a genus name followed by a species name—as in *Homo sapiens*. Scientific names are always italicized, and are also known as Latin names.

**sclereid** In plants, a relatively short type of sclerenchyma cell that usually functions in protection, such as in seed coats and nutshells. Compare with **fiber**.

**sclerenchyma cell** In plants, a cell that has a thick secondary cell wall and provides support; typically contains the tough structural polymer lignin and usually is dead at maturity. Includes fibers and sclereids. Compare with **collenchyma cell** and **parenchyma cell**.

**scrotum** A sac of skin containing the testes and suspended just outside the abdominal body cavity of many male mammals.

**second law of thermodynamics** The principle of physics that the entropy of the universe or any closed system always increases.

**second-male advantage** The reproductive advantage, in some species, of a male who mates with a female last, after other males have mated with her.

**second messenger** A nonprotein signaling molecule produced or activated inside a cell in response to stimulation at the cell surface. Commonly used to relay the message of a hormone or other extracellular signaling molecule.

**secondary active transport** Transport of an ion or molecule in a defined direction that is often against its electrochemical gradient, in company with an ion or molecule being transported along its electrochemical gradient. Also called *cotransport*.

**secondary cell wall** The thickened inner layer of a plant cell wall formed by certain cells as they mature and have stopped growing; in water-conducting cells, contains lignin. Provides support or protection.

**secondary consumer** A carnivore; an organism that eats herbivores. Compare with **primary consumer**.

**secondary growth** In plants, an increase in the width of stems and roots due to the activity of cambium. Compare with **primary growth**.

**secondary immune response** The adaptive immune response to a pathogen that the immune system has encountered before. Normally much faster and more efficient than the primary response, due to immunological memory. Compare with **primary immune response**.

**secondary metabolites** Molecules that are closely related to compounds in key synthetic pathways and that often function in defense.

**secondary oocyte** A cell produced by meiosis I of a primary oocyte in the ovary. If fertilized, will complete meiosis II to produce an ootid (which develops into an ovum) and a polar body.

**secondary spermatocyte** A cell produced by meiosis I of a primary spermatocyte in the testis. Can undergo meiosis II to produce spermatids.

**secondary structure** In proteins, localized folding of a polypeptide chain into regular structures (i.e., alpha-helix and beta-pleated sheet) stabilized by hydrogen bonding between atoms of the peptide backbone. In nucleic acids, elements of structure (e.g., helices and hairpins) stabilized by hydrogen bonding and hydrophobic interactions between complementary bases. Compare with **primary**, **tertiary**, and **quaternary structures**.

**secondary succession** Gradual colonization of a habitat after an environmental disturbance (e.g., fire, windstorm, logging) that removes some or all previous organisms but leaves the soil intact. Compare with **primary succession**.

**secretin** A peptide hormone produced by cells in the small intestine in response to the arrival of food from the stomach. Stimulates secretion of bicarbonate ($HCO_3^-$) from the pancreas.

**sedimentary rock** A type of rock formed by gradual accumulation of sediment, particularly sand and mud, as in riverbeds and on the ocean floor. Most fossils are found in sedimentary rocks.

**seed** A plant reproductive structure consisting of an embryo, associated nutritive tissue (endosperm), and an outer protective layer (seed coat). In angiosperms, develops from the fertilized ovule of a flower.

**seed bank** A repository where seeds, representing many different varieties of domestic crops or other species, are preserved.

**seed coat** A protective layer around a seed that encases both the embryo and the endosperm.

**segment** A well-defined, repeated region of the body along the anterior–posterior body axis, containing structures similar to other nearby segments.

**segmentation** Division of the body or a part of it into a series of similar structures; exemplified by the body segments of insects and worms and by the somites of vertebrates.

**segmentation genes** A group of genes that control the formation and patterning of body segmentation in embryonic development. Includes maternal genes, gap genes, pair-rule genes, and segment polarity genes.

**segregation, principle of** The concept that each pair of hereditary elements (alleles of the same gene) separate from each other during meiosis. One of Mendel's two principles of genetics.

**selective adhesion** The tendency of cells of one tissue type to adhere to other cells of the same type.

**selective permeability** The property of a membrane that allows some substances to diffuse across it much more readily than other substances.

**selectively permeable membrane** Any membrane across which some solutes can move more readily than others.

**self-fertilization** The fusion of two gametes from the same individual to form offspring. Also called *selfing*.

**self molecule** A molecule that is synthesized by an organism and is a normal part of its cells and/or body; as opposed to nonself, or foreign, molecules.

**semen** The combination of sperm and accessory fluids that is released by male mammals and reptiles during ejaculation.

**semiconservative replication** The way DNA replicates, in which each strand of an existing DNA molecule serves as a template to create a new complementary DNA strand. It is called semiconservative because each newly replicated DNA molecule conserves one of the parental strands and contains another, newly replicated strand.

**seminal vesicle** In male mammals, either of a pair of reproductive glands that secrete a sugar-containing fluid into semen, which provides energy for sperm movement.

**senescence** The genetically programmed, active process of aging.

**sensor** Any cell, organ, or structure with which an animal can sense some aspect of the external or internal environment. Usually functions, along with an integrator and effector, as part of a homeostatic system.

**sensory neuron** A nerve cell that carries signals from sensory receptors to the central nervous system. Compare with **interneuron** and **motor neuron**.

**sepal** One of the protective leaflike organs enclosing a flower bud and later part of the outermost portion of the flower.

**septum** (plural: septa) Any wall-like structure. In fungi, septa divide the filaments (hyphae) of mycelia into cell-like compartments.

**serotonin** A neurotransmitter involved in many brain functions, including sleep, pleasure, and mood.

**serum** The liquid that remains when cells and clot material are removed from clotted blood. Contains water, dissolved gases, growth factors, nutrients, and other soluble substances. Compare with **plasma**.

**sessile** Permanently attached to a substrate; not capable of moving to another location.

**set point** A normal or target value for a regulated internal variable, such as body heat or blood pH.

**sex chromosome** Chromosomes that differ in shape or in number in males and females. For example, the X and Y chromosomes of many animals. Compare with **autosome**.

**sex-linked inheritance** Inheritance patterns observed in genes carried on sex chromosomes. In this case, females and males have different numbers of alleles of a gene. Often creates situations in which a trait appears more often in one sex. Also called *sex-linkage*.

**sexual dimorphism** Any trait that differs between males and females.

**sexual reproduction** Any form of reproduction in which genes from two parents are combined via fusion of gametes, producing offspring that are genetically distinct from both parents. Compare with **asexual reproduction**.

**sexual selection** A type of natural selection that favors individuals with traits that increase their ability to obtain mates. Acts more strongly on males than females. (Compare with **ecological selection**.)

**shell** A hard, protective outer structure.

**Shine–Dalgarno sequence** See **ribosome binding sequence**.

**shoot** In a plant embryo, the combination of hypocotyl and cotyledons, which will become the aboveground portions of the plant.

**shoot apical meristem (SAM)** A group of undifferentiated plant stem cells at the tip of a plant stem that can differentiate into mature shoot tissues.

**shoot system** The aboveground part of a plant comprising stems, leaves, and flowers (in angiosperms).

**short-day plant** A plant that blooms in response to long nights (usually in late summer or fall in the Northern Hemisphere). Compare with **day-neutral** and **long-day plant**.

**short tandem repeats (STRs)** Relatively short DNA sequences that are repeated, one after another, down the length of a chromosome. See **microsatellite**.

**shotgun sequencing** A method of sequencing genomes that is based on breaking the genome into small pieces, sequencing each piece separately, and then figuring out how the pieces are connected.

**sieve plate** In plants, a pore-containing structure at each end of a sieve-tube element in phloem.

**sieve-tube element** In plants, an elongated sugar-conducting cell in phloem that lacks nuclei and has sieve plates at both ends, allowing sap to flow to adjacent cells.

**sigma** A bacterial protein that associates with the core RNA polymerase to allow recognition of promoters.

**signal** In behavioral ecology, any information-containing behavior or characteristic.

**signal receptor** Any cellular protein that binds to a particular signaling molecule (e.g., a hormone or neurotransmitter) and triggers a response by the cell. Receptors for lipid-insoluble signals are transmembrane proteins in the plasma membrane; those for many lipid-soluble signals (e.g., steroid hormones) are located inside the cell.

**signal recognition particle (SRP)** An RNA–protein complex that binds to the ER signal sequence in a polypeptide as it emerges from a ribosome and transports the ribosome–polypeptide complex to the ER membrane, where synthesis of the polypeptide is completed.

**signal transduction** The process by which a stimulus (e.g., a hormone, a neurotransmitter, or sensory information) outside a cell is converted into an intracellular signal required for a cellular response. Usually involves a specific sequence of molecular events, or signal transduction pathway, that may lead to amplification of the signal.

**signal transduction cascade** See **phosphorylation cascade**.

**silencer** A regulatory sequence in eukaryotic DNA to which repressor proteins can bind, inhibiting gene transcription.

**silent mutation** A point mutation that changes the sequence of a codon without changing the amino acid that is specified.

**simple eye** An eye with only one light-collecting apparatus (e.g., one lens), as in vertebrates and cephalopods. Compare with **compound eye**.

**simple fruit** A fruit (e.g., apricot) that develops from a single flower that has a single carpel or several fused carpels. Compare with **aggregate** and **multiple fruit**.

**simple sequence repeat** See **microsatellite**.

**SINEs (short interspersed nuclear elements)** The second most abundant class of transposable elements in human genomes; can create copies of itself and insert them elsewhere in the genome. Compare with **LINEs**.

**single nucleotide polymorphism (SNP)** A site on a chromosome where individuals in a population have different nucleotides. Can be used as a genetic marker to help track the inheritance of nearby genes.

**single-strand DNA-binding proteins (SSBP)** A protein that attaches to separated strands of DNA during replication or transcription, preventing them from re-forming a double helix.

**sink** Any tissue, site, or location where an element or a molecule is consumed or taken out of circulation (e.g., in plants, a tissue where sugar exits the phloem). Compare with **source**.

**sinoatrial (SA) node** In the right atrium of the vertebrate heart, a cluster of cardiac muscle cells that initiates the heartbeat and determines the heart rate. Compare with **atrioventricular (AV) node**.

**siphon** A tubelike appendage of many mollusks, often used for feeding or propulsion.

**sister chromatids** The paired strands of a recently replicated chromosome, which are connected at the centromere and eventually separate during anaphase of mitosis and meiosis II. Compare with **non-sister chromatids**.

**sister species** Closely related species that occupy adjacent branches in a phylogenetic tree.

**skeletal muscle** The muscle tissue attached to the bones of the vertebrate skeleton. Consists of long, unbranched muscle fibers with a characteristic striped (striated) appearance; controlled voluntarily. Compare with **cardiac** and **smooth muscle**.

**sliding-filament model** The hypothesis that thin (actin) filaments and thick (myosin) filaments slide past each other, thereby shortening the sarcomere. Shortening of all the sarcomeres in a myofibril results in contraction of the entire myofibril.

**slow muscle fiber** Type of skeletal muscle fiber that is red in color due to the abundance of myoglobin, ates ATP by oxidative phosphorylation, and c...cts slowly but does not fatigue easily. Also ca... *slow oxidative*, or *Type I, fiber*.

**small intestine** The portion of the digestive tract between the stomach and the large intestine. The site of the final stages of digestion and of most nutrient absorption.

**small nuclear ribonucleoproteins** See **snRNPs**.

**smooth endoplasmic reticulum (smooth ER)** The portion of the endoplasmic reticulum that does not have ribosomes attached to it. Involved in synthesis and secretion of lipids. Compare with **rough endoplasmic reticulum**.

**smooth muscle** The unstriated muscle tissue that lines the intestine, blood vessels, and some other organs. Consists of tapered, unbranched cells that can sustain long contractions. Not voluntarily controlled. Compare with **cardiac** and **skeletal muscle**.

**snRNPs (small nuclear ribonucleoproteins)** Complexes of proteins and small RNA molecules that function as components of spliceosomes during splicing (removal of introns from pre-mRNAs).

**sodium–potassium pump** A transmembrane protein that uses the energy of ATP to move sodium ions out of the cell and potassium ions in. Also called $Na^+/K^+$-ATPase.

**soil organic matter** Organic (carbon-containing) compounds found in soil.

**solute** Any substance that is dissolved in a liquid.

**solute potential ($\psi_S$)** A component of the potential energy of water caused by a difference in solute concentrations at two locations. Can be zero (pure water) or negative. Compare with **pressure potential ($\psi_P$)**.

**solution** A liquid containing one or more dissolved solids or gases in a homogeneous mixture.

**solvent** Any liquid in which one or more solids or gases can dissolve.

**soma** See **cell body**.

**somatic cell** Any type of cell in a multicellular organism except eggs, sperm, and their precursor cells. Also called *body cells*.

**somatic hypermutation** Mutation that occurs in the variable regions of immunoglobulin genes when B cells are first activated and in memory cells, resulting in novel variation in the receptors that bind to antigens.

**somatic nervous system** The part of the peripheral nervous system (outside the brain and spinal cord) that controls skeletal muscles and is under voluntary control. Compare with **autonomic nervous system**.

**somatostatin** A hormone secreted by the pancreas and hypothalamus that inhibits the release of several other hormones.

**somite** A block of mesoderm that occurs in pairs along both sides of the developing neural tube in a vertebrate embryo. Gives rise to muscle, vertebrae, ribs, and the dermis of the skin.

**sori** In ferns, a cluster of spore-producing structures (sporangia) usually found on the underside of fronds.

**source** Any tissue, site, or location where a substance is produced or enters circulation (e.g., in plants, the tissue where sugar enters the phloem). Compare with **sink**.

**space-filling model** A representation of a molecule where atoms are shown as balls—color-coded and scaled to indicate the atom's identify—attached to each other in the correct geometry.

**speciation** The evolution of two or more distinct species from a single ancestral species.

**species** An evolutionarily independent population or group of populations. Generally distinct from other species in appearance, behavior, habitat, ecology, genetic characteristics, and so on.

**species–area relationship** The mathematical relationship between the area of a certain habitat and the number of species that it can support.

**species diversity** The variety and relative abundance of the species present in a given ecological community.

**species richness** The number of species present in a given ecological community.

**specific heat** The amount of energy required to raise the temperature of 1 gram of a substance by 1°C; a measure of the capacity of a substance to absorb energy.

**sperm** A mature male gamete; smaller and more mobile than the female gamete.

**sperm competition** Competition between the sperm of different males to fertilize eggs inside the same female.

**spermatid** An immature sperm cell.

**spermatogenesis** The production of sperm. Occurs continuously in a testis.

**spermatogonium** (plural: spermatogonia) Any of the diploid cells in a testis that can give rise to primary spermatocytes.

**spermatophore** A gelatinous package containing sperm cells that is produced by males of species that have internal fertilization without copulation.

**sphincter** A muscular valve that can close off a tube, as in a blood vessel or a part of the digestive tract.

**spicule** Stiff spike of silica or calcium carbonate that provides structural support in the body of many sponges.

**spindle apparatus** The array of microtubules responsible for moving chromosomes during mitosis and meiosis; includes kinetochore microtubules, polar microtubules, and astral microtubules.

**spines** In plants, modified leaves that are stiff and sharp and that function in defense.

**spiracle** In insects, a small opening that connects air-filled tracheae to the external environment, allowing for gas exchange.

**spleen** A dark red organ, found near the stomach of most vertebrates, that filters blood, stores extra red blood cells in case of emergency, and plays a role in immunity.

**spliceosome** In eukaryotes, a large, complex assembly of snRNPs (small nuclear ribonucleoproteins) that catalyzes removal of introns from primary RNA transcripts.

**splicing** The process by which introns are removed from primary RNA transcripts and the remaining exons are connected together.

**sporangium** (plural: sporangia) A spore-producing structure found in seed plants, some protists, and some fungi (e.g., chytrids).

**spore** (1) In bacteria, a dormant form that generally is resistant to extreme conditions. (2) In eukaryotes, a single haploid cell produced by mitosis or meiosis (not by fusion of gametes) that is capable of developing into an adult organism.

**sporophyte** In organisms undergoing alternation of generations, the multicellular diploid form that arises from two fused gametes and produces haploid spores. Compare with **gametophyte**.

**sporopollenin** A watertight material that encases spores and pollen of modern land plants.

**stabilizing selection** A mode of natural selection that favors phenotypes near the middle of the range of phenotypic variation. Reduces overall genetic variation in a population. Compare with **disruptive selection** and **directional selection**.

**stamen** The male reproductive structure of a flower. Consists of an anther, in which pollen grains are produced, and a filament, which supports the anther. Compare with **carpel**.

**standing defense** See **constitutive defense**.

**stapes** The last of three small bones (ossicles) in the middle ear of vertebrates. Receives vibrations from the tympanic membrane and by vibrating against the oval window passes them to the cochlea.

**starch** A mixture of two storage polysaccharides, amylose and amylopectin, both formed from $\alpha$-glucose monomers. Amylopectin is branched, and amylose is unbranched. The major form of stored carbohydrate in plants.

**start codon** The AUG triplet in mRNA at which protein synthesis begins; codes for the amino acid methionine.

**statocyst** A sensory organ of many arthropods that detects the animal's orientation in space (e.g., whether the animal is flipped upside down).

**statolith** A tiny stone or dense particle found in specialized gravity-sensing organs in some animals such as lobsters, and in gravity-sensing tissues of plants.

**statolith hypothesis** The hypothesis that amyloplasts (dense, starch-storing plant organelles) serve as statoliths in gravity detection by plants.

**stem cell** Any relatively undifferentiated cell that can divide to produce a daughter cell that remains a stem cell and a daughter cell that can differentiate into specific cell types.

**stems** Vertical, aboveground structures that make up the shoot system of plants.

**stereocilium** (plural: stereocilia) One of many stiff outgrowths from the surface of a hair cell that are involved in detection of sound by terrestrial vertebrates or of waterborne vibrations by fishes.

**steroid** A class of lipid with a characteristic four-ring hydrocarbon structure.

**sticky ends** The short, single-stranded ends of a DNA molecule cut by a restriction endonuclease. Tend to form hydrogen bonds with other sticky ends that have complementary sequences.

**stigma** The sticky tip at the end of a flower carpel to which pollen grains adhere.

**stolon** A modified stem that runs horizontally over the soil surface and produces new plants at the nodes (a form of asexual reproduction). Compare with **rhizome**.

**stoma** (plural: stomata) Generally, a pore or opening. In plants, a microscopic pore, surrounded by specialized cells that open the pore, on the surface of a leaf or stem through which gas exchange occurs. See also **guard cells**.

**stomach** A tough, muscular pouch in the vertebrate digestive tract between the esophagus and small intestine. Physically breaks up food and begins digestion of proteins.

**stop codon** Any of three mRNA triplets (UAG, UGA, or UAA) that cause termination of protein synthesis. Also called a *termination codon*.

**strain** The lowest, most specific level of taxonomy that refers to a population of individuals that are genetically very similar or identical.

**striated muscle** Muscle tissue containing protein filaments organized into repeating structures that give the cells and tissues a banded appearance.

**stroma** The fluid matrix of a chloroplast in which the thylakoids are embedded. Site where the Calvin cycle reactions occur.

**structural formula** A two-dimensional notation in which the chemical symbols for the constituent atoms are joined by straight lines representing single (–), double (=), or triple (≡) covalent bonds. Compare with **molecular formula**.

**structural homology** Similarities in adult organismal structures (e.g., limbs, shells, flowers) that are due to inheritance from a common ancestor.

**style** The slender stalk of a flower carpel connecting the stigma and the ovary.

**suberin** Waxy substance found in the cell walls of cork tissue and in the Casparian strip of endodermal cells.

**subspecies** A population that has distinctive traits and some genetic differences relative to other populations of the same species but that is not distinct enough to be classified as a separate species.

**substrate** (1) A reactant that interacts with a catalyst, such as an enzyme or ribozyme, in a chemical reaction. (2) A surface on which a cell or organism sits.

**substrate-level phosphorylation** Production of ATP or GTP by the transfer of a phosphate group from an intermediate substrate directly to ADP or GDP. Occurs in glycolysis and in the citric acid cycle.

**succession** In ecology, the gradual colonization of a habitat after an environmental disturbance (e.g., fire, flood), usually by a series of species. See **primary** and **secondary succession**.

**sucrose** A disaccharide formed from glucose and fructose. One of the two main products of photosynthesis.

**sugar** Synonymous with carbohydrate, though usually used in an informal sense to refer to small carbohydrates (monosaccharides and disaccharides).

**summation** The additive effect of different postsynaptic potentials on a nerve or muscle cell, such that several subthreshold stimulations can cause or inhibit an action potential.

**supporting connective tissue** A type of connective tissue distinguished by having a firm extracellular matrix. Includes bone and cartilage.

**surface metabolism model** Hypothetical explanation for chemical evolution whereby small molecules reacted with one another through catalytic activity associated with a surface, such as the mineral deposits found in deep-sea hydrothermal vents.

**surface tension** The cohesive force that causes molecules at the surface of a liquid to stick together, thereby resisting deformation of the liquid's surface and minimizing its surface area.

**survivorship** On average, the proportion of offspring that survive to a particular age.

**survivorship curve** A graph depicting the percentage of a population that survives to different ages.

**suspension feeder** Any organism that obtains food by filtering small particles or small organisms out of water or air. Also called *filter feeder*.

**sustainability** The planned use of environmental resources at a rate no faster than the rate at which they are naturally replaced.

**sustainable agriculture** Agricultural techniques that are designed to maintain long-term soil quality and productivity.

**swamp** A wetland that has a steady rate of water flow and is dominated by trees and shrubs.

**swim bladder** A gas-filled organ of many ray-finned fishes that regulates buoyancy.

**symbiosis** (adjective: symbiotic) Any close and prolonged physical relationship between individuals of two different species. See **commensalism**, **mutualism**, and **parasitism**.

**symmetric competition** Ecological competition between two species in which both suffer similar declines in fitness. Compare with **asymmetric competition**.

**sympathetic nervous system** The part of the autonomic nervous system that stimulates fight-or-flight responses, such as increased heart rate, increased blood pressure, and decreased digestion. Compare with **parasympathetic nervous system**.

**sympatric speciation** The divergence of populations living within the same geographic area into different species as the result of their genetic (not physical) isolation. Compare with **allopatric speciation**.

**sympatry** Condition in which two or more populations live in the same geographic area, or close enough to permit interbreeding. Compare with **allopatry**.

**symplast** In plants, the space inside the plasma membranes. The symplast of adjacent cells is often connected through plasmodesmata. Compare with **apoplast**.

**symporter** A cotransport protein that allows an ion to diffuse down an electrochemical gradient, using the energy of that process to transport a different substance in the same direction *against* its concentration gradient. Compare with **antiporter**.

**synapomorphy** A shared, derived trait found in two or more taxa that is present in their most recent common ancestor but is missing in more

distant ancestors. Useful for inferring evolutionary relationships.

**synapse** The interface between two neurons or between a neuron and an effector cell.

**synapsis** The physical pairing of two homologous chromosomes during prophase I of meiosis. Crossing over is observed during synapsis.

**synaptic cleft** The space between two communicating nerve cells (or between a neuron and effector cell) at a synapse, across which neurotransmitters diffuse.

**synaptic plasticity** Long-term changes in the responsiveness or physical structure of a synapse that can occur after particular stimulation patterns. Thought to be the basis of learning and memory.

**synaptic vesicle** A small neurotransmitter-containing vesicle at the end of an axon that releases neurotransmitter into the synaptic cleft by exocytosis.

**synaptonemal complex** A network of proteins that holds non-sister chromatids together during synapsis in meiosis I.

**synthesis (S) phase** The phase of the cell cycle during which DNA is synthesized and chromosomes are replicated.

**system** A defined set of interacting chemical components under observation.

**systemic acquired resistance (SAR)** A slow, widespread response of plants to a localized infection that protects healthy tissue from invasion by pathogens. Compare with **hypersensitive response**.

**systemic circulation** The part of the circulatory system that sends oxygen-rich blood from the lungs out to the rest of the body. It is separate from the pulmonary circulation in mammals and birds.

**systemin** A peptide hormone, produced by plant cells damaged by herbivores, that initiates a protective response in undamaged cells.

**systems biology** The study of the structure of networks and how interactions between individual network components such as genes or proteins can lead to emergent biological properties.

**systole** The portion of the cardiac cycle during which the heart muscles are contracting. Compare with **diastole**.

**systolic blood pressure** The force exerted by blood against artery walls during contraction of the heart's left ventricle. Compare with **diastolic blood pressure**.

**T cell** A type of lymphocyte that matures in the thymus and, with B cells, is responsible for adaptive immunity. Involved in activation of B cells ($CD4^+$ helper T cells) and destruction of infected cells ($CD8^+$ cytotoxic T cells). Also called *T lymphocytes*.

**T-cell receptor (TCR)** A type of transmembrane protein found on T cells that can bind to antigens displayed on the surfaces of other cells. Composed of two polypeptides, called the alpha chain and beta chain, that consist of variable and constant regions. See **antigen presentation**.

**T tubule** Any of the membranous tubes that extend into the interior of muscle cells, propagating action

**...ntials** throughout the cell and triggering release ...rium from the sarcoplasmic reticulum.

**tag...a** (singular: tagma) Prominent body regions in arthropods, such as the head, thorax, and abdomen in insects.

**taiga** A vast forest biome throughout subarctic regions, consisting primarily of short coniferous trees. Characterized by intensely cold winters, short summers, and high annual variation in temperature.

**taproot** A large, vertical main root of a plant's root system.

**taste bud** A sensory structure, found chiefly in the mammalian tongue, containing spindle-shaped cells that respond to chemical stimuli.

**TATA-binding protein (TBP)** A protein that binds to the TATA box in eukaryotic promoters and is a component of the basal transcription complex.

**TATA box** A short DNA sequence in many eukaryotic promoters about 30 base pairs upstream from the transcription start site.

**taxon** (plural: taxa) Any named group of organisms at any level of a classification system.

**taxonomy** The branch of biology concerned with the classification and naming of organisms.

**tectorial membrane** A membrane, located in the vertebrate cochlea, that takes part in the transduction of sound by bending the stereocilia of hair cells in response to sonic vibrations.

**telomerase** An enzyme that adds DNA to the ends of chromosomes (telomeres) by catalyzing DNA synthesis from an RNA template that is part of the enzyme.

**telomere** The end of a linear chromosome that contains a repeated sequence of DNA.

**telophase** The final stage in mitosis or meiosis during which daughter chromosomes (homologous chromosomes in meiosis I) have separated and new nuclear envelopes begin to form around each set of chromosomes.

**temperate** Having a climate with pronounced annual fluctuations in temperature (i.e., warm summers and cold winters) but typically neither as hot as the tropics nor as cold as the poles.

**temperature** A measurement of thermal energy present in an object or substance, reflecting how much the constituent molecules are moving.

**template strand** An original nucleic acid strand used to make a new, complementary copy based on hydrogen bonding between nitrogeneous bases.

**temporal lobe** In the vertebrate brain, one of the four major areas in the cerebrum.

**tendon** A band of tough, fibrous connective tissue that connects a muscle to a bone.

**tentacle** A long, thin, muscular appendage typically used for feeling and feeding. Occurs in different forms in diverse animals such as cephalopod mollusks and sea anemones.

**termination** (1) In enzyme-catalyzed reactions, the final stage in which the enzyme returns to its original conformation and products are released. (2) In transcription, the dissociation of RNA polymerase from DNA. (3) In translation, the dissociation of a ribosome from mRNA when it reaches a stop codon.

**territory** An area that is actively defended by an animal from others of its species and that provides exclusive or semi-exclusive use of its resources by the owner.

**tertiary consumers** In a food chain or food web, organisms that feed on secondary consumers. Compare with **primary consumer** and **secondary consumer**.

**tertiary structure** The overall three-dimensional shape of a single polypeptide chain, resulting from multiple interactions among the amino acid side chains and the peptide backbone. In single-stranded nucleic acids, the three-dimensional shape is formed by hydrogen bonding and hydrophobic interactions between complementary bases. Compare with **primary**, **secondary**, and **quaternary structure**.

**testcross** The breeding of an individual that expresses a dominant phenotype but has an unknown genotype with an individual having only recessive alleles for the traits of interest. Used to order to infer the unknown genotype from observation of the phenotypes seen in offspring.

**testis** (plural: testes) The sperm-producing organ of a male animal.

**testosterone** A steroid hormone, produced and secreted by the testes, that stimulates sperm production and various male traits and reproductive behaviors.

**tetrad** The structure formed by synapsed homologous chromosomes during prophase of meiosis I. Also known as a *bivalent*.

**tetrapod** Any member of the lineage that includes all vertebrates with two pairs of limbs (amphibians, mammals, and reptiles, including birds).

**texture** A quality of soil, resulting from the relative abundance of different-sized particles.

**theory** An explanation for a broad class of phenomena that is supported by a wide body of evidence. A theory serves as a framework for the development of new hypotheses.

**thermal energy** The kinetic energy of molecular motion.

**thermocline** A steep gradient (cline) in environmental temperature, such as occurs in a thermally stratified lake or ocean.

**thermophile** A bacterium or archaean that thrives in very hot environments.

**thermoreception** A sensory system in which receptors are activated by changes in heat energy.

**thermoreceptor** A sensory cell or an organ specialized for detection of changes in temperature.

**thermoregulation** Regulation of body temperature.

**thick filament** A filament composed of bundles of the motor protein myosin; anchored to the center of the sarcomere. Compare with **thin filament**.

**thigmotropism** Growth or movement of an organism in response to contact with a solid object.

**thin filament** A filament composed of two coiled chains of actin and associated regulatory proteins; anchored at the Z disk of the sarcomere. Compare with **thick filament**.

**thorax** A region of the body; in insects, one of the three prominent body regions, along with the head and abdomen, called tagmata.

**thorn** A modified plant stem shaped as a sharp, protective structure. Helps protect a plant against feeding by herbivores.

**threshold potential** The membrane potential that will trigger an action potential in a neuron or other excitable cell. Also called simply *threshold*.

**thylakoid** A membrane-bound network of flattened sac-like structures inside a plant chloroplast that functions in converting light energy to chemical energy. A stack of thylakoid discs is a granum.

**thymus** An organ, located in the anterior chest or neck of vertebrates, in which immature T cells that originated in the bone marrow undergo maturation.

**thyroid gland** A gland in the neck that releases thyroid hormone (which increases metabolic rate) and calcitonin (which lowers blood calcium).

**thyroid hormones** Either of two hormones, triiodothyronine ($T_3$) or thyroxine ($T_4$), produced by the thyroid gland. See **triiodothyronine** and **thyroxine**.

**thyroid-stimulating hormone (TSH)** A peptide hormone, produced and secreted by the anterior pituitary, that stimulates release of thyroid hormones from the thyroid gland.

**thyroxine ($T_4$)** A lipid-soluble hormone, derived from the amino acid tyrosine, containing four iodine atoms and produced and secreted by the thyroid gland. Acts primarily to increase cellular metabolism. In mammals, $T_4$ is converted to the more active hormone triiodothyronine ($T_3$) in the liver.

**Ti plasmid** A plasmid carried by *Agrobacterium* (a bacterium that infects plants) that can integrate into a plant cell's chromosomes and induce formation of a gall.

**tight junction** A type of cell–cell attachment structure that links the plasma membranes of adjacent animal cells, forming a barrier that restricts movement of substances in the space between the cells. Most abundant in epithelia (e.g., the intestinal lining). Compare with **desmosome** and **gap junction**.

**tip** The end of a branch on a phylogenetic tree. Represents a specific species or larger taxon that has not (yet) produced descendants—either a group living today or a group that ended in extinction. Also called *terminal node*.

**tissue** A group of cells that function as a unit, such as muscle tissue in an animal or xylem tissue in a plant.

**tolerance** In ecological succession, the phenomenon in which early-arriving species do not affect the probability that subsequent species will become established. Compare with **facilitation** and **inhibition**.

**tonoplast** The membrane surrounding a plant vacuole.

**tool-kit genes** A set of key developmental genes that establishes the body plan of animals and plants; present at the origin of the multicellular lineages and elaborated upon over evolutionary time by a process of duplication and divergence. Includes *Hox* genes.

**top-down control** The hypothesis that population size is limited by predators or herbivores (consumers).

**topoisomerase** An enzyme that prevents the twisting of DNA ahead of the advancing replication fork by cutting the DNA, allowing it to unwind, and rejoining it.

**torpor** An energy-conserving physiological state, marked by a decrease in metabolic rate, body temperature, and activity, that lasts for a short period (overnight to a few days or weeks). Occurs in some small mammals when the ambient temperature drops significantly. Compare with **hibernation**.

**totipotent** Capable of dividing and developing to form a complete, mature organism.

**toxin** A poison produced by a living organism, such as a plant, animal, or microorganism.

**trachea** (plural: tracheae) (1) In insects, any of the small air-filled tubes that extend throughout the body and function in gas exchange. (2) In terrestrial vertebrates, the airway connecting the larynx to the bronchi. Also called *windpipe*.

**tracheid** In vascular plants, a long, thin, water-conducting cell that has pits where its lignin-containing secondary cell wall is absent, allowing water movement between adjacent cells. Compare with **vessel element**.

**trade-off** In evolutionary biology, an inescapable compromise between two traits that cannot be optimized simultaneously. Also called *fitness trade-off*.

**trait** Any observable characteristic of an individual.

**transcription** The process that uses a DNA template to produce a complementary RNA.

**transcription factor** General term for a protein that binds to a DNA regulatory sequence to influence transcription. It includes both regulatory and basal transcription factors.

**transcriptional activator** A eukaryotic regulatory transcription factor that binds to regulatory DNA sequences in enhancers or promoter-proximal elements to promote the initiation of transcription.

**transcriptional control** Regulation of gene expression by various mechanisms that change the rate at which genes are transcribed to form messenger RNA. In negative control, binding of a regulatory protein to DNA represses transcription; in positive control, binding of a regulatory protein to DNA promotes transcription.

**transcriptome** The complete set of genes transcribed in a particular cell.

**transduction** The conversion of information from one mode to another. For example, the process by which a stimulus outside a cell is converted into a response by the cell.

**transfer RNA (tRNA)** An RNA molecule that has an anticodon at one end and an amino acid attachment site at the other. Each tRNA carries a specific amino acid and binds to the corresponding codon in messenger RNA during translation.

**transformation** (1) Incorporation of external DNA into a cell. Occurs naturally in some bacteria; can be induced in the laboratory. (2) Conversion of a normal mammalian cell to one that divides uncontrollably.

**transgenic** A plant or animal whose genome contains DNA introduced from another individual, often from a different species.

**transition state** A high-energy intermediate state of the reactants during a chemical reaction that must be

achieved for the reaction to proceed. Compare with **activation energy**.

**transitional feature** A trait that is intermediate between a condition observed in ancestral (older) species and the condition observed in derived (younger) species.

**translation** The process by which a polypeptide (a string of amino acids joined by peptide bonds) is synthesized from information in codons of messenger RNA.

**translational control** Regulation of gene expression by various mechanisms that alter the life span of messenger RNA or the efficiency of translation.

**translocation** (1) In plants, the movement of sugars and other organic nutrients through the phloem by bulk flow. (2) A type of mutation in which a piece of a chromosome moves to a nonhomologous chromosome. (3) The movement of a ribosome down a messenger RNA during translation.

**transmembrane protein** See **integral membrane protein**.

**transmission** The passage or transfer of (1) a disease from one individual to another or (2) electrical impulses from one neuron to another.

**transpiration** Loss of water vapor from aboveground plant parts. Occurs primarily through stomata.

**transporter** See **carrier protein**.

**transposable elements** Any of several kinds of DNA sequences that are capable of moving themselves, or copies of themselves, to other locations in the genome. Include LINEs and SINEs.

**tree of life** The phylogenetic tree that includes all organisms.

**trichome** A hairlike appendage that grows from epidermal cells in the shoot system of some plants. Trichomes exhibit a variety of shapes, sizes, and functions depending on species.

**triiodothyronine ($T_3$)** A lipid-soluble hormone, derived from the amino acid tyrosine, containing three iodine atoms and produced and secreted by the thyroid gland. Acts primarily to increase cellular metabolism. In mammals, $T_3$ has a stronger effect than does the related hormone thyroxine ($T_4$).

**triose** A monosaccharide (simple sugar) containing three carbon atoms.

**triplet code** A code in which a "word" of three letters encodes one piece of information. The genetic code is a triplet code because a codon is three nucleotides long and encodes one amino acid.

**triploblast** (adjective: triploblastic) An animal whose body develops from three basic embryonic cell layers or tissues: ectoderm, mesoderm, and endoderm. Compare with **diploblast**.

**trisomy** The state of having three copies of one particular type of chromosome in an otherwise diploid cell.

**tRNA** See **transfer RNA**.

**trochophore** A larva with a ring of cilia around its middle that is found in some lophotrochozoans.

**trophic cascade** A series of changes in the abundance of species in a food web, usually caused by the addition or removal of a key predator.

**trophic level** A feeding level in an ecosystem.

**trophoblast** The exterior of a blastocyst (the structure that results from cleavage in embryonic development of mammals).

**tropomyosin** A regulatory protein present in thin (actin) filaments that blocks the myosin-binding sites on these filaments in resting muscles, thereby preventing muscle contraction.

**troponin** A regulatory protein, present in thin (actin) filaments, that can move tropomyosin off the myosin-binding sites on these filaments, thereby triggering muscle contraction. Activated by high intracellular calcium.

**true navigation** The type of navigation by which an animal can reach a specific point on Earth's surface. Also called *map orientation*.

**trypsin** A protein-digesting enzyme present in the small intestine that activates several other protein-digesting enzymes.

**tube foot** One of the many small, mobile, fluid-filled extensions of the water vascular system of echinoderms; the part extending outside the body is called a podium, while the bulb within the body is the ampulla. Used in locomotion, feeding, and respiration.

**tuber** A modified plant rhizome that functions in storage of carbohydrates.

**tuberculosis** A disease of the lungs caused by infection with the bacterium *Mycobacterium tuberculosis*.

**tumor** A mass of cells formed by uncontrolled cell division. Can be benign or malignant.

**tumor suppressor** A protein (e.g., p53 or Rb) that prevents cell division, such as when the cell has DNA damage. Mutant genes that code for tumor suppressors are associated with cancer.

**tundra** The treeless biome in polar and alpine regions, characterized by short, slow-growing vegetation, permafrost, and a climate of long, intensely cold winters and very short summers.

**turbidity** Cloudiness of water caused by sediments and/or microscopic organisms.

**turgid** Swollen and firm as a result of high internal pressure (e.g., a plant cell containing enough water for the cytoplasm to press against the cell wall). Compare with **flaccid**.

**turgor pressure** The outward pressure exerted by the fluid contents of a living plant cell against its cell wall.

**turnover** In lake ecology, the complete mixing of upper and lower layers of water of different temperatures; occurs each spring and fall in temperate-zone lakes.

**tympanic membrane** The membrane separating the middle ear from the outer ear in terrestrial vertebrates, or similar structures in insects. Also called the *eardrum*.

**ubiquinone** See **coenzyme Q**.

**ulcer** A hole in an epithelial layer, exposing the underlying tissues to damage.

**ultimate causation** In biology, the reason that a trait or phenomenon is thought to have evolved; the adaptive advantage of that trait. Also called *ultimate explanation*. Compare with **proximate causation**.

**umami** The taste of glutamate, responsible for the "meaty" taste of most proteins and of monosodium glutamate.

**...ical cord** The cord that connects a develop-...mammalian embryo or fetus to the placenta and ...th which the embryo or fetus receives oxygen and nutrients.

**unequal crossover** An error in crossing over during meiosis I in which the two non-sister chromatids match up at different sites. Results in gene duplication in one chromatid and gene loss in the other.

**unsaturated** Referring to lipids in which at least one carbon-carbon bond is a double bond. Double bonds produce kinks in hydrocarbon chains and decrease the compound's melting point. Compare with **saturated**.

**upstream** In genetics, opposite to the direction in which RNA polymerase moves along a DNA strand. Compare with **downstream**.

**urea** The major nitrogenous waste of mammals, adult amphibains, and cartilaginous fishes. Compare with **ammonia** and **uric acid**.

**ureter** In vertebrates, a tube that transports urine from one kidney to the bladder.

**urethra** The tube that drains urine from the bladder to the outside environment. In male vertebrates, also used for passage of semen during ejaculation.

**uric acid** A whitish excretory product of birds, reptiles, and terrestrial arthropods. Used to remove from the body excess nitrogen derived from the breakdown of amino acids. Compare with **ammonia** and **urea**.

**urochordates** One of the three major chordate lineages (Urochordata), comprising sessile or floating, filter-feeding animals that have a polysaccharide covering (tunic) and two siphons through which water enters and exits; include tunicates and salps. Compare with **cephalochordates** and **vertebrates**.

**uterus** The organ in which developing embryos are housed in mammals and some other viviparous vertebrates.

**vaccination** Artificially producing immunological memory against a pathogen by using isolated antigens or altered versions of the pathogen to stimulate an adaptive immune response in the absence of disease.

**vaccine** A preparation designed to stimulate an immune response against a particular pathogen without causing illness. Vaccines consist of inactivated (killed) pathogens, live but weakened (attenuated) pathogens, or parts of a pathogen (subunit vaccine).

**vacuole** A large organelle in plant and fungal cells that usually is used for bulk storage of water, pigments, oils, or other substances. Some vacuoles contain enzymes and have a digestive function similar to lysosomes in animal cells.

**vagina** The birth canal of female mammals; a muscular tube that extends from the uterus through the pelvis to the exterior.

**valence** The number of unpaired electrons in the outermost electron shell of an atom; often determines how many covalent bonds the atom can form.

**valence electron** An electron in the outermost electron shell, the valence shell, of an atom. Valence electrons tend to be involved in chemical bonding.

**valence shell** The outermost electron shell of an atom.

**valve** In circulatory systems, any of the flaps of tissue that prevent backward flow of blood, particularly in veins and in the heart.

**van der Waals interactions** A weak electrical attraction between two nonpolar molecules that have been brought together through hydrophobic interactions. Often contributes to tertiary and quaternary structures in proteins.

**variable number tandem repeat** See **minisatellite**.

**variable (V) region** The amino acid sequence that changes in polypeptides used to make antibodies, B-cell receptors, and T-cell receptors, This portion of the protein is highly variable within an individual and forms the epitope-binding site. Compare with **constant (C) region**.

**vas deferens** (plural: vasa deferentia) A muscular tube that stores and transports semen from the epididymis to the ejaculatory duct. Also called the *ductus deferens*.

**vasa recta** In the vertebrate kidney, a network of blood vessels that runs alongside the loop of Henle of a nephron. Functions in reabsorption of water and solutes from the filtrate.

**vascular bundle** In a plant stem, a cluster of xylem and phloem strands that run the length of the stem.

**vascular cambium** One of two types of cylindrical meristem, consisting of a ring of undifferentiated plant cells in the stem and root of woody plants; produces secondary xylem (wood) and secondary phloem. Compare with **cork cambium**.

**vascular tissue** In plants, tissue that transports water, nutrients, and sugars. Made up of the complex tissues xylem and phloem, each of which contains several cell types. Also called *vascular tissue system*.

**vector** A biting insect or other organism that transfers pathogens from one species to another. See also **cloning vector**.

**vegetative development** The phase of plant development that involves growth and the the production of all plant structures except the flower.

**vein** Any blood vessel that carries blood (oxygenated or not) under relatively low pressure from the tissues toward the heart. Compare with **artery**.

**veliger** A distinctive type of larva, found in mollusks.

**vena cava** (plural: venae cavae) Either of two large veins that return oxygen-poor blood to the heart.

**ventral** Toward an animal's belly and away from its back. The opposite of dorsal.

**ventricle** (1) A thick-walled chamber of the heart that receives blood from an atrium and pumps it to the body or to the lungs. (2) Any of several small fluid-filled chambers in the vertebrate brain.

**venule** Any of the body's many small veins (blood vessels that return blood to the heart).

**vertebrae** (singular: vertebra) The cartilaginous or bony elements that form the backbones of vertebrate animals.

**vertebrates** One of the three major chordate lineages (Vertebrata), comprising animals with a dorsal column of cartilaginous or bony structures (vertebrae) and a skull enclosing the brain. Includes fishes, amphibians, mammals, and reptiles (including birds). Compare with **cephalochordates** and **urochordates**.

**vessel element** In vascular plants, a short, wide, water-conducting cell that has gaps through both the primary and secondary cell walls, allowing unimpeded passage of water between adjacent cells. Compare with **tracheid**.

**vestigial trait** A reduced or incompletely developed structure that has no function or reduced function, but is clearly similar to functioning organs or structures in closely related species.

**vicariance** The physical splitting of a population into smaller, isolated populations by a geographic barrier.

**villi** (singular: villus) Small, fingerlike projections (1) of the lining of the small intestine or (2) of the fetal portion of the placenta adjacent to maternal arteries. Function to increase the surface area available for absorption of nutrients and gas exchange.

**virion** The infectious extracellular particle that is produced from a viral infection; used for transmitting the virus between hosts. It consists of a DNA or RNA genome enclosed within a protein shell (capsid) that may be further enveloped in a phospholipid bilayer. Compare with **virus**.

**virulence** (adjective: virulent) Referring to the ability of pathogens to cause severe disease in susceptible hosts.

**virus** An obligate, intracellular parasite that is acellular, but uses host-cell biosynthetic machinery to replicate. Compare with **virion**.

**visceral mass** One of the three main parts of the mollusk body; contains most of the internal organs and external gill.

**visible light** The range of wavelengths of electromagnetic radiation that humans can see, from about 400 to 700 nanometers.

**vitamin** Any of various organic micronutrients that usually function as coenzymes.

**vitelline envelope** A fibrous sheet of glycoproteins that surrounds mature egg cells in many vertebrates. Surrounded by a thick gelatinous matrix (the jelly layer) in some aquatic species. In mammals, called the *zona pellucida*.

**viviparous** Producing live young (instead of eggs) that develop within the body of the mother before birth. Compare with **oviparous** and **ovoviviparous**.

**volt (V)** A unit of electrical potential (voltage).

**voltage** Potential energy created by a separation of electric charges between two points. Also called *electrical potential*.

**voltage clamping** A technique for imposing a constant membrane potential on a cell. Widely used to investigate ion channels.

**voltage-gated channel** An ion channel that opens or closes in response to changes in membrane voltage. Compare with **ligand-gated channel**.

**voluntary muscle** Muscle that contracts in response to stimulation by voluntary (somatic), but not involuntary (parasympathetic or sympathetic), neural stimulation.

**vomeronasal organ** A paired sensory organ, located in the nasal region, containing chemoreceptors that bind odorants and pheromones.

**wall pressure** The inward pressure exerted by a cell wall against the fluid contents of a living plant cell.

**Wallace line** A line in the Indonesian region that demarcates two areas, each of which is characterized by a distinct set of animal species.

**water potential (ψ)** The potential energy of water in a certain environment compared with the potential energy of pure water at room temperature and atmospheric pressure. In living organisms, ψ equals the solute potential ($\psi_S$) plus the pressure potential ($\psi_P$).

**water-potential gradient** A difference in water potential in one region compared with that in another region. Determines the direction that water moves, always from regions of higher water potential to regions of lower water potential.

**water table** The upper limit of the underground layer of soil that is saturated with water.

**water vascular system** In echinoderms, a system of fluid-filled tubes and chambers that functions as a hydrostatic skeleton.

**watershed** The area drained by a single stream or river.

**Watson–Crick pairing** See **complementary base pairing**.

**wavelength** The distance between two successive crests in any regular wave, such as light waves, sound waves, or waves in water.

**wax** A class of lipid with extremely long, saturated hydrocarbon tails. Harder and less greasy than fats.

**weather** The specific short-term atmospheric conditions of temperature, moisture, sunlight, and wind in a certain area.

**weathering** The gradual wearing down of large rocks by rain, running water, temperature changes, and wind; one of the processes that transform rocks into soil.

**weed** Any plant that is adapted for growth in disturbed soils.

**white blood cell** Any of several types of blood cells, including neutrophils, macrophages, and lymphocytes, that circulate in blood and lymph and function in defense against pathogens.

**wild type** The most common phenotype seen in a wild population.

**wildlife corridor** Strips of wildlife habitat connecting populations that otherwise would be isolated by human-made development.

**wilt** To lose turgor pressure in a plant tissue.

**wobble hypothesis** The hypothesis that some tRNA molecules can pair with more than one mRNA codon by tolerating some non-standard base pairing in the third base, so long as the first and second bases are correctly matched.

**wood** Xylem resulting from secondary growth; forms strong supporting material. Also called *secondary xylem*.

**worm** An animal with a long, thin, tubelike body lacking limbs.

**Woronin body** A dense organelle in certain fungi that plugs pores in damaged septa to prevent leakage of cytoplasm.

**X-linked inheritance** Inheritance patterns for genes located on the mammalian X chromosome. Also called *X-linkage*.

**X-ray crystallography** A technique for determining the three-dimensional structure of large molecules, including proteins and nucleic acids, by analysis of the diffraction patterns produced by X-rays beamed at crystals of the molecule.

**xenoestrogens** Foreign chemicals that bind to estrogen receptors or otherwise induce estrogen-like effects.

**xeroderma pigmentosum (XP)** A human disease characterized by extreme sensitivity to ultraviolet light. Caused by an autosomal recessive allele that inactivates the nucleotide excision DNA repair system.

**xylem** A plant vascular tissue that conducts water and ions; contains tracheids and/or vessel elements.

Primary xylem develops from the procambium of apical meristems; secondary xylem, or wood, from the vascular cambium. Compare with **phloem**.

**Y-linked inheritance** Inheritance patterns for genes located on the mammalian Y chromosome. Also called *Y-linkage*.

**yeast** Any fungus growing as a single-celled form. Also, a specific lineage of Ascomycota.

**yolk** The nutrient-rich cytoplasm inside an egg cell; used as food for the growing embryo.

**Z disk** The structure that forms each end of a sarcomere. Contains a protein that binds tightly to actin, thereby anchoring thin filaments.

**Z scheme** Model for changes in the potential energy of electrons as they pass from photosystem II to photosystem I and ultimately to NADP$^+$ during the light-dependent reactions of photosynthesis. See also **noncyclic electron flow**.

**zero population growth (ZPG)** A state of stable population size due to fertility staying at the replacement rate for at least one generation.

**zona pellucida** The gelatinous layer around a mammalian egg cell. In other vertebrates, called the *vitelline envelope*.

**zone of (cellular) division** In plant roots, a group of apical meristematic cells just behind the root cap where cells are actively dividing.

**zone of (cellular) elongation** In plant roots, a group of young cells, derived from primary meristem tissues and located behind the apical meristem, that are increasing in length.

**zone of (cellular) maturation** In plant roots, a group of plant cells, located several millimeters behind the root cap, that are differentiating into mature tissues.

**zygosporangium** (plural: zygosporangia) The distinctive spore-producing structure in fungi that are members of the Zygomycota.

**zygote** The cell formed by the union of two gametes; a fertilized egg.

# Credits

## Photo Credits

**Frontmatter** **Title page** Eric Isselée/Fotolia **p. iii** IFE, URI-IAO, UW, Lost City Science Party; NOAA/OAR/OER; The Lost City 2005 Expedition **p. v** R. B. Taylor/Photo Researchers, Inc. **p. vi** Brian Johnston **p. viii** Anthony Bannister/Photo Researchers, Inc. **p. x** Tim Laman/National Geographic Stock **p. xiii** Lee W. Wilcox **p. xiv** Steve Winter/National Geographic/Getty Images **p. xvi** Associated Press/Gerald Herbert **p. xviii (bottom left)** Natalie B. Fobes Photography

**Chapter 1** **Opener** Thierry Montford/Biosphoto/Photo Researchers Inc. **1.1a** Biophoto Associates/Photo Researchers, Inc. **1.1b** Brian J. Ford **1.1c** The Print Collector/Alamy **1.6a** Steve Gschmeissner/Photo Researchers, Inc. **1.6b** Kwangshin Kim/Photo Researchers, Inc. **1.7** Corbis Premium RF/Alamy **1.10** Reproduced with permission from H. Wolf. 2011. Odometry and Insect Navigation. *Journal of Experimental Biology* 214: 1629–1641.

**Chapter 2** **Opener** IFE, URI-IAO, UW, Lost City Science Party; NOAA/OAR/OER; The Lost City 2005 Expedition **2.1** Dragan Trifunovic/Shutterstock **2.6c** Zedcor Wholly Owned/Photos.com **2.11** LianeM/Alamy **2.15b** Dietmar Nill/Getty Images **2.15c** John Sylvester/First Light/AGE fotostock **2.29** picture-alliance/Judaica-Samml/Newscom

**Chapter 3** **3.9ab** Janice Carr, CDC

**Chapter 4** **Opener** SSPL/The Image Works **4.5** National Cancer Institute

**Chapter 5** **Opener** Peter Arnold/Alamy

**Chapter 6** **6.2a** Multiart/iStockphoto **6.2b** lepas2004/iStockphoto **6.2c** ilker canikligil/Shutterstock **6.6L** Dr. rer. nat. Markus Drechsler **6.15** Jack W. Szostak **6.18** Don W. Fawcett/Photo Researchers, Inc.

**Chapter 7** **Opener** Dr. Torsten Wittmann/SPL/Photo Researchers, Inc. **7.1** SPL/Photo Researchers, Inc. **7.2a** Gopal Murti/Photo Researchers, Inc. **7.2b** Biology Pics/Photo Researchers, Inc. **7.3** Eye of Science/Photo Researchers, Inc. **7.4** Eye of Science/Photo Researchers, Inc. **7.7** Don W. Fawcett/Photo Researchers, Inc. **7.8** Omikron/Photo Researchers, Inc. **7.9LR** Don W. Fawcett/Photo Researchers, Inc. **7.10** Biophoto Associates/Photo Researchers, Inc. **7.11** Don W. Fawcett/Photo Researchers, Inc. **7.12** E.H. Newcomb & W.P Wergin/Biological Photo Service **7.13** Fawcett/Friend/Photo Researchers, Inc. **7.14** Don W. Fawcett/Photo Researchers, Inc **7.15** E.H. Newcomb & W.P. Wergin/Biological Photo Service **7.16a** Dr. Don Fawcett/S. Ito & A. Like/Photo Researchers, Inc. **7.16b** Don W. Fawcett/Photo Researchers, Inc. **7.16c** Biophoto Associates/Photo Researchers, Inc. **7.16d** From "*Caveolin-1* expression is essential for proper nonshivering thermogenesis in brown adipose tissue." Cohen, A. W., Schubert, W., Brasaemle, D. L., Scherer, P. E., Lisanti, M. P. *Diabetes*. 2005 Mar; 54(3): 679–86, Fig. 6. **7.17** Don W. Fawcett/Photo Researchers, Inc. **7.26** Micrograph by Dr. Conly L. Rieder, Wadsworth Center, Albany, New York 12201-0509 **7.27ab** Reproduced by permission of the American Society for Cell Biology from *Molecular Biology of the Cell* 9 (12), December 1998, cover. ©1999 by the American Society for Cell Biology. Image courtesy of Bruce J. Schnapp, Oregon Health Sciences University. **7.28** John E. Heuser, M.D., Washington University School of Medicine, St. Louis, Missouri **7.29a** SPL/Photo Researchers, Inc. **7.29b** Biomedical Imaging Unit, Southampton General Hospital/Photo Researchers, Inc. **7.30** Don W. Fawcett/Photo Researchers, Inc.

**Chapter 8** **Opener** Richard Megna/Fundamental Photographs **8.3** Thomas Eisner

**Chapter 9** **Opener** Raiden32/Used under the Creative Commons license. http://creativecommons.org/licenses/by-sa/3.0/deed.en **9.1a** Oliver Hoffmann/Shutterstock **9.1b** Gergo Orban/Shutterstock **9.8** Terry Frey **9.16** Michael Delannoy

**Chapter 11** **Opener** Roger J. Bick & Brian J. Poindexter/UT-Houston Medical School/Photo Researchers, Inc. **11.1** Jochen Tack/imagebroker/Alamy **11.2** Biophoto Associates/Photo Researchers, Inc. **11.3b** ©ROCKWATER, Inc./*Journal of Bone and Joint Surgery*, 1997, 79, Instructional Course Lectures, The American Academy of Orthopaedic Surgeons—Articular Cartilage. Part I: Tissue Design and Chondrocyte-Matrix Interactions, Buckwalter, 600–611 **11.5** Biophoto Associates/Photo Researchers, Inc. **11.7aLR** Don W. Fawcett/Photo Researchers, Inc. **11.8** Don W. Fawcett/Photo Researchers **11.10a** Dr. Don Fawcett/Photo Researcher's, Inc. **11.10b** E. H. Newcomb & W.P. Wergin/Biological Photo Service **11.17a** A. Nern and R. A. Arkowitz. 2000. "G proteins mediate changes in cell shape by stabilizing the axis of polarity." *Molecular Cell* 5(5): 853–864, Fig. 2C. **11.17b** R. H. Kessin. 2003. "Cell motility: Making streams." *Nature* 422: 481–482. ©2003 Nature Publishing Group. Used with permission.

**Chapter 12** **Opener** G. Gimenz-Martin/SPL/Photo Researchers, Inc. **12.1T** Gopal Murti/Photo Researchers, Inc. **12.1B** Biophoto Associates/Photo Researchers, Inc. **12.5(1–7)** Micrographs by Conly L. Rieder, Department of Biology, Rensselaer Polytechnic Institute, Troy, New York. **12.8a** Ed Reschke/Getty **12.8b** Michael Danilchik

**Chapter 13** **Opener** David Phillips/The Population Council/Photo Researchers, Inc. **13.1** Look at Sciences/Photo Researchers, Inc. **13.6** Jupiterimages/Photos.com **13.7(1–9)** Warren Rosenberg/Fundamental Photographs **13.15** Dr. Rebecca Shulte

**Chapter 14** **Opener** Brian Johnston **14.9a** Benjamin Prud'homme/Nicolas Gompel **14.9bLR** From "Learning to Fly: Phenotypic Markers in Drosophila." A poster of common phenotypic markers used in Drosophila genetics. Jennifer Childress, Richard Behringer, and Georg Halder. 2005. *Genesis* 43(1). Cover illustration. **14.16** Carla Fernanda Reis

**Chapter 15** **Opener** Dr. Gopal Murti/Science Photo Library/Photo Researchers, Inc. **15.1** Eye of Science/Photo Researchers, Inc. **15.5** Reproduced by permission of Matthew S. Meselson, Harvard University, from M. Meselson and F.W. Stahl, "The replication of DNA in Escherichia coli." *PNAS* 44(7): 671–682 (July 1958), p. 675, Fig. 4. **15.7** Dr. Gopal Murti/Science Photo Library/Photo Researchers, Inc.

**Chapter 16** **Opener** J. Craig Venter Institute **16.4a** Rod Williams/Nature Picture Library **16.4b** Clint Cook & Janet P. Crossland, The Peromyscu Genetic Stock Center at the U. of South Carolina **16.9** Courtesy of Hesed M. Padilla-Nash and Thomas Ried. Affiliation is Section of Cancer Genomics, Genetics Branch, Center for Research, National Cancer Institute, National Institutes of Health, Bethesda, MD 20892

**Chapter 17** **Opener** Oscar Miller/SPL/Photo Researchers, Inc. **17.5** Bert W. O'Malley, M.D., Baylor College of Medicine **17.8** From Hamkalo and Miller, "Electronmicroscopy of Genetic Material," Figure 6a, p. 379. Reproduced with permission, from *Annual Review of Biochemistry*, Volume 42. ©1973 by Annual Reviews, Inc. **17.9** Dr. Elena Kiseleva/Photo Researchers, Inc.

**Chapter 19** **19.2** Ada Olins/Don Fawcett/Photo Researchers, Inc. **19.4TB** ©2002 from *Molecular Biology of the Cell* 4/e Fig. 4-23 by Bruce Alberts et al. Reproduced by Permission of Garland Science Taylor & Francis Books, Inc., and Dr. Barbara Hamkalo.

**Chapter 20** **Opener** International Rice Research Institute (IRRI) used under Creative Commons 2.0 license. http://creativecommons.org/licenses/by-nc-sa/2.0/deed.en **20.1** Brady-Handy Photograph Collection, Library of Congress. Reproduction number: LC-DIG-cwpbh-02977. **20.12** Science Source/Photo Researchers, Inc. **20.15BLR** Golden Rice

**Chapter 22** **Opener** Anthony Bannister/Photo Researchers, Inc. **22.1a** From "The BMP antagonist Gremlin regulates outgrowth, chondrogenesis and programmed cell death in the developing limb." R. Merino, J. Rodriguez-Leon, D. Macias, Y. Ganan, A.N. Economides and J. M. Hurle. *Development* 126: 5515-5522 (1999), Fig. 6 E & F Juan M. Hurle. **22.1b** Reproduced by permission of Elsevier Science from K. Kuida et al., "Reduced apoptosis and cytochrome c–mediated caspase activation in mice lacking caspase 9. *Cell* 94:325-337 (1998), Figs. 2E and 2F. ©1998 by Elsevier Science Ltd. Image courtesy of Keisuke Kuida, Vertex Pharmaceuticals. **22.2** John Chadwick/Agence France Presse/Newscom **22.3a** Richard Hutchings/Photo Researchers, Inc. **22.3b** From Drs. Adamson and Walls, "Embryonic and Neonatal Phenotyping of Gentically Engineered Mice." *ILAR Journal* 47(2), Fig. 12A, Optical projection tomogratphhy (OPT) image of a day 12.5 mouse embryo. (The rotation of the embryo and the art overlays do not appear in original paper.) **22.5** Christiane Nüsslein-Volhard, Max Planck Institute of Developmental Biology, Tubingen, Germany **22.6** Wolfgang Driever, University of Freiburg, Germany **22.7ac** Jim Langeland, Stephen Paddock, and Sean Carroll, University of Wisconsin at Madison **22.7b** Stephen J. Small, New York University **22.8L** Thomas Deerinck, NCMIR/Photo Researchers, Inc. **22.8M** David Scharf/Science Source/Photo Researchers, Inc. **22.8R** Eye of Science/Photo Researchers, Inc. **22.11ab** Reprinted from "The Origin of Form" by Sean B. Carroll, *Natural History*, November 2005. Burke, A. C. 2000. *Hox* Genes and the Global Patterning of the Somitic Mesoderm. In *Somitogenesis*. C. Ordahl (ed.) *Current Topics in Developmental Biology*, Vol. 47. Academic Press.

**Appendix A: Answers**  **A7.1ab** Don W. Fawcett/Photo Researchers, Inc.
**A7.1c** Biophoto Associates/Photo Researchers, Inc. **A7.1d** From "*Caveolin-1*
expression is essential for proper nonshivering thermogenesis in brown adipose
tissue." Cohen, A. W., Schubert, W., Brasaemle, D. L., Scherer, P. E., Lisanti, M. P.
*Diabetes.* 2005 Mar; 54(3): 679–86, Fig. 6.

**Appendix B: BioSkills**  **B9.3** Reproduced by permission from J. P. Ferris, et al.
"Synthesis of long prebiotic oligomers on mineral surfaces." *Nature* 381: 59–61
(1996), Fig. 2. ©1996 Macmillan Magazines Ltd. Image courtesy of James P. Ferris,
Rensselaer Polytechnic Institute. **B11.1a** Biology Media/Photo Researchers, Inc.
**B11.1b** Janice Carr/Centers for Disease Control and Prevention (CDC)
**B11.2ab** Michael W. Davidson/Molecular Expressions **B11.3** Rosalind Franklin/
Photo Researchers, Inc. **B12.1aL** National Cancer Institute **B12.1aR** E.S. Anderson/
Photo Researchers, Inc. **B12.1b** Sinclair Stammers/Photo Researchers, Inc.
**B13.1a** Kwangshin Kim/Photo Researchers, Inc. **B13.1b** Richard L. (Larry) Blanton,
Ph.D. **B13.1c** Holt Studios International/Photo Researchers, Inc. **B13.1d** Custom
Medical Stock Photo, Inc. **B13.1e** Graphic Science/Alamy Images **B13.1f** Sinclair
Stammers/Photo Researchers, Inc. **B13.1g** dra_schwartz/iStockphoto

## Illustration and Text Credits

**Chapter 1**  **1.3** Based on S. P. Moose, J. W. Dudley, and T. R. Rocheford. 2004. Maize
selection passes the century mark: A unique resource for 21st century genomics.
*Trends in Plant Science* 9 (7): 358–364, Fig. 1a; and the Illinois long-term selection
experiment for oil and protein in corn (University of Illinois at Urbana–Champaign).
**1.7a** Based on T. P. Young and L. A. Isbell. 1991. Sex differences in giraffe feeding
ecology: Energetic and social constraints. *Ethology* 87: 79–80, Figs. 5a, 6a. **1.9** Adapted
by permission of AAAS and the author from M. Wittlinger, R. Wehner, and H. Wolf.
2006. The ant odometer: Stepping on stilts and stumps. *Science* 312: 1965–1967,
Figs. 1, 2, 3. (http://www.sciencemag.org/content/312/5782/1965.short).

**Chapter 2**  **T2-1** Data: D. R. Lide (editor). 2008. Standard thermodynamic properties
of chemical substances. In *CRC Handbook of Physics and Chemistry*. 89th ed. Boca
Raton, FL: CRC Press. **2.21** After S. L. Miller. 1953. A production of amino acids
under possible primitive Earth conditions. *Science* 117 (3046): 528–529.

**Chapter 3**  **Opener** PDB ID: 2DN2. S. Y. Park, T. Yokoyama, N. Shibayama, et al.
2006. 1.25 Å resolution crystal structures of human hemoglobin in the oxy, deoxy
and carbonmonoxy forms. *Journal of Molecular Biology* 360: 690–701. **3.8a** PDB ID:
1TGH. Z. S. Juo, T. K. Chiu, P. M. Leiberman, et al. 1996. How proteins recognize
the TATA box. *Journal of Molecular Biology* 261: 239–254. **3.8b** PDB ID: 2X9K.
F. Korkmaz-Ozkan, S. Koster, W. Kuhlbrandt, et al. 2010. Correlation between the
OmpG secondary structure and its pH-dependent alterations monitored by FTIR.
*Journal of Molecular Biology* 401: 56–67. **3.8c** PDB ID: 2PTC. M. Marquart, J. Walter,
J. Deisenhofer, et al. 1983. The geometry of the reactive site and of the peptide groups
in trypsin, trypsinogen and its complexes with inhibitors. *Acta Crystallographica*
Section B39: 480–490. **3.8d** PDB ID: 1CLG. J. M. Chen, C. D. E. King, S. H.
Feairheller, et al. 1991. An energetic evaluation of a "Smith" collagen microfibril
model. *Journal of Protein Chemistry* 10: 535–552. **3.11b, left** PDB ID: 2MHR.
S. Sheriff, W. A. Hendrickson, and J. L. Smith. 1987. Structure of myohemerythrin in
the azidomet state at 1.7/1.3 resolution. *Journal of Molecular Biology* 197: 273–296.
**3.11b, middle** PDB ID: 1FTP. N. H. Haunerland, B. L. Jacobson, G. Wesenberg, et al.
1994. Three-dimensional structure of the muscle fatty-acid-binding protein isolated
from the desert locust *Schistocerca gregaria*. *Biochemistry* 33: 12378–12385.
**3.11b, right** PDB ID: 1IXA. M. Baron, D. G. Norman, T. S. Harvey, et al. 1992.
The three-dimensional structure of the first EGF-like module of human factor IX:
Comparison with EGF and TGF-alpha. *Protein Science* 1: 81–90. **3.12a** PDB ID:
1D1L. P. B. Rupert, A. K. Mollah, M. C. Mossing, et al. 2000. The structural basis for
enhanced stability and reduced DNA binding seen in engineered second-generation
Cro monomers and dimers. *Journal of Molecular Biology* 296: 1079–1090.
**3.12b** PDB ID: 2DN2. S.Y. Park, T. Yokoyama, N. Shibayama, et al. 2006. 1.25
Å resolution crystal structures of human hemoglobin in the oxy, deoxy and
carbonmonoxy forms. *Journal of Molecular Biology* 360: 690–701. **3.14a** PDB ID:
1DMO. M. Zhang, T. Tanaka, and M. Ikura. 1995. Calcium-induced conformational
transition revealed by the solution structure of apo calmodulin. *Nature Structural
Biology* 2: 758–767. **3.14b** PDB ID: 3CLN. Y. S. Babu, C. E. Bugg, and W. J. Cook.
1988. Structure of calmodulin refined at 2.2 A resolution. *Journal of Molecular Biology*
204: 191–204. **3.16** PDB ID: 2PTC. M. Marquart, J. Walter, J. Deisenhofer, et al. 1983.
The geometry of the reactive site and of the peptide groups in trypsin, trypsinogen
and its complexes with inhibitors. *Acta Crystallographica* Section B39: 480–490.

**Chapter 4**  **T4-1** PDB ID: 1EHZ. H. Shi and P. B. Moore. 2000. The crystal structure
of yeast phenylalanine tRNA at 1.93 Å resolution: A classic structure revisited.
*RNA* 6: 1091–1105. **4.11** PDB ID: 1X8W. F. Guo, A. R. Gooding, and T. R. Cech.
2004. Structure of the *Tetrahymena* ribozyme: Base triple sandwich and metal ion at
the active site. *Molecular Cell* 16: 351–362.

**Chapter 5**  **5.6** H. M. Florman, K. B. Bechtol, and P. M. Wassarman. 1984. Enzymatic
dissection of the functions of the mouse egg's receptor for sperm. *Developmental
Biology* 106: 243–255. Also H. M. Florman and P. M. Wassarman. 1985. O-linked
oligosaccharides of mouse egg ZP3 account for its sperm receptor activity. *Cell*
41: 313–324; J. D. Bleil and P. M. Wassarman. 1988. Galactose at the nonreducing
terminus of O-linked oligosaccharides of mouse egg zona pellucida glycoprotein ZP3
is essential for the glycoprotein's sperm receptor activity. *PNAS* 85: 6778–6782.

**Chapter 6**  **Opener** CHARMM-GUI Archive—Library of Pure Lipid Bilayer (www.
charmm-gui.org/?doc=archive&lib=lipid_pure), POPE Bilayer Library (pope_n256.
pdb). Reference: S. Jo, T. Kim, and W. Im. 2007. Automated builder and database of
protein/membrane complexes for molecular dynamics simulations. *PLoS ONE*
2 (9): e880. **6.10** Data: J. de Gier, J. G. Mandersloot, and L. L. van Deenen. 1968.
Lipid composition and permeability of liposomes. *Biochimica et Biophysica Acta* 150:
666–675. **6.21** Data: C. E. Bear, F. Duguay, A. L. Naismith, et al. 1992. Purification
and functional reconstitution of the cystic fibrosis transmembrane conductance
regulator (CFTR). *Cell* 68: 809–818. **6.22** PDB ID: 2ZZ9. K. Tani, T. Mitsuma,
Y. Hiroaki, et al. 2009. Mechanism of aquaporin-4's fast and highly selective water
conduction and proton exclusion. *Journal of Molecular Biology* 389: 694–706.
**6.23** PDB ID: 1K4C. Y. Zhou, J. H. Morais-Cabral, A. Kaufman, et al. 2001.
Chemistry of ion coordination and hydration revealed by a $K^+$ channel–Fab complex
at 2.0 Å resolution. *Nature* 414: 43–48. **6.23** PDB ID: 3FB7. L. G. Cuello, V. Jogini,
D. M. Cortes, et al. Open KcsA potassium channel in the presence of $Rb^+$ ion. (To
be published.) **7.18** A. D. Mills, R. A. Laskey, P. Black, et al. 1980. An acidic protein
which assembles nucleosomes in vitro is the most abundant protein in *Xenopus*
oocyte nuclei. *Journal of Molecular Biology* 139: 561–568. Also C. Dingwall, S. V.
Sharnick, and R. A. Laskey. 1982. A polypeptide domain that specifies migration of
nucleoplasmin into the nucleus. *Cell* 30: 449–458.

**Chapter 7**  **7.5** Reprinted with permission from Springer Science+Business
Media B.V. from David S. Goodsell, *The Machinery of Life*. 2nd ed., 2009.

**Chapter 8**  **8.8** PDB ID: 1Q18. V. V. Lunin, Y. Li, J. D. Schrag, et al. 2004. Crystal
structures of *Escherichia coli* ATP-dependent glucokinase and its complex with
glucose. *Journal of Bacteriology* 186: 6915–6927. **8.8** PDB ID: 2Q2R. A. T. Cordeiro,
A. J. Caceres, D. Vertommen, et al. 2007. The crystal structure of *Trypanosoma cruzi*
glucokinase reveals features determining oligomerization and anomer specificity
of hexose-phosphorylating enzymes. *Journal of Molecular Biology* 372: 1215–1226.
**8.14a&b** Data: N. N. Nawani, B. P. Kapadnis, A. D. Das, et al. 2002. Purification and
characterization of a thermophilic and acidophilic chitinase from Microbispora sp.
V2. *Journal of Applied Microbiology* 93: 865–975, Figs. 7, 8a. Also N. N. Nawani and
B. P. Kapadnis. 2001. One-step purification of chitinase from *Serratia marcescens*
NK1, a soil isolate. *Journal of Applied Microbiology* 90: 803–808, Figs. 3, 4. **8.15** PDB
ID: 2ERK. B. J. Canagarajah, A. Khokhlatchev, M. H. Cobb, et al. 1997. Activation
mechanism of the MAP kinase ERK2 by dual phosphorylation. *Cell* (Cambridge, MA)
90: 859–869. **8.15** PDB ID 3ERK. Z. Wang, B. J. Canagarajah, J. C. Boehm, et al. 1998.
Structural basis of inhibitor selectivity in MAP kinases. *Structure* 6: 1117–1128.

**Chapter 9**  **9.7** PDB ID: 4PFK. P. R. Evans and P. J. Hudson. 1981.
Phosphofructokinase: Structure and control. *Philosophical Transactions R. Soc.
Lond. B: Biol. Sci.* 293: 53–62. **9.13** Data: X. Li, R. K. Dash, R. K. Pradhan, et al.
2010. A database of thermodynamic quantities for the reactions of glycolysis and the
tricarboxylic acid cycle. *Journal of Physical Chemistry B* 114: 16068–16082, Table
4. **9.14** Data: D.F . Wilson, M. Erecinska, and P. L. Dutton. 1974. Thermodynamic
relationships in mitochondrial oxidative phosphorylation. *Annual Review of
Biophysics and Bioengineering* 3: 203–230, Tables 1, 3. Also V. D. Sled, N. I.
Rudnitzky, Y. Hatefit, et al. 1994. Thermodynamic analysis of flavin in mitochondrial
NADH: Ubiquinone oxidoreductase (complex I). *Biochemistry* 33: 10069–10075.
**9.17** E. Racker and W. Stoeckenius. 1974. Reconstitution of purple membrane vesicles
catalyzing light-driven proton uptake and adenosine triphosphate formation. *Journal
of Biological Chemistry* 249: 662–663.

**Chapter 11**  **11.4** Reprinted with kind permission from Springer Science+Business
Media B.V. from David S. Goodsell, *The Machinery of Life*. 2nd ed., 2009.
**11.7b** B. Alberts, A. Johnson, J. Lewis, et al. 2002. *Molecular Biology of the Cell*.
4th ed., Fig. 19.5, p. 1069. **11.9** K. Hatta and M. Takeichi. 1986. Expression of
N-cadherin adhesion molecules associated with early morphogenetic events in
chick development. *Nature* 320: 447–449. Also M. Takeichi. 1988. The cadherins:
Cell–cell adhesion molecules controlling animal morphogenesis. *Development* 102:
639–655.

**Chapter 12**  **12.6** G. J. Gorbsky, P. J. Sammack, and G. G. Borisey. 1987.
Chromosomes move poleward during anaphase along stationary microtubules that
coordinately dissemble from their kinetochore ends. *Journal of Cell Biology* 104: 9–18.
**12.9** Based on J. L. Ptacin, S. F. Lee, E. C. Garner, et al. 2010. A spindle-like apparatus
guides bacterial chromosome segregation. *Nature Cell Biology* 12: 791–798, Fig. 5.
**12.10** Y. Masui and C. L. Markert. 1971. Cytoplasmic control of nuclear behavior
during meiotic maturation of frog oocytes. *Journal of Experimental Zoology* 177:

5. **12.13** Data: the website of the National Cancer Institute (www.cancer.gov), Common Cancer Types, November 2010.

**Chapter 13** **13.13** Data: National Down Syndrome Society, 2012. **13.15** L. T. Morran, O. G. Schmidt, I. A. Gelarden, et al. 2011. Running with the red queen: Host-parasite coevolution selects for biparental sex. *Science* 333: 216–218.

**Chapter 14** **14.3** G. Mendel. 1866. Versuche über Pflanzen-hybriden. *Verhandlungen des naturforschenden Vereines in Brünn* 4: 3–47. English translation available from Electronic Scholarly Publishing (www.esp.org). **T14.2** Data: G. Mendel. 1866. Versuche über Pflanzen-hybriden. *Verhandlungen des naturforschenden Vereines in Brünn* 4: 3–47. **14.13** Data: T. H. Morgan. 1911. An attempt to analyze the constitution of the chromosomes on the basis of sex-limited inheritance in *Drosophila. Journal of Experimental Zoology* 11: 365–414. **14.20** Data: Pan American Health Organization/WHO. 2004. *Epidemiological Bulletin* 25: 9–13, Graph 1.

**Chapter 15** **15.2** A. D. Hershey and M. Chase. 1952. Independent functions of viral protein and nucleic acid in growth of bacteriophage. *Journal of General Physiology* 36: 39–56. **15.5** Adapted by permission of Dr. Matthew Meselson after M. Meselson and F. W. Stahl. 1958. The replication of DNA in *Escherichia coli. PNAS* 44: 671–682, Fig. 6. **15.14** Data: R. C. Allsopp, H. Vaziri, C. Patterson, et al. 1992. Telomere length predicts replicative capacity of human fibroblasts. *PNAS* 89: 10114–10118. **15.18a** Data: J. E. Cleaver. 1970. DNA repair and radiation sensitivity in human (xeroderma pigmentosum) cells. *International Journal of Radiation Biology* 18: 557–565, Fig. 3. **15.18b** Data: J .E. Cleaver. 1972. Xeroderma pigmentosum: Variants with normal DNA repair and normal sensitivity to ultraviolet light. *Journal of Investigative Dermatology* 58: 124–128, Fig. 1. **15.UN2** Graph adapted by permission of the Radiation Research Society from P. Howard-Flanders and R. P. Boyce. 1966. DNA repair and genetic recombination: Studies on mutants of *Escherichia coli* defective in these processes. *Radiation Research Supplement* 6: 156–184, Fig. 8.

**Chapter 16** **16.2** Data: A. M. Srb and N. H. Horowitz. 1944. The ornithine cycle in *Neurospora* and its genetic control. *Journal of Biological Chemistry* 154: 129–139.

**Chapter 17** **17.2a** PDB ID: 3IYD. B. P. Hudson, J. Quispe, S. Lara-Gonzalez, et al. 2009. Three-dimensional EM structure of an intact activator-dependent transcription initiation complex. *PNAS* 106: 19830–19835. **17.11** Based on M. B. Hoagland, M. L. Stephenson, J. F. Scott, et al. 1958. A soluble ribonucleic acid intermediate in protein synthesis. *Journal of Biological Chemistry* 231: 241–257, Fig. 6. **17.13** PDB ID: 1ZJW: I. Gruic-Sovulj, N. Uter, T. Bullock, et al. 2005. tRNA-dependent aminoacyl-adenylate hydrolysis by a nonediting class I aminoacyl-tRNA synthetase. *Journal of Biological Chemistry* 280: 23978–23986. **17.14b** PDB IDs: 3FIK, 3FIH. E. Villa, J. Sengupta, L. G. Trabuco, et al. 2009. Ribosome-induced changes in elongation factor Tu conformation control GTP hydrolysis. *PNAS* 106: 1063–1068.

**Chapter 19** **Opener** PDB ID: 1ZBB. T. Schalch, S. Duda, D. F. Sargent, et al. 2005. X-ray structure of a tetranucleosome and its implications for the chromatin fibre. *Nature* 436: 138–141. **19.5** I. Sandovici, N. H. Smith, and M. D. Nitert. 2011. Maternal diet and aging alter the epigenetic control of a promoter–enhancer interaction at the *Hnf4a* gene in rat pancreatic islets. *PNAS* 108: 5449–5454. **19.7b** PDB ID: 1MDY. P. C. Ma, M. A. Rould, H. Weintraub, et al. 1994. Crystal structure of MyoD bHLH domain–DNA complex: Perspectives on DNA recognition and implications for transcriptional activation. *Cell* (Cambridge, MA) 77: 451–459.

**Chapter 22** **22.10a&b** Reproduced by permission from Macmillan Publishers Ltd after J. C. Pearson, D. Lemons, and W. McGinnis. 2005. Modulating *Hox* gene functions during animal body patterning. *Nature Reviews Genetics* 6: 893–904, Fig. 1.

**Chapter 28** **28.4c** Data adapted by permission of the publisher from M. A. Nikaido, P. Rooney, and N. Okada. 1999. Phylogenetic relationships among cetartiodactyls based on insertions of short and long interspersed elements: Hippopotamuses are the closest extant relatives of whales. *PNAS* 96: 10261–10266, Figs. 1, 7. ©1999 National Academy of Sciences, USA. **28.6, 28.7, 28.8** Data: International Commission on Stratigraphy, "International Stratigraphic Chart, 2009" (www.stratigraphy.org/column.php?id=Chart/TimeScale). The data on this site are modified from F. M. Gradstein and J. C. Ogg (eds.). 2004. *A Geologic Time Scale 2004.* Cambridge, UK: Cambridge University Press; and J. G. Ogg, G. Ogg, and F. M. Gradstein. 2008. *The Concise Geologic Time Scale.* Cambridge, UK: Cambridge University Press. **28.9** B. G. Baldwin, D. W. Kyhos, and J. Dvorak. 1990. Chloroplast DNA evolution and adaptive radiation in the Hawaiian Silversword Alliance (Asteraceae–Madiinae). *Annals of the Missouri Botanical Garden* 77 (1): 96–109, Fig. 2. **28.10c** J. B Losos, K. I. Warheit, and T. W. Schoener. 1997. Adaptive differentiation following experimental island colonization in Anolis lizards. *Nature* 387: 70–73. **28.13** Data: J. W. Valentine, D. H. Erwin, and D. Jablonski. 1996. Developmental evolution of metazoan body plans: The fossil evidence. *Developmental Biology* 173: 373–381, Fig. 3. Also R. de Rosa et al. 1999. *Hox* genes in brachiopods and priapulids and protostome evolution. *Nature* 399: 772–776; D. Chourrout, F. Delsuc, P. Chourrout, et al. 2006. Minimal *ProtoHox* cluster inferred from bilaterian and cnidarian *Hox* complements. *Nature* 442: 684–587. **28.14** Data: M. J. Benton. 1995. Diversification and extinction in the history of life. *Science* 268: 52–58.

**Chapter 29** **29.12** Data: D. F. Wilson, M. Erecinska, and P. L. Dutton. 1974. Thermodynamic relationships in mitochondrial oxidative phosphorylation. *Annual Review of Biophysics and Bioengineering* 3: 203–230, Tables 1, 3. **30.1** S. M. Adl, A. G. Simpson, M. A. Farmer, et al. 2005. The new higher level classification of eukaryotes with emphasis on the taxonomy of protists. *Journal of Eukaryotic Microbiology* 52: 399–451. Also N. Arisue, M. Hasegawa, and T. Hashimoto. 2005. Root of the eukaryota tree as inferred from combined maximum likelihood analyses of multiple molecular sequence data. *Society for Molecular Biology and Evolution, Molecular Biology and Evolution* 22: 409–420; V. Hampl, L. Hug, J. W. Leigh, et al. 2009. Phylogenomic analyses support the monophyly of Excavata and resolve relationships among eukaryotic "supergroups." *PNAS* 106 (10): 3859–3864, Figs. 1, 2, 3; J. D. Hackett, H. S. Yoon, S. Li, et al. 2007. Phylogenomic analysis supports the monophyly of cryptophytes and haptophytes and the association of Rhizaria with chromalveolates. *Molecular Biology and Evolution* 24: 1702–1713, Fig. 1; P. Schaap, T. Winckler, M. Nelson, et al. 2006. Molecular phylogeny and evolution of morphology in the social amoebas. *Science* 314: 661–663.

**Chapter 30** **30.1, 30.7** S. M. Adl, A. G. Simpson, M. A. Farmer, et al. 2005. The new higher level classification of eukaryotes with emphasis on the taxonomy of protists. *Journal of Eukaryotic Microbiology* 52: 399–451. Also N. Arisue, M. Hasegawa, and T. Hashimoto. 2005. Root of the eukaryota tree as inferred from combined maximum likelihood analyses of multiple molecular sequence data. *Society for Molecular Biology and Evolution, Molecular Biology and Evolution* 22: 409–420; V. Hampl, L. Hug, J. W. Leigh, et al. 2009. Phylogenomic analyses support the monophyly of Excavata and resolve relationships among eukaryotic "supergroups." *PNAS* 106 (10): 3859–3864, Figs. 1, 2, 3; J. D. Hackett, H. S. Yoon, S. Li, et al. 2007. Phylogenomic analysis supports the monophyly of cryptophytes and haptophytes and the association of Rhizaria with chromalveolates. *Molecular Biology and Evolution* 24: 1702–1713, Fig. 1; P. Schaap, T. Winckler, M. Nelson, et al. 2006. Molecular phylogeny and evolution of morphology in the social amoebas. *Science* 314: 661–663.

**Chapter 33** **33.2** A. M. A. Aguinaldo, J. M. Turbeville, L. S. Linford, et al. 1997. Evidence for a clade of nematodes, arthropods, and other moulting animals. *Nature* 387: 489–493, Figs. 1, 2, 3. Also C. W. Dunn, A. Hejnol, D. Q. Matus, et al. 2008. Broad phylogenomic sampling improves resolution of the animal tree of life. *Nature* 452: 745–750, Figs. 1, 2. **33.7** Based on J. R. Finnerty, K. Pang, P. Burton, et al. 2004. Origins of bilateral symmetry: *Hox* and *Dpp* expression in a sea anemone. *Science* 304: 1335–1337.

**Chapter 34** **34.1** A. D. Chapman. 2009. *Numbers of Living Species in Australia and the World.* 2nd ed. Canberra: Australian Biological Resources Study. **34.2** A. M. A. Aguinaldo, J. M. Turbeville, L. S. Linford, et al. 1997. Evidence for a clade of nematodes, arthropods, and other moulting animals. *Nature* 387: 489–493, Figs. 1, 2, 3. Also C. W. Dunn, A. Hejnol, D. Q. Matus, et al. 2008. Broad phylogenomic sampling improves resolution of the animal tree of life. *Nature* 452: 745–750, Figs. 1, 2. **34.28, 34.30** Based on data in J. Regier, J. W. Schultz, A. Zwick, et al. 2010. Arthropod relationships revealed by phylogenomic analysis of nuclear protein-coding sequences. *Nature* 463: 1079–1083. **34.UN1** Based on M. Averof and N. H. Patel. 1997. Crustacean appendage evolution associated with changes in *Hox* gene expression. *Nature* 388: 682–686, Fig. 4.

**Chapter 35** **35.1** After C. W. Dunn, A. Hejnol. D. Q. Matus, et al. 2008. Broad phylogenomic sampling improves resolution of the animal tree of life. *Nature* 452: 745–750, Figs. 1, 2. Also F. Delsuc, H. Brinkmann, D. Chourrout, et al. 2006. Tunicates and not cephalochordates are the closest living relatives of vertebrates. *Nature* 439: 965–968, Fig. 1. **35.12** J. E. Blair and S. B. Hedges. 2005. Molecular phylogeny and divergence times of deuterostome animals. *Molecular Biology and Evolution* 22: 2275–2284, Figs. 1, 3, 4. **35.13** Data: American Museum of Natural History; BirdLife International (birdlife.org); FishBase (www.fishbase.org); IUCN 2010. *The IUCN Red List of Threatened Species* (http://www.iucnredlist.org); The Reptile Database (reptile-database.org). **35.16** Based on E. B. Daeschler, N. H. Shubin, F. A. Jenkins, et al. 2006. A Devonian tetrapod-like fish and the evolution of the tetrapod body plan. *Nature* 440: 757–763, Fig. 6. Also N. H. Shubin, E. B. Daeschler, F. A. Jenkins, et al. 2006. The pectoral fin of *Tiktaalik roseae* and the origin of the tetrapod limb. *Nature* 440:764–771, Fig. 4. **35.20** Color plate by Michael DiGiorgio. From Q. Li, K.-Q. Gao, J. Vinther, et al. 2010. Plumage color patterns of an extinct dinosaur. *Science* 327, Fig. 4, p. 1371. Reprinted by permission of the artist, Michael DiGiorgio. **35.22** J. E. Blair and S. B. Hedges. 2005. Molecular phylogeny and divergence times of deuterostome animals. *Molecular Biology and Evolution*, 22: 2275–2284, Figs. 1, 3, 4. Also F. R. Liu, M. M. Miyamoto, N. P. Freire, et al. 2001. Molecular and morphological supertrees for eutherian (placental) mammals. *Science* 291: 1786–1789; A. B. Prasad, M. W. Allard, E. D. Green, et al. 2008. Confirming the phylogeny of mammals by use of large comparative sequence data sets. Oxford University Press, *Molecular Biology and Evolution* 25: 1795–1808. **35.36** A. B. Prasad, M. W. Allard, E. D. Green, et al. 2008. Confirming the phylogeny of mammals by use of large comparative sequence data sets. Oxford University Press, *Molecular Biology and Evolution* 25 (9):1795–1808, Figs. 1, 2, 3. **35.37** Data: D. E. Lieberman. 2009. Palaeoanthropology: *Homo floresiensis* from head to toe. *Nature* 459: 41–42.

**T35.1** S. L. Robson and B. Wood. 2008. Hominin life history: Reconstruction and evolution. *Journal of Anatomy* 212: 394–425. **35.39** J. Z. Li, D. M. Absher, H. Tang, et al. 2008. Worldwide human relationships inferred from genome-wide patterns of variation. *Science* 319: 1100–1104, Fig. 1. **35.40** After L. L. Cavalli-Sforza and M. W. Feldman. 2003. The application of molecular genetic approaches to the study of human evolution. *Nature Genetics Supplement* 33: 266–275, Fig. 3; Data: Genographic Project at National Geographic: https://genographic.nationalgeographic.com/genographic/lan/en/atlas.html; dates from August 2009 summary map: http://ngm.nationalgeographic.com/big-idea/02/queens-genes; M. Rasmussen, X. Guo, Y. Wang, et al. 2011. An Aboriginal Australian genome reveals separate human dispersals into Asia. *Science* 334: 94–98.

**Chapter 42** **42.2** A. M. Kerr, S. N. Gershman, and S. K. Sakaluk. 2010. Experimentally induced spermatophore production and immune responses reveal a trade-off in crickets. *Behavioral Ecology* 21: 647–654. **42.10** Data: K. Schmidt-Nielsen. 1984. *Scaling: Why Is Animal Size So Important?* Cambridge, UK: Cambridge University Press. **42.11** Adapted by permission of The Company of Biologists from P. R. Wells and A. W. Pinder. 1996. The respiratory development of Atlantic salmon. II. Partitioning of oxygen uptake among gills, yolk sac and body surfaces. *Journal of Experimental Biology* 199: 2737–2744, Figs. 1A, 3.

**Chapter 43** **43.13** Anterolateral view reproduced by permission from Macmillan Publishers Ltd after S. E. Pierce, J. A. Clack, and J. R. Hutchinson. 2012. Three-dimensional limb joint mobility in the early tetrapod *Ichthyostega*. *Nature* 486: Fig. 1, p. 523. **43.14** Adapted by permission of Elsevier from K. J. Ullrich, K. Kramer, and J. W. Boyer. 1961. Present knowledge of the counter-current system in the mammalian kidney. *Progress in Cardiovascular Diseases* 3: 395–431, Figs. 5, 7. ©1961. **43.19** J. R. Davis and D. F. DeNardo. 2007. The urinary bladder as a physiological reservoir that moderates dehydration in a large desert lizard, the Gila monster *Heloderma suspectum*. *Journal of Experimental Biology* 210 (8): 1472–1480. Reprinted with permission from The Company of Biologists.

**Chapter 45** **45.7** Based on Y. Komai. 1998. Augmented respiration in a flying insect. *Journal of Experimental Biology* 201: 2359–2366, Fig. 7. **45.9** R. A. Berner. 1999. Atmospheric oxygen over Phanerozoic time. *PNAS* 96: 10955–10957. Fig. 2. Copyright ©1999 National Academy of Sciences, USA. Reprinted with permission. **45.12** W. Bretz and K. Schmidt Nielsen. 1971. Bird respiration: Flow patterns in the duck lung. *Journal of Experimental Biology* 54: 103–118. **45.21** Data: E. H. Starling. 1896. On the absorption of fluids from the connective tissue spaces. *Journal of Physiology* 19: 312–326. **45.23** J. E. Blair and S. B. Hedges. 2005. Molecular phylogeny and divergence times of deuterostome animals. *Molecular Biology and Evolution* 22: 2275–2284, Figs. 1, 3, 4.

**Chapter 46** **46.10** Data: O. Loewi. 1921. Über humorale Übertragbarkeit der Herznervenwirkung. *Pflügers Archiv European Journal of Physiology* 189: 239–242. **46.22** Data: R. Q. Quiroga, L. Reddy, G. Kreiman, et al. 2005. Invariant visual representation by single neurons in the human brain. *Nature* 435: 1102–1107, Fig. 1B. **46.24a&c** Based on K. C. Martin, A. Casadio, H. Zhu, et al. 1997. Synapse-specific, long-term facilitation of *Aplysia* sensory to motor synapses: A function for local protein synthesis in memory storage. *Cell* 91: 927–938.

**Chapter 47** **47.2a&b** Data: J. E. Rose, J. E. Hind, D. J. Anderson, et al. 1971. Some effects of stimulus intensity on response of auditory nerve fibers in the squirrel monkey. *Journal of Neurophysiology* 34: 685–699. **47.9** K. Pohlmann, J. Atema, and T. Breithaupt. 2004. The importance of the lateral line in nocturnal predation of piscivorous catfish. *Journal of Experimental Biology* 207: 2971–2978. **47.15** Based on D. M. Hunt, K. S. Dulai, J. K. Bowmaker, et al. 1995. The chemistry of John Dalton's color blindness. *Science* 267: 984–988, Fig. 3. **47.UN1** Reprinted by permission from Macmillan Publishers Ltd. from M. K. McClintock. 1971. Menstrual synchrony and suppression. *Nature* 229: 244–245, Fig. 1.

**Appendix B: BioSkills** **TB16.1** A. Crowe, C. Dicks, and M. P. Wenderoth. 2008. Biology in bloom: Implementing Bloom's Taxonomy to enhance student learning in Biology. *CBE–Life Sciences Education* 7: 368–381, Table 3.

# Index

**Boldface** page numbers indicate a glossary entry; page numbers followed by an *f* indicate a figure; those followed by *t* indicate a table.

**Boldface** page numbers indicate a glossary entry; page numbers followed by an
*f* indicate a figure; those followed by *t* indicate a table.

I:4    INDEX

**Boldface** page numbers indicate a glossary entry; page numbers followed by an
*f* indicate a figure; those followed by *t* indicate a table.

**6**    INDEX

**Boldface** page numbers indicate a glossary entry; page numbers followed by an *f* indicate a figure; those followed by *t* indicate a table.

**I:10** INDEX

Boldface page numbers indicate a glossary entry; page numbers followed by an
*f* indicate a figure; those followed by *t* indicate a table.

Boldface page numbers indicate a glossary entry; page numbers followed by an *f* indicate a figure; those followed by *t* indicate a table.

on global carbon cycle, 1161–62
global climate change from (see Global climate change)
on global net primary productivity, 1156
on global water cycle, 1160
human population growth and, 1101–2, 1117–18
on nutrient cycling, 1158
protection of metapopulations from, 1118–20
on soil erosion, 779–81
Human population
age structure of, 1115–16
analyzing changes in growth rate of, 1116–18
biodiversity loss and growth of, 1173, 1189
global climate change and growth of, 1163–64
impact of global growth of, 1101–2
impacts of, 1069
survivorship curves for, 1105
Human reproduction. See also Animal reproduction
accessory fluids in semen in, 1023t
childbirth and maternal mortality rates in, 1034
contraception in, 1029–30
female reproductive systems in, 1024–25
gametogenesis in, 1016–18f
male reproductive system in, 1021–23
menstrual/ovarian cycle in, 1027–30
pregnancy and gestation in, 1031–33
puberty in, 1026–27
Hummingbirds, 594
Humoral response, 1051–53
Humus, 778–79f, 1156–57
Huntington's disease, 278, 378–82
Hutchinson, G. Evelyn, 1125
Hutterites, 470
Huxley, Andrew, 932–36
Huxley, Hugh, 974
Hybridization, 498–502
Hybrid sterility as postzygotic isolation, 491t
Hybrid viability as postzygotic isolation, 491t
Hybrid zones, 500–501
Hybrids, 258t, 259
Hydrocarbons, 85–86, 90. See also Lipids
Hydrochloric acid, 28, 890–91
Hydrogen
electronegativity of, 21
lipids, hydrocarbons, and, 85–86
in living organisms, 19
molecules of, 21–23f, 33–36, 142–43
in protein secondary structure, 48–49
simple molecules from, 23
Hydrogen bonds, 25
of amino acids, 43f
DNA complementary base pairing and, 62–63, 287
in plant water transport, 765
protein structure and, 48–50f
RNA complementary base pairing and, 65–66
specific heat of liquids and, 27t
of water, 25–28
Hydrogen cyanide, 34–35
Hydrogen ions, 28–30
Hydroids, 653–54
Hydrolysis, 45
of ATP to drive endergonic reactions, 143–44

of carbohydrates by enzymes to release glucose, 80–81
lysosomses, digestive enzymes, and, 114
of polymers to release monomers, 45
Hydronium ions, 28–29
Hydrophilic side chains, 44
Hydrophilic substances, 25, 44, 63, 87f
Hydrophobic interactions, 25–26, 49–50f
Hydrophobic side chains, 44
Hydrophobic substances, 25, 63, 85–87f
Hydroponic growth, 777–78
Hydrostatic skeletons, 644, 661–63, 980–81
Hydrostats, 981
Hydrothermal vents. See Deep-sea hydrothermal vents
Hydroxide ions, 28–30
Hydroxyl functional group, 37t–38, 58, 73–74, 85–87, 298, 318
Hyenas, 1024–25f
Hygiene hypothesis, 1056
Hyperosmotic solutions, 862–63
Hyperpolarization, 933–34, 936
Hyperpolarized membranes, sensory transduction and, 953–54
Hypersensitive reaction, 1055–56
Hypersensitive response (HR), 815–17, 818t
Hypertension, 923
Hypertonic solutions, 93
Hyphae, 574, 616–18, 624, 784
Hypocotyl, 434, 833
Hypodermic insemination, 1020
Hypophasphatemia (vitamin D-resistant rickets), 279
Hyposmotic solutions, 863–64
Hypothalamic–pituitary axis, 1005, 1026–27
Hypothalamus, 856, 1004
hormones of, in mammalian puberty, 1026–27
photoperiod, sex hormones, and, 999, 1000f
regulation of hormone production by, 1004–6
thermoreception and, 967
in thermoregulation, 856–57
Hypotheses, 3–5, 9–12, B:7
Hypotonic solutions, 92, 755

**I**

Ice, floating of, 26–27
Ichthyosaurs, 509–10, 985, 986
*Ichthyostega*, 984–85
Identification, species, 490, 492–93
Iguanas, 481
Imaging techniques, 119, B:18–B:21
Immigration, 482, 1103, 1120, 1143–44
Immune systems, 713, 1037–58
adaptive immunity activation in, 1047–51
adaptive immunity recognition in, 1041–47
adaptive immunity responses and memory in, 1051–55
coevolution of, 1133
failures of, 1055–56
fitness trade-offs and, 843–45
HIV and helper T cells of human, 713–14
*HLA* genes in human, 469–70
inbreeding and, 471–72
innate immunity in, 1038–41, 1042t
micrograph of human, 1037f

pathogens, immunity, and three processes of, 1037–38
sexual selection, carotenoids, and, 475–76
Immunity, 1037
Immunization, 1054–55
Immunodeficiency diseases, 383–85, 724–25, 1056. See also AIDS (acquired immune deficiency syndrome); HIV (human immunodeficiency virus)
Immunoglobulins, 1044–47. See also Antibodies
Immunological memory, 1053, 1054–55
Immunostaining, cell, B:18–B:19
Impact hypothesis, 521–23
Imperfect flowers, 827
Implantation, 1031
Import, nutrient, 1157–58
In situ conservation, 1189–91
In situ hybridization, 411–12, 440, 458–59f
In vitro metabolic pathway research, 158
In vitro protein-synthesis systems, 326–27
In vitro translation systems, 324
In vivo vs. in vitro, 122
Inactivated virus vaccines, 1055
Inbreeding, 470–72
Inbreeding depression, 471–72, 1180
Inclusive fitness, 1096–97
Incomplete digestive tracts, 886–87
Incomplete dominance, 272, 273f, 276, 277t
Incomplete metamorphosis, 672
Independent assortment, principle of, 247–48, 249f, 263–64, 265–67, 270
Independent variables, graphing, B:4–B:6
Indeterminate growth, 732
Indole acetic acid (IAA). See Auxin
Induced fit, 145
Inducers, 338, 343
Inducible defenses, 815, 1130, 1131f
Industrial pollutants, 1182
Inertia, population growth, 1116
Infant diarrhea, 727
Infection threads, nitrogen-fixing bacteria, 788
Infectious diseases. See Diseases, animal; Diseases and disorders, human
Infidelity, bird, 1020
Inflammatory response, 1040–41, 1042t
Influenza viruses, 712, 713f, 723–24, 728, 1039, 1055
Information
as characteristic of life, 69
gene regulation and, 337–39f
genetic, 2, 64, 67, 256–57 (see also Genes)
hormones as carriers of, 209–10t
plant processing of, 794–96
Ingestion, 563–64, 637, 882–83f, 884–86
Inhalation, 909–11f
Inheritance. See also Chromosome theory of inheritance; Genetics; Mendelian genetics
of acquired characters, 257, 446, 459
autosomal, 269
epigenetic, 352–53
human, 277–79
hypotheses on, 257
particulate, 261–63
polygenic, 275–76, 277t
sex-linked, 268–69, 277t

Inhibition, enzyme, 149, 150
Inhibition, successional, 1141
Inhibitory postsynaptic potentials (IPSPs), 940–42
Initiation factors, 330
Initiation phase
enzyme catalysis, 146f–47
eukaryotic transcription, 353–56 (see also Transcriptional control, eukaryotic)
transcription, 318–20
translation, 329–30
Innate behavior, 1084
Innate immune response, 1039–41, 1042t. See also Immune systems
Innate immunity, 1038–41, 1042t. See also Immune systems
Inner cell mass (ICM), 424
Inner ear, 956
Inorganic soil elements, 778–79f
Inositol triphosphate (IP$_3$), 213t
Inoue, Shin-ichiro, 797
Insecticides, 555, 1152–53
Insects, 675. See also Arthropods
altruism in, 1097–98
characteristics and orders of, 675–76t
competition in, 1083–84
exoskeletons of, 983
fungal infections of, 628–29
fungal mutualisms with, 623
honeybee language in, 1092–93
metamorphosis in, 651, 672, 991f, 998
mimicry in, 1129–30
mutualisms of, 1133–35
open circulatory systems of, 917
osmoregulation in, 869–71
photoreception by eyes of, 960
plant defense responses to, 815, 817–19
pollination by, 593–94, 608–9f
as protostomes, 657–58
taxon-specific survey of, 1175
terrestrial adaptations of, 659
tracheae of, 907–9
Insemination, hypodermic, 1020
Instantaneous rate of increase, 1111f
Insulin, 47–48, 210t, 369, 897–99, 992
Integral membrane proteins, 95
Integrated pest management, 1133
Integrators, 854, 1001
Integrins, 203f–4
Interactions. See Cell-cell interactions; Species interactions
Interbreeding, 499–502
Intercalated discs, 922
Intercellular attachments. See Cell-cell attachments
Intercellular communication. See Cell-cell gaps
Intercellular connections, 204–9
Intergovernmental Panel on Climate Change (IPCC), 1164–66
Interleukin 2, 992
Intermediate filaments, 128t, 129
Intermediate hosts, 666
Intermediate (fast oxidative) muscle fibers, 979–80
Intermediate phenotypes, 273f
Intermediates, catabolic, 157–58
Internal consistency, evolution and, 451–53
Internal environments, eukaryotic differential gene expression and, 349
Internal fertilization, animal, 650, 1019–20
Internal membranes, 108, 110

Boldface page numbers indicate a glossary entry; page numbers followed by an f indicate a figure; those followed by t indicate a table.

fungus, 625–27
land plant, 589–90, 823–25
plant, 433f
protist, 566–69
Life histories, 1105, **1106**–7, 1118. *See also* Life tables
Life spans, protein, 360
Life tables, **1104**–5, 1106f, 1118, 1119f. *See also* Life histories
Lifelong plant growth, 436
Ligaments, **982**
Ligand-gated channels, **940**
Ligands, **940**
Ligase. *See* DNA ligases
Light-capturing reactions, photosynthetic, 177–90. *See also* Photosynthesis
absorption of light energy by pigments, 179–82
in chloroplasts, 178–79f
discovery of, 177–78
electromagnetic spectrum and, 179
electron excitation in, 182–84
photosystem I in, 186–87
photosystem II in, 184–86
Z-scheme model for photosystem interactions in, 187–90
Light chain polypeptides, **1044**–46
Light energy
animal sight and, 647t (*see also* Photoreception, animal)
in aquatic biomes, 1074, 1075f
capture of, in photosynthesis (*see* Light-capturing reactions, photosynthetic)
carbohydrate storage of, as chemical energy, 80
chemical evolution and, 31, 34–35
in chemical reactions, 137
electromagnetic spectrum of, 179
land plant adaptations to, 584–85
in mating, 1087–88
in plant water transport, 765
primary producers and, 1149–50
prokaryotic photosynthesis and, 541
in terrestrial biomes, 1068–69
transformation of, into biomass, 1149–50
in tropical and polar climates, 1066
vegetative development and, 436
Light microscopy, 119, 241, 557–58, B:18
Lightning, chemical evolution and, 31, 33–34
Lignin, **202**, **585**, **745**
in decomposition rates, 1157
fungal digestion of, 612–15, 623–24
in secondary cell walls, 202, 585, 745, 763
Likens, Gene, 1149–50
Limbs
animal movement and, 649–50f
arthropod, 670–71
evolutionary loss of, 416, 644
as structural homology, 450
tetrapod, 448, 689, 692–93
Limiting factors, population size and growth, 1109–12
Limiting nutrients, **777**
Limnetic zone, **1077**
Lincoln, Abraham, 273
Lindeman, Raymond, 1150
Line of best fit, scatterplot, B:5
Lineages, **491**–93, **507**, B:10–B:11. *See also* Clades; Monophyletic groups
Lines, scatterplot, B:5
Lingual lipase, **889**, 895t

Linkage, **270**–71, 274f, 277t
Linkage maps, **379**. *See also* Genetic maps
Linked genes. *See* Linkage
Linnaeus, Carolus, 8–9
Lipid bilayers, **88**. *See also* Plasma membranes
artificial membranes as experimental, 88–89
in chemical evolution, 93–94
membrane proteins and, 94–101
permeability of, 89–92
space-filling model of, 84f
Lipid-insoluble hormones, 209, 210–11
Lipid-soluble hormones, 209, 210, 211f, 996, 1006
Lipids, **85**
animal digestion of, 888, 889, 894–96
bond saturation and hydrocarbon structure of, 85–86
in characteristics of domains of life, 529t
chemical evolution of, 88
nucleic acid polymerization and, 60–61
prokaryotic glycolipids and, 109
smooth ER and, 114
structure of membrane, 87–88, 90
types of, 86–87
Lipopolysaccharide (LPS), 845
Liposomes, 88–89, 90, 92–93
Liquids, specific heat of some, 27t
Literature, primary, B:26–B:27
Littoral zone, **1077**
Live virus vaccines, 1055
Liver, 115, 162, 848f, 887f, **894**
Liverworts, 601
Lizards
adaptive radiations of, 516
extinction rates of, 1183–84
impacts of global climate change on, 1167
life table and life history of, 1104–6
mating in, 1087–89
movement of, 972f
niche concept and interspecific competition of, 1125
pineal eye of, 999, 1000f
range of, 1102–3
as reptiles, 702
urine formation in, 878f–79
ln notation, logarithms and, B:9
Loams, 778
Lobe-finned fishes, **699**
Lobes, brain, 944
Lobsters, 677
Lock-and-key model, enzyme catalysis, 54, 144–45
Locomotion, animal, **973**, 983–88. *See also* Animal movement
Locomotion, protist, 565–66
Locus (loci), gene, **266**
Loewi, Otto, 938–39
Log notation, logarithms and, B:9
Logarithms, B:9
Logistic population growth, **1108**–12
Lohmann, Kenneth, 1090–91
Long-day plants, **802**
Long interspersed nuclear elements (LINEs), **396**, 397f
Loop of Henle, 872, **874**–77f, 878t
Loose connective tissue, 846t, **847**
Lophophores, **660**–61f
Lophotrochozoans, 638t, **645**, 658, 659f, 660–70. *See also* Protostomes
Lorenz, Konrad, 1084

Lorises, 704
Losos, Jonathan, 516
Loss-of-function alleles, **305**
Loss-of-function mutations, 471, 481–82, 485
Lou Gehrig's disease (ALS), 408
Love darts, 1020
Lovejoy, Thomas, 1180
Low-order cognitive (LOC) skills, B:20–B:30t
LUCA (last universal common ancestor), **8**, **32**
Lumen, **112**, **178**
Luminescence, 377
Lungfish, 448, 692–93, 699
Lungs, 692–93, **909**–12, 916
LUREs, 832
Luteal phase, **1027**
Luteinizing hormone (LH), **1006**, **1026**, 1027–30
Lycophytes (club mosses), 603
Lyme disease, 546
Lymph, **919**, **1043**
Lymph nodes, **1043**
Lymphatic system, 233f, 919, **1043**
Lymphocytes, **1042**–48. *See also* B cells; T cells
Lynx, 1113–15
Lysine, 311
Lysogeny, **721**–22
Lysosomes, **114**, 117t
Lysozyme, 716, **1039**
Lytic cycle, viral, **716**. *See also* Replicative growth, viral

## M

M phase, **220**, 223–29, 232
M phase-promoting factor (MPF), **229**–31
MacArthur, Robert, 1143–44
MacArthur–Wilson model, 1143–45
McClintock, Barbara, 396
McClintock, Martha, 967
McGinnis, William, 415
Macromolecular machines, **50**
Macromolecules, **44**, 54, 157–58, B:13–B:14, B:20–B:21. *See also* Carbohydrates; Lipids; Molecules; Nucleic acids; Organic molecules; Proteins
Macronutrients, **777**, 780t
Macrophages, **1040**–41, 1042t
Mad cow disease, 53
MADS box, **441**
Maggot flies, 496–97
Magnesium, 777, 780t, 885t
Magnetic fields, 646, 647t, 968–69, 1090–91
Magnetite, 108, 534, 1090
Magnetoreception, **968**–69
Magnetoreceptors, **953**
Magnifications, microscope, B:18
Maidenhair ferns, 498
Maize, 5–6, 579
Major histocompatibility (MHC) proteins, **1048**–51, 1053
Maladaptive traits, **192**
Malaria, **554**–55, 573, 1132
Malaria, avian, 1062
Male gametes. *See* Sperm
Male reproductive systems, 1016–17, 1019–23
Males
in age structure of human population, 1115–16

chromosomes of, 238
female mate choice and, 475–76, 1088–89
female-mimicking behaviors of, 1094–95
gametangia of, 587
male-male competition of, 476–77
plant flower parts, 827
plant gametophytes, 828–29
sex chromosomes of, 268
sex hormones of, 999
sex-linked diseases of, 278–79
sexual selection and, 475–78
sperm as reproductive cells of, 237
visual cues from, in mating, 1088
Malignant tumors, **233**
Malpighian tubules, **870**–71
Malthus, Thomas Robert, 453, 1116
Mammals, **696**. *See also* Animal(s); Vertebrates
amniotic eggs in, 693–94
in Cenozoic era, 515
citric acid cycle in, 162
cleavage in, 423–24
cloning of, 409
digestive enzymes of, 895t
diversification of, 522–23
ecological efficiency of biomass production by, 1152
fungal mutualisms with, 629
gametogenesis in, 1016–18f
hormones in growth of, 999
house mouse as model organism for, B:26
lineages of, 696, 700–701
mouthparts of, 884, 885f
nitrogenous wastes of, 865
osmoregulation in, 871–79
ovarian cycle of, 1027f
overhunting of, 1181
parental care in, 694
pregnancy in, 1029–34
primates, hominids, and humans, 704–8 (*see also* Human[s])
reproduction in, 1021–30
seed dispersal by, 835
Mammary glands, **696**
Mandibles, arthropod, **677**
Manipulation, altruism and, 1097–98
Mantle, **662**–63
Map orientation (true navigation), migration and, 1089, 1090–91
Mapping
biodiversity hotspots and, 1177
communities, 1137
concept, B:28
genetic (*see* Genetic maps)
species richness and endemism, 1176
Marfan syndrome, 272–73
Margulis, Lynn, 560
Marine biomes
carbon cycle in, 556–57
characteristics of, 1075, 1078–79
impacts of global climate change on net primary productivity of, 1168–69
loss of biodiversity from overfishing of, 1181
net primary production of, 1154–56
osmoregulation in, 862–63, 866–68
Mark-recapture studies, 1103f, 1113, 1115
Markow, Therese, 469–70
Marshes, **1077**
Marsupials, 696, **701**, 1031
Martindale, Mark, 642, 663–64

Boldface page numbers indicate a glossary entry; page numbers followed by an *f* indicate a figure; those followed by *t* indicate a table.

Microtektites, 521–22f
Microtubule organizing centers
  (MTOCs), **129**, 224–25, 226t
Microtubules, **129**. *See also* Cytokinesis
  image of, 106f
  in meiosis, 241
  in mitosis, 224–27
  structure and function of, 128t, 129–31
Microvilli, **873–74**, **892**
Midbrain, **688**
Middle ear, **956**
Middle lamella, 204
Migration, **1089**
  allopatric speciation by, 494–95
  hypotheses on ultimate causation
    of, 1091
  magnetoreception in bird, 968–69
  metapopulation extinction vs.,
    1112f–13
  navigation strategies in proximate
    causation of, 1089–91
Miller, Stanley, 33–34, 59
Millipedes, 675
Millivolt (mV), **930**
Milner, Brenda, 945
Mimicry, 1094–95, **1129–30**
Mineralocorticoids, **1003**
Minerals, **884**
  as essential nutrients for animals and
    humans, 884, 885t
  nucleic acid polymerization and,
    60–61
  as nutrients for plants, 776–79f, 780t
    (*see also* Nutrients, plant)
  synthesis of monosaccharides
    from, 74
Minisatellites, **396–98f**
Miscarriages, 470
Misfolding, protein, 53
Mismatch repair, DNA, **298–99**
Missense mutations, **313–14t**
Mistakes, DNA synthesis, 297–301,
  313–14
Mistletoe, 789, 790f
Mitchell, Peter, 169
Mitochondria, **115**
  citric acid cycle in, 162–65
  functions of, 115–16
  origin of, in protists, 560–61
  oxidation of NADH and FADH$_2$ in,
    166–68
  in parietal cells, 891
  in proximal tubules, 874
  replacement rate for, 119
  structure and function of, 117t
Mitochondrial DNA (mtDNA), 500–501,
  560–61
Mitochondrial matrix, **115**, **161**, 162–65
Mitogen-activated protein kinase
  (MAPK), 150, **213–14**
Mitosis, **219–29**
  asexual reproduction vs. sexual
    reproduction and, 247
  cell cycle and, 222–23
  daughter cell production by
    cytokinesis in, 227–29
  discovery of phases of, 220–22
  events in, 223–26
  meiosis and, in cell cycle, 219–20, 244t,
    245f (*see also* Cell cycle; Meiosis)
  movement of chromosomes during
    anaphase of, 226–27
Mitosis-promoting factor (MPF), 406
Mitotic spindle forces, 226
Mockingbirds, 449–50

Model organisms, 257, B:23–B:26. *See
  also Escherichia coli (E. coli)*; Fruit
  flies; Mustard plant; Roundworms;
  *Saccharomyces cerevisiae*
  bread mold, 305, 629
  cellular slime mold (*Dictyostelium
    discoideum*), B:23–B:25
  characteristics of, B:23
  in developmental biology, 408
  genomes of, 392
  liverworts, 601
  peas as, in Mendelian genetics, 257–66
  protostome, 658
Models
  animal, of disease, 382
  condensed eukaryotic DNA, 348f
  DNA synthesis, 289–95
  eukaryotic transcription initiation,
    356, 357f
  mathematical, of genetic drift, 480f
  molecular, 24, B:12–B:13
Mode of transmission, **277**
Modified leaves, 739–40, 790
Modified roots, 734–35
Modified stems, 736–37
Moisture
  in decomposition rates, 1157
  terrestrial biomes and, 1068–69 (*see
    also* Precipitation; Water)
Molaison, Henry Gustav, 945
Molarity, **29**
Mold, bread, 305, 629
Mole, **29**
Molecular biology, 304, 305, 307–9, 368–
  69, B:13–B:16. *See also* Genetic
  engineering
Molecular chaperones, **52–53**, **331–32**
Molecular formulas, **24**, B:12–B:13
Molecular level, anatomy and physiology
  at, 849f
Molecular machines, 108
Molecular phylogenies
  of animals, 638, 640f
  eukaryote and protist, 558, 559f
  of fungi, 618–19
  green plant, 582–83
  human, 707–8
  vertebrate, 691
Molecular weight, **29**
Molecules, **21**. *See also* Macromolecules
  atomic structure and, 19–21
  in bottom-up research approach to
    chemical evolution, 32–33
  carbon and organic, 36–38 (*see also*
    Organic molecules)
  cell-cycle regulatory, 229–31
  in chemical reactions, 24
  covalent bonding and, 21–23
  development of phylogenetic tree of
    life from rRNA, 6–8
  DNA (*see* DNA [deoxyribonucleic
    acid])
  enzyme catalysis and substrate, 54
  ionic bonding and, 22–23f
  measuring amounts of, using
    radioimmunoassay, B:16
  nuclear transport of, 119–21
  reading chemical structures of,
    B:13–B:13
  research on proteins as first self-
    replicating, 42, 55
  RNA (*see* RNA [ribonucleic acid])
  separating and visualizing, B:13–B:16
  shapes and geometry of simple, 23–24
  simple, from carbon, hydrogen,
    nitrogen, and oxygen, 23

solutes as (*see* Solutes)
  visualizing, in 3-D, B:20–B:21
Mollusks, 638t, 657–58, 662–64,
  668–69, 1175
Molting, **670**, 983
Molybdenum, as plant nutrient,
  777, 780t
Momentum, population growth, 1116
Monarch butterflies, 1091
Monkeys, 704–5, 724–25, 1098
Monoamines, 941t
Monocots, **596**, 742f, 834, 837
Monod, Jacques, 307–8, 338–39f,
  342–43, B:23
Monoecious species, **827**, 828f
Monogamy, 722
Monohybrid crosses, **259–61**
Monomers, **44–46**, 58–59, 72–75. *See
  also* Polymerization
Monophyletic groups, **491–93**, **507–8**,
  **536**, 557, B:10–B:11. *See also*
  Clades; Lineages
Monosaccharides, **72–75**. *See also*
  Carbohydrates
Monosodium glutamate (MSG), 965
Monotremes, **696**, **700**, 1031
Morgan, Thomas Hunt, 267–71,
  274f, B:25
Morphogens, **410–14**, 435–36
Morphology, **107**, **450**
  adaptive radiations and, 517
  of eukaryotic lineages, 558t
  evolution of animal (*see* Evolutionary
    innovations, animal)
  fungal, 615–18
  of green plants, 580–81
  lophotrochozoan, 660–61
  morphospecies concept and, 490–91
  phylogenies based on, 510, 511f
  of prokaryotic and eukaryotic
    cells, 107
  of protists, 557–58
  structural homology in, 450–51
  viral, 715, 725
Morphospecies concept, **490–91**, 492t
Mortality rates. *See* Death rates, animal
Mosquitos, 555, 672
Mosses, 176f, 581, 601–2, 824f–25
Moths, 952–53, 966–67
Motility. *See* Movement
Motor neurons, **929**, 976–77
Motor proteins, 54, **128–31**, 133,
  228, 241
Mountain pine beetles, 1166t, 1167
Mountain ranges, climate and, 1066–67
Mouse, 392, B:24f, B:25. *See also* Mice
Mouths
  digestion in, 888–89
  human, 887f
  lophotrochozoan, 662
  mammalian, 701
  mouthpart adaptations for, 884–86
  protostome vs. deuterostome,
    644–45, 658
  taste as chemoreception by, 964–65
Movement
  animal (*see* Animal movement)
  cell (*see* Cell movement)
  prokaryotic, 109, 536, 537f
  protist, 565–66
  wind/touch responses and plant, 806
Mucins, 889
Mucosal-associated lymphoid tissue
  (MALT), **1043**
Mucous cells, **890**
Mucus, 889, **1038**, 1042

Mudslides, 779–81
Müller, Fritz, 1130
Müllerian inhibitory substance, **999**
Müllerian mimicry, **1130**
Multicellularity, **204**, **562**, 846
  cell–cell interactions for, 200–201
  cell–cell signaling and, 209–10t
  in characteristics of domains of
    life, 529t
  in eukaryotes, 8, 553
  gene regulation and, 348–49
  intercellular connections and, 204–9
  origin of, in animal evolution, 638–40
  in Paleozoic era, 515
  protist, 562–63
Multichambered hearts, 919–21
Multidrug resistance, 456
Multinucleate muscle cells, 977
Multiple allelism, **271–72**, 277t
Multiple fertilization, prevention of,
  421–23
Multiple fruits, **834**, 835f
Multiple sclerosis (MS), **937–38**, 1056
Multiplication rule, probability, B:8
Mumps virus, 728
Münch, Ernst, 768
Muscle cells, 162, 200f, 427–29, 637
Muscle contraction, 637, 973–77. *See
  also* Animal movement
  actin-myosin interactions in, 974–76
  animal locomotion and, 984–88
  endoskeletons and, 982
  in evolution of animal movement,
    972–73
  exoskeletons and, 983
  initiation of, by neurons, 976–77
  of skeletal muscles, 979–80
  sliding-filament model of, 973–74
Muscle fibers, **973–74**, 979–80
Muscle tissues, **847–48**, 973–74, 977–80
Muscular dystrophy, 200f
Muscular hydrostats, 981
Musculoskeletal structure, 984–85. *See
  also* Skeletal systems
Mushrooms, 612f, 614, 617, 626–27, 630.
  *See also* Fungi
*Mus musculus*, 392, B:24f, B:26. *See also*
  Mice
Mussels, 662, 668, 1130, 1131f, 1137–38
Mustard plant
  in blue-light phototropism
    research, 797
  in cytokinin research, 808
  embryogenesis in, 434f
  in flowering hormone research, 803
  genome of, 392
  in gravitropic response research, 804
  as model organism for plants, 433,
    B:24f, B:25
  in phloem loading research, 770–71
  in plant active ion exclusion research,
    786–87
  in population ecology, 1106–8
  reproductive development of, 438–41
  stages of development of, 433f
  vegetative development of, 436–38
  in wind/touch response research, 805
Mutagens, **339**
Mutants, **268**. *See also* Mutation(s)
  creating experimental, 305, 339
  histone, 351
  homeotic, 413
  in study of flower development,
    439–41
  in study of hormones and homestasis,
    1001–3

*Boldface* page numbers indicate a glossary entry; page numbers followed by an *f* indicate a figure; those followed by *t* indicate a table.

**Boldface** page numbers indicate a glossary entry; page numbers followed by an *f* indicate a figure; those followed by *t* indicate a table.

Boldface page numbers indicate a glossary entry; page numbers followed by an f indicate a figure; those followed by t indicate a table.

:32    INDEX

**Boldface** page numbers indicate a glossary entry; page numbers followed by an *f* indicate a figure; those followed by *t* indicate a table.

I:34   INDEX

**Boldface** page numbers indicate a glossary entry; page numbers followed by an *f* indicate a figure; those followed by *t* indicate a table.

:36   INDEX

Boldface page numbers indicate a glossary entry; page numbers followed by an *f* indicate a figure; those followed by *t* indicate a table.

Boldface page numbers indicate a glossary entry; page numbers followed by an f indicate a figure; those followed by t indicate a table.

**Boldface** page numbers indicate a glossary entry; page numbers followed by an
f indicate a figure; those followed by t indicate a table.